W9-CBW-020

environmental
science

FOURTH EDITION

a Canadian perspective

BILL FREEDMAN

Dalhousie University

PEARSON

Prentice
Hall

Toronto

Library and Archives Canada Cataloguing in Publication

Freedman, Bill
    Environmental science : a Canadian perspective / Bill Freedman. — 4th ed.

Includes bibliographical references and index.
ISBN 0-13-200041-5

    1. Environmental sciences—Textbooks. I. Title.
GE160.C3F74 2007   363.7   C2006-901015-3

Copyright © 2007, 2004, 2001, 1998 Pearson Education Canada, a division of Pearson Canada Inc., Toronto, Ontario

Pearson Prentice Hall. All rights reserved. This publication is protected by copyright, and permission should be obtained from the publisher prior to any prohibited reproduction, storage in a retrieval system, or transmission in any form or by any means, electronic, mechanical, photocopying, recording, or likewise. For information regarding permission, write to the Permissions Department.

0-13-200041-5

Vice President, Editorial Director: Michael J. Young
Editor-in-Chief: Gary Bennett
Executive Marketing Manager: Marlene Olsavsky
Developmental Editor: Rema Celio
Production Editor: Mary Ann Field
Copy Editor: Kelly Davis
Production Coordinator: Andrea Falkenberg
Composition: Heidi Palfrey
Photo Research: Sandy Cooke
Interior and Cover Design: Julia Hall
Cover Image: Getty Images/Daryl Benson

Statistics Canada information is used with the permission of Statistics Canada. Users are forbidden to copy this material and/or redisseminate the data, in its original or modified form, for commercial purposes, without the express permission of Statistics Canada. Information on the availability of the wide range of data from Statistics Canada can be obtained from Statistics Canada's regional offices, its website at http://www.statcan.ca, and its toll-free access number, 1-800-263-1136.

 2 3 4 5   11 10 09 08 07

Printed and bound in Hong Kong.
GCC/02

This book is printed on recycled paper.

There is absolutely no inevitability
as long as there is a willingness
to contemplate what is happening.

Marshall McLuhan,
The Medium is the Massage (1967).

About the Author

Bill Freedman is a professor of Biology at Dalhousie University in Halifax, Nova Scotia, where he has taught for the past 25 years. He earned his M.Sc. and Ph.D. from the Department of Botany at the University of Toronto. Bill has researched many aspects of environmental science, including the ecological effects of forestry, acidification, toxic metals, sulfur dioxide, pesticides, eutrophication, and urban ecology. Bill is a Director of and Science Advisor to the Nature Conservancy of Canada. In addition to this book, he has written another titled *Environmental Ecology* (Academic Press, 1995), co-edited a book on arctic ecology, and written over 200 scientific papers and research reports.

In his spare time, Bill enjoys natural history, especially birding and botanizing in wild places, collecting antiques and folk art, and playing squash. Bill and his spouse, George-Anne Merrill, have two college-age kids, Jonathan and Rachael.

Brief Contents

Contents

Contents

Feature Boxes
and Canadian Cases

Canadian Cases

Preface

Environmental Literacy

Environmental literacy can be defined as: "the degree to which people have a well-informed understanding of environmental issues." Today, an understanding of environmental issues is crucial. Humans are presently engaged in a frenzy of destructive behaviour that is causing enormous damage to the ecosystems that sustain both our species and Earth's legacy of biodiversity. All around us, we see collapsing fisheries, deforestation, soil degradation, species extinctions, pollution, and other awful damages.

Nevertheless, we need not be overly pessimistic. If our society takes constructive actions now, it is not too late to prevent or repair these terrific environmental problems, which threaten the welfare of people and most other species. Within limits, humans are prescient creatures, and our society is capable of implementing sustainable economies that can support our livelihoods as well as healthy ecosystems.

It is clear, however, that any sustainable economy will involve very different ways of doing business, and will also require fundamental changes in the lifestyles of many people. This is especially the case in wealthy countries such as Canada. Ultimately, such socio-economic transformations must involve much less use of energy, materials, and other resources, in comparison with what many of us take for granted today. A more respectful attitude toward the natural world will also be needed.

Achieving such a transformation will depend on citizens having a sound understanding of environmental issues. Any imposition of restrictions on access to resources will initially be uncomfortable for many people. I believe, however, that people will be more willing to soften their lifestyle if they understand the reasons for those changes in the context of economic sustainability and the livelihoods of future generations. With such an understanding, most people will support economic and social changes that conserve the quality of their environment.

Environmental literacy will be a key requirement if a country such as Canada is to achieve the difficult transition into an ecologically sustainable economy. I hope that this book will make it easier for more Canadians to become literate about important environmental issues.

A Canadian Text

This textbook is intended to provide the core elements of a curriculum for teaching environmental science at the introductory level in Canadian colleges and universities. This book is suitable for students starting in environmental science or environmental studies programs, for arts students who require a science elective, and for science students who require a non-major elective.

Only a few introductory textbooks in environmental science include much Canadian content. It is regrettable that many Canadian students of environmental subjects have used books that are so lacking in information about their own country. Canada has unique national and regional perspectives that should be understood by Canadian students.

One of the main goals of this book is to address the needs of Canadian students. Canadian information and examples are integrated throughout the text, along with international data that provide a broader context. Special Canadian Focus Boxes illustrate Canadian applications of important concepts. And special Canadian Case Studies provide additional examples in a Canadian context.

To help make a difference, I am donating a percentage of the proceeds from the sale of this book to the Nature Conservancy of Canada, a charitable organization that is dedicated to preserving Canadian biodiversity through the acquisition and protection of ecologically significant property. By purchasing and learning from this textbook, you too are taking a constructive step towards establishing Canadian sustainability.

Approach and Organization

Environmental science draws on knowledge and methods from many fields of the sciences and social sciences, including biology, chemistry, economics, ethics, geography, geology, medicine, physics, political science, sociology, and statistics. Many environmental specialists adopt an interdisciplinary approach to integrate these different kinds of knowledge in order to help understand and prevent environmental damage.

This book also adopts an interdisciplinary approach by drawing on different disciplines. At the same time, the choice of topics and the interpretations offered reflect my own experience and world view as an ecologist.

The book is organized into twenty-seven chapters grouped into six parts. Part I (Ecosystems and Humans) consists of one chapter that serves as an introduction. It defines environmental science and ecology, explains the principles of the ecosystem approach, briefly considers environmental stressors caused by human activities, and describes various world views.

Part II (The Biosphere: Characteristics and Dynamics) consists of eight chapters that provide a scientific foundation for much of what follows. It discusses the scientific approach (Chapter 2); the geological, hydrological, and atmospheric dynamics of planet Earth (Chapter 3); energy (Chapter 4); the flows and cycles of nutrients (Chapter 5); evolution (Chapter 6); biodiversity and the classification of organisms (Chapter 7); biomes and ecozones (Chapter 8); and ecology (Chapter 9).

As its name implies, Part III (The Human Population) deals with the structure, growth, and implications of the human population. It consists of two chapters: one on global populations (Chapter 10) and one on the Canadian population (Chapter 11).

Part IV (Resources) consists of three chapters that deal with the natural resources that humans and all other species need to sustain their livelihoods. It discusses the relation between resources and sustainable development (Chapter 12), the limited supplies of non-renewable resources (Chapter 13), and potentially renewable resources (Chapter 14).

Part V (Environmental Damages) consists of twelve chapters dealing with the damage caused by humans (individually and collectively) during the course of their activities. It discusses pollution and disturbance as environmental stressors (Chapter 15), gaseous air pollution (Chapter 16), atmospheric and climatic change (Chapter 17), toxic elements (Chapter 18), acidification (Chapter 19), additional problems of surface waters (Chapter 20), oil spills (Chapter 21), pesticides (Chapter 22), the environmental effects of forestry (Chapter 23), agriculture and

the environment (Chapter 24), urban ecology (Chapter 25), and the biodiversity crisis (Chapter 26).

Part VI (Ecologically Sustainable Development) consists of one chapter (Chapter 27) that serves as a synthesis and conclusion. It discusses the process of assessing environmental impacts and it considers the prospects for Canada and for spaceship Earth.

New to This Edition

In addition to the clarification of explanations and the extensive updating of data, many new boxes have been added that highlight environmental issues relevant to Canada and its international context. There is also an entirely new category of boxes, titled Global Focus—these are intended to reinforce the global context of key issues. There are also three new Canadian cases with CBC video supplements:

- Canadian Case 1—The Fur Industry
- Canadian Case 3—Fished Out
- Canadian Case 4—Oily Birds

The end of chapter material has also been enhanced by adding a new *Conclusions* section that puts the entire chapter into a tighter context. There are also additional *Questions for Review*, which provide questions that test students' understanding of the material presented in the chapter, as well as *Questions for Discussion*, which provide thought-provoking questions that help stimulate careful reflection and class discussion. Also new are *Exploring Issues*, which provide self-directed activities and exercises to help students delve deeper into environmental issues. These various changes allow the fourth edition of this textbook to keep pace with the highly dynamic realm of environmental science, both in Canada and globally.

All of the boxes have been reviewed and updated, but there are also many new ones. The key changes to boxes in the fourth edition involve the following elements:

- Canadian Focus 1.1 David Suzuki—A Canadian Environmentalist
- Global Focus 3.1 A Killer Tsunami
- In Detail 5.1 Too Much of a Good Thing—Pollution by Nutrients
- In Detail 6.3 Genetically Modified Organisms
- Canadian Focus 7.1 Medicinal Plants

Features

A special effort has been made with this book to incorporate features that will facilitate learning and enhance an understanding of environmental science.

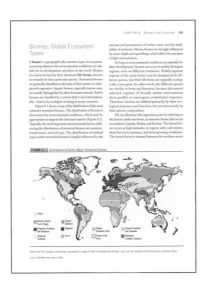

- **Chapter Objectives** at the beginning of each chapter summarize the skills and knowledge to be learned in that chapter.

- **Key terms** are boldfaced where they are defined in the text and are listed at the end of each chapter. For easy reference, all the key terms and their definitions are collated in a **Glossary** near the end of the book.

- **Canadian Focus** boxes illustrate the application of important concepts to the Canadian environment.

■ **Global Focus** boxes enhance the global context for learning about environmental issues.

■ **In Detail** boxes provide additional technical information.

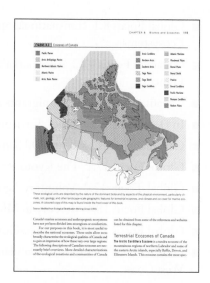

■ **Figures**, **Tables**, and **Photos** are abundant throughout the book, each with an explanatory caption.

■ **Canadian Case Studies** provide further examples of important applications and include their own Questions for Discussion. A special CBC video segment supplements accompanies each Canadian Case Study.

■ **Questions for Review** at the end of each chapter provide questions that test students' factual and conceptual understanding of the material presented in the chapter.

■ **Questions for Discussion** at the end of each chapter provide thought-provoking questions which help stimulate careful reflection and class discussion.

■ **Exploring Issues** at the end of each chapter provide activities and exercises that help students delve deeper into environmental issues.

■ **References** are listed at the end of each chapter to help guide users to further reading.

■ **Informative Websites** at the end of each chapter direct users to useful Internet sites.

- Appendix A lists some standard **Units of Measurement and Conversions**.
- Appendix B lists **Environmental Legislation** at the federal and international levels.
- Appendix C, **Detailed Data Tables**, includes more detailed versions of some text tables.

- A comprehensive **Index** makes looking up items easy.
- For convenience, a colour version of Figure 8.3 (**Ecozones of Canada**) is given on the inside front cover, and a colour version of Figure 8.1 (**Distribution of Earth's Major Terrestrial Biomes**) is given on the inside back cover.

Supplements

The following supplements have been carefully prepared to accompany this new book:

- An *Instructor's Manual with Transparency Masters* which includes suggested answers to all the Questions for Review and Questions for Discussion at the end of each chapter and at the end of each Canadian Case Study. The *Transparency Masters* include all the Figures and Tables in the text.
- *Electronic Transparencies* consisting of full-colour versions of all the Photos, Figures, and Tables in the text.
- A *Test Item File* of questions, organized by chapter, with the level of difficulty (i.e., easy, moderate, or difficult) indicated for each question.
- *Pearson TestGen*, a special computerized version of the Test Item File that enables instructors to view and edit the existing questions, add questions, generate tests, and print the tests in a variety of formats. Powerful search and sort functions make it easy to locate questions and arrange them in any order desired. TestGen also enables instructors to administer tests on a local area network, have the tests graded electronically, and have the results prepared in electronic or printed reports. Issued on a CD-ROM, the Pearson TestGen is compatible with IBM or Macintosh systems.
- *CBC/Pearson Education Canada Video Library for Environmental Science*, a special compilation of six video segments from news magazines of the Canadian Broadcasting Corporation. Each video segment has been carefully selected to accompany one of the Canadian Case Studies in the book.

Acknowledgements

A number of acknowledgements are in order. Numerous colleagues provided an extremely valuable service by informally reviewing draft material for this book and by making important ideas and information available to me. Inevitably, I was not able to incorporate all of the criticisms and suggestions, sometimes because they did not correspond with my own views or interpretations of the subject matter. However, the great majority of suggestions and criticisms offered by these people resulted in changes in preliminary manuscripts, and they improved the quality, and sometimes the accuracy, of the material. These helpful colleagues are: Gordon Beanlands, Christine Beauchamp, Stephen Beauchamp, Karen Beazley, Marian Binkley, Chris Corkett, Ray Cote, Roger Cox, Les Cwynar, Roger Doyle, Peter Duinker, William Ernst, Tracy Fleming, George Francis, David Gauthier, Chuck Geale, William Gizyn, Patricia Harding, Chris Harvey-Clarke, Owen Hertzman, Jeff Hutchings, Adrian Johnston, Joseph Kerekes, Allan Kuja, Roshani Lacoul, Brian Le, Judy Loo, Annette Luttermann, Paul Mandell, Moira McConnell, Ian McLaren, Chris Miller, Pierre Mineau, Gunther Muecke, Neil Munro, Ram Myers, David Nettleship, David Patriquin, Allan Pinder, Stephen Price, Nigel Roulet, Robert Scheibling, Tara Steeves, Donald Stewart, Tony Turner, Torgney Viegerstad, Richard Wassersug, Peter Wells, Mary-Anne White, Hal Whitehead, Sheilagh Whitley, Martin Willison, Stephen Woodley, and Vince Zelazney.

In addition, I am grateful to the following instructors for providing formal reviews of part or all of the manuscript:

Patrick Lane
Susan Bare
Peter Feige
Kate Turner
Jon Hornung

A number of the professional staff at Pearson Canada have been of great assistance in the preparation of this book, especially Stephen Broadbent, Mary Ann Field, and Andrea Falkenberg.

Several personal acknowledgements are also in order. I thank my spouse, George-Anne Merrill, for her patient and uncomplaining tolerance of my work habits and lifestyle, and for being my best friend in spite of everything I do and don't do. Also, my son, Jonathan, and daughter, Rachael, for mysterious motivations that succeeding generations engender in their parents, for tolerating my often

busy days, and for not minding too much that I am frequently away from home.

If readers of this book have any comments, suggestions, or criticisms about the material or the approach, I would be grateful if you would communicate your ideas to me for future improvements.

Bill Freedman,
Department of Biology
Dalhousie University
Halifax, Nova Scotia
B3H 4J1

Ecosystems and Humans 1

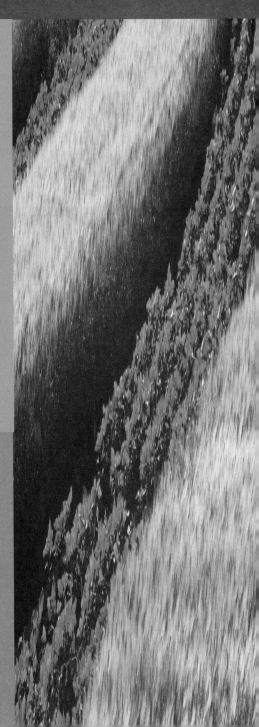

CHAPTER OBJECTIVES

After completing this chapter, you will be able to

1. Define environmental science and ecology and distinguish between them.
2. Outline a hierarchical framework of the universe that includes consideration of life on Earth at various scales.
3. Identify important principles of the ecosystem approach.
4. Compare humans and other species in terms of their abilities to cope with environmental constraints.
5. Describe how environmental stressors and disturbances can affect species and ecosystems.
6. List three direct ways in which humans influence their environment.
7. Identify four broad classes of environmental values.
8. Describe five important world views.
9. Classify the issues of the environmental crisis into three categories and give examples of each.
10. Discuss environmental effects of humans as a function of both population and lifestyle.

CHAPTER OUTLINE

- Environmental Science
- The Larger Context: Earth, Life, and Ecosystems
- Species and Ecosystems
- Stressors and Responses
- Human Activities: Important Environmental Stressors
- Environmental Ethics and World Views
- The Environmental Crisis
- Conclusions

Environmental Science

Environmental science is concerned with the rapidly increasing human population, the use and abuse of resources, damage caused by pollution and disturbance, and the endangerment and extinction of species and natural ecosystems. Typical questions that might be examined in environmental science include the following:

1. What might the human population be in Canada, or on Earth, in 50 or 200 years?

2. How can fossil fuels and other non-renewable resources be integrated into a sustainable Canadian and global economy?

3. How can we harvest cod in Atlantic Canada, wild salmon in British Columbia, or wheat in the Prairie provinces without degrading the resource?

4. What kinds of ecological damage are caused by acid rain, pesticides, and other kinds of pollution, and how can these be prevented or repaired?

5. How quickly are species and natural ecosystems becoming endangered or extinct, both in Canada and globally, and how can these calamities be prevented?

Environmental scientists examining these and similar questions use several disciplines in their study. The most relevant of these are atmospheric science, biology, chemistry, computer science, ecology, geography, geology, mathematics, medical science, oceanography, physics, and statistics. Ecology and geography are also interdisciplinary fields.

Environmental science involves just the science-related aspects of *environmental studies*, which is also a highly *interdisciplinary* field. The field of environmental studies encompasses a wide diversity of disciplines, all relevant to studying the effects of humans and their activities on environmental quality. Important non-science disciplines include anthropology, art, business, economics, ethics, law, literature, philosophy, political studies, psychology, religion, and sociology. The interdisciplinary nature of environmental studies is illustrated in Figure 1.1.

This book deals mainly with environmental science, although relevant non-science topics are also discussed, such as ethics, philosophy, and economics.

Of all the academic disciplines, ecology is the most relevant to environmental science, and, in fact, the two terms are often confused by many people and the popular media. **Ecology** can be defined simply as the study of the interrelationships of organisms and their environment. Ecology is mostly a biological area of study, but knowledge of chemistry, computer science, mathematics, physics, geology, and other fields is also important. Figure 1.2 highlights the interdisciplinary nature of ecology.

Geography is another highly interdisciplinary field that is central to environmental science. Geography can be simply defined as the study of the natural features of Earth's surface, including climate, topography, soil, and vegetation, as well as intersections with the human economy. Obviously, ecology and geography are closely related fields.

Most academic ecologists do not study the relationships between human activities and environmental quality. Rather, they research and write about the structures and functions of ecosystems and the factors that influence these. However, increasing numbers of ecologists are focusing on the study of human (or *anthropogenic*) influences on ecosystems. This applied specialization is sometimes called *environmental ecology*: the ecological effects of pollution and disturbance. Major subject areas of environmental ecology are

Photo 1.1   Earth is the third closest planet to the sun, and it is the only place in the universe definitely known to sustain life and ecosystems.

Source: NASA/Karen Taylor

FIGURE 1.1 | The Interdisciplinary Nature of Environmental Studies

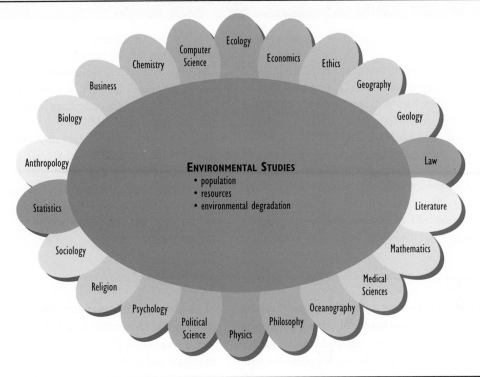

1. the management of biological resources, such as those important in agriculture, fisheries, and forestry;

2. the prevention or repair of ecological problems, such as those related to endangered biodiversity, restoration of degraded land or water, and management of greenhouse gases (such as carbon dioxide); and

3. the management of ecological processes, such as productivity, nutrient cycling, hydrology, and erosion.

Ecologists are specialists who study relationships among organisms and their environment. *Environmental scientists*, on the other hand, are generalists, using any science-related knowledge relevant to environmental quality, such as air or water chemistry, climate modelling, or the ecological effects of pollution or disturbance. Four well-known Canadian environmental scientists are Tom Hutchinson of Trent University, who studies how human influences degrade terrestrial ecosystems, Hamish Kimmins of the University of British Columbia, who works in sustainable forest management, William Rees of the University of British Columbia, who studies ecological economics and footprints, and David Schindler of the University of Alberta, who studies the effects of pollution and climate change on lakes.

A third group of people, known as **environmentalists**, has significant involvement with environmental issues, especially in the sense of advocacy. Advocacy involves taking strong public stances, either for or against, on particular environmental issues. David Suzuki is perhaps the most famous environmentalist in Canada, because he so effectively influ-

FIGURE 1.2 | Ecology Is also an Interdisciplinary Field

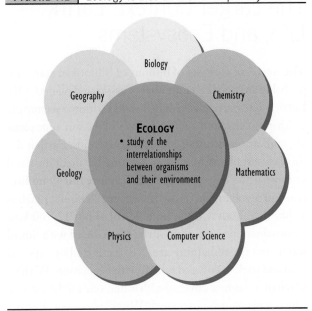

Canadian Focus 1.1

David Suzuki—A Canadian Environmentalist

David Suzuki was born in Vancouver in 1936. In 1964 he became a high-profile biology professor at the University of British Columbia, where he specialized in fruit fly genetics. Beginning in the mid-1970s, Suzuki became heavily engaged in media ventures aimed at popularizing knowledge about scientific issues important to society, most notably through the *Quirks and Quarks* (radio) and *Nature of Things* (television) series of the CBC. Through these avenues, as well as his prolific books, magazine and newspaper articles, and public lectures, Suzuki has been instrumental in informing a broad public in Canada and other countries about the gravity of environmental problems, including their scientific and socio-economic dimensions. His work is now being advanced through the activities of the David Suzuki Foundation, an advocacy and research organization he founded in 1990 with the aim of enhancing progress toward an ecologically sustainable human economy (see www.davidsuzuki.org/). Suzuki has built a worldwide following of a broad constituency of people concerned about environmental damage and social equity. By doing this, he has contributed greatly to the identification and resolution of environmental problems in Canada and the world.

ences the attitudes of Canadians through the popular media of television, newspapers, and books. Another well-known Canadian is Paul Watson, a direct-action environmentalist who operates under the auspices of the Sea Shepherd Society. He has been involved in non-governmental "policing" actions, such as the sabotage of ships engaged in illegal whaling and fishing. However, anyone who cares about the quality of the environment and who advocates change for the better can be called an environmentalist. Environmentalists often pursue their advocacy in so-called non-governmental organizations (NGOs; see Chapter 27 for a discussion of the role of NGOs in Canada and internationally).

The Larger Context: Earth, Life, and Ecosystems

The universe consists of billions of billions of stars and probably an even larger number of associated planets. Our Earth is one particular planet, located within a seemingly ordinary solar system, which consists of the sun, nine planets, and various orbiting comets and asteroids. Earth is the third closest planet to the sun, orbiting the medium-sized star every 365 days at an average distance of 149 million km, and revolving on its own axis every 24 hours. Earth is a spherical body with a diameter of about 12 700 km. Approximately 70% of its surface is covered with liquid water, and the remaining area, characterized by exposed land and rock, is covered mostly with vegetation. With so much of its surface covered with water, one might wonder why our planet was not named "Water" instead of "Earth."

Like any other planet in the universe, Earth has its own unique characteristics. What makes Earth particularly exceptional are certain qualities of its environment that have led to the genesis and subsequent evolution of living organisms and ecosystems. These favourable environmental factors include aspects of Earth's chemistry, surface temperature, and strength of gravity.

The beginning of life on Earth occurred about 3.5 billion years ago, perhaps only 1 billion years following the origin of the planet during the formation of the solar system. We do not know exactly how life first evolved from inanimate matter, although almost all biologists today believe that life began spontaneously. In other words, genesis happened naturally, as a direct result of appropriate physical–chemical conditions occurring in the same place at the same time. These conditions involved chemistry, temperature, solar radiation, pressure, and other critical factors.

Aside from the musings of science fiction, Earth is celebrated as the only place in the universe known to sustain life and its associated ecological processes. Of course, this observation simply reflects our present state of knowledge. We do not actually know that living organisms do not exist elsewhere—only that life or its signals have not yet been discovered anywhere else in the universe. In fact, many (but not all) scientists believe that, because of the extraordinary diversity of environments that must exist among the innumerable planets that exist in the multitudinous solar systems of the universe, it is statistically likely that life forms have developed elsewhere. Nevertheless, the fact remains that Earth is the only planet definitely known to support organisms and ecosystems. This makes Earth an extraordinarily special place in the greater scheme of things.

We can consider the universe at various hierarchical levels (Figure 1.3). The scale ranges from the extremely small, such as sub-atomic particles and photons (an energy unit), to the fantastically large, such as galaxies and, ultimately, the universe.

Life on Earth occupies several intermediate levels of this hierarchy. The realm of ecology encompasses

1. **individual organisms**, which are living entities that are genetically and physically discrete;

2. **populations**, or individuals of the same species that occur together in time and space;

3. **communities**, or populations of various species, also co-occurring at the same time and place;

4. **landscapes** and **seascapes**, which are spatial integrations of various communities over large areas; and

5. the entire **biosphere**, composed of all life and ecosystems on Earth.

Species and Ecosystems

A **species** is an aggregation of individuals and populations that can potentially interbreed and produce fertile offspring (see Chapter 7). The word "species" is both singular and plural. The word **ecosystem** is a generic term used to describe one or more communities of organisms that are interacting with their environment as a defined unit. As such, ecosystems can be organized in a hierarchy. Ecosystems can range from small units occurring in discrete microhabitats (e.g., an aquatic ecosystem contained in a pitcher plant or in a garden surrounded by pavement) to larger units (e.g., landscapes and seascapes). Even the biosphere can be viewed as a single ecosystem.

Ecological interpretations of the natural world consider the diverse, web-like interconnections among the many components of ecosystems in a holistic manner. This **ecosystem approach** does not view each ecosystem as a random grouping of populations, species, communities, and environments—it confirms all of these as intrinsically connected and mutually dependent, although in varying degrees.

Another important ecological principle is that all species are sustained by environmental resources: the "goods and services" provided by ecosystems. All organisms require specific necessities of life, such as inorganic nutrients, food, and habitat with particular biological and physical qualities. Green plants, for example, need an adequate supply

FIGURE 1.3 | Hierarchical Organization of the Universe

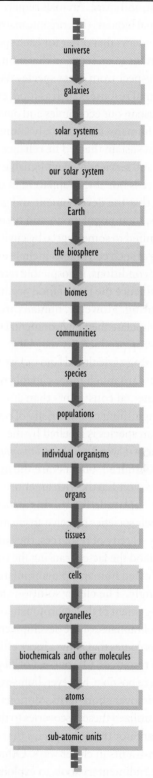

universe

galaxies

solar systems

our solar system

Earth

the biosphere

biomes

communities

species

populations

individual organisms

organs

tissues

cells

organelles

biochemicals and other molecules

atoms

sub-atomic units

This diagram focuses on Earth, its ecosystems, and life, and suggests a linear structure to the organization of the universe. However, it is important to understand that all elements are interconnected.

of moisture, inorganic nutrients (such as nitrate and phosphate), sunlight, and space. Animals require suitable foods of plant or animal biomass (i.e., organic matter), along with habitat requirements that differ for each species.

It is important to understand that humans are no different in this respect from other species. We also depend on environmental resources such as food, energy, shelter, and water to sustain our economies and ourselves. Like all other species, humans are intimately connected with the ecosystems that sustain them. The reliance of humans on natural goods and services is an undeniable fact, although this dependence is not always apparent in our daily lives.

It follows that the development and growth of individual humans, their populations, and their societies and cultures are limited to some degree by environmental factors. Examples of such constraints include excessively cold or dry climatic conditions, inhospitable terrain, and other factors that influence the rate of food production by agriculture or hunting. However, humans are often able to favourably manipulate their environmental circumstances. For example, crop productivity may be increased by irrigating or fertilizing agricultural land or by managing pests. In fact, humans are much more capable of overcoming their environmental constraints than any other species. This is a distinguishing characteristic of our species.

The human species is labelled by the scientific term *Homo sapiens*, a two-word name (or *binomial*) that is Latin for "wise man." Indeed, humans are the most intelligent of all the species on Earth, with an enormous cognitive ability (i.e., an aptitude for solving problems). When humans and their societies perceive an environmental constraint, such as scarcity of resources, they often have been able to understand the factors causing the constraint. This insight has allowed humans to manipulate the environment accordingly. The clever solutions have generally involved management of the environment or other species to the benefit of humans, or the development of social systems and technologies that allow a more efficient exploitation of natural resources. Of course, not all problems have solutions. Where possible, however, humans generally have been able to discover short-term solutions to their problems and have utilized these discoveries to their advantage.

Humans are not the only species that can cope with ecological constraints in clever ways. Other species have learned to use rudimentary tools to exploit the resources of their environment more efficiently. For example, the woodpecker finch of the Galapagos Islands uses cactus spines to pry its food of insects out of fissures in bark and rotting wood. Chimpanzees modify twigs and use them to extract termites, a favourite food, from termite mounds.

Egyptian vultures pick up stones in their beak and drop them on ostrich eggs, breaking them and allowing access to the rich food inside.

Some modern innovations or "discoveries" by other species have also been observed. About 50 years ago in England, whole milk was hand-delivered to homes in glass bottles that had a bulbous compartment at the top to collect the cream as it separated from the milk. A few great tits (small, chickadee-like birds) discovered that they could feed on the nutritious cream by tearing a hole in the cardboard cap of the bottle. Other great tits observed this behavioural novelty and enthusiastically adopted it. The feeding tactic became widespread and was even adopted by several other species, such as the blue tit. Cream-eating was certainly a clever innovation, allowing access to a new and valuable food resource.

Although other species have developed behavioural changes that allow more efficient exploitation of their environment, none have approached the number and variety of innovations developed by humans. Moreover, no other species has developed a cumulative expertise for intensively exploiting such a broad range of useful resources. And no other species has managed to spread these capabilities as extensively as humans have, in an increasingly global culture. The human ability to exploit resources is extraordinary. Unfortunately, humans also have an unparalleled ability to degrade resources, to disturb and pollute ecosystems, and to cause the endangerment or extinction of other species. The intense damage caused by humans and their activities is, of course, a major element of the subject matter of environmental science.

Stressors and Responses

The development and productivity of individual organisms, populations, communities, and ecosystems are naturally constrained by environmental factors. These environmental constraints can be viewed as **environmental stressors** (Figure 1.4). For example, an individual plant may be stressed by inadequate nutrition, perhaps caused by infertile soil or by competition with nearby plants for scarce resources. Less-than-optimal access to nutrients, water, or sunlight results in physiological stress, which causes the plant to be less productive than it is genetically capable of being. One result of this stress–response relationship is that the plant may develop relatively few seeds during its lifetime. Because evolutionary success is related to the number of progeny an organism produces to carry

FIGURE 1.4 | Conceptual Model of the Ecological Effects of Environmental Stress

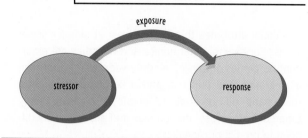

Environmental stressors are always present at some variable intensity, which is referred to as "exposure." Effects on individuals, species, communities, or larger ecological units occur in response to exposure to one or more environmental stressors.

on its genetic lineage, the realized success of this individual plant is less than its potential.

Similarly, the development and productivity of an animal (including any human) are constrained by the environmental conditions under which it lives. For instance, an individual may have to deal with stresses caused by food shortage or related to interactions with other animals through predation, parasitism, or competition for scarce resources.

The most benign (or least stressful) natural environments on Earth are characterized by conditions in which environmental factors such as moisture, nutrients, and temperature are not unduly constraining to biological processes, while extensive disturbances associated with wildfire, windstorm, disease, or other cataclysms are rare. These relatively benevolent conditions allow Earth's most complex and biodiverse ecosystems to develop, namely old-growth rainforests and coral reefs. Other environments, however, are characterized by conditions that are more stressful, and ecological development is therefore limited to less complex ecosystems, such as prairie, tundra, or desert.

All of Earth's ecosystems change profoundly, and quite naturally, over time. Many ecosystems are relatively dynamic, regularly experiencing large changes in their component species, quantities of biomass, and rates of productivity and nutrient cycling (these are described in following chapters). For example, ecosystems that occur in strongly seasonal climates usually have a discrete growing season followed by a dormant period when little or no growth occurs. To varying degrees, all of the natural ecosystems of Canada are seasonally dynamic: a warm growing season is followed by a dormant period characterized by

cold temperatures during which no plant productivity or growth occurs. Animals may survive the difficult time of winter by migrating, hibernating, or feeding on plant biomass remaining from the previous growing season.

Ecosystems that have been stressed by a recent **disturbance** (i.e., an episode of destruction) are particularly dynamic because they are undergoing a process of ecological recovery known as **succession**. Succession occurs in response to changes associated with natural disturbances such as wildfire, windstorms, and insect and disease epidemics. These cataclysmic factors may kill many of the dominant organisms in an ecosystem, creating opportunities for relatively short-lived species, which may dominate the earlier years of the post-disturbance, successional recovery.

Natural disturbance dynamics can be far-reaching, in some cases affecting extensive landscapes. For example, in most years, millions of hectares of the conifer-dominated boreal forest of northern Canada are disturbed by wildfires. Similarly extensive areas of forest may be affected by sudden increases in the abundance of spruce budworm, a moth whose caterpillars can kill most mature trees in fir–spruce stands, or by the mountain pine beetle, which kills pine trees. An even more extensive cataclysm ended about 15 000 years ago, when glaciation covered virtually all of Canada with enormous ice-sheets, several kilometres thick in places. All of the current ecosystems in Canada have developed since the melt-back of that glacial advance.

Disturbances can also be local in scale. For example, the death of a large tree within an otherwise intact forest creates a local zone of damage, referred to as a *microdisturbance*. This small-scale disturbance induces a local *microsuccession* of vigorously growing plants that attempt to achieve individual success by occupying the newly available gap in the forest canopy.

Even Earth's most stable ecosystems change inexorably over time. However, the dynamics of change in tropical rainforest and in the communities of the deepest regions of the oceans are generally slow. Catastrophic disturbances may affect these stable ecosystems, but under natural conditions they are rare. Nevertheless, as with all of Earth's ecosystems, these relatively stable types are profoundly influenced by widespread changes in climate and by other long-term dynamics, such as evolution.

In fact, natural environmental and ecological changes have caused the extinction of almost all of the species that have ever lived on Earth since life began about 3.5 billion years ago. Many of these extinctions occurred because species could not cope with the demands of changes in fac-

In Detail 1.1

Systems and Complexity

The concept of systems is important in the hierarchical organization of environmental science. The simplest definition of a system is "an organized whole." For our purposes, however, a system is defined as a group or combination of regularly interacting and interdependent elements, which form a collective entity, but one that is more than the sum of its constituents. A system can be isolated for purposes of examination. Systems can occur in various spheres of life, including

- biosystems (or biological systems), represented by any of the levels of organization of life and organisms (ranging from biochemistry to the biosphere);
- ecosystems (or ecological systems), which are biosystems consisting of one or more ecological communities that are interacting with their environment as a defined unit;
- technological systems, consisting of technologies integrated to produce manufactured goods, to harvest or manage natural resources, or to achieve some other human goal;
- information systems, or ways of handling and analyzing complex sets of data or other knowledge;
- organizational systems, or ways of integrating groups of specialized people to achieve some common, often institutional goal;
- economic systems, or integrated activities that produce goods and services in an economy;
- socio-cultural systems, which consist of the organization of specialized people, information, and technologies to achieve some goal; and
- numerous others including many that are less relevant to environmental science, such as a musical symphony, physical art such as a painting, and, for that matter, the words and data in this book.

Note that these various systems are not mutually exclusive. For example, an agroecosystem includes elements of biosystems, ecosystems, and socio-cultural systems.

Systems have so-called collective properties, which are based on the summation of their parts. One such property might be the total number of organisms present in some defined area, which is measured as the sum of all of the individual plants, animals, and microorganisms estimated to be present.

Systems also have emergent properties, which are revealed only when their components interact to develop functional attributes that do not exist at simpler, lower levels. For example, harmonies and melodies are emergent properties of music, as when vocalists, a drummer, a bass and lead guitarist, and a keyboard player of a rock band all integrate to create a pleasing song. Emergent properties are complex and are extremely difficult to predict or manage.

Biological systems provide numerous examples of emergent properties (see Chapter 9). For example, certain kinds of fungi and algae join together in an intimate, mutually beneficial relationship (a mutualism), as a life form known as a lichen. The biological properties of a lichen are different from those of the partner species (which cannot, in fact, live apart in nature), and they are impossible to predict based only on knowledge of the alga and the fungus.

Similarly, assemblages of various species occurring in the same place and time (an ecological community) develop emergent properties based on interactions such as herbivory, predation, competition, and disease. This complexity makes it difficult to predict the changes caused by the introduction of a new disease, herbivore, or predator to a community (including the harvesting of certain species by humans). Assemblages of communities over large areas, known as landscapes and seascapes, also have emergent properties, as does the biosphere as a whole. Emergent properties are extremely difficult to predict and often emerge as "surprises," occurring when, for example, ecosystems are stressed by some human influence. The interconnections within systems are particularly important: any effects on particular components will inevitably affect all others. This source of extreme complexity is one of the defining attributes of life and ecosystems, in contrast with physical (i.e., non-biological) systems, which are less complex.

Systems analysis is the study of the characteristics of systems, including their components, the relationships among those elements, and their collective and emergent properties. Systems analysis is used to study scientific, industrial, and commercial operations, usually with the goal of improving their efficiency. It can also be applied to improve the management of ecosystems being exploited to provide goods and services for use by humans. Ecologists also use systems analysis to better understand the organization and working of natural ecosystems, regardless of any direct relationship to the harvesting of resources by people. A key result of many such analyses is that the complexity of the system precludes accurate predictions.

tors such as climate or in biological interactions such as predation, competition, or disease. However, many of the extinctions appear to have occurred synchronously (i.e., at about the same time) and were presumably caused by unpredictable, catastrophic disturbances, such as a meteorite colliding with the Earth. (See Chapters 7 and 26 for discussions of natural extinctions and extinctions caused by human influences.)

Environmental stressors and disturbances have always been an important, natural context for life on Earth. So, too, have been the resulting ecological responses, including changes in species and the dynamics of their communities and ecosystems.

Human Activities: Important Environmental Stressors

These days, of course, ecosystems are influenced not only by "natural" environmental stresses. In many situations, human influences are the major constraining factor on the productivity of species, and on ecosystems more generally. Throughout the history of *Homo sapiens*, the scale, frequency, and intensity of environmental stressors and disturbances have been altered through the activities of humans. These anthropogenic influences have intensified enormously in modern times.

Anthropogenic influences can be direct or indirect. Humans directly affect ecosystems and species in three ways: (a) by harvesting economically valuable biomass, such as trees and hunted animals; (b) by causing toxicity through pollution; and (c) by converting natural ecosystems to agricultural, industrial, or urban land-uses.

These actions also engender many indirect effects. For example, the harvesting of trees alters conditions for the diversity of plants, animals, and microorganisms that require forested habitat, thereby affecting their populations. At the same time, timber harvesting indirectly changes functional properties of the landscape, such as the quantity of water flowing in streams, erosion, and productivity. Both the direct and indirect effects of humans on ecosystems are important.

Humans have always left "footprints" in nature; that is, to some degree, they have influenced the ecosystems of which they are a component. During most of the more than one million years of evolution of *Homo sapiens*, that footprint was relatively shallow. This was because the capability of humans for exploiting their environment was not much different from that of other similarly abundant, large

Photo 1.2 Modern consumerism results in huge demands for material and energy resources to manufacture and operate machines.

animals. However, during the cultural evolution of humans, the ecological changes associated with our activities intensified progressively. This process of **cultural evolution** has been characterized by increasingly more sophisticated methods, tools, and social organizations used to secure resources by exploiting the environment and other species.

Certain innovations occuring during the cultural evolution of humans represented great increases in capability. Because of their enormous influence on human success, these advances are referred to as "revolutions." Examples of early technological revolutions include

1. methods of making weapons to hunt animal prey;

2. domestication of the dog, which greatly facilitated hunting;

3. methods for the domestication of fire, which provided warmth and allowed for cooked, more digestible foods;

4. ways of cultivating and domesticating plants and livestock, which resulted in huge increases in food availability; and

5. techniques for smelting metal-containing minerals and working the raw metals into tools, which were much better than those made of wood, stone, or bone.

The rate of new discoveries has increased enormously over time. More recent technological revolutions include

1. methods of utilizing fuels and machines to accomplish work previously done by humans or draught animals;

2. further advances in the domestication and cultivation of plants and animals;

3. discoveries in medicine and sanitation; and

4. extraordinary strides in communications and information-processing technologies.

These and other revolutionary innovations all led to substantial, and sometimes enormous, increases in the ability of humans to exploit the resources of their environment and to achieve population growth (see Chapter 10). Unfortunately, enhanced exploitation has rarely been accompanied by the development of a compensating cultural ethic—that is, one that encourages conservation of the resources needed for survival. Even the early hunting societies of more than 8000 years ago caused the extermination of species that were hunted too effectively (see Chapter 26). Enthusiastic over-harvesting of resources continues today and occurs much more efficiently than in prehistoric times.

The diverse effects of human activities on environmental quality are vital issues, and we will discuss them in detail later. For now, we emphasize the message that intense environmental stress associated with diverse human activities is forcing ecological changes on Earth. Many of these changes are reducing the ability of the environment and ecosystems to sustain humans and their societies. Human activities are also causing enormous degradation of natural ecosystems, including the habitats required to support other species.

In fact, the environmental and ecological damage caused by humans is so severe that an appropriate metaphor for the human enterprise is that of a malignancy, or cancer. This is a sobering image. It is useful to dwell on it so that its meaning does not escape our understanding. **Humans and their activities are endangering species and natural ecosystems at such a tremendous scale and rate that the integrity of Earth's life-support systems is at risk.** From the ecological perspective, the pace and intensity of these changes is truly staggering. Moreover, the damage will become substantially worse before corrective actions are (hopefully) undertaken to stop and reverse the degradation and allow an ecologically sustainable human enterprise to become possible. From a pessimistic perspective, however, it may prove to be beyond the capability of human societies to act effectively to reverse the damage and to design and implement solutions for sustainability.

These are, of course, only opinions, albeit the highly informed, expert opinions of many environmental scientists. Anticipating the future is always uncertain, and things may turn out to be less grim than is now commonly predicted. For example, we might be wrong about the amounts of resources needed to sustain future generations of humans. Still, the clear indications from recent patterns of change are that the environmental crisis is severe and that it will worsen in the foreseeable future.

The belief that humans are causing grievous damage to the life-support systems of Earth, and the metaphor of human activities as a malignancy, should not be dismissed as the opinions of misanthropic people. These beliefs are remarkably common among ecologists and environmental scientists. These opinions result from objective interpretations of recent trends in environmental quality and from reasonably anticipated changes in the future. If many ecologists and environmental scientists have predicted correctly, the future may, indeed, be quite grim. The causes of this future predicament are environmental damage and resource shortages caused by human activities.

But all this damage is not inevitable. There is sincere hope that human societies will yet make appropriate adjustments and will choose to pursue options that are more sustainable than those now being followed.

Environmental Ethics and World Views

Human actions can influence environmental quality by affecting the availability of resources, by causing pollution, and by endangering species and natural ecosystems. Decisions influencing environmental quality are influenced by two types of considerations: *knowledge* and *ethics*.

For the purposes of this book, *knowledge* refers to information and understanding about the natural world, and *ethics* refers to the perception of right and wrong and the appropriate behaviour of people toward each other, other species, and nature. Humans can, of course, choose to interact with the environment and ecosystems in various ways. On the one hand, knowledge provides guidance about the consequences of alternative choices, including damage that might be caused and actions that might be taken to avoid that damage. On the other hand, ethics provides guidance about which alternative actions should be favoured or even allowed to occur.

The influence of both knowledge and ethics on choices is critical because modern humans have enormous power to utilize and damage the environment. And we can choose from among various alternatives. For example, individual people can choose whether to have children, purchase an automobile, or eat meat, while society can decide whether to allow whale hunting, clear-cutting of forests, or the construction of nuclear-power plants. All of these choices have implications for resource consumption, pollution, biodiversity, and other elements of environmental quality.

Perceptions of *value* (i.e., of merit or importance) profoundly influence interpretations of the consequences of human actions. **Environmental values** can be divided into two broad classes: utilitarian and intrinsic.

Utilitarian values (also known as *instrumental values*) are based on the known importance of something to the welfare of humans (see also the discussion of the anthropocentric world view, below). Accordingly, components of the environment and ecosystems are only considered important if they are resources necessary to sustain humans, that is, if they bestow economic benefits, provide livelihoods, and contribute to the life-support system. Humans harvest materials from nature because they have utilitarian value. These include water, timber, fish and animals hunted in wild places, and agricultural crops grown in managed ecosystems.

Ecological values are somewhat broader utilitarian values—they are based partly on the needs of humans, but also those of other species and natural ecosystems. Ecological values often take a longer-term view. *Aesthetic values* are also utilitarian but are based on an appreciation of beauty. They are subjective and influenced by cultural perspectives. Aesthetics might value natural wilderness over human-dominated ecosystems, and free-living whales over whale meat. Maintaining aesthetic values can provide substantial cultural, social, psychological, and economic benefits.

Intrinsic value is based on the belief that components of the natural environment (such as species and natural ecosystems) have inherent value and a right to exist, regardless of any positive, negative, or neutral relationships with humans. Under this system, it would be wrong for humans to treat other creatures cruelly, to take actions that cause other natural entities to become endangered or extinct, or to fail to prevent such an occurrence.

As noted previously, ethics concerns the perception of right and wrong and the values and rules that should govern human conduct. Clearly, ethics of all kinds depend upon the values that people believe are important. **Environmental ethics** deals with the responsibilities of the present human generation to future generations of people and other species to ensure that the world will continue to function in an ecologically healthy way, and to provide adequate resources and livelihoods (this is a key element of sustainable development; see Chapter 12). The environmental values discussed above underlie this system of ethics. Applying environmental ethics often means analyzing and balancing standards that may conflict, because utilitarian, ecological, aesthetic, and intrinsic values rarely all coincide with each other (see Canadian Focus 1.2 and In Detail 1.2).

There is also tension between ethical considerations that are individualistic and those that are holistic. For example, animal-rights activists are highly concerned with issues involving the treatment of individual organisms. Ecologists, however, are typically more concerned with holistic values, such as populations, entire species, and entire ecosystems. As such, an ecologist might advocate a cull of overabundant deer in a park in order to favour the survival of populations of endangered plants.

Values and ethics, in turn, support larger systems known as world views. *World views* are comprehensive philosophies of human life and the universe, and of the

Photo 1.3   According to the biocentric and ecocentric world views, all species have equal intrinsic value. This does not, however, mean that one species cannot exploit another.

Canadian Focus 1.2

Old-Growth Forest: A Case of Values in Competition

Ethics and values are greatly influenced by cultural attitudes. Because the attitudes of people vary considerably, proposals to exploit natural resources as economic commodities often give rise to controversy. Consider the case of old-growth rainforest on Vancouver Island.

Old-growth forest in the coastal zone of British Columbia contains many ancient trees, some of which are hundreds of years old and of gigantic height and girth (see Chapter 23). The cathedral-like aesthetics of old-growth forest are inspiring to many people, providing them with a deeply natural, even religious experience. Major elements of the culture of the First Nations of coastal British Columbia are based on values associated with old-growth forest. Whatever their culture, however, few people fail to be inspired by a walk through a tract of old-growth forest on Vancouver Island.

Old-growth forest is also a special kind of natural ecosystem, different from other forests, supporting species that cannot survive elsewhere. These ecological qualities give the old-growth forest of coastal B.C. an intrinsic value that is not replicated elsewhere in Canada. This ecosystem represents a distinct element of our natural heritage.

Old-growth forest is also an extremely useful resource because it contains large trees that can be harvested and manufactured into lumber or paper. If utilized in this manner, old-growth forest can provide livelihoods for people and revenues for local, provincial, and national economies. Old-growth forest also supports other economic values, including deer and salmon that can be harvested by hunters and fishers, and birds and wildflowers that entice ecotourists to visit these special ecosystems. Intact old-growth forest also provides other valuable services, such as yielding a supply of clean streamwater and helping to regulate atmospheric concentrations of such gases as oxygen and carbon dioxide.

At one time, old-growth forest was widespread on Vancouver Island, but it is now endangered both there and almost everywhere else in Canada. This has happened largely because old-growth forest has been extensively harvested and replaced by younger, second-growth forest. The second-growth forest is harvested as soon as it becomes economically mature, which happens long before it can develop into old-growth forest. The net result is a rapidly diminishing area of old-growth forest and endangerment of both the ecosystem and some of its dependent species.

Obviously, the different values concerning old-growth forest on Vancouver Island are in severe conflict. Proposals to harvest old-growth timber to supply raw material to sawmills and pulp mills are incompatible with other proposals to protect this special ecosystem in parks and ecological reserves. The conflicting perceptions of values have resulted in emotional confrontations between loggers and preservationists, in some cases resulting in civil disobedience, arrests, and jail terms. Ultimately, these controversies can only be resolved by finding a balance among the utilitarian, ecological, aesthetic, and intrinsic values of old-growth forest, and by ensuring that all these values are sustained in the future.

relationship between humans and the natural world. World views include traditional religions, philosophies, and science, as well as other belief systems. Three important environmental world views are known as anthropocentric, biocentric, and ecocentric, while the frontier and sustainability world views are more directly related to the use of resources by humans.

The **anthropocentric world view** considers humans as the centre of moral consideration. Humans are seen as more worthy than any other species and as being uniquely disconnected from the rest of nature. Thus, the anthropocentric world view judges the importance and worthiness of everything, including other species and ecosystems, in terms of the implications for human welfare.

The **biocentric world view** focuses on living entities and considers all species (and individuals) as having intrinsic value. Humans are seen as a unique and special species, but no more worthy than other species. As such, the biocentric world view rejects discrimination against other species, known as *speciesism* (a term similar to racism or sexism).

The **ecocentric world view** considers the direct and indirect connections among species within ecosystems to be invaluable. It also includes consideration for non-living entities, such as rocks, soil, and water. It incorporates the biocentric world view but goes beyond it by stressing the importance of interdependent ecological functions, such as productivity and nutrient cycling.

In Detail 1.2

Scientific and Non-scientific Considerations

Environmental scientists have a responsibility to provide citizens, politicians, regulators, corporations, and other decision makers with sound advice regarding the causes and consequences of environmental damage associated with human activities. By influencing the choices made, scientific information can affect environmental quality. However, decision makers also consider other kinds of non-science information, principally social, when deliberating on alternative choices that can affect environmental quality. Examples of non-science information and considerations include

- political gain or loss;
- aspects of social equity, including the distribution of wealth;
- ethical and philosophical considerations;
- aesthetic quality; and
- proximity effects (e.g., will the effects be felt by myself or by someone else, locally or far away, now or in the future?).

Both social and scientific considerations are important, because together they influence choices about human actions that affect environmental quality. For this reason, both are considered when examining the potential environmental consequences of proposed developments (this planning process is known as *environmental impact assessment* and is described in Chapter 27).

The importance of science and non-science considerations in an environmental issue can be illustrated by the example of tobacco use in our society. Many studies by toxicologists and epidemiologists have shown that certain chemicals in tobacco fumes are poisonous, and that serious medical risks are associated with smoking and even with exposure to second-hand smoke. (Note, however, that there is not scientific consensus about these issues—a small minority of scientists is willing to support claims by the tobacco industry that smoking does not cause health problems.) Decision makers in government agencies consider this scientific information, along with economic data and non-science advice concerning the political implications of alternative actions and other factors. They then decide whether to ban cigarettes or other forms of tobacco; to otherwise regulate the use of these products (e.g., by restricting the age at which people can purchase tobacco or by banning smoking in public places); or to discourage people from smoking (e.g., by prohibiting advertising or by publishing health advisories). However, whatever the action taken by government, ultimately it is individual people who make the decision to smoke or not. Each person bases this decision on his or her understanding of the risks and benefits of smoking, using both science and non-science information, and guided to some degree by government regulation.

The **frontier world view** asserts that humans have a right to exploit nature by consuming natural resources in boundless quantities. Based on utilitarian values and derived from the anthropocentric world view, the frontier world view claims that humans are superior and have a right to "subdue" and exploit nature. Moreover, the supply of resources to sustain humans is considered to be limitless, because new resources or substitutes can always be discovered. The consumption of resources is considered to be good because it enables economies to grow. Nations and individuals should be allowed to consume resources aggressively, as long as no humans are hurt in the process.

The **sustainability world view** acknowledges that humans must have access to vital resources, but the exploitation of those resources should be governed by

appropriate ecological, aesthetic, and intrinsic values. The sustainability world view can assume various forms. The **spaceship world view**, for example, is quite anthropocentric. It focuses only on sustaining those resources needed by people, and it assumes that humans can exert a great degree of control over natural processes and can safely pilot "spaceship Earth." In contrast, **ecological sustainability** is more ecocentric. It considers humans within an ecological context and focuses on sustaining all components of Earth's life-support system by preventing human actions that would degrade them. In an *ecologically sustainable economy*, natural goods and services should be utilized only in ways that do not compromise their future availability and do not endanger the survival of species or natural ecosystems.

Photo 1.4   Places where people live, work, grow food, and harvest natural resources are affected by many kinds of anthropogenic stressors. These result in ecosystems that are not very natural in character, such as the pavement and grassy edges of this major highway in Toronto.

The attitudes of humans and their societies toward other species, natural ecosystems, and resources have enormous implications for environmental quality. Extraordinary damages have been legitimized by attitudes based on a belief in the inalienable right of humans to harvest whatever they desire from nature, without considering pollution, threats to species, or the availability of resources for future generations of people. One of the keys to resolving the environmental crisis is to achieve a widespread adoption of ecocentric and ecological sustainability world views.

The Environmental Crisis

The current environmental crisis embraces many issues. In large part, however, we can classify the issues into three categories: population, resources, and environmental quality.

Population

In 2005, the human population numbered more than 6.4 billion globally, including about 32 million in Canada. The human population has been increasing because of changes in the balance between certain *demographic* parameters, particularly the excess of the *birth rate* over the *death rate*. The recent explosive population growth, and the poverty of so many people, is a root cause of much of the environmental crisis. Directly or indirectly, population growth leads to extensive deforestation, expanding deserts, erosion, water shortages, climate change, endangerment and extinction of species, and other problems. Considered together, these damages represent changes in the character of Earth's biosphere that are as cataclysmic as major geological events, such as glaciation. We will discuss the human population in more detail in Chapters 10 and 11.

Resources

We can distinguish between two types of natural resources. A **non-renewable resource** is present on Earth in a finite quantity. These resources can only be mined, and so as they are used, they are available in smaller and smaller quantities for future generations. Non-renewable resources include metals and fossil fuels such as petroleum and coal.

A **renewable resource** can regenerate after harvesting and, if managed suitably, can provide a supply that is sustainable virtually forever. To be renewable, however, the ability of the resource to regenerate cannot be compromised by environmental damage or inappropriate management practices. Examples of renewable resources include fresh water; the biomass of trees, agricultural plants, and livestock; and hunted animals such as fish and deer. Ultimately, sustainable economies are supported by renewable resources. Too often, however, potentially renewable resources are not used wisely, thereby impairing their renewal and representing a type of mining. Resources will be discussed in Chapters 12, 13, and 14.

Environmental Quality

Environmental quality deals with anthropogenic pollution and disturbance and the effects of these on humans, their economies, other species, and natural ecosystems. Pollution can be caused by pesticides, gases emitted by power plants and vehicles, and hot water discharged by factories into lakes. Examples of disturbance include clearcutting, fishing, and forest fires. We will study the consequences of pollution and disturbance in terms of their effects on biodiversity, climate change, resource availability, risks to human health, and other aspects of environmental quality in Chapters 15 to 26.

Environmental Impacts of Humans

In general terms, the cumulative impact of humans on the biosphere is a function of two factors: the size of the pop-

TABLE 1.1	The Relative Environmental Impacts of Canada, China, and India

The environmental impacts of Canada, China, and India and their individual citizens can be roughly compared using energy use and gross domestic product as simple indicators.

COUNTRY	POPULATION (MILLIONS)	USE OF ENERGY		GROSS DOMESTIC PRODUCT	
		PER CAPITA (10^9 JOULE)	NATIONAL (10^{18} J)	PER CAPITA (10^3 $US)	NATIONAL (10^9 $US)
Canada	31.9	317	10.1	26.1	834
China	1322	35	45.6	1.07	1410
India	1097	18	20.1	0.55	599

Note: Population data are for 2005; energy-use for 2001; GDP for 2003 in current $US.

Source: Data from World Resources Institute (2005)

ulation and the per capita environmental impact. The human population varies greatly among and within countries as does the per capita impact, which depends on the nature and degree of economic development.

How does Canada's impact on the environment compare with that of more populous countries, such as China and India? Let us use energy use and gross domestic product (GDP, the annual value of all goods and services produced by a country) as simple *indicators* of the environmental impact of both individual people and national economies. Energy use is a helpful indicator because energy is required in virtually all activities in a modern society, including driving automobiles, heating homes, mining metal ores and fossil fuels, harvesting forests and fish, manufacturing industrial products, growing and processing food, running computers, and watching television. Gross domestic product represents all of the economic activities in a country, each of which results in some degree of environmental impact.

Canada, with a population of 32 million in 2005, has a much smaller population than China (1.3 billion) or India (1.1 billion), which are the two most populous countries in the world (Table 1.1). However, as indicated by per capita energy use and per capita GDP, individuals in Canada affect the environment much more intensely than do people in China or India. This difference is an inevitable consequence of the affluent nature of the Canadian lifestyle (which can be euphemistically referred to as "affluenza"). Overall, in terms of national energy use and national GDP, the environmental impacts of Canada, China, and India are rather similar.

This is a remarkable observation. Although the population of Canada is relatively small, the intensive resource use by Canadians means that their aggregate effect on the environment is large and comparable to that of much more populous India or China. We can conclude that **the environmental crisis is due to both overpopulation and excessive resource consumption**.

Conclusions

Environmental science is a highly interdisciplinary field that is concerned with issues associated with the rapidly increasing human population, the use and diminishing stocks of natural resources, damage caused by pollution and disturbance, and effects on biodiversity and the biosphere. These are extremely important issues, but they involve complex and poorly understood systems. They also engage conflicts between direct human interests and those of other species and the natural world. Ultimately, the design and implementation of an ecologically sustainable human economy will require a widespread adoption of new world views based on environmental and ecological ethics, which include consideration for the needs of other species and natural ecosystems. This will be the best way of dealing with the so-called "environmental crisis," a modern phenomenon associated with rapid population growth, resource depletion, and environmental damage. This crisis is caused by the combined effects of population increase and an intensification of per capita environmental damage.

Key Terms

environmental science	disturbance
ecology	succession
geography	cultural evolution
environmentalist	environmental values
individual organism	environmental ethics
population	anthropocentric world view
community	biocentric world view
landscape	ecocentric world view
seascape	frontier world view
biosphere	sustainability world view
species	spaceship world view
ecosystem	ecological sustainability
ecosystem approach	non-renewable resource
environmental stressor	renewable resource

Questions for Review

1. Define environmental science, environmental studies, and ecology. List the disciplinary fields of knowledge that each includes.

2. Describe the hierarchical structure of the universe and list the elements that encompass the realms of biology and ecology.

3. Identify the key environmental stressors that may be affecting an ecosystem in your area (e.g., a local park). Make sure that you consider both natural and anthropogenic stressors.

4. What is the difference between morals and knowledge, and how are these conditioned by personal and societal values?

Questions for Discussion

1. Describe how you are connected with ecosystems, both through the resources that you consume (i.e., food, energy, and materials) and through your recreational activities. Which of these connections could you do without?

2. How are your personal ethical standards related to utilitarian, ecological, aesthetic, and intrinsic values? Think about your world view and discuss how it relates to the anthropocentric, biocentric, and ecocentric models of world views.

3. According to information presented in this chapter, Canada might be regarded as being as overpopulated as India and China. Do you believe this is a reasonable conclusion? Justify your answer.

4. Using data available in Appendix C, choose two countries of similar population, one developed and the other less developed, and use simple indicators to compare aspects of their per capita and national environmental impact.

Exploring Issues

1. You have been asked by the United Nations to devise an index of national and per capita environmental impacts that will be used to compare various developed and less-developed countries. Until now, the United Nations has used extremely simple indicators, such as energy use and gross domestic product, but they now want to use more realistic data. How would you design better indicators? What do you think would be the most important components of the indicators and why?

References

Armstrong, S.J. and R.G. Botzler. 2003. *Environmental Ethics: Divergence and Convergence.* Columbus, OH: McGraw-Hill.

Botkin, D. 1992. *Discordant Harmonies. A New Ecology for the 21st Century.* 2nd ed. New York: Oxford University Press.

Callicott, J.B. 1988. *In Defence of the Land Ethic: Essays in Environmental Philosophy.* Albany, NY: State University of New York Press.

DesJardins, J.R. 2000. *Environmental Ethics: An Introduction to Environmental Philosophy.* 3rd ed. Belmont, CA: Wadsworth.

Devall, B. and G. Sessions. 1985. *Deep Ecology: Living as if Nature Mattered.* Salt Lake City, UT: Peregrine Smith Books.

Evernden, L.L.N. 1985. *The Natural Alien: Humankind and Environment.* Toronto, ON: University of Toronto Press.

Evernden, L.L.N. 1992. *The Social Creation of Nature.* Baltimore, MD: Johns Hopkins Press.

Freedman, B. 1995. *Environmental Ecology: The Ecological Effects of Pollution, Disturbance, and Other Stresses.* San Diego, CA: Academic Press.

Hargrove, E.C. 1989. *Foundations of Environmental Ethics.* Englewood Cliffs, NJ: Prentice Hall.

Kuhn, T.S. 1996. *The Structure of Scientific Revolutions.* 3rd ed. Chicago, IL: University of Chicago Press.

Leopold, A. 1949. *A Sand County Almanac.* New York: Oxford University Press.

Livingston, J.A. 1994. *Rogue Primate: An Exploration of Human Domestication.* Toronto, ON: Key Porter Books.

Miller, G.T. 2003. *Living in the Environment.* Pacific Grove, CA: Brooks Cole.

Nash, R.F. 1988. *The Rights of Nature: A History of Environmental Ethics.* Madison, WI: University of Wisconsin Press.

Regan, T. 1984. *Earthbound: New Introductory Essays in Environmental Ethics*. New York: Random House.

Rowe, J.S. 1990. *Home Place: Essays on Ecology*. Edmonton, AB: NeWest Pub.

Schumacher, E.F. 1973. *Small Is Beautiful*. New York: Harper & Row.

Singer, P. 2003. *Ethics*. Oxford, UK: Oxford University Press.

Singer, P. 2004. *Animal Liberation*. New York: Ecco Press.

Wackernagle, M. and E.E. Rees. 1996. *Our Ecological Footprint: Reducing Human Impact on the Earth*. Gabriola Island, BC: New Society Publishers.

White, L. 1967. The Historical Roots of Our Ecologic Crisis. *Science* **155**: 1203–07.

Wilson, E.O. 1984. *Biophilia*. Cambridge, MA: Harvard University Press.

World Resources Institute. 2004. *World Resources 2002–04*. New York: Oxford University Press.

World Resources Institute. 2005. *Earth Trends. The Environmental Information Portal*. Washington, DC: WRI.

Informative Websites

Environmental Literacy Council. www.enviroliteracy.org/

This wide-ranging website provides information on various environmental issues with an aim to educate and foster environmental literacy.

New Ethic: The Independent Ethics Site. www.ethics1.org/

This website provides an overview of ethical considerations in many contexts, including environmental ones. It also has an excellent section that provides links to other websites.

Revisiting Carrying Capacity: Area-Based Indicators of Sustainability. www.dieoff.org/page110.htm

This comprehensive article by William E. Rees of the University of British Columbia discusses sustainability and provides examples and diagrams to support his argument.

Welcome to Enviroethics. www.jiscmail.ac.uk/lists/ENVIROETHICS.html

This site is a forum for discussing environmental ethics.

The Fur Industry

It is likely that the very first items of clothing that early humans wore were made from the skins of animals that they had hunted and killed as a source of meat. Much later on, the killing of wild mammals primarily for their fur became an important commercial activity. In fact, almost immediately upon the European discovery of the regions we now know as Canada, the aggressive pursuit of the fur trade became a critical economic activity. This early fur trade stimulated much of the exploration of the interior of North America.

For most of the history of the fur trade in Canada, fur-bearing mammals were trapped or shot by people living in remote regions of the country, where prey was relatively abundant. The dried and stretched animal skins would be taken to trading posts, such as those operated by the Hudson's Bay Company and the Northwest Company, where they would be exchanged for goods or money. This kind of commercial trapping of fur-bearers still goes on in rural regions of Canada, and it provides employment for many people who might otherwise have trouble finding jobs. Aboriginal peoples have been particularly involved in the harvesting of fur-bearers. In addition, some fur-bearing animals, such as fox and mink, are also cultivated on "ranches."

There is still a strong market for furs today because they are widely used in the garment industry. Although the fur markets have had their ups and downs during the past several decades, they are currently strong and demand is increasing, particularly in Europe and China.

Many people, however, have a deep ethical objection to the fur trade. They disapprove because they consider the killing of wild animals for their pelts to be unnecessary in view of the synthetic replacements that are easily available. Opponents of the fur trade also believe that trapping, the usual method of harvesting wild fur-bearers, is a cruel way of killing animals.

These views are, of course, opposed by the individual people and economic interests that are engaged in the fur trade and also by much of the fashion industry. These interests consider furs to be a natural resource that can be harvested in ways that do not threaten the future supply, while also contributing to the rural economy. Supporters of the fur trade also point to the increasing use of killing methods that are less cruel to the animals.

The views of many supporters and opponents of the fur trade are diametrically opposed, and their differences may be irresolvable. This important controversy also has parallels with other issues involving the cruel treatment and killing of animals, such as the meat trade and the use of animals in biomedical research. These topics are important in environmental studies and function as useful ways of exploring ethical dimensions of the interaction of the human economy with the natural world. These issues are explored in the accompanying CBC video resource.

Questions

1. Do you think that it is OK to wear garments made of or decorated with fur or leather, even though there are suitable synthetics that could be substituted for most uses of these materials? If you think it is acceptable to wear fur or leather, then explain why. If not, why not?

2. What is a renewable natural resource? Is it appropriate to view wild fur-bearing mammals in this manner? Remember, some fur-bearers exist in numbers that are large enough that some animals could be harvested at a rate that would not deplete the population. Is this any different from killing wild animals as a source of meat?

Video Resource

"Fur Industry," CBC The National, January 10, 2003.

Selected References

International Fur Trade Association. http://www.iftf.com/
Library and Archives Canada. 2001. *The Fur Trade and Hudson's Bay Company.*
http://www.canadiana.org/hbc/intro_e.html
The Coalition to Abolish the Fur Trade.
http://www.caft.org.uk/

Science as a Way of Understanding the Natural World

2

CHAPTER OBJECTIVES

After completing this chapter, you will be able to

1. Describe the nature of science and its usefulness in explaining the structure and function of the natural world.
2. Distinguish among facts, hypotheses, and theories.
3. Outline the methodology of science, including the critical importance of tests designed to disprove hypotheses.
4. Discuss the importance of uncertainty in many scientific predictions and the relevance of this to environmental controversies.

CHAPTER OUTLINE

- The Nature of Science
- Inductive and Deductive Logic
- Goals of Science
- Facts, Hypotheses, and Experiments
- Uncertainty
- Conclusions

The Nature of Science

Science can be defined as the systematic study of the character and behaviour of the physical and biological world. Science is also a rapidly expanding body of knowledge about the natural world. A goal of science is to discover the simplest general principles that explain the enormous complexity of the natural world. These principles can be used to gain insights about the structure and function of nature and to make predictions about future change.

Science is a relatively recent way of learning about natural phenomena, having largely replaced the influences of other, less objective methods and world views. The major alternatives to science are belief systems that are influential in all cultures, including those based on religion, morality, and aesthetics. These belief systems are primarily directed toward different ends, such as finding meaning that transcends the natural world, learning how people ought to behave toward each other, or understanding the value of art.

Modern science evolved from natural philosophy, a way of learning developed by classical Greeks that was concerned with rational investigations of existence, knowledge, and phenomena. Compared with modern science, however, investigations in natural philosophy use relatively unsophisticated technologies and methods and are not particularly quantitative, sometimes involving only the application of logic.

Modern science began with the systematic investigations of such famous sixteenth- and seventeenth-century scientists as

1. Nicolaus Copernicus (1473–1543), a Polish astronomer who first conceived the modern theory of the solar system;

2. William Gilbert (1544–1603), an Englishman who worked on magnetism;

3. Galileo Galilei (1564–1642), an Italian who conducted research on the physics of objects in motion as well as astronomy;

4. William Harvey (1578–1657), an Englishman who described the circulation of the blood; and

5. Isaac Newton (1642–1727), an Englishman who made important contributions to understanding gravity, laws of motion, the nature of light, and the mathematics of calculus.

Inductive and Deductive Logic

The English philosopher Francis Bacon (1561–1626) was also highly influential in the development of modern science. Bacon was not an actual practitioner of science but was a strong proponent of its emerging methodologies. He promoted the usefulness of **inductive logic**, in which conclusions are objectively developed from the accumulating evidence of experience and the results of experiments. Inductive logic can lead to unifying explanations based on large bodies of data and observations of natural phenomena. Consider the following illustration of inductive logic, applied to an environmental topic:

Observation 1: Marine mammals off the Atlantic coast of Canada have large residues of DDT and other chlorinated hydrocarbons in their fat and other body tissues.

Observation 2: So do marine mammals off British Columbia.

Observation 3: As do marine mammals in the Arctic Ocean, although in lower concentrations.

Inductive conclusion: There is widespread contamination of marine mammals with chlorinated hydrocarbons. Further research may demonstrate a global contamination. This suggests a potentially important environmental problem.

In contrast, the application of **deductive logic** involves making one or more initial assumptions and then drawing logical conclusions from those premises. Consequently, the truth of deductive conclusions depends entirely on the veracity of the original assumptions. If those assumptions are based on false information or on incorrect supernatural belief, then any deduced conclusions about natural phenomena are likely to be wrong. Consider the following illustration of deductive logic:

Assumption 1: TCDD, an extremely toxic chemical in the dioxin family, is poisonous when present in even the smallest concentrations in food and water—even a single molecule can cause toxicity.

Assumption 2: Exposure to anything that is poisonous in even the smallest concentrations is unsafe.

Assumption 3: No exposure that is unsafe should be allowed.

Deductive conclusion 1: No exposure to TCDD is safe.

Deductive conclusion 2: No emissions of TCDD should be allowed.

The two conclusions are consistent with the original assumptions. However, scientists disagree about those assumptions. Many toxicologists believe that exposures to TCDD (and other potentially toxic chemicals) must exceed a "threshold of biological tolerance" before any poisoning will result (see Chapter 15). In contrast, other scientists believe that even the smallest exposure to TCDD carries some degree of toxic risk. In this and many other cases in the environmental field, the science issues are not yet resolved, and may never be.

In general, inductive logic plays a much stronger role in modern science than deductive logic. In both cases, however, the usefulness of any conclusions depends greatly on the accuracy of the observations and data on which they were based. Poor data may lead to an inaccurate conclusion through the application of inductive logic, as will inappropriate assumptions in deductive logic.

Goals of Science

The goals of science are to understand natural phenomena and to explain any changes in them. To achieve those goals, scientists undertake investigations that are based on information, inferences, and conclusions developed through a systematic application of inductive logic. Scientists observe natural phenomena and conduct experiments.

A higher goal of scientific research is to formulate laws that describe the workings of the universe in general terms. (See, for example, Chapter 4 for a discussion of the laws of thermodynamics, which describe the transformations of energy among its various states.) Universal laws, along with *theories* and *hypotheses*, are used to understand and explain natural phenomena. Many natural phenomena, however, are extremely complex and may never be fully understood in terms of physical laws. This is particularly true of the ways that organisms and ecosystems work and are organized.

Scientific investigations may be *pure* or *applied*. Pure science is driven by curiosity—it is the unfettered search for knowledge and understanding, without regard for its usefulness in human welfare. Applied science is more goal-oriented and deals specifically with practical difficulties and problems of one sort or another. Applied science might examine how to improve the technological instruments available to society, how to solve problems in the man-agement of natural resources, or how to reduce pollution or deal with other kinds of environmental damage associated with human activities.

Facts, Hypotheses, and Experiments

A **fact** is an event or thing that is definitely known to have happened, to exist, and to be true. Facts are based on experience and scientific evidence. In contrast, a **hypothesis** is a proposed explanation of the occurrence or cause of a phenomenon. Scientists formulate hypotheses as statements and test them through experiments and other forms of research. Hypotheses are developed using logic, inference, and mathematical arguments in order to explain the nature of observed phenomena. It must always be possible to refute scientific hypotheses. Thus, the hypothesis that "cats are so intelligent that they prevent humans from discovering it" cannot be logically refuted, and so it is not a scientific hypothesis.

Theory is a broader term that refers to a set of laws, rules, and explanations. These are supported by a large body of experimental and observational evidence, all leading to robust, internally consistent conclusions. Some of the most famous theories in science are:

1. the theory of evolution by natural selection, published simultaneously in 1858 by the English naturalists Charles Darwin (1809–82) and Alfred Russel Wallace (1823–1913);

2. the theory of gravitation, first proposed by Isaac Newton (1642–1727); and

3. the theory of relativity, identified by the German–Swiss physicist Albert Einstein (1879–1955).

Celebrated theories such as these are strongly supported by large bodies of evidence, and they will likely persist for a long time. It cannot, however, be said that these (or any other) theories are known with certainty to be true—some future experiments may yet falsify even these famous theories.

The **scientific method** begins with the identification of a question involving the structure or function of the natural world, which is often developed using inductive logic (Figure 2.1). The question is interpreted in terms of existing theory, and specific hypotheses are formulated to

Photo 2.1 Charles Darwin (1809–82), regarded by some as the greatest naturalist of all time, is best known for the theory of evolution by natural selection. Darwin and Alfred Russel Wallace (1823–1913) announced the theory simultaneously in 1858.

Source: CP/AP Photo

explain the character and causes of the natural phenomenon. Observations made in nature, and especially in carefully controlled experiments, usually give scientists reasons to reject various hypotheses rather than to accept them. Most hypotheses are rejected because their predictions are not borne out during the course of research. Any viable hypotheses are further examined through additional research, again largely involving experiments designed to disprove each hypothesis. Once a large body of evidence accumulates in support of a hypothesis, it can be used to corroborate the original theory.

The scientific method can be used to investigate only those questions that can be critically examined through observation and experiment. Consequently, science cannot by itself resolve value-laden questions such as the meaning of life, good versus evil, or the existence and nature of God or any other supernatural being or force.

An **experiment** is a test or investigation that is designed to provide evidence in support of, or preferably against, a hypothesis. **Natural experiments** are conducted by observing actual variations of phenomena in nature, and then developing explanations for them by analysis of possible causal mechanisms. **Manipulative experiments** involve the deliberate alteration of factors that are hypoth-

esized to influence phenomena. These manipulations are carefully planned and controlled in order to determine whether predicted responses will occur, thereby uncovering causal relationships.

By far the most useful working hypotheses in scientific research are **null hypotheses** that we seek to disprove rather than support. Null hypotheses are specific testable hypotheses that deny something implied by the main hypothesis under investigation. Unless null hypotheses are eliminated on the basis of contrary evidence, we cannot be confident of the main hypothesis.

This is a very important aspect of scientific investigation. A hypothesis might, for example, be supported by a large number of confirming experiments or observations. This does not, however, serve to "prove" the hypothesis, only to support its conditional acceptance. As soon as a clearly defined hypothesis is falsified by an appropriately designed and well-conducted experiment, it is disproved for all time (provided that the assumptions in the experiment were not later disproved). This is why experiments designed to disprove hypotheses are a key aspect of the scientific method.

Revolutionary advances in understanding may occur when important hypotheses and theories are rejected due

FIGURE 2.1 Diagrammatic Representation of the Scientific Method

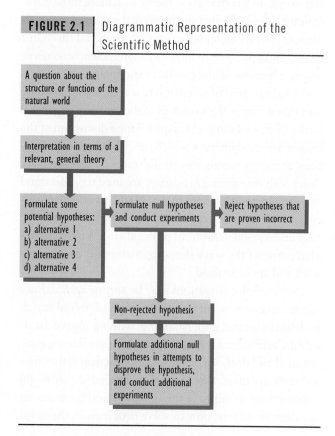

Source: Modified from Raven and Johnson (1992)

to the discoveries of science. For instance, once it was discovered that the Earth is not flat, it became possible to confidently sail beyond the visible horizon without fear of falling off the planet. Another example involved the important discovery by Copernicus that the planets of our solar system revolve around the sun, and the related concept that the sun is an ordinary star among many—these revolutionary ideas replaced the previously dominant one that the planets, sun, and stars all revolved around the Earth. Thomas Kuhn (1922–95) was a philosopher of science who emphasized the important role of so-called "scientific revolutions" in achieving great advances in understanding about the structure and function of the natural world. In essence, Kuhn said that scientific revolutions occur when well-established theories are rigorously tested and then collapse under the accumulating weight of new facts and observations that cannot be explained, and so render the original ideas obsolete, to be replaced by a new, more informed **paradigm** (i.e., a set of assumptions, concepts, practices, and values that constitutes a way of viewing reality and is shared by an intellectual community).

Factors believed to influence natural phenomena are called **variables**. For example, a scientist might hypothesize that the productivity of a wheat crop is potentially limited by such variables as the availability of water or of nutrients such as nitrogen and phosphorus. Some of the most powerful scientific experiments involve the manipulation of *key* (or controlling) variables and the comparison of the results of these treatments with those of a **control** that was not manipulated. In the example just described, the specific variable that controls wheat productivity could be identified by conducting an experiement in which test populations of wheat are provided with varying amounts of water, nitrogen, and phosphorus, alone and in combination, and then comparing the results with a non-manipulated control.

In some respects, the explanation of the scientific method offered above is uncritical. It perhaps suggests a too-orderly progression in terms of logical, objective experimentation and comparison of alternative hypotheses. These are, in fact, important components of the scientific method. However, it is also important to understand that the insights and personal biases of scientists are significant in the conduct and progress of science. In most cases, scientists design experiments that they think will "work"; that is, experiments that will yield useful results and contribute to the orderly advancement of knowledge in their field. Karl Popper (1902–94), a famous European philosopher, noted that scientists tend to use their "imaginative pre-

conception" of the workings of the natural world and design experiments based on those informed insights. This means that effective scientists must be more than knowledgeable and technically skilled—they must also be capable of a certain degree of insightful creativity when forming their ideas, hypotheses, and research.

Uncertainty

Much scientific investigation involves the collection of observations and data by measuring and monitoring phenomena in the natural world. Another important aspect of science involves making predictions about the future values of variables. Such projections require some degree of understanding of the relationships among variables and their influencing factors, and of recent patterns of change. However, many types of scientific information and predictions are subject to *inaccuracy*. Often, measured data are only approximations of the true values of phenomena, and predictions are rarely fulfilled exactly. The accuracy of observations and predictions is influenced by various factors, including those described in the following sections.

Phenomena Can Be Predictable or Uncertain

Some phenomena are highly predictable, but most are uncertain. A few phenomena are considered to have a universal character and are consistent wherever and whenever they are accurately measured. One of the best examples of such a universal constant is the speed of light, which always has a value of 2.998×10^8 m/s, regardless of where it is measured or of the speed of the body from which the light is emitted. Similarly, certain relationships describing transformations of energy and matter, known as the laws of thermodynamics (Chapter 4), always give reliable predictions.

Most natural phenomena, however, are not universally consistent—depending on circumstances, there are exceptions to general predictions about these phenomena. This circumstance is particularly true of biology and ecology, related fields of science in which virtually all general predictions have exceptions. We have not yet discovered any inviolate laws or unifying principles of biology or ecology, in contrast to the several esteemed laws and 11 universal constants of physics. For this reason, biologists and ecologists have great difficulties making accurate predictions about responses of organisms and ecosystems to environmental change. This is why biologists and ecologists are sometimes said to have "physics envy."

In large part, the inaccuracies of biology and ecology occur because key functions are controlled by complexes of poorly understood, and sometimes unidentified, environmental influences. Consequently, predictions about future values of biological and ecological variables or the causes of changes are seldom accurate. For example, even though ecologists in eastern Canada have been monitoring the population size of spruce budworm (an important pest of conifer forests) for some years, they cannot accurately predict its future abundance in particular stands of forest or in larger regions. This is because the abundance of this moth is influenced by a complex of environmental factors, including tree-species composition, age of the forest, abundance of its predators and parasites, quantities of its preferred foods, weather at critical times of year, and insecticide use to reduce its populations (see Chapter 21). Biologists and ecologists still do not fully understand this complexity, and perhaps they never will.

Variable Phenomena

Many natural phenomena vary in space and time. This is true of physical and chemical variables as well as of biological and ecological ones. Within a forest, for example, the amount of sunlight reaching the ground varies temporally, depending on time of day and season of the year. It also varies spatially, depending on the density of foliage over the place where sunlight is being measured. Similarly, the density of a particular species of fish within a river typically varies greatly in response to changes in habitat conditions and other influences. Most fish populations also vary greatly over time, especially migratory species such as salmon. In environmental science, replicated (that is, independently repeated) measurements and statistical analyses are used to measure and account for these kinds of spatial and temporal variations.

Accuracy, Precision, and Significant Figures

Accuracy refers to the degree to which a measurement or observation reflects the actual, or true, value of the subject. For example, the insecticide DDT and the metal mercury are potentially toxic chemicals that occur in trace concentrations in all organisms, but their small residues are difficult to analyze chemically. Some of the analytical methods used to determine DDT and mercury concentrations are more accurate than others and therefore provide relatively useful and reliable data compared with less accurate methods. In fact, analytical data are usually approximations of the real values—exact accuracy is rarely attainable.

Precision is different from accuracy and is related to the degree of *repeatability* of a measurement or observation. For example, suppose that the actual number of caribou in a particular migrating herd is 10 246 animals. A wildlife ecologist might estimate that there were about 10 000 animals in that herd, which for practical purposes is a reasonably accurate approximation of the actual number of caribou. If other ecologists also independently estimate the size of the herd at about 10 000 caribou, there is a good degree of precision among the values. If, however, some systematic bias existed in the methodology used to count the herd, giving consistent estimates of 15 000 animals (remember, the actual population is 10 246 caribou), these estimates would be considered precise, but not particularly accurate.

Precision is also related to the number of digits with which data are reported. If you were using a flexible tape to measure the lengths of 10 large, wriggly snakes, you would probably measure the reptiles only to the nearest centimetre. The strength and squirminess of the subjects make more precise measurements impossible. The reported average length of the 10 snakes should reflect the original measurements and might be given as 204 cm and not a value such as 203.8759. The latter number might be

Photo 2.2 An experiment is a controlled investigation designed to provide evidence for, or preferably against, a hypothesis about the working of the natural world. This laboratory experiment exposed test populations of a grass to different concentrations of toxic chemicals.

displayed as a calculated average by a calculator or computer, but it is unrealistically precise.

Significant figures are also related to accuracy and precision and can be defined as the number of digits used to report data from analyses or calculations. Significant figures are best understood by examples. The number 179 has three significant figures, as does the number 0.0849 and also 0.000 794 (i.e., the zeros preceding the significant integers do not count). However, the number 195 000 000 has nine significant figures (i.e., the zeros following are meaningful), although the number 195×10^6 has only three significant figures (see also Appendix A). It is rarely useful to report environmental or ecological data with more than two to four significant figures. This is because any more would generally exceed the accuracy and precision of the methodology used in the estimation and would therefore be unrealistic. For example, the approximate population of Canada in 2005 was 31.9 million people (or 31.9×10^6; both of these notations have three significant figures). However, the population should not be reported as 31 900 000, which implies an unrealistic accuracy and precision of eight significant figures.

The Need for Scepticism in Environmental Science

Environmental science is filled with examples of uncertainty—in present values and in future changes of environmental variables, as well as in predictions of biological and ecological responses to those changes. To some degree the difficulties associated with scientific uncertainty can be mitigated by developing and using improved technologies for analysis and by modelling and studying changes occurring in ecosystems in different parts of the world. The latter approach enhances our understanding by providing convergent evidence about the occurrence and causes of natural phenomena.

Scientific information and understanding will always, however, be subject to some degree of uncertainty. Therefore, predictions will always be, to some extent, inaccurate. Uncertainty must always be considered when trying to understand and deal with the causes and consequences of environmental and ecological changes. As such, all information and predictions in environmental science must be critically interpreted with uncertainty in mind. This should be done whenever one is learning about an environmental issue, whether it involves listening to a speaker in a classroom, at a conference, or on television or

the radio, or when reading an article in a newspaper, magazine, textbook, or respected scientific journal. Because of the uncertainty of many predictions in science, and particularly in environmental science, a certain amount of scepticism and critical analysis is always useful.

Environmental issues are acutely important to the welfare of humans and other species. Science and its methods allow for the critical and objective identification of important issues, the investigation of their causes, and a degree of understanding of the consequences of environmental change. Scientific information influences decision making about environmental issues, including whether to pursue expensive strategies to avoid further, but often uncertain, damage.

Scientific information is, however, only one consideration for decision makers, who are also concerned with the political, economic, and cultural contexts of environmental problems (see In Detail 1.2 and Chapter 27). In fact, when deciding how to deal with the causes and consequences of environmental changes, decision makers may give greater weight to non-scientific (or social and economic) considerations than to scientific ones, especially when there is uncertainty about the latter. The most important decisions about environmental issues are made by politicians and senior bureaucrats in government, or by private managers, not by environmental scientists. Decision makers typically worry about the short-term implications of their decisions on their chances for re-election or continued employment, and on the economic activity of a company or society at large, as much as they do about the consequences of environmental damage (see also Chapter 27).

Conclusions

The procedures and methods of science are important in identifying, understanding, and resolving environmental problems. At the same time, however, social and economic issues are also vital considerations. Although science has made tremendous progress in helping us to understand the natural world, the extreme complexity of organisms and ecosystems makes it difficult for environmental scientists to make reliable predictions about the consequences of many human economic activities and other influences. This context underscores the need for continued study of the scientific and socio-economic dimensions of environmental problems, even while practical decisions are made to deal with obvious issues as they arise.

Key Terms

science

inductive logic

deductive logic

fact

hypothesis

theory

scientific method

experiment

natural experiment

manipulative experiment

null hypothesis

paradigm

variable

control

accuracy

precision

significant figures

Questions for Review

1. Outline the reasons why science is a rational way of understanding the natural world.

2. Describe the differences between inductive and deductive logic. Why is inductive logic most often used by scientists when formulating hypotheses and generalizations about the natural world?

3. Why are null hypotheses an efficient way to conduct scientific research? Identify a hypothesis suitable for examining a specific problem in environmental science and suggest a corresponding null hypothesis that could be examined through research.

4. What are the causes of variation in natural phenomena? Choose an example, such as differences in the body weights of a defined group of people, and suggest reasons for the natural variation.

Questions for Discussion

1. What are the key differences between science and less objective belief systems, such as religion?

2. What factors result in legitimate scientific controversies about environmental issues? Contrast these with environmental controversies that exist because of differing values and world views.

3. Explain why there are no scientific "laws" that explain the structure and function of ecosystems.

4. Many natural phenomena are highly variable, particularly ones that are biological or ecological. What are the implications of this variability for understanding and predicting the causes and consequences of environmental changes? How do environmental scientists cope with this challenge of a variable natural world?

Exploring Issues

1. Come up with an environmental question of interest to you. Suggest useful hypotheses to be investigated, identify the null hypotheses, and outline experiments that might be conducted.

2. During a research project investigating mercury, an environmental scientist performed a series of chemical analyses of fish caught in Lake Canuck, a large body of water. The sampling program involved seven species of fish obtained from various habitats within the lake. A total of 360 fish of various sizes and sexes were analyzed. It was discovered that 30% of the fish had residue levels greater than 0.5 ppm of mercury, the upper level of contamination recommended by Health Canada for fish eaten by humans. The scientist reported these results to a governmental regulator, who was alarmed by the high mercury levels because of Lake Canuck's popularity as a place where local people fish for food. The regulator asked the scientist to recommend whether it was safe to eat any fish from the lake or whether to avoid only certain sizes, sexes, species, or habitats. What sorts of data analyses should the scientist perform to develop useful recommendations? What other scientific and non-scientific aspects should be considered?

References

AAAS. 1989. *Science for All Americans*. Washington, DC: American Association for the Advancement of Science (AAAS).

Barnes, B. 1985. *About Science*. London, UK: Blackwell Ltd.

Giere, R.N. 1996. *Understanding Scientific Reasoning*. 4th ed. New York: Wadsworth Publishing.

Kuhn, T.S. 1996. *The Structure of Scientific Revolutions*. 3rd ed. Chicago, OH: University of Chicago Press.

McCain, G. and E.M. Siegal. 1982. *The Game of Science*. Boston, MA: Holbrook Press Inc.

Moore, J.A. 1999. *Science as a Way of Knowing*. Boston, MA: Harvard University Press.

Popper, K. 1979. *Objective Knowledge: An Evolutionary Approach*. Oxford, UK: Clarendon Press.

Raven, P.H., G.B. Johnson, S. Singer, and J. Leves. 2004. *Biology*. Columbus, OH: McGraw-Hill.

Silver, B.L. 2000. *The Ascent of Science*. Oxford, UK: Oxford University Press.

Informative Websites

BadScience. www.ems.psu.edu/~fraser/BadScience.html

This is one professor's attempt to clarify well-understood phenomena that are persistently explained incorrectly.

Method for Finding Scientific Truth.

www.astronomynotes.com/scimethd/s1.htm

Scientific theory, correlation, induction, assumptions, and ways of finding the truth are all discussed here.

National Center for Science Education.

www.natcenscied.org/article.asp

The National Center for Science Education is an interest group whose mandate involves the teaching of science and evolution in public schools. This website includes readings about the differences between science and religion and related issues.

Project 2061. A Program of the American Association for the Advancement of Science (AAAS).

www.project2061.org/default_flash.htm

This website of the AAAS provides an overview of issues related to science literacy, as well as many useful links.

The Association for Science Education (ASE).

www.ase.org.uk/

The ASE is a U.K.-based organization that promotes excellence in teaching and achievement in science.

The GLOBE Program. www.globe.gov/globe_flash.html

The GLOBE program is a U.S.-based but international program that fosters hands-on science education.

3

The Physical World

CHAPTER OBJECTIVES

After completing this chapter, you will be able to

1. Explain the geological structure and dynamics of planet Earth.
2. Describe the importance of glaciation and other geological forces in modifying the landscapes of Canada.
3. Outline the four major elements of Earth's water cycle.
4. Describe Earth's atmosphere and its circulation.
5. Explain the elements of climate and weather.

CHAPTER OUTLINE

- Introduction
- Planet Earth
- Geological Dynamics
- The Hydrosphere
- The Atmosphere
- Climate and Weather
- Conclusions

Introduction

In this chapter we examine various aspects of the physical world, including the origin of Earth and the nature and dynamics of its physical and geological attributes. Understanding these subjects is important in environmental science because they provide a context for interpreting the changes being caused by human activities.

Planet Earth

The sun is an ordinary star, one of billions of billions that exist in the universe. The universe is thought to have originated as many as 15–20 billion years ago during an immense cataclysm known as the "big bang." Initially, virtually all of the mass of the universe consisted of the two lightest elements, hydrogen and helium, which existed as an extremely diffuse gaseous mass. Eventually, under the influence of gravity, the hydrogen and helium aggregated and became compressed under enormously high pressure and temperature into developing stars. This caused the formation of heavier elements through nuclear fusion, accompanied by the release of tremendous amounts of energy. Because of these processes, there are now 87 naturally occurring elements. Hydrogen and helium are, however, still the most abundant elements, comprising more than 99.9% of the mass of the universe.

The sun, its nine orbiting planets, miscellaneous comets, meteors, asteroids, and other local materials (such as space dust) are collectively known as the **solar system**. This particular region of the universe is organized and held together by a balance of the attractive force of gravitation and the repulsive forces associated with rotation and orbiting (these same forces, along with continuing expansion from the initial big bang, also organize the universe). The age of the solar system (and of Earth) is at least 4.5 billion years.

Earth is a dense planet, as are the other so-called terrestrial planets located relatively close to the sun: Mercury, Venus, and Mars. The mass of these planets consists almost entirely of heavier elements such as iron, nickel, magnesium, aluminum, and silicon. These inner planets were formed by a selective condensing of heavier elements out of the primordial planetary nebula (i.e., the disk of gases and other matter that slowly rotated around the sun during the early stages of formation of the solar system). This happened because the inner planets were subjected to relatively intense heating by solar radiation, which allowed heavier elements to liquefy and solidify, while much of the lighter gases such as hydrogen and helium ended up in the outer, cooler planets. Consequently, the more distant planets in the solar system, such as Jupiter and Saturn, are relatively large, gaseous, and diffuse in character. Most of their volume is composed of an extensive atmosphere of hydrogen and helium, although these planets may contain heavier elements in their cores.

Earth, the third closest planet to the sun, is the only place in the universe definitely known to sustain life. It is quite possible, however, that other places in the cosmos also sustain life. Although there is no direct evidence, many scientists nevertheless consider it likely that life has evolved elsewhere. One estimate suggests that the universe contains 10^{20} (i.e., 10^{11} billion) stars, with perhaps 10% of them having planetary systems (i.e., 10^{19} systems). It is highly probable that at least some of the billions of billions of other planetary systems in the universe support suitable conditions for the genesis of life.

Earth is a spherical body with a diameter of about 12 000 km. It revolves around the sun in an elliptical orbit, at an average distance of about 149 million km, completing an orbit in 365.26 days, or one year. Earth also rotates on its axis every 24 hours, or one day. Earth's single moon has a diameter of about 3500 km and a mass about 1.2% that of Earth. The Moon revolves around Earth in an elliptical orbit at an average distance of about 385 000 km, completed every 27.3 days (the lunar month).

Earth's sphere is thought to be composed of four layers—the core, mantle, lithosphere, and crust—arranged in concentric layers like an onion. Earth's massive **core** has a diameter of about 3500 km and is made up mostly of hot, molten metals, particularly iron and nickel. The internal heat of Earth is generated by the slow, radioactive decay of unstable isotopes of elements such as uranium.

The **mantle** is a less dense region enclosing the core, about 2800 km thick and composed of minerals in a plastic, semi-liquid state known as *magma*. The mantle contains large amounts of relatively light elements, notably silicon, oxygen, and magnesium, occurring as various mineral compounds. Magma from the upper mantle sometimes erupts to the surface at mountainous vents known as volcanoes and is usually spewed from the surface as lava, which cools to form basaltic rock. The next layer, the **lithosphere**, is only about 80 km thick and is made of rigid, relatively light rocks, especially basaltic, granitic, and sedimentary ones. These rocks contain elements found in the mantle as well as enriched quantities of aluminum, carbon, calcium, potassium, sodium, sulphur, and other lighter elements.

The outermost layer is known as the **crust**. Oceanic crust is relatively thin, averaging 10–15 km, while continental crust is 20–60 km thick. Earth's crust has an extremely complex mineralogical composition, in contrast to the mantle and especially the core, which are thought to be relatively uniform in their structure and constitution. The most abundant elements in the crust are oxygen (45%), silicon (27%), aluminum (8.0%), iron (5.8%), calcium (5.1%), magnesium (2.8%), sodium (2.3%), potassium (1.7%), titanium (0.86%), vanadium (0.17%), hydrogen (0.14%), phosphorus (0.10%), and carbon (0.032%).

The rocks forming the crust can be grouped into three basic types: igneous, sedimentary, and metamorphic. **Igneous rocks** include basalt and granite, which are formed by the cooling of molten magma. The mineral forms depend on the rate of cooling and other factors. Basalt is a heavy, dark, extremely fine-grained rock that sometimes forms vertical, columnar structures. Basaltic rocks are the major constituent of oceanic crust, originating in submarine places where magmic lava erupts to the sea-floor surface, such as deep-ocean spreading zones and abyssal volcanoes. Basalt can also be formed at terrestrial volcanoes—for instance, it forms the basement rock of the Hawaiian archipelago and other volcanic islands. Granitic rocks dominate the continental crust and are typically relatively light in colour and density and are coarse-grained, with readily distinguishable crystals. The complex crystalline structure includes the minerals quartz and feldspar, and mica and hornblende are often present.

Sedimentary rocks include limestone, dolomite, shale, sandstone, and conglomerates. These form from particles eroded from other rocks or from precipitated minerals such as calcite ($CaCO_3$), which become lithified (turned into stone) under great pressure in deep oceanic deposits. Sedimentary rocks typically overlie basaltic or granitic rocks.

Metamorphic rocks are formed from igneous or sedimentary ones that were changed under the combined influences of geological heat and pressure. These conditions are encountered when the primary rocks are carried deep into the lithosphere by crustal movements, such as those associated with mountain building (described below). Gneiss, for example, is a metamorphic rock derived from granite, while marble is derived from limestone, and slate from shale.

About 30% of Earth's surface is covered by the solid substrates of continents and islands. The other 70% of Earth's surface is liquid water, virtually all of which is oceanic. In addition, Earth's dense sphere is immersed in a gaseous envelope known as the atmosphere, which extends to a distance of about 1000 km. However, about 99% of the mass of the atmosphere occurs within 30 km of the planet's surface.

Geological Dynamics

Throughout its history, Earth has been subject to enormous geological forces that have greatly affected its mineralogical composition and surface features. The predominant influences are **tectonic forces**, which are associated with crustal movements and other processes that cause structural deformation of rocks and minerals. Geological forces also cause the continents and their underlying plates to slowly move about Earth's surface, much like rafts of solid rock riding upon a sea of plastic magma. Mountain ranges are built where crustal plates collide and push up surface rocks.

Earthquakes and *volcanoes* are also tectonic phenomena, influencing Earth's crust and surface with extremely powerful, sometimes disastrous events. Other massive geological forces include rare, cataclysmic strikes into our planet by *meteorites* and extensive *glaciation* associated with climatic cooling. Slower but still pervasive geological forces are *erosion* (caused by water, wind, and gravity) and *weathering* (the fracturing of rocks and dissolution of minerals).

Over geological time, these various physical processes have profoundly influenced the present character of Earth. Geological forces continue to have enormous influences on Earth and its ecosystems, over both short- and long-term time scales. Environmental changes associated with Earth's geological dynamics provide a natural context for the substantial changes that humans are now causing through various economic activities.

Meteorites

Earth is frequently struck by fast-moving, rocky or metallic objects from space known as **meteorites**. Although meteorites are relatively small objects (by planetary standards), they have immense momentum because of their speed, which typically ranges from 10–100 km/s. The smallest, most numerous meteorites reaching Earth typically burn up or explode in the atmosphere because of heat generated by friction, but larger ones can survive to strike the surface. It has been estimated that each day a meteorite weighing at least 100 g impacts somewhere in Canada.

Very large meteorites are extremely rare, but they can cause enormous damage. The impact site is typically obliterated, and a large crater is formed because vast quantities of crustal materials are ejected into the atmosphere. Immense *sea waves* can also be caused by a meteorite impact. The two largest of the several dozen large meteorite craters known in Canada are an ovoid depression with a diameter of 140 km near Sudbury, Ontario, and a doughnut-shaped lake with a diameter of 100 km at Manicouagan, Quebec. These were created by collisions with meteorites more than 570 million years ago. These extraordinary events must have caused tremendous damage to the species and ecosystems of the time.

Earth's evolutionary history has been punctuated by a number of catastrophic events of mass extinction, when most of the existing biota disappeared in a short period of time, to be later replaced by new species (see Chapter 6). Paleontologists recognize these cataclysms by rapid changes in Earth's fossil record, which point to the transition between stages in the geological time scale (Table 3.1). According to surviving evidence, the most intense mass extinction event occurred 245 million years ago at the end of the Permian period, when an astonishing 96% of species may have become extinct. Another mass extinction occurred 65 million years ago at the end of the Cretaceous period, when perhaps 76% of species became extinct, including the last of the dinosaurs.

According to one theory, the end-of-Cretaceous extinctions were caused when a 10–15-km-wide meteorite impacted the Earth. It is thought that huge amounts of fine dust were spewed into the upper atmosphere, resulting in a climatic cooling that large animals and many ecosystems could not tolerate. Some geologists believe that the impact site was near the Yucatan coast of Mexico, where a buried, 170-km-wide ring structure exists, dated to about 65 million years old. Although controversial, the theory of rare, meteorite-caused catastrophes has also been used to explain other mass extinctions in the geological record.

Plate Tectonics and Related Processes

The theory of *plate tectonics* concerns the dynamics of Earth's surface crustal materials. In simple terms, this theory suggests that Earth's crust and mantle behave as an enormous convecting system. This is characterized by slow surface movements of huge plates of rigid crustal

TABLE 3.1	The Geological Time Scale

Divisions between geological time stages are largely assigned on the basis of rapid changes in species composition of the fossil record. These are related to events of mass extinction, followed by the evolutionary radiation of new species and families. The record is most detailed for relatively recent times, because their fossil records are more complete.

Time is given in millions of years and indicates the beginning of each time stage (e.g., the Holocene epoch ranges from 10 000 years ago to the present; the Pleistocene ranges from 1.6 million years ago to 10 000 years ago).

ERA	PERIOD	EPOCH	TIME ($\times 10^6$ YEARS)
Cenozoic	Quaternary	Holocene (recent)	0.01 (i.e., 10 000)
		Pleistocene	1.6
	Tertiary	Pliocene	5
		Miocene	26
		Oligocene	38
		Eocene	54
		Paleocene	65
Mesozoic	Cretaceous		140
	Jurassic		210
	Triassic		245
Paleozoic	Permian		290
	Carboniferous		365
	Devonian		413
	Silurian		441
	Ordovician		504
	Cambrian		570
Precambrian	Proterozoic		2400
	Archaean		>4500

material from zones where it is created toward zones where it is destroyed by downward movement into the upper zone of the mantle. New crust forms where there is an upwelling of magma from the upper mantle. The magma rises to the surface, solidifies, and then extends laterally in a process known as sea-floor spreading. In other zones, there is a compensating *subduction* of sea-floor crust back down into the mantle, where it is re-melted and convected laterally. The magma may eventually reach another magmatic upwelling region and be carried to the crust again. The slowly moving, rigid plates of surface crust have a basement of basaltic rock, with lighter, granitic-based continents rafting on the surface of some of the oceanic plates (Figure 3.1).

FIGURE 3.1 | Tectonic Forces

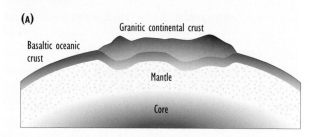

(A)

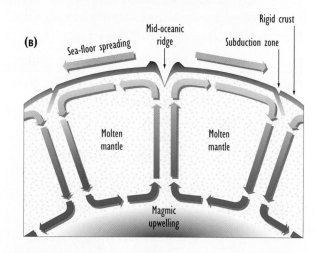

(B)

(A) The continents are viewed as granitic islands rafting upon plates of basaltic oceanic crust. **(B)** Heat and density gradients in the mantle cause a slow, convective circulation to develop in the molten magma. This circulation forms new basaltic crust at zones of magmic upwelling known as mid-oceanic ridges, followed by lateral sea-floor spreading and eventual subduction back to the mantle at the boundary with another crustal plate.

For example, in the Atlantic Ocean, about halfway between the Americas and Europe and Africa, the deep-sea Mid-Atlantic Ridge runs in a roughly north–south direction. This abyssal ridge is a zone of sea-floor spreading, from which the two continental regions are diverging at a slow but steady rate of 2–4 cm/y. In contrast, parts of the continental landmass in the western Americas are riding on regions of plates that are subducting beneath the oceanic Pacific Plate. However, along most of southwestern North America, the Pacific and North American Plates are moving in opposite but parallel directions, causing southern California and the Baja Peninsula to slowly move northward relative to the rest of the continent. This process is occurring along an extended contact between the plates (i.e., a *fault*) known as the San Andreas Fault.

These tectonic forces result in frequent earthquakes and volcanic eruptions along the Pacific coasts of North and South America, the Aleutians, and eastern Asia. Geologists refer to this geologically active region around the Pacific Ocean as the "ring of fire" because of its many volcanoes. In addition to these discrete but intense geological events, there is active building of the relatively young mountains in this region. The mountain building is caused by crustal materials being pushed upward as continents collide with each other and with their underlying oceanic plates. In a similar manner, the lofty Himalayas of southwestern Asia were and still are being created by the immense, uplifting forces generated as the northward-drifting Indian subcontinent pushes into the larger Asian landmass.

It is thought that the continents were initially arranged separately and then aggregated into a single mass during the Permian period, about 240 million years ago. This ancient super-continent, referred to as Pangea, was surrounded by a single, global ocean. Divergent forces of crustal plates moving in different directions then pulled Pangea apart, initially into two masses known as Laurasia and Gondwanaland, and then into the existing continents of North and South America, Africa, Eurasia, Australia, and Antarctica.

An **earthquake** is a trembling or movement of the earth caused by a sudden release of geological stresses at some point within the crust or upper mantle. Earthquakes are most often caused when crustal plates slip across or beneath each other at their faults. Earthquakes can also be caused by a volcanic explosion. Although their seismic energy can affect a large area, earthquakes have a spatial focus, known as the epicentre and defined as the surface position lying above the deep point of energy release. Intense earthquakes can cause great damage to buildings, and the collapsing structures, fires, and other destruction can take a toll on human lives.

In 1556 an earthquake struck Shanxi Province in China and caused about 830 000 deaths, making it the most deadly earthquake in recorded history. The most famous catastrophic earthquake in North America was the San Francisco event in 1906, caused by slippage along the San Andreas Fault, which killed 503 people and resulted in tremendous physical damage. Other twentieth-century earthquakes resulted in much greater losses of human lives, including one in 1976 that killed 242 000 people in Tangshan, China; another in 1927 that killed 200 000 in Nan-Shan, China; and one in Tokyo–Yokohama, Japan, that killed 200 000 in 1926. More

Global Focus 3.1

A Killer Tsunami

A tsunami, or seismic sea wave, is a great surge of the ocean's surface caused by an underwater earthquake. A tsunami may be almost indiscernible in the deep water of the open ocean, but it can become enormous when it reaches shallow coastal water and builds to a height capable of causing great destruction. The greatest tsunami of recent times was triggered by an undersea, so-called "megathrust" earthquake on December 26, 2004. Its epicentre was located about 40 km off the coast of Aceh in northern Sumatra, an Indonesian island, and it registered a massive 9.0 on the Richter scale (making it the largest earthquake in 40 years). The tremor generated an immense tsunami (actually, a close series of individual seismic sea waves) that gathered to a height up to 15 m when it impacted shallow-sloping coasts of countries fringing the Indian Ocean. Unfortunately, none of the countries that bore the brunt of the devastation were forewarned of the impending catastrophe, and so no action was taken to move people from low-lying coastal areas to higher ground. This happened mostly because there was no tsunami-detection system in the Indian Ocean, although negligence was also involved because the extremely large earthquake should have alerted civil authorities to a potential catastrophe. The colossal tsunami waves were moving at speeds of about 60 km/hr when they impacted the shore. They caused widespread devastation and more than 290 000 deaths by drowning and injuries caused by floating debris and collapsing buildings. The hardest-hit places were Sumatra (which suffered at least 237 000 dead and missing), Sri Lanka (35 000), the eastern coast and islands of India (17 000), and Thailand (8000). At least 7000 of the deaths were nationals from developed countries, mostly Swedes and Germans who were visiting coastal resorts during their Christmas–New Year holiday break. In addition to the mortality, tens of millions of people were displaced from their homes and livelihoods by the flooding. In many of the worst-hit places, the damage was made much more severe because of increased coastal vulnerability caused by the removal of previously abundant mangrove forest, mostly to develop tourist resorts and brackish ponds for shrimp aquaculture. Where mangroves remained intact, the coastal forest provided a sea-wall that helped to absorb and retain some of the awesome force of the tsunami, providing a measure of protection to areas further inland. Responding to the overwhelming toll of death and destruction, citizens and governments of many non-affected countries delivered large donations of aid for rescue and subsequent recovery, including money (pledges totalled about US$5.4 billion), specialized personnel, food and water, and materials for reconstruction. Relatively wealthy, developed countries were particularly generous, being led by donations of US$815 million from Australia, $680 million from Germany, $500 million from Japan, and $350 million from the United States. Another $800 million was contributed from private sources, including individuals and companies across the world. Canada contributed US$80 million and deployed a military emergency response facility to provide medical services and clean water to a badly affected area in Sri Lanka. From the environmental perspective, important lessons to be learned from this devastating tsunami include the facts that natural disasters are unpredictable and inevitable, and that the ensuing destruction can be made much worse by inappropriate land-use practices and a lack of emergency planning and response capability.

recently, the 1995 earthquake that devastated Kobe, Japan, killed 5500 people, displaced 300 000 from their homes, and caused about US$147 billion in structural damage (EQE, 1995).

The events in San Francisco and Tokyo affected large cities. The powerful tremors caused great damage, partly because of weak architectural designs that were unable to withstand the strong forces. In both cases, however, about 90% of the actual destruction resulted from fires. Earthquakes can also cause soil to lose some of its mechanical stability, resulting in destructive landslides and subsidence (i.e., sinking) of land and buildings.

Undersea earthquakes can trigger fast-moving, sea-surface phenomena known as *tsunami* or seismic sea waves. A tsunami is barely noticeable at sea, but it can become gigantic when the wave reaches shallow water and piles up to heights that can swamp coastal villages and towns. In 1929, an earthquake off eastern Canada generated a seismic sea wave that killed 29 people in Newfoundland and Cape Breton. In 1946, a large earthquake, centred on Umiak Island in the Aleutian Islands, caused a tsunami to strike Hawaii, 4500 km away, with an 18 m crest. In 2004, a tsunami in the Indian Ocean killed more than 290 000 people.

Volcanoes are vents in the Earth's surface that spew molten lava onto the ground and eject liquid, solid, and gaseous materials into the atmosphere. The largest volcanic eruptions can literally explode mountains, ejecting immense quantities of material into the environment and causing enormous damage and loss of life. For example, an eruption of Mount Vesuvius in the year 79 CE buried the Roman city of Pompeii, killing most of its inhabitants. A 1902 explosion of Mont Pelée on the Caribbean island of Martinique killed 30 000 people.

The greatest eruption of modern times involved Tambora, a volcano in Indonesia that exploded in 1815 and blew more than 300 km³ of material into the atmosphere (including the top 1300 m of the mountain). Some of the finer particulates of this massive eruption were blown into the upper atmosphere (the stratosphere), causing an increase in Earth's reflectivity that resulted in global cooling. The year 1816 became known as the "year without a summer" in Europe and North America because of its unusually cool and wet weather, including frost and snowfall during the summer months.

Another famous Indonesian eruption was that of Krakatau in the Sunda Strait in 1883, which ejected 18–21 km³ of material as high as 50–80 km into the atmosphere. The 30-m-high tsunami associated with this eruption killed about 36 000 people in coastal villages.

Large volcanic eruptions can also disturb great expanses of forest and other ecosystems. For instance, the 1980 explosion of Mount St. Helen's in the state of Washington blew down about 21 000 ha of coniferous forest, killed another 10 000 ha of forest by heat injury, and otherwise damaged another 30 000 ha. Mudslides also devastated large areas, and a vast region was covered by particulate debris (known as tephra) that settled from the atmosphere to a depth of up to 50 cm.

Some volcanoes produce chronic lava flows and venting of gases. These volcanoes tend to form distinctive, cone-shaped mountains from their accumulated lava, which solidifies into finely crystalline, glassy rocks. An active example of this spectacular process is Mount Kilauea in Hawaii, which often erupts continuously for years. The slowly flowing lava from these volcanoes can destroy buildings and vegetation but is not otherwise dangerous because people and animals can avoid the molten streams.

Glaciation

Glaciers, or persistent sheets of ice, are common features in high-latitude environments of the Arctic and Antarctic.

Glaciers also occur at high altitude on mountains, even in some tropical countries such as equatorial New Guinea. Glaciers are formed from deep, persistent snowpacks, which become compressed into ice as their weight accumulates. Most glaciers occur on land, but some extend onto the ocean or exist as extensive oceanic ice shelves. At the present time, about 10% of the land surface of Earth (or about 15 million km²) is covered with glaciers, the largest of which are the continental ice sheets of Antarctica. The largest glaciers in the Northern Hemisphere are in Greenland, but parts of Baffin and Ellesmere Islands in the Canadian Arctic are also extensively covered with glacial ice, as are some mountainous areas in western Canada.

Glaciation refers to an extensive advance of ice sheets caused by extended global cooling, sometimes known as an ice age. There have been a number of glacial periods during Earth's history. However, significant details are known only about the most recent glaciation, occurring during the Pleistocene epoch, because most traces of earlier events have been obliterated. The most recent glacial period, known as the Wisconsin, began about 100 000 years ago and ended about 10 000 years ago. (Note that this should not be referred to as the "last" glaciation, which has not yet happened!)

At the height of the Wisconsin glaciation, ice covered about 30% of Earth's land surface, including virtually all of what is now Canada and also extensive areas of the continental shelf that are now beneath the ocean. (Sea level was about 100 m lower during the Wisconsin glaciation because so much water was tied up in ice on land.) The greatest ice mass in Canada was the Laurentide Ice Sheet, which reached a thickness of about 4 km. The Cordilleran Ice Sheet of the western mountains contained ice up to 2 km thick.

The present Holocene (recent) epoch is relatively warm and ice-free and is referred to as an *interglacial* stage. Climate has not, however, been uniformly warm during the present interglacial. For example, the period of 1450 to 1850 is known as the Little Ice Age because of its relatively cool climate. During that period there was a moderate expansion of glaciers and snowfields in many parts of the world, including the Arctic and western mountains of Canada.

Glaciers are extremely erosive forces that crush, scour, and excavate the underlying terrain with their massive weight. Glaciers also move huge quantities of excavated debris around the landscape. These solid materials are eventually deposited when the glaciers melt, tumbling from the ablating (i.e., melting) ice mass or being carried away by running meltwater. Extensive deposits of glacial debris are common over virtually all of Canada, often occurring as distinctive landforms, such as the following:

1. moraines, which are series of long, mounded hills, usually lying perpendicular to the glacier's flow, containing mixed rocky debris known as till

2. drumlins, or teardrop-shaped hills that are elongated in the direction of movement of the glacier and composed of a mixture of rocky materials

3. eskers, which are long, serpentine mounds of crudely sorted debris deposited by rivers running beneath a glacier

4. erratics, or rounded boulders that can be incongruously scattered over the landscape

5. long, U-shaped valleys in mountainous terrain, carved from pre-existing river valleys by the erosive forces of glaciers

6. fjords, which are long, narrow, steep-sided inlets of the ocean

7. outwash plains, which contain a mixture of rocky materials that were deposited over a relatively wide area by streams and rivers fed by glacial meltwaters

8. the former basins of extensive lakes of glacial meltwater, which today are characterized by flat, fine-grained, often fertile plains (e.g., southern Manitoba has extensive former lakebeds of postglacial Lake Agassiz, while in southern Ontario and Quebec, flat areas were once part of the more-extensive basins of what are now the Great Lakes and St. Lawrence River)

The tremendous ice sheets that once obliterated almost all of Canada were largely gone by 8000–10 000 years ago, although glacial remnants still occur on islands in the Arctic and on mountains of western Canada. The Canadian landscape has been profoundly shaped by the impressive geological signatures of the advance and retreat of the immense continental glaciers. Since then, the terrain and landforms have been greatly modified by other geological forces, such as erosion and weathering, and by the redevelopment of ecosystems after the retreat of the immense ice sheets. However, these forces have had a

Photo 3.1   As recently as 15 000 years ago, virtually all of Canada was covered by glaciers. Remnants still occur, such as this ice cap on Ellesmere Island.

relatively small influence on the enduring, essentially glacial character of the Canadian landscape.

Weathering and Erosion

Meteorite impacts, earthquakes, volcanic explosions, and glaciation are all tremendous environmental forces, capable of obliterating both natural and anthropogenic ecosystems. Other, less forceful geological dynamics are also important, although they exert their influences more pervasively, by operating relatively slowly over longer time scales rather than as extremely destructive events.

Weathering refers to the physical and chemical processes by which rocks and minerals are broken down by environmental agents. Non-biological agents include rain, wind, and temperature changes (especially freeze–thaw cycles), and biological influences include the rock-cracking forces that can be exerted by plant roots. Weathering proceeds by the physical fracturing of rocks and by the chemical decomposition (i.e., solubilization) of minerals by acidic rainwater and corrosive solutions secreted by plant roots and microorganisms. Weathering is an in situ (i.e., "in place") phenomenon—the weathered rocks and minerals are not necessarily transported elsewhere.

Erosion refers to the physical removal of rocks and soil through the actions of flowing water, ice, wind, and gravity. Erosion is a pervasive geological process, occurring at various rates in all environments. Usually it is gradual, occurring as particles are slowly removed by flowing water or blowing wind, or as dissolved minerals are carried away by underground and surface flows of water. It also occurs as mass events, such as landslides and mudslides in steep terrain. Over extremely long periods of time, weathering and erosion tend to create a relatively flat and homogeneous landscape, known as a *peneplain*.

Even geological features as immense as mountains are slowly eroded away, with their enormous mass gradually deposited in lower regions. For instance, the Precambrian Shield that is so extensive in regions of Canada is composed of the granitic basement rocks of ancient mountains that were slowly eroded away by the actions of water, wind, and glaciers. The somewhat less ancient hills of the Appalachians of eastern North America, which extend into New Brunswick, Nova Scotia, and Newfoundland, are also the eroded relics of a once-great mountain range. The youngest mountain range in North America, the Rocky Mountains, extends from the western United States north into Alberta, British Columbia, the Yukon, and the western Northwest Territories. The Rockies still have many towering, sharp peaks because they have not yet been much reduced by the mass-wasting forces of erosion.

Rates of natural weathering and erosion are influenced by many factors, including the hardness of rocks, degree of consolidation of soil and sediment, amount of vegetation cover, rate of water flow, slope of the land, speed and direction of winds, and frequency of storm events and other types of disturbances. Some of these factors can be greatly influenced by human actions. When we disturb vegetation, for example, its moderating influence on erosion is reduced or eliminated. In fact, human activities associated with agriculture, forestry, and road building have greatly increased rates of erosion in almost all regions of the world. In many cases, the increased losses of soil have had serious consequences for the productivity of agricultural land and for natural biodiversity. We will examine anthropogenic influences on erosion in Chapters 14, 20, 23, and 24.

Materials eroded from mountains and other uplands must, of course, go somewhere. These materials are carried to lower altitudes and much of the mass is eventually deposited in the oceans, settling to the bottom in a process known as **sedimentation**. Over extremely long periods of time (i.e., tens or more millions of years), as the mass of sedimented material builds up, sufficient pressure is exerted on underlying sediment to cause it to aggregate, become more densely packed, and cement into sedimentary rock in a process called **lithification**. Common examples of sedimentary rocks are sandstone, mudstone, shale, limestone, and mixtures of these known as conglomerates (the latter may also contain eroded, non-sedimentary rocks such as granites and basalts).

Eventually, under the influence of tectonic forces, enormously slow and powerful collisions of crustal plates can cause areas of deep-oceanic, sedimentary rocks to *uplift*, sometimes raising them to great altitudes and forming new mountain ranges underwater or on the continents. Geological uplift is the means by which oceanic rocks and marine fossils can find their way to the tops of Earth's highest mountains. Uplift and mountain building are important stages in the geological recycling of some of the continental mass that was wasted down-slope during millions of years of erosion.

The Hydrosphere

Earth's **hydrosphere** is the portion of the planet that contains water (H_2O), including the oceans, the atmosphere, the land surface, and underground. The **hydrologic,** or **water, cycle** refers to the rates of movement (**fluxes**) of water among these various reservoirs (**compartments**). The hydrologic cycle is a global phenomenon, although it also operates on local scales. The major elements of the hydrologic cycle are illustrated in Figure 3.2.

Each compartment of the hydrologic cycle has input and output fluxes, and the sum of all of these comprises the cycle. If the rate of input equals the rate of output, then a compartment is in a flow-through equilibrium and its size does not change. Of course, if input exceeds output, the compartment increases in size over time (and it decreases if input is less than output).

On the global scale, the major compartments of the hydrological cycle are in a long-term equilibrium condition. This is not, however, generally true on a local scale, particularly over shorter intervals of time. For example, areas may temporarily flood or dry out. In addition, local hydrological conditions can change over the long term. Glaciation, for example, stores immense quantities of solid water on land, and excessive use of groundwater can deplete artesian reservoirs (aquifers).

We can distinguish four major compartments of the hydrological cycle (see Table 3.2):

1. The **oceans** are the largest hydrological compartment, accounting for about 97.4% of all water on the planet.

FIGURE 3.2 | Major Elements of the Hydrologic Cycle

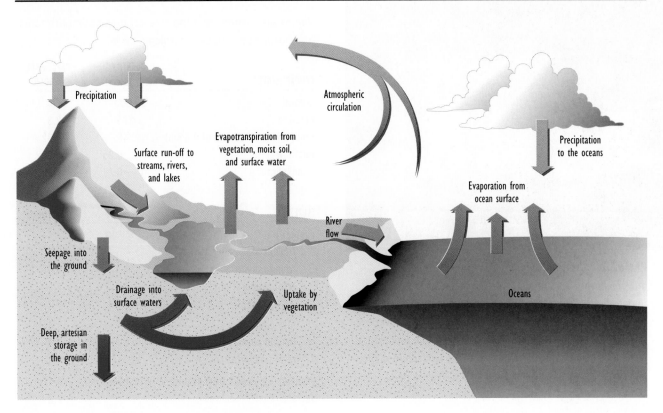

2. **Surface waters** occur on Earth's landmasses and account for 2.3% of global water. Virtually all surface water is tied up in glaciers, mostly in Antarctica. Lakes, ponds, rivers, streams, and other surface bodies containing liquid water amount to only 0.002% of global water.

3. **Groundwater** accounts for 0.32% of Earth's water. Groundwater can occur in relatively shallow soil horizons, where it is accessible for uptake by plants, or it can drain laterally into surface waters such as lakes and streams. Deeper groundwater is inaccessible for these purposes and forms *artesian reservoirs* in spaces within porous or fractured bedrock. Such aquifers receive water infiltrating by **deep drainage** from above or by long-distance underground transport from nearby upland areas.

4. Atmospheric moisture accounts for only about 0.001% of Earth's water. **Atmospheric water** can occur as a gas, vapour (tiny, suspended droplets), or solid (ice crystals), all of which are highly variable over space and time. Clouds are dense aggregations of liquid or solid water in the atmosphere, while gaseous water is invisible. Note that the maximum amount of water a volume of atmosphere can hold is highly dependent on temperature, with warmer air having a much greater water-storage capacity than cold air. The term **humidity** refers to the actual concentration of water in the atmosphere (measured in g/m³), while **relative humidity** expresses actual humidity as a percentage of the *saturation value* for a particular temperature.

The four major fluxes among the five major compartments of the hydrological cycle are listed in Table 3.2. The more important fluxes are described below.

Evaporation is a change of state of water from a liquid to a gas, or from a solid, such as snow or ice, directly to a gas (this is more properly referred to as sublimation). Globally, about 86% of evaporation is from the oceans, and the rest is from terrestrial surfaces. On terrestrial landscapes, water can evaporate from bodies of surface water, from moist soil and rocks, and from vegetation. **Transpiration** refers specifically to the evaporation of water from plants, while **evapotranspiration** refers to all sources of evaporation from a landscape.

Photo 3.2   The global hydrologic cycle involves water movement through the atmosphere, on the surface, and underground, as well as storage in oceans, lakes, glaciers, and groundwater. Ultimately, rivers like the Niagara River, which flows north from Lake Erie to Lake Ontario, represent a flow to the ocean of water deposited to the landscape as precipitation. Niagara Falls is located on the Niagara River.

TABLE 3.2	The Hydrologic Cycle		
Values are estimates of the sizes of major compartments and fluxes of the global hydrologic cycle.			
COMPARTMENTS	**QUANTITY (10^{14} tonnes)**	**PERCENTAGE OF TOTAL**	
oceans	12 300	97.4	
glaciers	286	2.3	
groundwater (to depth of 0.8 km)	40	0.32	
inland waters	0.25	0.002	
atmosphere	0.13	0.001	
FLUXES	**QUANTITY (10^{14} t/year)**		
evaporation			
from oceans	3.8		
from land surfaces	0.6		
total evaporation	4.4		
precipitation			
to oceans	3.4		
to land surfaces	1.0		
total precipitation	4.4		
atmospheric export from oceans to terrestrial	0.4		
surface runoff from land	0.2		

Sources: Data from Odum (1983) and Botkin and Keller (1995)

Precipitation is the deposition of water from the atmosphere as liquid rain or as solid snow or hail. In addition, vapour-phase water in the atmosphere can condense or freeze onto surfaces as dew or frost, respectively. As previously noted, most global evaporation is from the oceans, much of which precipitates back to them. Some, however, is transported by moving air masses over the continents, resulting in a net import of evaporated water from Earth's oceans to its land surfaces. Precipitation volumes can be especially large in hilly or mountainous areas. This phenomenon is known as **orographic precipitation** (In Detail 3.1).

Surface flows involve water that is transported in brooks, streams, and rivers. (In contrast, lakes and ponds are relatively static storage reservoirs.) Surface flows move in response to gravitational gradients associated with altitude (in other words, water flows downhill). Most surface flows ultimately carry water to the oceans, thereby balancing the net import of moisture evaporated from the oceans, plus the excess moisture of terrestrial precipitation over evapotranspiration. Consequently, there is a net export of flowing water from Earth's terrestrial surfaces to the oceans.

Groundwater drainage involves the infiltration of water into the ground. Shallow groundwater can drain laterally, eventually draining into surface waters. It can also be taken up by plant roots, almost all of which is later tran-

spired into the atmosphere through foliage. However, deeper groundwater is not available for plant uptake or to re-charge surface waters. It accumulates in underground artesian reservoirs, which can be very large.

The hydrologic cycle is extremely important. Water is required by natural ecosystems for the metabolic needs of organisms, for cooling, and as a ubiquitous solvent that allows water-soluble nutrients to be absorbed by organisms. Water is also required by humans for use in agriculture, industry, and recreation. In many regions, unfortunately, water and its biological resources (such as fish) have been used excessively, and water quality has been degraded through pollution. These damages to water and its resources are common but regrettable themes in many chapters in this book.

The Atmosphere

Earth's **atmosphere** is the envelope of gases that surrounds the planet and is held in place by the attractive forces of gravity. The density of the atmospheric mass is greater at lower altitudes and decreases rapidly with increasing altitude.

In Detail 3.1

Orographic Precipitation

The spatial pattern of precipitation in coastal British Columbia illustrates orographic precipitation. Moisture-laden air masses, blown by the prevailing westerly winds from the Pacific Ocean, encounter mountains of the Coast Range. As they rise, the air masses cool (by 0.5–0.8°C for every 100 m increase in elevation), which greatly reduces their ability to hold water. This causes much of the moisture to condense into clouds and then precipitate from the atmosphere as snow and rain.

As the air mass descends on the other side of the mountains, it warms again, increasing its moisture-holding capacity. Therefore, precipitation is sparser on the *rain-shadow* side of the mountains. Consequently, coastal Vancouver has much more rainfall (about 110 cm/y) than Penticton in the inland Okanagan Valley (28 cm/y). Rainfall just in the Greater Vancouver area ranges from about 50 cm/y in the southern suburbs, such as Delta, to as much as 250 cm/y in places nearer the mountains, such as North Vancouver.

Orographic Precipitation along a Transect through Coastal British Columbia

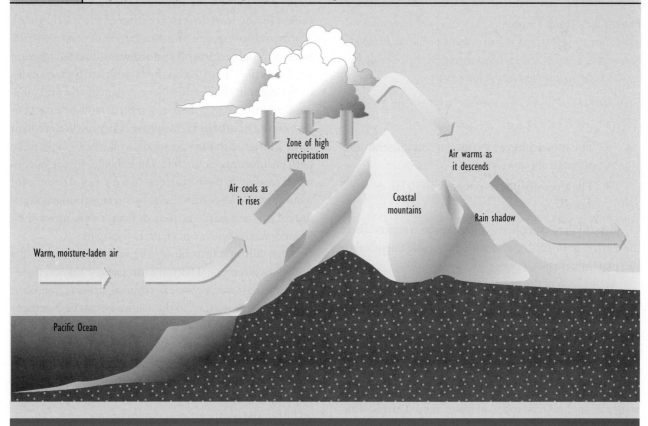

The atmosphere consists of four layers, the boundaries of which vary over time and space:

1. The **troposphere** contains 85–90% of the atmospheric mass and extends from the surface 8–20 km (being thinner at high latitudes and thicker at equatorial latitudes, as well as varying seasonally). Air temperature typically decreases with increasing altitude within the troposphere, and convective air currents (winds) are common. Consequently, the troposphere is sometimes called the "weather layer."

2. The **stratosphere** extends from the troposphere to as high as about 50 km, depending on season and latitude. Air temperature varies little with altitude within the stratosphere, and there are few convective air currents.

Photo 3.3 The atmosphere is composed of a mixture of gases, fine particulates, and water vapour occurring as clouds. This view of a cloudy atmosphere, mountains, and a foggy valley was taken in the highlands of Bolivia.

3. The **mesosphere** extends beyond the stratosphere to about 75 km.

4. The **thermosphere** extends to 450 km or more.

Beyond the atmosphere is **outer space**, a region where the Earth's atmosphere exerts no detectable chemical or thermal influences.

About 78% of the mass of the atmosphere is nitrogen gas (N_2), while 21% is oxygen (O_2), 0.9% argon (Ar), and 0.037% carbon dioxide (CO_2). The rest is various trace gases, including potentially toxic chemicals such as ozone (O_3) and sulphur dioxide (SO_2) (see Chapter 16). The atmosphere also contains highly variable concentrations of water vapour, which can range from only 0.01% in frigid winter air in the Arctic to 5% in warm, humid, tropical air. On average, the total weight of Earth's atmospheric mass exerts a pressure at sea level of around 1.0×10^5 Pa, or *one atmosphere*, equivalent to the weight of a 1.0 kg mass per square centimetre. Air pressure is, however, variable over space and time.

Earth's atmosphere is a highly dynamic medium. This is particularly true of the troposphere, within which temperature and energy gradients are most pronounced. To even out these energy gradients, there is a streaming of atmospheric mass from regions of relatively high pressure to those with lower pressure. These more-or-less lateral atmospheric movements are known as **wind**, the vigour and speed of which can range from barely perceptible to several hundred kilometres per hour in extremely turbulent, rotating air masses such as tornadoes or hurricanes. In general, winds are caused when air heated by the sun becomes less dense and rises in altitude, to be replaced at the surface by an inflow of cooler, denser air. Simply interpreted, this movement of atmospheric mass represents an enormous, gaseous, convective cell. These atmospheric movements occur on both local and global scales and are extremely variable over space and time. At the global level, however, a broad general pattern of circulation is discernible (Figure 3.3).

As noted above, wind directions are influenced by the relative locations of high and low atmospheric pressures. Wind directions are also influenced by the **Coriolis effect**, caused by the west-to-east rotation of the Earth. In the Northern Hemisphere, the distribution of pressure in the lower atmosphere provides a northward-directed force on wind direction. The Coriolis force, which deflects motions to the right in that hemisphere, balances the pressure-gradient force so that the winds tend to blow from west to east. In the Southern Hemisphere, the pressure gradient force is directed toward the south, while the Coriolis force deflects motions to the left. On balance, this results in winds tending to blow from east to west. Local patterns of wind flow are also influenced by surface topography—mountains are barriers that deflect winds upward or around, while valleys can channel wind flow.

Prevailing winds blow relatively continuously in a dominant direction. There are three major classes of prevailing winds: *trade winds* are tropical airflows that blow from the northeast (i.e., to the southwest) in the Northern Hemisphere, and from the southeast in the Southern Hemisphere; *westerlies* are mid-latitude winds that blow from the southwest in the Northern Hemisphere, and from the northwest in the Southern Hemisphere; and *polar easterlies* blow from the northeast at high northern latitudes, and from the southeast near Antarctica.

Climate and Weather

Climate refers to the prevailing atmospheric conditions of temperature, precipitation, humidity, wind speed and direction (together, these are wind velocity), insolation (i.e., incoming solar radiation), visibility, fog, and cloud cover in a place or region. Climatic data are usually calculated as statistics (such as averages or ranges of values)

FIGURE 3.3 | Atmospheric Circulation in the Western Hemisphere

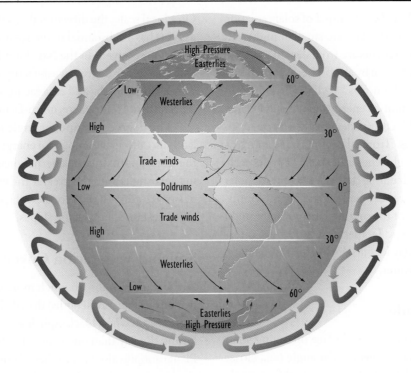

Note that air masses tend to circulate from areas of relatively high pressure to areas of lower pressure. In such cases, surface winds blow from high pressure toward low pressure and are replaced by a higher-altitude flow of air in the opposite direction.

Source: Modified from Botkin and Keller (1995)

using data obtained from several decades or more of monitoring (the preferred period for the calculation of "normal" climatic parameters is at least 30 years).

In contrast, **weather** refers to relatively short-term, day-to-day or instantaneous meteorological conditions (the latter is referred to as "real-time" weather). Because weather is related to short-term conditions, it is much more variable over time and space than climate.

Many aspects of Earth's climate are functions of solar insolation and how this incoming energy is absorbed, reflected, and re-radiated by the atmosphere, oceans, and terrestrial surfaces. It is not practical here to discuss this complex subject in detail. Nevertheless, we can describe several ecologically important aspects (see also the discussion of physical energy budgets in Chapter 4).

Give Thanks to the Sun

If it were not for the warming influence of solar radiation, the temperature of Earth's surface and atmosphere would approach the coldest that is physically possible—absolute zero, or –273°C (0 on the Kelvin scale). Although Earth

has a limited ability to generate its own heat, by the decay of radioactive elements in its core, this is insufficient to provide much warming at the surface. Solar energy is critical to maintaining Earth's surface temperature within a range that organisms can tolerate.

Atmospheric Reflection and Absorption

Conditions in Earth's atmosphere have a great influence on climatic factors. For instance, cloud cover and tiny particulates are highly reflective of many visible wavelengths of incoming solar radiation and so have a cooling effect on the lower atmosphere and the surface. In addition, the atmosphere contains trace concentrations of gases that absorb some of the infrared radiation that the planet emits to cool itself of the heat obtained from solar radiation. Most important in this regard are water vapour, carbon dioxide, and methane. Because of the influence of these so-called "greenhouse gases," Earth's surface temperature is maintained at an average of about 15°C, or 33°C warmer than the –18°C it would be without this moderating effect (see Chapters 4 and 17).

Night and Day

At any place on Earth's surface the input of solar radiation is relatively high during the day and small at night. (At night, the only radiation inputs are from distant stars and from solar radiation reflected by atmospheric particulates and the moon—inputs known as "skylight.") The daily, 24-hour (*diurnal*) variations in energy input result in large changes in weather. This effect varies greatly between tropical and polar latitudes. Tropical regions have approximately equal day and night lengths of about 12 hours each, which do not vary much during the year. In contrast, polar latitudes are much more seasonal, with virtually continuous light during part of the summer and constant night during part of the winter. Temperate latitudes are intermediate, with longer day lengths during the summer and shorter ones during winter.

Effects of Latitude

Places at tropical latitudes tend to face incoming solar radiation on a relatively perpendicular angle (i.e., closer to 90° at noon). Polar latitudes have a more oblique angle of solar incidence, and temperate latitudes are intermediate in this regard. The more perpendicular the angle of incidence of solar radiation, the smaller the surface area over which the incoming energy is distributed, and the more intense the resulting heating. The angle of solar incidence has a strong influence on differences in unit-area solar radiation received at various latitudes and is a major reason (along with seasonality) why the tropics are warmer than polar regions.

Seasons

Earth's axis tilts at a 23.5° angle relative to the incidence of solar radiation. Consequently, during Earth's annual revolution around the sun, there are seasonal differences in energy received between the Northern and Southern Hemispheres. In the Northern Hemisphere, the angle of incidence is closer to perpendicular from March 21 to September 22, giving relatively warmer conditions, while the angle is more oblique from September 22 to March 21, resulting in cooler conditions. These seasons are reversed in the Southern Hemisphere. Because Earth's orbit is elliptical, climatic seasons are also influenced by the varying distance from the sun. This effect is relatively small, however, compared with that of the inclination of Earth's axis.

Aspect and Slope

On a local scale, the direction that a slope faces (known as **aspect**) has a substantial influence on the amount of solar radiation received. In the Northern Hemisphere, south- and, to a lesser degree, west-facing slopes are relatively warm, while north- and east-facing slopes are cooler. (In the Southern Hemisphere, north-facing slopes are warmer.)

The degree of **slope**, or angle of inclination of the land, also affects the amount of energy received. The closer the slope approximates a perpendicular angle to incoming solar radiation, the greater the energy input per unit of surface area. In the Northern Hemisphere, this effect is greatest on south-facing slopes.

Soil and Vegetation Cover

Darker surfaces absorb much more solar radiation (particularly visible wavelengths) than do lighter surfaces. This is the reason why a black asphalt surface gets much hotter during the day than one made of light-coloured cement. Plant canopies also vary in their absorption and reflection characteristics, depending on the colour of the foliage and on the angle at which it is oriented to incoming solar radiation. Major changes in the character of vegetation, as occur when forest is converted into agricultural or urban land-use, can affect local, and sometimes regional, weather and climate.

Snow and Ice Cover

Because snow and ice are highly reflective to solar radiation, relatively little insolation is absorbed by snow- or ice-covered surfaces. The melting of snow cover in the springtime exposes a much more absorptive ground surface, and warming then accelerates.

Evaporation of Water

Moist surfaces are cooled by the evaporation of water, a process that absorbs thermal energy. Therefore, the transpiration of water from plant foliage has a cooling effect, as does the evaporation of sweat from the body surface of a human.

The above factors influence the input, reflection, absorption, and dissipation of solar radiation, resulting in large variations of air, water, and surface temperatures over Earth's surface. The energy gradients that develop result in global processes that attempt to distribute the energy more evenly, by movements of air masses in the atmosphere (winds) and currents of water in the oceans. In addition, prevailing wind directions can interact with oceanic currents to generate circular water flows known as *gyres*. Subtropical gyres rotate clockwise in the Northern Hemisphere and counter-clockwise in the Southern Hemisphere, while subpolar gyres rotate in the opposite directions.

Climate has an important influence on the character of ecological development in any region or place. Climatic conditions can vary on a large scale, called **macroclimate**, and thereby affect the nature of ecosystems over a large area. Climatic conditions can also vary on much smaller scales, called **microclimates**, caused, for example, by topog-

raphy, proximity to the ocean or a large lake, or understorey conditions beneath a dense canopy of tree foliage.

Four important climatic factors particularly affect the development of ecosystems. Of these, variations of precipitation and temperature generally have the greatest influence.

Precipitation volumes are greatly affected by the flow of prevailing winds, the humidity of air masses, and the influence of topography (see In Detail 3.1). Dry climates can support only desert vegetation, whereas wetter conditions may allow old-growth forest and wetlands to develop.

Temperature is relatively warm in tropical latitudes and at lower altitude in mountainous terrain, and cooler at high latitude and high altitude. In general, places with cold temperatures develop tundra vegetation, whereas

Canadian Focus 3.1

Climates of Canada

Canada is a huge country, the second-largest in the world after Russia. The wide range of latitude means that Canadian climates vary from cold polar in the High Arctic to warm temperate in southern Ontario and southern British Columbia. Canada also has extremely varied topography, with extensive regions at low level and many areas at high elevation, particularly in the mountains of Labrador, the eastern Arctic Islands, and the Rocky Mountains. Thus, Canada's regions are characterized by huge differences in climate. The data below reflect "normal" or average values calculated for the period 1961 to 1990.

	ST. JOHN'S NF	HALIFAX NS	MONTREAL QC	TORONTO ON	WINNIPEG MN	REGINA SK	EDMONTON AB	PENTICTON BC	VANCOUVER BC	YELLOWKNIFE NT	RESOLUTE NU
TEMPERATURE (°C)											
Annual average	4.8	6.1	6.5	7.3	2.2	2.2	3.1	8.9	9.8	−5.4	−16.6
Coldest	−23.3	−26.1	−37.8	−31.1	−45.0	−50.0	−48.3	−27.2	−17.8	−51.1	−52.2
Warmest	30.6	34.5	37.8	38.3	40.6	43.3	34.4	40.6	33.3	32.2	18.3
GROWING DEGREE-DAYS											
(warmer than 5°C)	1196	1694	2113	2127	1785	1677	1560	2136	1994	1027	33
PRECIPITATION (cm/y)											
Annual total	152	149	95	77	53	40	49	29	111	28	13
Annual rainfall	116	122	72	64	41	29	35	22	105	15	5
Annual snowfall	36	27	23	13	12	11	14	7	6	13	8
Average windspeed (km/h)	24	18	16	15	19	21	14	13	12	16	22
Bright sunshine (h/y)	1497	1885	2054	2045	2321	2331	2264	2032	1920	2277	1505
Days with fog (d/y)	124	122	20	35	20	29	17	1	45	21	62
Days with rain (d/y)	156	125	114	99	72	59	70	78	156	46	20
Days with snow (d/y)	88	64	62	47	57	58	59	29	15	82	82
Days with wind >63 km/h	23	3	1	<1	1	9	0	<1	<1	<1	25
Frost-free period (d)	131	155	157	149	121	109	140	148	216	111	9

Source: Data from Phillips (1990)

warmer temperatures may support forest. Temperate and polar latitudes have large, seasonal fluctuations in temperature. Tropical forest develops in moist regions where temperature remains uniformly warm, while temperate and boreal forests are dominated by tree species that can tolerate cold temperatures during the winter.

Wind can also have a substantial ecological influence, although this is typically less important than that of precipitation and temperature. Very windy locations may not be able to support forest, even though precipitation and temperature are otherwise favourable. This occurs in many coastal habitats in Canada where windy conditions result in shrub-dominated ecosystems developing rather than the forest that occurs farther inland.

Extreme events of weather, such as drought, flooding, hurricanes, and tornadoes, can also be important. Severe disturbances influence ecological development, especially where they occur frequently. For example, frequent drought or severe windstorms may restrict the development of forest in some regions even though the average climatic conditions may be favourable.

Major elements of the climates of Canada are described in Canadian Focus 3.1. We will discuss their relationship with ecological development in Chapter 8.

Conclusions

Knowledge of the physical world is a central aspect of environmental science—it provides essential context for understanding the causes and consequences of almost all changes associated with human activities. The physical and structural attributes of Earth influence the geological and geographical forces affecting its surface (both water and land) and atmosphere. In addition, the amount and spectral quality of incoming sunlight have a profound influence on Earth's energy budget and climate. Increasingly, human activities are having a large, cumulative effect on these natural influences and are transforming the surface attributes of the planet, by affecting erosion, surface cover, environmental chemistry, and even global climate.

Key Terms

solar system

core

mantle

lithosphere

crust

igneous rock

sedimentary rock

metamorphic rock

tectonic force

meteorite

earthquake

volcano

glacier

glaciation

weathering

erosion

sedimentation

lithification

hydrosphere

hydrologic (water) cycle

flux

compartment

ocean

surface water

groundwater

deep drainage

atmospheric water

humidity

relative humidity

evaporation

transpiration

evapotranspiration

precipitation

orographic precipitation

surface flow

groundwater drainage

atmosphere

troposphere

stratosphere

mesosphere

thermosphere

outer space

wind

Coriolis effect

prevailing wind

climate

weather

aspect

slope

macroclimate

microclimate

Questions for Review

1. What are the various layers of Earth's solid sphere and atmosphere? Describe the characteristics of these layers.

2. What causes tectonic forces, and what are their consequences on the crustal dynamics of the Earth?

3. What is glaciation? Describe the major surface features it leaves behind.

4. What are key factors affecting regional climate and microclimate?

Questions for Discussion

1. What major geological forces have influenced landscape features in the region where you live?

2. Where does your drinking water come from? Trace its origins and disposal in terms of the hydrologic cycle.

3. Outline the differences between climate and weather. Discuss the influences of climate and weather on your daily and annual life.

4. Natural disasters, such as events of extreme weather (e.g., a tornado, hurricane, ice storm, or tsunami), are rare but inevitable events. What is the history of natural disasters in the place where you live? Do you think that land-use and other human influences may have increased the possibility of worse damage being caused by these unpredictable events?

Exploring Issues

1. You are part of a research team investigating the potential ecological effects of climate change in a region of hilly topography. Your responsibility is to characterize the climatic conditions in the study area, giving sufficient detail so the team can understand the overall conditions as well as the local ones (for example, in valleys, on slopes, and on hilltops). What types of factors would you have to consider when designing the climate-monitoring program? Consider the following aspects: (a) the number of monitoring sites, (b) where monitoring sites should be located, (c) what variables to measure (e.g., wind, temperature, precipitation, sunlight), and (d) how long you must monitor conditions before determining the normal climate (as opposed to the weather).

References

Alvarez, W., E.G. Kauffman, F. Surlyk, L.W. Alvarez, F. Asaro, and H.V. Michel. 1984. Impact Theory of Mass Extinctions and the Invertebrate Fossil Record. *Science*, **223**: 1135–41.

Botkin, D.B. and E.A. Keller. 2002. *Environmental Science: Earth as a Living Planet.* 4th ed. New York: J. Wiley & Sons.

Bryant, E.A. 1997. *Climate Process and Change.* Cambridge, UK: Cambridge University Press.

Cowen, R. 2000. *History of Life.* 3rd ed. London, UK: Blackwell Sci. Pub.

EQE International. 1995. The January 17, 1995 *Kobe Earthquake.* Houston, TX: EQE; www.eqe.com/publications/kobe/kobe.htm

Flint, R.F. and B.J. Skinner. 1987. *Physical Geology.* New York: J. Wiley & Sons.

Jablonski, D. 1991. Extinctions: A Paleontological Perspective. *Science*, **253**: 754–7.

Keller, E.A. 1999. *Environmental Geology.* 8th ed. Upper Saddle River, NJ: Prentice Hall.

Margulis, L. and L. Olendzenski (eds.). 1992. *Environmental Evolution.* Cambridge, MA: MIT Press.

Montgomery, K. 2002. *Environmental Geology.* Columbus, OH: McGraw-Hill.

Phillips, D. 1990. *The Climates of Canada.* Ottawa, ON: Environment Canada.

Pielou, E.C. 1991. *After the Ice Age: The Return of Life to Glaciated North America.* Chicago, IL: University of Chicago Press.

Raup, D.M. 1986. *The Nemesis Affair.* New York: Norton Pub. Co.

Schneider, S.H. 1989. The Changing Climate. *Scientific American*, **261 (3)**: 70–9.

Tarbuck, E.J. and F.K. Lutgens. 2002. *Essentials of Geology. 8th ed.* Upper Saddle River, NJ: Prentice Hall.

Tarbuck, E.J., F.K. Lutgens, and T. Dennis. 2002. *Earth: An Introduction to Physical Geology.* 7th ed. Englewood Cliffs, NJ: Prentice Hall.

Van Andel, T.H. 1985. *New Views on an Old Planet: Continental Drift and the History of the Earth.* Cambridge, UK: Cambridge University Press.

Informative Websites

Earth Science World. www.earthscienceworld.org/

The American Geological Institute sponsors this site that outlines current events in the earth sciences, links to relevant news articles, and links to other earth sciences resources.

How the Weatherworks. www.weatherworks.com/

You will find weather FAQs, links to related sites, educational services and activities, and school-to-school weather projects at this comprehensive website.

Natural Disasters.
http://library.thinkquest.org/16132/frames.html?tqskip1=1

This website provides an overview of natural disasters in a multimedia format, and also links to other useful websites.

Natural Resources Canada. www.nrcan.gc.ca/

This bilingual site has information on climate change and provides Canadian examples of floods, earthquakes, landslides, and forest fires. Links to databases, libraries, maps, and related publications are also available.

The Earthquake Museum.
www.olympus.net/personal/gofamily/quake/famous.html

This website provides interesting information about famous earthquakes and the damage they caused.

The Weather Network.
www.theweathernetwork.com/weather/cities/indexcan.htm

Will you be able to wear shorts tomorrow, or will a parka be more appropriate? Find out the weather forecast for your area here.

USGS Educational Resources. www.usgs.gov/education/

The U.S. Geological Survey sponsors this site, which discusses how biology, geology, hydrology, and geography can help us understand our changing world.

Water in a Changing World.
www.esa.org/Science/Issues/FileEnglish/issue9.pdf

This pdf document of the Ecological Society of America explains how humans are affecting the hydrology of the planet.

World Meteorological Organization. www.wmo.ch/

A United Nations specialized agency, this organization deals with weather prediction, air pollution research, ozone layer depletion studies, and tropical storm forecasting.

4

Energy and Ecosystems

CHAPTER OBJECTIVES

After completing this chapter, you will be able to

1. Describe the nature of energy, its various forms, and the laws that govern its transformations.
2. Discuss how Earth is a flow-through system for solar energy.
3. Identify the three major components of Earth's energy budget.
4. Describe energy relationships within ecosystems, including the fixation of solar energy by primary producers and the passage of that fixed energy through other components of the ecosystem.
5. Explain why the trophic structure of ecological productivity is pyramid-shaped and why ecosystems cannot support many top predators.
6. Compare the feeding strategies of humans living a hunting and gathering lifestyle and those of modern cultures living in cities and towns.

CHAPTER OUTLINE

- Introduction
- The Nature of Energy
- Forms of Energy
- Energy Units
- Energy Transformations and the Laws of Thermodynamics
- Earth: An Energy Flow-Through System
- Earth's Energy Budget
- Energy in Ecosystems
- Conclusions

Introduction

Earth's **ecosystems** are not closed, self-sustaining systems. In fact, without continuous access to an external source of energy, ecosystems would quickly deplete their quantities of stored energy and cease to function. The external source of energy is solar energy, which is stored mainly as biomass and heat.

Solar energy is absorbed by green plants and algae and is utilized to *fix* carbon dioxide and water into simple sugars through a process known as *photosynthesis*. Ultimately, this biological fixation of solar energy provides the energetic basis for almost all organisms and ecosystems (the few exceptions are described later).

Energy is critical to the functioning of physical processes throughout the universe and of ecological processes on Earth. In this chapter we will examine the physical nature of energy, the laws that govern its behaviour and transformations, and its role in ecosystems.

The Nature of Energy

Energy is a fundamental physical entity and is defined simply as the capacity of a body or system to accomplish work. In physics, **work** is defined as the result of a force being applied over a distance. In all of the following examples of work, energy is transformed and some measurable outcome is achieved:

- A hockey stick strikes a puck, causing it to speed toward a target.
- A book is picked up from the floor, lifted, and then laid on a table.
- A vehicle is driven along a road.
- Heat from a stove is absorbed by water in a kettle, causing it to become hotter and eventually boil.
- The photosynthetic pigment chlorophyll absorbs sunlight, converting the electromagnetic energy into a form that plants and algae can utilize to synthesize sugars.

Forms of Energy

Energy can exist in various states, each of which is fundamentally different from the others. Under suitable conditions, however, any energy state can be converted into another through various physical or chemical transformations. The states can be grouped into three categories of energy: electromagnetic, kinetic, and potential.

Electromagnetic Energy

Electromagnetic energy (or electromagnetic radiation) is associated with *photons*, which are entities having properties of both particles and waves that travel through space at a constant speed of 3×10^8 m/s (i.e., at the speed of light). Electromagnetic energy exists in a continuous spectrum of wavelengths, which (ordered from the shortest to longest wavelengths) are known as gamma, X-ray, ultraviolet, visible light, infrared, microwave, and radio (Figure 4.1). The human eye can perceive electromagnetic energy with wave-

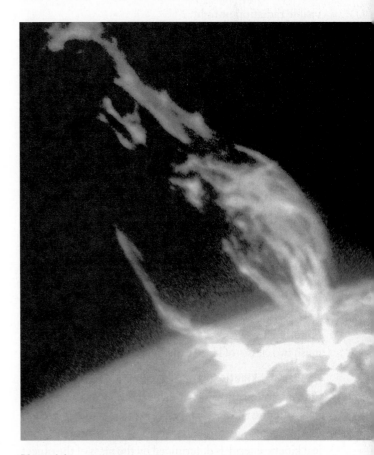

Photo 4.1   The energy of the sun is derived from nuclear fusion reactions involving hydrogen nuclei. The reactions generate enormous quantities of thermal and electromagnetic energy. Solar electromagnetic energy is the most crucial source of energy sustaining ecological and biological processes on Earth.

Source: ©NSO/SEL/Roger Rossmeyer/CORBIS/MAGMA

| FIGURE 4.1 | The Electromagnetic Spectrum |

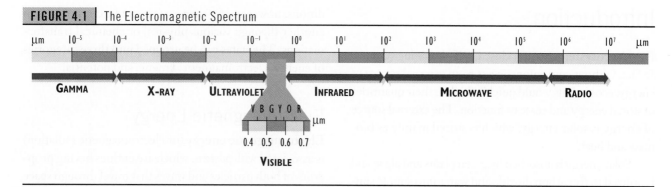

The spectrum is divided into major components on the basis of wavelength and is presented on a logarithmic scale ($\log_{10}$) in units of micrometers ($\mu m = 10^{-3}$ mm $= 10^{-6}$ m). Note the expansion of the visible component and the wavelength ranges for red, orange, yellow, green, blue, and violet colours.

lengths of about 0.4–0.7 μm (1 μm, or 1 micrometer, is 10^{-6} m; see Appendix A), a range commonly referred to as visible radiation or light.

Electromagnetic energy is given off (or radiated) by all objects with a surface temperature greater than absolute zero (i.e., greater than –273°C). The surface temperature of the body determines the rate and spectral quality of the emitted radiation. Compared with cooler bodies, hotter ones have much greater emission rates, and their radiation is dominated by shorter, higher-energy wavelengths. The sun has an extremely hot surface temperature, about 6000°C (the interior of the sun is much hotter still), and most of its radiation is ultraviolet (0.2–0.4 μm), visible (0.4–0.7 μm), and near infrared (0.7–2 μm). Because the surface temperature of Earth averages only about 15°C, it radiates much smaller quantities of longer-wavelength energy (peaking at a wavelength of about 10 μm).

Kinetic Energy

Kinetic energy is associated with motion. We can distinguish two classes of kinetic energy: mechanical and thermal.

Mechanical kinetic energy is associated with objects in motion, for example, a baseball flying through the air, a deer running through a forest, water flowing in a stream, or a planet moving through space. The quantity of mechanical kinetic energy is determined by the mass of the object and its speed.

Thermal kinetic energy is associated with the rate of vibration of atoms or molecules. Such vibrations are frozen at –273°C (absolute zero), but they are progressively more vigorous at higher temperatures, reflecting a larger content of thermal kinetic energy. Thermal energy is sometimes referred to as *heat*.

Potential Energy

Potential energy is the stored ability to perform work. To actually perform work, potential energy must be transformed into electromagnetic or kinetic energy. There are various types of potential energy associated with gravity, chemicals, electrical potential, compressed gases, and the subatomic organization of matter.

Gravitational potential energy results from the attractive forces between objects (i.e., gravity). For example, water stored at some height above sea level contains gravitational potential energy. This can be converted into kinetic energy if a pathway allows the water to flow downhill in response to gravity. Gravitational potential energy can be converted into electrical energy through the technology of hydroelectric power plants.

Chemical potential energy is stored in the bonds between atoms within molecules. Chemical potential energy can be liberated by *exothermic reactions* (i.e., those which lead to a net release of thermal energy); for example,

- Chemical potential energy is stored in the molecular bonds of sulphide minerals (such as iron sulphide, FeS_2), and some of this energy is released when the sulphides are oxidized. Specialized bacteria can metabolically tap the potential energy of sulphides to support their own productivity, through a process known as *chemosynthesis* (discussed later in this chapter).

- The ionic bonds of salts also store chemical potential energy. For example, when table salt (sodium chloride, NaCl) is dissolved in water, ionic potential energy is released as heat, slightly increasing the water temperature.

- Hydrocarbons store energy in the bonds between their hydrogen and carbon atoms (hydrocarbons contain only these atoms). The chemical potential energy of gasoline, a mixture of liquid hydrocarbons, is liberated in an internal combustion engine and mechanically transformed to achieve the kinetic energy of vehicular motion.

- Organic compounds (biochemicals) produced metabolically by organisms also store large quantities of potential energy in their interatomic bonds. Carbohydrates typically contain about 16.8 kJ/g, proteins about 21.0 kJ/g, and lipids or fats about 38.5 kJ/g. Many organisms store their energy reserves as fats because these biochemicals have such a high energy density.

Electrical potential energy results from differences in the quantity of electrons. Electrons, which are subatomic, negatively charged particles, flow from areas of high density to areas of lower density. When an electrical switch is used to complete a circuit connecting two areas with different electrical potentials, electrons flow along the electron gradient. The electric energy may then be transformed into light, heat, or work performed by a machine. The difference in electrical potential is known as voltage, and the current of electrons must flow through a conducting material, such as a metal.

Compressed gases also store potential energy, which can do work when the gases are allowed to expand. This type of potential energy is present in a cylinder containing compressed or liquefied gas.

Nuclear potential energy results from the extremely strong binding forces that exist within atoms. This is by far the densest form of energy. Huge quantities of electromagnetic and kinetic energy are liberated when nuclear energy is released by processes that convert matter into energy. **Fission reactions** involve the splitting of isotopes of certain heavy atoms, such as uranium-235 and plutonium-239, to generate smaller atoms plus enormous amounts of energy. Fission reactions occur in nuclear explosions and, under controlled conditions, in nuclear reactors used to generate electricity.

Fusion reactions involve the combining of certain light elements, such as hydrogen, to form heavier atoms under conditions of extremely high temperature and pressure, while liberating huge quantities of energy. Fusion reactions involving hydrogen occur in stars and are responsible for the unimaginably large amounts of energy that these celestial bodies generate and radiate into space. It is thought that all heavy atoms in the universe were produced by fusion reactions occurring in stars (see Chapter 3). Fusion reactions also occur in a type of nuclear explosion known as a hydrogen bomb. A technology has not yet been developed to allow controlled fusion reactions; if and when available, controlled fusion could be used to generate virtually unlimited amounts of electricity (see Chapter 13).

Energy Units

As we explained above, energy can exist in various forms, all of which can be measured in the same or equivalent units. The *SI* recommended unit (Système International d'Unités, the internationally accepted system for scientific units) is the **joule** (abbreviation J). A joule is defined as the energy required to accelerate 1 kg of mass at 1 m/s^2 (1 meter per second per second) for a distance of 1 m.

A **calorie** (or gram-calorie, abbreviation cal) is another unit of energy. A calorie, defined as being equivalent to 4.184 J, is equal to the amount of energy required to raise the temperature of 1 g of pure water by 1°C (specifically, from 15°C to 16°C). Note that the dietician's "Calorie" is equivalent to 1000 calories (i.e., 1 Calorie = 1 kcal).

Photo 4.2 Organic matter and fossil fuels contain potential chemical energy, which is released during combustion to generate heat and electromagnetic radiation. This forest fire was ignited naturally by lightning and burned the organic matter of boreal forest vegetation.

Source: T. Keith

However, the energy content of many food products is now listed in kJ in countries using the SI system of units, such as Canada.

Energy Transformations and the Laws of Thermodynamics

As was previously noted, energy can be transformed among its various states. For example, when solar electromagnetic radiation is absorbed by a dark object, it is transformed into thermal energy and the absorbing body increases in temperature. The gravitational potential energy of water stored at a height is converted into the kinetic energy of flowing water at a waterfall, or it may be used in hydro-electric technology to spin a turbine and generate electrical energy. As well, visible wavelengths of solar radiation are absorbed by chlorophyll, a green pigment in the foliage of plants, and some of the absorbed energy is converted into chemical potential energy of sugars through the biochemistry of photosynthesis.

All transformations of energy must behave according to certain physical principles, known as the **laws of thermodynamics**. These are universal principles, meaning they are always true, regardless of the circumstances.

The First Law of Thermodynamics

The **first law of thermodynamics**, also known as the law of conservation of energy, can be stated as follows: *energy can undergo transformations among its various states but it is never created or destroyed; thus, the energy content of the universe remains constant*. A consequence of this law is that there is always a zero balance among the energy inputs to a system, any net storage within the system, and the energy output from the system.

Consider the case of an automobile driving along a highway. The vehicle consumes gasoline, an energy input that can be measured. The potential energy of the fuel is converted into various other kinds of energy, including kinetic energy embodied in forward motion of the automobile, electrical energy powering the lights and windshield wipers, heat from friction between the vehicle and the atmosphere and road surface, and the hot exhaust gases (thermal energy) and unburned fuel (chemical potential energy) that are vented through the tailpipe. Overall, in accordance with the first law of thermodynamics, an accurate account of all of these transformations would find that,

while the energy of the gasoline was converted into various other forms, the *total* amount of energy was *conserved* (it remained constant).

The Second Law of Thermodynamics

We can express the **second law of thermodynamics** as follows: *transformations of energy can occur spontaneously only under conditions in which there is an increase in the entropy of the universe*. **Entropy** is a physical attribute related to disorder and is associated with the degree of randomness in the distributions of matter and energy. As the randomness (i.e., disorder) increases, so does entropy. A decrease in disorder is referred to as negative entropy.

Consider, for example, an inflated balloon. Because of the potential energy of its compressed gases, that balloon may slowly leak its contents to the surrounding atmosphere; alternatively, it may burst. Either of these events can occur spontaneously, because both processes would represent increases in the entropy of the universe. This is because compressed gases are more highly ordered than gases dispersed in the atmosphere. In contrast, the dispersed gases in the atmosphere would never spontaneously relocate to inflate a balloon. A balloon can be inflated only if energy is expended through a local application of work (e.g., by a person blowing into the balloon). In other words, energy must be expended to locally decrease entropy in a system. Note that this energy cost itself gives rise to an increase in the entropy of the universe. For instance, the effort of a balloon blower involves additional respiration, which uses biochemical energy and results in heat being expelled into the environment.

Another example concerns planet Earth. Earth continuously receives solar radiation, almost all of which is comprised of visible and near-infrared wavelengths in the range of about 0.4–2.0 μm. Some of this electromagnetic energy is absorbed and converted to thermal energy, heating Earth's atmosphere and surface. The planet cools itself in various ways, but ultimately Earth dissipates all of the absorbed solar radiation by emitting its own electromagnetic energy to outer space as longer-wave infrared radiation (of a spectral quality that peaks at a wavelength of 10 μm). In this case, relatively short-wavelength solar radiation is ultimately transformed into the longer-wavelength radiation emitted by Earth, a process that represents a spontaneous degradation in quality of the energy and an increase in the entropy of the universe.

An important corollary (or secondary proposition) of the second law of thermodynamics is that energy transformations can never be completely efficient—some of the initial content of energy must always be converted to heat so that entropy increases. This helps to explain why, even when using the best available technology, only about 30% of the potential energy of gasoline can be converted into the kinetic energy of a moving automobile, and no more than about 40% of the energy of coal can be transformed into electricity in a generating station. There are also thermodynamic limits to the efficiency of photosynthesis, by which plants convert visible radiation into biochemicals, even under ideal ecological conditions with optimal supplies of nutrients, water, and light.

A superficial assessment might suggest that life in general appears to contradict the second law of thermodynamics. Plants, for example, absorb visible wavelengths of electromagnetic radiation and use this highly dispersed form of energy to fix simple inorganic molecules (carbon dioxide and water) into extremely complex and energy-dense biochemicals. The plant biomass may then be consumed by animals and microbes, which synthesize their own complex biochemicals. These various biological syntheses represent energy transformations that greatly decrease local entropy because relatively dispersed electromagnetic energy and simple inorganic compounds are actively converted into the complex, highly ordered biochemicals of organisms. Do these biological transformations contravene the second law of thermodynamics?

This seeming paradox of life can be successfully resolved using the following logic: the localized bio-concentration of negative entropy can only occur because the system (i.e., life on Earth) receives a constant input of energy in the form of solar radiation. If this external source of energy were terminated, all the organisms and organic materials would quickly and spontaneously degrade, releasing simple inorganic molecules and heat and thereby increasing entropy in the universe. Life and ecosystems cannot survive without continual inputs of solar energy, which are required to organize and maintain their negative entropy. In this sense, the biosphere can be viewed as representing an island (system) of negative entropy, localized in space and time, and continuously fuelled by the sun as an external source of energy.

Earth: An Energy Flow-Through System

Solar electromagnetic radiation is by far the major input of energy that drives Earth's ecosystems. Solar energy heats the planet, circulates its atmosphere and oceans, evaporates its water, and sustains almost all its ecological productivity. Eventually, all solar energy absorbed by Earth is re-radiated back to space in the form of electromagnetic radiation of a longer wavelength than what was originally absorbed. Therefore, Earth maintains a virtually perfect balance between these inputs and outputs of electromagnetic energy. In other words, Earth is a **flow-through system**, with an input of solar energy, an output of re-radiated energy, and no net storage of energy.

In addition, Earth's ecosystems absolutely depend on solar radiation as the source of energy that photosynthetic organisms (such as green plants) utilize to synthesize simple organic compounds (such as sugars) from inorganic molecules (such as carbon dioxide and water). Plants then use the chemical potential energy in these sugars, plus inorganic nutrients, to synthesize a huge diversity of biochemicals through various metabolic reactions. Plants grow and reproduce by using these biochemicals and their potential energy. Moreover, plant biomass is used as food by the enormous numbers of organisms that are incapable of photosynthesis. These organisms include *herbivores*, which eat plants directly; *carnivores*, which eat other animals; and *detritivores*, which feed on dead biomass. (The energy relationships within ecosystems are described later in more detail.)

Less than 0.02% of the solar energy received at Earth's surface is absorbed and fixed by photosynthetic plants and algae. Although this represents a quantitatively trivial component of Earth's energy budget, it is extremely important qualitatively. This biologically absorbed and fixed energy is the foundation of ecological productivity.

Ultimately, however, the solar energy fixed by plants and algae is released to the environment again as heat and is eventually radiated back to outer space. This reinforces the idea of Earth as a flow-through system for energy.

Earth's Energy Budget

An **energy budget** of a system describes the rates of energy input and output as well as any internal transformations among its various states, including changes in stored quantities. Figure 4.2 illustrates key aspects of Earth's physical energy budget.

The rate of input of solar radiation to Earth averages about 8.36 J/cm^2•min (equivalent to 2.00 cal/cm^2•min), measured at the outer limit of the planet's atmosphere. About half of this energy input is visible radiation and half is near-infrared. The output of energy from Earth also occurs at a rate of about 8.36 J/cm²·min. Because the rates of energy input and output are equal, there is no net storage of energy, and Earth's average surface temperature remains stable. Therefore, as was previously noted, the energy budget of Earth can be characterized as a zero-sum, flow-through system.

However, the above is not exactly true. Over extremely long geological time scales, a small storage of solar energy has occurred through the accumulation of undecomposed biomass that eventually transformed into fossil fuels. Minor long-term fluctuations in Earth's surface temperature also occur, representing an important element of climate change. These are, however, quantitatively trivial exceptions to the statement that Earth is a zero-sum, flow-through system for solar energy.

Even though the quantity of energy emitted by Earth eventually equals the amount of solar radiation that is absorbed, many ecologically important transformations occur between the initial absorption and eventual re-radiation. These are the internal elements of the planet's physical energy budget (see Figure 4.2). The most important components are described below.

Reflection

On average, Earth's atmosphere and surface reflect about 30% of incoming solar energy back to outer space. Earth's reflectivity (*albedo*) is strongly influenced by such factors as the angle of the incoming solar radiation (which varies during the day and over the year), amounts of cloud cover and atmospheric particulates (also highly variable), and

---

FIGURE 4.2 | Important Components of Earth's Physical Energy Budget

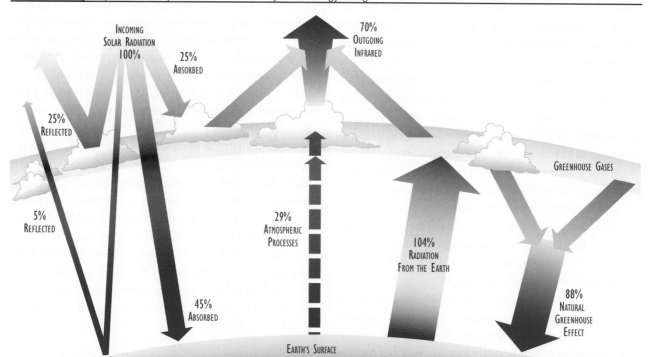

About 30% of the incoming solar radiation is reflected by atmospheric clouds and particulates and by Earth's surface. The remaining 70% is absorbed and then dissipated in various ways. Much of the absorbed energy heats the atmosphere and terrestrial surfaces, and most is then re-radiated as long-wave infrared radiation. Atmospheric moisture and greenhouse gases interfere with this process of re-radiation, keeping Earth's surface warmer than it would be otherwise (see also Chapter 17). The numbers refer to the percentage of incoming solar radiation. See text for a more detailed description of important factors in this energy budget.

Source: Modified from Schneider (1989)

the character of the surface, especially the types and amounts of water (including snow and ice) and vegetation.

Absorption by the Atmosphere

About 25% of incident solar radiation is absorbed by gases, vapours, and particulates in the atmosphere, including clouds. The rate of absorption is wavelength-specific, with portions of the infrared range being intensively absorbed by the so-called "greenhouse" gases (especially water vapour and carbon dioxide; see Chapter 17). The absorbed energy is converted to heat and re-radiated as infrared radiation of a longer wavelength.

Absorption by the Surface

On average, about 45% of incoming solar radiation passes through the atmosphere and is absorbed at Earth's surface by living and non-living materials, increasing the temperature of the absorbing surfaces. This figure of 45% is highly variable, however, depending on atmospheric conditions, especially cloud cover, and also on whether the incident light has passed through a plant canopy.

Over the longer term (i.e., years), and even the medium term (i.e., days), the global net storage of heat is virtually zero. In some places, however, there may be substantial changes in the net storage of thermal energy within the year. This occurs everywhere in Canada because of the strong seasonality of its climate (i.e., Canadian environments are warmer during summer than during winter). Most of the absorbed energy is eventually dissipated by re-radiation from the surface as long-wave infrared.

Evaporation of Water

Some of the thermal energy of living and non-living surfaces causes water to evaporate in a process known as **evapotranspiration.** Evapotranspiration has two components: **evaporation** of water from lakes, rivers, streams, moist rocks, soil, and other non-living substrates, and **transpiration** of water from any living surface, particularly from plant foliage, but also from moist body surfaces and lungs of animals.

Melting of Snow and Ice

Absorbed thermal energy can also cause ice and snow to melt, representing an additional energy transformation associated with a change of state of water from a solid to a liquid form.

Wind and Water Currents

Thermal energy on Earth's surface has a highly uneven distribution, with some regions being quite cold (e.g., the Arctic) and others relatively warm. Because of this irregular allocation of heat, Earth's surface develops processes to diminish the energy gradients by transporting mass around the globe, such as by winds, water currents, and waves on the surface of waterbodies (see also Chapter 3).

Biological Fixation

A very small but ecologically critical portion of incoming solar radiation (globally averaging less than 0.02%) is absorbed by chlorophyll in plants and algae and used to drive photosynthesis. This biological fixation allows some of the solar electromagnetic energy to be temporarily stored as potential energy in biochemicals, thereby serving as the energetic basis for ecological productivity and life on Earth.

Energy in Ecosystems

Ecological energy budgets focus on the absorption of energy by photosynthetic organisms and the transfer of that fixed energy through the *trophic levels* of ecosystems ("trophic" refers to the means of organic nutrition). Ecologists classify organisms in terms of the sources of energy they utilize.

Autotrophs are capable of synthesizing their complex biochemicals using simple inorganic compounds and an external source of energy to drive the process. Most autotrophs are **photoautotrophs**, which use sunlight as their external source of energy. Photoautotrophs capture solar radiation using photosynthetic pigments, the most important of which is chlorophyll. Green plants are the most abundant examples of photoautotrophs, but algae and some bacteria are also photoautotrophic.

A much smaller number of autotrophs are **chemoautotrophs**, which harness some of the energy content of certain inorganic chemicals to drive *chemosynthesis*. The bacterium *Thiobacillus thiooxidans*, for example, oxidizes sulphide minerals to sulphate and uses some of the energy liberated during this reaction to chemosynthesize organic molecules.

Because autotrophs are the biological foundation of ecological productivity, ecologists refer to them as **primary producers**. The total fixation of solar energy by all the primary producers within an ecosystem is known as **gross primary production (GPP)**. Primary producers use some

Photo 4.3 Plant productivity is sustained by solar energy, which is fixed by chlorophyll in the plant and used to combine carbon dioxide, water, and other simple inorganic compounds into the complex molecular structures of organic matter. These ecologists are studying the productivity of a plant community on Sable Island, Nova Scotia.

of this production for their own **respiration** (R)—that is, for the physiological functions needed to maintain themselves in a healthy condition. Respiration, the metabolic oxidation of biochemicals, requires a supply of oxygen and releases carbon dioxide and water as waste products. **Net primary production (NPP)** refers to the fraction of gross primary production that remains after primary producers have used some of their GPP for their own respiration. In other words: NPP = GPP – R.

The energy fixed by primary producers is the basis for the productivity of all other organisms, known as heterotrophs. **Heterotrophs** rely on other organisms, living or dead, to supply the energy they need; they cannot fix solar energy themselves. Animal heterotrophs that feed on plants are known as **herbivores** (or **primary consumers**), three familiar examples being deer, geese, and

grasshoppers. Heterotrophs that consume other animals are known as **carnivores** (or **secondary consumers**), for example, timber wolves, peregrine falcons, sharks, and spiders. Some species feed on both plant and animal biomass and are known as **omnivores**—the grizzly bear is a good example, as is our own species. Many other heterotrophs feed primarily on dead organic matter and are called **decomposers** or **detritivores**; examples include vultures, earthworms, and most fungi and bacteria.

Productivity is production expressed as a rate function, that is, per unit of time and area. Productivity in terrestrial ecosystems is often expressed in units such as kilograms of dry biomass (or its energy equivalent) per hectare per year (i.e., kg/ha•y or kJ/ha•y), while aquatic productivity is often given as grams per cubic metre per year (g/m^3•y).

Numerous studies have been made of the productivity of the different trophic levels in various types of ecosystems. For example, studies of a natural oak–pine forest in New York found that the total fixation of solar energy by the vegetation (i.e., the annual gross primary productivity) was equivalent to 48 100 kJ/m^2•y (4.81 × 10^4 kJ/m^2•y) (Odum, 1983). This fixation rate was equivalent to less than 0.01% of the annual input of solar radiation to the forest. Because the plants used 2.72 × 10^4 kJ/m^2•y during respiration, the net primary productivity in the ecosystem was 2.09 × 10^4 kJ/m^2•y, represented mainly by the growing biomass of the trees. The various heterotrophic organisms in the forest used 1.26 × 10^4 kJ/m^2•y to support their respiration. Ultimately, the net accumulation of biomass by all the organisms in the ecosystem (referred to as the **net ecosystem productivity**) was equivalent to 0.84 × 10^4 kJ/m^2•y.

The primary productivities of the world's major classes of ecosystems are summarized in Table 4.1. Note that the rate of production is greatest in tropical forests, wetlands, coral reefs, and estuaries. The production for each ecosystem type is calculated as its productivity multiplied by its area. The largest amounts of production occur in tropical forests and the open ocean. Note that the open ocean has a relatively small productivity, but its global production is large because of its enormous area.

Ecological **food chains** are linear models of feeding relationships among species. An example of a simple food chain in northern Canada is lichens and sedges, eaten by caribou, eaten by wolves. **Food webs** are more complex models of feeding relationships, describing the connections among all food chains within an ecosystem. Wolves, for instance, are opportunistic predators that feed on snowshoe hare, voles, lemming, beaver, birds, and other prey

TABLE 4.1	Primary Production of Earth's Major Ecosystems

Productivity is the rate of production, standardized to area and time, while production is the total amount of biomass (in dry tonnes) produced by the global area of an ecosystem. Ecosystems are arranged in order of net primary productivity. See Chapter 8 for descriptions of biomes.

ECOSYSTEM	AREA	NET PRIMARY PRODUCTIVITY	GLOBAL NET PRODUCTION
	$(\times 10^6 \text{ km}^2)$	(t/ha·y)	$(\times 10^9 \text{ t/y})$
Wetlands	2.0	30.0	6.0
Tropical rain forest	17.0	22.0	37.4
Tropical seasonal forest	7.5	16.0	12.0
Temperate evergreen forest	5.0	13.0	6.5
Temperate deciduous forest	7.0	12.0	8.4
Savannah	15.0	9.0	13.5
Boreal forest	12.0	8.0	9.6
Open woodland	8.5	7.0	6.0
Cultivated land	14.0	6.5	9.1
Temperate grassland	9.0	6.0	5.4
Lake and stream	2.0	4.0	0.8
Tundra, arctic and alpine	8.0	1.4	1.1
Desert and semidesert scrub	18.0	0.9	1.6
Extreme desert	24.0	<0.1	0.1
TOTAL CONTINENTAL	149.0	7.8	117.5
Reefs and estuaries	2.0	18.0	3.7
Shelf and upwelling	27.0	3.6	9.8
Open ocean	332.0	1.3	41.5
TOTAL MARINE	361.0	1.5	55.0
WORLD TOTAL	510.0	3.4	172.5

Source: Modified from Whittaker and Likens (1975)

in addition to their usual prey of deer, moose, and caribou. Therefore, wolves participate in various food chains within their ecosystem. However, no natural predators feed on wolves, which are therefore referred to as *top carnivores* or *top predators*.

Figure 4.3 illustrates important elements of the food web of Lake Erie, one of the Great Lakes. In this lake, shallow-water environments support aquatic plants, while phytoplankton occur throughout the upper water column. The shallow-water plants are consumed by ducks, muskrat, and other herbivores, while phytoplankton are consumed by tiny crustaceans (zooplankton) and bottom-living filter-feeders such as clams. Zooplankton are eaten by small fish such as smelt, which are fed upon by larger fish, which may eventually be eaten by cormorants, bald eagles, or humans. Dead biomass from any level of the food web may settle to the bottom, where it enters a detrital food web.

There it is eaten by small animals and ultimately decomposed by bacteria and fungi.

In accordance with the second law of thermodynamics, the transfer of energy in food webs is always inefficient because some of the fixed energy is converted into heat. For example, when herbivores consume plant biomass, only some of the energy content can be assimilated and transformed into herbivore biomass. The rest is excreted in feces or utilized in respiration (Figure 4.4). Consequently, in all ecosystems the amount of productivity by autotrophs is always much greater than that of herbivores, which in turn is always greater than that of their predators. As a broad generalization, there is about a 90% loss of energy at each transfer stage. In other words, the productivity of herbivores is only 10% of that of their plant food, and the productivity of the first carnivore level is only 10% of that of the herbivores they feed upon.

FIGURE 4.3 | Major Elements of the Food Web in Lake Erie

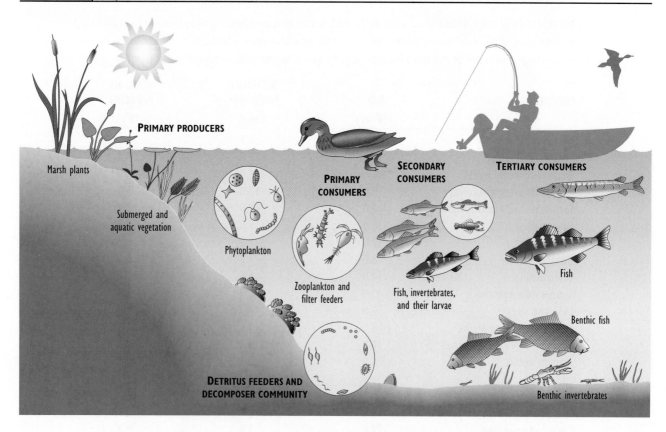

These productivity relationships can be displayed graphically using so-called **ecological pyramids** to represent the **trophic structure** of an ecosystem. Ecological pyramids are organized with plant productivity on the bottom, that of herbivores above the plants, and carnivores above the herbivores. If the ecosystem sustains top carnivores, they are represented at the apex of the pyramid. The sizes of the trophic boxes in Figure 4.4 suggest the pyramid-shaped structure of ecosystem productivity.

The second law of thermodynamics applies to ecological productivity, a function that is directly related to energy flow. The second law does not, however, directly explain the accumulated biomass of an ecosystem. Consequently, it is only the productivity trophic structure that is always pyramid shaped. In some ecosystems, other variables may have a pyramid-shaped trophic structure, such as amounts of biomass (*standing crop*) present at specific times, or the sizes or densities of populations. These particular variables are not, however, pyramid shaped in all ecosystems.

For example, in the open ocean, phytoplankton are the primary producers, but they often maintain a biomass similar to that of the small zooplankton that feed upon them. The phytoplankton cells are relatively short-lived,

and their biomass turns over quickly because of their high productivity. In contrast, the individual zooplankton are longer-lived and much less productive than the phytoplankton. Consequently, the productivity of the phytoplankton is much larger than that of the zooplankton, even though at any particular time both of these trophic levels may have a similar biomass.

Some ecosystems may even have an inverted pyramid of biomass, characterized by a smaller biomass of plants than of herbivores. This sometimes occurs in grasslands, in which the dominant plants are relatively small, herbaceous species that can be quite productive but do not maintain a large biomass. In comparison, some of the herbivores that feed on the plants are relatively large, long-lived animals, which may maintain a larger total biomass than the vegetation. Some temperate and tropical grasslands have an inverted biomass pyramid, especially during the dry season when there may be large populations (and biomass) of long-lived herbivores such as deer, bison, antelope, gazelle, hippopotamus, rhino, or elephant. However, in accordance with the second law of thermodynamics, the annual (or long-term) productivity of the plants in these grasslands is always much larger than that of the herbivores.

FIGURE 4.4 | Model of Energy Transfer in an Ecosystem

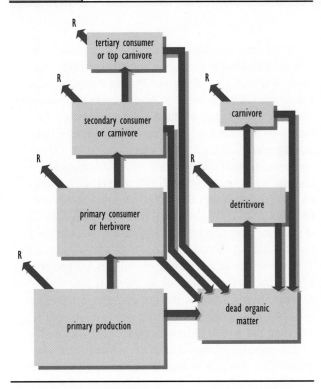

Note that lower levels of the food web always have a greater productivity than higher levels, so the trophic structure is roughly pyramidal. Although not drawn to an appropriate scale, this relationship is roughly indicated by the relative areas of the boxes. "R" indicates respiration.

In addition, the population densities of animals are not necessarily smaller than those of the plants that they eat. For instance, insects are the most important herbivores in many forests and they commonly maintain large populations. In contrast, the numbers of trees are much smaller, because each individual plant is large and occupies a great deal of space. Forests typically maintain many more herbivores than trees and other plants, so the pyramid of numbers is inverted in shape. As in all ecosystems, however, the pyramid of forest productivity is much wider at the bottom than at the top.

Because of the inefficiency of the energy transfer between trophic levels, there are energetic limits to the numbers of top carnivores (such as wolves, killer whales, eagles, and sharks) that can be sustained by an ecosystem. To sustain a viable population of top predators, there must be a suitably high productivity of prey that these animals can exploit. This prey must in turn be sustained by an appropriately high plant productivity. Because of these ecological constraints, only extremely productive or very extensive ecosystems can support top predators.

Of all Earth's terrestrial ecosystems, none supports more species of higher-order carnivores than the savannahs and grasslands of Africa. The most prominent of these top predators are the cheetah, lion, leopard, spotted and striped hyena, and wild dog. This unusually high richness of top predators can be sustained because these African ecosystems are extensive and quite productive of vegetation, except during years of drought. In contrast, the tundra of northern Canada can support only one natural species of top predator, the wolf, because, although extensive, tundra is a relatively unproductive ecosystem.

Some pre-industrial human populations functioned as top predators, including aboriginal peoples of Canada such as the arctic Inuit and many subarctic First Nations cultures. As an ecological consequence of their higher-order feeding strategy within the food web, these cultures were not able to maintain very large populations. In most modern economies, however, humans interact with ecosystems in an omnivorous manner—we harvest an extremely wide range of foods and other biomass products of microbes, fungi, algae, plants, and invertebrate and vertebrate animals.

Conclusions

Energy can exist in various states, but transformations from one to another must obey the laws of thermodynamics. Organisms and ecosystems would spontaneously degrade if they did not have continuous access to external sources of energy. Ultimately, sunlight is the key source of energy supporting almost all life and ecosystems. Sunlight is used by photoautotrophs to combine carbon dioxide and water into simple organic molecules through the metabolic process of photosynthesis. The fixed energy of plant biomass supports ecological food webs. Plants may be eaten by herbivores and the energy obtained is used to support their own growth. Herbivores may then be eaten by carnivores. Dead biomass supports a decomposer food web. Sunlight also drives important planetary functions, such as the hydrologic and climatic systems. Human activities can have a large and degrading influence on food webs, and even on Earth's climatic system by influencing the intensity of the planet's greenhouse effect.

In Detail 4.1

Vegetarianism and Energy Efficiency

Most people have an omnivorous diet, meaning they eat a wide variety of foods of both plant and animal origin. Vegetarians, however, do not eat meat or other foods produced by killing mammals, birds, fish, or other animals. Some vegetarians, known as vegans, do not eat any foods of animal origin, including milk, cheese, or eggs. People choose to adopt a vegetarian lifestyle for various reasons, including those that focus on the ethics of the cultivation and slaughter of animals and the health benefits of a balanced diet that does not include animal products. Moreover, there are tangible environmental benefits of vegetarianism related to avoiding certain air, water, and soil pollutants, and reducing the conversion of natural habitat into agroecosystems used for livestock rearing. In addition, it generally takes much less energy to feed a population of vegetarian humans than omnivorous ones.

Cultivated animals eat a great deal of food. In the industrial agriculture practised in developed countries, including Canada, livestock are mostly raised on a diet of plant products, including cultivated grain. Some vegetarians argue that if that grain were fed directly to people, the total amount of cereals and agricultural land needed to support the human population would be substantially less. This argument is based on the inefficiency of energy transfer between trophic levels, which we examined elsewhere in this chapter in a more ecological context. This energy-efficiency argument is, however, most compelling for animals fed on grain and other concentrated foods. It is much less relevant to livestock that spend all or part of their life grazing on wild rangeland—in that ecological context, ruminant animals such as cows and sheep are eating plant biomass that humans could not directly consume and are producing food that would not otherwise be available.

Similarly, many pigs, chickens, and other livestock are fed food wastes (e.g., from restaurants) and processing by-products (e.g., vegetable and fruit culls and peelings, and grain mash from breweries) that are considered unsuitable for human consumption.

It has been estimated that about 25% of global cropland is being used to grow grain and other foods for livestock, and that 37% of the world's cereal production is fed to agricultural animals. In North America, however, about 70% of the grain production is fed to livestock. And there are immense numbers of agricultural animals: globally, there are about 1.8 billion sheep and goats, 1.3 billion cows, 0.86 billion pigs, and 17 billion chickens. In Canada, there are about 14.7 million cows, 14.8 million pigs, 1.0 million sheep, 526 million chickens, and 20 million turkeys (in 2003; chicken and turkey data are annual slaughters; see Chapter 24). The world's cows alone eat the equivalent of the caloric needs of 8–9 billion people.

Assimilation efficiency is a measure of the percentage of the energy content of an ingested food that is actually absorbed across the gut wall and is therefore available to support the metabolic needs of an animal, including the growth of new biomass. Assimilation efficiency varies among groups of animals and also depends on the type of food being eaten. Herbivorous animals typically have an assimilation efficiency of 20–50%; the smaller rate is relevant to tough, fibrous, poor-quality foods such as grass and straw, while the larger rate applies to higher-quality foods such as grain. Carnivores have a higher assimilation efficiency, around 80%. Overall, it takes about 16 kg of feed to produce 1 kg of beef in a feedlot. The ratios for other livestock are 6:1 for pork, 3:1 for chicken, and 2:1 to 3:1 for farmed fish. These assimilation inefficiencies would be avoided if people directly ate the grain consumed by livestock.

Ecological energetics is not the only consideration in the energy efficiency of vegetarianism. Huge amounts of energy are also used to convert natural ecosystems into farmland, to cultivate and manage the agroecosystems, to transport commodities, to process and package foods, and to transport, treat, or dispose of waste materials. These energy expenditures would also be substantially reduced if more people had a vegetarian diet and lifestyle. It should also be noted that vegetarians have a smaller "ecological footprint" associated with their feeding habits (see Table 25.1 in Chapter 25).

Key Terms

ecosystem	photoautotroph
energy	chemoautotroph
work	primary producer
electromagnetic energy	gross primary production (GPP)
kinetic energy	
potential energy	respiration
fission reaction	net primary production (NPP)
fusion reaction	heterotroph
joule	herbivore
calorie	primary consumer
laws of thermodynamics	carnivore
first law of thermodynamics	secondary consumer
second law of thermodynamics	omnivore
entropy	decomposer
flow-through system	detritivores
energy budget	net ecosystem productivity
evapotranspiration	food chain
evaporation	food web
transpiration	ecological pyramid
autotroph	trophic structure

Questions for Review

1. What are the forms of energy discussed in this chapter? How can each be changed into other forms?

2. What are the first and second laws of thermodynamics? How do they govern transformations of energy?

3. What are the major elements of Earth's physical energy budget?

4. Why is the trophic structure of ecological productivity pyramid-shaped?

Questions for Discussion

1. According to the second law of thermodynamics, systems always spontaneously move toward a condition of greater entropy. Yet life and ecosystems on Earth represent local systems where negative entropy is continuously being generated. What conditions allow this apparent paradox to exist?

2. Why are there no natural higher-order predators that kill and eat lions, wolves, and sharks?

3. Why would it be more efficient for humans to be vegetarians? Discuss your answer in view of the pyramid-shaped structure of ecological productivity.

4. Make a list of the key sources and transformations of energy that support you and your activities on a typical day. What is the ultimate source of each of the energy resources you used (e.g., sunlight, fossil fuels)?

Exploring Issues

1. As part of a study of the cycling of pollutants, you have been asked to describe the food web of two local ecosystems. One of the ecosystems is a natural forest and the other is an area used to grow wheat. How would you determine the major components of the food webs of these ecosystems, the species occurring in their trophic levels, and the interactions among the various species present?

References

Botkin, D.B. and E.A. Keller. 2002. *Environmental Science: Earth as a Living Planet.* 4th ed. New York: Wiley & Sons.

Freedman, B. 1995. *Environmental Ecology.* 2nd ed. San Diego, CA: Academic Press.

Gates, D.M. 1985. *Energy and Ecology.* New York: Sinauer.

Hinrichs, R.A. and M. Kleinbach. 2001. *Energy: Its Use and the Environment.* 3rd ed. Florence, KY: Brook Cole.

Liu, P.I. 1997. *Introduction to Energy and the Environment.* New York: Wiley & Sons.

Odum, E.P. 1983. *Basic Ecology.* New York: Saunders College Publishing.

Priest, J. 1991. *Energy.* New York: Addison-Wesley.

Schneider, S.H. 1989. The Changing Climate. *Scientific American,* **261(3)**: 70–9.

Whittaker, R.H. and G.E. Likens. 1975. The Biosphere and Man. pp. 305–28. In: *Primary Productivity of the Biosphere.* (H. Lieth and R.H. Whittaker, eds.). New York: Springer-Verlag.

Informative Websites

EarthSave Canada. www.earthsave.bc.ca/links/

EarthSave Canada is an organization that promotes awareness of the consequences (including environmental) of food choices.

Entropy on the World Wide Web.
www.math.uni-hamburg.de/home/gunesch/entropy.html

This website promotes the understanding of entropy and its implications.

Ethical Vegetarian Alternative.
http://www.vegetarisme.be/?menu=eng

This website provides a discussion of the environmental and ethical benefits of a vegetarian lifestyle.

Sierra Club Critical Ecoregions Program.
www.sierraclub.org/ecoregions/

This program offers a practical, long-term strategy to buttress the "web of life" on Earth. A clickable map of North America can help you learn more about the ecosystem in your region.

Thermodynamics.
http://en.wikipedia.org/wiki/Thermodynamics

This Wikipedia site and its links provide an excellent overview of the principles and applications of thermodynamics.

5

Flows and Cycles of Nutrients

CHAPTER OBJECTIVES

After completing this chapter, you will be able to

1. Explain what nutrients are and give examples.
2. Discuss the concept of nutrient cycling and describe important compartments and fluxes.
3. Describe the factors that affect the development of major soil types.
4. Describe key aspects of the cycles of carbon, nitrogen, phosphorus, and sulphur.

CHAPTER OUTLINE

- Nutrients
- Nutrient Flows and Cycles
- The Soil Ecosystem
- The Carbon Cycle
- The Nitrogen Cycle
- The Phosphorus Cycle
- The Sulphur Cycle
- Conclusions

Nutrients

Nutrients are any chemicals required for the proper functioning of organisms. We can distinguish two basic types of nutrients: inorganic chemicals required by autotrophic organisms for use in photosynthetic reactions and metabolism, and organic compounds ingested by heterotrophic organisms. This chapter deals with the inorganic nutrients.

Plants absorb a wide range of inorganic nutrients from their environment, typically as simple compounds. For example, most plants obtain their carbon as gaseous carbon dioxide (CO_2) from the atmosphere, their nitrogen as the ions nitrate (NO_3^-) or ammonium (NH_4^+), their phosphorus as phosphate (PO_4^{-3}), and their calcium and magnesium as simple ions (Ca^{2+} and Mg^{2+}, respectively). The various ions are obtained from soil water. Plants utilize these nutrients in photosynthetic reactions and other metabolic processes to manufacture all of the biochemicals required for their growth and reproduction.

Some inorganic nutrients, referred to as *macronutrients*, are required by plants in relatively large quantities. These are carbon, oxygen, hydrogen, nitrogen, phosphorus, potassium, calcium, magnesium, and sulphur. Carbon and oxygen are needed in the largest amounts because carbon typically comprises 45–50% of the dry weight of plant biomass and oxygen somewhat less. Hydrogen accounts for about 6% of dry plant biomass, while nitrogen and potassium occur in concentrations of 1–2%. The concentrations of calcium, phosphorus, magnesium, and sulphur are about 0.1–0.5%. *Micronutrients*, required by plants in much smaller quantities, include boron, chlorine, copper, iron, manganese, molybdenum, and zinc. Each micronutrient accounts for less than 0.01% of plant biomass and as little as a few parts per million (i.e., ppm or 10^{-6}; 1 ppm is equivalent to 0.0001%; see Appendix A).

Heterotrophs obtain the nutrients they require by eating plants, other heterotrophs, or both. This ingested biomass contains nutrients in various organically bound forms. The animals digest the organic forms of nutrients and assimilate them into simple organic or inorganic compounds, which they use to synthesize their own necessary biochemicals through various metabolic processes.

Nutrient Flows and Cycles

Earth does not receive much mass from outer space, and it also loses little to that enormous void. Earth does gain small amounts of space materials through meteorite showers, but these extraterrestrial inputs are insignificant in comparison with Earth's mass. Earth is, therefore, essentially an isolated system in terms of matter. Because of this fact, at the global and biospheric levels, nutrients and other materials "cycle" within and between ecosystems. In contrast, energy (discussed in Chapter 4) always "flows through" ecosystems and the biosphere.

Nutrient cycling refers to the transfers, chemical transformations, and recycling of nutrients in ecosystems. A **nutrient budget** is a quantitative estimate of the rates of nutrient input and output to and from some designated ecosystem, as well as the amounts present and transferred within the system.

The major elements of a nutrient cycle are shown in Figure 5.1. The outer boundary of the diagram defines the limits of an ecosystem. (It could even represent the entire biosphere, in which case there would be no significant inputs to or outputs from the system.) More commonly, in ecological studies, the system is defined as a particular landscape, lake, or *watershed* (i.e., the terrestrial basin from which water drains into a stream or lake). Each of these systems has inputs and outputs of nutrients, the rates of which can be measured.

Photo 5.1 The productivity of a natural ecosystem is often limited by the supply of nutrients, a phenomenon that can be investigated by experimentally fertilizing the system. In this case, nitrogen fertilizer was added to a meadow in the arctic tundra, resulting in increased productivity. The experimental plot is a slightly darker colour.

FIGURE 5.1 A Representative Nutrient Cycle

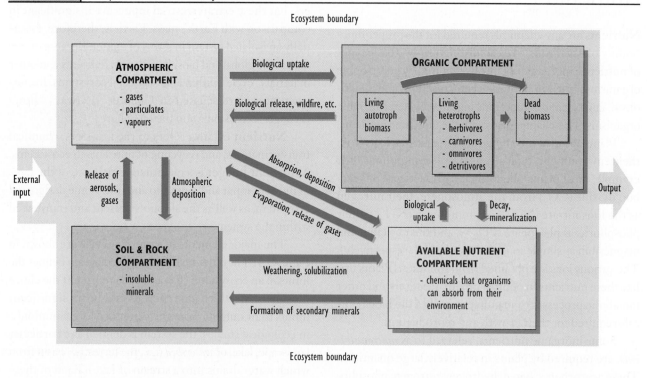

This shows the major elements of a representative nutrient cycle for a particular, defined ecosystem, such as a watershed. The boxes represent compartments that "store" materials. The arrows represent fluxes, or transfers of material between compartments.

Source: Modified from Likens *et al.* (1977)

The boxes within the boundary represent **compartments**, each of which stores quantities of materials. Compartment sizes are commonly expressed in units of mass per unit of surface area. Examples of such units are kilograms per hectare (kg/ha) or tonnes per hectare (t/ha). In aquatic studies, compartment sizes may be expressed per unit of volume of water (e.g., g/m^3). The arrows in the diagram represent **fluxes**, or transfers of material between compartments. Fluxes are rate functions, measured in terms of mass per area per time (e.g., kg/ha•y).

We can divide the system into four major compartments:

1. The atmosphere consists of gases and small concentrations of suspended particulates and water vapour.

2. Rocks and soil consist of various insoluble minerals that are not directly available for uptake by organisms.

3. Available nutrients, present in chemical forms that are water soluble to some degree, can be taken up by organisms from their environment and contribute to their mineral nutrition.

4. The organic compartment consists of nutrients present within living and dead biomass. The organic compartment can be divided into three functional groups: living autotrophs such as plants, algae, and autotrophic bacteria; living heterotrophs including herbivores, carnivores, omnivores, and detritivores; and all forms of dead biomass.

The major transfers of material between compartments, the fluxes, are also shown in Figure 5.1. These are the critically important transfer pathways within nutrient cycles. For instance, insoluble forms of nutrients in rocks and soil become available for uptake by organisms through various chemical transformations, such as *weathering* or *solubilization*, that render the nutrients soluble in water. This is reversed by reactions that produce insoluble compounds from soluble ones. These reactions form *secondary minerals* such as clays, carbonates (e.g., $CaCO_3$, $MgCO_3$), oxides of iron and aluminum (e.g., Fe_2O_3, $Al(OH)_3$), sulphides (e.g., FeS_2), and other compounds that are not directly available for biological uptake.

Other fluxes in nutrient cycles include the biological uptake of nutrients from the atmosphere or from the available nutrient pool in soil. Plant foliage, for example, assimilates carbon dioxide (CO_2) from air, and roots absorb nitrate (NO_3^-) and ammonium (NH_4^+) ions dissolved in soil water. These nutrients can be fixed by plants into their growing biomass. The organic nutrients then enter the food web and are eventually deposited as dead biomass. Organic nutrients in dead biomass are recycled through the processes of decay and mineralization, which regenerate the supply of available nutrients.

We further investigate these concepts in the following sections. Initially, we examine the soil ecosystem, which is where most nutrient cycling occurs within terrestrial habitats. We will then examine important aspects of the cycling of carbon, nitrogen, phosphorus, and sulphur.

The Soil Ecosystem

Soil is a complex and variable mixture of fragmented rock, organic matter, moisture, gases, and living organisms that covers almost all of Earth's terrestrial landscapes. It provides mechanical support for growing plants, even for trees as tall as 100 m. Soil also stores supplies of water and critical nutrients for plants and other organisms. It also provides habitat for the many organisms that are active in the decomposition of organic matter and recycling of its nutrient content. Soil is a component of all terrestrial ecosystems, but it can also be studied as a dynamic ecosystem in and of itself.

Soils develop over long periods of time toward a mature condition. Fundamentally, they are derived from so-called parent materials, which are rocks and minerals that occur within a metre or so of the surface. Parent materials in most of Canada were deposited as a result of glacial processes, often as a complex mixture known as till, which contains rock fragments of various sizes and mineralogies. In some areas, however, the parent materials were deposited beneath immense inland lakes, usually in post-glacial times. Such places are typically rather flat and have relatively uniform, fine-grained soils ranging in texture from clay to sand. (Clay particles have diameters less than 0.002 mm, while silt ranges from 0.002–0.05 mm, sand from 0.05–2 mm, and gravel from 2–20 mm. Coarse gravel and rubble are larger than 20 mm.) Figure 5.2 presents a textural classification of soil based on the percentage of clay-, silt-, and sand-sized particles.

In other regions, parent materials known as loess are derived from silts that were transported by the wind from

Photo 5.2   Soil in natural ecosystems often develops a vertical stratification, with organic-rich horizons on the surface and mineral-rich ones below. This soil "pit" was dug in a stand of an aspen–grassland ecosystem in northern Saskatchewan known as "parkland." Beneath the dark, organic surface layer is a horizon moderately stained with organic matter leached from the surface. Below this is the mineral, lighter-coloured parent material.

Source: D. Gauthier

other places. Because of their very small particle size, clay soils have an enormous surface area, giving them important chemical properties such as the ability to bind many nutrient ions.

The characteristics of the parent material have an important influence on the type of soil. Soil development is also, however, profoundly affected by biological processes and climatic factors such as precipitation and temperature.

FIGURE 5.2 | A Textural Classification of Soils

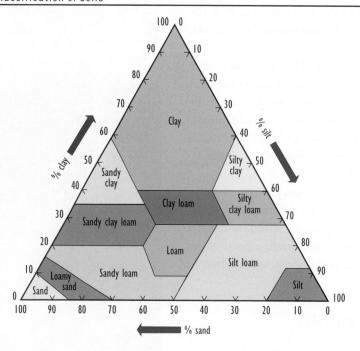

The percentage composition of clay-, silt-, and sand-sized particles is used to classify soils into the 12 types represented here.

Source: Modified from Foth (1990)

For example, water from precipitation can dissolve certain chemicals from parent materials and carry them downwards. This process, known as **leaching**, modifies the chemistry and mineralogy of both the surface and the deeper parts of the soil. In addition, inputs of litter and other debris from plants increase the content of organic matter in mature soils. Fresh litter is a food substrate for many species of soil-dwelling animals, fungi, and bacteria. These organisms progressively oxidize the organic debris into carbon dioxide, water, and inorganic nutrients such as ammonium, with some material remaining as complex organic matter, known as humus.

As soils develop, they assume a vertical stratification known as a **soil profile**, which can have discrete, easily recognizable layers known as horizons. From the surface downward, the major horizons of a well-developed soil profile are as follows:

HORIZON	DESCRIPTION
L	Litter layer contains organic matter that is readily identifiable as being plant litter.
F	Fermentation or duff layer contains partly decomposed organic matter with small litter fragments still visible.
H	Humus layer contains well-decomposed (humified) organic matter with few readily identifiable fragments.
A_1	Transitional A horizon has a high organic concentration mixed with inorganic materials.
A_2 or A_e	Eluviated A horizon has a relatively light colour with low concentrations of organic matter and certain minerals (such as iron and aluminum) that have been leached downward (or eluviated) by percolating water.
B	Accumulation horizon has a darker colour because of the deposition of clay, iron, and organic matter leached from the A horizon.
C	Parent material, a layer in which the original parent material has been little influenced by soil-forming processes.
R	Regolith or underlying rock.

Soils modified by human influences can be stratified quite differently from that just described. In cultivated land, for example, a rather homogeneous plough layer (A_p) of 15–20 cm develops on the surface of the soil. The plough layer is uniform in structure because it has been mixed up repeatedly for many years. In addition, the soil of agricultural land is often highly deficient in organic matter, compacted by the repeated passage of heavy machinery, and degraded in structure, nutrient concentration, and other qualities important to its potential ability to support crop productivity. These subjects are discussed in more detail in Chapters 14 and 24.

Broadly speaking, soils within a particular kind of ecosystem, such as tundra, conifer forest, hardwood forest, or prairie, tend to develop in a distinctive way. Soils are classified by the ecological conditions under which they developed. The highest level of classification arranges soils into *orders*, which can themselves be divided into more complex groups. The most important soil orders in Canada are the following:

SOIL ORDER	DESCRIPTION
Chernozem	Forms in cool temperate climates with sufficient rainfall to support tall-grass and mixed-grass prairie. Has a thick, blackish, organic-rich A horizon, rich in calcium carbonate at the surface. The B horizon is lighter coloured, and the C horizon is again rich in calcium carbonate. A fertile soil, also known as "black earth."
Podzol	Forms in cool, temperate, humid climates especially under coniferous and mixed conifer and angiosperm (hardwood) forest. Has a thick, acidic, LFH layer, a highly leached A_e horizon, and often a reddish B horizon due to the deposition of iron oxides. Also known as spodosol.
Brunisol	Forms in temperate, humid climates under angiosperm forest, and usually from calcium-rich parent material. Little accumulation of litter, with a dark-brown A horizon and a lighter coloured B horizon. Also known as brown forest soil.
Luvisol	Develops under a range of climatic conditions from boreal to temperate, and under a range of forest types from coniferous to angiosperm. Little accumulation of litter, with a slightly acidic A_e horizon and a neutral, clay-rich B horizon.
Regosol	Develops under various climatic conditions from poorly consolidated parent materials such as sand or silt. Has little profile development.
Gleysol	Develops in cool, temperate climates on sites subject to periodic waterlogging, usually because the C horizon is not fully permeable to downward movement of water. The waterlogged surface layers become anoxic (oxygen-depleted), fostering the leaching of iron and manganese compounds which deposit lower down in grey-red mottled bands.
Solonetz	Develops in semi-desert to arid climates under moderate drainage and somewhat saline conditions that support salt-tolerant plants. Has a thin surface layer over a darker, alkaline horizon.
Organic	Develops in a cool, humid climate in wetlands such as bogs and fens. It is characterized by surface peat deposits that can be up to 10 m thick.

The Importance of Soil

The soil ecosystem is extremely important ecologically. Terrestrial plants obtain their water and much of the nutrients they need for growth from the soil, absorbing these through their underground roots, rhizomes, and mycorrhizae. Soil also provides habitat for a great diversity of animals and microorganisms that play a crucial role in litter decomposition and nutrient cycling.

Soil is also economically important because it critically influences the kinds of agricultural crops that can be grown in a region (Chapter 14 discusses soil factors and crop productivity). Some of the most productive soils for agriculture are alluvial soils, typically found along rivers and their deltas where periodic flooding and silt deposition bring in abundant supplies of nutrients. As long as they are not too stony, chernozems and brunisols are also fertile and favourable for agriculture. Much prairie agriculture is developed on chernozem soils of various types, while much of the fertile agricultural land of southern Quebec and Ontario contains brunisols.

The Carbon Cycle

Carbon is one of the basic building blocks of life and the most abundant element in organisms, accounting for about 50% of typical dry biomass. Key aspects of the global carbon cycle are presented in Figure 5.3 (see also Chapter 17 and Figure 17.1). Gaseous carbon dioxide (CO_2) is the most important atmospheric form of carbon, occurring in a concentration of about 375 ppm, although methane (CH_4, about 1.8 ppm) is also significant.

Atmospheric CO_2 is a critical nutrient for photosynthetic organisms, such as plants, which absorb this gas through tiny pores in their foliage, fix it into organic matter, and then use the fixed energy to support their respiration and to achieve growth and reproduction. Some of the organic matter of plants and other autotrophs is consumed by heterotrophs and passed through ecological food webs. All organisms release CO_2 to the atmosphere as a waste product of their respiratory metabolism.

CO_2 is also the most common emission associated with the decomposition of dead organic matter. However, if this process occurs under *anaerobic* conditions (i.e., oxygen [O_2] is not available), CH_4 and CO_2 are both emitted. Anaerobic decomposition is relatively inefficient, which explains why dead organic matter in wetlands, such as swamps and bogs, often accumulates, eventually forming peat. Under suitable geological conditions (i.e., anaerobic, deep burial, high pressure, high temperature), peat may be slowly transformed into carbon-rich fossil fuels such as coal, petroleum, and natural gas (see Chapter 13).

Atmospheric CO_2 also dissolves into oceanic water, forming the bicarbonate ion (HCO_3^-), which can be taken up and fixed into organic matter by photosynthetic algae and bacteria. These autotrophic organisms are the base of the marine food web. Various marine organisms also use oceanic CO_2 and HCO_3^- to manufacture their shells of calcium carbonate ($CaCO_3$), an insoluble mineral that slowly accumulates in sediments and may eventually lithify into limestone (also $CaCO_3$).

FIGURE 5.3 | Model of the Global Carbon Cycle

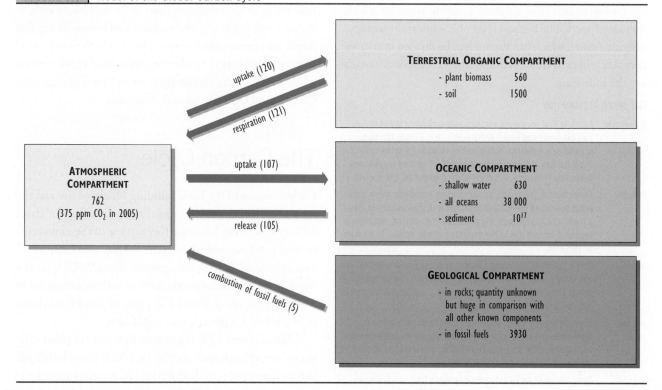

The amounts of carbon stored in the various compartments are expressed in units of billions of tonnes of carbon (10^9 t), while fluxes between compartments are in 10^9 t/y.

Sources: Modified from Blasing (1985), Solomon *et al.* (1985), and Freedman (1995)

Overall, the amount of CO_2 absorbed by the global biota from the atmosphere is similar to the amount released through respiration and decomposition. Consequently, the cycling of this nutrient can be viewed as a steady-state system. In modern times, however, anthropogenic emissions have significantly upset the atmospheric carbon balance. Global emissions of CO_2 and CH_4 are now larger than the uptake of these gases, an imbalance that has led to their increasing concentrations in the atmosphere. This phenomenon may be important in intensifying Earth's greenhouse effect (see Chapter 17).

The Nitrogen Cycle

Nitrogen is another critically important nutrient for organisms, being an integral component of many biochemicals, including amino acids, proteins, and nucleic acids. Like the carbon cycle, the nitrogen cycle has an important atmospheric phase, but unlike carbon, nitrogen is not a significant constituent of rocks and minerals. Consequently, the atmospheric reservoir of nitrogen plays a paramount role in its environmental cycling (Figure 5.4).

Virtually all atmospheric nitrogen occurs in the form of nitrogen gas (N_2, sometimes referred to as dinitrogen), which is present in a concentration of 78%. Other gaseous forms of nitrogen include ammonia (NH_3), nitric oxide (NO), nitrogen dioxide (NO_2), and nitrous oxide (N_2O). These trace gases typically occur in the atmosphere in concentrations considerably less than 1 ppm, although there may be larger amounts in environments influenced by anthropogenic emissions (see Chapter 16). Nitrogen also occurs in trace atmospheric particulates containing nitrate (NO_3^-) and ammonium (NH_4^+), such as ammonium nitrate (NH_4NO_3) and ammonium sulphate (($NH_4)_2SO_4$), both of which can be important pollutants (see Chapters 16 and 19).

Nitrogen occurs in many other chemical forms in terrestrial and aquatic environments. "Organic nitrogen" refers to the great variety of nitrogen-containing molecules in living and dead biomass. These chemicals range in character from simple amino acids, through proteins

FIGURE 5.4 | Model of the Global Nitrogen Cycle

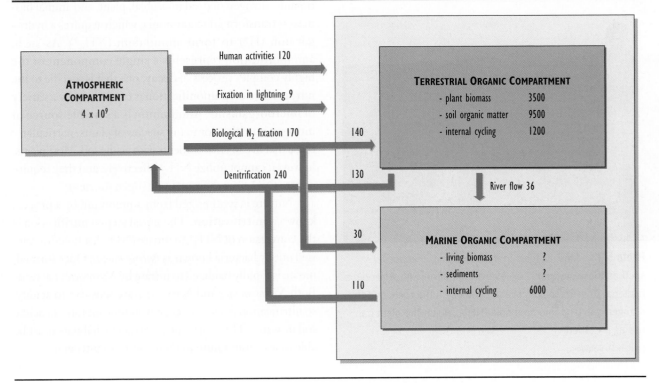

The amounts of nitrogen stored in compartments are in millions of tonnes (10^6 t of N), while fluxes between compartments are in 10^6 t/y.

Sources: Modified from Hutzinger (1982) and Freedman (1995)

and nucleic acids, to large and complex molecules (known as humic substances) that are important components of dead organic matter in ecosystems. Nitrogen in ecosystems also occurs in a small number of inorganic compounds, the most important of which are N_2 and NH_3 gases and the ions nitrate, nitrite (NO_2^-), and ammonium. The nitrogen cycle involves the transformation and cycling of the various organic and inorganic forms of nitrogen within ecosystems.

Nitrogen Fixation

Because the two nitrogen atoms in dinitrogen gas are held together by a strong triple bond, N_2 is a virtually inert compound. For this reason, N_2 can be directly utilized by only a few specialized organisms even though it is extremely abundant in the environment. These so-called nitrogen-fixing species, all of which are microorganisms, have the ability to metabolize N_2 into NH_3 gas. The microorganisms can then use the "fixed" nitrogen for their own nutrition. More importantly, the NH_3 also becomes available to the

great majority of autotrophic plants and microorganisms that cannot fix N_2 themselves.

Biological **nitrogen fixation** is a critical process—most ecosystems depend on it to provide the nitrogen nutrition that sustains their primary productivity. In fact, because nitrogen is not an important constituent of rocks and soil minerals, N_2 fixation is ultimately responsible for almost all of the organic nitrogen in the biomass of the world's organisms and ecosystems. The only other significant sources of fixed nitrogen for ecosystems are atmospheric depositions of nitrate and ammonium through precipitation and dustfall, and the direct uptake of NO and NO_2 gases by plants. These are usually, however, minor sources in comparison with biological N_2 fixation.

The best known of the N_2-fixing microorganisms are bacteria called *Rhizobium*, which live in specialized nodules on the roots of certain species of leguminous plants, such as peas and beans. Some other plants, such as alders, also live in a **mutualism** (i.e., a mutually beneficial *symbiosis*; see Chapter 9) with N_2-fixing microorganisms. So do most lichens, which are a mutualism between a fun-

Photo 5.3   Most species in the pea family (*Fabaceae*), such as these soybeans, develop a mutualism with *Rhizobium* bacteria. The *Rhizobium* live in nodules on the roots and fix nitrogen gas (N_2) into ammonia (NH_3), which the plant can use as a nutrient.

Source: D. Patriquin

gus and an alga. Many other N_2-fixing microbes are free-living in soil or water, for example cyanobacteria (blue-green bacteria).

Non-biological nitrogen fixation also occurs naturally, for instance during a lightning event when atmospheric N_2 combines with O_2 under conditions of great heat and pressure. Humans also cause N_2 to be fixed in various ways. Nitrogen fertilizer is manufactured by combining N_2 with hydrogen gas (H_2, which is manufactured from CH_4, a fossil fuel) in the presence of iron catalysts to produce NH_3. In addition, NO gas is formed in the internal combustion engine of vehicles, where N_2 combines with O_2 under conditions of high pressure and temperature. Large quantities of NO are emitted to the atmosphere in vehicle exhaust, contributing to air pollution (Chapter 16). Anthropogenic N_2 fixation now amounts to about 120 million t/y, about 83% of which is associated with the manufacturing of nitrogen fertilizers. This is a globally important component of the modern nitrogen cycle and is comparable in magnitude with non-human N_2 fixation (about 170 million t/y).

Ammonification and Nitrification

After organisms die, their organically bound nitrogen must be converted to inorganic forms; otherwise, the recycling of the fixed nitrogen would not be possible (Figure 5.5).

In **ammonification**, the initial stage of this process, the organic nitrogen of dead microbial, plant, and animal biomass is transformed to ammonia, which acquires a hydrogen ion (H^+) to form ammonium (NH_4^+). As such, ammonification represents a single component of the highly complex process of **decay**, one that is specific to the nitrogen cycle. Ammonification is carried out by a variety of microorganisms. Ammonium is a suitable source of nitrogen nutrition for many species of plants, particularly those that live in environments with acidic soil. Most plants, however, cannot utilize NH_4^+ effectively, and they require nitrate (NO_3^-) as their main nitrogen nutrient.

Nitrate is synthesized from ammonium by a process known as **nitrification**. The initial step in nitrification is the conversion of NH_4^+ to nitrite (NO_2^-), a function carried out by bacteria known as *Nitrosomonas*. Once formed, nitrite is rapidly oxidized to nitrate by *Nitrobacter* bacteria. Both *Nitrosomonas* and *Nitrobacter* are sensitive to acidity, so nitrification does not occur at significant rates in acidic soil or water. This is why plants in acidic habitats must be able to use ammonium as their source of nitrogen.

Denitrification

In **denitrification**, also performed by a wide variety of microbial species, nitrate is converted to either of the gases N_2O or N_2, which are emitted to the atmosphere. Denitrification occurs under anaerobic (O_2-poor) conditions, and its rate is greatest when concentrations of nitrate are large, for example in fertilized agricultural land that is temporarily flooded. In some respects, denitrification can be considered a counter-balancing process to nitrogen fixation. In fact, global rates of nitrogen fixation and denitrification are in a rough balance, so the total quantity of fixed nitrogen in Earth's ecosystems is not increasing or decreasing substantially over time.

The Phosphorus Cycle

Phosphorus is a key constituent of many biochemicals, including lipids, nucleic acids such as DNA and RNA, and energy-carrying molecules such as ATP. Phosphorus is, however, required by organisms in considerably smaller quantities than nitrogen or carbon. Compared with the rates of cycling of carbon and nitrogen, relatively small amounts of phosphorus cycle in ecosystems. Because phosphorus is often in short supply, it is a critical nutrient in many ecosystems, particularly in freshwater and agriculture.

FIGURE 5.5 | Important Transformations of Fixed Nitrogen in Ecosystems

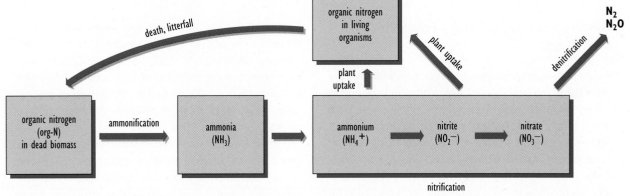

Source: Modified from Freedman (1995)

Unlike the carbon and nitrogen cycles, the phosphorus cycle does not have a significant atmospheric phase. Phosphorus compounds do occur in the atmosphere, as particulates present in trace quantities; however, atmospheric inputs to ecosystems are typically small compared with the amounts available from soil minerals or from artificial fertilization of agricultural lands.

Phosphorus tends to move from the terrestrial landscape into surface waters and eventually into the oceans, where it deposits to sediments that act as a long-term sink. Some phosphorus minerals in oceanic sediments are eventually recycled back to the land by geological uplift associated with mountain building. However, this is an extremely slow process and is not meaningful in ecological time scales. Therefore, aspects of the global phosphorus cycle represent a flow-through system.

Certain ecological mechanisms do return some marine phosphorus to portions of the continental landscape. For example, some species of fish spend most of their life at sea but migrate up rivers to breed. When they are abundant, fish such as salmon import substantial quantities of organic phosphorus to the higher reaches of rivers, where it becomes decomposed to phosphate after the fish spawn and die. Fish-eating marine birds are also locally important in returning oceanic phosphorus to land. Their phosphorus-rich excrement is so abundant on some islands that it is mined as fertilizer.

Soil is the principal source of phosphorus nutrition for terrestrial vegetation. The phosphate ion (PO_4^{-3}) is the most important form of plant-available phosphorus. Although phosphate ions are typically present in small concentrations in soil, they are constantly produced from slowly dissolving minerals such as calcium, magnesium, and iron phosphates ($Ca_3(PO_4)_2$, $Mg_3(PO_4)_2$, and $FePO_4$, respectively). Phosphate is also produced by the microbial oxidation of organic phosphorus, a component of the more general decay process. Water-soluble phosphate is quickly absorbed by microorganisms and plant roots and used in the synthesis of their biochemicals.

Aquatic autotrophs also utilize phosphate as their principal source of phosphorus nutrition. In fact, phosphate is commonly the most important **limiting factor** in freshwater ecological productivity. This means that the primary productivity of most freshwater ecosystems will increase if they are fertilized with phosphate, but not if they are treated with sources of nitrogen or carbon (unless they first have sufficient PO_4^{-3} added; see Chapter 20). Lakes and other aquatic ecosystems receive most of their phosphate supply from runoff from the terrestrial parts of their watershed, and through the recycling of phosphorus from sediment and organic phosphorus suspended in the water column.

Humans are greatly affecting the global cycling of phosphorus by mining it, manufacturing fertilizers, and applying these to agricultural land to increase its productivity. For some time, the major source of phosphorus fertilizers was guano, the dried excrement of marine birds. Guano is mined on islands, such as those off coastal Chile and Peru, where colonies of breeding seabirds are abundant and the climate is dry, allowing the guano to accumulate over time. During the twentieth century, however, deposits of sedimentary phosphate minerals were discovered in several places, such as southern Florida. Phosphorus became geologically concentrated in sedimentary deposits in these places through the deposition of marine organisms over millions of years. These deposits are now being

In Detail 5.1

Too Much of a Good Thing—Pollution by Nutrients

As is emphasized throughout this chapter, nutrients are essential to the healthy metabolism of organisms and to the proper functioning of ecosystems. Often, an increase in the supply of nutrients will enhance the productivity of wild and cultivated plants—this is the principle behind the common practice of fertilizer addition in agriculture. There are, however, many instances in which an excessive supply of nutrients has resulted in important environmental problems.

We learned in this chapter that the supply of available forms of nitrogen (particularly NO_3^- and NH_4^+) is often a limiting factor to plant productivity; consequently, nitrogen is the most abundant ingredient in most agricultural fertilizers. However, the use of agricultural fertilizer can result in concentrations of NO_3^- in drinking water that are high enough to be toxic to humans, especially to infants (see Chapter 24). We also know that plants can take up gaseous NO and N_2O from the atmosphere and use them as nutrients, along with NO_3^- and NH_4^+ from precipitation and soil water. Yet, gaseous NO and N_2O are important air pollutants in areas where

they occur in high concentrations, particularly in sunny environments where they are involved in the photochemical production of toxic ozone (see Chapter 16). Furthermore, large amounts of NO_3^- and NH_4^+ in rain and snow may contribute to the acidification of precipitation (e.g., acid rain) and weakly buffered surface waters (see Chapter 19).

There are other examples of environmental problems caused by excessive nutrients. For instance, CO_2 is one of the most important plant nutrients because carbon comprises about half of plant biomass. But this critical nutrient occurs in a relatively small atmospheric concentration—only about 0.04%. However, the concentration of CO_2 in the atmosphere has increased by about 40% during the past two centuries and it continues to amplify; this well-documented change is contributing to global warming, an important environmental problem (see Chapter 17). Eutrophication, or an excessive productivity of waterbodies, is most often caused by an excess of the nutrient PO_4^{-3}, usually because of sewage dumping or runoff from fertilized agricultural land (see Chapter 20). Clearly, these examples show that there is a fine balance between chemicals serving as beneficial nutrients, or as damaging pollutants.

mined to supply mineral phosphorus used to manufacture agricultural fertilizer. When these easily exploitable mineral deposits become exhausted, however, phosphorus may turn out to be a limiting factor for agricultural production in the not-so-distant future.

About 50 million tonnes of phosphorus fertilizer are now manufactured each year. This is a highly significant input to the global phosphorus cycle in view of the estimate that about 200 million tonnes of phosphorus per year are absorbed naturally from soil by vegetation.

The Sulphur Cycle

Sulphur, another important nutrient, is a key constituent of certain amino acids, proteins, and other biochemicals. Sulphur is relatively abundant in many minerals and rocks and also has a significant presence in soil, water, and the atmosphere.

Atmospheric sulphur occurs in various compounds, some of which are important air pollutants (see Chapter 16). Sulphur dioxide (SO_2), a gas, is naturally emitted by volcanic eruptions and forest fires. SO_2 is also emitted in large quantities by coal-fired power plants and metal smelters. SO_2 is toxic to many plants at concentrations lower than 1 ppm. In some places, important ecological damage has been caused by this gas, such as the Sudbury area (see Chapter 16).

In the atmosphere, SO_2 becomes oxidized to the *anion* (i.e., negatively charged ion) sulphate (SO_4^{-2}), which occurs as tiny particulates or dissolved in droplets of moisture. In this form, the negative charges of sulphate must be balanced by positive charges of *cations* such as ammonium (NH_4^+), calcium (Ca^{2+}), or the hydrogen ion (H^+, an important element of "acid rain"; see Chapter 19).

Hydrogen sulphide (H_2S), which has a strong smell of rotten eggs, is emitted from volcanoes and deep-sea vents. It is also emitted from ecosystems in which organic sulphur compounds are decomposed under anaerobic conditions, and from oxygen-poor aquatic systems where SO_4^{-2} is reduced to H_2S. Dimethyl sulphide is another reduced-sulphur gas that is produced in the oceans and emitted to the atmosphere. In oxygen-rich environments, such as the atmosphere, H_2S is oxidized to sulphate—as is dimethyl sulphide, but more slowly.

Most emissions of SO_2 to the atmosphere are associated with human activities, but almost all H_2S emissions are natural. An important exception is the emission of H_2S from sour-gas wells and processing facilities—for example, in Alberta. Overall, the global emission of all sulphur-containing gases is equivalent to about 251 million tonnes of sulphur per year. About 41% of this emission is anthropogenic and the rest is natural (see Chapter 16 for more details).

Sulphur occurs in rocks and soils in a variety of mineral forms, the most important of which are sulphides, which occur in compounds with metals. Iron sulphides (such as FeS_2, called pyrites when they occur as cubic crystals) are the most common sulphide minerals, but all of the heavy metals (e.g., copper, lead, nickel) can occur in this mineral form. Whenever metal sulphides become exposed to an oxygen-rich environment, certain bacteria begin to oxidize the sulphide, generating sulphate as a product. These autotrophic bacteria, known as *Thiobacillus thiooxidans*, use energy from this chemical transformation to sustain their growth and reproduction. This type of primary productivity is called **chemosynthesis** (in parallel with the photosynthesis of plants). In places where large quantities of sulphide are oxidized, high levels of acidity are associated with the sulphate product, a phenomenon referred to as "acid-mine drainage" (see Chapter 19).

Sulphur also occurs in a variety of organically bound forms in soil and water. These compounds include proteins and other sulphur-containing chemicals from dead organic matter. Soil microorganisms oxidize organic sulphur to sulphate, an ion that plants can readily use in their nutrition.

Plants satisfy their nutritional requirements for sulphur by assimilating its simple mineral compounds from the environment, mostly by absorbing sulphate dissolved in soil water, which is taken up by roots. In environments where the atmosphere is somewhat contaminated by SO_2, plants can absorb this gas through their foliage (although too much absorption can be toxic—there is a fine line between SO_2 as a plant nutrient and as a poison).

As was already mentioned, human activities have significantly influenced the rates of certain fluxes of the sulphur cycle. Important environmental damage has been caused by SO_2 toxicity, acid rain, acid-mine drainage, and other sulphur-related problems. Sulphur is also, however, an important mineral commodity, with many industrial uses in manufacturing and as an agricultural fertilizer. Most commercial sulphur is obtained by cleaning "sour" natural gas (methane, CH_4) of its H_2S content and by removing SO_2 from waste gases at metal smelters.

Conclusions

Nutrients are chemicals that are essential for the metabolism of organisms and ecosystems. If they are insufficient in quantity, then productivity is less than it potentially could be. Nutrients can also be present in excess, causing environmental damage through eutrophication and other problems. Nutrients routinely cycle among inorganic and organic forms within ecosystems. Key aspects of nutrient cycles are illustrated by the carbon, nitrogen, phosphorus, and sulphur cycles.

Key Terms

nutrient

nutrient cycling

nutrient budget

compartment

flux

soil

leaching

soil profile

nitrogen fixation

mutualism

ammonification

decay

nitrification

denitrification

limiting factor

chemosynthesis

Questions for Review

1. What are the basic aspects of a nutrient cycle? In your answer, include the roles of compartments and fluxes.

2. How are soils formed from parent materials? Include the influences of physical and biological processes in your answer.

3. What are the major types of soil? How do they differ?

4. What are the key chemical transformations in the nitrogen cycle, and which ones are affected by human influences?

Questions for Discussion

1. Compare and contrast key aspects of the cycling of carbon, nitrogen, phosphorus, or sulphur.

2. Nitrogen and phosphorus fertilizers are critically important to the practice of modern agriculture, yet these materials are manufactured from non-renewable resources and may not be so readily available in the future. What would be the consequences for agricultural production if nitrogen and phosphorus fertilizers were to become more expensive and less available?

3. How do your daily activities affect key aspects of the carbon cycle?

4. If soil becomes acidic, the process of nitrification may no longer occur. What would the consequences of this change be for the nutrition of plants?

Exploring Issues

1. A sewage-treatment plant has applied for permission to dispose its nutrient-rich sludge onto nearby agricultural land. You have been asked to design a study that would examine the effects of the sludge on the cycling of nitrogen and phosphorus in the agroecosystem. What key response variables should be measured during the study? What experiments would you recommend for examining the potential effects of the sludge on nutrient cycling and crop productivity?

References

Atlas, R.M. and R. Bartha. 1998. *Microbial Ecology: Fundamentals and Applications.* 4th ed. Menlo Park, CA: Benjamin/Cummings.

Blasing, T.J. 1985. Background: Carbon Cycle, Climate, and Vegetation Responses. pp. 9–22. In: *Characterization of Information Requirements for Studies of CO$_2$ Effects: Water Resources, Agriculture, Fisheries, Forests, and Human Health.* Washington, DC: DOE/ER-0236, U.S. Department of Energy.

Botkin, D.B. and E.A. Keller. 2002. *Environmental Science: Earth as a Living Planet.* 4th ed. New York: Wiley & Sons.

Brady, N.C. and R.R. Weil. 2003. *Elements of the Nature and Properties of Soils.* 2nd ed. New York: Prentice Hall.

Foth, H.D. 1990. *Fundamentals of Soil Science.* New York: Wiley & Sons.

Freedman, B. 1995. *Environmental Ecology.* 2nd ed. San Diego, CA: Academic Press.

Hutzinger, O. (ed.) 1982. *The Handbook of Environmental Chemistry.* New York: Springer-Verlag.

Likens, G.E., and F.H. Bormann. 1999. *Biogeochemistry of a Forested Ecosystem.* 2nd ed. New York: Springer-Verlag.

Margulis, L., C. Matthews, and A. Haselton. 2000. *Environmental Evolution.* 2nd ed. Cambridge, MA: MIT Press.

Plaster, E.J. 2002. *Soil Science and Management.* 3rd ed. Florence, KY: Delmar Thomson Learning.

Post, W.M., T. Peng, W.R. Emanual, A.W. King, V.H. Dale, and D.L. DeAngelis. 1990. The Global Carbon Cycle. *American Scientist,* **78**: 310–26.

Schlesinger, W.H. 1997. *Biogeochemistry: An Analysis of Global Change.* 2nd ed. San Diego, CA: Academic Press.

Solomon, A.M., J.R. Trabolka, D.E. Reichle, and L.D. Voorhees. 1985. The Global Cycle of Carbon. pp. 1–13. In: *Atmospheric Carbon Dioxide and the Global Carbon Cycle,* Washington, DC: DOE/ER-0239, U.S. Department of Energy.

Informative Websites

Ecosystem Services: Benefits Supplied to Human Societies by Natural Ecosystems.
www.esa.org/Science/Issues/FileEnglish/issue2.pdf

This pdf document of the Ecological Society of America explains the importance of ecosystem services to both the natural world and the human economy.

Human Alteration of the Global Nitrogen Cycle: Causes and Consequences.
www.esa.org/Science/Issues/FileEnglish/issue1.pdf

This pdf document published by the Ecological Society of America explains the effects of human activities on nitrogen cycles.

The Health of Our Soils: Toward Sustainable Agriculture in Canada. http://res2.agr.gc.ca/publications/hs/index_e.htm

This website of Agriculture and Agri-Food Canada discusses the importance of soil health for agriculture.

Something to Grow On.
www.hort.cornell.edu/department/faculty/good/growon/

All you ever wanted to know about nutrients, soil testing, fertilizing, liming, field-grown trees and shrubs, soils, nitrogen cycle, pH, and soluble salt—you can find it all at this website.

Evolution

CHAPTER OBJECTIVES

After completing this chapter, you will be able to

1. Explain major differences in environmental conditions before and after the genesis of life.
2. Discuss the differences between creationism and evolution as explanations of the origin of life and species.
3. Describe the theory of evolution by natural selection.
4. Explain the role of genetics in understanding evolution as well as differences among individual organisms and species.

CHAPTER OUTLINE

In the Beginning...

Based on geological and astronomical data, the planet Earth is believed to have originated by the condensation of interstellar dust about 4.5 billion years ago. The primordial, pre-life environments of Earth were quite different from what exists today. For example, it appears that the initial atmosphere contained large concentrations of hydrogen sulphide (H_2S), methane (CH_4), ammonia (NH_3), carbon dioxide (CO_2), and other gases that today exist only in trace concentrations. In contrast, the modern atmosphere has large concentrations of oxygen (O_2) and nitrogen (N_2).

A major reason for these profound changes in atmospheric chemistry was the evolution of photosynthetic organisms that emit O_2 as a waste product of their autotrophic metabolism. The presence of large amounts of O_2 changed Earth's atmosphere from one that favoured reducing reactions (in which the reaction products have a net gain in electrons) to one in which oxidizing reactions predominate. H_2S, CH_4, and NH_3 are all chemically reduced compounds, but in an O_2-rich atmosphere, they become oxidized to sulphate (SO_4^{-2}), CO_2, and nitrate (NO_3^-), respectively. In addition, O_2 can react photochemically to produce small amounts of ozone (O_3). Ozone in the upper atmosphere absorbs solar ultraviolet radiation and thereby shields organisms from many of the damaging effects of this kind of electromagnetic energy.

The genesis of life on Earth is thought to have occurred in a primordial aquatic environment about 3.5 billion years ago, only about 1 billion years after the origin of the planet. It is not known exactly how life first began from inanimate matter, although biologists believe that it occurred spontaneously. In other words, the origin of life happened naturally, as a consequence of the existence of appropriate conditions of chemistry, temperature, pressure, energy, and other environmental factors.

As such, the origin of life could have happened as a series of random events occurring under suitable conditions. Some biologists, however, believe that genesis could have occurred in a more purposeful manner, under the influence of autocatalytic (self-catalyzed) reactions that favoured the synthesis and persistence of particular organic chemicals. Under these selective influences, molecules and their interrelationships became increasingly complicated, and they eventually developed the qualities that define the simplest forms of life: metabolism, growth, and reproduction.

The appropriate conditions for the genesis of life probably included the presence of many simple organic compounds in primordial waters. It is believed that simple

Photo 6.1   Dinosaurs (order Dinosauria) were dominant animals on Earth for about 160 million years, but the last species became extinct 65 million years ago. We know that dinosaurs used to exist because their fossilized bones have been discovered on all continents. Modern reptiles are relatives of dinosaurs, and birds are considered to be their surviving descendants. This model of *Troodon formosus,* a predatory dinosaur, is located in the Museum of Nature in Ottawa.

organic compounds were naturally synthesized by inorganic (i.e., non-living) reactions among the ammonia, methane, hydrogen sulphide, and other compounds occurring in Earth's pre-life atmosphere. These reactions were favoured because the atmosphere at that time was a high-energy environment associated with ultraviolet radiation and lightning strikes. The resulting organic compounds were deposited into the primordial oceans by rainfall, where they became progressively concentrated, especially in pools on the oceanic shores.

Modern scientists have performed simple laboratory experiments that simulate primordial conditions. In airtight flasks, mixtures of water and gaseous CH_4, NH_3, and H_2S are sparked by electric arcs. These experiments yield various types of hydrocarbons, amino acids (precursors of proteins), nitrogenous bases (precursors of nucleic acids), and other organic chemicals. Scientists think something similar happened prior to the origin of life on Earth.

It is still, however, an enormous step from the occurrence of appropriate environmental conditions to the spontaneous genesis of living microorganisms. Scientists do not yet understand how this momentous process—the origin of the first organisms—occurred. In fact, the boundary between complex chemical systems and living organisms is thought to be somewhat arbitrary (viruses, for example, exist at this boundary). Nevertheless, there is a broad consensus among scientists that microorganisms did appear in Earth's oceans about 3.5 billion years ago (Table 6.1). These first microorganisms were heterotrophic consumers of the rich soup of organic compounds that had accumulated in Earth's pre-biological oceans over hundreds of millions of years. The first chemoautotrophic microorganisms evolved several hundred million years later, and the first photosynthetic ones about 2.5 billion years ago.

The earliest cellular life forms were **prokaryotes** (i.e., single-celled organisms without an organized nucleus containing the genetic material, which was likely DNA or RNA; see In Detail 6.1). Eventually, **eukaryotes** (having an organized nucleus bounded by a membrane) evolved from simpler, prokaryotic predecessors.

More complex microorganisms, containing subcellular *organelles* such as mitochondria, plastids, and cilia, are thought to have evolved through symbiotic associations among different species. According to this theory, smaller microorganisms became encapsulated within larger ones in a mutually beneficial **symbiosis** (a **mutualism**; see Chapter 9). Some smaller microorganisms evolved into specialized energy-processing organelles known as mitochondria. Other encapsulated microbes were specialized to capture light and to use that energy in photo-synthesis; they became chloroplasts. Mitochondria and chloroplasts in living organisms contain small quantities of DNA that is distinctive in character and is believed to be residual from ancient times when these organelles were independent microorganisms.

Multicellular organisms were the next major category of life form to appear, likely in late Precambrian times (see Tables 6.1 and 3.1, page 31). The evolution and radiation of these relatively complex organisms were driven by physiological and ecological adaptations associated with interactions of specialized cell types. The first multicellular organisms were relatively small and simple, but these eventually evolved into the larger, more complex organisms that are now so prominent on Earth, including vertebrates, the *phylum* of animals to which humans belong.

"Progression" of Life

Modern biologists believe that all living species are similarly "advanced." The two reasons are that all species have had the same amount of time to evolve since the first organ-

TABLE 6.1	Estimated Dates of the Origins of Important Life Forms

The data represent the time of first appearance of each type of organism in the fossil record.

EVOLUTIONARY EVENT	MILLIONS OF YEARS AGO
Formation of planet Earth	4500
First life, anaerobic microorganisms	3500
Chemoautotrophic microorganisms	3100
Photosynthetic microorganisms	2500
First eukaryotes	1200
First multicellular organisms	600
Animals with external skeletons	570
Lampreys	550
Crustaceans and mollusks	500
Plants	435
Jawed fish	415
Land plants	410
Amphibians	355
Insects	310
Reptiles	300
Conifers	270
Dinosaurs	223
Mammals	214
Birds	150
Angiosperm plants	135
Anthropoid primates	43
Hominids	5.5
Genus *Homo*	2
Homo sapiens	0.5

Source: Modified from Raven and Johnson (1992)

isms appeared and that they are all well adapted to coping with the opportunities and constraints presented by the environments in which they live. Therefore, all species, from the smallest and simplest, such as bacteria tinier than 1 μm, to enormous blue whales exceeding 30 m in length, represent similarly advanced, well-adapted, and marvellous examples of the diversity of living organisms.

This is not to say that species do not vary enormously in their complexity, which of course they do. We should, however, be careful when we use the terms "simple" and "complex," because these concepts are difficult to define precisely. All living organisms display a mixture of traits, some of which evolved in ancient times while others are more recent adaptations. For example, most organisms (except some viruses) have DNA as their genetic material, so this is an ancient trait. Other attributes, such as flight in bats or intelligence in humans, represent specific adaptations that occurred relatively late in particular evolutionary lineages.

In Detail 6.1

A Primer on Genetics

Every organism has an individual complement of genetic information contained in the specific arrangement of nucleotides in its DNA or RNA. The following is a brief outline of the storage and translation of genetic information in organisms.

DNA, or deoxyribonucleic acid, carries the genetic information in most species. In some viruses, however, the genetic information is contained in RNA (see below). DNA, a nucleic acid, is a linear sequence of only four nucleotides that are differentiated by their bases: adenine, cytosine, guanine, and thymine. The linear sequences are arranged as two strands, which coil as a double helix (spiral). The two strands in the double helix are held together by hydrogen bonds between complementary pairs of nucleotides: adenine with thymine, and cytosine with guanine. The genetic information is carried in the precise sequence of the nucleotides.

RNA, or ribonucleic acid, is composed of a single strand of nucleotides. In RNA, a fifth base, uracil, substitutes for the thymine of DNA. RNA occurs in all organisms, and it permits the translation of the genetic information of DNA into the structure of proteins (see below).

Chromosomes are composed of DNA and protein and contain the genetic information of the cell. Chromosomes are self-duplicating structures, which means they create exact copies of themselves through the process of replication (see below). An exact copy is passed to each daughter cell when the cell divides. Chromosomes in the body (somatic) cells of plants and animals occur as complementary pairs (known as homologous pairs). The number of pairs of chromosomes varies greatly among species, from one to hundreds.

Genes are regions of a chromosome that determine the development of a particular trait by coding for a specific protein during transcription (see below). Because chromosomes occur in pairs, the genes also are paired. Genes commonly occur in more than one form, each of which is called an allele. Frequently, one allele is dominant (D) and another recessive (r). The dominant one is expressed when both alleles in the gene pair are of this type (i.e., DD), and also when both dominant and recessive alleles occur (i.e., rD or Dr). Recessive alleles are expressed only if both alleles are of this type (i.e., rr). The condition in which both alleles are the same (i.e., DD or rr) is referred to as homozygous, while the mixed condition (rD or Dr) is heterozygous.

Replication is the biochemical process during which the nucleotide sequence of each strand of DNA is copied, producing two identical DNA molecules. Replication is necessary for cellular division because each new cell requires identical copies of the DNA from the parent. During replication, the double helix of the DNA "unzips," allowing free nucleotides to hydrogen-bond with those in each strand, producing new but identical DNA molecules. An error occurring during replication can result in a change in the genetic information known as a mutation.

Transcription involves DNA unzipping and a complementary strand of RNA being made on one of the DNA strands, in a manner similar to replication. Then the RNA floats free and the DNA zips up again. Three types of RNA can be made: ribosomal RNA (rRNA), which forms small bodies in the cytoplasm called ribosomes; messenger RNA (mRNA), which transports the information from the DNA to the ribosome; and transfer RNA (tRNA), discussed below.

Translation occurs when the mRNA, which contains information from a portion of a DNA strand, attaches to a ribosome in the cytoplasm. There, tRNA molecules bind to specific amino acids and transport them to the mRNA in the correct sequence for protein synthesis. (Amino acids are the building blocks of proteins. Only 20 amino acids are common, but these make up the extraordinary diversity of proteins found in organisms. Proteins are extremely important, mainly as structural chemicals and metabolism-regulating enzymes.) The information on the mRNA, copied from the information on the DNA, determines the exact sequence of amino acids in a protein, and therefore its function.

Meiosis is important in sexual reproduction, in which two "sex" cells, one from each parent, combine to start a new life. If those cells were somatic cells, they would have the same number of chromosomes as the parent (the diploid number), and the progeny would then have double the number of the parent. This does not occur—the sex cells are not diploid. Instead, through a process called meiosis, the number of chromosomes in sex cells is halved (to haploid), so the progeny has the same number of chromosomes as the parent.

During meiosis, the paired chromosomes separate, with one of each pair going randomly to each daughter "sex" cell. Just before they separate, exchanges of genetic material may occur between the paired chromosomes—a phenomenon known as crossing-over. Both of these processes increase the variability of genetic information in sex cells. When the haploid sex cells (one from each parent) combine, a diploid progeny results. Having chromosomes from each parent, the progeny is genetically different from them, but also similar. This is, essentially, how parents pass their genetic information to their progeny.

Genotype refers to the unique genetic information of individual organisms, as embodied in the nucleotide sequences of their DNA. This unique genotype of an individual is fixed and constant (except for rare mutations). However, the genotypes of populations and species are quite variable, although this is restricted by the range of genetic variation among the constituent individuals.

Phenotype refers to the actual expression of an individual's genotype in terms of anatomical development, behaviour, and biochemistry. For example, recessive alleles, unless in a homozygous condition, are not expressed, even though they appear in the genotype.

The expression of genetic potential is affected by environmental conditions and other circumstances. For instance, a geranium plant, with a fixed complement of genetic information, may be relatively tall and robust if grown under well-watered, fertile, uncrowded conditions. However, if that same individual were grown under drier, less fertile, more competitive conditions, its productivity and form would be different. Such varying growth patterns of the same genotype represent a phenotypically "plastic" response to environmental conditions. In contrast, the flower colour of individual geraniums (which can be white, red, or pink) is fixed genetically and is not affected by environmental conditions.

The ability of a species to exhibit phenotypically plastic responses to environmental variations is itself genetically determined to some extent. Therefore, **phenotypic plasticity** reflects both genetic capability and varying expression of that capability, depending on environmental circumstances.

The fossil record clearly demonstrates that, over time, a progression of life forms has existed on Earth. The first prokaryotic organisms were relatively tiny and simple, but through evolution, these led to the development of larger, more complex eukaryotic microorganisms, and so on until large, exceedingly complex animals and plants evolved. This evolutionary pattern implies a clear temporal sequence. It is important to understand, however, that relatively complex, more recent species (including humans) do not represent the epitome of evolution, nor have they inherited the Earth and its opportunities. Rather, all living species share this bountiful planet, the only place in the universe known to sustain life.

Evolution

Evolution can be defined as genetically based changes in populations of organisms, occurring over successive generations. Evolution is a critically important theory because it accounts for the natural development of existing species from progenitors that may have been quite unlike their descendants in form and function. The reality of evolution is widely accepted by modern scientists, as much so as the theory of gravity, which explains how the Earth revolves around the sun.

Evolution occurs in response to various driving forces. The modern theory of evolution suggests that natural selection is an especially important cause of evolutionary change. In essence, **natural selection** predicts that individual organisms that are better adapted to coping with the opportunities and limitations of their environment will have an increased probability of leaving descendants. If the adaptive advantages are genetically determined, they will be passed to some of their progeny, then to subsequent generations, and so on. This will result in evolutionary change.

Evolution can also occur in response to catastrophic influences on populations of organisms, such as a forest fire or flood. This may result in more haphazard (random) changes in the genetic structure of a population. Small populations are particularly subject to such *non-selective* evolutionary influences.

It is important to understand that individual organisms do not evolve. Evolution is a process of genetic change from generation to generation, occurring in populations or higher-order groupings of organisms (such as species). This is not to say that individual organisms cannot display variable responses to environmental conditions. These responses are, however, constrained by the degree of biochemical, developmental, and behavioural flexibility allowed by the genetic complement of each individual (its genotype; see In Detail 6.1). The variable expression of the genetic information of an individual is called phenotypic plasticity, but this kind of response to variations in environmental conditions is not evolutionary change. For evolution to occur, there must be change in the collective genetic information of a population or species.

Evolution can occur at various scales. For convenience, evolutionary biologists use the term **microevolution** to refer to relatively subtle changes occuring within a population or species, often within only a few generations, that may lead to the evolution of a variety, race, or subspecies. In contrast, the term **macroevolution** describes the evolution of new species or higher taxonomic groups, such as genera, families, or classes. Evolutionary biologists continue to debate and discuss the linkages of these scales of evolution. Are patterns of macroevolutionary change simply the cumulative effects of many microevolutionary changes over long periods of time? Or is macroevolution actually large changes occurring over a short time, each representing a great step (or saltation) of evolution? Or does macroevolution happen in both ways?

Despite debates regarding its details, the theory of evolution is a unifying theme in biology because it can be used successfully to understand so many phenomena in nature. Evolution is commonly used by scientists to explain both the origin of life and the extraordinary changes that have occurred in organisms over the billions of years of life on Earth.

Relatedness and Descent of Species

A biological definition of **species** is "a group of organisms that is reproductively isolated from other such groups." Within a species, individual organisms tend to resemble each other, but more importantly, they can breed with each other and produce fertile offspring. An inability to successfully interbreed implies reproductive isolation (see In Detail 6.2).

That species have evolved from progenitors is a well-established biological theory, richly supported by evidence. Two of the most compelling lines of argument, showing evolutionary patterns of relatedness and descent, follow.

Patterns Inferred from the Fossil Record

A well-known example of evolution evidenced by the fossil record is that of the horse lineage. One of the earliest

horse-like progenitors was *Eohippus*, a dog-sized creature that lived 50 million years ago. Its foot had two fused and three separate toes. Comparison of the morphology (structure) of fossil bones suggests that *Eohippus* was an ancestor of *Mesohippus*, a larger animal that lived 35 million years ago. Its foot had three fused central toes and two free outer ones. Further evolution led to *Merychippus*, a somewhat larger animal living 20 million years ago that also had three fused and two free toes. Next came *Pliohippus*, a pony-sized animal living 10 million years ago, that had all five toes fused into a hoof. Modern horses evolved several million years ago and have a hoof like that of *Pliohippus*. They include the horse (*Equus caballus*), ass or donkey (*E. asinus*), Mongolian wild horse (*E. przewalskii*), and zebra (*E. burchelli*).

Inferences from Modern Species

Modern species display many obvious similarities and dissimilarities that can be used to group them on the basis of inferred relatedness. Early studies of this sort mostly involved comparative anatomy. Research on animals relied mostly on the characteristics of bones, shells, skins, and other enduring structures, while studies of plants largely involved the anatomy of flowers and fruits. More recent studies gather a much wider range of comparative information to examine relatedness among groups of species, including information about behaviour, ecology, proteins, and—most recently—specific base sequences of DNA. For example, studies involving DNA and blood proteins have clearly shown that humans are closely related to other great apes, such as the chimpanzee, orangutan, and gorilla. Of these, humans are most closely related to chimpanzees—in fact, these species share about 99% of the information encoded in their DNA. These observations do not suggest that humans evolved from modern apes. Rather, the appropriate interpretation is that humans and living apes share common, ape-like ancestors.

Evolution Observed

As was just described, patterns of relatedness and descent can be inferred from comparative studies of the fossil record and of modern species. It is important to understand, however, that the evolution of a new species has never been directly observed. This is because it takes a very long time for populations of related organisms to diverge enough to become new species—perhaps hundreds of thousands of

In Detail 6.2

The Nature of Species

A species is defined as a group of organisms that is reproductively isolated from other such groups. Moreover, only individuals of the same species can successfully mate with each other and have fertile offspring. In practice, however, it can be difficult to demonstrate reproductive isolation. For example, two populations of small animals may be separated by a mountain range and may never interact. However, if they could encounter one another, they might interbreed. This can be tested by attempting to breed them in captivity, but this might not be representative of their behaviour in nature. Limitations such as this have led some biologists to alter their working definition of species. However, definitions of the term "species" are not cast in stone; rather, the meaning is a human construct.

In all species, individual organisms share many physical, chemical, and behavioural attributes, and they look similar. However, there can also be stunning differences among individuals:

- *Sex:* Male lions are larger than females and have an impressive mane framing the head. And vive la différence in the sexual dimorphism of humans!
- *Life-history stage:* Compare frogs of different ages—an egg, a tadpole, and the legged adult.
- *Phenotypic plasticity:* If growing in stressful conditions beneath a forest canopy, a 50-year-old sugar maple may be only 20 cm tall and have fewer than 10 leaves. Under ideal conditions, the same individual might be 15 m tall.
- *Differentiation of populations:* Compare the size and shape of Canada geese from different parts of their range. The duck-sized "cackling goose" (*Branta canadensis minima*) of the Aleutians weighs only 1.3–1.5 kg, while the "giant Canada goose" (*B.c. maxima*) found in many urban areas is about 5 kg.
- *Selection by humans:* Tiny Chihuahua dogs can fit into a soup bowl, but mighty Newfoundland dogs can exceed 100 kg. These and all breeds of dog are the same species, *Canis familiaris*.

In spite of the differences, each of these cases represents variations of individuals of the same species, because they can still interbreed. (At least potentially—in the case of the Chihuahua and Newfoundland dogs, there is a physical incompatibility, although it could be overcome by artificial insemination.)

A classic example of reproductive incompatibility concerns two related species, the horse (*Equus caballus*) and donkey (*E. asinus*). Interbreeding produces live young: a mule is a cross between a male horse and a female donkey, while a hinney is the reverse cross. Mules have many favourable attributes, including an ability to work hard as a beast of burden. Mules and hinneys are, however, biological and evolutionary dead ends because they are sterile. Although horses can interbreed with donkeys, the result is not evolutionarily "successful," and the two are considered different species.

On the other hand, consider the savannah sparrow, a common songbird of grassy habitats throughout North America, with a streaky brown colour and a body length of 11–14 cm. For many years, the larger (15–16 cm) and paler Ipswich sparrow, which only breeds on Sable Island off Nova Scotia, was considered a species named *Passerculus princeps*. However, a few cases of successful interbreeding of Ipswich and savannah sparrows were found, and so these two are now lumped as one species, *P. sandwichensis*. (The Ipswich retains sub-species rank, as *P. s. princeps*.)

The discovery of hybrids does not always result in changes in taxonomy. For example, hybridization is common among species of willow (*Salix* spp.), particularly if there is a habitat intermediate to those typically used by the parent species. In such cases, botanists commonly retain the parents as separate species, because they are generally identifiable as unique and different and hybridize only under unusual circumstances. The botanists are partly being pragmatic, recognizing that the taxonomic system must have practical value to scientists studying plants in the field.

Bird taxonomists are also starting to adopt this view of the nature of species and are de-emphasizing the importance of occasional hybridization. Consequently, some birds that were once considered different species, such as the savannah and Ipswich sparrows, and were later "lumped" because of interbreeding may be separated again as distinct species.

A species is often simply defined as "a group of organisms that is reproductively isolated from other such groups." Perhaps a better working definition is "species are groups of organisms that differ in one or more characteristics and do not successfully interbreed extensively if they occur together in nature."

years, and in many cases, millions. In spite of this, biologists have no doubt that new species have been evolving for billions of years—in fact, throughout the history of life.

Although speciation has not been observed in nature, examples of microevolution are known. These cases provide key evidence in support of the theory of evolution.

Industrial Melanism

One example of microevolution is that of the peppered moth (*Biston betularia*) of western Europe. This moth's normal coloration is a mottled, whitish tan. During the day, the moth commonly rests on lichen-covered trees where it is difficult to see against the bark. This camouflage is important to the moth's survival because its predators, such as birds, hunt using vision.

About a century ago in England, it was observed that some populations of peppered moths had developed a black coloration, known as melanism. This had apparently occurred in response to changes in the tree bark, which had lost its lichen cover because of air pollution and had become blackened by soot deposition. Under such habitat conditions in industrial areas, the normal light-coloured moths were highly visible to predators and were at a distinct disadvantage compared to blacker moths. Studies showed that melanism is genetically based, and that melanistic moths occurred, but were rare, in unpolluted habitats. However, melanistic individuals became dominant in populations of peppered moths living in polluted habitats, representing a population-level genetic change. This famous example of microevolution, which has also been demonstrated in other species of moths, is known as "industrial melanism."

Interestingly, air quality has greatly improved over most of western Europe in recent decades, largely due to clean-air legislation that has reduced the use of coal as a source of energy. As a result, lichens are again growing on trees and bark surfaces have less soot. These recoveries have been accompanied by the reappearance of light-coloured peppered moths in places where their populations had been dominated by melanistic moths—another evolutionary response to changing environmental conditions.

Metal-Tolerant Ecotypes

In another example of observed evolution, several plant species were found growing on sites in England and Wales that were polluted by metal-rich mine waste. Although the soil was toxic to most plants, local populations of several plant species were thriving. The most common species were grasses, such as bent-grass (*Agrostis tenuis*). Research showed that these local populations had a genetically based, physiological tolerance of the toxic metals, and that they differed in this respect from other populations of the same species growing on non-polluted sites. The locally adapted populations, referred to as "metal-tolerant ecotypes," were found to have evolved in as few as several years after their first exposure to the toxic soil. (This example was the first one to be documented and is famous for that reason. Canadian examples of metal-tolerant ecotypes, discovered later, are described in Chapter 18.)

Religion and Evolution

Some religious groups have long attacked the theory of evolution. This intensified after the publication of Charles Darwin's ideas about the role of natural selection in evolution (see the next section). The Biblical description of creation is one of the oldest written explanations of the origin of life on Earth, the existence of so many species and ecosystems, and the roles and responsibilities of humans in their interactions with the natural world. But science and religion are not irreconcilable. Indeed, for many people, physical concerns belong to the domain of science, whereas spiritual ones belong to the domain of religion.

Nevertheless, some religious groups insist upon a literal interpretation of the Bible as the ultimate authority for

Photo 6.2   These are metal-tolerant ecotypes of the grass *Deschampsia caespitosa*, growing in metal-polluted soil close to a smelter near Sudbury, Ontario.

all knowledge. For example, **creationists** reject the theory of evolution in favour of a literal interpretation of Genesis, the first book of the Old Testament of the Bible. Creationists assert that the account given in Genesis means that God created the universe and all living organisms during a six-day period, culminating with the creation of humans. Humans were created in the physical image of God and were given powers to freely use the resources of Earth:

> *And God said, let us make Man in our image, after our likeness; and let them have dominion over the fish of the sea, and over the fowl of the air, and over the cattle, and over all the Earth and over every creeping thing that creepeth over the Earth.*

Humans were furthermore instructed to increase their populations and to exploit nature:

> *Be fruitful, and multiply, and replenish the Earth, and subdue it.*[1]

Based on their literal interpretation of Genesis and other passages in the Bible, creationists have drawn the following conclusions relevant to evolution:

1. Earth and its species are not ancient because creation occurred only a few thousand years ago.

2. Species are essentially immutable, having been created as entities that have not changed since their creation.

3. Because species were individually created, existing species did not descend from earlier ones through evolution.

4. Humans are particularly special, having been created in the Creator's image. Therefore, they are not related to or descended from any other species.

However, these four points do not accord with scientific findings:

1. The geological record clearly demonstrates that Earth and the solar system are extremely old, having begun to develop at least 4.5 billion years ago. Life is also ancient, having originated about 3.5 billion years ago. Earth and organisms date back much further than a few thousand years.

2. The fossil record gives numerous signs of great changes in the characteristics of groups of species over time, as do some living species. Species are not immutable. Moreover, Earth's existing complement of species represents only a small sample of all those that have ever lived. The fossil record demonstrates that most species that evolved during Earth's long biological history are now extinct. Many of the extinct species, families, and even phyla have no descendants—their entire lineage is extinct (see also Chapter 7).

3. The fossil record presents clear evidence of lineages among groups of organisms, indicating that living species have descended from earlier ones. In almost all cases, the progenitor species are now extinct. There are even a few examples in the fossil record of links between major groups. Perhaps the most famous of these is *Archaeopteryx*, a metre-long creature that lived about 150 million years ago. It had teeth and other typically dinosaurian characters, but it also had a feathered body and could fly. *Archaeopteryx* is considered to be a link between extinct dinosaurs and living birds. Quite recently, fossils were found of small dinosaurs with feather-like scales, possibly evolved for insulation, separate from the evolutionary development of flight.

4. Fossil and genetic information clearly indicate that humans are descended from earlier, now-extinct species. Fossil records show that the human species (*Homo sapiens*) is derived from an evolutionary lineage of anthropoid apes. There are a few other surviving species in that lineage, with chimpanzees, and to a lesser degree gorillas and orangutans, being the closest living relatives of humans. All surviving members of the ape family are descended from now-extinct progenitors.

People known as **scientific creationists** also insist that their interpretation of Genesis is the most reliable source of knowledge about the origin and evolution of life. Scientific creationists have attempted to explain some of the discrepancies between their beliefs and current scien-

---

[1] Note, however, that there is some controversy about the meaning of the word "replenish" in this biblical passage. Some people have interpreted it in the sense of conservation, as in to re-fill or restore resources as they are used. Others, however, maintain that the original meaning was "to fill up," and, in this sense, it referred to filling the Earth with humans and their economic activities.

tific understanding of evolution. For example, some acknowledge that geological and fossil evidence do suggest that Earth and life are ancient phenomena and that most species have become extinct. Most scientific creationists also acknowledge that species have changed over time, but only through microevolution—they do not agree that macroevolution has led to the development of new species from earlier ones. By extension, scientific creationists also do not believe that humans are descended from previous species of hominids or are related to other ape-like creatures or other primates. Moreover, the theory of scientific creationism does not abandon the notion that, at one particular time in the past, God created all species that have ever lived on Earth.

Science proceeds by observation and hypothesis testing. But scientific creationism rests on a belief, not a hypothesis, concerning a literal interpretation of the Bible as representing "truth." Most predictions of scientific creationists cannot be tested by rigorous methodology; when they can be, they are refuted by the evidence. In short, despite its name, scientific creationism is not science.

The Theory of Evolution by Natural Selection

Virtually all species are genetically variable: that is, individual organisms differ in the information encoded in their genetic material, DNA (see In Detail 6.1). All observable attributes of an individual (its phenotype) are influenced by its specific genetic information (its genotype), including morphology, physiology, behaviour, and other traits.

However, not all variations of an organism's phenotype are due only to genetic differences. The phenotype is related to both genetic information and environmental influences on the expression of that genetic potential. Individual organisms display phenotypic plasticity, or differential growth, physiology, and behaviour, that depends in part on environmental circumstances (see In Detail 6.1).

Because organisms vary in character, they also differ in their abilities to deal successfully with stresses and opportunities in their environment. Under certain conditions, an individual with a particular phenotype (which is substantially determined by its genotype) may be relatively successful compared with others having different genotypes and phenotypes.

In the sense meant here, the "success" of an individual means successful reproduction: having progeny that themselves go on to reproduce successfully. This is also

referred to as **fitness**, or the proportionate genetic contribution made by an individual to all of the progeny in its population. A central tenet of evolutionary theory is that individuals maximize their fitness by optimizing the degree to which their own genetic attributes will influence future generations of their species.

Biologists believe that evolution proceeds mainly by natural selection, which operates when genetically based variation exists among individuals within a population, making some individuals better adapted to deal with the prevailing environmental conditions. On average, the fitter organisms are more successful in reproduction, and so have a disproportionate influence on the evolution of subsequent generations.

The theory of evolution by natural selection is perhaps the greatest unifying concept in modern biology, giving context to virtually all aspects of the study of life. This theory was co-announced publicly in 1858 by the English naturalists Charles Darwin (1809–82) and Alfred Russel Wallace (1823–1913). Darwin, however, had been working on aspects of the theory for about 20 years prior to its publication, and he had collected detailed evidence in support of natural selection as a mechanism of evolution. This evidence was marshalled in Darwin's famous book, *On the Origin of Species by Means of Natural Selection*, published in 1859. Because of this book, Darwin has become more closely linked than Wallace to the theory of evolution by natural selection. Darwin is also the more famous of the two scientists, largely because of his great contributions toward understanding the mechanisms of evolution. Perhaps the most influential biologist of all time, Darwin undertook an astonishingly broad range of research projects on a great variety of species and biological topics.

In his *Origin of Species*, Darwin summarized natural selection in the following way:

> *Can we doubt...that individuals having any advantage, however slight, over others, would have the best chance of surviving and of procreating their kind? On the other hand, we may feel sure that any variation in the least degree injurious would be rigidly destroyed. This preservation of favourable variations, I call Natural Selection.*

In an essay that Wallace sent to Darwin for review, natural selection was expressed in a rather similar fashion:

> *The life of wild animals is a struggle for existence...in which the weakest...must always succumb...giving rise to successive variations departing further and further from the original type.*

Darwin's and Wallace's theory was based on the following line of reasoning:

1. It is known that the fecundity of all species is high enough that they could easily overpopulate their habitats, yet this does not generally happen.

2. It is also known that the resources that species need to sustain themselves are limited, particularly in relatively stable habitats.

3. Therefore, in view of potential population growth and limited resources, there must be intense competition among individuals of each species for access to the requirements of life. Only some individuals can survive this struggle for existence.

4. Because individuals within a species are different from each other, and much of this variation is heritable, it is reasonable to suggest that survival in the struggle for existence is partly influenced by genetically determined differences in abilities.

5. Individuals that are more capable will have a better chance of surviving and reproducing, and their genetically based attributes will be disproportionately represented in future generations.

6. Over long periods of time, this process of natural selection will lead to evolutionary changes within populations and, eventually, to the evolution of new species.

When it was first presented publicly in 1858, the theory of evolution by natural selection created a sensation among scientists and also within society. The excitement and controversy occurred largely because the theory provided the first convincing body of evidence in support of the three notions that evolution occurs, that it proceeds under natural influences, and that it has resulted in the great diversity of living species. This was a radically different view from that of creationism, which was the prevailing explanation of the origin of life and species in the mid-nineteenth century. According to the notion of creation widely believed at the time, all species had been directly created by God during a short period of time only several thousands of years previously, and those species had not substantially changed since then.

Interestingly, Charles Darwin's writings did not directly challenge the existence of a divine Creator. Darwin discussed mainly the causes of change in species over time: he did not suggest that their initial ancestors had not been created by God. Modern theories about the spontaneous genesis of life on Earth are based on relatively sophisticated science that was unknown to Darwin. Nor did he know of the mechanisms of genetics and the inheritance of traits.

Modern extensions of the theory of evolution by natural selection suggest that new species evolve from progenitors. This is thought to happen when populations become spatially isolated by intervening barriers such as mountain ranges, extensive glaciers, or other habitat discontinuities. Isolation is important in speciation because it reduces or eliminates genetic interchange, allowing differentiation to proceed more effectively. Isolated populations that experience different environmental conditions are subject to differing selection pressures and can evolve in dissimilar ways. Eventually, there may be enough evolutionary change that the populations can no longer interbreed successfully, even if they become spatially re-united. At this point, the populations have achieved reproductive isolation and, therefore, have become closely related but different species.

Speciation is also thought to occur in a more linear fashion, as when progenitor species gradually evolve over time in response to changes in environment. Eventually, the ancestral species may become extinct, but new species evolved from the progenitor may survive to continue the evolutionary chain.

The Importance of Genetics

Knowledge of genetics in Darwin's time was based on a highly incomplete understanding of how an organism's traits are passed to its offspring. One popular theory, the *inheritance of acquired traits*, was based on the observation that the morphology, behaviour, and/or biochemistry of individual organisms varied in response to environmental change. According to the theory, these plastic responses to environmental conditions could be passed along to the individual's progeny. For example, during periods of drought or intense competition for food, individual short-necked ancestors of giraffes might have stretched their necks as far as they could to reach scarce foliage higher up in trees, resulting in the development of a longer neck. The long-neckedness would have been passed to the giraffe's progeny, who developed it still further. Eventually, populations developed the familiar, long neck of modern giraffes.

Natural selection suggests a different mechanism: within populations of short-necked giraffes there existed a genetically determined variation in neck length among

Photo 6.3   Humans can artificially select varieties of animals or plants for traits useful in agriculture or for some other reason such as preferences for breeds of dogs. Charles Darwin referred to this evolutionary process as "cultural selection."

Source: Mark Burnside/Tony Stone Images

individuals. Because long-necked giraffes were better able to find food, they were more likely to survive and reproduce. This meant that more of the next generation had the long-necked trait, and this trait became increasingly prominent in the evolving population.

Modern observations and experiments have shown that "acquired traits" are just a manifestation of phenotypic plasticity. There is no evidence that they can become genetically fixed in an individual and passed along to its offspring. In contrast, the science of genetics has provided convincing evidence in support of the theory of evolution by natural selection. The biochemical mechanisms that determine the genotype of an individual organism and how it is passed to progeny have been discovered. These topics are described briefly in In Detail 6.1, but the subject matter is rather complicated and cannot be dealt with in much depth here. It is, however, useful to examine the key experiments that first suggested the existence of genes.

This research was conducted by Gregor Mendel (1822–84), an Austrian scientist (and monk) who devel-

oped important ideas about inheritance through breeding experiments with the garden pea (*Pisum sativum*). Mendel was interested in producing pea hybrids, which involves crossing two parent plants, each having distinctive traits. Prior research had shown that certain traits were fixed in cultivated varieties of peas, including flower colour (white or purple) and whether the seeds have a wrinkled or smooth coat. In total, Mendel worked with 32 traits of this sort. Pea flowers are bisexual, containing both female (pistil, containing the ovules) and male (anther, containing pollen) parts. These are compatible within the same individual, so self-fertilization can occur. However, Mendel experimented by cross-fertilizing selected parents, producing known hybridizations.

In each experiment, Mendel cross-bred two inbred varieties in which certain traits "bred true" (were homozygous, e.g., white or purple flower colour; see In Detail 6.1 for definitions of genetic terms). The progeny (first generation) were all the same: all had purple flowers. Crosses between the first-generation plants, however, yielded a ratio of about 3:1 purple flowers to white flowers in the second generation. This fits the prediction for two generation crosses between two homozygous lines, as follows:

1. Represent the original purple variety as AA. This trait is dominant over the white flower trait (called recessive).

2. Represent the original white variety as aa.

3. When the two plants are crossed, the first-generation progeny all have purple flowers but are heterozygous (Aa).

4. A cross between the first-generation plants yields four possible outcomes: AA, Aa, aA, and aa. Each is equally probable among the progeny. Because A is dominant to a, the AA, Aa, and aA progeny have purple flowers. Only aa has white flowers. Therefore, the expected ratio of purple to white among the second-generation progeny is 3:1.

The most important conclusion to emerge from Mendel's work was that the inheritance of genetic information occurred in a "particulate" form (which we now refer to as genes), often involving dominant and recessive alleles. Inheritance is not a blended condition—in the example previously described, a cross of purple- and white-flowered pea plants does not yield progeny of an intermediate colour. Therefore, flower colour and many other traits are discrete units that remain intact during inheritance and either are or are not expressed in progeny.

In Detail 6.3

Genetically Modified Organisms

GMOs, or genetically modified organisms, are a highly controversial topic. But what, exactly, is meant by the term?

Strictly speaking, GMOs are organisms whose genotype has been influenced by human intervention. But people have been doing this for an extremely long time. As early as about 10 000 years ago, when humans began to cultivate other species as crops, they selectively bred individual plants and animals that had traits favourable to husbandry (see Chapter 10 for a discussion of socio-cultural evolution, including the early development of agriculture). This "artificial selection" rapidly led to the evolution of crop varieties that were more responsive to management and had greater yields than their wild progenitors. In this sense, almost all domesticated species of plants, animals, and microorganisms that are cultivated as sources of food, material, or energy are "genetically modified organisms." They were produced using conventional methods of selective breeding, a process that is not very controversial.

More recently, however, new techniques in biotechnology, specifically in molecular biology, have been used to create novel genetic modifications of organisms. These techniques allow biologists to selectively insert portions of the DNA of one species into another, unrelated one. This is a fundamentally different kind of genetic modification than conventional selective breeding, and it should be referred to as transgenic modification, or recombinant bioengineering. There are potential benefits to this kind of genetic modification of crop species, including the development of varieties that are resistant to diseases or pests and that require less fertilizer or pesticide. In spite of these seeming benefits, there is intense controversy over transgenic biotechnology and the commercial use of GMOs, largely because of the following issues:

- Should scientists be interfering with the very foundation of life—the genetics of species—by using methods of genetic "engineering" that do not normally occur in nature?

- Do novel, transgenic organisms represent "new" varieties of designed and manufactured life that are appropriate for patenting and use for commercial gain? (In fact, various legal rulings have stated that this can be done, and some transgenic crops have become extremely profitable to the owners of the patents.)

- Are important ecological risks associated with the cultivation of transgenic organisms? Because many biological and ecological unknowns are associated with this practice, "surprises" are likely to follow from the release of these organisms into the environment, including unanticipated damage to crops, wild species, and natural ecosystems.

These are contentious and precautionary issues, and the controversy is not resolved. Nevertheless, some GMO products have already been widely commercialized and are now routinely used. For instance, transgenic GMO varieties of soybean and canola have been developed to be resistant to glyphosate, meaning that this herbicide can be used on these crops. This provides savings to farmers in terms of reduced costs of energy and machinery needed to control weeds of these crops. In a similar vein, transgenic varieties of maize (corn) have been developed that contain modified DNA of the insecticidal bacterium *Bacillus thuringiensis*, which provides resistance to important insect pests and allows farmers to use less insecticide. These and other transgenic crops are now widely cultivated in North America (although they are banned in other countries, including most of Europe and Brazil), but there is relatively little known about the biological and ecological risks that may arise when their transgenic factors escape to wild plants.

Mendel first published his results in 1865 in a relatively obscure journal. As a result, the work was unknown to the mainstream of science for many years. However, Mendel's work was re-discovered and re-published in 1900 and quickly became the basis of modern theories of genetic inheritance.

Mendel's work and the subsequent flourishing of the science of genetics have been extremely important in biology and in the development of the modern theory of evolution. This is because genetics allows a rational explanation of inheritance as a mechanism by which genetically fixed traits can be passed along to offspring. Subsequent research has found that new genotypes can arise through mechanisms such as hybridization, polyploidism (i.e., a spontaneous increase in the number of chromosomes), and mutations. Genetic variation is, of course, the menu of possibilities from which natural selection can choose so that adaptive evolution can occur.

It is important to recognize that much genetic information in an individual does not appear to code for functional enzymes or other proteins and, hence, does not code for traits that could be selected for or against. Because of its neutrality with respect to natural selection, this type of genetic material is sometimes referred to as "junk DNA." However, we may be ignorant of other roles that so-called junk DNA may play in the functioning of the genome.

Other Mechanisms of Evolution

Although natural selection is the most important mechanism of evolution, it is not the only one. **Artificial selection**, for example, involves the deliberate breeding of plants, animals, and microorganisms to enhance certain traits that humans view as desirable. Artificial (or cultural) selection has obvious parallels to natural selection in that individual organisms with particular, genetically based traits experience greater success in life and in breeding, so they become over-represented in subsequent generations. However, traits that are favoured in artificial selection may not be adaptive in the natural world. In addition, evolutionary change typically occurs much more rapidly under artificial selection than under natural selection because the breeding of desired genotypes can be controlled.

For example, maize, or corn (*Zea mays*), is an important crop that, through artificial selection, now differs enormously from its closest wild progenitor, a Mexican grass known as teosinte (*Euchlaena mexicana*). Artificial selection has caused many specific evolutionary changes in maize. For example, the fruiting head (consisting of the seeds and cob) is much larger than in wild ancestors of corn; the seeds have different coloration; the seeds implant securely onto the cob so they do not scatter before harvesting; the ripe fruit is tightly wrapped within enclosing leaves known as bracts, again to prevent pre-harvest losses; and there are vigorous growth responses to fertilizer application, weed control, and other cultivation practices. Moreover, without the intervention of humans through cultivation, maize would likely become extinct within only a few generations. This is partly because artificial selection has rendered maize seeds virtually incapable of detaching from the cob, which, in any event, is tightly bound in leafy bracts. Unaided seed dispersal, therefore, is virtually impossible.

All domesticated plant, animal, and microbial species have undergone similar artificial selection for desirable traits. Sometimes, however, artificial selection proceeds in bizarre directions, with the fostering of genetic traits that are viewed as desirable for aesthetic reasons. For example, oriental breeders of pet fish have produced some amazing varieties of goldfish (*Carassius auratus*) and koi (a golden-coloured variety of carp, *Cyprinus carpio*). These varieties, often with grotesque shapes and behaviours, would be rapidly eliminated in wild populations but are prized as unusual and valuable varieties by aficionados of these aquatic pets. Similar comments could be made about some curious varieties of pigeons, dogs, cats, and horticultural plants.

Evolution can also occur through a process known as *genetic drift*, or random changes in the frequencies of genes occurring in small, isolated populations. Such populations often exist on small islands or may be created through a catastrophic reduction of a larger population because of disease, disturbance, or some other factor. The relatively small genetic base of small populations is sometimes called a "bottleneck." Subsequent evolution is based on the restricted genetic variation of only a few individuals, which may become further reduced through the effects of inbreeding (i.e., reproduction between closely related individuals, such as siblings). Given the small amount of genetic variation, the evolution of a small population may proceed very differently from the evolution of a larger population.

Conclusions

Planet Earth is the only place in the universe that is definitely known to sustain life and ecosystems. It is thought that life spontaneously arose on Earth about 3.5 billion years ago, because of the existence of environmental conditions appropriate for its genesis. Since that origin, profound changes have occurred in the morphology and functionality of organisms through a process known as evolution. Evolution may be simply defined as changes in the genetic makeup of populations and species over time (individual organisms do not evolve). Although evolution has influenced life on Earth ever since it began, there is controversy over the mechanisms of the process. Most biologists believe that natural selection has been the most important cause of evolutionary change, but others think that geological catastrophes (such as meteorite strikes of the planet or intense volcanic eruptions) have also had a large influence.

Key Terms

prokaryote	genotype
eukaryote	phenotype
symbiosis	phenotypic plasticity
mutualism	evolution
DNA	natural selection
RNA	microevolution
chromosome	macroevolution
gene	species
replication	creationist
transcription	scientific creationist
translation	fitness
meiosis	artificial selection

Questions for Review

1. How has the evolution of living organisms, especially those capable of photosynthesis, resulted in important changes in the chemistry of the environment?
2. What key evidence supports the theory of evolution?
3. How is natural selection a mechanism of evolution? What are other means by which evolution can occur?
4. How does artificial selection result in the evolution of domesticated species?

Questions for Discussion

1. Why are most biologists reluctant to describe certain species as being "more advanced" or "more highly evolved" than others?
2. How might environmental conditions have affected your own development? How do influences of these conditions relate to phenotypic plasticity?
3. Why is knowledge of genetics important to the understanding of evolutionary processes?
4. Do you think there is enough scientific evidence in support of the idea of spontaneous generation of life on Earth to replace the faith-based notion of divine creation?

Exploring Issues

1. You have been asked to participate in a debate about the evolution of life on Earth. What kinds of evidence would you use to support the theory that life evolved from inanimate matter billions of years ago? What evidence supports the theory that humans evolved from earlier ancestors that are now extinct?

References

Bengtson, S. (ed.). 1995. *Early Life on Earth*. New York: Columbia University Press.

Cowen, R. 1995. *History of Life*. London: Blackwell Scientific.

Coyne, J.A. and H.A. Orr. 2004. *Speciation*. Sunderland, MA: Sinauer Associates.

Darwin, C.D. 1859. *On the Origin of Species by Means of Natural Selection, or the Preservation of Favoured Races in the Struggle for Life*. London: Murray.

Dawkins, R. 1986. *The Blind Watchmaker*. New York: Penguin.

Eldredge, N. 1999. *The Pattern of Evolution*. San Francisco, CA: W.H. Freeman & Co.

Gould, S.J. (ed.). 1993. *Book of Life*. London: Hutchinson.

Horgan, J. 1991. In the Beginning... *Scientific American*, **264**: 116–25.

Klug, W.S. and M.R. Cummings. 2002. *Concepts of Genetics*. 7th ed. Upper Saddle River, NJ: Prentice Hall.

Lewin, R. 1991. *Thread of Life: The Smithsonian Looks at Evolution*. Washington, DC: Smithsonian Books.

Mayr, E. 1982. *The Growth of Biological Thought*. Cambridge, MA: Harvard University Press.

National Research Council. 1990. *The Search for Life's Origins*. Washington, DC: National Academy Press.

Numbers, R.L. 1993. *The Creationists: The Evolution of Scientific Creationism*. Berkeley, CA: University of California Press.

Raven, P.H. and G.B. Johnson. 2004. *Biology*. 7th ed. Columbus, OH: McGraw-Hill.

Ridley, M. 2003. *Evolution*. 3rd ed. Boston, MA: Blackwell Science.

Romaniuk, Roman B. 1997. *Roman's Notes on DNA*. Toronto: Trifolium.

Shapiro, R. 1986. *Origins: A Sceptic's Guide to the Creation of Life on Earth*. New York: Simon & Schuster.

Strickberger, M.W. 2000. *Evolution*. 3rd ed. Boston: Jones & Bartlett.

Informative Websites

Exploration of the Universe Division.
http://universe.gsfc.nasa.gov/

This NASA (National Space and Aeronautics Administration) website gives information about cosmology and the changing structure of the universe.

National Center for Science Education.
www.natcenscied.org/article.asp

The National Center for Science Education is an interest group whose mandate involves promoting the teaching of science and evolution in public schools. The website includes interesting readings and useful links.

The Talk Origins Archive. www.talkorigins.org

Critics of evolutionary theory may want to visit this comprehensive site to test the creation theory. Many essays are provided to support what Darwin first hypothesized.

World Resources Institute. www.wri.org/wrisites.cfm

From the genetic diversity of agriculture to zoological parks, this site provides links to everything resource-related.

Biodiversity and the Systematic Organization of Life

7

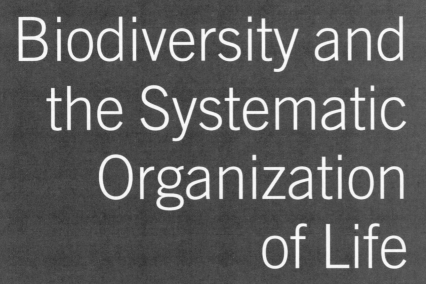

CHAPTER OBJECTIVES

After completing this chapter, you will be able to

1. Outline the concept of biodiversity and explain its constituent elements.
2. Discuss the reasons why biodiversity is important and should be preserved.
3. Define the classification of life in terms of species, genus, family, order, class, phylum, and kingdom.
4. Describe the five kingdoms of life.

CHAPTER OUTLINE

Biodiversity

Biodiversity can be defined as the richness of biological variation. It is often considered to have three levels of organization: genetic variation within populations and species; numbers of species (also known as species richness); and the variety and dynamics of ecological communities on larger scales, such as landscapes and seascapes.

Genetic Variation

In almost all species, individuals differ genetically—that is, in terms of the information encoded in their DNA. This variation constitutes genetic biodiversity at the level of populations and ultimately of the species.

There are, however, exceptions to this generalization. Some plants, for example, have little or no genetic variability within their populations, usually because the species relies on asexual (vegetative) mechanisms of propagation. In such species, genetically uniform *clones* can develop, consisting of plants that, although discrete, nevertheless constitute the same genetic "individual." For example, clones of trembling aspen (*Populus tremuloides*) can develop naturally through vegetative propagation, in some cases covering more than 40 ha and consisting of thousands of trees. Such aspen clones may be the world's largest "individual" organisms (in terms of total biomass). Similarly,

Photo 7.1   Species are one of the familiar elements of biodiversity. The arctic tern (*Sterna paradisaea*) breeds widely in Canada.

the tiny plant known as duckweed (*Lemna minor*), which grows on the surface of fertile waterbodies, propagates by developing small buds on the edge of its single leaf. These break off to produce "new" plants, resulting in a genetically uniform population. These interesting cases are exceptions, however, and most populations and species contain a great deal of genetic variation.

A high level of genetic diversity in a population is generally considered desirable. With greater genetic diversity, populations are more likely to survive, to have enhanced fecundity and resistance to disease, and to be more adaptable to changes in environmental conditions. Very small populations with low genetic diversity are thought to be at extreme risk because of inbreeding and low adaptability. Examples of such populations include the several hundred beluga whales (*Delphinapterus leucas*) living in the estuary of the St. Lawrence River and the population of only 30–50 panthers (*Felis concolor coryi*) in Florida.

Richness of Species

Another level of biodiversity concerns **species richness**, or the number of species in a particular ecological community or in some other defined area, such as a park, county, province, country, or, ultimately, the biosphere. Species richness is the aspect of biodiversity that most people can easily relate to and understand.

It is well known that many tropical countries support a greater richness of species than do temperate countries (such as Canada). Tropical rainforests, in fact, support more species than any other kind of ecosystem. Unfortunately, species-rich rainforest in tropical countries is rapidly being destroyed, mostly through conversion into agricultural land-use and other disturbances. These ecological changes are causing the endangerment or extinction of many species and are the overwhelming cause of the modern-day biodiversity crisis (see Chapter 26). The magnitude of this crisis is much smaller in Canada. Nevertheless, many of our native species have become **extinct** or **extirpated** because of over-exploitation or habitat loss, and hundreds of other species are considered to be at risk (see Chapter 26).

In total, about 1.9 million species have been identified and given a scientific name. About 35% of these known species live in the tropics, 59% in the temperate zones, and the remaining 6% in boreal or polar latitudes (Table 7.1). It is important to recognize, however, that the identification of species on Earth is very incomplete. This is especially true of tropical ecosystems, which have not yet been

TABLE 7.1	Numbers of Species in Major Climatic Zones

Estimates suggest that whatever the total number of species, most live in tropical rainforests. These data include only plants and animals.

ZONE	NUMBER OF IDENTIFIED SPECIES ($\times 10^6$)	ESTIMATED TOTAL NUMBER OF SPECIES	
		ASSUME 5×10^6	ASSUME 10×10^6
Boreal	0.1	0.1	0.1
Temperate	1.0	1.2	1.3
Tropical	0.6	3.7	8.6
TOTAL	1.7	5.0	10.0

Source: Modified from World Resources Institute (1986)

thoroughly explored and characterized. According to some estimates, the total richness of species could range as high as 30–50 million species, with 90% of them living in the tropics, particularly in rainforests.

Most of the species that biologists have described and named are invertebrates, with insects making up the bulk of that total, and beetles (order Coleoptera) comprising most of the insects (Table 7.2). The scientist J.B.S. Haldane (1892–1964) was once asked by a theologian to succinctly tell, based on his knowledge of biology, what he could discern of God's purpose. Haldane reputedly said that God has "an inordinate fondness of beetles." This reflects the fact that, in any random sampling of all the known species on Earth, there is a strong likelihood that a beetle would be the chosen specimen.

Furthermore, it is believed that many tropical insects have not yet been described by biologists— perhaps more than another 30 million species, with many of these being small beetles. This remarkable conclusion initially emerged from research by T.L. Erwin, an entomologist studying tropical rainforest in South America. Erwin treated small areas of tropical-forest canopy with a fog of insecticide, which resulted in a "rain" of dead arthropods that was collected in sampling trays on the ground. In the trays were large numbers of

previously undescribed species of insects, most of which have a very localized distribution, being limited to only a single type of forest or even to a particular species of tree.

Clearly, biologists know remarkably little about the huge numbers of relatively small, unobtrusive species that occur in poorly explored, tropical habitats. However, even in a relatively well-prospected country like Canada, many indigenous species of invertebrates, lichens, microbes, and other small organisms have not yet been discovered and

TABLE 7.2	Numbers of Species in Various Groups of Organisms

The numbers of identified species are based on recent tallies, while the estimated numbers are based on the opinions of biologists about how many species will eventually be discovered in the major groups of organisms.

GROUP	WORLD		CANADA	
	Identified	Estimated	Identified	Estimated
Viruses	5 000	500 000	200	150 000
Bacteria	4 000	3 000 000	2 400	23 200
Fungi	72 000	1 500 000	11 310	16 500
Protozoans	40 000	100 000	1 000	2 000
Algae	40 000	350 000	5 303	7 300
Lichens	14 000	18 000	2 500	2 800
Non-vascular plants	16 000	20 000	1 500	1 800
Vascular plants	250 000	300 000	4 153	4 400
Mollusks	70 000	200 000	1 500	1 635
Crustaceans	40 000	150 000	3 139	4 550
Arachnids	75 000	750 000	3 275	11 006
Insects	950 000	8 000 000**	29 913	54 566
Fishes	25 000	27 000	1 100	1 600
Amphibians	4 522	5 000	42	44
Reptiles	6 900	7 400	42	42
Birds	9 672	10 000	430	430
Mammals	4 629	5 000	194	194
TOTAL*	1 627 000	15 000 000**	68 000	282 000

*Rounded figures
**This is a conservative number. Some recent estimates suggest more than 30 million species of insects living in tropical forests alone (see text).

Sources: Modified from Groombridge (1992), Heywood (1995), Environment Canada (1997), World Resources Institute (2000), and United Nations Environment Program (2001).

studied. Of course, larger plants and animals are relatively well known, partly because, for most people (including scientists), these have greater "charisma" than small beetles, microbes, and the like. Still, even in Canada and the U.S., new species of vascular plants and vertebrate animals are being discovered.

Compared with invertebrates and microbes, the species richness of other groups of tropical-forest organisms is better known. For example, a survey of rainforest in Sumatra, Indonesia, found 80 species of tree-sized plants (i.e., with diameter larger than 20 cm) in an area of only 0.5 ha. A study in Sarawak, Malaysia, found 742 woody species in a 3-ha plot of rainforest, with 50% of the species being represented by only a single individual. A similar study in Amazonian Peru found 283 tree species in a 1-ha plot, with 63% of the species represented by only one individual and another 15%, by only two. In marked contrast, temperate forest in North America typically has fewer than 9–12 tree species in plots of this size. The richest temperate forest in the world, in the Great Smokies of the eastern U.S., contains 30–35 tree species, far fewer than in tropical forest. More northern boreal forest, which covers much of Canada, has only 1–4 species of trees present.

Only a few studies have been made of the richness of bird species in tropical rainforest. A study of Amazonian forest in Peru found 245 resident bird species, plus another 74 migrants, in a 97-ha plot. Another study found 239 species of birds in a rainforest in French Guiana. In contrast, temperate forest in North America typically supports 30–40 species of birds.

Few systematic studies have been made of other types of biota in tropical ecosystems. In one study, a 108-km^2 area of dry tropical forest in Costa Rica was found to contain about 700 species of plants, 400 vertebrate species, and 13 000 species of insects, including 3140 species of moths and butterflies.

Richness of Communities

Biodiversity at the level of landscape (or seascape) is associated with the number of different communities occurring within a certain area, as well as their relative abundance, size, shape, connections, and spatial distribution. An area uniformly covered with a single type of community would be judged as having little biodiversity at the landscape level, compared with an area having a rich and dynamic mosaic of different communities.

Because natural landscapes contain many species and communities that have evolved together, it is as important to protect community- and landscape-level diversity as it is to protect genetic and species diversity. Natural communities, landscapes, and seascapes are being lost in all parts of the world, particularly through the destruction of tropical rainforest and coral reefs. Dramatic losses of this level of biodiversity are also occurring in Canada:

- Only about 0.2% of the original area of tallgrass prairie remains, the rest having been converted to agricultural use.

- Virtually all of the Carolinian forest of southern Ontario has been destroyed, mostly by conversion to agricultural and urbanized landscapes.

- The survival of old-growth forest in coastal British Columbia is at risk, with the dry coastal Douglas fir forest being especially depleted to only about 7% of its original extent. The loss of old-growth forest is mostly due to harvesting of the trees, which converts the ecosystem into a younger, second-growth forest (see Chapter 23).

- Throughout southern Canada, wetlands of all kinds have been destroyed or degraded by pollution, in-filling, and other disturbances.

- Natural fish populations have been widely decimated, including mixed-species communities in the Great Lakes, communities of salmonid species (salmon and trout) in western Canada, and cod and redfish off the Atlantic Provinces.

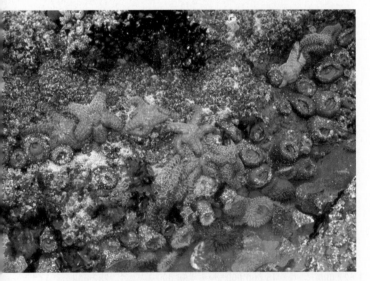

Photo 7.2   This marine intertidal community in Pacific Rim National Park on the west coast of Vancouver Island sustains various species of algae, barnacles, mussels, starfish, and other species that vary in their tolerance of environmental stress associated with tidal cycles.

In all of these Canadian examples, only *remnant* patches of endangered natural communities, landscapes, and seascapes remain. These are at great risk because they are no longer components of robust, extensive, naturally organizing ecosystems.

The Value of Biodiversity

Biodiversity is valuable and important for many reasons. These can be categorized into several groups.

Direct Utilitarian Value

Humans are not isolated from the rest of the biosphere, mostly because we need the products of certain elements of biodiversity. Because of this requirement, humans exploit species and ecosystems as sources of food, biomaterials, and energy—in other words, for their **utilitarian value**. Virtually all human foods are ultimately derived from biodiversity. Moreover, about one-quarter of the prescription drugs dispensed in North America contain active ingredients extracted from plants. In addition, there may be a wealth of other, as yet undiscovered, products of biodiversity that are potentially useful to humans. Research on wild species of plants, animals, and microorganisms has discovered many new bio-products useful to people as food, as medicines, or for other purposes. Like many of the species already known to be useful to humans, some of the newly discovered ones have a potentially enormous economic value.

To illustrate the importance of medicinal plants, take the case of the rosy periwinkle (*Catharantus roseus*), a small plant native to the island of Madagascar. One method used in the search for anti-cancer drugs involves screening large numbers of wild plants for the presence of chemicals that slow tumour growth. During one study, an extract of rosy periwinkle was found to counteract the reproduction of cancer cells. Further research identified the active chemicals as several alkaloids, probably synthesized by the rosy periwinkle to deter herbivores. These natural biochemicals are now used to prepare the drugs vincristine and vinblastine, which are extremely useful in chemotherapy to treat childhood leukemia, a cancer of the lymph system known as Hodgkin's disease, and several other cancers. Children with leukemia now have a 94% chance of remission, compared with 5% prior to the discovery of the therapeutic properties of periwinkle extracts. Hodgkin's patients now have a 70% chance of survival, compared with less than 1% previously. Therefore, an obscure species of plant,

Photo 7.3   Many elements of biodiversity provide products useful to people as food, materials, and medicines. In the 1990s, a chemical called taxol extracted from species of yews was found to be useful in treating certain kinds of cancers, particularly ovarian cancer. Commercial harvests are now being made of two yews native to Canada to supply biomass from which taxol can be extracted. These are the Pacific yew (*Taxus brevifolia*) of British Columbia and the Canada yew (*Taxus canadensis*) of eastern Canada. This image is of Canada yew growing in Prince Edward Island.

until recently known only to a few tropical botanists, has proven to be of great medicinal benefit to humans.

Human exploitation of wild biodiversity can be conducted in ways that allow the renewal of harvestable stocks. Unfortunately, many potentially renewable biodiversity resources are managed as if they were non-renewable resources (i.e., they are being "mined"; see Chapters 12

Canadian Focus 7.1

Medicinal Plants

Plants and products derived from them have always been vital to human survival, being used as sources of food, medicine, material, and energy. For instance, most foods eaten by people are the biomass of plants; the rest is animal or microbial products, but even these are produced indirectly from plants. Moreover, useful products are derived from a great richness of plant species—about 1800 medicinal plants are commercially available in North America, and perhaps 20 000 are known worldwide. It is also important to recognize that all biomass products are potentially renewable resources that can be available indefinitely, assuming they are harvested and managed on a sustainable basis (see Chapter 12).

Studies by anthropologists have repeatedly shown that Aboriginal peoples are intimately aware of the useful medicinal plants that grow within their local ecosystems. This so-called "traditional ecological knowledge" has been important in identifying potentially useful plants for further investigation by scientists. Nevertheless, only a small fraction of the enormous richness of Earth's biodiversity has been investigated by scientists for its potential to supply us with useful products. Because of the likelihood of discovering new useful bioproducts, it is imperative that we continue to engage in "bio-prospecting" research. Work of this sort is ongoing in many countries, including Canada.

Canada supports about 3200 species of native plants, of which as many as 1000 have been used for medicinal purposes, mostly by Aboriginal peoples. Of this relatively large number, several tens of species have become widely enough used that they are of significant commercial value. Some of them are being cultivated to supply the emerging herbal medicine markets; others are still harvested from the wild. A few notable examples of Canadian species that are of particular interest and value as medicinal plants include the following:

- *Achillea millefolium* (yarrow) is a widespread perennial herb of disturbed habitats and meadows that can be taken (often in capsule form) to treat the common cold, diarrhea, fever, and some other maladies, or used as a poultice to stanch the flow of blood from wounds. It is easily cultivated or may be gathered from the wild.
- *Echinacea pallida* var. *angustifolia* (purple coneflower) is a perennial herb native to prairie habitats that is

widely drunk as a root extract. The root may also be chewed or taken in other forms to prevent or treat the common cold, sore throat, bacterial infections, and other ills. It is easily cultivated and is one of the most widely used herbal medicines in North America.

- *Oenothera biennis* (evening primrose) is a widespread biennial herb of disturbed habitats and meadows that may be taken as a whole-plant infusion to treat asthma and gastrointestinal disorders or as a pressed-oil product in the form of a nutritional supplement, particularly to supply linolenic acid. It is easily cultivated or can be gathered from the wild.
- *Panax quinquefolius* (ginseng) is a perennial understorey plant of eastern hardwood forest that may be taken as a root infusion as a general tonic or to treat headache, cramps, fever, rheumatism, and other maladies. It is cultivated on a 5- to 7-year rotation, and it may be the most widely used herbal medicine in the world. It should not be gathered from the wild because past over-harvesting has rendered it endangered.
- *Taxus brevifolia* and *T. canadensis* (Pacific yew and Canadian yew) are tree- and shrub-sized woody plants of the humid west coast or eastern forests, respectively. An extract of bark or leaves containing the chemical taxol has proven useful in the treatment of certain malignancies, particularly ovarian and breast cancers. Biomass for processing is gathered from wild plants, but local over-harvesting is an issue in some areas; plantations of Pacific yew and other yews are being established to relieve the pressure on the slow-growing populations of wild plants.
- *Vaccinium macrocarpon* (cranberry) is a widespread dwarf shrub of bog wetlands that may be taken as a pressed juice as a source of vitamin C, to treat urinary tract infections and kidney ailments, and for other purposes for which its diuretic properties are useful. The species is extensively cultivated and is also gathered from wild habitats.

Reference and Additional Information

Small, E. and P.M. Catling. 1999. *Canadian Medicinal Plants*. Ottawa, ON: NRC Research Press.

Deur, D. and N. Turner (eds.). 2005. *Keeping It Living: Traditions of Plant Use and Cultivation on the Northwest Coast of North America*. Seattle, WA: University of Washington Press.

and 14), usually by excessive harvesting and inadequate fostering of regeneration. This results in biological resources becoming degraded in quantity and quality.

Sometimes, over-exploited species become locally extirpated or are even rendered globally extinct, and their unique resource values are no longer available for use by humans. The great auk, passenger pigeon, and sea mink are examples of Canadian species that were made extinct by over-harvesting. Local and regional extirpations have been more numerous and include the cougar, grizzly bear, timber wolf, and wild ginseng over most of their former ranges (see Chapters 14 and 26 for details).

Provision of Ecological Services

Examples of **ecological services** provided by biodiversity include nutrient cycling, biological productivity, cleansing of water and air, control of erosion, provision of atmospheric oxygen, removal of carbon dioxide, and other functions important to maintaining the stability and integrity of ecosystems. Even though all of these services are critical to the welfare of humans and other species, they are not usually assigned economic value by society. In part, this is because we do not yet have sufficient understanding and appreciation of the "importance" of ecological services and of the particular species and communities that provide them. According to Peter Raven, a famous botanist and advocate of biodiversity, "In the aggregate, biodiversity keeps the planet habitable and ecosystems functional."

Intrinsic Value

Biodiversity has its own **intrinsic value**, regardless of any direct or indirect worth in terms of the needs or welfare of humans. Its intrinsic value suggests certain ethical questions about actions that threaten biodiversity. Do humans have the "right" to impoverish or exterminate unique and irretrievable elements of biodiversity, even if our species is technologically able to do so? Is the human existence somehow impoverished by extinctions caused by our actions? These are philosophical issues, and they cannot be resolved by science. However, enlightened people and societies do not facilitate the endangerment or extinction of species or natural communities.

Biodiversity Is Worthwhile

Many people firmly believe that wild biodiversity and natural ecosystems are worthwhile and important. They cite the above reasons but also mention less tangible opinions, such as the charisma of many species (lions, pandas, and baby harp seals among others) and the spirituality of natural places (such as towering old-growth forest and other kinds of wilderness). Because this belief is becoming increasingly widespread and popularized, it is having a major influence on politicians, who are now including biodiversity issues in their agendas. Threats to biodiversity have therefore become politically important.

Undoubtedly, there is an undiscovered wealth of products of biodiversity that are potentially useful to humans. Many of these bio-products will be found in tropical species that have not yet been "discovered" by biologists. Clearly, the most important argument in favour of preserving biodiversity is the need to maintain natural ecosystems so they can continue to provide their vast inventory of useful products and their valuable ecological services. Biodiversity must also, of course, be preserved for its own, intrinsic value.

Classification of Organisms

Biologists classify species into higher-order groupings on the basis of their relatedness and similarities. Similarity is judged using information about anatomy, development, biochemistry, behaviour, and habitat selection. These classifications are made by systematists (biologists who study the evolutionary relationships among groups of organisms) and taxonomists (who focus on naming groups of organisms).

The systematic of life is traditionally organized hierarchically, with the levels ranging through sub-species, species, genus, family, order, class, phylum, and kingdom. This system is illustrated in Table 7.3.

Individual species are always described using two Latin words, known as a binomial. In cases where a subspecies is also recognized, the name has three Latin words. Many species also have a scientifically recognized "common name," and they may have informal common names as well. For example, the "proper" (scientifically recognized) common name of the widespread tree *Populus tremuloides* is trembling aspen, but this species is also known as aspen, golden aspen, mountain aspen, poplar, quaking asp, quaking aspen, trembling poplar, and that old-time favourite, "popple." Some of these common names have only a regional use and are unknown in other parts of the range of the species. Common names may also overlap among species—for instance, balsam poplar (*Populus balsamifera*) and large-toothed aspen (*P. grandidentata*) are both often called "poplar."

TABLE 7.3	Biological Classification			

The hierarchical, systematic classification of organisms is illustrated by three representative species.

GROUPING	DOUGLAS FIR (INTERIOR)	MONARCH BUTTERFLY	HUMANS
Kingdom	Plantae	Animalia	Animalia
Phylum (Division)	Coniferophyta	Arthropoda	Chordata
Class	Gymnospermae	Insecta	Mammalia
Order	Coniferales	Lepidoptera	Primates
Family	Pinaceae	Danaidae	Hominidae
Genus	*Pseudotsuga*	*Danaus*	*Homo*
Species	*menziesii*	*plexippus*	*sapiens*
Sub-species	*glauca*	*plexippus*	(not recognized)
Scientific name	*Pseudotsuga menziesii glauca*	*Danaus plexippus plexippus*	*Homo sapiens*

To avoid these ambiguities associated with common names, all species are assigned a globally recognized scientific binomial and sometimes a "proper" common name. Therefore, biologists working in Canada, the U.S., Mexico, Germany, Turkey, Russia, China, and other countries where the animal *Ursus arctos* occurs all know it by its binomial. In English, this animal is known as the grizzly or brown bear, and in other languages, by other common names. But no one is confused by its scientific binomial name.

Photo 7.4   Landscapes and seascapes are elements of biodiversity that are composed of spatial mosaics of various communities occurring at relatively large scales. This flat landscape in northwestern Newfoundland is characterized by extensive wetlands and intervening drier areas supporting tundra and low forest.

The Systematic Organization of Life

Most biologists divide all of Earth's species into five major groups, known as kingdoms. Although somewhat controversial and subject to ongoing refinement, this systematic organization is believed to reflect the evolutionary relationships among groups of organisms. The five kingdoms of living organisms and their major characteristics are briefly described below.

Monera

Monerans are the simplest of single-celled microorganisms and include bacteria and blue-green bacteria, the latter being photosynthetic. Monerans are **prokaryotes**, which means their genetic material is not contained within a membrane-bounded organelle (called a nucleus). Organisms in the other kingdoms have nuclei within their cells and are called **eukaryotes**. Prokaryotic microorganisms also do not have other kinds of organelles, such as chloroplasts, mitochondria, or flagella, and they differ from eukaryotes in other respects as well. Prokaryotes were the first organisms to evolve, about 3.5 million years ago. It was not until 2 billion years later (i.e., 1.5 billion years ago) that the first eukaryotes appeared.

About 4800 species of bacteria have been named, but there are many additional species that have not yet been described by microbiologists. The diversity of bacteria includes species capable of exploiting a phenomenal range of ecological and metabolic opportunities. Many are

In Detail 7.1

Non-living Entities: Viruses and Prions

In addition to the living organisms described in this chapter, there are other entities that display some, but not all, of the characteristics of life. These "pseudo-organisms" are incapable of reproduction, or even of metabolism, unless they have first invaded and parasitized a living cell. The best known of these "non-living" entities are viruses, which consist of bits of nucleic acid (DNA or RNA) surrounded by a protein capsule. Viruses cannot reproduce themselves, but they can invade specific living cells, take over the genetic metabolism, and use it to replicate themselves.

Some viruses cause diseases. Some viral diseases of humans include colds and flus and more serious mal-adies such as smallpox, yellow fever, rabies, herpes, polio, and acquired human immunodeficiency syndrome (AIDS). Some viral diseases can be controlled by vaccination, which involves infecting hosts with non-virulent, attenuated, or dead viruses, causing the host to develop resistance to the virulent strains. This practice has allowed the recent eradication of smallpox, a lethal disease.

Prions are another kind of infectious particle, consisting only of bits of transmissible protein. Prions are known to cause certain lethal diseases, including scrapies in sheep and bovine spongiform encephalopathy or "mad cow disease." The human form of mad cow disease is known as variant Creutzfeldt-Jakob syndrome, which may be caused be eating the organs or meat of a prion-infected cow.

decomposers, found in "rotting" biomass. Some species are photosynthetic, others are chemosynthetic, and still others can utilize virtually any organic substrate for their nutrition, either in the presence or absence of oxygen. Some species of bacteria can tolerate extreme environments, living in hot springs at temperatures as torrid as 78°C, while others are active in sub-zero temperatures as deep as 400 m in glacial ice.

Many bacterial species live in *mutualistic symbioses* with more complex organisms. For example, some live as a community in the rumens of cows and sheep and others live in the human gut, in both cases aiding in the digestion of complex organic foods. Other bacteria, known as *Rhizobium*, live in a mutualism with the roots of leguminous plants (such as peas and clovers), fixing atmospheric nitrogen gas into a form (ammonia) that plants can utilize as a nutrient (see Chapter 5).

Many bacteria are parasites of other species, causing various diseases. For example, *Bacillus thuringiensis* is a pathogen of many species of moths, butterflies, and black-flies and has been used as a biological insecticide against certain pests in agriculture and forestry. Species of bacteria also cause important diseases of humans, including bacterial pneumonia, cholera, diphtheria, gonorrhea, Legionnaire's disease, leprosy, scarlet fever, syphilis, tetanus, tooth decay, tuberculosis, whooping cough, most types of food poisoning, and the "flesh-eating disease" caused by a virulent strain of *Streptococcus*.

Protista

Protists include a wide range of simple, eukaryotic organisms, comprising both unicellular and multicellular species. Familiar protists include protozoans, foraminifera, slime moulds, single-celled algae, and multicellular algae. The latter group includes the large seaweeds known as kelps, some of which are over 10 m long. The kingdom Protista consists of 14 phyla and about 40 000 named species, which vary enormously in their genetics, structure, and function. Systematists will eventually divide the Protista into several kingdoms because of increasing evidence of key differences among certain groups and recognition that the other, relatively complex eukaryotic kingdoms (i.e., fungi, plants, and animals) evolved from different protistan ancestors.

Several phyla of protists, broadly known as algae, are photosynthetic. These groups include the diatoms (Bacillariophyta), green algae (Chlorophyta), dinoflagellates (Dinoflagellata), euglenoids (Euglenophyta), red algae (Rhodophyta), and brown algae, such as kelps (Phaeophyta). Algae are important primary producers in aquatic ecosystems, both marine and freshwater. Some seaweeds are harvested as a natural resource, mostly to extract chemicals known as alginates, which are important additives to many foods and cosmetics. Uncommon marine phenomena known as "red tides" are natural blooms of certain species of dinoflagellates that produce extremely toxic metabolites.

Other phyla of protists are heterotrophic in their nutrition. These groups include the ciliates (Ciliophora), forams (Foraminifera), slime moulds (Myxomycota), amoebae (Rhizopoda), and unicellular flagellates (Zoomastigina). Forams are unicellular microorganisms that form a shell of calcium carbonate, the remains of which may accumulate over geological time to form a mineral known as chalk. (The white cliffs of Dover in southern England are made of foram remains.) Trypanosomes are unicellular flagellates responsible for sleeping sickness, a debilitating disease of humans and other vertebrate animals. Certain species of amoebae are parasites of animals, and one species causes amoebic dysentery in humans. A ciliate known as *Giardia* causes a water-borne disease known as hiker's diarrhea (or beaver fever), which is the reason why even the cleanest-looking natural waters should be boiled or otherwise disinfected before drinking.

Fungi

This kingdom consists of yeasts, which are single-celled microorganisms, and fungi, which are multicellular and filamentous. Fungi evolved at least 400 million years ago, but they may be much older because their remains do not fossilize well. Fungal cells excrete enzymes into their surroundings, which then externally digest complex organic materials. The fungus then ingests the resulting simple organic compounds. All fungi are heterotrophic—most species are decomposers of dead organic matter, while others are parasitic on plants or animals.

There are three major divisions (phyla) of fungi, distinguished mainly by their means of sexual reproduction. (Asexual reproduction is also common in most species of fungi.)

The zygomycetes (division Zygomycota) achieve sexual reproduction by the direct fusion of hyphae (the thread-like tissues of fungi), which form resting spores known as zygospores. There are about 600 named species of zygomycetes, the most familiar of which are the bread moulds, such as *Rhizopus*, with their fluffy mycelium (loosely organized mass of hyphae).

The ascomycetes (division Ascomycota) include about 30 000 named species, some of which are commonly known as a cup fungus or morel. During their sexual reproduction, ascomycetes form many microscopic, cup-shaped bodies known as asci, located in specialized fleshy structures called ascocarps. Relatively familiar species of ascomycetes include yeasts, morels, and truffles, as well as the pathogenic fungi that cause chestnut blight and Dutch elm disease (see below).

The basidiomycetes (division Basiodiomycota) include about 16 000 named species. Sexual reproduction of basidiomycetes involves the development of a relatively complex spore-producing structure known as a basidium. Depending on its shape, a basidium may be commonly called a mushroom, toadstool, puffball, or shelf fungus. In Canada, the largest of these structures is developed by the giant puffball (*Calvatia* spp.), which can grow a ball-like basidium with a diameter of up to 50 cm.

Lichens are specific mutualisms between a fungus and either an alga or a blue-green bacterium. Most of the lichen biomass is fungal tissue, which provides habitat and inorganic nutrients for the photosynthetic partner, which provides organic nutrition to the fungus. Another type of mutualism, known as a mycorrhiza, involves an intimate relationship between plant roots and certain fungi. This relationship is highly beneficial to the plant because it allows more efficient absorption of inorganic nutrients from the soil, particularly phosphate. About 80% of plant species develop mycorrhizae.

Fungi are extremely important ecologically because they are excellent decomposers, allowing nutrients to be recycled and reducing the accumulation of dead biomass.

Economically important fungi spoil stored grains and other foods, are serious parasites of agricultural or forestry plants, and cause diseases in humans and other animals. Ringworm is a disease of the skin, usually the scalp, which can be caused by various species of fungi. The chestnut blight fungus (*Endothia parasitica*) was accidentally introduced to North America from Europe and wiped out the native chestnut (*Castanea dentata*), which used to be a prominent and valuable tree in eastern forests. The Dutch elm disease fungus (*Ceratocystis ulmi*), also introduced from Europe, is causing similar damage to native elm trees (especially white elm, *Ulmus americana*).

Economically useful fungi include a few species of yeast that have the ability to ferment sugars under anaerobic (O_2-deficient) conditions, yielding gaseous CO_2 and ethanol. The CO_2 produced during fermentation raises bread dough prior to baking, while brewers take advantage of the alcohol production to make beer, wine, and other intoxicating beverages. Other fungi are employed in the manufacture of cheese, tofu, soy sauce, food additives such as citric acid, and certain antibiotics such as penicillin.

Some mushroom-forming fungi are cultivated as a source of food; other edible species are collected from natural ecosystems. The most commonly cultivated species is the meadow mushroom (*Agaricus campestris*), while the most prized wild mushroom is the extremely flavourful truffle (*Tuber melanosporum*). Some wild mushrooms contain chemicals that induce hallucinations, feelings of well-being, and other pleasurable mental states, and are sought by people for religious or recreational use. These include the fly agaric (*Amanita muscaria*), a species widespread in Canada and elsewhere, and psilocybin (*Psilocybe* spp.) of more southern regions of North America and Central America. Some wild mushrooms are deadly poisonous even when eaten in tiny quantities. The most toxic species in Canada are the destroying angel (*Amanita virosa*) and deathcap (*A. phalloides*).

Plantae

Plants are photosynthetic organisms that manufacture their food by using the energy of sunlight to synthesize organic molecules from inorganic ones. Plants evolved from multicellular green algae about 430 million years ago, and the first tree-sized plants evolved about 300 million years ago. Plants are different from algae in that they are always multicellular; have cell walls rich in cellulose; synthesize a mixture of photosynthetic pigments, including chlorophylls *a* and *b* and carotenoids; and use starch as their principal means of storing energy. Plants are extremely important as photosynthetic fixers of CO_2 into organic carbon, and they are dominant in terrestrial ecosystems, where algae and blue-green bacteria are relatively unimportant.

Plants are generally separated into 12 divisions, which are aggregated into two functional groups.

Bryophytes

The relatively simple **bryophytes** lack vascular tissues and do not have a waxy cuticle covering their foliage, a character that restricts these plants to moist habitats. The bryophytes consist of the following:

- liverworts (division Hepaticophyta), of which there are about 6500 species
- mosses (Bryophyta), including about 10 000 species, which are prominent in some types of wetlands, especially in bogs, where the dead biomass of peat-mosses (species of *Sphagnum*) accumulates as a partially decayed material known as peat, which is mined as a horticultural soil conditioner and as a source of energy
- hornworts (Anthocerophyta), with 100 species

Vascular Plants

The relatively complex **vascular plants** have specialized, elongated, tube-like, vascular tissues in their stems for conducting water and nutrients. The nine divisions of vascular plants include the following:

- whisk ferns (division Psilophyta), containing several species
- club mosses and quillworts (Lycophyta), about 1000 species
- horsetails or scouring rushes (Sphenophyta), 15 species
- ferns (Pterophyta), 12 000 species
- cycads or sago palms (Cycadophyta), 100 species
- gnetums or mormon tea (Gnetophyta), 70 species
- ginkgo (Ginkgophyta), with only one relict, surviving species (*Ginkgo biloba*)
- conifers (Coniferophyta), including about 550 species of firs, hemlocks, pines, redwoods, spruces, yews, and others
- flowering plants (Anthophyta), containing a diverse assemblage of about 235 000 species

The flowering plants are also known as **angiosperms**, because their ovules are enclosed within a specialized membrane and their seeds, within a seedcoat. The conifers, ginkgo, and gnetums lack these structures and are referred to as **gymnosperms**. Together, the angiosperms and gymnosperms are known as *seed plants*. Their seeds develop from a fusion between specialized haploid cells known as pollen and ovules, in a process called pollination.

The seed plants are extremely diverse in their form and function. The tallest species are redwood trees (*Sequoia sempervirens*), which can exceed 100 m in height. The smallest is an aquatic plant known as watermeal (*Wolffia* spp.), only the size of a pinhead. Many seed plants live for less than one year (these are "annual" plants), while the age of others can exceed 4500 years—for example, the oldest bristlecone pines (*Pinus aristata*).

Many flowering plants grow as shrubs or trees. Rigid, woody tissues in their stems confer mechanical strength that allows these plants to grow tall against the forces of gravity and wind. Other species of angiosperms lack these rigid stem tissues and grow as herbaceous plants that die back to the ground at the end of the growing season.

Species of angiosperms are the most important crop plants in agriculture, while both conifer and angiosperm trees are important in forestry. Plants are also economically important as sources of biochemicals in industry and medicine, and because they provide the food and habitat required by so many other organisms, including many species of animals that are hunted by humans for food.

Animalia

Animals are multicellular organisms, and most are mobile during at least some stage of their life history, having the ability to move about to search for food, to disperse, or to reproduce. Animals are heterotrophs: they must ingest their food, ultimately consuming the photosynthetic products of plants or algae.

Most animals (except the sponges) have their cells organized into specialized tissues that are further organized into organs. Almost all animals reproduce sexually, a process involving the joining of haploid gametes from males and females to produce a fertilized egg. Animals comprise the bulk of identified species of organisms, with insects being the most diverse group. Apart from these broad generalizations, animals are extremely diverse in their form and function. They range in size from the largest blue whales (*Balaenoptera musculus*), which can reach 32 m in length and 136 t in weight, to the smallest beetles and soil mites, which are less than 1 mm long and weigh a few milligrams.

The animal kingdom includes about 35 phyla. The majority of these are exclusive to marine habitats, with a smaller number occurring in freshwater and on land. All animals in all the phyla except one are considered **invertebrates** (no backbone), while the phylum Chordata includes the **vertebrates**—animals with backbones.

The most prominent phyla of animals are described below.

Sponges

Sponges (phylum Porifera) include a marine group of about 5000 species plus about 150 freshwater species. Sponges are simple, sessile (non-mobile) animals, with no differentiation of their tissues into organs. Sponges filter-feed on organic matter suspended in water. The slow flow of water through sponges is driven by surface cells that use flagella, tiny whip-like structures, to move water over their surface.

Cnidarians

Cnidarians (phylum Cnidaria) include about 9000 species, almost all of which are marine. Familiar cnidarians include jellyfish, sea anemones, hydroids, and corals. Cnidarians have a simple, rather gelatinous body structure. They display radial symmetry, meaning a cross-section in any direction through their central axis yields two parts that are mirror images. Jellyfish are weakly swimming or floating animals, with a body form known as a medusa. Most other cnidarians are sessile as adults, being firmly attached to a bottom substrate. Cnidarians are carnivores, capturing their prey using tentacles that ring their mouth opening, often after subduing the prey by stinging it with specialized cells. Corals develop a protective casement of calcium carbonate and are important reef-building organisms in shallow tropical seas.

Flatworms and Tapeworms

The flatworms and tapeworms (phylum Platyhelminthes) include about 12 000 species of soft-bodied, ribbon-shaped animals. Many flatworms are free-living scavengers or predators of small animals, while tapeworms and flukes are internal parasites of larger animals, including humans.

Nematodes and Roundworms

Nematodes (phylum Nematoda) include 12 000 species of small, worm-like creatures. These animals are round in cross-section and are abundant in almost all habitats containing other forms of life, ranging from aquatic habitats to the driest deserts. Many species are parasites, living in or on their hosts. Virtually all plants and animals are parasitized by one or more species of nematodes, which are often specialized to live in a particular host. Species of hookworms, pinworms, and roundworms are important parasites of humans. The *Trichinella* roundworm causes a painful disease known as trichinosis, while *Filaria* causes filariasis, a tropical disease.

True Worms

The worms (phylum Annelida) include about 12 000 species of long, tubular, segmented, soft-bodied animals. Most worm species are marine, but others occur in freshwater and moist terrestrial habitats. Worms are divided into three major groups: bristleworms, or polychaetes; typical worms, or oligochaetes (including earthworms); and leeches or hirudineans. Most feed on dead organic matter, but leeches are blood-sucking parasites of larger animals. Earthworms provide an important ecological service by helping to recycle dead biomass in many terrestrial habitats, including some agricultural ecosystems.

Mollusks

Mollusks (phylum Mollusca) comprise about 110 000 species of clams, cuttlefish, octopuses, oysters, scallops, slugs, snails, and squid. Many mollusks have a hard shell made of calcium carbonate which protects the soft body parts inside. Other mollusks, such as squid and octopuses, lack this hard shell. Mollusks are most abundant in marine and freshwater habitats, with far fewer terrestrial species. Most mollusks are herbivores or scavengers, but a few are predators of other animals. Various species of mollusks are an important resource used by humans as food. Several species produce pearls, valuable for making jewellery. Some species of slugs and snails are pests in agriculture, while others are alternative hosts for certain parasites, such as the tropical fluke that causes schistosomiasis in humans.

Arthropods

Arthropods (phylum Arthropoda) comprise the largest phylum of organisms. There are about 900 000 named species of arthropods and probably millions of others that have not yet been described. Arthropods have an exterior skeleton (exoskeleton) made of a polysaccharide known as chitin, with the body parts segmented to allow movement. They have at least three pairs of legs. The most important groups of arthropods are the spiders and mites (class Arachnida), crustaceans (Crustacea), centipedes (Chilopoda), millipedes (Diplopoda), and insects (Insecta). Insects alone make up more than half of all named species.

Arthropods are of great economic importance, with some species being used by humans as food (e.g., lobster, crayfish), and others used to produce food (e.g., the honey of certain species of bees). Some other species are important pests. Termites damage buildings by eating wood, while various insects are important pests in agriculture. Species of mosquitoes, blackflies, fleas, and ticks spread diseases of humans and other animals, including malaria, yellow fever, encephalitis, and plague.

Echinoderms

Echinoderms (phylum Echinodermata) include about 6000 species of marine animals, such as brittle stars, sand dollars, sea stars, sea cucumbers, and sea urchins. Echinoderms have radial symmetry as adults. Most have an exoskeleton rich in calcium carbonate, some are covered with spiny projections, and some move about using large numbers of small, tube-like feet. Sea urchins and sea cucumbers are harvested as a minor source of food, popular in some Asian countries.

Chordates

Chordates (phylum Chordata) are the most familiar group of animals. Distinctive characters (in at least the embryonic phase) include a hollow nerve cord that runs along the dorsal (top) surface, and a flexible, rod-like dorsal structure (the notochord), which is replaced by the vertebral column in adult vertebrates.

There are about 42 500 species of chordates, divided among three sub-phyla. The tunicates (Urochordata) are composed of about 1000 species of marine animals, including sea grapes and sea peaches. Tunicates have a small notochord and are sessile filter-feeders as adults. The lancets (Cephalochordata) consist of 23 species of filter-feeding marine animals, which have a long, laterally compressed body.

The vertebrates (Vertebrata) are a group of about 41 000 species, most of which have a vertebral column as adults. The major classes of living vertebrates are the following:

The jawless fishes (class Agnatha) include 63 species of lampreys and hagfishes, which first evolved 470 million years ago. These marine or freshwater animals have a notochord throughout their life and a skeleton made of cartilage (i.e., cartilaginous).

The cartilaginous jawed fishes (class Chondrichthyes) consist of 850 species of dogfish, rays, sharks, and skates, all of which occur in marine habitats. Cartilaginous fishes evolved more than 410 million years ago.

The bony fishes (class Osteichthyes) include 18 000 species of typical fish, such as cod, salmon, tuna, and guppies. The first bony fishes evolved about 390 million years ago.

The amphibians (class Amphibia) consist of 4000 species of frogs, salamanders, toads, and legless caecilians. The first amphibians evolved about 330 million years ago. Early stages in the life history (egg and larva) are usually aquatic, but adult stages of many species can live in terrestrial habitats.

The reptiles (class Reptilia) include 6000 species of crocodilians, lizards, snakes, and turtles. Reptiles first evolved about 300 million years ago. Extinct groups include the dinosaurs, plesiosaurs, and pterosaurs, the last of which became extinct about 65 million years ago. Reptiles were the first fully terrestrial animals, capable of completing all stages of their life history on land (although some species, such as turtles, are highly aquatic as adults). Reptiles have a dry skin and lay eggs on land. Their young are miniature versions of the adults.

The birds (class Aves) consist of 9000 living species, which first evolved about 225 million years ago from small, dinosaurian ancestors. All birds are homeothermic (warmblooded), are covered in feathers, lay hard-shelled eggs, and have a specialized horny covering of the jaws known as a beak. Most species of birds can fly, the exceptions being the largest birds, penguins, and many species that evolved on islands lacking predators.

The mammals (class Mammalia) consist of 4500 living species, which first evolved about 220 million years ago (the earliest fossil mammals are difficult to distinguish from reptiles). Mammals became especially prominent after the extinction of the last dinosaurs, about 65 million years ago. Mammals are homeotherms, have at least some hair on their body, feed their young with milk, and have a double circulation of the blood (i.e., a four-chambered heart and fully separate circulatory systems for oxygen-poor and oxygen-rich blood).

There are three major groups of mammals. The *monotremes* are a few species of egg-laying mammals that live in Australia and New Guinea—the duck-billed platypus (*Ornithorhynchus anatinus*) and several species of echidnas. *Marsupials* bear live young that are at an extremely early stage of development. After birth, the tiny young migrate to a special pouch (the marsupium) on the mother's belly where they develop further while feeding on milk. Examples of marsupials include kangaroos, koala, and wallabies, which live only in Australia, New Guinea, and nearby islands, and the opossum of North and South America. The *placental mammals* include many familiar species of the Americas, Africa, and Eurasia. Placental mammals give birth to live young that are suckled by the mother. Humans are a species of placental mammal.

Conclusions

Biodiversity is the richness of biological variation—it exists at the levels of genetics, species richness, and community diversity. Biodiversity is important to the survival of humans and their economy, and also to all other species. Biodiversity also has inherent value. Human activities have resulted in the extinction of many elements of biodiversity, and the survival of many others is being placed at grave risk. Damage to biodiversity is a principal aspect of the environmental crisis.

Key Terms

biodiversity	eukaryote
species richness	bryophyte
extinct	vascular plant
extirpated	angiosperm
utilitarian value	gymnosperm
ecological service	invertebrate
intrinsic value	vertebrate
prokaryote	

Questions for Review

1. What are the major components of biodiversity? Provide an example of each.

2. Pick a species. Illustrate the hierarchical classification of life by giving the scientific names of its species, genus, family, order, class, phylum, and kingdom.

3. What are the five kingdoms of life? Identify several of the groups within each of the kingdoms.

4. What are the characteristics of a "living" entity? Why are viruses and prions not considered living organisms?

Questions for Discussion

1. Why is biodiversity important? Outline several reasons.

2. Discuss the notion that all species are similarly "advanced" in the evolutionary sense but may vary greatly in their complexity.

3. All elements of biodiversity are considered to have intrinsic, or existence, value. What does this value mean? Can it be fully justified in a strictly scientific context?

4. Choose an economically important "pest," such as the house mouse (*Mus musculus*), a disease-carrying mosquito (e.g., *Anopheles* species), or the group B *Steptococcus* bacterium that causes deadly infections. Now suppose that a new method has been discovered to eradicate that pest, which would cause its global extinction. Based on ideas about intrinsic value and other considerations, could you mount a logical defence of the pest species to argue against its extinction?

Exploring Issues

1. You are a biodiversity specialist, and a group of influential politicians has asked why they should spend public money to protect an endangered species occurring within their jurisdiction. You know that these people are sceptical, and that if you do not convince them to preserve the species

and its habitat, it may become extinct. What information and arguments would you include in your presentation to the politicians?

2. Make a comprehensive list of products of biodiversity that you use in a typical day. The list can include raw and processed foods, materials, and sources of energy.

References

Bolandrin, M.F., J.A. Klocke, E.S. Wurtele, and W.H. Bollinger. 1985. Natural plant chemicals: Sources of industrial and medicinal materials. *Science*, **228**: 1154–60.

Boyd, R. 1988. *General Microbiology*. St. Louis, MO: Mosby Year Book.

Ehrlich, P.R., and A. Ehrlich. 1981. *Extinction: The Causes and Consequences of the Disappearance of Species*. New York: Ballantine.

Environment Canada. 1997. *The State of Canada's Environment*. Ottawa: State of the Environment Reporting Organization, Environment Canada.

Erwin, T.L. 1991. How many species are there? Revisited. *Conserv. Biol.*, **5**: 330–33.

Freedman, B. 1995. *Environmental Ecology*. 2nd ed. San Diego, CA: Academic Press.

Gaston, K.J. (ed.). 1996. *Biodiversity: A Biology of Numbers and Difference*. Cambridge: Blackwell Science.

Gaston, K.J. and J.I. Spicer. 2004. *Biodiversity: An Introduction*. 2nd ed. Cambridge: Blackwell Science.

Groombridge, B. and M.D. Jenkins. 2002. *World Atlas of Biodiversity: Earth's Living Resources in the 21st Century*. Berkeley, CA: University of California Press.

Groombridge, G. 1992. *Global Biodiversity*. World Conservation Monitoring Center. London: Chapman & Hall.

Heywood, V.H. (ed.). 1995. *Global Biodiversity Assessment*. Cambridge: Cambridge University Press.

Janzen, D.H. 1987. Insect diversity in a Costa Rican dry forest: why keep it, and how. *Biol. J. Linn. Soc.*, **30**: 343–56.

Miller, K. and L. Tangley. 1991. *Trees of Life*. Boston: Beacon.

Myers, N. 1983. *A Wealth of Wild Species*. Boulder, CO: Westview.

Perlman, D.L. and G. Adelson. 1997. *Biodiversity: Exploring Values and Priorities in Conservation*. Cambridge, UK: Blackwell Science Publishers.

Pough, F.H., J.B. Hirser, and W.N. McFarland. 1996. *Vertebrate Life*. 4th ed. Upper Saddle River, NJ: Prentice Hall.

Raven, P.H. and G.B. Johnson. 1992. *Biology*. Toronto: Mosby Year Book.

Raven, P.R., G.B. Johnson, J. Losos, and S. Singer. 2004. *Biology*. New York: McGraw-Hill.

Reaka-Kudla, M.L., D.E. Wilson, and E.O. Wilson (eds.). 1997. *Biodiversity II: Understanding and Protecting Our Biological Resources*. Washington, DC: National Academy Press.

Terborgh, J., S.K. Robinson, T.A. Parker, C.A. Muna, and N. Pierpont. 1990. Structure and organization of an Amazonian forest bird community. *Ecol. Monogr.*, **60**: 213–38.

Townsend, C.R., M. Begon, and J.L. Harper. 2002. *Essentials of Ecology. 2nd ed.* Cambridge, UK: Blackwell Publishers.

United Nations Environment Program. 2001. *Global Biodiversity Outlook*. Montreal, PQ: Secretariat of the Convention on Biological Diversity.

Wilson, E.O. (ed.). 1988. *Biodiversity*. Washington, DC: National Academy Press.

WRI. 2000. *World Resources 2000-01. People and Ecosystems*. New York: Oxford University Press.

Informative Websites

Biodiversity. www.enviroliteracy.org/subcategory.php/4.html

The Environmental Literacy Council, a non-profit organization, organized this site, which discusses endangered species, exotic species, ecosystems, and conservation.

Biodiversity and Ecosystem Functioning: Maintaining Natural Life Support Processes.
www.esa.org/Science/Issues/FileEnglish/issue4.pdf

This pdf document of the Ecological Society of America explains the importance of biodiversity in maintaining ecosystems in a healthy condition.

Conservation International.
http://www.conservation.org/xp/CIWEB/home

Conservation International is an organization dedicated to studying and conserving global biodiversity.

Ecological Monitoring and Assessment Network.
www.eman-rese.ca/

This site has links to Environment Canada's community-based ecosystem health monitoring programs and to research findings of the network.

Sound Science Initiative. Biodiversity.
www.ucsusa.org/ssi/biodiversity/

The Union of Concerned Scientists is an international advocacy organization that deals with important science issues, including environmental ones. This website provides links to their statements and publications relevant to biodiversity issues.

Tree of Life Web Project.
http://tolweb.org/tree/phylogeny.html

The Tree of Life project provides information about the diversity of organisms on Earth, their history, and characteristics. The information is linked together in the form of the evolutionary tree that connects all organisms to each other.

United Nations Environment Programme (UNEP).
http://www.biodiv.org/welcome.aspx

The United Nations Environment Programme is responsible for the international Convention on Biological Diversity. This website explains the convention and provides much useful information.

World Resources Institute. Index: [Species].
www.wri.org/wrisites.cfm

From the genetic diversity of agriculture to zoological parks, this site provides links to everything resource-related.

8 Biomes and Ecozones

CHAPTER OBJECTIVES

After completing this chapter, you will be able to

1. Identify Earth's major biomes and outline their characteristics.
2. Identify Canada's ecozones and list their prominent species.
3. Outline the character of urban, agricultural, and industrial habitats in Canada.
4. Discuss the differences between natural and anthropogenic ecosystems.

CHAPTER OUTLINE

- Biomes: Global Ecosystem Types
- Major Biomes and Their Characteristics
- Ecozones of Canada
- Anthropogenic Habitats
- Conclusions

Biomes: Global Ecosystem Types

A **biome** is a geographically extensive type of ecosystem, occurring wherever the environmental conditions are suitable for its development, anywhere in the world. Biomes are characterized by their dominant **life forms**, but not necessarily by their particular species. Terrestrial biomes are generally identified on the basis of their mature or older-growth vegetation. Aquatic biomes, especially marine ones, are usually distinguished by their dominant animals. Earth's biomes are classified by a system that is used internationally—that is, by ecologists working in many countries.

Figure 8.1 shows a map of the distribution of the most extensive terrestrial biomes. The distribution of biomes is determined by environmental conditions, which must be appropriate to support the dominant species (Figure 8.2). Typically, the most important environmental factors influencing the distribution of terrestrial biomes are moisture, temperature, and soil type. The distribution of wetland types within terrestrial biomes is largely influenced by the

amount and permanence of surface water and the availability of nutrients. Marine biomes are strongly influenced by water depth and upwellings, which affect the amounts of light and nutrients.

As long as environmental conditions are suitable for their development, biomes can occur in widely divergent regions, even on different continents. Widely separate regions of the same biome may be dominated by different species, but their life forms are typically ecologically convergent. In other words, the different species are similar in form and function, because the natural selection regimes of broadly similar environments elicit parallel, or convergent, evolutionary responses. Therefore, biomes are defined primarily by their ecological structure and function, but not necessarily by their species composition.

We can illustrate this important point by referring to the boreal coniferous forest, an extensive biome that occurs in northern Canada, Alaska, and Eurasia. The boreal forest occurs at high latitudes, in regions with cold winters, short but warm summers, and moist growing conditions. The boreal forest is situated between the northern arctic

---

FIGURE 8.1 | Distribution of Earth's Major Terrestrial Biomes

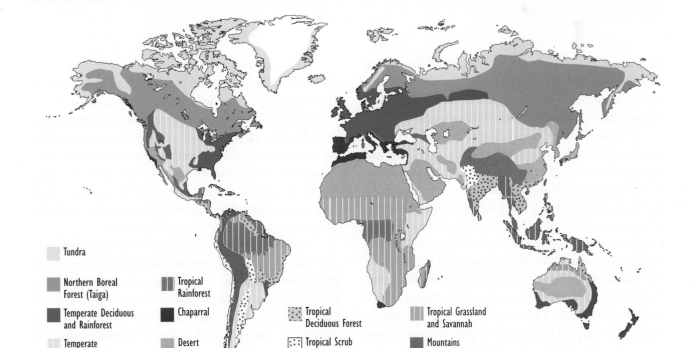

Legend:
- Tundra
- Northern Boreal Forest (Taiga)
- Temperate Deciduous and Rainforest
- Temperate Grassland
- Tropical Rainforest
- Chaparral
- Desert
- Tropical Deciduous Forest
- Tropical Scrub Forest
- Tropical Grassland and Savannah
- Mountains (Complex Zonation)

Note that the spatial complexity is greatest in regions with mountainous terrain, such as the western Americas and southern Asia.

Source: Modified from Odum (1983)

FIGURE 8.2 | Environmental Influences on the Distribution of Biomes

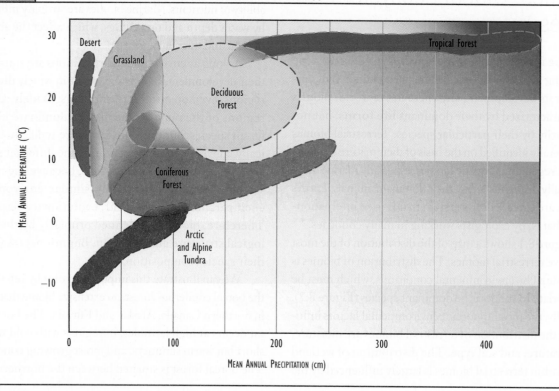

This figure suggests the reasons why temperature and moisture are believed to be the most important environmental factors affecting the distributions of terrestrial biomes.

Source: Modified from Odum (1983)

tundra and temperate forests to the south. The typical dominant vegetation of boreal forest is coniferous trees, especially species of fir, larch, pine, or spruce. However, the particular species vary from region to region.

Over much of northern Canada, the boreal coniferous forest is dominated by stands of black spruce. In some regions, however, white spruce, jack pine, balsam fir, or tamarack are dominant. In the boreal forest of northern Europe, Norway spruce (*Picea abies*) and Scotch pine (*Pinus sylvestris*) are the characteristic trees, while Siberia has different species of fir (*Abies sibirica*), larch (*Larix sibirica* and *L. gmelinii*), spruce (*Picea obovata*), and pine (*Pinus sibirica*). The boreal forests of northern Japan, Korea, and the Pacific coast of Russia occur in a more maritime climate, which is relatively moderate. These regions have yet other species of coniferous trees. However, all of these different forests are structurally and functionally convergent ecosystems within the same biome—the boreal coniferous forest. (The scientific names of Canadian species mentioned in this chapter are listed in Appendix 8A following the chapter.)

We should also note that biomes are described on the basis of the dominant, most extensive kind of ecosystems that they contain. For the coniferous boreal forest, this is stands of coniferous trees. However, biomes are not homogeneous; they also contain other kinds of ecosystems. For instance, parts of the boreal forest biome are dominated by broad-leaved (angiosperm) trees, especially species of alder, aspen, birch, poplar, and willow. Parts of the southern boreal forest, just north of the Canadian prairies, for example, contain extensive stands of trembling aspen.

In addition, because the boreal forest is subject to periodic catastrophic **disturbances**, the landscape is composed of a mosaic of stands in various stages of the process of ecological recovery, called **succession**. Disturbances of boreal forest are commonly caused by wildfire and sometimes by epidemics of insects, such as spruce budworm, that kill trees after several years of defoliation (see Chapter 22). The boreal forest biome also contains various wetland ecosystems, including bogs, fens, and marshes, as well as ponds, lakes, streams, and rivers.

Major Biomes and Their Characteristics

Earth's natural biomes are characterized by their dominant ecosystems, which are themselves composed of communities of plants, animals, and microorganisms. Earth also has anthropogenic ecosystems that are strongly influenced by humans and their activities, such as cities and agricultural land. In fact, all of Earth's modern biomes have been influenced by humans to some degree. At the very least, all organisms in even the most remote places now contain trace contaminations of organochlorine chemicals that humans have manufactured and dispersed into the environment, such as DDT and PCBs (see Chapter 22).

Ecologists have used a number of systems to divide the biosphere into major biomes (see Figure 8.1). The classification of global biomes described in this chapter is modified from a system proposed by the American ecologist E.P. Odum. In the following sections, we describe the world's biomes within continental and global contexts. This is appropriate because biomes are widespread ecological units, and their boundaries and species do not respect political boundaries.

Terrestrial Biomes

Tundra

The **tundra** is a treeless biome that occurs in environments with long, cold winters and short, cool growing seasons. There are two broad types of tundra, alpine and arctic. Alpine tundra occurs at higher elevations on mountains, even in some tropical countries. Arctic tundra occurs at high latitudes—that is, in the northern regions of the Northern Hemisphere and the southern parts of the Southern Hemisphere. Most tundras are meteorological deserts because they receive little precipitation (typically less than 25 cm/y). Nevertheless, tundra soil may be moist or even wet because the cold environment allows little evaporation to occur, and deep drainage of water is often prevented by frozen soil. The coldest, most northerly, high-arctic tundra is extremely unproductive and dominated by long-lived small plants, generally growing less than 5–10 cm above the surface. In less-cold environments of the lower Arctic, well-drained tundra can be dominated by shrubs as tall as 1–2 m, while wetter habitats develop productive meadows of sedge, cottongrass, and grass.

Photo 8.1   The tundra is a biome of short vegetation growing in climatically stressed environments of the Arctic and Antarctic and on mountaintops. This is a view of arctic tundra on Ellesmere Island.

Boreal Coniferous Forest

The **boreal coniferous forest**, or taiga, is an extensive biome of environments with cold winters, short but warm growing seasons, and moist soil. It is most extensive in the Northern Hemisphere. The boreal forest is dominated by coniferous trees, especially species of fir, larch, pine, and spruce. Some angiosperm trees may also be prominent, particularly aspen, birch, and poplar. Stands of boreal forest are poor in tree species, and may be dominated by only one or a few kinds. Most regions of boreal forest are subject to periodic disturbances, usually by wildfire, but sometimes by windstorms or insect epidemics.

Montane forest occurs at sub-alpine altitudes on mountains in temperate latitudes. It is similar in structure to high-latitude boreal forest and is also dominated by conifers.

Temperate Deciduous Forest

The **temperate deciduous forest** occurs in relatively moist, temperate climates with short, moderately cold winters and warm summers. This biome is dominated by a mixture of angiosperm tree species. Most of the tree species have seasonally deciduous foliage, meaning their leaves are shed each autumn and then regrown in the springtime. This is an adaptation to surviving the drought and other stresses associated with winter. Common trees of the temperate deciduous forest in North America are species of ash, basswood, birch, cherry, chestnut, dogwood, elm, hickory, magnolia, maple, oak, sassafras, tulip-tree, and walnut. These tree species are found in distinctive communities based on their preferences for particular qualities of soil moisture and fertility, soil and air temperature, and other environmental factors.

Temperate Rainforest

Temperate rainforest develops in a climate in which winters are mild and precipitation is abundant year-round. Because this climate is too moist to allow frequent wildfires, old-growth forest often develops. The old-growth forest is dominated by coniferous trees of mixed age and species composition. Some individual trees are extremely

Photo 8.2 The boreal coniferous forest (taiga) is extensive in northern regions of Canada, Alaska, and Eurasia. This photo shows a stand of black spruce with a carpet of feather mosses, near Inuvik in the Northwest Territories.

large and can be hundreds of years old. Common species of trees in temperate rainforest of the humid west coast of North America are Douglas-fir, hemlock, red cedar, redwood, Sitka spruce, and yellow cypress.

Temperate Grassland

Temperate grassland occurs in temperate regions where the annual precipitation is 25–60 cm/y. Under these conditions, soil moisture is adequate to prevent desert from developing, but insufficient to support forest. Temperate grassland is called prairie in North America and steppe in Eurasia, and this biome occupies vast regions in the interiors of both continents. North American prairie is commonly divided into three types according to height of the dominant vegetation: tall grass, mixed grass, and short grass. Tall-grass prairie is dominated by various species of grasses and herbaceous angiosperm plants, such as blazing stars and sunflowers, some as tall as 2–3 m. Fire is an important factor that prevents tall-grass prairie from developing into an open forest. Tall-grass prairie is a critically endangered ecosystem in North America because almost all of it has been converted into agricultural land. Mixed-grass prairie occurs where there is less rainfall and is characterized by shorter species of grasses and herbaceous angiosperms. Short-grass prairie develops where precipitation is even less, and it can be subject to unpredictable, severe drought.

Chaparral

Chaparral develops in south-temperate environments with a so-called Mediterranean climate, with winter rains and summer drought. Typical chaparral is characterized by dwarfed trees and shrubs with interspersed herbaceous vegetation. Periodic fires are characteristic of chaparral. In North America, chaparral is best developed in coastal southern California.

Desert

Desert can be temperate or tropical, commonly occurring in continental interiors or in rain shadows of mountains. The distribution of desert is determined by the amount of soil moisture, which, in the temperate zones, generally requires an annual precipitation of less than about 25 cm. The driest desert supports almost no plant productivity, while less dry conditions may support communities of herbaceous and succulent plants, both annual and perennial. Occasional moist places with perennial springs of groundwater develop relatively lush vegetation of shrubs or trees and are known as desert oases.

Tropical Grassland and Savannah

Tropical grassland and savannah occur in regions with as much as 120 cm of annual rainfall, but a pronounced dry season. Savannah is dominated by grasses and herbaceous angiosperms, with scattered shrubs and tree-sized plants that provide an open canopy. Some tropical grasslands and savannahs support large populations of big animals, including seasonally abundant migratory mammals. This is particularly true of Africa, where this biome supports a diverse community of large mammals, including elephant, gazelle and other antelopes, hippopotamus, rhinoceros, water buffalo, and various predators of these herbivores, such as cheetah, hyena, leopard, lion, and wild dog.

Semi-Evergreen Tropical Forest

This type of tropical forest develops in a warm climate with pronounced wet and dry seasons. Most trees and shrubs are seasonally deciduous, shedding their foliage in anticipation of the dry season. This biome supports a great richness of biodiversity, though less than tropical rainforest.

Evergreen Tropical Rainforest

This biome occurs in tropical climates with copious precipitation throughout the year. Tropical rainforest commonly develops into an old-growth condition because wildfire and other catastrophes are naturally uncommon in the wet climate. Old-growth tropical rainforest supports a tremendous richness of tree species of many sizes and ages, most of which retain their foliage throughout the year. This forest also sustains an extraordinary diversity of other plants, animals, and microorganisms. Tropical rainforest represents the peak of development of terrestrial ecosystems. The biome supports huge biomass, great productivity, and enormous biodiversity under relatively benign climatic conditions.

Freshwater Biomes

Lentic

Lentic ecosystems, such as lakes and ponds, contain standing or very slowly flowing water. The ecological character of lentic systems is greatly influenced by their water chemistry, particularly transparency and nutrient concentration.

Photo 8.3   The temperate deciduous forest contains various species of angiosperm trees, which drop their leaves in the autumn, plus some species of coniferous trees. This forest type is widespread south of the boreal forest. This stand is dominated by ashes, birches, and maples.

Waters well supplied with nutrients are highly productive (*eutrophic*), while infertile waters are unproductive (*oligotrophic*). In general, shallow waterbodies are much more productive than deeper ones of a comparable surface area. However, waterbodies with poor transparency are much less productive than might be predicted on the basis of nutrient supply. Waters that are brown-coloured because

Photo 8.4   Temperate grassland is widespread in the dry interior of North America and other continents, and it is dominated by species of grasses and other herbaceous plants. This view is of mixed-grass prairie in Saskatchewan.

Photo 8.5 Desert is a sparsely vegetated biome of extremely dry environments. This view is of arid habitat in Dinosaur Provincial Park in southern Alberta.

of dissolved organic matter, and turbid waters with fine suspended particulates, have poor transparency.

Lentic ecosystems are often characterized by zonations in two dimensions. Horizontal zonation is due to changes in water depth and is usually related to the slope and length of the shore. Vertical zonation occurs in deeper water and is related to the amount of light, changes in water temperature, and nutrient and oxygen concentrations. Lentic ecosystems often develop distinct communities

Photo 8.6 Evergreen tropical forest occurs in warm regions where rainfall is abundant throughout the year. Tropical rainforest, such as this one in Peru, sustains more species than any other ecosystem.

along their shore (known as the littoral zone), in their deeper open water (the pelagic zone), and on their sediment (the benthic zone).

Lotic

Lotic ecosystems are characterized by flowing water and include rivers, streams, and creeks. The quantity, velocity, and seasonal variations of water flow are important environmental factors in these ecosystems. Within streams or rivers, silt-sized particles are deposited in places with relatively calm water, leaving a fine-grained or muddy substrate. In contrast, the substrate of places with vigorous water flow is rocky in character because fine particles are selectively eroded from the bottom. For similar reasons, the turbidity of the water is greatest during times of high water flow. Turbidity is an ecologically important factor because it interferes with light penetration and thereby restricts primary productivity.

Lotic ecosystems sustain some productivity of algae and aquatic plants, but their primary production is not usually large. Most of the productivity of aquatic invertebrates and fish in lotic ecosystems is typically sustained by inputs of organic matter from upstream lakes and from the terrestrial watershed in the form of plant debris.

Wetlands

Freshwater **wetlands** (also known as mires) occur in wet places on land. There are four major types of wetland: **marsh**, **swamp**, **bog**, and **fen**. Marshes are the most productive kind of wetland; they are dominated by species of angiosperm plants that are rooted in sediment but grow as tall as several metres above the water surface, such as reed, cattail, and bulrush. Open-water areas of marshes have floating-leaved plants, such as water lily and lotus.

Swamps are forested wetlands that can be flooded seasonally or permanently. North American swamps are often dominated by such tree species as silver maple, white elm, or bald cypress.

Bogs are acidic, relatively unproductive wetlands that develop in cool, wet climates. Their supply of nutrients is very sparse because these ecosystems are fertilized only by atmospheric inputs in the form of dust, chemicals dissolved in precipitation, and gases. Bogs are typically dominated by species of *Sphagnum* moss (also known as peat moss).

Fens also develop in cool and wet climates, but since they have a better nutrient supply than bogs, they are less acidic and more productive.

Global Focus 8.1

Transnational Species and Ecosystems

Because biomes are defined as "geographically extensive ecosystems, occurring throughout the world wherever environmental conditions are suitable," they clearly have a global context. Temperate forest, for instance, occurs in all countries in which environmental conditions are favourable for its development. In comparison, ecozones are more specifically defined on the basis of their landforms, climate, species, and ecological communities. Because ecozones are identified on the basis of natural biophysical features, which are not related to national boundaries, the more southerly ecozones of Canada extend into the neighbouring United States. For instance, the humid forest of the Pacific Maritime Ecozone also occurs in adjacent Washington, Oregon, and Alaska. Similarly, the Prairies Ecozone extends into the central U.S., and the Mixedwood Plains and the Atlantic Maritime Ecozones into the northeastern states.

Species may also have a transnational context. The western red cedar (*Thuja plicata*), for instance, occurs in humid coastal forest throughout western North America, as does the white pine (*Pinus strobus*) in the east. The brown, or grizzly, bear (*Ursus arctos*) is even more widespread—its original range encompassed much of Eurasia and North America, extending from arctic regions of northwestern Canada, through much of the western U.S., to the semi-desert and temperate forest of Mexico.

Many species of animals are migratory, undertaking long-distance movements between their breeding and wintering ranges. Because of the great distances that may be involved, most migratory animals utilize ecosystems in various countries at different times of the year. This ecological habit is well known for the many species of migratory birds that venture to Canada to breed but spend the winter in warmer climes, and it is also true of some other kinds of animals.

The monarch butterfly (*Danaus plexippus*) is one of the most wide-ranging insects in the world, being native to North and South America, the Caribbean, Australia, New Zealand, and other Pacific islands, and also being recently introduced to Western Europe. The monarch is highly migratory in its North American range. At the end of the growing season, during September and October, adult monarchs migrate south to spend the winter in one of two areas. Most of them migrate to central Mexico, where they winter in dense, multi-million populations at only about 12 high-altitude, mountain roosts in the states of Michoacan and Mexico; a much smaller population of western monarchs migrates to roosts in coastal forest of southern California. The longest migrations are made by butterflies that were born in eastern Canada—these intrepid individuals fly thousands of kilometres to reach their wintering roosts in Mexico.

When spring comes, the overwintering monarchs begin a northward migration. When they find a sufficient abundance of milkweed plants (*Asclepias* spp.), the only food eaten by the larvae, the adult females lay about 400 eggs and die soon afterward. The larvae hatch, feed voraciously, and metamorphose into adults after 20–45 days (depending on environmental conditions, particularly temperature and food availability). The adults then continue the northward migration. After a breeding relay of three to five generations, adult monarchs reach the northernmost parts of their range in Canada, where they breed wherever milkweed is abundant. The last generation of the year, which transforms into adults in September, is the one that undertakes the astonishing migration to the wintering roosts in Mexico and southern California.

The conservation of the monarch butterfly is greatly complicated by its migratory habit, its use of various kinds of ecosystems at different times of the year, and the fact that all of its critical habitats must be conserved if the species is to survive. However, the greatest conservation risk for the monarch is the survival of the only 12 known winter roosts it uses in Mexico. These critical habitats are in natural, mature forest of oyamel fir (*Abies religiosa*) that is threatened by deforestation, illegal logging, and tourism development. Although the monarch butterfly is an abundant and familiar species, it could quickly become lost from most of its North American range if these winter roosts are not conserved. In addition, the species requires an abundance of milkweeds in its breeding range, and these native plants are being widely depleted by the use of herbicides in intensive agricultural management. As is the case for all transnational species and ecosystems, conservation of the monarch butterfly requires the cooperation of various countries, levels of government, and economic interests.

Photo 8.7   A swamp is a forested wetland. This swamp is located near Barrie, Ontario, in a flat area where the Nottawasaga River floods in the springtime, making it possible to canoe through the forest. The dominant trees are silver maple, red ash, and elm.

Marine Biomes

The Open Ocean

The open ocean consists of pelagic and benthic ecosystems. The ecological character of the pelagic (open-water) ecosystem is determined by physical and chemical fac-

Photo 8.8   A marsh is a relatively fertile wetland dominated by taller herbaceous plants, such as bulrush and cattail. Marshes are often productive of animal wildlife, such as this great blue heron.

tors, particularly waves, tides, currents, salinity, temperature, light intensity, and nutrient concentration. The primary productivity of this ecosystem is small, comparable to that of desert, the least productive of terrestrial biomes. The primary production is associated with phytoplankton, which range in size from extremely small photosynthetic bacteria to larger (but still microscopic) unicellular and colonial algae. Oceanic phytoplankton are grazed by tiny animals known as zooplankton (most of which are crustaceans), which are eaten in turn by larger zooplankton and small fish. Large predators such as bluefin tuna, sharks, squid, and whales are at the top of the pelagic food web.

The benthic ecosystem of the open ocean biome is supported by a sparse rain of dead biomass from the surface. The benthic ecosystem of the deep oceans is not yet well described, but it appears to be somewhat rich in species, low in productivity, and extremely stable over time.

Continental Shelf Waters

Oceanic waters near the shores of continents are relatively shallow because they overlie continental shelves, which are underwater projections of the landmass. Compared with the open ocean, nearshore waters are relatively warm and well supplied with nutrients. The nutrients come from inputs from rivers and from deeper, relatively fertile oceanic water, occasionally stirred from the bottom to the surface by currents or turbulence caused by severe windstorms. Because the nutrient supply of coastal waters is relatively high, phytoplankton are rather productive and support a higher productivity and biomass of animals than occurs in the open ocean. Some of the world's most important oceanic fisheries are supported by the continental shelf biome—for example, those on the Grand Banks and other shallow waters of northeastern North America, in the nearshore waters of western North and South America, and in the Gulf of Mexico.

Regions with Persistent Upwelling

Oceanographic conditions in certain regions favour the upwelling of relatively deep, nutrient-rich water to the surface. The increased nutrient supply allows areas with persistent upwelling to sustain relatively high rates of primary productivity. This ecological foundation supports great populations of animals, including large fish, sharks, marine mammals, and seabirds. Some of Earth's most productive fisheries occur in upwelling areas, such as those off the west coast of South America, and extensive regions of the Antarctic Ocean.

Estuaries

Estuaries are a complex group of coastal ecosystems that are open to the sea but semi-enclosed. Estuaries are transitional between marine and freshwater biomes, typically having large fluctuations of salinity associated with inflows of fresh water from the nearby land, twice-daily tidal cycles, and marine storm surges. Estuaries typically occur as coastal bays, river mouths, salt marsh, and tropical mangrove forest. They are highly productive ecosystems, largely because their semi-enclosed water circulation tends to retain much of the water-borne input of terrestrial nutrients. Estuaries provide critical habitat for juvenile stages of many commercially important species of fish, shellfish, and crustaceans.

Seashores

The interface of terrestrial and oceanic biomes supports a complex of ecosystems known as the seashore biome. This biome is locally influenced by physical environmental factors, especially bottom type, the intensity of wave action, and the frequency of major disturbances such as storms. Hard-rock and cobblestone bottoms in temperate regions usually develop ecosystems dominated by large species of seaweeds or kelp. These are productive ecosystems and can maintain large quantities of algal biomass. Areas with softer bottoms of sand or mud develop ecosystems supported by the primary productivity of benthic algae and inputs of organic detritus from elsewhere. These soft-bottom ecosystems are usually dominated by benthic invertebrates, especially mollusks, echinoderms, crustaceans, and marine worms.

Coral Reefs

Coral reefs are a tropical marine biome, developing in shallow, relatively infertile places close to land. The physical structure of coral reefs is composed of the calcium carbonate shells of dead coral and mollusks. Coral reefs support a biodiverse veneer of crustose algae, living corals, other invertebrates, and fish. The biome is physically dominated by corals, which are colonial animals that live in a mutualism with unicellular algae. Because this symbiosis is efficient in acquiring nutrients from water, coral reefs can sustain a high rate of productivity even though they occur in infertile water.

Human-Dominated Ecosystems

Urban–Industrial Techno-Ecosystems

This complex of anthropogenic ecosystems is characterized by urbanized areas and is dominated by the dwellings, businesses, factories, and other infrastructure of human society (see Chapter 25). This biome supports many species in addition to humans, but these are mostly non-native species introduced from other places. Typically, the alien species cannot live locally outside this biome (although they may occur in the foreign biome to which they are indigenous).

Rural Techno-Ecosystems

These anthropogenic ecosystems occur outside urbanized areas and consist of the extensive technological infrastructure of civilization. These ecosystems include rural transportation corridors (highways, railways, and electricity transmission corridors), as well as small towns that support industries involved in the extraction and processing of natural resources. Rural techno-ecosystems support a blend of introduced species, plus those native species that are tolerant of the disturbances and other stresses associated with human activities in rural areas.

Agroecosystems

An **agroecosystem** is a complex of agricultural ecosystems and is managed to cultivate products for use by humans. The most intensively managed agroecosystems involve **monocultures** (single-species crops) of non-native plants or animals that are cultivated in agriculture, forestry, or aquaculture. These valuable and necessary crops are grown under conditions enhanced for their productivity, although intensive management systems may cause many ecological problems (see Chapter 24). Some less intensive agroecosystems cultivate mixtures of species (polycultures), which may also provide habitat for some native species.

Ecozones of Canada

The terrestrial, freshwater, and marine ecosystems found in Canada have been described in various ways, including a hierarchical classification of distinctive types. The largest ecological zones in the national classification are referred to as **ecozones**. Ecozones are similar in many respects

Photo 8.9   Urban–industrial techno-ecosystems are dominated by the dwellings, businesses, factories, and other infrastructure of human society. These areas support the economic activities of large numbers of people, and are sustained by enormous flows of resources from the surrounding landscape, and even from other countries. This aerial view of Halifax shows an area used entirely for roads, hospitals, homes, schools, and recreational parks.

to biomes, particularly in that they represent extensive types of ecosystems. However, biomes are geographically extensive ecosystems, occurring throughout the world wherever environmental conditions are suitable. By comparison, ecozones are more regional in character, being characterized on the basis of specific biophysical features, particularly landforms, climate, soils, species, and ecological communities.

There are 15 terrestrial and five marine ecozones in Canada (Figure 8.3). These natural ecozones are characterized by key aspects of their physical environment, such as dominant landforms and climate, as well as their natural ecosystems and prominent species. Because so much of the Canadian landscape has been intensively

modified through human activities, we will also examine three anthropogenic ecosystems: urban, agricultural, and industrial.

It is important to recognize that each of the Canadian ecozones represents a hierarchical agglomeration of distinct ecosystems of more local character. *Ecoregions* are sub-ecozone units, characterized by distinctive regional factors related to climate and landform and, to some degree, by soil, vegetation, fauna, and land-use. There are 194 terrestrial ecoregions in Canada.

Ecodistricts are smaller elements within ecoregions that are themselves distinctive and characterized by more local assemblages of these same biophysical factors, particularly landform. There are 1020 terrestrial ecodistricts in Canada.

FIGURE 8.3 | Ecozones of Canada

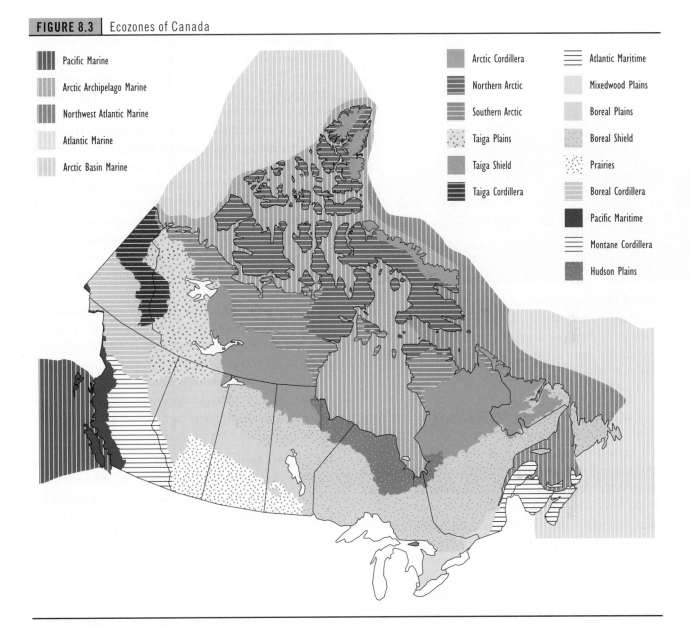

▮ Pacific Marine	▨ Arctic Cordillera
▨ Arctic Archipelago Marine	▨ Northern Arctic
▨ Northwest Atlantic Marine	▬ Southern Arctic
▨ Atlantic Marine	⣿ Taiga Plains
▨ Arctic Basin Marine	▨ Taiga Shield
	▬ Taiga Cordillera

▤ Atlantic Maritime	
▨ Mixedwood Plains	
▨ Boreal Plains	
⣿ Boreal Shield	
⣿ Prairies	
▤ Boreal Cordillera	
▮ Pacific Maritime	
▤ Montane Cordillera	
▨ Hudson Plains	

These ecological units are described by the nature of the dominant biota and by aspects of the physical environment, particularly climate, soil, geology, and other landscape-scale geographic features for terrestrial ecozones, and climate and ice cover for marine ecozones. A coloured copy of this map is found inside the front cover of this book.

Source: Modified from Ecological Stratification Working Group (1995)

Canada's marine ecozones and anthropogenic ecosystems have not yet been divided into ecoregions or ecodistricts.

For our purposes in this book, it is most useful to describe the national ecozones. These units allow us to broadly characterize the ecological qualities of Canada and to gain an impression of how these vary over large regions. The following descriptions of Canadian ecozones are necessarily brief overviews. More detailed characterizations of the ecological zonations and communities of Canada can be obtained from some of the references and websites listed for this chapter.

Terrestrial Ecozones of Canada

The Arctic Cordillera Ecozone is a tundra ecozone of the mountainous regions of northern Labrador and some of the eastern Arctic islands, especially Baffin, Devon, and Ellesmere Islands. This ecozone contains the most spec-

Photo 8.10 Pingos are ice-cored hills that slowly rise out of partially drained lakes in certain regions of permafrost. These unusual features are common near Tuktoyaktuk in the Southern Arctic Ecozone, where this 60-m-high pingo is located.

tacular mountains in eastern Canada, with elevations up to 2000 m, including extensive fields of glacial ice. The climate is cold and dry, with mean annual temperature ranging from –20°C to –6°C, average summer temperature from –2°C to 6°C, and precipitation from 10–60 cm/y. The growing season is short and cool but is enhanced by the almost continuous daylight of summer in these high latitudes. About 75% of the terrain is covered by glacial ice or exposed bedrock, and the rest is sparsely vegetated. Permafrost, or permanently frozen ground, is found throughout the ecozone. It occurs beneath a seasonally thawed *active layer* some 30–50 cm thick.

The climate at higher elevations is so extreme that the land is almost devoid of vegetation, with only a meagre cover of mosses, lichens, and a few hardy, low-growing vascular plants. Large mammals in this ecozone include sparse populations of caribou, muskox, and wolf, while smaller species include arctic fox, arctic hare, collared lemming, and ermine. Rock ptarmigan and raven are resident birds, while representative migratory species include gyrfalcon, hoary redpoll, peregrine falcon, ringed plover, and snow bunting.

The Northern Arctic Ecozone is a tundra ecozone in northern Quebec and the northeastern Northwest Territories and Nunavut, particularly on the arctic islands. The climate is cold and dry. Mean annual temperature ranges from –17°C to –11°C, average summer temperature from

–1.5°C to 4°C, and precipitation from 10–20 cm/y. The growing season is short and cool but is enhanced by almost continuous sunlight during the summer. There is a continuous distribution of permafrost. Precipitation is low enough for this ecozone to be characterized as a meteorological desert. However, rates of evaporation are low because of cool temperatures, and deep drainage is impeded by permafrost, so many sites are moist.

Because of the harsh climate, most of the terrain is sparsely vegetated and is referred to as arctic desert or semi-desert. However, protected lowlands and river valleys can be relatively warm, moist oases that sustain more productive vegetation and provide critical habitat for denser populations of animals (see Canadian Focus 8.1). Such oases are uncommon, accounting for only a few percent of the land area.

The Northern Arctic Ecozone supports mammal and bird populations similar to those of the Arctic Cordillera Ecozone. Additional migratory birds include Baird's sandpiper, Brant goose, Canada goose, greater snow goose, Lapland longspur, semipalmated sandpiper, and snowy owl. Sea ducks, such as common eider and oldsquaw, nest along the coast but feed in nearshore environments of the Arctic Archipelago Marine Ecozone.

The Southern Arctic Ecozone is also tundra, with extensive rolling hills and lowlands. Its low-arctic tundra is characterized by relatively taller, somewhat lusher vegetation than the two higher-arctic ecozones. This ecozone occurs in northern Quebec and across the northern part of the continental Northwest Territories and Nunavut. The climate is cold but moister than in higher-arctic ecozones. Mean annual temperature ranges from –11°C to –7°C, average summer temperature from 4°C to 6°C, and precipitation from 20–40 cm/y. The growing season is short and somewhat warm and is enhanced by long days. Permafrost is continuous, except beneath large lakes and rivers. Glacial deposits are common and highly evident, including long, sinuous mounds of mixed debris known as eskers. Ice in the soil (ground ice) causes unusual surface features to develop, including patterns on the ground created by underground ice wedges, and unusual hills, with a core of ice, up to 40–60 m tall. Known as pingos, they are common near Tuktoyaktuk, east of the Mackenzie Delta. Lakes, ponds, rivers, streams, and wetlands are common over most of this ecozone.

Compared with the higher Arctic, this ecozone is well vegetated. Shrubs can be as tall as several metres in protected sites, but are usually less than 1 m tall. Prominent shrubs include species of alder, birch, and willow. Drier,

Canadian Focus 8.1

Alexandra Fiord: A High-Arctic Oasis

Some important research in ecology has involved integrated studies of particular ecosystems, carried out by teams of ecologists, geographers, geologists, chemists, meteorologists, and other environmental scientists. From work of this kind, scientists can understand the physical, chemical, and biological factors that affect the structure and function of ecosystems and sustain their species.

Beginning in 1980, teams of Canadian scientists have studied a fine example of a high-arctic oasis, located on a coastal lowland beside Alexandra Fiord on Ellesmere Island, at 79° N. Their objectives were to describe the plant and animal communities of the oasis and to determine the environmental factors influencing its productivity and biodiversity. Specific research included studies of local and regional climate; geology; soil; plant species composition and distribution; productivity of plant communities; the ecological relationships of prominent plant species; responses of vegetation to experimental changes in environmental conditions; and animal populations and their habitat.

This was a multidisciplinary research program, but because all the component studies were carried out in the same place, the results could be integrated to develop a larger understanding of the oasis. This kind of knowledge is of scientific importance because arctic ecosystems have not yet been well studied. This research also contributes to the understanding required to assess the many kinds of ecological damage that are associated with increasing resource exploitation, eco-tourism, and climate change in the Arctic.

The team at Alexandra Fiord found that the climate of the lowland is, indeed, more moderate than that of the larger landscape. In general, air and soil temperatures are warmer, soil moisture is greater, and there is less wind. Dark-coloured cliffs on nearby uplands absorb solar radiation and then emit long-wave infrared energy. This warms the oasis in a manner similar to an oven being heated by its hot, enclosing walls. The lowland is also relatively sheltered, so heat-dispersing winds are less vigorous. In addition, snow meltwater from the surrounding uplands helps to keep local soils moist, so wet meadows and other communities that depend on moisture can develop.

The moderate environmental conditions allow the lowland to support well-developed vegetation, including lush meadows dominated by sedges and cottongrass. Vegetation in drier places is dominated by dwarf shrubs and cushion plants, which are woody, long-lived plants growing no taller than 5 cm above the surface. These include avens, bilberry, white heather, arctic willow, and purple saxifrage. Disturbed habitats beside rivers and streams or near human habitation (the lowland contains an abandoned Royal Canadian Mounted Police post) support profuse flowerings of herbaceous plants, such as arctic poppy and willow-herb.

These plant communities are much more productive than those of the prevailing polar desert, and consequently, the oasis supports relatively large populations of animals. Birds are especially abundant, including snow bunting, Baird's sandpiper, hoary redpoll, arctic tern, oldsquaw, greater snow goose, rock ptarmigan, parasitic jaeger, and another 22 species. Studies of the arctic skipper butterfly discovered that its slow-growing larvae take 14 years to accumulate enough energy to undergo metamorphosis to the adult stage, resulting in a remarkably long life cycle.

Because of its relatively small area (only 8 km^2), this lowland oasis is not able to support a population of muskox, the most important large herbivore in the greater landscape. However, small numbers of this impressive animal occasionally feed in the oasis while passing through on their way to larger oases nearby.

more exposed sites have shorter shrubs and herbaceous plants, and wet sites have meadows of sedges, cottongrass, and grasses. A few protected places support scattered, stunted trees of white spruce or balsam poplar.

The ecozone supports low densities of large mammals. However, large herds of caribou, which spend most of the year in or near the southern treeline, migrate to low-arctic tundra to calve and feed during the growing season. Other large mammals include grizzly bear, moose, muskox, and wolf. Smaller mammals include arctic ground squirrel, brown lemming, muskrat, red fox, snowshoe hare, and weasel. Willow ptarmigan and raven are resident birds, and migratory species include arctic and red-throated loon, Canada goose, common redpoll, golden eagle, gyrfalcon, Lapland longspur, lesser snow goose, sandhill crane, snow bunting, snowy owl, tundra swan, and various ducks, such as greater and lesser scaup and oldsquaw.

Photo 8.11 The Taiga Shield Ecozone is an extensive area of open boreal forest, rocky outcrops, and wetlands. This shows an open forest of black spruce near Nain in Labrador.

The Taiga Plains Ecozone is a northern ecozone characterized by rolling plains and uplands with a taiga (boreal) forest, mostly of relatively open stands of short trees. This ecozone is distributed in the western Northwest Territories, northern British Columbia, and northwestern Alberta and essentially encompasses the taiga regions of the drainage of the MacKenzie River, Canada's largest watercourse. The overall climate is cool and winters are very cold. Mean annual temperature ranges from –10°C to –1°C, average summer temperature from 7°C to 14°C, and precipitation from 20–50 cm/y. The growing season is moderately long and warm and is enhanced by long days. Permafrost is extensive but discontinuous. Although there is not much precipitation, soil moisture is generally adequate because evapotranspiration is low and permafrost keeps water from draining away in many places. Deposits of glacial debris are common and widespread. Surface waters and wetlands are common features.

The dominant vegetation is an open, slow-growing forest of black spruce. Some upland areas develop forests of lodgepole pine, white spruce, white birch, trembling aspen, or balsam poplar, and large white spruce and balsam poplar can occur along rivers. The open forests have well-developed shrub components, including species of willow, birch, and heaths such as Labrador tea and bearberry. Mosses and lichens are prominent in the ground vegetation, as are species of herbaceous plants. The forest is periodically subject to wildfire, and after a burn, spec-

tacular stands of purple-coloured fireweed appear during the early stages of succession.

Large mammals of this ecozone include black bear, moose, woodland caribou, wood bison, and wolf. Smaller mammals include lynx, pine marten, muskrat, snowshoe hare, and species of lemming and vole. Birds include common redpoll, fox sparrow, grey jay, northern shrike, peregrine falcon, raven, red-throated loon, and sharp-tailed grouse. The numerous ponds and lakes support breeding waterfowl, such as greater and lesser scaup, pintail, and Canada goose, as well as shorebirds such as greater and lesser yellowlegs and snipe. The Mackenzie corridor is an important migratory route for large numbers of waterfowl and shorebirds that breed in the tundra to the north.

The Taiga Shield Ecozone, a forested ecozone, overlies the hard, quartzitic bedrock and thin soil of the Canadian Shield of central Quebec, most of Labrador, southeastern Northwest Territories, southern Nunavut, and northern Saskatchewan and Manitoba. The taiga forest is composed of open stands of relatively short, unproductive trees. The climate is cool and winters are extremely cold. Mean annual temperature ranges from –8°C to 0°C, average summer temperature from 6°C to 11°C, and precipitation from 20–50 cm/y, although parts of the Labrador coast are wetter. The growing season is of moderate length and warmth and is enhanced by long days. Permafrost is widespread but discontinuous. Deposits of glacial debris are common and widespread, including frequent eskers, and surface waters and wetlands are abundant.

The dominant vegetation type is an open forest of black spruce, but in some areas, stands are dominated by balsam fir, balsam poplar, jack pine, tamarack, trembling aspen, white birch, or white spruce. Non-forest communities are also common, including tundra-like vegetation on open sites with shallow or no soil over bedrock, and many wetlands and open-water habitats.

Black and grizzly bear, caribou, moose, and wolf are prominent large mammals, while smaller species include arctic and red fox, beaver, lynx, and snowshoe hare. Some of the breeding birds include arctic and red-throated loons, grey-cheeked thrush, tree sparrow, white-crowned sparrow, willow ptarmigan, and yellow-rumped warbler.

The Boreal Shield Ecozone, another forested ecozone, largely occupies the quartzitic bedrock and thin soil of more southern reaches of the Canadian Shield, including northern Saskatchewan, central Manitoba, much of northern Ontario, most of southern Quebec, and Newfoundland. The general terrain is a rolling mosaic of upland forest and lowland wetlands and surface waters. Most of this ecozone has a continental climate (i.e., not influenced by proximity to an ocean), with long cold winters and warm summers. These conditions are moderated in areas closer to the Atlantic Ocean, where winters are less cold and summers less warm. Mean annual temperature ranges from –4°C in continental areas to 5.5°C in maritime Newfoundland, average summer temperature ranges from 11°C to 15°C, and precipitation ranges from 10–40 cm/y in continental places and from 90–160 cm/y in maritime areas. Deposits of glacial debris are widespread, and surface waters and wetlands are common.

The ecozone is dominated by closed forest of various species of conifers, especially balsam fir, black and white spruce, and tamarack. More southern parts of the ecozone also have stands of jack, red, and white pine; angiosperm species can be locally abundant, especially balsam poplar, trembling aspen, and white birch. Areas with shallow soil have more open communities, and bogs and fens are abundant in poorly drained places.

Prominent large mammals include black bear, caribou, moose, white-tailed deer, and wolf, while smaller species include bobcat, fisher, lynx, pine marten, raccoon, red squirrel, striped skunk, and eastern chipmunk. Some of the breeding birds include blue and grey jay, boreal owl, common loon, evening grosbeak, great horned owl, red-eyed vireo, white-throated sparrow, and species of warblers.

The Atlantic Maritime Ecozone, a forested ecozone, includes New Brunswick, Nova Scotia, Prince Edward Island, and adjacent parts of the Gaspé and southeastern Quebec. Bedrock and soils in this region are complex and include quartzitic rocks such as granite, gneiss, and greywacke, along with sedimentary limestone, sandstone, and shale. The terrain is rolling and extensively forested, with abundant wetlands and surface waters. The climate ranges from continental to maritime, with cold winters and warm summers, being more moderate closer to the Atlantic Ocean. Mean annual temperature ranges from 4°C to 7°C, average summer temperature from 13°C to 16°C, and precipitation from 90–150 cm/y. Glacial debris is widespread.

The forest is a relatively productive mosaic of mixed-species communities, with prominent trees being eastern hemlock, red spruce, red and sugar maple, red and white pine, and white and yellow birch. Boreal species are also prominent, such as black and white spruce, balsam fir, and jack pine. Understorey shrubs include alder, blueberry, cherry, spiraea, and viburnum.

Large mammals include black bear, coyote, moose, and white-tailed deer, while smaller species include bobcat, eastern chipmunk, mink, porcupine, raccoon, red squirrel, striped skunk, and various mice and voles. Breeding birds include barred owl, black duck, black-capped chickadee, broad-winged hawk, common crow, great horned owl, rose-breasted grosbeak, sharp-shinned hawk, and diverse warblers, vireos, and sparrows.

The Mixedwood Plains Ecozone, also forested, covers relatively southern regions of the Great Lakes–St. Lawrence River valley and includes the most southern regions of Ontario and Quebec. Bedrock in this region is mostly limestone, and soils are relatively deep and rich. The terrain is gently rolling and was originally forested, although most of the natural vegetation has been cleared and the land converted into agricultural and urban uses (about half of Canada's population lives in this rather small ecozone). Climate is continental, with cold winters and warm summers, but more moderate conditions occur closer to the Great Lakes and St. Lawrence River. Mean annual temperature ranges from 5°C to 8°C, average summer temperature from 16°C to 18°C, and precipitation from 70–100 cm/y. Glacial debris is widespread in some areas, but the relatively flat, former beds of the post-glacial Great Lakes and St. Lawrence River have deep, fine-textured, fertile soil. Ponds, small lakes, and wetlands are less common than in more northern ecozones.

The natural forests of the ecozone are much richer in species than anywhere else in Canada. Forest cover is, however, now reduced to less than 10% of the area, and some communities and many species are endangered or extirpated. Forest stands vary greatly in species composition. Some stands are dominated by red or white pine, others by rich mixtures of basswood, beech, eastern hemlock, sugar and red maple, white elm, and yellow birch. Remnant stands of Carolinian forest in southern Ontario have rare species of trees that are more typical of the eastern United States, such as black walnut, butternut, cucumber-tree, sassafras, sycamore, tulip-tree, and various species of southern ashes and hickories.

Black bear and white-tailed deer are the most prominent large mammals. Cougar used to occur, but this predator has been extirpated, and wolf has also been eliminated from most of the ecozone. Coyotes have invaded the region and are now abundant. Smaller mammals include cottontail rabbit, grey (or black) squirrel, groundhog, raccoon, and striped skunk. Many bird species breed in the ecozone, including blue jay, cardinal, red-shouldered hawk, and

Photo 8.12   The Prairies Ecozone is divided into categories depending on the height of the dominant species. The richest, most productive, and most endangered type is tall-grass prairie. This is a view of tall-grass prairie in southeastern Manitoba, where the Nature Conservancy of Canada and the provincial government are assembling remnants of this endangered ecosystem as a nature preserve.

Source: G. Fortney

northern oriole. Some relatively southern birds also breed in parts of this ecozone, including bob-white, Carolina wren, green-backed heron, orchard oriole, prothonotary warbler, and scarlet tanager.

The Boreal Plains Ecozone occurs as a broad, forested band extending from northeastern British Columbia, across northern Alberta, to central Saskatchewan and Manitoba. This ecozone is characterized by rolling terrain derived from extensive moraine deposits and by flatter landscapes with deep soil derived from post-glacial lake sediment. There are few exposures of bedrock. Climate is continental, with cold winters and warm summers. Mean annual tem-

perature ranges from –2°C to 2°C, the average summer temperature from 13°C to 16°C, and precipitation from 30–63 cm/y. Lakes are less abundant than on the Canadian Shield, but wetlands are extensive, covering more than 25% of most landscapes.

Conifer-dominated stands contain black and white spruce, jack pine, and tamarack. Angiosperm-dominated stands are more common in southern areas, closer to the forest–prairie border, and include balsam poplar, trembling aspen, and white birch.

Prominent large mammals include black bear, caribou, elk, moose, white-tailed and mule deer, coyote, and wolf. Smaller mammals include fisher, lynx, pine marten, striped skunk, and eastern chipmunk. Representative breeding birds include blue jay, boreal owl, evening grosbeak, great horned owl, and white-crowned sparrow. Lakes and wetlands support Caspian tern, double-crested cormorant, great blue heron, white pelican, and many species of waterfowl. The endangered whooping crane breeds in extensive wetlands in Wood Buffalo National Park.

The Prairies Ecozone is an open, mostly non-forested ecozone which occurs in southern regions of Alberta, Saskatchewan, and Manitoba. This ecozone is characterized by rolling terrain derived from extensive glacial moraine and by flatter landscapes with deep, fertile soil derived from post-glacial lake sediment. The climate is continental, with cold winters and hot summers. Mean annual temperature ranges from 2°C to 4°C, average summer temperature from 14°C to 16°C, and precipitation from 25–70 cm/y. Soil moisture is often limiting to plant growth during the summer. This occurs because of the relatively sparse precipitation, coupled with hot, windy summers that increase evapotranspiration. Small lakes and ponds with fringing wetlands, known as potholes and sloughs, are a common feature, particularly in relatively rainy years.

Grass and forb-dominated **prairie** is extensively developed throughout this ecozone (forb is a general term for broad-leaved, herbaceous, angiosperm plants). There are three types of prairie, identified by vegetation height and species composition. Tall-grass prairie has grasses 1–2 m tall, such as big bluestem, plus many tall species of forbs, such as blazing-stars and sunflowers. Mixed-grass prairie has a mixture of medium and short grasses and forbs, while short-grass prairie has only short species. These natural prairie types have been largely converted into agricultural land-uses. Tall-grass prairie is now an endangered natural ecosystem, as are the other kinds of natural prairie but to a lesser degree.

Northern parts of this ecozone support an open forest known as aspen parkland, dominated by groves of trembling aspen and balsam poplar, with intermittent, prairie-like glades. There are also small areas of desert in the southernmost parts of this ecozone, characterized by prickly pear cactus and other plants typical of dry habitats.

Large mammals of this ecozone include coyote, elk, white-tailed and mule deer, and pronghorn antelope, while smaller mammals include badger, black-tailed prairie dog, northern pocket gopher, Richardson's ground squirrel, and white-tailed jack rabbit. Buffalo were once important in this ecozone, but these large animals were extirpated from almost all of their natural range during the nineteenth century. Bird species include black-billed magpie, burrowing owl, ferruginous hawk, horned lark, northern oriole, prairie falcon, and Swainson's hawk. Large numbers of waterfowl and shorebirds breed in potholes and sloughs during wetter years, including American avocet, canvasback, coot, mallard, lesser scaup, pintail, and western grebe. Because so much of this ecozone has been converted into agriculture, the remnants of natural habitat tend to occur as small, isolated fragments. Consequently, some of the indigenous species of plants and animals are endangered.

The Taiga Cordillera Ecozone is a sub-arctic, largely forested ecozone occurring in northern Yukon and parts of the western Northwest Territories. The region covers the northernmost extension of the Rocky Mountains and contains steep terrain with deep valleys and wild rivers as well as more gently sloping foothills. The climate is continental arctic, with long, cold, dark winters and short, cool summers with long days. However, as in mountainous terrain everywhere, altitude, slope, and aspect are important influences on local climate. Mean annual temperature ranges from −10°C to −5°C, average summer temperature from 7°C to 10°C, and precipitation from 30–70 cm/y. Surface waters are mostly rivers and streams, with some mountain lakes. Ponds and lakes are more abundant on the flatlands around the Old Crow River and northern coastal plain. Most of the ecozone has continuous permafrost.

Vegetation of this complex ecozone ranges from alpine tundra at high elevation and arctic tundra on the coastal plain of Yukon, to open taiga at lower elevations in the south. The forest is dominated by white spruce and white birch, with a shrub understorey of dwarf birches and willows.

Large mammals include black and grizzly bear, caribou, Dall's sheep, moose, mountain goat, and wolf, while smaller mammals include arctic ground squirrel, hoary marmot, lynx, pika, and wolverine. Breeding birds include gyrfalcon, peregrine falcon, rock and willow ptarmigan, sandhill crane, white-crowned sparrow, yellow warbler, and many species of waterfowl and shorebirds. The Old Crow Flats are an important staging area for Canada goose, tundra swan, and other waterfowl during their southern migration.

The Boreal Cordillera Ecozone covers rugged mountainous terrain of northern British Columbia and southern Yukon. The region is characterized by steep terrain with deep, wide valleys, high-altitude plateaus, and gently sloping foothills and lowlands. The climate is continental, with long, cold winters and warm summers, although altitude and aspect greatly affect local climate. Mean annual temperature ranges from 1°C to 6°C, average summer temperature from 10°C to 12°C, and precipitation from 150 cm/y in high-elevation areas receiving orographic precipitation (see In Detail 3.1, page 39) to less than 30 cm/y in rain-shadow areas. Surface waters are largely streams and rivers, with some mountain lakes. Discontinuous permafrost is widespread in the northern part of the ecozone.

Southern areas of the ecozone have grasslands and open forest on relatively warm and dry south-facing slopes, and boreal forest on the northerly exposures. Dominant tree species are balsam poplar, black and white spruce, trembling aspen, and white birch, joined by alpine fir and lodgepole pine in southern areas. Alpine tundra occurs at higher elevations.

Large mammals include black and grizzly bear, caribou, Dall's sheep, moose, mountain goat, and wolf, while smaller mammals include arctic ground squirrel, hoary marmot, lynx, marten, and pika. Breeding birds include peregrine falcon, rock and white-tailed ptarmigan, white-crowned sparrow, and many other migratory species.

The Pacific Maritime Ecozone includes mainly rugged mountainous terrain of the coastal mainland and islands of British Columbia, where the climate is greatly moderated by the Pacific Ocean. The climate is humid temperate, with short, cool winters and long, warm summers, although altitude and aspect have a great influence on local climate. Mean annual temperature ranges from 5°C to 9°C and average summer temperature from 10°C to 16°C. Precipitation ranges from 60 cm/y in some of the relatively dry Gulf Islands to as much as 400 cm/y in places strongly influenced by orographic precipitation. More typically, however, precipitation ranges from 150–300 cm/y. Surface waters are mostly streams and rivers, with some lakes.

The dominant natural vegetation is a mixed-species, conifer-dominated, temperate rainforest. Because the humid climate makes disturbance by wildfire an uncommon occurrence, old-growth forests were naturally exten-

Photo 8.13 Although much less extensive now, old-growth rainforest is characteristic of the Pacific Maritime Ecozone. Old-growth forest has a complex structure, with large, old trees of various species, as well as standing dead trees (snags) and large logs lying on the ground. This is an old-growth forest near Maugher's Bay on Vancouver Island.

sive. These old-growth forests have, however, largely been replaced by younger, more productive, second-growth forests through logging and silviculture, and to some degree, they have also been converted into agricultural and urban land-uses. Prominent species of trees include amabalis and grand firs, Douglas-fir, mountain and western hemlock, red alder, Sitka spruce, western red cedar, and yellow cedar. Individual trees of some of these species can attain huge size and great age (sometimes older than 500 years) in old-growth forest. Higher-altitude sites can develop boreal-like montane forest or alpine tundra. Because the Queen Charlotte Islands and parts of Vancouver Island were not glaciated, they have some endemic sub-species and species that occur nowhere else.

Prominent large mammals in this ecozone include black and grizzly bear, black-tailed deer, elk, and wolf, while smaller species include river otter and raccoon. Representative birds include bald eagle, black oystercatcher, blue grouse, California and mountain quail, chestnut-backed chickadee, dipper, northwestern crow, Steller's jay, and many migratory species.

The Montane Cordillera Ecozone is a largely mountainous ecozone that covers most of southern British Columbia and adjacent southwestern Alberta. The climate is temperate, with cold winters and warm summers. Altitude and aspect greatly influence local climate. Mean annual temperature ranges from 1°C to 8°C and average summer temperature from 11°C to 17°C. Precipitation is highly variable, ranging from only 30 cm/y in drier valleys and plateaus in the rain shadow of coastal mountains to 120 cm/y at higher elevations along the Alberta–British Columbia border. Surface waters are mostly streams and rivers, with some lakes.

The ecozone is largely forested, but community types are highly diverse, reflecting the variable terrain and environmental conditions. Alpine tundra occurs at higher altitude with montane forest below, typically dominated by alpine fir, Engelmann spruce, and lodgepole pine. Forest at lower elevation often includes these species along with interior Douglas-fir, ponderosa pine, trembling aspen, western hemlock, western red cedar, and western white pine. Drier sites support semi-desert, with shrubs such as antelope bush, rabbit bush, and sagebrush, and various species of grasses and forbs.

Prominent mammals include bighorn sheep, black and grizzly bear, coyote, woodland caribou, elk, moose, mountain goat, and mule and white-tailed deer, while smaller species include Columbian ground squirrel and hoary marmot. Prominent birds include black-billed magpie, blue grouse, Clark's nutcracker, dipper, golden eagle, and Steller's jay.

The Hudson Plains Ecozone covers the broad lowlands of previously more extensive, post-glacial Hudson and James bays. It extends from northeastern Manitoba through northern Ontario to adjacent Quebec. Because of the influence of the cold waters of Hudson and James bays, the climate is more subarctic than might be expected on the basis of latitude, with long, cold winters and short, warm summers. Mean annual temperature ranges from –4°C to –2°C, average summer temperature from 11°C to 12°C, and precipitation from 40–80 cm/y. Permafrost is discontinuous and surface waters are abundant, with numerous streams, rivers, ponds, lakes, and wetlands.

Tidal habitats can develop into extensive *salt marshes* of salt-tolerant grasses and forbs. Shrub-dominated, low-arctic tundra is extensive closer to the coasts of Hudson and James bays. This tundra changes gradually to an open-canopied, short-treed taiga further inland, and then to a more closed-canopied boreal forest. The dominant trees are black spruce and tamarack. Much of the terrain is characterized by series of old, raised-beach ridges, representing former shorelines of Hudson and James bays. The relatively dry tops of these ridges are generally forested, while the lower areas develop into wetlands such as fens, bogs, and marshes.

Species of large mammals include black bear, caribou, moose, white-tailed deer, and wolf, while smaller ones include beaver, muskrat, river otter, and porcupine. Shorebirds and waterfowl, including Canada goose and snow goose, breed in large numbers in this ecozone.

Marine Ecozones of Canada

Canada's marine ecozones have not yet been fully designated. The descriptions that follow are somewhat tentative, but they illustrate the essential character of these distinctive ecological regions.

The Pacific Ecozone occurs in waters off the mainland and islands of western British Columbia. The climate is temperate, with long, warm summers and short, cool winters. There is no sea ice.

Various species of Pacific salmon, such as chum, coho, and sockeye, are important in this marine ecozone. These fish spend most of their adult life at sea but migrate up accessible rivers to spawn. Individual adult salmon return to their birth river for breeding. Pacific herring is another abundant species of fish. Prominent marine mammals in the Pacific Ecozone include grey whale, harbour seal, killer whale, northern fur seal, northern sea lion, sea otter, and sperm whale. Prominent seabirds include double-crested and pelagic cormorant, glaucous gull, marbled murrelet, pigeon guillemot, and tufted puffin. Many species of waterfowl winter in coastal habitats in this ecozone.

The Arctic Archipelago Ecozone occurs in waters between the islands of the Arctic, the Beaufort Sea, and Hudson Bay and James Bay. The climate is marked by long, cold winters and short, cool summers. The ice-free season is as long as several months, with the ocean surface covered with metres-thick ice for the rest of the year. In a few places, underwater seamounts force currents to the surface, creating ice-free areas known as *polynya*, which are a critical habitat for marine mammals and birds. The polynya are marine counterparts of the oases of the Arctic Cordillera and Northern Arctic Ecozones.

Arctic cod and char, a migratory salmonid fish, are abundant. Marine mammals include bearded seal, beluga, bowhead whale, narwhal, ringed seal, and walrus. Although polar bear usually have their young on land or den there when the sea ice has melted, they are essentially marine animals, hunting seals as their major food. On certain islands (such as King Christian Island in Lancaster Sound), thick-billed murres have huge colonies that can contain millions of breeding birds. Other seabirds include arctic tern, black guillemot, dovekie, fulmar, and glaucous gull. The most abundant sea ducks are common eider and oldsquaw.

The Arctic Basin Ecozone is a northern, deep-water marine ecozone that occurs north and west of the arctic islands of Canada. The climate is characterized by long, cold winters and short, cool summers. Ice cover is continuous in the more northern reaches of this ecozone, and almost continuous further south. Some regions break up into discontinuous pack ice that shifts about in a huge, counterclockwise movement because of a current known as the

Photo 8.14 The Pacific Ecozone is rich in marine life. Pictured here is a "forest" of large seaweeds known as kelps (*Nereocystis* spp.), which provide critical habitat for many animals, such as black rockfish (*Sebastes melanops*).

Source: C. Harvey-Clark

Photo 8.15   Most urbanized habitats in Canada are unnatural and support few indigenous species of plants and animals. However, a few urban habitats are well-used by wildlife, such as this area on the Toronto waterfront known as the Leslie Street Spit, which supports many species of plants, birds, and other animals.

arctic gyre, which is centred roughly on the North Pole.

Sparse populations of fish and marine mammals occur in this ecozone, living in regions of pack ice. Species of mammals include bearded and ringed seals, beluga, bowhead whale, narwhal, polar bear, and walrus. The ivory gull is a characteristic seabird.

The Northwest Atlantic Ecozone includes waters of the continental shelf off eastern Baffin Island, northern Quebec, Labrador, Newfoundland, and the Gulf of St. Lawrence. The southeast-flowing Labrador Current is a major water flow, and the Gulf of St. Lawrence is strongly influenced by the St. Lawrence River. The climate ranges from subarctic to boreal, with cold winters and cool summers. Sea ice forms extensively, but breaks up and melts completely in the spring or early summer.

Populations of fish are abundant and widespread, including capelin, cod, herring, and redfish. Marine mammals include grey, harbour, harp, and hooded seals; harbour porpoise; white-sided dolphin; and beluga, blue, fin, humpback, minke, pilot, and sperm whales. Seabirds include black guillemot, common murre, common and arctic tern, double-crested and great cormorant, fulmar, gannet, herring and black-backed gull, and razorbill. The

most abundant breeding sea duck is the common eider, but other ducks and loons winter in this ecozone.

The Atlantic Marine Ecozone extends offshore into waters of the continental shelf off eastern Newfoundland, Nova Scotia, and New Brunswick. Extensive shallower-water areas (less than about 150 m deep) are known as banks, but the ecozone also contains deep-water habitats. The climate is generally temperate, partly because of the influence of the Gulf Stream, which flows northward from the Caribbean Sea. Sea ice does not form, but icebergs drift south with the Labrador Current, and pack ice is imported from the Gulf of St. Lawrence after its spring breakup.

Populations of fish are abundant and widespread on the offshore banks, including cod, haddock, redfish, silver hake, and turbot. Marine mammals include grey and harbour seals and blue, bottlenosed, fin, humpback, minke, pothead, right, and sperm whales. Seabirds include black guillemot, common and arctic tern, common eider, common murre, common puffin, double-crested cormorant, fulmar, gannet, great cormorant, herring and black-backed gull, kittiwake, razorbill, and Wilson's storm petrel.

Anthropogenic Habitats

Anthropogenic ecosystems, such as urban, agricultural, and industrial habitats, are not natural. Rather, they are dominated by humans and include constructed and disturbed habitats and their associated species of plants and animals.

Urban Habitats

Urban habitats are characterized by the places where people live and work in metropolitan areas, cities, towns, and villages. Most of the natural ecozones have elements of urban habitat embedded in them, although to widely varying degrees. Urban habitats are developed most extensively in southern Canada, particularly within several hundred kilometres of the border with the United States.

The vegetation of urban habitats is extremely complex. Mature residential neighbourhoods commonly have an urban forest, but, in general, the most abundant trees are non-native species such as horse chestnut, linden, and Norway maple. These trees, and most of the shrubs and herbaceous plants cultivated in the urban ecosystem, were introduced to Canada from Europe, Asia, and elsewhere.

Some native trees are also planted in urban habitats—for example, American elm, Manitoba maple, and silver maple—but these are usually less common than alien species. Some additional native plants may survive in younger neighbourhoods that have been recently converted from natural habitats.

Along with humans, the most abundant mammals in urban habitats are domestic cat and dog, house mouse, and Norway rat, none of which are indigenous to Canada. Some native mammals, such as coyote, raccoon, and striped skunk, may also live in urban habitats. The most characteristic and abundant birds are house sparrow, rock dove (pigeon), and starling, all of which were introduced from Eurasia. Some native species also occur in urban habitats, including American crow, American robin, cardinal, black-capped chickadee, blue jay, and song sparrow.

Agricultural Habitats

Agricultural habitats occur in the *agroecosystems* of Canada, where plants and animals are grown for food, fibre, or energy for use by humans. These habitats were created through extensive conversions of natural ecosystems. Agricultural habitats are most extensive in the Prairie Provinces, but they occur wherever the soil and climate are suitable for the growth of crops, including much of southern Ontario and Quebec, the Atlantic Provinces, and southern British Columbia.

Agroecosystems in which food plants are grown are mostly dominated by species of annual crops, such as barley, canola (rapeseed), corn (maize), potato, soybean, tomato, and wheat, or by perennial fruit-bearing crops such as apple, blueberry, cherry, and peach. Except for blueberry, all of the above species were introduced to Canada as non-indigenous crop plants. Often, these crops are managed as *monocultures*, containing as few other species as possible that might compete with the crop species.

Agroecosystems in which livestock are raised are either pastures dominated by introduced species of grasses, or semi-natural grasslands containing native species adapted to being grazed by large animals. Grasslands are also harvested for their hay crop, which is supplemented by grains and other foods and fed to agricultural livestock. Increasingly, domestic livestock are cultivated indoors, in crowded, intensively managed, factory farms (see Chapters 14 and 24).

The most common large animals in agricultural habitats are cow, goat, horse, pig, and sheep, while smaller animals include chicken, domestic rabbit, and turkey. All of these animals were introduced to Canada as agricultural livestock (except perhaps for the turkey, which is native to North America). Many indigenous animals also use agricultural habitats, particularly if the land is not managed very intensively or sprayed with poisonous insecticides and other pesticides. However, the most intensively managed agroecosystems support few native species.

Intensively managed forestry plantations can also be considered agricultural habitats. Such plantations may be managed as virtual monocultures in which trees are grown as a long-lived crop. Usually, only one species of tree is planted, commonly in straight, evenly spaced rows, which optimizes growth rates and makes silvicultural management easier. Sometimes, non-native species of trees are planted, such as hybrid poplar, Norway spruce, Scotch pine, or Eurasian larch. More commonly, however, native trees are planted, such as Douglas-fir or species of pine or spruce. Some indigenous species of forest plants and animals can utilize these plantations as habitat, but many cannot.

Industrial Habitats

Industrial habitats are associated with the technological infrastructure of Canadian civilization and occur extensively in many rural landscapes. Transportation corridors such as highways and railroads are important industrial habitats, as are electricity transmission corridors. Also prominent are mine sites and other areas affected by the extraction, processing, and manufacturing of products from natural resources, such as metals, coal, petroleum, oil sand and natural gas.

Vegetation in this biome is typically highly disturbed, and it may be actively managed to keep it in an early stage of succession, usually by mowing or herbicide spraying. However, vegetation in industrial habitats is often dominated by indigenous plants, and useful habitat is available for many native animals. Like the plant species, these are mostly animals of early stages of succession.

Conclusions

Biomes are geographically extensive ecosystems that occur throughout the world wherever environmental conditions are suitable for their development. The same biome may occur in far-flung places, even on different continents, and, in such cases, it will be similar in structure and function but will usually be dominated by different species. Temperature and moisture availability are the most critical environmental factors affecting the distribution of terrestrial biomes; marine biomes are most influenced by depth, nutrient availability, and temperature. The natural landscapes of Canada are divided into biophysical regions known as ecozones—15 terrestrial and 5 marine. The ecozones are, in turn, divided into smaller units known as ecodistricts. Ecozones and ecodistricts are characterized by their natural landforms, climate, species, and ecological communities. The natural biomes of the world, and the ecozones of Canada, are being rapidly modified by human activities, and many of their inherent biodiversity values are becoming increasingly at risk. The effects are most intensive in regions where people live and work in high population densities, for example, in the more southern regions of Canada.

Key Terms

biome	lentic ecosystem
life form	lotic ecosystem
disturbance	wetland
succession	marsh
tundra	swamp
boreal coniferous forest	bog
montane forest	fen
temperate deciduous forest	estuary
temperate rainforest	agroecosystem
temperate grassland	monoculture
chaparral	ecozone
desert	prairie

Questions for Review

1. List Earth's biomes. What are the essential characteristics of each of them?

2. What are the natural ecozones occurring in the province or territory where you live? Describe the characteristics and key species of each.

3. What species occur in urban, agricultural, and industrial habitats in the province, territory, or region where you live? Which of these are native to Canada and which are introduced?

4. Select any Canadian ecozone. What are the most important environmental factors affecting the species and ecological communities of that ecozone? How do you think these factors have changed over the past century, and during the past several decades?

Questions for Discussion

1. Why is it useful to know about the species of plants and animals that live in some defined area, such as a park, county, or province? Is it useful to know about the ecological communities? Does this kind of information assist in planning for conservation and sustainable development?

2. Ecologists usually consider native species to have greater "value" than non-native ones. Why do they think this way? Is the rationalization only scientific, or does it include an element of non-objectivity?

3. Select any one of the more southerly Canadian ecozones, where human activities have become important factors affecting species and ecological communities. Describe any damage that you think human activities might have caused to the native species and natural ecosystems of that ecozone, and consider whether it might be possible to repair any of those effects.

Exploring Issues

1. You have been asked to characterize and map the various ecosystems occurring in a national park (choose one near where you live). How would you determine the distributions and characteristics of the various kinds of terrestrial, wetland, and aquatic ecosystems present in the park?

References

Barbour, M.G. and W.D. Billings. 1988. *North American Terrestrial Vegetation*. New York: Cambridge University Press.

Bolen, E.G. 1998. *Ecology of North America*. New York, NY: John Wiley & Sons.

Crabtree, P. (ed.). 1970. *The Illustrated Natural History of Canada* (9 vol.). Toronto: NSL Natural Science of Canada.

Ecological Stratification Working Group. 1995. *A National Ecological Framework for Canada*. Ottawa: Environment Canada.

Heywood, V.H. (ed.). 1995. *Global Biodiversity Assessment*. Cambridge: Cambridge University Press.

National Wetlands Working Group. 1988. *Wetlands of Canada*. Ecological Land Classification Series No. 24. Ottawa: Environment Canada.

Odum, E.P. 1993. *Ecology and Our Endangered Life-Support Systems*. Sunderland, MA: Sinauer.

Odum, E.P. and G.W. Barrett. 2004. *Fundamentals of Ecology*. Florence, KY: Brooks Cole.

Phillips, D. 1990. *The Climates of Canada*. Ottawa: Environment Canada.

Rowe, J.S. 1972. *Forest Regions of Canada*. Ottawa: Forestry Canada.

Schultz, J. 2004. *Ecozones of the World: The Ecological Divisions of the Geosphere*. 2nd ed. Berlin, Germany: Springer Verlag.

Scott, G.A.J. 1995. *Canada's Vegetation: A World Perspective*. Montreal: McGill-Queen's University Press.

Shelford, V.E. 1974. *The Ecology of North America*. Urbana, IL: University of Illinois Press.

Townsend, C.R., M. Begon, and J.L. Harper. 2002. *Essentials of Ecology*, 2nd ed. Cambridge, UK: Blackwell Publishers.

Walter, H. 1977. *Vegetation of the Earth*. New York: Springer.

Wiken, E., D. Gauthier, I. Marshall, K. Lawton, and H. Hirvonen. 1996. *A Perspective on Canada's Ecosystems: An Overview of the Terrestrial and Marine Ecozones*. Occ. Pap. No. 14. Ottawa: Canadian Council on Ecological Areas.

Woodward, S.L. 2003. *Biomes of the Earth: Terrestrial, Aquatic, and Human-Dominated*. Oxford, UK: Greenwood Press.

Informative Websites

Biom0es of the World.
http://mbgnet.mobot.org/sets/index.htm

Wondering what taiga means? Need a definition for tundra? Visit this well-designed site to find the answers to these questions as well as explanations of rainforest, desert, temperate, and grassland biomes.

EarthTrends: The Environmental Information Portal.
http://earthtrends.wri.org

This website of the World Resources Institute provides useful information about ecosystems, biodiversity, and resources.

Ecozones of Canada.
www.ec.gc.ca/soer-ree/English/Vignettes/default.cfm

This website from Environment Canada provides detailed information on the ecozones of Canada.

Mysterious Journey. http://library.thinkquest.org/26634/

A multiple-choice quiz and online treasure hunt game encourage you to explore this website and learn about the rainforest, desert, and grassland.

Plants

alpine fir, *Abies lasiocarpa*
amabalis fir, *Abies amabalis*
American elm, *Ulmus americana*
antelope bush, *Purshia tridentata*
arctic avens, *Dryas integrifolia*
arctic poppy, *Papaver lapponicum*
arctic willow, *Salix arctica*
balsam fir, *Abies balsamea*
balsam poplar, *Populus balsamifera*
basswood, *Tilia americana*
bearberry, *Arctostaphylos uva-ursi*
beech, *Fagus grandifolia*
big bluestem, *Andropogon gerardii*
bilberry, *Vaccinium uliginosum*
black spruce, *Picea mariana*
black walnut, *Juglans nigra*
blueberry, *Vaccinium angustifolium*
bulrush, *Scirpus* spp.
butternut, *Juglans cinerea*
cattail, *Typha latifolia*
cottongrass, *Eriophorum angustifolium*
cucumber-tree, *Magnolia acuminata*
Douglas-fir, *Pseudotsuga menziesii*
eastern hemlock, *Tsuga canadensis*
elm, *Ulmus americana*
Engelmann spruce, *Picea engelmannii*
fireweed, *Epilobium angustifolium*
grand fir, *Abies grandis*
horse chestnut, *Aesculus hippocastanum*
jack pine, *Pinus banksiana*
Labrador tea, *Ledum groenlandicum*
linden, *Tilia cordata*
lodgepole pine, *Pinus contorta*
Manitoba maple, *Acer negundo*
mountain hemlock, *Tsuga mertensiana*
Norway maple, *Acer platanoides*
Norway spruce, *Picea abies*
perennial sunflower, *Helianthus giganteus*
ponderosa pine, *Pinus ponderosa*
prickly pear cactus, *Opuntia fragilis*
purple saxifrage, *Saxifraga oppositifolia*

rabbit bush, *Chrysothamnus nauseosus*
red alder, *Alnus rubra*
red ash, *Fraxinus pennsylvanica*
red maple, *Acer rubrum*
red pine, *Pinus resinosa*
red spruce, *Picea rubens*
sagebrush, *Artemisia tridentata*
sassafras, *Sassafras albidum*
Scotch pine, *Pinus sylvestris*
sedges, *Carex membranacea* and *C. stans*
silver maple, *Acer saccharinum*
Sitka spruce, *Picea sitchensis*
sugar maple, *Acer saccharum*
sycamore, *Platanus occidentalis*
tamarack, *Larix laricina*
trembling aspen, *Populus tremuloides*
tulip-tree, *Liriodendron tulipifera*
western hemlock, *Tsuga heterophylla*
western red cedar, *Thuja occidentalis*
western white pine, *Pinus monticola*
white birch, *Betula papyrifera*
white elm, *Ulmus americana*
white heather, *Cassiope tetragona*
white pine, *Pinus strobus*
white spruce, *Picea glauca*
willow-herb, *Epilobium latifolium*
yellow birch, *Betula lutea*
yellow cedar, *Chamaecyparis nootkatensis*

Fish

arctic char, *Salvelinus alpinus*
arctic cod, *Boreogadus saida*
capelin, *Mallotus villosus*
chum salmon, *Oncorhynchus gorbuscha*
cod, *Gadus morhua*
coho salmon, *Oncorhynchus kisutch*
haddock, *Melanogrammus aeglefinus*
herring, *Clupea harengus*
redfish, *Sebastes fasciatus*
silver hake, *Merluccius bilinearis*
sockeye salmon, *Oncorhynchus nerka*
turbot, *Reinhardtius hippoglossoides*

Mammals

arctic fox, *Alopex lagopus*
arctic ground squirrel, *Spermophilus parryi*
arctic hare, *Lepus arcticus*
Atlantic white-sided dolphin, *Lagenorhynchus acutus*
badger, *Taxidea taxus*
bearded seal, *Erignathus barbatus*
beaver, *Castor canadensis*
beluga, *Delphinapterus leucas*
bighorn sheep, *Ovis canadensis*
black bear, *Ursus americanus*
black-tailed deer, *Odocoileus hemionus columbianus*
black-tailed prairie dog, *Cynomys ludovicianus*
blue whale, *Balaenoptera musculus*
bobcat, *Lynx rufus*
bottlenosed whale, *Hyperoodon ampullatus*
bowhead whale, *Balaena mysticetus*
brown lemming, *Lemmus sibiricus*
buffalo, *Bison bison*
caribou, *Rangifer tarandus*
collared lemming, *Dicrostonyx torquatus*
Columbian ground squirrel, *Spermophilus columbianus*
cottontail rabbit, *Sylvilagus floridanus*
cougar, *Felis concolor*
coyote, *Canis latrans*
Dall's sheep, *Ovis dalli*
domestic cat, *Felis catus*
domestic dog, *Canis familiaris*
eastern chipmunk, *Tamias striatus*
elk, *Cervus canadensis*
ermine, *Mustela erminea*
fin whale, *Balaenoptera physalus*
fisher, *Martes pennanti*
grey seal, *Halichoerus gryptus*
grey (or black) squirrel, *Sciurus carolinensis*
grey whale, *Eschrichtius robustus*
grizzly bear, *Ursus arctos*
groundhog, *Marmota monax*
harbour porpoise, *Phocoena phocoena*
harbour seal, *Phoca vitulina*

harp seal, *Phoca groenlandica*
hoary marmot, *Marmota caligata*
hooded seal, *Cystophora cristata*
house mouse, *Mus musculus*
humpback whale, *Megaptera novaeangliae*
killer whale, *Orcinus orca*
lynx, *Lynx lynx*
mink, *Mustela vison*
minke whale, *Balaenoptera acutorostrata*
moose, *Alces alces*
mountain goat, *Oreamnos americanus*
mule deer, *Odocoileus hemionus*
muskox, *Ovibos moschatus*
muskrat, *Ondatra zibethicus*
narwhal, *Monodon monoceros*
northern fur seal, *Callorhinus ursinus*
northern pocket gopher, *Thomomys talpoides*
northern sea lion, *Eumetopias jubata*
Norway rat, *Rattus norvegicus*
Pacific white-sided dolphin, *Lagenorhynchus obliquidens*
pika, *Ochotona princeps*
pilot or pothead whale, *Globicephala melaena*
pine marten, *Martes americana*
polar bear, *Ursus maritimus*
porcupine, *Erethizon dorsatum*
pronghorn antelope, *Antilocapra americana*
raccoon, *Procyon lotor*
red fox, *Vulpes vulpes*
red squirrel, *Tamiasciurus hudsonicus*
Richardson's ground squirrel, *Spermophilus richardsonii*
right whale, *Balaena glacialis*
ringed seal, *Phoca hispida*
river otter, *Lontra canadensis*
sea otter, *Enhydra lutris*
snowshoe hare, *Lepus americanus*
sperm whale, *Physeter catodon*
striped skunk, *Mephitis mephitis*
walrus, *Odobenus rosmarus*
white-tailed deer, *Odocoileus virginianus*
white-tailed jack rabbit, *Lepus townsendii*
wolf, *Canis lupus*
wolverine, *Gulo gulo*
wood bison, *Bison bison*

Birds

American avocet, *Recurvirostra americana*
American robin, *Turdus migratorius*
arctic loon, *Gavia arctica*
arctic tern, *Sterna paradisaea*
Baird's sandpiper, *Calidris bairdii*
bald eagle, *Haliaeetus leucocephalus*
barred owl, *Strix varia*
black duck, *Anas rubripes*

black guillemot, *Cepphus grylle*
black oystercatcher, *Haematopus bachmani*
black-backed gull, *Larus marinus*
black-billed magpie, *Pica pica*
black-capped chickadee, *Parus atricapillus*
blue grouse, *Dendragapus obscurus*
blue jay, *Cyanocitta cristata*
bob-white, *Colinus virginianus*
boreal owl, *Aegolius funereus*
Brant goose, *Branta bernicla*
broad-winged hawk, *Buteo platypterus*
burrowing owl, *Athene cunicularia*
California quail, *Callipepla californica*
Canada goose, *Branta canadensis*
canvasback, *Aythya valisineria*
cardinal, *Cardinalis cardinalis*
Carolina wren, *Thryothorus ludovicianus*
Caspian tern, *Sterna caspia*
chestnut-backed chickadee, *Parus rufescens*
Clark's nutcracker, *Nucifraga columbiana*
common crow, *Corvus brachyrhynchos*
common eider, *Somateria mollissima*
common loon, *Gavia immer*
common murre, *Uria aalge*
common puffin, *Fratercula arctica*
common redpoll, *Carduelis flammea*
common tern, *Sterna hirundo*
coot, *Fulica americana*
dipper, *Cinclus mexicanus*
double-crested cormorant, *Phalacrocorax auritus*
dovekie, *Alle alle*
evening grosbeak, *Hesperiphona vespertina*
ferruginous hawk, *Buteo regalis*
fox sparrow, *Passerella iliaca*
fulmar, *Fulmarus glacialis*
gannet, *Sula bassanus*
glaucous gull, *Larus hyperboreus*
golden eagle, *Aquila chrysaetos*
grey-cheeked thrush, *Catharus minimus*
grey jay, *Perisoreus canadensis*
great blue heron, *Ardea herodias*
great cormorant, *Phalacrocorax carbo*
great horned owl, *Bubo virginianus*
greater scaup, *Aythya marila*
greater snow goose, *Anser caerulescens atlanticus*
greater yellowlegs, *Tringa melanoleuca*
green-backed heron, *Butorides striatus*
gyrfalcon, *Falco rusticolus*
herring gull, *Larus argentatus*
hoary redpoll, *Carduelis hornemanni*
horned lark, *Eremophila alpestris*
house sparrow, *Passer domesticus*
ivory gull, *Pagophila eburnea*
kittiwake, *Rissa tridactyla*
Lapland longspur, *Calcarius lapponicus*

lesser scaup, *Aythya affinis*
lesser snow goose, *Anser caerulescens caerulescens*
lesser yellowlegs, *Tringa flavipes*
mallard, *Anas platyrhynchos*
marbled murrelet, *Brachyramphus marmoratus*
mountain quail, *Oreortyx pictus*
northern oriole, *Icterus galbula*
northern shrike, *Lanius excubitor*
northwestern crow, *Corvus caurinus*
oldsquaw, *Clangula hyemalis*
orchard oriole, *Icterus spurius*
parasitic jaeger, *Stercorarius parasiticus*
pelagic cormorant, *Phalacrocorax pelagicus*
peregrine falcon, *Falco peregrinus*
pigeon guillemot, *Cepphus columba*
pintail, *Anas acuta*
prairie falcon, *Falco mexicanus*
prothonotary warbler, *Protonotaria citrea*
raven, *Corvus corax*
razorbill, *Alca torda*
red-eyed vireo, *Vireo olivaceus*
red-shouldered hawk, *Buteo lineatus*
red-throated loon, *Gavia stellata*
ringed plover, *Charadrius hiaticula*
rock dove (or pigeon), *Columba livia*
rock ptarmigan, *Lagopus mutus*
rose-breasted grosbeak, *Pheucticus ludovicianus*
sandhill crane, *Grus canadensis*
scarlet tanager, *Piranga olivacea*
semipalmated sandpiper, *Calidris pusilla*
sharp-shinned hawk, *Accipiter striatus*
sharp-tailed grouse, *Tympanuchus phasianellus*
snipe, *Gallinago gallinago*
snow bunting, *Plectrophenax nivalis*
snow goose, *Chen caerulescens*
snowy owl, *Nyctea scandiaca*
song sparrow, *Melospiza melodia*
starling, *Sturnus vulgaris*
Steller's jay, *Cyanocitta stelleri*
Swainson's hawk, *Buteo swainsoni*
thick-billed murre, *Uria lomvia*
tree sparrow, *Spizella arborea*
tufted puffin, *Fratercula corniculata*
tundra swan, *Cygnus columbianus*
western grebe, *Aechmophorus occidentalis*
white pelican, *Pelecanus erythrorhynchos*
white-crowned sparrow, *Zonotrichia leucophrys*
white-tailed ptarmigan, *Lagopus leucurus*
white-throated sparrow, *Zonotrichia albicollis*
whooping crane, *Grus americana*
willow ptarmigan, *Lagopus lagopus*
Wilson's storm petrel, *Oceanites oceanicus*
yellow warbler, *Dendroica petechia*
yellow-rumped warbler, *Dendroica coronata*

9

Ecology: From Individuals to the Biosphere

CHAPTER OBJECTIVES

After completing this chapter, you will be able to

1. Outline how species are adapted to different levels of stress and disturbance in their habitat.
2. Explain the elements of population growth and the constraints on population size.
3. List major factors that influence the nature of ecological communities.
4. Describe an ecological landscape (or seascape) and the factors that influence its spatial and temporal dynamics.
5. Outline the Gaia hypothesis and discuss its applicability to the functioning of the biosphere.

Introduction

Ecology involves the study of the relationships between organisms and their environment. In the sense meant here, "environment" includes both non-living factors, such as temperature, moisture, nutrients, and physical disturbances, as well as living organisms, which exert biological influences through competition, herbivory, predation, and disease, and by providing elements of habitat (e.g., trees provide much of the habitat for species living in a forest). Because all organisms and ecosystems are subjected to a multiplicity of influences, it is extremely difficult to predict the ecological effects of changes in environmental conditions.

Some environmental influences are resources that organisms can exploit as opportunities, allowing them to gain the necessities of life and livelihood. Other environmental influences are **stressors**—constraints on productivity and reproductive success. Many environmental stressors operate in a relatively continuous (chronic) fashion, as is often the case for soil and water pollution, climatic factors, and many biological interactions. Other stressors affect organisms and ecosystems as events of **disturbance**, which cause great damage during a short period of time. Disturbance is followed by an extended period of ecological recovery called **succession**. Disturbances may be caused by natural forces such as wildfire and windstorms, and by anthropogenic influences such as clear-cutting of forests or ploughing of fields.

Photo 9.2   This population of northern gannets (*Morus bassanus*) breeds at Cape St. Mary's in southern Newfoundland.

Ecology considers the structure and function of the web of life at the following hierarchical levels:

1. **Individual organisms** can be defined, in an evolutionary context, as genetically unique entities. Some species, however, reproduce by asexual mechanisms, and, in these cases, clones of genetically identical "individuals" may develop.

2. **Populations** are groups of individuals of the same species that are co-occurring in time and space and that can potentially interbreed with each other.

3. A **species** consists of one or more populations that can potentially interbreed with each other and that are reproductively isolated from other such groups.

4. **Communities** consist of populations of various species that are co-existing at the same time and place and are interacting ecologically.

5. **Landscapes** and **seascapes** are spatial integrations of various communities over large areas. These comprise a dynamic mosaic known as a landscape in terrestrial environments and a seascape in marine environments.

6. The **biosphere** consists of all Earth's life and ecosystems and all the environments where they occur.

Photo 9.1   An individual organism is genetically unique and is different from other individuals of its species. This is a long-tailed duck (*Clangula hyemalis*) breeding on Ellesmere Island in arctic Nunavut.

Each of these levels of ecology is meaningful, and all are highly relevant to environmental science. These tiers

Photo 9.3 Coral reefs are shallow-water marine ecosystems in tropical seas, and they are extremely rich in species. Prominent species in this nearshore coral reef community near Grand Cayman, in the Caribbean Sea, are blue-striped grunts (*Haemulon sciurus*) and elkhorn coral (*Acropora palmata*).

Source: C. Harvey-Clark

of ecology are not, however, totally discrete—they are all interconnected, and each level influences every other level. This chapter discusses issues relevant to the various hierarchical levels of ecology.

Individuals and Species

Autecology is the field within ecology that deals with the study of individuals, populations, and species. Important topics in autecology include the following:

- differences among species in life-history characteristics and in adaptations to different kinds of environmental conditions

- influences of the environment on individual organisms, including effects on development and behaviour

- the causes of changes in the size and makeup of populations

Life-History Characteristics

Each species is unique and can be described by its physical, biochemical, behavioural, and ecological attributes. These characteristics are ultimately determined by the genetic variation existing within the unique individuals that comprise the species.

Although species are unique, they can still be aggregated into groups on the basis of similarities in their attributes. These affinities may be due to ancestral relatedness; that is, many species are somewhat alike because they share aspects of their evolutionary history (i.e., they have a similar phylogenetic lineage). For example, all maple trees (genus *Acer*) look rather similar and occur in comparable, temperate-forest habitats. All members of the cat family (Felidae) also bear a certain resemblance and are ecologically comparable in that all are predators, although of different species of prey and in different habitats or ecosystems.

Unrelated species may also display strikingly similar attributes, usually because they have undergone parallel changes through a phenomenon known as *evolutionary convergence* (sometimes called parallel evolution). Convergence suggests that, through natural selection, unrelated species in similar environments may evolve to resemble each other and play similar functional roles in their ecosystems.

There are numerous examples of evolutionary convergence among unrelated groups of organisms. For instance, all perennial (i.e., long-lived) plants growing in arid environments have a need to conserve moisture. This critical function is enhanced by growth forms that are adaptations for reducing water loss, such as relatively cylindrical trunks and branches; tissues protected by a thick, waxy outer cuticle; and no leaves. Thorniness is another useful trait in arid environments, because sharp spines deter herbivores from consuming plant biomass and stores of water. Desert-inhabiting plants in many families have developed one or more of these adaptations, including species of cacti (family Cactaceae), euphorbs (Euphorbiaceae), and succulents (Crassulaceae). Although species in these families are not related in an evolutionary sense, they often resemble each other because of evolutionary convergence.

Examples of convergence among animals include the similarities of the timber wolf (*Canis lupus*) of Eurasia and North America and the marsupial wolf (thylacine, *Thylacinus cynocephalus*) of Australia. A comparable example is the groundhog (*Marmota monax*) of North America and the marsupial wombat (*Vombatus ursinus*) of Australia. Also, the penguins (family Spheniscidae) of the Southern Hemisphere are similar to the guillemots, murres, puffins, and related auks (family Alcidae) of the Northern Hemisphere.

Ecologists often categorize plant species on the basis of their life (growth) forms. For example, a system proposed by the Danish botanist C. Raunkiaer classifies biennial and perennial plants largely on where the shoots or buds are positioned. Although this system is simplistic, it is useful in research examining the relationships between growth forms and habitat.

Another categorization is based on the adaptations of plants for coping with large differences in ecological conditions. The British ecologist Philip Grime has suggested that plant strategies can be divided into three categories, determined by life history and its relationship to habitat conditions. This system proposes that two groups of environmental factors, disturbance and stress, strongly influence the evolution of plant life-history strategies. Disturbance can be frequent or uncommon, and severe or mild in its intensity. Stress is a longer-term site condition, and it can be intense if associated with extreme shortages of moisture, light, or nutrients, or innocuous if these necessary factors are all available in adequate levels.

Any particular environment can be characterized by the importance of these two factors. This results in four kinds of habitat conditions:

1. low stress and rare disturbance
2. low stress but frequent disturbance
3. intense stress but rare disturbance
4. intense stress and frequent disturbance

Grime suggests that plants exhibit only three primary life-history strategies because they cannot cope with an environment that is both stressful and frequently disturbed (case 4 above). According to Grime, the three primary strategies of plants result in **competitors**, **ruderals**, and **stress-tolerators**:

Competitor plants are dominant in habitats in which disturbance is rare and environmental stresses are relatively unimportant. Under such conditions, competition is the major selective influence on plant evolution and on the organization of their communities. Competitive plants effectively acquire resources and use them to achieve a dominant position in their community by interfering with the productivity of other plants. Useful adaptations in competitors include rapid, tall growth, a spreading canopy, and a widely spreading root system—all of which effectively occupy space and take advantage of resources. Seedlings of competitive plants can also establish themselves beneath a closed canopy.

Ruderals are characteristic of frequently disturbed environments with abundant resources, so stress is not great. Ruderal plants are, therefore, well adapted to utilizing rich but temporary habitats. They are typically short-lived and intolerant of stress and competition. Ruderals produce large numbers of seeds, which usually have mechanisms for long-distance dispersal so that new habitats can be discovered and colonized.

Stress-tolerators are adapted to environments that are marginal in terms of climate, moisture, or nutrient supply, but are infrequently disturbed and therefore stable. Typical of arctic, desert, and other stressful environments, stress-tolerant plants are generally short, slow-growing, and intolerant of competition from more vigorous species.

Another system of categorizing organisms, more commonly applied to animals, involves two groups of life-history characteristics. One group consists of longer-lived organisms that produce relatively few progeny, but invest a great deal of energy in each to improve their chances of survival. These are known as *K-selected* species. The other group, referred to as *r-selected*, comprises short-lived species that produce large numbers of smaller offspring, each of which has a relatively small chance of survival. However, because of the enormous numbers of offspring, it is likely that some will manage to survive. K-selected species are dominant in relatively stable, mature habitats in which competition is the controlling influence on community structure; r-selected species occur in younger, recently disturbed habitats in which resources are freely available and rapid population growth is possible. (The source of the "K" and "r" labels comes from the logistic equation, a fundamental element of population ecology that, for simplicity, is not described here.)

Species can also be considered in terms of other elements of their reproductive strategy, for example how often they engage in reproduction. Some species only achieve one reproductive event during their lifetime, usually dying afterward. This type of reproduction, known as *semelparous*, is seen in annual and biennial plants, many insects and other invertebrates, and most species of salmon. Most semelparous species are short-lived, but some can live for many years, gradually accumulating enough energy to sustain one massive, "big-bang," reproductive effort. Semelparous reproduction is favoured in relatively rich habitats that are frequently disturbed, and it is common among ruderal and r-selected species.

Species that reproduce a number of times during their lives are known as *iteroparous*. These are typically long-lived species that live in relatively stable habitats. Iteroparous species may produce large numbers of small offspring (r-selected), or they may produce fewer, larger young, each of which receives a large investment of parental resources (K-selected).

Relationships of Individual Organisms with Their Environment

Autecology also deals with the lives of individual organisms and how they are influenced by their physical and biological environments.

As was discussed in Chapter 6, all individual organisms have a fixed complement of genetic information, known as their *genotype*. However, the expression of genetic information (the *phenotype*) is influenced by environmental conditions, a phenomenon known as *phenotypic plasticity*. If individuals experience difficult environmental conditions, their phenotypic expression of genetic potential may include sub-optimal growth rates and the production of few or no progeny. Other individuals that live in a more benign environment can achieve higher productivity and have many offspring. The latter, more prolific circumstance is highly desirable in terms of an individual achieving evolutionary "success." By definition, "successful" individuals have managed to maximize their *fitness*, that is, their genetic contribution to future generations of their population.

The success of an individual organism is also affected by unpredictable (stochastic) events of disturbance, which may result in untimely injury or premature death. Even if it is living in a relatively benign environment, with optimal access to resources and other necessities of life, an unlucky individual may just happen to be scorched by a wildfire, injured during a hurricane, devoured by a predator, debilitated by a disease, or hit by a truck.

Population Ecology

The study of populations of organisms is another aspect of autecology. The abundance of all species changes over time in response to environmental factors that affect four population-related (*demographic*) variables: birth rate (BR), immigration rate (IR), death rate (DR), and emigration rate (ER). The change in population size (ΔP) during a unit of time (say, a year) is described by the following equation:

$$\Delta P = BR - DR + IR - ER$$

This demographic relationship is true of all species, including humans. In some cases, isolated (closed) populations do not receive any immigration of new individuals and do not lose any individuals to emigration. Under such conditions, ΔP is calculated as $BR - DR$, a value known as the *natural rate of population change*.

Often, ΔP is expressed as a percentage change, by dividing its value by the initial population size (e.g., a population of 100 individuals that increases by 10 in one year has a 10% per year growth rate). If the percentage change in any population is constant, then there will be an accelerating rate of population increase or decrease, called *exponential change*.

Imagine a circumstance in which a fertile pair of individuals discovers a new habitat—one that is suitable but has not been previously occupied by their species. Under such conditions, the founder individuals will breed and the population will grow over time. Initially, resources will be abundant and will not constrain growth of the population. Consequently, the percentage rate of population increase will be constant, being limited only by how quickly progeny can be produced and become fertile (i.e., by birth and maturation rates), and countered only by longevity of individuals in the population. This maximum rate of population growth, limited only by the biology of the species in the given environment and not by competition for resources, is referred to as the *intrinsic rate of population increase*. Any population growing at the intrinsic rate of increase (or indeed at any fixed percentage rate) will quickly explode in abundance (see In Detail 9.1).

Eventually, however, as the **carrying capacity** of the available habitat is approached, space and resources become limiting. (The carrying capacity is related to the size of population that can be sustained without degrading the habitat.) At or beyond the carrying capacity, opportunities are constrained by the limited availability of resources, and individuals in the population must compete with each other. Intense competition produces physiological stress, which generally results in a decrease in the birth rate and an increase in the death rate.

In some cases, the rate of population increase may then decrease to zero (i.e., birth rate equals death rate—a condition referred to as *zero population growth*, or ZPG). If ZPG is maintained, the population size will eventually

In Detail 9.1

Exponential Growth

A constant rate of increase leads to extremely rapid growth in the sizes of populations. This happens for the same reason that money invested at a fixed rate of interest can quickly increase in quantity. This phenomenon, known in finance as compound interest, is illustrated below.

Consider, for example, an investment of $100 at an interest rate of 10% per year, locked in for a 10-year period. After one year, the initial deposit grows to $110, representing the initial investment plus accumulated interest. In the second year, the 10% interest rate is applied to the $110, so the earned interest is larger ($11) than in the first year ($10). In the third year, the 10% interest is applied to the accumulated $121, so the earned interest is larger yet ($12.10), and the accumulated value of the investment is $133.10. At the end of the fourth year, the initial investment of $100 is worth $146.41; it is $161.05 at the end of the fifth year, and $259.37 at the end of the tenth year, representing an impressive 159% return on the initial investment. Clearly, the compound interest leads to an extremely rapid increase in capital.

Exponential growth refers to the accelerating growth of an initial quantity due to a constant rate of increase. Sometimes an important parameter known as *doubling time* is calculated—that is, the time required for a two-fold increase in capital. The doubling time can be roughly calculated as 70 divided by the rate of increase. In the example above, 70 divided by 10% per year yields 7 years. Therefore, the initial $100 would double in amount in only 7 years, and the accumulated $200 would again double (to $400) in another 7 years, and so on as long as the investment conditions do not change.

The mathematics of compound interest can also be applied to the exponential growth of populations of organisms. One example will suffice: In 2000, the global human population was about 6 billion people, growing at about 1.4% per year. Therefore, in only 49 years (i.e., 70 divided by 1.4% per year), the human population could double to 12 billion (as long as the growth rate remains the same). The ecological implications of such a population increase are awesome (see Chapter 10).

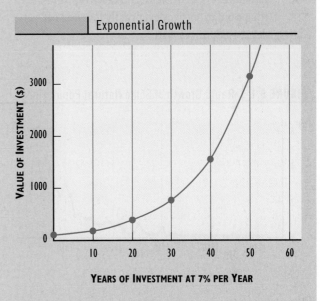

This curve shows the growth of an initial deposit of $100 invested at a compound interest rate of 7% per year. Biological populations also grow at exponential rates if their rate of increase is constant. However, when resources become limiting, the rate of increase decreases, and the population may ultimately crash.

level off, perhaps at a level appropriate to the carrying capacity of the habitat.

However, the earlier exponential population growth may have resulted in an abundance that exceeded what the habitat could support. Such an *over-population* would over-exploit the environment, resulting in its degradation and a decrease in its carrying capacity. If this happens, the population size will decrease through a rapid increase in the mortality rate, or perhaps by a surge of emigration in search of new habitats. These events may result in a rapid and uncontrolled crash in the numbers of individuals in the population. Usually, a

crash takes the population to a level below the carrying capacity of the habitat, creating a circumstance for renewed population growth. In small habitats, however, the population crash can be massive enough to extirpate a local population.

Population ecologists have developed mathematical models of population dynamics that account for the influences of such factors as the intrinsic rate of population increase, the carrying capacity of habitats, the effects of predation and disease, and even the effects of unpredictable disturbance events. These models are described in introductory textbooks of ecology and are not dealt with here in any detail. For present purposes, there are several important points to understand about population ecology:

- Populations of all species are dynamic. They change over time due to varying rates of birth, death, immigration, and emigration.

- Populations of all species can, potentially, increase very rapidly, under conditions in which resource availability and other factors are not constraining. Several examples of rapid population growth are illustrated in Figure 9.1. However, unlimited growth cannot be sustained forever—in all of the cases in Figure 9.1, the population sizes eventually levelled off, decreased, or crashed.

- Ultimately, the abundance of a species that can be sustained is limited by the carrying capacity of the available habitat. Two examples of population growth that level off at the carrying capacity of the habitat are illustrated in Figure 9.2.

- Some populations are relatively stable. Usually these exist in environments in which resource availability is predictable so that a balance can be achieved with the carrying capacity. For example, relatively little change occurs in the year-to-year populations of trees growing in old-growth forest, unless a rare, catastrophic disturbance occurs.

FIGURE 9.1 | Rapid Growth of Some Natural Populations

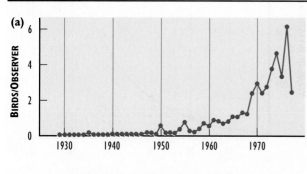
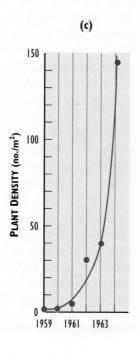
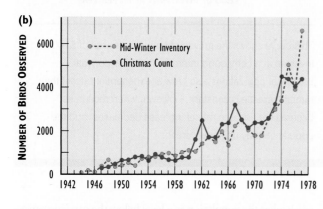
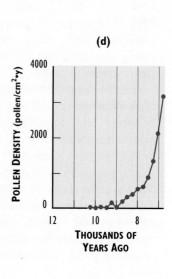

(a) The population of mourning doves (*Zenaida macroura*) wintering in southern Ontario over 48 years. This used to be a rare species, but it has apparently benefited from a warming climate, improved suburban habitat, and winter feeding. **(b)** The population of mallards (*Anas platyrhynchos*) wintering in southern Ontario over 35 years, illustrated with two independent sets of data. This duck has expanded its breeding and wintering ranges into eastern Canada, largely in response to habitat made available by the clearing of forested land. **(c)** The population of wild oats (*Avena fatua*) in an annually ploughed field over six years. This grass is an invasive weed in agriculture. **(d)** The population of lodgepole pine (*Pinus contorta*) near Snowshoe Lake, British Columbia, occurring during natural afforestation following deglaciation about 7000–9000 years ago. In this case, tree populations are indicated by the amounts of pollen recovered from dated layers of lake sediment.

Sources: Modified from (a) Freedman and Riley (1980); (b) Goodwin *et al.* (1977); (c) Silverton (1987); (d) MacDonald and Cwynar (1991)

FIGURE 9.2	Population Growth Ceasing at Carrying Capacity

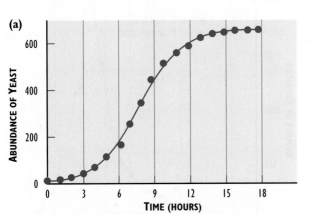 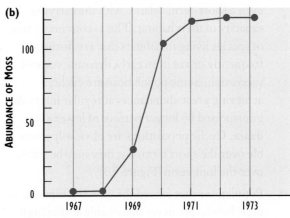

(a) The population growth of yeast cells cultivated in a flask is initially exponential but then levels off at the carrying capacity of the habitat. Carrying capacity is determined by the volume of the flask, the quantity of nutrients available, and the increasing concentrations of toxic metabolites, including ethyl alcohol. **(b)** The population of a moss colonizing a suitable, but initially bare, rock substrate in Iceland. The carrying capacity is limited by the amount of two-dimensional space available.

Sources: (a) Modified from Krebs (1985); (b) Modified from Silverton (1987)

FIGURE 9.3	Cyclic Populations

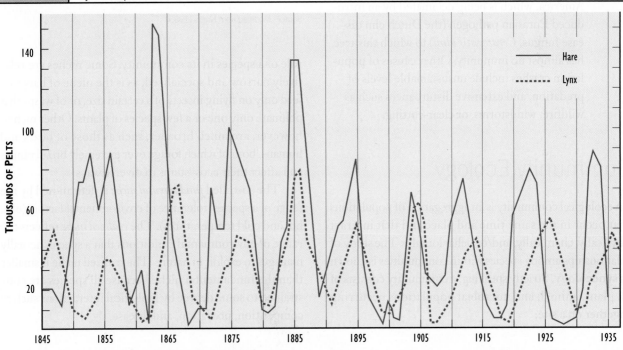

Populations of lynx (*Lynx canadensis*) and snowshoe hare (*Lepus americanus*) over much of northern Canada, as indicated by the numbers of pelts received from fur trappers by the Hudson Bay Company. Ecologists interpret these data as suggesting 10-year population cycles, with the predatory lynx responding to changes in abundance of snowshoe hare, its major prey.

Source: Modified from Odum (1983)

- Other populations are relatively dynamic, changing greatly over time and rarely achieving even a short-term balance with the carrying capacity of their habitat. This is commonly true of species living in habitats that are disturbed frequently or are in an early, dynamic stage of succession. Some populations are cyclic, achieving great abundances at regular intervals, interspersed by longer periods of lower abundance. Cyclic populations are obviously unstable over the short term, but they may be stable over the long term (Figure 9.3).

- Populations that exceed the carrying capacity of their habitat are never sustainable at that high level, partly because of the environmental damage they cause. Unsustainable populations eventually crash to a smaller abundance and sometimes to extinction. Figure 9.4 shows an example of rapid population growth, resulting in habitat degradation and a subsequent population crash. Populations can also crash for other reasons, such as the sudden occurrence of a deadly disease. This is happening with the native white elm (*Ulmus americana*) of North America, which is being decimated by an introduced Eurasian pathogen (the Dutch elm disease fungus, *Ceratocystis ulmi*) to which this tree has almost no immunity. Other causes of population crashes include unsustainable levels of predation, and extensive disturbances such as wildfire, windstorms, or clear-cutting.

Community Ecology

An ecological community is an aggregation of populations that occur in the same time and place and that interact physically, chemically, and/or behaviourally. The study of relationships among species within communities is known as **synecology**. Strictly speaking, a community consists of all plant, animal, and microbial populations occurring together on a site.

The Niche

Each species within a community exploits the environment and interacts with other species in a particular manner. This can be considered to be its "occupation" or livelihood. Ecologists use the word **niche** to describe the

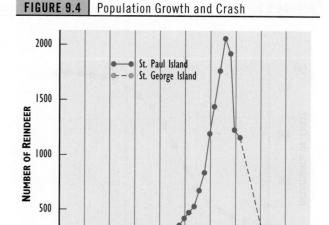

FIGURE 9.4 | Population Growth and Crash

In 1910, reindeer (*Rangifer tarandus tarandus*; the Eurasian subspecies of caribou) were introduced to two islands in the Aleutian chain off western Alaska in an attempt to establish a new resource of meat and hides for local use. On both islands, the reindeer population increased rapidly. They exceeded the carrying capacity of the habitat and caused severe damage through overgrazing. The populations then crashed.

Source: Modified from Krebs (1985)

role of a species in its community. Some niches are relatively narrow and specialized, as is the niche of bats that feed only on flying insects of a certain size, or of wasps that pollinate only one or a few species of plants. Other niches, however, are much broader, such as those of bears and humans, both of which forage over extremely broad ranges and affect their ecosystems in diverse ways.

The so-called *fundamental niche* is determined by the range of a species' tolerance of environmental factors (e.g., hot and cold temperatures). The *realized niche* reflects the range of environmental conditions that a species actually manages to exploit in nature. The realized niche is smaller than the fundamental niche because all species are constrained to some degree by biological interactions such as competition, predation, and disease.

Functional Communities

Because of their complexity, entire communities are rarely studied by ecologists. Ecological studies are usually limited by the amounts of funding, person-power, and breadth of expertise available. Instead, community-level research usually involves the examination of selected functional "communities" of similar organisms, such as insect, fish, bird, plant, or microbial communities. Although the scope of such work is limited, it does allow ecologists to investigate important aspects of community ecology.

Forest communities, for example, contain a wide range of organisms of various species and sizes, including plants, animals, and microorganisms. The populations of these diverse species interact with each other in myriad ways. Trees, for instance, contribute most of the physical structure of the habitat, provide food for many species of herbivorous animals, and drop leaf litter that is decomposed by animals and microorganisms who recycle the nutrients through the detrital food web. Other ecological interactions within a forest community include predatory, parasitic, and disease relationships among species, as well as many symbioses, such as pollination, seed dispersal, and root mycorrhizae. Because of the inherent complexity of forest communities, most ecological studies only investigate selected components.

This pragmatic approach to community-level forest research can be illustrated by studies of the ecological effects of forestry conducted in the Maritimes by my students and I. We divided the larger community into the following *functional groups*:

1. trees, which we define as woody plants with a stem diameter greater than 10 cm

2. shrubs, which have a stem diameter less than 10 cm, are taller than 1 m, and include shrub-sized, young individuals of tree species as well as "true" shrubs

3. ground vegetation, which includes all plants, mosses, and lichens that are growing within 1 m of the ground surface

4. epiphytes that grow on other plants, such as species of lichens and mosses that grow on the bark-covered surfaces of trees

5. small mammals such as mice, shrews, voles, squirrels, and marten

6. large mammals such as deer, bear, and coyote

7. birds

8. reptiles and amphibians

9. insects

10. fungi and other microorganisms living in the soil

During some of our relatively detailed studies of birds, specific work was done with species that nest in holes in trees. These species comprise a "cavity-requiring" element of the larger avian community. Similarly, studies of insects and other invertebrates have involved functional groups that live in soil, in rotting deadwood, or on foliage. Even with all of these (and other) functional groups, we did not manage to examine all of the important elements of the forest communities that we were studying.

Factors Influencing Communities

Ecological communities are affected by various environmental factors, particularly those described below.

Species Present

Obviously, only those species that are present in a habitat, or are capable of dispersing into it, can play a role in the community that develops. A species' ability to colonize an available habitat is influenced by its biology, intervening barriers such as a mountain range or ocean, the disturbance regime in the habitat, and other factors. Increasingly, humans are influencing the species composition of communities, often by introducing non-indigenous species beyond their natural range.

Appropriate Habitat

If a habitat is unsuitable, then a particular species will not be able to utilize it even if it is capable of dispersing to the site. There are many aspects of habitat suitability, and all of these must be satisfied within the limits of tolerance of a species if it is to become a component of a local community.

Interactions with Other Species

Species interact through herbivory, predation, competition, disease, and symbiosis, the latter including mutualism, commensalism, and parasitism. All of these interactions can influence the presence and abundance of different species within communities. The following examples illustrate these influences.

Herbivory: Larvae of the hemlock looper (*Lambdina fiscellaria*) are voracious feeders on the foliage of spruce, fir, and other coniferous trees. When conditions are suitable, this moth can proliferate rapidly, causing severe damage over a large area of forest, as periodically happens in eastern Canada. Forests defoliated for several years have many dead trees, representing an important element of community change. The loss of much of the forest canopy

Photo 9.4 Species interact with each other in various ways, such as herbivory, predation, competition, disease, and symbiosis. This photo shows elk (*Cervus canadensis*) grazing on plants in a lawn in Jasper National Park, Alberta.

has many indirect effects, such as allowing understorey plants to grow more vigorously. The changes in vegetation affect the habitat available for species of insects, birds, and other animals. Microorganisms and other detritivores are also affected, because large quantities of dead tree biomass are available to be decomposed.

Predation: An extremely effective predator can greatly reduce the abundance of its prey, thereby changing the structure of the community. For instance, during the summer, most forest birds feed on insects, spiders, and other invertebrates, which are nutritious food for both adults and their rapidly growing nestlings. Avian predation can greatly change the invertebrate community, as has been demonstrated by studies in which small areas of forest were enclosed with netting. Avian predators were excluded, but invertebrates could move in or out. Under these conditions, the abundance of many species of insects and other avian prey increased, with species particularly vulnerable to avian predation benefiting the most.

Competition: This occurs when the biological demand for an ecological resource exceeds the supply, causing organisms to interfere with each other. Plants, for example, often compete for access to limited supplies of sunlight, water, nutrients, and space. Animals may compete for food, nesting sites, mates, and other resources. *Intraspecific competition* occurs when individuals of the same species vie for access to resources, while *interspecific competition* occurs between different species. If a species is particularly effec-

tive at co-opting resources to its own benefit, it may displace other species, a phenomenon known as competitive displacement (or, in extreme cases, competitive exclusion). This affects the presence and relative abundance of species in the community. For example, sugar maple (*Acer saccharum*) is a very competitive tree in hardwood forests of eastern Canada. Where environmental conditions are well suited for this species, it can dominate mature stands. If large sugar maple trees are removed from a stand, perhaps by a selective timber harvest, other tree species (as well as small sugar maples) will benefit greatly from the reduced competition, and will grow more vigorously.

Disease: The health of individuals and of populations is affected by their vulnerability to certain diseases. Virulent diseases can cause enormous changes in the composition of ecological communities. In the early 1900s, the American chestnut (*Castanea dentata*) was afflicted by chestnut blight (*Endothia parasitica*), an introduced fungal pathogen. Because chestnuts have little immunity to this disease, the species was virtually eliminated from the forests of eastern North America by the 1950s. This change released other tree species from competition with the previously dominant chestnut, and they quickly filled gaps in the canopy created by its demise.

Symbiosis: This refers to intimate relationships among species. Some symbioses involve obligate relationships in which the symbionts cannot live apart, but more commonly, the association is somewhat flexible. Symbioses can greatly influence the success of species in particular environments by improving their competitive ability and decreasing their vulnerability to predation, disease, or other stresses.

The main types of **symbiosis** are **mutualism**, in which both partners benefit; **parasitism**, in which one organism benefits and the other is harmed; and **commensalism**, in which one organism benefits without harming the other. While symbioses are critical to one or both partners, they can also indirectly affect the habitat and the resources available to other members of the community.

Lichens are a familiar example of a mutualism. They are an obligate association between a fungus and either an alga or a blue-green bacterium. The fungus benefits from the productivity of the photosynthetic partner, while the latter gains a relatively moist microhabitat and improved access to inorganic nutrients.

Another mutualism, called a mycorrhiza, is an intimate association between fungi and the roots of vascular plants. The plant benefits through enhanced access to nutrients,

Photo 9.5 A mutualism is an intimate symbiosis in which both partners benefit from the relationship. Lichens, such as the light-coloured *Parmelia saxatilis* in the centre of the photo, are an obligate mutualism between a fungus and an alga, meaning that the two species cannot live apart in nature. Thus, taxonomists treat them as a single "species."

especially phosphate, while the fungus receives nutritious exudates from the roots of the plant. This mutualism also provides a broad, community-level benefit through increased primary productivity. Some species of legumes live in a mutualism with the bacterium *Rhizobium japonicum*, which fixes nitrogen gas (N_2) into ammonia, a critical nutrient.

Another mutualism involves species of Dinoflagellates (single-celled algae) that live within corals (small, colonial animals), where they receive protection and access to nutrients. The corals benefit through access to the photosynthetic productivity of the algae.

Many animals eat plant biomass, but few are able, on their own, to digest complex polymeric biochemicals such as cellulose and lignin. Consequently, many herbivores live in a mutualism with microorganisms, which inhabit their gut and secrete enzymes that digest cellulose and lignin, making those abundant sources of nutrition available to the animal. Cows, deer, and sheep host their digestion-aiding microorganisms in a specialized pouch of their fore-stomach, called the rumen. Humans also harbour a diverse community of microorganisms in their gut, many of which are important to our nutrition.

Other mutualisms include the many species of flowers that are pollinated by specific insects. Pollination is crucial to the reproductive success of plants, while the insects benefit from an abundant food source of nectar or pollen. In addition, herbivores in the community benefit from the fruits that are produced because of pollination, and, in turn, they may disperse the plant seeds.

An example of commensalism is the epiphyte community of plants, lichens, and mosses that often grows on large trees. The epiphytes achieve an ecological benefit from the relationship, but the host trees are not affected to any meaningful degree. There are many familiar examples of parasitism, including fleas on a dog and tapeworms in humans. The parasite benefits by taking nutrition from the host, but the host usually suffers, and may even die.

Disturbance

All ecological communities are dynamic, changing over time in their species composition and functional attributes (such as productivity, decomposition, and nutrient cycling). The nature and rate of community change depend on the stability of environmental conditions. The most dynamic communities are associated with the younger stages of *succession* after *disturbance*. As we noted in Chapter 1, disturbance can occur on two spatial scales.

Stand-replacing disturbances are caused by wildfire, a disease epidemic, glaciation, clear-cutting, and other cataclysmic events. This kind of disturbance is relatively extensive and results in the immediate replacement of a community with a different one, followed by successional recovery. Over time, succession may regenerate a community similar to what existed before the disruption, or a different community may result.

The younger stages of a *sere* (or successional sequence) are especially dynamic in terms of the rate of community change. During the initial years of recovery, competition is not intense, and ruderal, r-selected species dominate. Later stages of succession are much less dynamic, and K-selected species dominate.

Microdisturbances are local disruptions, affecting small areas within an otherwise intact community. A microdisturbance may, for instance, be associated with the death of an individual tree or a small group of trees within a forest. Such a microdisturbance results in a gap in the canopy, within which community change is relatively dynamic as species compete to take advantage of the temporary resource opportunity of additional sunlight. Similarly, the deaths of individual coral heads represent microdisturbance within a coral reef community. Although ecological changes

Photo 9.6   Ecosystems are occasionally subjected to catastrophic disturbances, such as this forest fire in La Mauricie National Park, Quebec.

Source: L. Foisy

are dynamic within a gap created by a recent micro-disturbance, at the stand level the community is relatively stable. Gap-phase community dynamics occur in all eco-systems but are most important during later stages of succession, for example in older-growth forests.

Spatial Variation of the Environment

Environmental conditions are always variable from place to place, and sometimes extremely so. These spatial vari-ations greatly influence the character of ecological com-munities, as described below.

Gradual spatial changes in environmental conditions are associated with varying altitude on a mountain, chang-ing climate over large distances across continents, and other relatively continuous gradients. This type of spatial change is reflected in gradual variations of communities, because of individual species' different but overlapping tolerances and requirements of environmental conditions. This results in overlaps of the distributions of species, which can make it difficult for ecologists to determine the locations of boundaries (*ecotones*) between some types of communities.

Rapid spatial changes in environmental conditions occur at sharp boundaries between distinctive types of soil or bedrock, at interfaces between aquatic and terrestrial habi-tats, and in places affected by different disturbance regimes. The latter influence can occur, for instance, between a burned and unburned area of forest or between an eco-logical reserve and its surrounding area, which may be affected by agriculture or forestry. Relatively discrete changes in environmental conditions favour large differences in community types, with distinct, readily identifiable boundaries between them.

Landscape Ecology

Landscapes (or seascapes in the marine context) are a mosaic of patches, each of which represents an ecological community. A landscape may contain various kinds of communities because

- each reflects particular environmental conditions, such as different soil or bedrock types or variations of standing water (as in lakes, streams, or wetlands);

- they represent various stages in succession, such as communities of different ages after wildfire or insect damage; and

- they are related to the nature of land-use, as when parts of landscapes are affected by urbanization, agriculture, forestry, transmission corridors, roads, or other human influences.

Over time, the spatial patterns of communities in landscapes are highly dynamic. This largely reflects the influence of disturbances and successional recovery. A patch that today is a pasture, or a recent clear-cut or burn, may be a mature forest after 50 years of succession. Similarly, a pond may in-fill over the centuries and become a wetland, which with further time may transform into a forest. Ecologists use the term "shifting mosaic" to integrate the spatial and temporal variations of communities within landscapes. The following important factors affect the shifting mosaic of communities in landscapes.

Patch size relates to the area of particular stands of communities (a "stand" is a community in a particular place). All species need some minimal area of habitat to support their populations over the long term, and small patches of ecosystem may not be adequate for this purpose. Relatively small patches may, however, help to support a population living in several patches on the landscape (an extensive population of this sort is known as a *metapopulation*). This can happen if the patches are connected by corridors to other suitable habitat, or if the species is capable of dispersing through surrounding, inhospitable habitats (i.e., the landscape matrix must be "permeable" to movements of the species).

The amount of edge is also important, largely because it influences the length of ecotone habitat associated with the patch. A circular patch has the smallest ratio of edge to area, and smaller patches have higher ratios than larger ones of the same shape. Ecotones between patch types are a habitat and may be selectively utilized by so-called "edge species." However, the greater the ratio of edge to area, the less "interior" habitat there is (interior habitat is uninfluenced by ecological conditions associated with ecotones). Ecologists have identified "interior species" that are less successful if they try to use habitat close to an edge. Certain forest birds, for instance, experience greater rates of predation and nest parasitism in small remnants of mature forest (see Chapter 26).

Connectedness refers to the presence of links between otherwise discrete patches of similar habitat. These may be used by species as corridors to move among patches, allowing metapopulations to function on the landscape. As was noted previously, connectedness is also related to the abil-

Photo 9.7 Landscapes are subjected to patch dynamics associated with natural disturbances, such as wildfire, windstorms, and insect outbreaks. However, the patch dynamics of forested landscapes in Canada are being increasingly structured by forestry. In this aerial view of an area in New Brunswick, the natural forest is being harvested by clearcutting (the lighter patches are snow in the clear-cuts), which initiates a succession that restores a forest for another harvest in 60–80 years. Unless areas are set aside for protection, this entire landscape may become used in this way.

Source: M. Sullivan

ity of a species to disperse among habitable patches through the surrounding, inhospitable habitat.

Age-class adjacency is important in a landscape in which patches represent different stages of a successional sequence. This commonly occurs in landscapes affected by disturbances such as wildfire, insect epidemics, clear-cutting, or agriculture. In general, patches of a similar post-disturbance age will be comparable in many aspects of habitat quality, while patches of different age will be less similar. This can be an important consideration for movements of species among patches suitable as habitat.

Complex habitat requirements are characteristic of some larger species of animals, such as deer, bears, and wolf. These species need different kinds of habitat patches for various purposes at various times of year. Because these animals participate in various kinds of communities, all the habitat patches they need must be present on the landscape if viable metapopulations are to be sustained.

Landscape-level biodiversity is related to the richness of community types over a large area (see Chapter 7). A landscape uniformly covered by a single community has less biodiversity than one composed of a rich and dynamic mosaic of different communities.

Landscape-level functions operate over extensive areas, and they integrate the influences of many kinds of communities. A **watershed**, for example, is defined as the expanse of terrain from which water drains into a stream, lake, or some other kind of waterbody. Most watersheds contain various types of habitat patches, each with particular influences on hydrology and water chemistry. In general, watersheds covered with mature forest yield the cleanest flows of water. Other environmental services provided by well-vegetated landscapes include evapotranspiration, control of erosion, moderation of climatic extremes, and absorption of atmospheric carbon dioxide and release of oxygen.

Landscape ecology is an important subject area in environmental science. Humans commonly affect individual stands of particular kinds of communities, but many of the ecological effects of these actions must be managed at the scale of landscapes and seascapes.

The Biosphere

The biosphere consists of all life and ecosystems on Earth. It is bounded by the presence of living organisms, and it is the only place in the universe known to support life.

Ecological processes at the level of the biosphere include global climatic, oceanic, and atmospheric regimes (Chapter 3), Earth's energy budget (Chapter 4), and planetary nutrient cycles (Chapter 5). These biospheric processes influence all life and ecosystems. It is important to recognize, however, that Earth's life and ecosystems also influence biosphere-level processes.

The Gaia Hypothesis

Some scientists have suggested that there may be a degree of homeostatic control, or feedback, between the reciprocal influences of Earth's ecosystems and their biosphere-level environment. A notion describing these global biosphere–environment relationships is known as the **Gaia hypothesis**, a controversial idea popularized by the British scientist James Lovelock. Lovelock suggests that Earth's organisms and ecosystems have caused substantial changes to occur in certain physical and chemical attributes of the environment, resulting in improvements in living conditions on the planet. The hypothesis envisions all of Earth's species and ecosystems as encompassed by a sort of "super-organism," or Gaia. According to Lovelock, Gaia attempts to optimize environmental conditions toward enhancing its own health and continuity, and uses feedback mechanisms that help maintain conditions within the range that life can tolerate.

The ancient Greeks believed that Gaia (or Gaea) was the prolific ancestor of many of their most important gods. The Romans, who adopted many Greek gods and ideas as their own, also believed in Gaia, whom they knew as Terra. More recently, the Gaian myth has been personified as "mother Earth."

The Gaian idea is attractive and interesting, largely because it integrates so many ideas and large-scale observations into a single, consolidated belief and world view. However, Earth is the only planet in the universe known to support life and ecosystems, and therefore it is the only known replicate in the great experiment of life. Consequently, the Gaia hypothesis cannot be tested by rigorous, scientific experimentation, and for this reason, many scientists reject many of its inferences. Except in the broadest of terms, Gaian ideas may not be very useful in helping humans to manage the detrimental impacts of their increasing population and agroindustrial activities on the biosphere.

Nevertheless, some intriguing lines of evidence can be marshalled in support of the Gaian notion. Two examples follow.

Atmospheric Oxygen

Earth's primordial atmosphere did not contain oxygen (O_2). This gas appeared only after the first photosynthetic organisms, blue-green bacteria, evolved. These, and the somewhat later evolved green algae, give off O_2 as a waste product of photosynthesis. The present concentration of O_2 in the atmosphere, 21%, has resulted entirely from photosynthesis and is a critical environmental factor for most of Earth's species and many key ecological processes.

Atmospheric O_2 concentrations have probably been stable for as long as several billions of years. This suggests a long-term equilibrium between O_2 production by photoautotrophs and its consumption by respiration, including decomposition. Interestingly, if the concentration of oxygen were much higher than 21%, say about 25%, then biomass would be much more combustible. This condition would lead to more frequent and extensive wildfires, which would severely damage Earth's terrestrial ecosystems.

All this can be interpreted as suggesting the existence of a homeostatic control of the concentration of atmospheric O_2, operating at the biospheric scale. This control may achieve a balance between sufficient O_2 to sustain Earth's most abundant organisms (which have an aerobic metabolism), and larger O_2 concentrations that would result in extremely destructive conflagrations.

Earth's Greenhouse Effect

The concentration of atmospheric carbon dioxide (CO_2) is substantially regulated by a complex of physical and biological processes by which this gas is emitted and absorbed. Atmospheric CO_2 is important in Earth's greenhouse effect, which maintains the surface temperature within a range that organisms can tolerate (see Chapters 4 and 17). Earth's greenhouse effect helps maintain an average surface temperature of about 15°C, compared with the –18°C that would otherwise occur and would be too cold for organisms to tolerate. Advocates of the Gaia hypothesis suggest that these observations imply a direct homeostatic control of atmospheric CO_2 and an indirect control of the greenhouse effect and climate.

There is clear evidence that organisms and ecosystems cause substantial changes in their environment and that they are also affected by environmental conditions. The scientific community does not, however, widely support the notion that Earth's species and ecosystems have somehow integrated into a mutually benevolent symbiosis aimed at maintaining a comfortable range of environmental conditions.

The Gaia hypothesis is nevertheless useful in environmental science. Gaian ideas emphasize the diverse connections within and among ecosystems, as well as the damaging consequences of human actions that are increasingly causing environmental and ecological changes. If these changes exceed the biospheric limits of homeostatic tolerance and repair, the consequences for the planet's geophysiology and ecology could be catastrophic.

Applied Ecology

The application of ecological principles to dealing with economic and environmental problems is known as **applied ecology** (or as environmental ecology). The major subject areas of applied ecology are

1. *the management of renewable resources*, such as those important in agriculture, fisheries, and forestry;

2. *the prevention or repair of ecological damages*, such as those related to endangered biodiversity, the restoration of degraded land or water, and the management of greenhouse gases; and

3. *the management of ecological processes*, such as productivity, nutrient cycling, hydrology, and erosion.

Later chapters in this textbook contain many examples of the use of applied ecology to deal with problems of resource management, pollution, and disturbance. Although the subject is not dealt with here in detail, it can be illustrated by the following examples:

■ **Setting Harvest Limits:** Ecologists can estimate the rate of forest productivity in a region by repeatedly measuring trees in plots that are re-sampled over the years or by coring populations of trees and examining the annual ring-width of their recent wood. This information can be used to set limits on the amount of timber that can be harvested without degrading the resource. Analogous methods of measuring productivity can be used to manage the harvesting of populations of mammals, birds, and fish.

■ **Increasing Biological Productivity:** Through research, ecologists can determine the possibility of increasing the productivity of biological resources—for example, whether forest productivity could be increased by applying fertilizer, thinning dense stands, or establishing plantations. Research can also predict other ecological implications of these sorts of management practices, including the effects on indigenous biodiversity and water quality.

■ **Remediation, Reclamation, and Restoration:** Ecologists can provide research-based advice for improving conditions in areas that have been degraded by pollution or disturbance (see In Detail 9.2). Various kinds of schemes can be used to deal with ecological degradation:

In Detail 9.2

Restoration Ecology

Restoration ecology involves activities that ecologists might undertake to repair environmental damage, with a view to restoring a natural, self-maintaining ecosystem.

Endangered species and their habitat are a common focus of restoration ecology. Typically, ecologists might try to increase the abundance of an endangered species by preventing any exploitation, developing a program of captive breeding and release, and managing habitat to ensure its suitability. Another focus of restoration ecology is to increase the area of an endangered ecosystems, for example, by protecting remnants of the ecosystem and repairing them if they are in a degraded condition. Restoration ecologists might also try a reconstruction effort, by introducing constituent species to a suitable site while managing the environment to foster community development.

Ecologists may also be involved in the reclamation of areas damaged by industrial activities, for example, the reclamation of abandoned strip-mines, waste-disposal areas, or disused building sites into an ecologically acceptable condition. These projects are not necessarily intended to restore a natural ecosystem, but rather to develop a stable, self-maintaining cover of vegetation. Non-native species are often used in industrial reclamation rather than strictly using native ones, as would be the case in a restoration project. An example of such a project is described in Canadian Focus 18.1 involving the reclamation of a waste-disposal area near Sudbury.

Restoring indigenous biodiversity is always difficult, often because of an incomplete understanding of the structure and function of imperilled communities, including the ecological relationships among key species. In part, this problem is due to ecology being a relatively recent science.

Often, small fragments of natural ecosystems persist in degraded landscapes, but it is not known if they are representative of what used to occur more widely or whether the remnants are themselves damaged. For example, tall-grass prairie was once an extensive ecosystem in central North America, including southwestern Ontario and southeastern Manitoba. This natural ecosystem has become critically endangered because almost all of its original area has been converted into agricultural use. Only a few remnants of tall-grass prairie have survived, but ecologists do not know how typical they are of the original ecosystems or whether part of the original complement of species is now missing.

Another difficulty is that most natural ecosystems require a long time to develop their mature character. Therefore, it is difficult for individual ecologists, and for society, to commit to the restoration of some natural ecosystems that take decades or centuries to develop. For example, old-growth forest may not reach an equilibrium of species composition and biomass until three to five centuries have passed since the most recent, stand-replacing disturbance. Any initiative to reconstruct old-growth forest on degraded land must be designed with this long time frame in mind.

In many cases, environmental conditions have changed significantly, even permanently, from those existing before anthropogenic damage was caused. Under a changed environmental regime, it may not be feasible to restore original ecosystems, and ecologists may have to pursue alternative, less lofty goals.

Although the challenges faced by restoration ecologists are daunting, there are great benefits of restoring natural ecosystems and endangered species. Restoration ecology tests our knowledge of ecological principles and of environmental influences on species and communities. It takes a deep understanding of ecology to convert degraded environments into self-maintaining populations and facsimiles of natural ecosystems.

Examples of Ecological Restoration

Most projects in restoration ecology have focused on the conservation of endangered species. In some cases, success only required a stop to the killing of the species. For example, on the Pacific coast, populations of the sea otter (*Enhydra lutris*) were so depleted by the nineteenth-century fur trade that the species was thought extinct. However, small populations were discovered in the 1930s. These were strictly protected, allowing them to grow and colonize other suitable habitat, aided by some introductions by humans (including to the west coast of Vancouver Island). The sea otter is no longer so endangered. Other recoveries achieved by controlling hunting include the pronghorn antelope (*Antilocapra americana*), elk (*Cervus canadensis*), beaver (*Castor canadensis*), northern fur seal (*Callorhinus ursinus*), grey whale (*Eschrichtius robustus*), and humpback whale (*Megaptera novaeangliae*). All of these species had been over-exploited but rebounded after hunting was stopped or strictly regulated.

Other depleted species have been restored by controlling hunting while also enhancing their habitat. For example, the wood duck (*Aix sponsa*) was endangered by the combined effects of over-hunting and habitat loss by wetland drainage and timber cutting in forested wetlands (swamps). It has recovered substantially because of limits on hunting, the conservation of swamp habitat, and the provision of nest boxes. A terrestrial nest-box program has also allowed some recovery of eastern and western bluebirds (*Sialla sialis* and *S. mexicana*).

Other endangered species have benefited from programs of captive breeding and release to supplement their wild populations or to re-introduce the species to habitat from which it had been extirpated. The whooping crane (*Grus americana*) is being assisted in this way, and its abundance has increased from only 15 individuals in 1941 to more than 300 today. The release of captive-bred animals has also enhanced the peregrine falcon (*Falco peregrinus anatum*; see Canadian Focus 21.1), trumpeter swan (*Cyanus buccinator*), wild turkey (*Meleagris gallopavo*), and pine marten (*Martes americana*).

Some endangered species need active management of their degraded habitat. For example, the endangered Kirtland's warbler (*Dendroica kirtlandii*) only breeds in stands of jack pine (*Pinus banksiana*) in Michigan. Its critical habitat is maintained by conserving natural forest, planting jack pine, using burns to develop appropriate stand conditions, and reducing the abundance of the brown-headed cowbird (*Molothrus ater*), an important nest parasite (see Chapter 26). This intensive habitat management is helping the endangered warbler to maintain its small breeding population, although it remains threatened by habitat loss in its Caribbean wintering area.

In a few cases, restoration ecologists have focused their efforts on entire ecosystems. This may be done by protecting remnants of an endangered ecosystem. For example, tall-grass prairie now covers less than 1% of its

Photo 9.8   The principles of restoration ecology can be applied to the naturalization of urban land. This residential greenspace has been converted into a replica of tall-grass prairie by sowing seed, transplanting species, and managing the area to favour prairie plants.

Source: Larry Lamb

original area, and remnant habitats are being acquired by the Nature Conservancy of Canada and governments for conservation within ecological reserves. However, these protected areas must be managed properly, including periodic light burning to prevent the development of shrubs or oak-dominated forest.

The ultimate application of restoration ecology is in the reconstruction of facsimiles of natural ecosystems. This approach is, however, rarely used because of its inherent difficulty and expense. The best examples of this bottom-up restoration involve the re-establishment of prairie. Prairie plants are re-introduced by transplanting or sowing seed, while the habitat is managed (including the use of prescribed burns) until a self-maintaining ecosystem develops.

Restoration ecology helps to repair some of the damage caused by human activities. However, it is always better to avoid the damage in the first place. Restraint in the exploitation of wild species and natural ecosystems and acting to preserve natural values in large protected areas are by far the best ways to conserve the Earth's biodiversity.

- • **Remediation** involves specific actions undertaken to deal with particular problems, such as liming lakes and rivers to decrease their acidity, planting tolerant species of plants in polluted environments, or undertaking programs of captive breeding and release to increase the abundance of endangered species.

- • **Reclamation** involves more comprehensive actions to establish a productive ecosystem on degraded land. For example, an old landfill or a disused industrial site may be reclaimed with a permanent cover of vegetation, such as a pasture.

- • **Restoration** has a loftier goal: attempting to establish a self-maintaining facsimile of a natural ecosystem on degraded land. For instance, the techniques of restoration ecology might be used to convert abandoned farmland back to a native prairie or forest.

- ■ **Offsets for Greenhouse Gases:** Ecologists can predict the amount of forest that must be grown and protected in order to offset industrial emissions of greenhouse gases. This can allow companies and nations to reduce their net emissions of CO_2 or CH_4 and to make progress toward meeting international agreements to deal with climate change.

- ■ **Reducing Erosion:** Some areas are degraded through erosion caused by deforestation and other land-use changes. Ecologists can help find ways to deal with this problem—for example by reforestation, establishing other kinds of permanent plant cover, using terraced agricultural fields, or controlling local hydrology to reduce erosion caused by overland or subsurface water flows.

Conclusions

Ecology is the study of the relationships of organisms with the environmental factors that provide the requirements of life and livelihood. These factors include resources such as nutrients and food, the influences of other organisms through competition and predation, as well as stressors such as disturbance and pollution. Knowledge of ecology is central to understanding many of the most important damages that the human economy is wreaking upon the biosphere. Applied ecological knowledge is essential to managing renewable resources on a sustainable basis, to conserving biodiversity, and to avoiding and repairing damage caused by pollution and other destructive influences of humans.

Key Terms

ecology
stressor
disturbance
succession
individual organism
population
species
community
landscape
seascape
biosphere
autecology
competitor
ruderal
stress-tolerator

carrying capacity
synecology
niche
symbiosis
mutualism
parasitism
commensalism
watershed
landscape ecology
Gaia hypothesis
applied ecology
remediation
reclamation
restoration

Questions for Review

1. Distinguish between autecology and synecology. Give examples to illustrate each.

2. What are birth rate, death rate, immigration rate, and emigration rate? How do these demographic factors influence population growth?

3. What environmental and biological influences affect the structure and function of an ecological community with which you are familiar?

4. What are the attributes of an ecological landscape (or seascape)? Illustrate your answer with examples from a landscape in the region where you live.

5. In a general sense, what are the goals and methods of a project in restoration ecology?

Questions for Discussion

1. Use the principles of autecology to discuss the resource needs and environmental tolerances of humans.

2. How are humans integrated into ecological communities?

3. How are the ideas and lessons of population ecology relevant to population changes of humans?

4. What are the core elements of the Gaia hypothesis? What evidence exists to support this hypothesis? How are Gaian ideas relevant to environmental science?

5. It is extremely difficult to successfully implement a large-scale project in restoration ecology. Under what sorts of conditions do you think such a project might be worthwhile?

Exploring Issues

1. The niche has sometimes been described as the "occupa-tion" of a species—what it does for a living, the resources it uses, and its habitat. You have been asked to make a pre-sentation to a group of non-ecologists, in which you must describe the niche of humans. What information would you include in your presentation?

References

Freedman, B. and J. Riley. 1980. Population trends of various species of birds wintering in southern Ontario. *Ontario Field Biologist*, **34**: 49–79.

Goodwin, C. E., B. Freedman, and S. M. McKay. 1977. Population trends in waterfowl wintering in the Toronto region, 1929–1976. *Ontario Field Biologist*, **31**: 1–28.

Grime, J.P. 1979. *Plant Strategies, Vegetation Processes and Ecosystem Properties*. 2nd ed. London: J. Wiley.

Harris, J.A., P. Birch, and J. Palmer. 1996. *Land Restoration and Reclamation: Principles and Practices*. Reading, MA: Addison-Wesley.

Kimmins, J.P. 2003. *Forest Ecology*. 3rd ed. New York: Prentice Hall.

Krebs, C.J. 1985. *Ecology: The Experimental Analysis of Distribution and Abundance*. New York: Harper & Row.

Lovelock, J.E. 1995. *The Ages of Gaia: A Biography of Our Living Earth*. New York: W. Norton & Co.

MacDonald, G.M. and L.C. Cwynar. 1991. Post-glacial popu-lation growth rates of *Pinus contorta* ssp. *latifolia* in west-ern Canada. *J. Ecol.*, **79**: 417–29.

Mills, S. 1996. *In Service of the Wild: Restoring and Reinhabiting Damaged Land*. Boston: Beacon Press.

Odum, E.P. 1997. *Ecology: A Bridge Between Science and Society*. New York: Sinauer Associates.

Odum, E.P. and G.W. Barrett. 2004. *Fundamentals of Ecology*. Florence, KY: Brooks Cole.

Silverton, J. 1987. *Introduction to Plant Population Ecology*. Harlow, UK: Longman Scientific and Technical.

Smith, L.E. 1991. *Gaia: The Growth of an Idea*. New York: St. Martin's.

Townsend, C.R., M. Begon, and J.L. Harper. 2002. *Essentials of Ecology*. 2nd ed. Cambridge, UK: Blackwell Publishers.

Informative Websites

British Ecological Society (BES).
www.britishecologicalsociety.org

The BES is the world's oldest society of professional ecologists. Their website contains numerous resources.

Ecological Society of America. Issues in Ecology.
www.esa.org/Science/Issues

You'll need Adobe Acrobat to view the reports available at this site. Sample titles include Human Alteration of the Global Nitrogen Cycle: Cause and Consequences; Ecosystem Services: Benefits Supplied to Human Societies by Natural Ecosystems; and Nonpoint Pollution of Surface Waters with Phosphorus and Nitrogen.

Ecology.com. http://www.ecology.com/

This website provides useful information about many facets of ecology and environmental science.

Ecology WWW Page. www.botany.net/Ecology/

This site has hundreds of ecology links listed alphabetically.

The Virtual Library of Ecology and Biodiversity.
http://conbio.net/vl/

This website reviews Internet information sources related to ecology and biodiversity.

10 Global Populations

CHAPTER OBJECTIVES

After completing this chapter, you will be able to

1. Outline the process of cultural evolution and describe how it has resulted in changes in the environment's carrying capacity for the human population.
2. Describe the growth of the human population during the past 10 000 years.
3. Explain the causes of global population growth during the past several centuries.
4. Discuss the reasons for differences in population growth rates between developed and less developed countries.
5. Explain the influences of the demographic transition and age-class structure on population growth.
6. List the major methods of birth control.
7. Discuss the reasons why certain methods of birth control are controversial.
8. Explain population policies and possible future influences on the global human population.
9. Discuss possible causes of a population crash.

CHAPTER OUTLINE

Introduction

About 10 000 years ago, there were only a few million humans on Earth. In 2005, there were more than 6.4 billion and the number is climbing steadily (by about 80 million per year). In terms of consequences for the biosphere, the enormous growth of the human population is the most significant event to occur in the past 15 000 years or so (i.e., since the most recent glaciation; see Chapter 3).

The global population of humans has been increasing for several millennia, but the growth rate been particularly rapid during the past few centuries. Moreover, there is every indication that the present, extremely large population will continue to increase in the foreseeable future. We will examine some possible scenarios of future population growth later in this chapter.

The environmental consequence of the presence of any human population is a function of two interacting factors: the actual number of people and the per capita environmental impact. The per capita impact is related to both the lifestyles of individual people and the level of tech-nological development of their society. Both of these influence resource use, pollution, and the degradation of ecosystems (see also Chapter 1).

The growth of the human population during the past several millennia is quite remarkable and may be unprecedented in scale during the history of life on Earth. This inference is based on

- the long period of time during which population growth has been sustained;

- the extraordinary abundance that has been achieved;

- the similarly impressive collateral population growth of mutualist species (such as cows, pigs, chickens, and agricultural plants); and

- the remarkable variety of species and ecosystems that are being exploited as resources to support the human enterprise.

In large part, these phenomenal achievements of *Homo sapiens* have been realized through the benefits of **cultural evolution**, or the progression of adaptive discoveries of

Photo 10.1 The human population is growing rapidly and now numbers more than six billion. This scene shows an urban market in Hong Kong.

increasingly sophisticated tools and social systems. The capacity of humans to learn from the experience of others, including the passage of information from one generation to the next, has allowed cultural evolution to proceed. In turn, cultural evolution has allowed humans to be more efficient in the capture of resources by exploiting other species, ecosystems, and non-renewable natural capital (Chapter 12). Cultural evolution has allowed humans to achieve unparalleled success in their domestication of planet Earth.

Unfortunately, intense damage has been caused to the biosphere by the combined effects of increases in population and in per capita environmental impact. Some of this damage represents a substantial reduction in the **carrying capacity** of the biosphere for humans (i.e., the abundance that can be sustained without degrading the habitat). Moreover, the extent of natural ecosystems has been severely reduced through human actions, which is causing a great reduction in Earth's carrying capacity for innumerable other species (see Chapter 26). This ecological damage is so increasingly extensive, and of such great intensity, that it has produced a global environmental crisis that is worsening with time. Regrettably, enhancing the human enterprise through cultural evolution has largely been achieved by reducing the ability of the biosphere to support many other species and natural ecosystems.

The increased size of the human population is not, on its own, the root cause of the environmental crisis. The rapid escalation of per capita resource usage is also important. However, we cannot achieve a sustainable resolution of the environmental crisis without knowing about, and ultimately dealing with, the explosive growth in the abundance of people on Earth.

In this chapter we examine the remarkable changes that have occurred in the human population during the past 10 000 or so years and in the intensity of resource use during cultural evolution. We also look at predictions of population change in the near future. Global patterns of change are emphasized in this chapter; we will examine the population of Canada in Chapter 11.

Cultural Evolution, Carrying Capacity, and Population

The biological history of hominids, including *Australopithecus africanus*, extends to perhaps four million years. The genus *Homo*, of which *Homo sapiens* is the only surviving species, goes back about two million years. For almost all of the

evolutionary history of our species, relatively small populations were engaged in subsistence lifestyles, foraging over extensive areas while hunting wild animals and gathering edible plants. These people likely roamed the landscape in small family groups, searching for food and other resources and using simple weapons and tools made of wood, bone, stone, shells, and other natural materials. The hunter-gatherer lifestyle characterized the first 99% or so of human history, and during that lengthy time, the population of our species was likely less than one million individuals.

By some 12 000–15 000 years ago, all of the major habitable landmasses had been discovered by early humans, including the Americas. The latter were colonized relatively late, when small groups of people roved eastward across a broad (up to 1000 km wide) but temporary land bridge connecting Siberia and Alaska, through what is now the Aleutian Islands. The land bridge was present as recently as about 11 000 years ago, and it existed because so much water was tied up in continental glaciers that sea level was about 100 m lower than it is now. (Note, however, that some archaeologists believe there may have been an earlier colonization of the Americas, occurring as early as 60 000 years ago.)

The wandering Siberians found a landscape with bountiful resources that had never before been exploited by humans. Descendants of the first human colonists of the Americas spread quickly, like an expanding wave, to occupy and exploit all habitable regions of North, Central, and South America. Coincident with the colonizing surge of humans was a mass extinction of many species of large mammals and birds. Probably naïve to the lethal prowess of the novel two-legged predators that hunted in well-coordinated packs, these unfortunate animals were unable to adapt to the onslaught (see Chapters 12 and 26).

Cultural evolution was not static during the protracted phase of foraging societies, and there were many adaptive innovations of culture and technology, such as:

- improvements of tools and weapons;
- discoveries of edible and medicinal species;
- development of improved social organizations to more efficiently exploit natural resources;
- the mastery of fire;
- the domestication of the dog, which allowed more efficient hunting, provided a pack animal, and helped keep encampments clean.

Each of these prehistoric breakthroughs enhanced the ability of humans to exploit natural resources. This increased the effective carrying capacity of the ecosystems they were utilizing and allowed the population to increase. By the end of this period (about 9000–10 000 years ago), when most societies engaged in foraging lifestyles, the global population was likely between one and five million individuals.

About 10 000 years ago, the first significant developments of primitive agriculture began, marking the beginning of the neolithic revolution (also known as the new stone age; Figure 10.1). The first agricultural innovations included the initial stages of domestication of a few edible plants and animals, such as barley and sheep, and the discoveries of simple ways of cultivating them to achieve greater yields. Because crops must be tended and protected, the adoption of agricultural practices required a relatively sedentary lifestyle. The eventual achievement of agricultural food surpluses allowed some people to be supported as non-agricultural workers in villages. This eventually fostered the development of city-states and then nation-states, along with their relatively sophisticated cultures and technologies.

The development of agriculture and its associated socio-cultural systems was one of the great leaps of human cultural evolution. The neolithic revolution provided an enormous increase in the carrying capacity of the environment for humans and their domesticated species. Steady population growth was one result of this change, because even primitive agricultural systems could support many more people than could subsistence lifestyles based on foraging for wild plants and animals.

The initial development of agriculture was followed by innovations that greatly increased crop yields. These improvements included the domestication of additional species of crop plants and animals, their genetic improvement through artificial selection (selective breeding), and the discovery of better ways of managing the environment to increase crop productivity. There were also many non-agricultural enhancements of the carrying capacity, including the discoveries of the properties of metals and their

---

FIGURE 10.1 | History of Human Population Growth

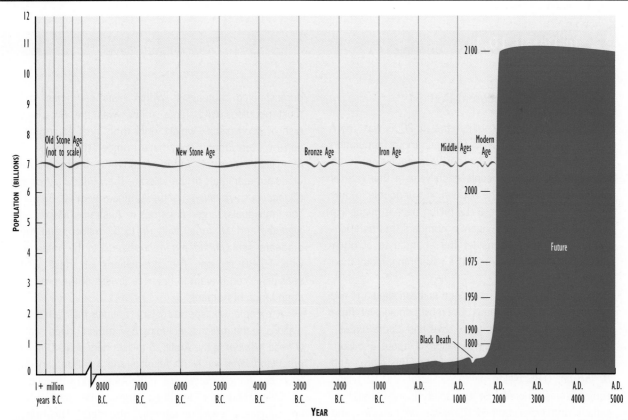

For most of the history of *Homo sapiens*, the global population remained relatively stable at several millions or less. Progressive innovations through cultural evolution allowed more efficient exploitation of natural resources, so the effective carrying capacity for humans increased. This process has intensified greatly during the past several millennia and especially during the past few centuries. The human population is now exhibiting explosive growth of a magnitude that is probably unprecedented for any large animal in the history of the biosphere.

Source: Modified from Population Reference Bureau (2005)

alloys, which allowed the manufacturing of tools and weapons that were superior to those made of bone, wood, or stone. Further, the domestication of beasts of burden and the invention of wheeled vehicles and ships made it easier to transport large quantities of valuable commodities, greatly stimulating trade.

Even this brief outline suggests that the cultural evolution of human sociotechnological systems has involved a long series of adaptive discoveries and innovations. Each of these increased the ability of people to exploit the resources of their environment. This increased the effective carrying capacity for people, which fostered growth of the population of humans and their mutualist species.

As a result of this adaptive progression, there were about five million people alive at the dawn of agriculture about 10 000 years ago, 200–300 million at the beginning of the Common Era 2000 years ago (0 CE), and 500 million in 1650.

The rate of population growth then began to increase markedly, a trend that has been maintained to the present. These recent, extremely rapid increases in the human pop-

ulation have occurred for several reasons. Of primary importance have been the discoveries of increasingly effective technologies in sanitation and medicine, which resulted in great decreases in death rates. Protection from lethal communicable diseases has been especially important in this regard.

In addition, recently discovered technologies allow increasingly effective extraction of resources, manufacturing of improved products, and better methods and infrastructures for transportation and communications. These have been achieved as a result of the "industrial revolution," which began in the mid-eighteenth century. Agricultural systems have also been enormously enhanced through the development of new crop varieties and improved cultivation methods, both of which have greatly increased yields. Again, all of these progressions of cultural evolution have further increased the carrying capacity of the environment for humans.

The global population of humans reached 1 billion in 1850, 2 billion in 1930, 4 billion in 1975, and 6.4 billion in 2005 (see In Detail 10.1). Between 8000 BCE and

In Detail 10.1

The Human Population in Context

The global population of humans in 2005 was more than 6 billion individuals. That enormous population was growing by about 1.3% per year, equivalent to an additional 80 million people each year. If that rate of growth is maintained, the population will double in only 54 years, at which time 9–12 billion people might live on Earth. To put these gigantic numbers into perspective, it is useful to consider the abundance of other species of "large" animals (i.e., weighing more than 44 kg, or 100 pounds).

Some large animals have been domesticated and live in a mutualism with humans. The most populous of these include sheep and goats (*Ovis aries* and *Capra hircus*), which have a combined population of about 4 billion. There are also about 1.3 billion cows (*Bos taurus* and *B. indica*), 0.85 billion pigs (*Sus scrofa*), 0.12 billion equines (mostly horses, *Equus caballus*), and 0.16 billion camels and water buffalo (*Camelus dromedarius* and *Bubalus bubalis*). Some smaller mutualists of humans are even more abundant, including an estimated 18 billion fowl, most of which are chickens (*Gallus gallus*).

It is doubtful that any wild, large animals ever had such enormous populations as do humans and their

domesticated mutualists. Within historical times, the most populous wild, large animal was the American bison (*Bison bison*), which, prior to its near extermination by over-hunting, may have numbered as many as 60 million individuals. At the present time, the most populous large animals in the wild are the white-tailed deer (*Odocoileus virginianus*) of the Americas with 40–60 million individuals, large kangaroos in Australia (*Macropus gigantea* and *M. rufus*) with up to 57 million, and the crabeater seal (*Lobodon carcinophagus*) of the Antarctic with 15–30 million. The populations of these wild species are equivalent to only 1% or less of the present abundance of humans.

A few other wild species of large animals maintain populations in the millions, including 6–7 million ringed seals (*Phoca hispida*) in the Arctic, 5 million harp seals (*Phoca groenlandica*) in the North Atlantic, and 3 million caribou (reindeer, *Rangifer tarandus*) in the Arctic and subarctic.

Clearly, humans and their large-animal mutualists are unusually, even unnaturally, abundant. The huge populations of domesticated large animals (humans included) can be maintained only by using an extremely large fraction of the productivity of Earth's ecosystems. Some ecologists have estimated that fraction to be as large as 50% (Vitousek *et al.*, 1986).

1650 CE, the human population increased from 5 million to 500 million; the average **doubling time** was 1500 years, and the growth rate was about 0.01% per year (Table 10.1). During the late 1960s, however, the growth rate of the global population was at about its historical maximum, equal to about 2.1% per year. At this rate of increase, the human population is capable of doubling in only 33 years. Population growth rates have slowed significantly since then, to about 1.3% in 2005. If maintained, however, even this rate of increase would double the population in only 54 years. In fact, there is now an annual net addition of about 80 million people to the global population. For perspective, this annual increase is equivalent to about two and a half times the population of Canada.

The cultural evolution of social, technological, and economic systems has allowed lifestyle improvements for many people. The main advancements are in food and health security, resulting from better access to sanitation, health care, food, shelter, and other elements of subsistence. (In the sense meant here, "security" is related to the likelihood of living to old age and of having access to the necessities and amenities of life.) The quality of life has also been improved through greater access to aesthetic resources and amenities, such as culture and recreation. Of course, these betterments of lifestyle are not shared equally among all people—they are essentially unavailable to enormous numbers of poor people.

This is not to say that hunter-gatherers did not enjoy aspects of their lifestyle. These people undoubtedly had a rich cultural life, and many were able to satisfy their subsistence requirements by "working" only a few hours each day, leaving much time for relaxing and socializing. In fact, the transitions to agricultural and then industrial societies may have involved greater workloads for average people and less time for relaxation. The additional work has, how-

TABLE 10.2	Cultural Evolution and Energy Usage

These are estimates of the per capita energy use by people engaged in various kinds of lifestyles. Energy use is presented here as a simple indicator of environmental impacts.

STAGE OF CULTURAL EVOLUTION	PER CAPITA ENERGY USE (MJ/day)
Foraging	20
Primitive agriculture	48
Advanced agriculture	104
Industrial society	308
Advanced industrial society	1025

Source: Modified from Goldemberg (1992)

ever, reaped benefits of the sort noted above, and for much larger numbers of people.

Nevertheless, the many improvements in human security have involved a great intensification of per capita environmental impacts. We can easily understand this important change by examining patterns of energy usage, which is the best simple indicator of per capita impacts (Table 10.2; see also Chapter 1). Compared with hunter-gatherers, people living in an advanced technological society use at least 50 times more energy, and their environmental impact is greater by at least a similar degree.

The intensification of per capita energy usage has been especially great during the past century or so of accelerating technological development and innovation. In fact, during the present century, average per capita economic output and fuel consumption have both increased more rapidly than the human population (Table 10.3). These changes have, of course, been most substantial in industrialized countries such as Canada. Per capita consumption of commercial energy in industrialized countries averages about 219 GJ/y (i.e., gigajoules/year), compared with 36 GJ/y in less-developed countries (WRI, 2004). Although industrialized countries account for about 20% of the human population, they use about 70% of the global production of commercial energy (WRI, 2004).

Regional Variations

The data cited to this point have been global in scale. It is important to recognize, however, that modern rates of population growth vary enormously among regions and countries. In recent decades, some countries have achieved natural rates of population growth as high as 4%

TABLE 10.1	Growth and Doubling Times of the Human Population	
DATE	GLOBAL POPULATION (MILLIONS)	DOUBLING TIME (YEARS)
8000 BCE	5	1500
1650 CE	500	200
1850	1000	80
1930	2000	45
1975	4000	36
2000	6055	55
2004	6396	54

Sources: Data from Ehrlich *et al.* (1977) and Population Reference Bureau (2005)

| TABLE 10.3 | A Century of Change in Global Population and Per Capita Environmental Impact |

Economic activity is given in 1995 U.S. dollars, so inflation does not account for the increases over time. Environmental impact is indicated by annual use of commercial energy; see text for discussion.

| YEAR | POPULATION (BILLIONS) | ECONOMIC ACTIVITY | | COMMERCIAL ENERGY CONSUMPTION | |
		GROSS WORLD PRODUCT (GWP) (1995$ $\times 10^9$)	PER CAPITA GWP (1995$ $\times 10^3$)	TOTAL (10^5 petajoules)	PER CAPITA (gigajoules)
1900	1.6	1.1	0.7	0.2	15
1950	2.5	5.3	2.2	0.7	28
1986	5.0	23.8	4.7	2.8	56
2004	6.4	33.3	5.2	4.3	69

Sources: Data from World Resources Institute (1998, 2004) and U.S. Department of Commerce (1999)

per year, which, if maintained, would double their populations in only 18 years.

Populations are growing most quickly in Africa, with a rate of increase of about 2.5% per year (Table 10.4). Although African countries vary considerably, as a whole, the continent is the world's poorest region. Its condition is due partly to legacies of its colonial history, including national boundaries that often make little sense in view of the distributions of ethnic and tribal groups. In some countries, other factors also detract from development, especially endemic corruption in government and business and strife between tribes. Moreover, the exploding populations of African countries are also making it extremely difficult to deal with the problem of chronic poverty. The population of Africa was about 224 million in 1950, 795 million in 2000, and an anticipated 1941 million (or 1.94 billion) in 2050. With human populations doubling every 25 years

or so, and the amounts of agricultural land and other resources remaining static or even declining because of over-exploitation, it will be a formidable challenge to avert social and ecological catastrophes in many African countries. Resolving these problems will require both national fortitude and generous international assistance.

Populations are growing least quickly in Europe, where the present change is about 0.0% per year, a rate that is expected to hold for several decades. Populations are growing somewhat more quickly in North America, currently at 0.8% per year (doubling time of 87 years), and projected to remain similar up to 2010.

Much of the population growth in Canada and the United States is due to relatively free immigration from other countries rather than to **intrinsic population change** (see Chapter 11). The major source regions of this immigration are Asia, Central and South America, and

| TABLE 10.4 | Regional Population Growth |

Data for 2025 and 2050 are estimated from recent trends in demographic parameters (i.e., in rates of birth, immigration, death, and emigration).

| COUNTRY | POPULATION (MILLIONS) | | | | INTERVAL GROWTH RATE (%/y) | | |
	1950	2004	2025	2050	1985–90	1995–2000	2005–10
WORLD	2524	6396	7934	9276	1.7	1.3	1.2
Africa	224	885	1323	1941	2.8	2.4	2.5
Asia	1402	3875	4778	5385	1.9	1.4	1.2
North America	172	326	386	457	1.0	0.9	0.8
Latin America + Caribbean	149	549	685	778	2.0	1.7	1.4
Europe	547	728	722	668	0.4	0.0	−0.1
Oceania	13	33	41	47	1.6	1.3	1.3

Sources: Data from World Resources Institute (1998, 2004) and Population Reference Bureau (2005)

Africa, mostly from countries with growing populations and few prospects for poor people to improve their lifestyle. Substantial immigration is also coming from parts of eastern Europe where there is little or no population growth but much unemployment and economic hardship.

Populations of Particular Countries

Data for recent population growth in selected countries are listed in Table 10.5 and Appendix C (Table 1). Countries with the most rapidly increasing populations are located in Africa and Asia, and, to a somewhat lesser degree, in Central and South America. Populations are increasing rapidly in almost all countries in those regions.

There are, however, some anomalous situations. Afghanistan, for instance, had a population decrease of 2.0% per year during 1980–85. This was largely because that country's devastating civil war killed so many of its citizens, while many others emigrated to neighbouring Pakistan and Iran. In contrast, the population of Afghanistan increased during 1990–95 by an extraordinary 6.7% per year. This happened because many displaced civilians returned after a sporadic ceasefire restored relative peace to the country. Overall, the intrinsic rate of increase of the Afghani population has been 3.0–3.5% per year. In 1950, the population of Afghanistan was 9 million; by 2004 it had increased 3.2-fold to 29 million, and it is projected to reach 50 million by 2025 and 82 million by 2050.

Some countries have had recent population growth even more rapid than Afghanistan. In Nigeria, for example, the population was 33 million in 1950 and is projected to reach 206 million in 2025, a 6.2-fold increase. (Note that such predictions for Nigeria and some other countries will likely prove inaccurate because of mortality that will result from the accelerating AIDS epidemic or some other disaster; see the last section of this chapter and Global Focus 10.1 on p. 170) In Iran, the population increase over the same period is projected to be about five-fold. Try to imagine the ecological and resource stresses associated with population explosions like these! Contemplate being a politician or government bureaucrat who is charged with the responsibility of ensuring livelihoods and an acceptable quality of life for so many citizens, while also protecting the ecological heritage and environmental quality of the country! The challenges are extraordinarily daunting.

The countries with the most stable populations occur mainly in Europe (Appendix C, Table 1). The populations of most European countries are growing at less than 0.5% per year, and the doubling times are longer than 100 years. As was previously noted, the intrinsic rates of population increase in Canada and the United States are similar to these values, although, because of substantial immigration, their populations are still growing at about 1% per year.

Some countries are showing rapid decreases in their rate of population increase (Table 10.5). China, for exam-

| TABLE 10.5 | Population Growth in Selected Countries |

See Appendix C, Table 1 for additional country data of this type.

COUNTRY	POPULATION (MILLIONS)			INTERVAL GROWTH RATE (%/y)		
	1950	2004	2025	1985–90	1995–2000	2005–10
RAPIDLY GROWING POPULATION						
Iran	17	67	85	3.8	1.7	2.4
Nigeria	33	137	206	2.9	2.4	2.6
DECLINING RATE OF POPULATION GROWTH						
Canada	*14*	*32*	*36*	*1.4*	*1.0*	*0.7*
China	555	1300	1476	1.5	0.9	0.7
India	358	1087	1363	2.1	1.6	1.3
RELATIVELY SLOW OR NO POPULATION GROWTH						
Japan	84	128	121	0.4	0.2	0.0
Germany	68	83	82	0.4	0.1	0.1

Sources: Data from World Resources Institute (1998, 2004) and Population Reference Bureau (2005)

ple, had population growth rates exceeding 3% per year early last century, but this decreased to 0.9% per year in 2000, and is expected to be 0.7% per year in 2010. The slowdown is occurring because the national government of China has recognized the acute nature of that country's population problem, has developed policies to slow the growth, and is starting to implement them in an effective manner. China's government has imposed its population policy with a determination that has sparked debates over human rights. The controversial measures include coerced sterilization and the enforcement (particularly in urban areas) of a one-child-per-family guideline. Nonetheless, China appears to be firmly on the road to rapidly decreasing its rate of population growth. We can only hope this necessary action has occurred in time. China's population in 2004 was 1.3 billion people, and even with its aggressive population policy, this will increase to 1.5 billion by 2025. These are immense numbers of people to accommodate within the bounds of China's landmass and natural resources, which are not increasing in area or quantity.

The situations in Brazil, India, Indonesia, Korea, Mexico, and Thailand are similar, although none of these countries is experiencing declining rates of population growth as rapid as that of China. India, the world's second-most populous country, had 1.1 billion people in 2004, and may somehow have to support 1.4 billion in 2025. Although all of these countries have started to develop population policies aimed at reducing growth rates, they are not being implemented as effectively as in China.

In general, countries that are experiencing rapid population growth are relatively undeveloped and poor, and they tend to be tropical and subtropical in distribution. However, not all poor countries have high population growth rates. The population growth rates of Cuba, for example, have been consistently less than 1% per year since the 1950s. Although Cuba is relatively poor, almost all of its citizens are literate. Its social system also provides ready access to housing, food, social security, and health care, including effective means of birth control.

It can be broadly generalized that the wealth and state of development of nations correlate inversely with their population growth rate. Nevertheless, any country with an appropriate and effectively delivered population policy can achieve a measure of control of the rate at which its population is increasing. The case of Cuba demonstrates this fact.

The explosive population increase in so many poor countries is straining the ecosystems that must somehow sustain the burgeoning numbers of people and their livelihoods. For instance, the population of central Sudan was 2.9 million in 1917, but it had irrupted (an *irruption* is a rapid increase) to 18.4 million by 1977, an increase of 6.4 times (Olsson and Rapp, 1991). Because most Sudanis are engaged in agricultural livelihoods, the populations of livestock also increased tremendously during that period. The number of cattle increased 20-fold (to 16 million); camels, 16-fold (to 3.7 million); sheep, 12.5-fold (to 16 million); and goats, 8.5-fold (to 10.4 million). Such enormous growth in the abundance of humans and livestock has extensively degraded the carrying capacity of rangelands in Sudan and other regions of Africa. Extensive damage has also been caused to natural ecosystems.

Another example concerns the number of people in the province of Rondonia in Amazonian Brazil. Between 1970 and 1988, this population increased 12-fold, mostly because of immigration of poor people from overpopulated cities in southern Brazil to this region of Amazonia, which is considered a development frontier. During the same period, the population of cattle increased 30-fold. Inevitably, these enormous population increases have been accompanied by intense ecological damage, as tropical forest is cleared to develop land needed to sustain humans and their livelihoods. Commonly, the cleared land has proved unsuitable for agricultural use and has been abandoned in a highly degraded condition while the farmers move on to clear additional forest elsewhere.

It must be remembered, however, that comparable economic growth occurred in Europe and North America in previous centuries. In Britain, for example, deforestation and other habitat losses resulted in the extirpation of many species of indigenous wildlife. In addition, deforestation and the grazing of hillsides in Scotland have virtually eliminated the native forest that once covered those hills. These ecologically destructive activities have largely been forgotten, and most inhabitants of Britain now regard the transformed landscape of their country as being "natural."

Birth and Death Rates

Human societies living in relatively primitive, undeveloped conditions have always tended to have high birth rates and death rates, typically about 40–50 per thousand. (Birth and death rates are expressed as the average number per thousand individuals in the population per year.) These were the usual rates of natality and mortality throughout virtually all of human history. As long as both birth and death rates remained high and similar, population growth was small or zero. It is only during the past several centuries that explosive growth has occurred.

This has happened because death rates have decreased substantially in all countries. The death rate declined because of improved sanitation, medicine, immunization, and social welfare, along with widespread access to education (which teaches awareness of the benefits of sanitation and medicine).

The benefits of sanitation, immunization, and medicine are particularly consequential for younger people, especially those less than five years old. This group tends to have the highest death rates under "primitive" conditions. Other relatively vulnerable groups that have benefited significantly include the elderly and women during childbirth. As well, reductions in deadly infectious diseases, such as diphtheria, plague, smallpox, tuberculosis, and yellow fever, have been important in reducing death rates.

These medical and social benefits have not been shared equally among the world's countries or among disparate income groups within nations. For this reason, poorer, less developed cultures or income groups have considerably higher death rates than do wealthier, more developed ones. This trend is readily apparent if data for death rates in poorer countries with increasing populations are compared with those of wealthier countries having more stable populations (Table 10.6 and Appendix C, Table 2).

Compared with the relatively large decreases in death rate in virtually all of the world's nations and cultures, decreases in birth rates have been less rapid and less uniform (Table 10.6 and Appendix C, Table 2). In general, the world's wealthiest, most developed countries have relatively low birth rates, typically about 10 per thousand. Moreover, these are almost in balance with death rates, so the rate of natural population increase is low or zero. In large part, the relatively low birth rates of these countries result from the development of a cultural inclination to have small families, which can be achieved because effective methods of birth control are readily available.

Changes in cultural attitude about family size appear to be a natural outcome of increasing affluence and health in developed societies. Such cultural changes are critically important for dealing with the potentially explosive population growth of modern times. It is not known exactly how these changes in attitude came about. In less developed societies, children are often viewed as sources of inexpensive labour and providers of material comfort for their parents in old age. In wealthier countries, however, children are considered to be substantial economic and social responsibilities for their parents—they are expensive consumers of space, education, energy, food, clothing, and other necessities. This is especially true in relatively affluent societies, in which each child is an expensive investment. This context provides an incentive for having a smaller family.

Birth rates have remained quite high in most less developed countries. Because death rates have fallen considerably in those countries, their populations are growing rapidly (Table 10.6). In general, birth rates have

---

TABLE 10.6 | Demographic Data for Selected Countries

Note that birth rate minus death rate is equal to the intrinsic rate of population change. A difference of +10 units is equal to a 1% increase per year. Fertility rate is the number of children born to an average woman over her lifetime. Life expectancy is the average number of years lived from birth. See Appendix C, Table 2 for additional country data of this type.

COUNTRY	BIRTH RATE (BIRTHS/1000)		DEATH RATE (DEATHS/1000)		FERTILITY RATE (BIRTHS/WOMAN)		LIFE EXPECTANCY (YEARS)	
	1975–80	2004	1975–80	2004	1975–80	2004	1975–80	2004
RAPIDLY GROWING POPULATION								
Iran	45	18	15	6	6.5	2.5	59	69
Nigeria	47	42	20	13	6.5	5.7	45	52
RELATIVELY SLOW OR NO POPULATION GROWTH								
Canada	15	11	7	7	1.8	1.5	74	79
China	22	12	9	6	3.3	1.7	65	71
Japan	15	9	7	8	1.8	1.3	76	82
United States	15	14	9	8	1.8	2.0	73	77

Sources: Data from World Resources Institute (1998, 2004) and Population Reference Bureau (2004)

remained high because of cultural preferences for larger families—a factor that may have been influenced by historically high death rates, particularly of young children. Fifty years ago, a family might have had six children with only three surviving; today, all six might survive. Some religions also influence birth rates because they favour large families or strongly disapprove of modern methods of birth control, resulting in a lag in the cultural adjustment of birth rate to offset the rapid decline in mortality rate. The ensuing imbalance has resulted in the rapid population growth seen in most less developed countries.

Actually, the situation is not quite as simple as this. In many countries, fertility rates are maintained at a considerably higher level than many people, particularly women of childbearing age, might freely choose. This happens because many women do not have sufficient access to effective means of birth control. Exceptions are countries such as China, and to a lesser degree Brazil, India, Indonesia, Korea, Sri Lanka, and Thailand, all of which are substantially reducing their population growth rates, mainly by ensuring that their citizens have access to effective means of controlling their fertility.

The Demographic Transition

During most of human history, which was characterized by relatively primitive living conditions, relatively low or **zero population growth (ZPG)** occurred because high death rates were balanced by high birth rates. In modern times, ZPG occurs in relatively "developed" nations and cultures in which low death rates are balanced by low birth rates.

Unfortunately, it typically takes a rather long time, usually several generations, for societies to make it through the so-called **demographic transition** from a condition of high birth and death rates to one of low birth and death rates (Figure 10.2). During this period of demographic transition, populations typically grow at relatively high rates. This imbalance occurs because modern sanitation, immunization, medicine, and related measures all contribute to achieving rapid reductions of death rates. However, the declines in mortality occur without similar, off-setting decreases in birth rates. If, for example, annual birth rates remained at 51 per thousand while death rates declined to 21 per thousand, the population would grow at 3.0% per year. If this situation continued, the population would double in only 23 years. These numbers are, by the way, actual demographic parameters for the African country of Malawi in 2004. These are not exceptional data

for poorer countries, as can be seen by inspection of data for birth and death rates in Appendix C, Table 2.

No cultures prefer high death rates, but people often prefer large families. Recent history has shown that it takes one or two generations to overcome cultural inclinations toward having large families and for birth rates to decline to a level that is in balance with modern death rates.

Many of the world's developed countries had the great fortune of passing through their demographic transition during times when their populations were relatively small, and under circumstances in which their "surplus" people could be exported to other places. Many European countries, in particular, encouraged their surplus of poor, landless people to emigrate to colonial "frontiers" in the Americas, Australia, and elsewhere. Many countries, such as Argentina, Australia, Brazil, Canada, Chile, Mexico, New Zealand, South Africa, the United States, and Venezuela, were then colonies of European nations. These were considered to be "underpopulated" places with bountiful resources, capable of assimilating a large amount of immigration.

In actual fact, these regions were already occupied by Aboriginal peoples at the time of their European "discovery." Nevertheless, in the socio-political context of that time (sixteenth to nineteenth centuries), European powers seized ownership of foreign regions, displaced or subjugated the original inhabitants, and colonized the freed-up land through an emigration of their poor or otherwise mobile citizens. To a substantial degree, the notion of underpopulation lingers today, particularly in Canada, the United States, and Australia, which still allow relatively high rates of immigration of people from other countries. As a result, population growth rates in those countries substantially exceed their birth to death ratio, which are almost in balance and reflect passage through the demographic transition.

Immigrants from Europe (and elsewhere) in recent centuries have greatly swelled the populations of Canada and the United States. For example, at the time of the first United States census, in 1790, that country had a population of four million. Sixty years later, in 1850, the population had increased almost six-fold to 23 million. This growth was largely achieved through emigration from Britain and other European countries. (The natural increase in population during that period was also vigorous, adding four to eight million of those people.) Similar changes occurred in Canada (see Chapter 11). The ability of many European countries to export so much of their surplus population was critical to their relatively smooth passage through the demographic transition.

FIGURE 10.2 | The Demographic Transition

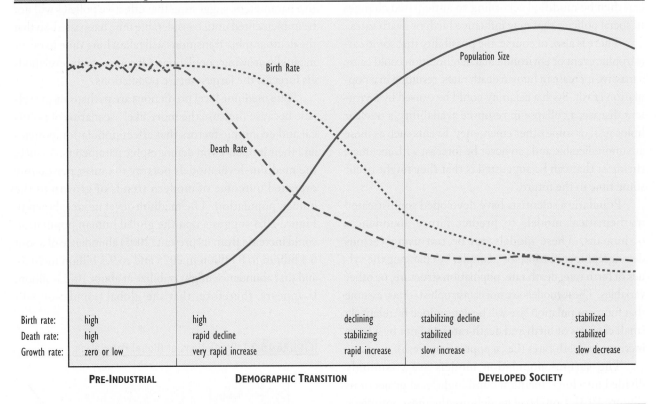

Birth rate:	high	high	declining	stabilizing decline	stabilized
Death rate:	high	rapid decline	stabilizing	stabilized	stabilized
Growth rate:	zero or low	very rapid increase	rapid increase	slow increase	slow decrease

PRE-INDUSTRIAL — **DEMOGRAPHIC TRANSITION** — **DEVELOPED SOCIETY**

This illustration models the transition that must be made from a condition of high birth and death rates to one of low birth and death rates. Typically, death rates fall more quickly than birth rates, and the corresponding imbalance has an explosive influence on population growth. Zero population growth occurs when birth and death rates offset each other. If the birth rate falls below the death rate, the population size will decrease.

Today, only a few countries still allow and even encourage a substantial rate of immigration (notably Canada, the United States, and Australia). However, the actual number of people involved in transnational immigration to developed countries, several million per year, is small in comparison with global population growth (about 80 million per year in 2005). Moreover, there is no reason to expect that these and other host nations will continue to be willing, or able, to absorb population surpluses from other countries.

One of the bitter truths of modern times is that the relatively poor, less developed countries of the world, with the most explosive population growth, have no significant outlets for their burgeoning surpluses of people. More nations today have access to the mortality-reducing benefits of modern sanitation and medicine, but in most countries, these are not being balanced by effective control of birth rates. Consequently, many less developed countries are faced with a pressing need to bridge their demographic

transition much more quickly than today's developed countries ever had to do. Moreover, this daunting feat must be accomplished without emigration. There are no underpopulated frontiers left on Earth—local population crises can no longer be exported somewhere else.

Future Populations

All trends in demographic indicators strongly indicate that the human population will continue to grow rapidly in the foreseeable future. Fortunately, there are convincing signals of decreasing rates of population growth in almost all countries. This is encouraging, but it does not negate the fact that the global population is growing rapidly (although not as quickly as it was several decades ago).

It is never possible to foretell the future accurately. Nevertheless, by extrapolating from recent trends it is possible to infer the likely future values of birth and death rates and other demographic variables. Such predictions can then be modified according to anticipated changes in social policies that may influence birth or death rates.

There is also, of course, the possibility that some catastrophic event or environmental deterioration could cause a massive increase in human death rates, resulting in a population crash. Such a calamity could be caused by a virulent disease, a collapse in resource availability, a nuclear holocaust, or some other emergency. Events such as these are unpredictable and can never be forecast with accuracy; the most that can be suggested is that they might occur some time in the future.

Population scientists have developed sophisticated mathematical models to predict future abundances of humans. These models can be run using various demographic scenarios, for example, by changing the values of birth rate, death rate, population structure, or other variables. These models are not catastrophist—they assume that future population size will be determined by relatively small changes of birth and death rates and not by a huge increase in death rates (i.e., a population crash).

The various population models are commonly divided into low-, medium-, and high-level projections (Figure 10.3). Low-level models use the most optimistic demographic predictions; they assume that effective population policies will be implemented rapidly and will allow stable populations to be achieved as quickly as can be

hoped. The high-level models use relatively conservative parameters, suggesting that effective policies will not be implemented until considerable time has passed, so that the demographic transitions will take a long time to occur in rapidly growing populations. Of course, high-level models forecast the largest future populations.

The medium-level predictions are perhaps most realistic because they use the more likely scenarios of political and economic factors that affect population policies and their influences on demographic parameters. As such, the medium-level models portray the most reasonably expected outcome of modern trends of growth of the human population. The medium-level model shown in Figure 10.3 suggests that the global human population could increase from its present (2005) abundance of about 6.4 billion to 8 billion in 2025 and to 9.3 billion in 2050, and that abundance might stabilize at about 10–11 billion. It appears, therefore, that the global population will

---

FIGURE 10.3 Predictions of Global Population

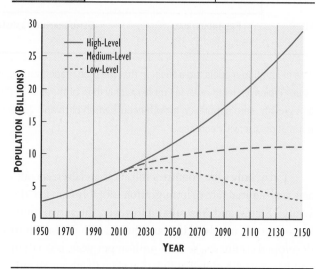

Three population scenarios are presented here, ranging from low-level to high-level in terms of the assumptions of demographic parameters. The low-level model makes optimistic and probably unrealistic assumptions about the development and implementation of population policies; it predicts relatively small populations in the future. The high-level model is more conservative and assumes that the imbalance between birth and death rates will be addressed more slowly. The low-level model assumes that average fertility will stabilize at 1.55 children per woman; the medium-level, at 2.10; and the high-level, at 2.35. In 2005, the global average fertility was 2.7 children per woman.

Source: Modified from World Resources Institute (1998 and 2004)

Photo 10.2 In less developed countries, governments will have to find livelihoods for increasingly larger numbers of young people, even as free space, resources, and environmental quality are rapidly diminishing. These students live in Padung Pajung, Sumatra, Indonesia.

FIGURE 10.4 Predicted Populations in Less Developed and Developed Regions

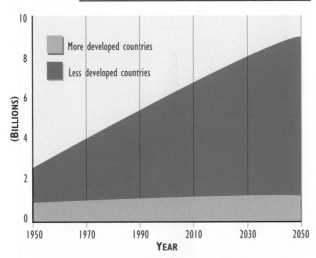

These predictions are based on medium-level population projections.

Source: Modified from Population Reference Bureau (2005)

increase greatly from its present level before it stabilizes. This assumes, of course, that there is no intervening catastrophe such as a collapse of the environmental carrying capacity for our species, an unprecedented pandemic, or a global war.

Moreover, it appears that the populations of almost all of the world's countries will increase. The population growth will not, however, be equitably shared between the less developed and more developed regions of the world. In 1950, about 31% of the world's population of 2.5 billion lived in developed countries. However, recent population growth has been much more rapid in less developed countries, so that in 2005, only about 18% of the world's 6.4 billion people lived in developed regions. This disparate trend will intensify in the near future, and by 2050, only 14% of the world's 10–11 billion people may be living in developed regions (Figure 10.4).

Age-Class Structure

A *population structure* describes the relative abundances of specified groups of people in an area. The most important is the **age-class structure**, or the proportions of individuals in various age groups. This type of population structure differs greatly between growing and stable populations and has important implications for their future growth.

Populations that have been stable for some time have similar proportions of people in various age classes (Figure 10.5). In other words, there are roughly comparable numbers of people aged 5–10, 10–15, 15–20, 20–25 years, and so on. This equitable distribution of population structure holds for most age-classes, except for the elderly, who always have a higher risk of mortality.

In marked contrast, the age-class distribution of a rapidly growing population reflects the fact that there are many more younger than older individuals. Consequently, growing populations have a triangular age-class structure—that is, much wider at the bottom than at the top. In fact, almost one-half of the people in a rapidly growing population are typically less than 15 years old (Table 10.7 and Appendix C, Table 3). This kind of population structure suggests an enormous potential for future growth as increasingly larger numbers of young people mature to reproductive age.

The growth potential (or inertia) of populations with a triangular age structure is an extremely important demographic fact. Because of this inertia, it is difficult for populations to *stop* growing quickly, and it usually takes several generations to pass through the demographic transition. For example, a "young" population (i.e., one with a triangular age-class structure) might rapidly achieve a **replacement fertility rate**, such that the number of progeny would only replace their parents (equivalent to about 2.1 children per family; slightly larger than 2 per family to account for the fact that some people are infertile). Nevertheless, the population would continue to grow for some time, although at a slowing rate of increase. This happens because, for several decades, increasingly larger

TABLE 10.7 Age Structure of the Populations of Selected Countries in 2004

See Appendix C, Table 3 for additional country data of this type.

COUNTRY	PERCENTAGE OF POPULATION		
	<15	15–65	>65
RAPIDLY GROWING POPULATION			
Iran	33	62	5
Nigeria	44	53	3
RELATIVELY SLOW OR NO POPULATION GROWTH			
Canada	18	69	13
Japan	14	67	19
United States	21	67	12

Source: Data from Population Reference Bureau (2005)

FIGURE 10.5 | Age-Class Structure of the Global Population

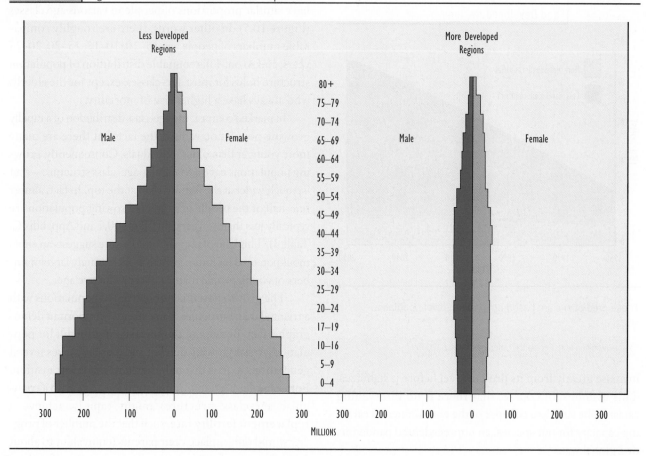

Compare the age-class structures of a relatively young, rapidly growing population (the less developed world, in 2005) with a stable population (developed countries).

Source: Modified from Population Reference Bureau (2005)

numbers of people come to reproductive age, a circumstance related to the initial, triangular age-class structure of the population. Eventually, replacement fertility rate would bring about a stable age-class structure, and zero population growth would finally occur.

The national population policy of China advocates one-child families, a fertility rate considerably smaller than that which would replace the numbers of parents. During the past decade or so, the one-child policy has been pursued with varying levels of official enthusiasm, generally more aggressively in urbanized areas than in rural ones. Most families of childbearing age are subjected to intense social pressure to follow the one-child guideline and to significant economic disincentives such as fines and lack of educational opportunities for second children. Many parents have been sterilized against their will.

In addition, there is a strong cultural preference in China for male children because of the prevailing system of inheritance of family lineage and property by the first-born son. This cultural attitude has led to widespread abortion of female fetuses, giving up female newborns for adoption, and even cases of female infanticide. These are not agreeable choices, but they are taken so that another attempt can be made to ensure that the single child allowed the family will be male. If female abortion and infanticide become widespread, an imbalance in the female to male ratio will develop in the population. This will have important social implications when many men have difficulties finding a spouse and starting a family.

Some of the population-control measures that occur in China are regrettable. And from some points of view, they abuse human rights. However, the Chinese federal government considers such measures to be necessary in view of their country's enormous population and the further growth implicit in its triangular age-class structure. In other words, in countries where population growth is causing a desperate situation, a vigorous implementation of aggressive population policies seems appropriate.

Distribution of Populations

Another important element of population structure is the spatial distribution of people and how this changes over time. This is a highly complex topic because the distribution of people varies enormously within countries (compare, for example, urban and rural populations) and also among countries in different stages of development.

As we previously noted, most of the world's people live in relatively poor, less developed countries, largely in the tropics and subtropics. Because populations are growing most quickly in those areas, this pattern of global distribution will intensify further over time (see Figure 10.4). The exploding populations in those countries present enormous challenges to national and global governments, international aid agencies, and more broadly, the security of human society. Even today, many of the great masses of poor people in less developed countries do not have access to reasonable livelihoods, or even to minimally acceptable standards of food, shelter, education, health care, and other necessities of life, not to mention the cultural and entertainment amenities that help make life an enjoyable experience. Faced with rapidly increasing populations, will these poor countries be able to do better in the future? Will wealthier countries be willing to help them to the degree that is necessary?

Urbanization (i.e., the development of cities and towns) is another critical aspect of population distribution. Most of the world's countries are urbanizing rapidly. In fact, urbanization is occurring much more rapidly than population growth. Increasing urbanization is being driven by several interacting factors, but particularly population growth and the migration of people to cities and towns in search of employment, services, and cultural attractions. On average, about three-quarters of the population of developed countries lives in urban environments, and one-third in the less developed parts of the world (World Resources Institute, 2004). By 2025, it is expected that the urban population will double to more than 5 billion and that 90% of that increase will be in developing countries. Global urbanization represents an extraordinary change in the distribution of people, compared with the essentially agrarian societies of only one century ago, when more than 95% of people lived in rural areas.

Populations of the world's greatest metropolitan areas, or **megacities**, are shown in Table 10.8. Most of the world's largest urbanized areas are located in developing countries, a trend which will increase in the future.

TABLE 10.8   Megacities

The data illustrate growth of some of the world's great megacities (or agglomerations), ranked by their population in 2003.

CITY	COUNTRY	POPULATION (MILLIONS) 1975	2003	2015	GROWTH RATE (%/y; 1975–2000)
Tokyo	Japan	26.6	35.0	36.2	1.0
Mexico City	Mexico	10.7	18.7	20.6	2.1
New York	United States	15.9	18.3	19.7	0.5
Sao Paulo	Brazil	9.6	17.9	20.0	2.3
Bombay	India	7.3	17.4	22.6	3.1
Delhi	India	4.4	14.1	20.9	4.1
Calcutta	India	7.9	13.8	16.8	2.0
Buenos Aires	Argentina	9.1	13.0	14.6	1.3
Shanghai	China	11.4	12.8	12.7	0.5
Jakarta	Indonesia	4.8	12.3	17.5	3.3
Los Angeles	United States	8.9	12.0	12.9	1.1
Dacca	Bangladesh	2.2	11.6	17.9	6.2
Osaka	Japan	9.8	11.2	11.4	0.5
Rio de Janeiro	Brazil	7.6	11.2	12.4	1.4
Karachi	Pakistan	4.0	11.1	16.2	3.7
Beijing	China	8.5	10.8	11.1	1.0
Cairo	Egypt	6.4	10.8	13.1	1.9
Moscow	Russia	7.6	10.5	10.9	1.1
Manila	Philippines	5.0	10.4	12.6	2.8
Lagos	Nigeria	1.9	10.1	17.0	6.1

Source: Data from United Nations Department of Economic and Social Affairs (2005). The United Nations is the author of the original material.

Urban people live under relatively densely crowded conditions, and their livelihoods tend to involve manufacturing, government administration, financial institutions, commerce, education, and services (see also Chapter 25). In addition, many urban people depend on social assistance. No cities are self-sufficient in food, energy, or raw materials for building and manufacturing, and few have enough potable water. Urban areas depend on trade with the surrounding countryside and with foreign nations to provide these necessities of life and economy. The development and maintenance of the complex physical, economic, and social infrastructures required to care for enormous numbers of urban people is an extraordinary challenge for governments, particularly in relatively poor countries.

Birth Control

Many individual people and families make conscious choices about their reproduction, including how many children to have. Historically, the available methods of controlling pregnancy were few, unreliable, and sometimes unsafe.

One of the best methods of **birth control** is the avoidance of sexual intercourse before marriage (or a non-married spousal partnership). This is because society generally accepts that matrimony is a social institution involving a commitment by both parents to care for their children. Avoidance of sexual intercourse affects population-level birth rates by delaying and spacing reproduction. A complementary effect is gained by delaying marriage until relatively late in life, which, if accompanied by pre-marital chastity, also delays reproduction and decreases birth rates. Coitus interruptus, or withdrawal of the penis prior to ejaculation, likewise contributes to lower rates of impregnation associated with copulation. This practice has been widely used throughout history. In addition, breast-feeding mothers have a lower probability of conceiving another child, so delaying the weaning of children helps to space births.

Some birth control practices have long been used, even by hunter-gatherer and early agricultural cultures, particularly when they had to deal with resource crises such as insufficient food. These include

- the use of traditional medicines to prevent conception or to induce abortion;

- infibulation, or the insertion of small pebbles or other objects into the uterus, where they may be retained for years, preventing implantation of fertilized ova;

- the use of mechanical means of inducing abortion;

- infanticide, or the killing of newborn infants; and

- mechanical means of raising the temperature within the scrotum, such as wearing a warm pouch, which inhibits sperm production and reduces fertility of the male.

The Polynesian culture inhabits islands in the southwestern Pacific Ocean. Perhaps because of the obvious resource constraints associated with living on islands, the Polynesians were aware of overpopulation and carrying capacity and practised several methods of birth control. Prior to the modern era, Polynesians engaged in a subsistence economy, cultivating various crop plants (particularly coconut, sweet potato, taro, and yam), raising pigs and chickens, and hunting marine mammals, fish, mollusks, and other edible invertebrates in shallow waters. Their populations were closed to varying degrees, depending on the isolation of their island homes. On some islands, such as Easter Island, there was likely no exchange of people after the initial colonization.

The methods of population control practised by the Polynesians included polyandry (in which one woman has several husbands at the same time), non-marriage of men who did not own land, abstention from sex for some time after birth of a child, coitus interruptus, abortion, and infanticide. However, these methods were not always sufficient to prevent population growth. Consequently, the Polynesians are well known for their voyages of colonization, undertaken during times of population pressure. They constructed sea-going outrigger sailing canoes and provisioned them with stores of water, crop plants, pigs, and chickens. Family units then embarked and headed toward the vast Pacific horizon in search of habitable but unpopulated islands. These courageous, extremely risky dispersals allowed some of the population surplus to discover new ecological opportunities, although many unfortunate people must have perished at sea.

Today, there are many means of birth control which are safer and more effective than most of the methods available in the past (see In Detail 10.2). Consequently, individuals and families in many countries can now control

In Detail 10.2

Methods of Birth Control

The methods listed below vary greatly in their effectiveness in achieving birth control, and all have various physiological and psychological drawbacks.

Contraceptives work by preventing ovulation, implantation of ova, or entry of sperm into the cervical canal. Oral contraceptives are most common and have a typical failure rate of less than 1% if properly used (the failure rate is the number of pregnancies per year while using the method, compared with no birth control). Depo-Provera, an injectible hormone, prevents ovulation for three months. The morning-after pill (RU486) is taken within 72 hours of intercourse and is 75–95% effective. These methods are reversible, so conception is possible soon after stopping use.

Spermicides are chemicals that kill sperm and are applied by women using a sponge, foam, jelly, or cream inserted into the vagina. The failure rate is 3–20% (the higher failures are associated with improper use of the method; this also applies to ranges cited for other methods).

An **intrauterine device (IUD)** is inserted into the uterus where it prevents implantation of ova, probably by mechanically stimulating an inflammatory response. IUDs have a failure rate of 1–5%. This method is being used less frequently because of risks of pelvic inflammation and infertility.

A **cervical cap** is a mechanical block, inserted by a woman to block access of sperm to the cervix. The failure rate is 3–10%.

A **contraceptive diaphragm** blocks entrance to the cervix and is used with spermicidal jelly and/or foam. The failure rate is 3–14%.

Condoms provide a mechanical barrier that contains sperm after ejaculation, thereby preventing entry into the vagina. The failure rate is 2–10%.

Douching involves flushing the vaginal area with water (often containing a spermicide) after intercourse.

Douching is not very effective because it does not completely remove sperm, so the failure rate is about 40%.

Coitus interruptus (withdrawal) involves the male withdrawing his penis from the woman's vagina prior to ejaculation. This method is not reliable because it runs contrary to powerful sexual urges and because sperm are present in pre-ejaculation fluids emitted from the penis. The failure rate is 9–20%.

The rhythm method involves the timing of sexual intercourse to avoid the days during which the woman is fertile. This method has a high failure rate (13–20%), largely because it is difficult to accurately determine the fertile period.

Vasectomy is a method of sterilization for males. It involves cutting and/or tying the vas deferens, the tube that carries the sperm from the testis before mixing with seminal fluids. This method has a failure rate of less than 0.2%.

Tubal ligation is a method of sterilization for women, in which the oviduct (fallopian tube) connecting the ovary and the uterus is tied, preventing the passage of ova. This method has a failure rate of less than 0.1%.

Abortion involves the use of medication or surgery to terminate a pregnancy before the fetus is viable (i.e., before it is capable of living unassisted outside the womb). In rarer cases, late-term abortions may occur, even in the third trimester of pregnancy. Abortion is an effective method of birth control and is relatively safe if carried out by qualified medical personnel (although the procedure is not without medical risk).

Abstinence is avoiding heterosexual intercourse.

No birth control—on average, heterosexual intercourse without any birth control will result in fertilization and pregnancy about 10% of the time. If pregnancy is not desired, this would correspond to a failure rate of 90%.

Sources: Health and Welfare Canada (1980), Kane (1983), Solomon *et al.* (1990), Leisinger and Schmitt (1994), and United Nations Population Fund (2005)

their reproduction, choosing from a range of safe and readily available methods of birth control.

However, the use of birth control raises questions beyond the purely medical and scientific, including religious, ethical, and philosophical questions. For example, because of beliefs regarding the sanctity of human procreation, the Roman Catholic Church opposes almost all methods of birth control. So do most fundamentalist Christian, Jewish, and Muslim denominations.

In Canada and the United States, one of the most contentious methods of birth control is abortion. On the one hand, anti-abortionists (also known as "pro-life" activists) contend that abortion violates the sanctity of life and should never be permitted. On the other hand, pro-abortion activists (also known as "pro-choice") argue that a fetus is not a viable life and that in a free and democratic society each woman should have the right to make decisions regarding her own body and reproduction. The acrimonious debate over abortion has erupted in both legal and illegal demonstrations, including the picketing of clinics and hospitals. In some cases, radical fringe elements opposing abortion have committed arson and even the murder of physicians and other medical personnel.

Population Policies

The topic of **population policies** is closely related to that of birth control. However, population policies do not include individual choices in reproduction, but refer to larger social strategies, designed and implemented by governments. Whether or not they have an official population policy, all nations have a population issue. From the perspective of environmental studies, these population problems can be divided into two groups, which differ significantly in their nature and in their prospects for effective action through the implementation of a population policy.

Less Developed Countries

As previously discussed, less developed countries are relatively poor and have not progressed far in industrial and socio-economic development. Their populations are growing rapidly because of an excess of births over deaths. Under such conditions, unfettered population growth is a huge barrier to the development process—it is an enormous undertaking just to provide the minimal requirements of life to rapidly increasing numbers of people, let

alone to achieve the improved standards of living that result from socio-economic development.

Although many people migrate from these countries to wealthier ones, there are not enough emigrants to make much of a difference in the overpopulated home countries. Wealthy countries control the numbers of immigrants they are willing to receive, and, compared with global population growth, those numbers are relatively small. When they were going through their own demographic transition some 100–200 years ago, wealthy nations exported much of their surplus population to colonies in the Americas and elsewhere. This option is not available to poorer countries today.

National population policies in less developed countries must focus on reducing birth rates as quickly as possible so that population growth can be arrested and hopefully even reversed (this is known as negative population growth, NPG). Ideally, this would be achieved by educating the populace about the national importance of population issues so that individuals and families would make appropriate free choices about family size and reproductive planning. Also, ideally, there would be ready access to effective means of birth control in support of this enlightened, population-level initiative.

In addition, a more equitable distribution of wealth in less developed countries would contribute greatly to achieving the necessary population goals, because better-off people are more inclined to have smaller families. For a similar reason, many people and agencies (such as the United Nations Population Fund) support the idea of a transfer of some wealth from developed to less developed countries. This could include both direct transfers and relief of the foreign-held debt loads of poorer countries.

A less desirable, but effective, alternative to these population policies involves coercive initiatives in family planning, such as social and/or economic disincentives to having more than one or two children per family. Forcing people to use family-planning practices infringes on their human rights, even if there are clear, long-term social and environmental benefits. Consequently, coercion presents a social and ethical dilemma for governments. Such actions may, however, be necessary if free choices do not result in sufficient reductions of population growth.

There is, of course, a clear alternative, which is easily implemented by all societies and governments. Instead of designing and adopting effective population policies, governments could do nothing to reduce birth rates, thereby allowing populations to grow rapidly. This would intensify the severe environmental damage already being caused in most less developed countries, decreasing further the carrying capacity for humans, their economy, and other species. The population and resource crises would then eventually resolve themselves in a natural, biological fashion, as would happen for any species. There would be a catastrophic increase in the death rate—a crash.

Developed Countries

Developed countries are relatively wealthy and their average citizens have access to desirable lifestyles compared to typical conditions in less developed countries. Moreover, most developed countries have completely passed through the demographic transition or have substantially done so. Consequently, their natural rate of population growth is relatively slow.

Progress through the demographic transition requires new cultural attitudes about appropriate family size and access to effective means of controlling reproduction. As such, population policies in developed countries tend to ensure that people are sympathetic with small-family goals and that they have easy access to safe and effective means of birth control.

A major issue concerning the population policies of developed countries is the allowable rate of immigration. There are huge numbers of poor people living in less developed countries who would happily migrate to wealthier countries in search of better economic, lifestyle, and social opportunities. In fact, some economists and politicians believe that immigration should be encouraged. They believe that it is desirable for developed countries to have a growing population, which would be an increasing marketplace for saleable commodities while providing an abundant source of inexpensive labour. In contrast, ecologically minded economists and environmental specialists argue that there are severe limits to such population and economic growth. This is because the relatively intensive lifestyles of growing numbers of people living in developed countries would require disproportionately increasing amounts of resources.

The characteristically high per capita environmental impact of people living in wealthier societies integrates closely with population issues. As we saw in Chapter 1, people living a resource-rich lifestyle cause a greater intensity of per capita environmental damage than do typical people in poorer countries. This fact must be recognized in the development of population policies in wealthier countries—the governments of those countries must acknowledge that there are limits to the numbers of resource-intensive people that can be sustained within their national boundaries.

Photo 10.3 Compared with people living in wealthy countries, such as Canada, inhabitants of less developed countries use fewer material and energy resources. Therefore, on a per capita basis, the environmental impacts of poorer people are relatively small. This family is engaged in subsistence agriculture in eastern Nepal.

Possible Causes of a Population Crash

Environmental scientists have suggested that uncontrolled growth of the human population could eventually lead to a population crash. If such a catastrophe occurred, it would probably be due to one of the following scenarios.

New, Virulent Diseases

A population crash could be caused by the emergence of one or more new, deadly, communicable diseases to which humans have little or no immunity. There are historical precedents for such a phenomenon. The best example is the bubonic plague, or Black Death, caused by the bacterium *Pasteurella pestis*. Bubonic plague is thought

Global Focus 10.1

AIDS and Population Projections

AIDS (acquired immunodeficiency syndrome) is a disease that has only recently begun to afflict humans. It was first noticed in the late 1970s and was not reported in North America until 1981. Caused by a virus (HIV, human immunodeficiency virus), AIDS results in a syndrome of intensifying sickness and body-wasting that over a period of years eventually proves lethal in most people who harbour the pathogen (i.e., who test positive in an antibody assay). AIDS is passed from person to person through sexual relations, poorly sterilized hypodermic needles, transfusions of blood products, organ transplants, and from mother to fetus during or shortly after birth.

Numbers of People with HIV/AIDS at the End of 2001, by Major Geographic Regions

Nations in the "advanced economies" group are the world's most developed countries and include Canada, the United States, Japan, and nations of Western Europe.

Region	Numbers With HIV/AIDS (millions)	Percentage Of Adult Population (%; age 15-49 y)
Sub-Saharan Africa	28.1	8.4
South & Southeast Asia	6.1	0.6
Latin America	1.4	0.5
Advanced Economies	1.5	0.4
Caribbean	0.42	2.2
Eastern Europe & Central Asia	1.0	0.5
East Asia & Pacific	1.0	0.1
North Africa & Middle East	0.44	0.2

Source: Data from World Health Organization (2001)

The AIDS virus is present in all countries, and in 2005 more than 40 million people were infected, about half of them women. About 95% of the HIV-positive people live in developing countries, while the rate of new infections in developed countries is slowing. In 2003, about 5 million people became newly infected with HIV, and 3 million died from AIDS. The cumulative mortality since the epidemic began is more than 25 million. In North America, more than one million people were HIV-positive in 2004, equivalent to 0.6% of the adult population. The highest rate of infection is in sub-Saharan Africa, where more than 25 million people are HIV-positive, equivalent to 7.5% of the adult population. Although the infection rate is lower in Asia, it is increasing rapidly.

The death rate from AIDS is relatively low in developed countries, where people are comparatively wealthy and have access to modern drugs that can slow the development of the disease. Few people in less developed countries have access to these treatments (nor do many poorer people in wealthier countries); in fact, most HIV-positive people in less developed countries do not even know that they are HIV-positive. This situation could, however, be greatly improved if all people suffering from AIDS, or who are potentially exposed to it, had ready access to information about the disease and its means of transmission and could obtain medical care to diagnose AIDS and inhibit its development.

Some countries in Africa have been hit especially hard by AIDS (about two-thirds of HIV-positive people live in Africa). In Botswana, for example, 37% of adults were HIV-positive in 2003, about double the number only seven years previously. AIDS-related mortality will have an enormous effect on life expectancy in that country, which is projected to fall to a mere 41 years by 2005, compared with 70 years in the absence of AIDS. The huge increase in mortality will, of course, greatly slow the rate of population increase in Botswana and other afflicted countries. However, since the birth rate in Botswana is quite high, the national population is still expected to keep growing and is predicted to double between 1995 and 2050.

The effect of AIDS on population growth in Botswana reflects, on a relatively small scale, the potential effect of AIDS on global population increase. This terrible illness, which is so devastating for afflicted individuals and their families, is already contributing to slowing the rate of increase of the human population. Nevertheless, this medical calamity does not mean that world governments no longer need to develop and implement rational population policies. The human population is still expected to grow substantially from its present huge size. Like population growth, the AIDS epidemic is only partially recognized by most governments, and like population growth, it can be dealt with if appropriate policies are developed and effective actions are taken.

to have originated in a species of rat. Under unsanitary conditions, humans and rats may live in close proximity, allowing rat fleas to bite people and spread bubonic plague. The first major outbreak of bubonic plague occurred in the early fourteenth century, starting in central Asia and spreading through Europe. An extremely virulent disease with no known cure at the time, it killed as much as half of some human populations. Around 1320, the population of Europe was about 85 million, but this fell to about 60 million by 1400 as a result of bubonic deaths. Today, bubonic plague is treated with antibiotics, and rat populations are controlled by routine sanitation measures.

Another killer plague swept the world in 1918–19, caused by an epidemic of a novel strain of influenza. As many as 20–40 million people died. Other virulent diseases will probably emerge in the future, perhaps transferred to humans by close contact with other species, most likely chickens or primates. A recent example is Ebola virus, which causes a rare but deadly hemorrhagic (bleeding) fever. It was probably spread to humans from a species of rainforest monkey in central Africa. Two other examples are a virulent strain of avian flu, which would likely jump to humans from domestic chickens or ducks, and severe acute respiratory syndrome (SARS), whose origin is believed to be wild carnivores killed as food for people. Yet another prospect is Creutzfeldt-Jakob disease, which is characterized by degeneration of the brain and other neural tissues. This affliction is caused by a transmissible protein known as a prion and is apparently spread when humans eat beef contaminated by so-called mad-cow disease, or eat the brains of infected monkeys or apes. Some epidemiologists believe that acquired immunodeficiency syndrome (AIDS), a slowly developing but almost always lethal syndrome, also has the potential to cause catastrophic mortality in human populations (see Global Focus 10.1). So could new, deadly, antibiotic-resistant strains of Group B *Staphylococcus* and other pathogenic bacteria.

So far, medical science has managed to deal with most of these new, lethal, communicable diseases. However, science may not be able to cope with some of the new pestilences. If this is true, there could be catastrophic results for dense, vulnerable populations of modern humans. Such an event could be caused by the emergence of a new virulent pathogen, but it could also be initiated by germ-warfare terrorism, for example using the anthrax or smallpox germs.

Famine

The spectre of famine has been present throughout human history. Famines can arise from various factors, including insect outbreaks, insufficient rainfall causing drought, excessive precipitation causing flooding, and warfare and other socio-political upheavals. Ancient historical records are full of descriptions of deadly famines in many cultures. Some of the most catastrophic famines of pre–twentieth-century Asia and Europe killed hundreds of thousands of people.

Even more enormous famines occurred in the twentieth century. For example, as many as 5–10 million people may have starved in the Soviet Union during 1932–34. This happened as a combined result of drought and social upheaval associated with the forced collectivization of private farms by the communist government. Another famine in West Bengal killed two to four million people in 1943. More recent famines have occurred in various parts of Africa and Asia, caused by crop failures due to drought and other weather extremes, and often aggravated by the chaos of war or revolution.

Overpopulation exacerbates most factors that contribute to famine. Regions or countries are vulnerable to developing famine conditions if

- they have large and dense populations;
- they have small reserves of stored food;
- environmental conditions for agriculture are marginal, partly because population pressure has led to land being cultivated in semi-arid regions susceptible to drought;
- there is little foreign exchange to purchase food from elsewhere during times of shortage, so people and governments must rely on goodwill and aid; and
- the economic and political systems do not foster the stable governments and social systems that are required for effectively dealing with crisis.

Decline of Carrying Capacity

Environmental catastrophists suggest that the ecological carrying capacity for the extremely large human population may collapse. If this were to happen, extensive mass starvation would follow. It is already clear that some of the most important potentially renewable resources are being severely overharvested and that stocks of non-renewable resources are being rapidly depleted (see Chapters 12, 13, and 14). Collapsing fish stocks, declines in agricultural soil capability, desertification, deforestation, and depleted groundwater are all evidence of this pressing phenomenon. Declining resources decrease the carrying capacity of the biosphere for the human enterprise.

A Nuclear Holocaust

Enormous numbers of people have died prematurely through the direct and indirect consequences of warfare. The most lethal conflicts in history were the First World War, which killed as many as 20 million people, and the Second World War, during which at least 38 million died. Potentially, however, modern humans are capable of killing enormously larger numbers through the unbridled use of nuclear weapons. The world's nuclear powers have enormous arsenals of sophisticated, extremely powerful weaponry, particularly the United States and Russia. The explosive power of their thousands of nuclear weapons is unbelievably huge and is capable of causing environmental damage so extreme as to return any surviving people back to the stone age. Conventional military theory holds that nuclear arsenals are most useful as deterrents against other nuclear-power nations, and recent treaties have resulted in large reductions in arsenals. Nevertheless, the remaining stockpiles remain active and immense, and it is not difficult to imagine scenarios of political instability and conflict that could lead to a nuclear holocaust. Until all nuclear weapons are beaten into ploughshares, a global nuclear disaster cannot be ruled out.

A Natural Big Bang

Although extraordinarily unlikely, it is conceivable that Earth and its ecosystems could suffer a natural, unpredictable, environmental catastrophe such as a meteorite impact. There are precedents for such a rare event, with clear evidence from the geological record (see Chapter 3). For instance, it appears that, about 65 million years ago, Earth may have been struck by a meteorite, an accident that caused enormous environmental damage and likely resulted in a mass-extinction event (see Chapters 6 and 26). Fortunately, cosmic calamities of this tremendous intensity are extremely rare, occurring only every 25–30 million years or so. It is much more likely that any crash that might occur in the human population would be caused by a virulent disease or collapse of carrying capacity, rather than by a big-bang cataclysm from a meteorite strike.

Conclusions

The human population has been growing exponentially in recent centuries. Further growth will occur in the foreseeable future, but likely at decreasing rates. Demographic models suggest that the population will eventually stabilize, but this may happen at a level at least 50% larger than the more than six billion people alive today.

Accompanying the growth of the human population has been an even more rapid increase in per capita environmental impact. In combination, these have changed the biosphere on a scale and intensity that is comparable to the effects of such enormous geological events as full-blown glaciation. The damage includes deforestation, depletion of virtually all kinds of resources, pollution, and mass extinction. It is clearly apparent that the cumulative, anthropogenic impacts on the environment will escalate even further with increases in the abundance of people.

A key to decreasing the growth of the human population is to get less developed countries through their demographic transition, which involves decreasing birth rates to a level that balances the already low death rates. If this is to happen, a widespread cultural change in favour of smaller families will have to occur or else governments will have to coerce people to have fewer children. In either case, it will be necessary to achieve widespread access to safe and effective means of birth control for all people, but particularly women.

The enormous growth of the human population must be kept in mind whenever environmental problems are considered. To some degree, the environmental effects of people and their economies can be avoided or mitigated by technological strategies such as pollution control and the conservation of natural resources. However, the size of the human population remains a root cause of the ecological damage caused by our species.

Key Terms

cultural evolution

carrying capacity

doubling time

intrinsic population change

zero population growth (ZPG)

demographic transition

age-class structure

replacement fertility rate

urbanization

megacity

birth control

population policy

Questions for Review

1. What are the major stages in cultural evolution? How do these relate to changes in carrying capacity and growth of the human population?

2. How is demographic transition defined? Compare its dynamics in developed and less developed countries.

3. Why is age-class structure so important in future population growth?

4. Describe the possible reasons why the human population will eventually level off or decrease.

Questions for Discussion

1. What is the recent pattern of growth of the human population? Discuss the possible scenarios for future growth.

2. Compare demographic parameters and population growth rates in developed and less developed countries. What can explain the differences?

3. What are the major means of birth control? Discuss controversies associated with their use.

4. What is the likelihood of a human population crash? What are the potential causes?

5. Why is HIV/AIDS much more prevalent in poorer countries than in wealthier ones?

Exploring Issues

1. The government of a poor country has asked for your help in designing a population policy. You will visit the country for several months to get a personal appreciation for the environmental and socio-economic problems that exist and to help you understand cultural conditions important in designing the population policy. What kinds of studies would you want to make during your visit? What cornerstones would you recommend for the population policy?

2. The personal choice to use birth control can be difficult and is further complicated by specific considerations about the various methods and technologies available. Make a list of the key ethical, social, and economic issues associated with any three methods of birth control (you can select them from In Detail 10.2). Consider both the personal dimensions of choice (e.g., personal ethics and views) as well as those that are relevant to society at large (e.g., group pressure, whether a particular method is legal, the ease of access to particular methods).

References

Bates, D.G. and E.M. Franklin. 2002. *Cultural Anthropology*. 3rd ed. Upper Saddle River, NJ: Allyn & Bacon.

Brown, L.R. 2003. *Plan C: Rescuing a Planet Under Stress and a Civilization in Trouble*. New York: W.W. Norton and Company.

Ehrlich, P.R. and A.H. Ehrlich. 1990. *The Population Explosion*. New York: Simon & Schuster.

Ehrlich, P.R., A.H. Ehrlich, and J.P. Holdren. 1977. *Ecoscience: Population, Resources, Environment*. San Francisco: W.H. Freeman.

Freedman, B. 1995. *Environmental Ecology*. 2nd ed. San Diego, CA: Academic Press.

Goldemberg, J. 1992. Energy, technology, development. *Ambio*, **21**: 14–17.

Health and Welfare Canada. 1980. *Facts and fancy about birth control, sex education, and family planning*. Ottawa: Health and Welfare Canada, Health Promotion Directorate.

Hollingsworth, W.D. 1996. *Ending the Explosion: Population Policies and Ethics for a Human Future*. Santa Ana, CA: Seven Locks Press.

Jennings, J.D. 1979. *The Prehistory of Polynesia*. Cambridge, MA: Harvard University Press.

Joint United Nations Programme on HIV/AIDS (UNAIDS) A Global Overview of the AIDS Epidemic. www.unaids.org/bangkok2004/GAR2004_html/GAR2004_03_en.htm#P237_35114

Kane, P. 1983. *The Which? Guide to Birth Control*. London: Hodder & Stoughton.

Kessler, B.A. (ed.). 1992. Special issue on population. *Ambio*, **21**: 1–120.

Leisinger, K.M. 2003. *Six Billion and Counting: Population Growth and Food Security in the 21st Century*. Washington, CD: International Food Policy Research Institute.

Leisinger, K.M. and K. Schmitt. 1994. *All Our People: Population Policy with a Human Face*. Washington, DC: Island Press.

Mongabay. Index of Population Estimates. http://books.mongabay.com/population_estimates/full/

Olsson, H. and A. Rapp. 1991. Dryland degradation in central Sudan and conservation for survival. *Ambio*, **20**: 192–5.

Polunin, N. (ed.). 1998. *Population and Global Security*. New York: Cambridge University Press.

Population Reference Bureau. 2004. *World Population Data Sheet.* www.prb.org/pdf04/04WorldDataSheet_Eng.pdf

Raven, P.H. and L.R. Berg. 2003. *Environment.* 4th ed. Hoboken, NJ: Wiley.

Shah, A. 1998. *Ecology and the Crisis of Overpopulation: Future Prospects for Global Sustainability.* London: Edward Elgar.

Solomon, E.P. 2003. *Introduction to Human Anatomy and Physiology.* New York: Saunders.

Tanner, J.T. 1975. Population limitation today and in ancient Polynesia. *BioScience*, **25**: 513–6.

United Nations Population Fund. 2004. *Demographic Yearbook, 2003.* New York: UNPF.

Vitousek, P.M., P.R. Ehrlich, A.H. Ehrlich, and P.A. Matson. 1986. Human appropriation of the products of photosynthesis. *Bioscience*, **36**: 368–73.

World Health Organization. 2005. *A Global Overview of the AIDS Epidemic.* Geneva, Switzerland: WHO.

World Resources Institute (WRI). 1998. *World Resources 1998–99: A Guide to the Global Environment: Global Change and Human Health.* New York: Oxford University Press.

World Resources Institute (WRI). 2004. *World Resources 2002–2004: Decisions for the Earth: Balance, Voice, and Power.* Washington, DC: WRI.

World Resources Institute (WRI). 2004. *World Resources, 2003–04. People and Ecosystems: The Fraying Web of Life.* Washington, DC: WRI.

Wrigley, E.A. 2004. *Poverty, Progress and Population.* Cambridge, UK: Cambridge University Press.

Yaukey, D. and D.L. Anderton. 2001. *Demography: The Study of Human Population.* 2nd ed. Long Grove, IL: Waveland Press.

Informative Websites

Joint United Nations Programme on HIV/AIDS (UNAIDS). A Global Overview of the AIDS Epidemic. www.unaids.org/bangkok2004/GAR2004_html/GAR2004_03_en.htm#P237_35114

This website is an excellent source of information about the global HIV/AIDS crisis.

Population Dynamics. www.enviroliteracy.org/subcategory.php/30.html

You'll find links to many other population websites as well as papers, fact sheets, and statistics here.

Population Reference Bureau. www.prb.org

The Population Reference Bureau is an excellent source of information about population issues and demographic data.

United Nations Population Fund. www.unfpa.org/

You can search this comprehensive site by region, sub-region, or country to find literacy percentages, contraceptive knowledge, life expectancy, total population, and other information.

World Resources Institute. Populations, Health, and Human Well-Being. http://population.wri.org

The WRI is a leading environmental organization that provides excellent information about population and resource issues.

The Canadian Population

11

Introduction

In Chapter 10 we examined the dynamics of human populations in different countries as well as globally. This information provides an international context for examining population issues in Canada.

Canada ranks among the top 20% of nations in terms of its human population (about 32 million in 2005). Canada also ranks among the wealthiest of nations in terms of per capita indicators of economic development, resource use, and anthropogenic impacts on environmental quality (see Chapter 1). Because its citizens have an environmentally intensive lifestyle, Canada has a much greater impact on Earth and its resources than would be predicted on the basis of its population alone.

Because Canada has achieved a relatively high level of economic and social development, it has an opportunity and a responsibility to manage its environmental quality in a sustainable manner. Canada also has a responsibility to control its population growth within sustainable limits. Moreover, because of Canada's privileged and wealthy status, it has an obligation to demonstrate a vision of sustainable development to other nations, including poorer countries that are hoping to emulate our national achievements. A central element of sustainable development is the implementation of a sensible population policy.

It is important that Canadians become knowledgeable about national and global population issues. If Canadians understand these matters, they will be sympathetic to population policies that are appropriate both within Canada and abroad.

Aboriginal Populations

Around 1000 CE, the Norse explorer Leif Ericsson made several landfalls along the northeast coast of North America. The Norse attempted a brief colonization, including a settlement at l'Anse aux Meadows in Newfoundland, but this failed. About 500 years later, other European explorers encountered vast regions in the Americas that were previously unknown to them. They did not, however, find unpopulated lands. In fact, all of the Americas were fully occupied by various **indigenous cultures** (also known as **First Nations**). At the end of the fifteenth century (at the time of the voyages of Christopher Columbus and John Cabot), the First Nations of the Americas had an estimated population of 35 million people. About 30 million of these people lived in South and Central America, and 5 million in North America.

Some of the First Nations had developed advanced cultures, particularly the Aztecs and Maya of Central America and the Inca of South America. These people built elaborate cities that contained great pyramids and other magnificent buildings. Their nations were supported by complex physical and social infrastructures. Like cities everywhere, those of advanced Amerindian cultures relied on the surrounding agricultural landscape for supplies of food, water, and other resources. Furthermore, taxes were collected from people living in the producing regions to support the rulers, administrators, soldiers, and artisans living in the urbanized centres.

Photo 11.1 Although population densities are high in Canadian cities (illustrated by this view of a crowd listening to musical buskers in Halifax), they are much lower in the country as a whole. Most of Canada is not suitable for supporting a large human population, mainly because of a difficult climate.

The First Nations cultures in what is now Canada were diverse, comprising 12 distinct language groups and many additional dialects. Some of the Aboriginal cultures, such as the Huron and Iroquois of the eastern temperate woodlands, were essentially agrarian societies. These people supplemented their agricultural livelihood by foraging for useful wild plants and by hunting deer, birds, fish, and other animals. They lived in grand longhouses in stockaded villages, surrounded by fields in which they cultivated maize, beans, pumpkin, squash, sunflower, and other indigenous crops.

Other First Nations of Canada subsisted largely through hunting and foraging lifestyles. The Bella Coola, Haida, Nootka, Tlingit, and related nations of the humid west coast exploited a relatively abundant and predictable resource base, and, consequently, they lived in permanent settlements. These people were mostly fishers of salmon, mollusks, and other inshore resources. They supplemented these aquatic foods with wild plants, deer, and other terrestrial resources.

Most of the Aboriginal cultures of the western plains, such as the Assiniboine, Blackfoot, and Piegan, were semi-nomadic hunters of the enormous herds of buffalo and other prairie animals that existed at the time. The more northern Athapaskans, Chipewyan, Cree, Dene, Innu, and Montagnais of the sweeping boreal forest hunted mostly caribou, moose, beaver, and waterfowl, and fished streams and lakes for grayling, trout, whitefish, pike, and other fishes. The Beothuk, Mi'kmaq, and Malacites of the Atlantic region also hunted moose, deer, and caribou, fished in freshwaters, and gathered shellfish in shallow, marine waters. The northernmost Inuit hunted caribou when those migratory animals were nearby, but they subsisted mostly on marine mammals, including ringed seal, walrus, beluga whale, narwhal, and even great bowhead whales. All of these peoples also gathered wild plant foods when they were seasonally abundant.

We know little about the population sizes of these First Nations of Canada. Reasonable estimates are based on assumptions about their lifestyles and the presumed carrying capacity of their habitats. At about the time when the first Europeans came to Canada, the total population of Aboriginal Canadians is estimated to have been about 300 000.

The European colonization of the Americas began in the early sixteenth century, following the "discovery" of these lands in 1492 by Christopher Columbus, a Genoan sailing on behalf of the Spanish Crown. Columbus was searching for an oceanic passage to the rich spices and silks of China, India, Japan, and Southeast Asia. In 1497, John Cabot, another Genoan employed by the King of England, sighted Newfoundland and possibly Cape Breton Island.

Within a century of the arrival of the Europeans, the numbers of Aboriginal people began to fall precipitously. By the end of the nineteenth century, the population of the First Nations in North America was only about 20% of their initial five million. Infectious diseases, particularly measles, smallpox, tuberculosis, and influenzas, were the most important causes of this calamitous mortality. Europeans were relatively tolerant of these diseases that they brought to the Americas, but the indigenous peoples were extremely vulnerable. Epidemiologists refer to populations that are hypersensitive to infectious diseases as **virgin fields**. Such populations can suffer intense mortality from introduced diseases (known as virgin-field epidemics).

In addition, huge numbers of Aboriginal peoples died as a direct and indirect result of conflicts associated with the European conquest. Others died during inter-tribal wars, some of which were precipitated when competing European nations upset previous balances of power among indigenous groups, in part by providing their Aboriginal allies with advanced weaponry. In addition, many people starved when they were dispossessed of their resources and livelihoods by European colonists and governments. For example, the rapacious nineteenth-century slaughter of the great buffalo herds of North America was partly a stratagem to deprive the Plains First Nations of their critical resource base.

In 1500 CE, there were about 300 000 indigenous people in Canada, a population that subsequently collapsed to perhaps 60 000. In 2004, the First Nations of Canada comprised more than 700 000 people. This number refers to Canadians who are registered as Indians under the federal Indian Act (Statistics Canada, 2004). However, as many as 1.2 million Canadians may consider themselves to be of Aboriginal origin.

Early Immigration from Europe

The initial wave of European colonists coming to Canada consisted mostly of French and British adventurers seeking furs, fish, timber, agricultural land, and trade. Compared with their European homelands, which even then were relatively densely populated, Canada represented an enormous frontier to these colonists, containing boundless opportunities to make money and develop livelihoods. The fact that these lands were already occupied by indigenous cultures did not matter much to the European colonists. The dominant world views at that time were harsh, aggressive, and imperialist. These beliefs served to legitimize the displacement of the First Nations people by the technologically empowered Europeans.

Slowly for the first century or so, and then as a great flood of immigration, colonists came to Canada from France and Britain, and later from many other countries. Today, the population of Canada is an amalgam derived from a rich diversity of immigrants from virtually all parts of the world, plus descendants of the original First Nations.

Between about 1500 and 1700, the population of the North American continent increased to about six million people. This included about one million black slaves, all of whom had been brought unwillingly from Africa to the southeastern colonies to work on plantations. Under laws of the time, slaves were the human property of their "owners," having no personal freedom and few rights. People in the northern colonies had few slaves, but they had large numbers of indentured servants, mostly of European origin, who were legally bound to their employers by contracts and debts that in many cases were impossible to pay off.

Following this initial phase of colonization, the pace of immigration quickened markedly. Data are not available for the entire period, but between 1820 and 1930, at least 50 million Europeans migrated to colonies and former colonies around the world, particularly to the Americas. This immense dispersal involved about one-fifth of the population of Europe during that period. The mass migration was stimulated by a combination of factors: rapid population growth in Europe, a shortage of arable land there, famine in Ireland and other countries, and rivalries among the imperial powers to develop empires and dominate world trade. In addition, religious and ethnic minorities in European countries were frequently persecuted, and many of these oppressed peoples emigrated to North America and elsewhere.

As was noted in Chapter 10, this great nineteenth- and twentieth-century dispersal was a critical factor in allowing the European countries to have a relatively easy passage through the early stages of their demographic transitions.

Growth of the Canadian Population

Reliable information is available describing early population growth in some regions of Canada, notably in

New France (see Canadian Focus 11.1 and 11.2). The first credible estimate of the population of all of Canada is for 1851, when there were about 2.4 million people (Figure 11.1). By 1867, the year of Confederation, there were 3.3 million people in Canada. By the turn of the twentieth century, the population had increased to 5.4 million. Much of the population growth resulted from a natural increase of 1.3–2.0% per year, with birth rates of 36–45 per 1000 people in the population, and death rates of 18–21 per 1000. In fact, because of a relatively depressed economy during the first several decades after Confederation, immigrants to Canada were fewer than emigrants from the country.

During the twentieth century, birth and death rates both declined steadily, although the natural rate of population increase remained greater than 1% per year until the mid-1970s. This natural growth, coupled with vigorous immigration, led to rapid increases in the Canadian population. Population growth rates were as high as 3% per year and averaged about 1.6% per year overall. By 1950 there were about 14 million Canadians, and in 2005 more than 32 million.

The natural rate of growth of the Canadian population (i.e., birth rate minus death rate) has slowed markedly during the past century or more (Tables 11.1 and 11.2). This has happened mainly because of rapid decreases in birth rates, which now almost counterbalance the death rates (which had declined earlier).

An exception to the general decline in birth rates is a demographic anomaly known as the baby boom that occurred between 1945 and 1965. This period of relatively

FIGURE 11.1 | The Population of Canada

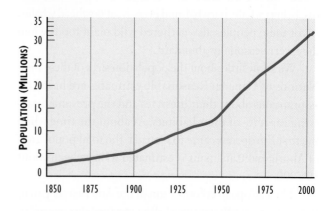

In 1851, the Canadian population was about 2.4 million. This graph shows the steady growth of the population up to 2003, when the Canadian population was 31.6 million.

Source: Data from Statistics Canada (1992, 1995b, 2004)

Canadian | Focus 11.1

The Legacy of Daniel LeBlanc and Françoise Gaudet

In 1650, Daniel LeBlanc emigrated from France to Acadia. He married Françoise Gaudet and settled into subsistence farming near what is now Annapolis Royal in Nova Scotia. Many families during that time were large, especially because children helped with the onerous labour of clearing the forest, tending crops and livestock, and taking care of the home and extended family. In fact, fecundity remained high among French Canadians for more than three centuries until the 1950s and 1960s, when birth rates began to plummet.

Daniel and Françoise had seven children—six sons and a daughter. Five of their sons married, presenting Daniel and Françoise with 35 grandchildren. Today, the LeBlanc family has an enormous legacy of descendants of Daniel and Françoise. The extended family is estimated to number more than 300 000 in Canada and the United States (many of whom have the anglicized surname White). The LeBlanc clan is the largest of the Acadian lineages that have persisted into modern times. Although the LeBlancs' case is extraordinary, it demonstrates the awesome power of human population growth.

high fecundity was due largely to several decades of social optimism that followed the end of the Second World War. In addition, during the war many couples delayed marriage and childbearing because many young men went to fight overseas and women were employed in factories and other wartime occupations. After the war ended, men and women turned their attention back to raising families. During the **baby boom**, the birth rate in Canada averaged about 27 per 1000 and the natural growth rate of the population was 1.9% per year.

An important reason for the end of the baby boom phenomenon was the growing affluence and urbanization of typical Canadians, which led to a general desire for smaller families. Also important was the increasingly easy access to, and social acceptance of, methods of birth control. By the year 2003 the birth rate in Canada was 10 per 1000, and the natural rate of increase of the population was about 0.3% per year.

Immigration has always been an important factor in the population growth of Canada, as can be readily appreciated by examining the data in Table 11.2. During most of Canada's history, considerably more migrants have moved to this country than away from it. The major exception was during the latter decades of the nineteenth century, when many people emigrated from Canada to the United States. During the twentieth century, however, Canada had consistently high rates of immigration.

Immigration has been especially vigorous since the 1960s, when the government of Canada loosened restrictions associated with national and ethnic origins of immigrants. These were replaced with criteria based on education, occupational skills, and wealth. Since the early 1970s there has been a substantial increase in the numbers of immigrants coming to Canada. Between 1972 and 1981, an annual average of 145 000 people immigrated to Canada; 143 000 per year came during 1982–91. This was followed by a substantial increase to 253 000 per year during 1992–93.

TABLE 11.1	Components of Natural Growth of the Canadian Population

These data are standardized per 1000 people in the population and are annual rates. Note that an annual growth rate of 10/1000 is equivalent to 1% per year.

DATE	BIRTH RATE	DEATH RATE	NATURAL GROWTH RATE
1921	29.3	10.6	18.7
1931	23.2	10.1	13.1
1941	22.4	10.0	12.4
1946	27.2	9.4	17.8
1951	27.2	9.0	18.2
1956	28.0	8.2	19.8
1961	26.1	7.7	18.4
1966	19.4	7.5	11.9
1971	16.8	7.3	9.5
1976	15.7	7.3	8.4
1981	15.3	7.0	8.3
1986	14.8	7.2	7.6
1991	14.3	7.0	7.3
1996	12.2	7.1	5.0
2001	10.8	7.1	3.7
2003	10.4	7.2	3.2

Sources: Data from Kalbach (1988), Dumas and Belanger (1994, 1998), and Statistics Canada (2004)

Canadian Focus 11.2

A Remarkable Legacy of New France

The best early demographic data for any area of Canada are for New France. This region encompassed the valley of the St. Lawrence River in southern Quebec, and the Acadian regions of what are now Nova Scotia, New Brunswick, and Prince Edward Island.

The first French colonization effort occurred in 1604, when Samuel de Champlain (1567–1635) led an expedition that settled near Annapolis Royal in the lower Bay of Fundy, followed by another mission that founded Quebec City in 1608. In the early 1600s, there were about 500 French colonists in the region known as New France. In 1663, after a half-century of tentative colonization, a census reported 3215 people of French origin in Quebec; another census in 1671 found about 400 in Acadia. Most were single men who had journeyed to the Canadian frontier as soldiers, as priests hoping to convert indigenous people to Roman Catholicism, as government administrators, or as adventurers seeking their fortune through the fur trade.

In the following decade, the pace of colonization quickened markedly because of sponsorship by the French government. Families of settlers arrived from France, intent on developing agriculture in the fertile lowlands of Acadia and along the St. Lawrence River. The immigration of single women was also encouraged to offset the substantial deficit of females in the early population of New France. Many of these young women were recruited from Parisian orphanages and were known as *les filles du roi*. In 1673, there were about 6700 francophones in New France.

Immigration then slowed greatly because of dwindling prospects for finding work in the colonies and because royal sponsorship of emigrants had ended. French immigration to Acadia ceased when that area was ceded to Britain in 1713, and then to Isle Royale (Cape Breton Island) after the fortress of Louisbourg was lost to a British siege in 1758. Immigration to Quebec also ended after the British victory at the Plains of Abraham in 1759, which effectively ended the French colonization of eastern Canada. Population growth after these times was due to a natural increase, owing to the excess of births over deaths.

Birth rates were high in New France (and elsewhere) during the eighteenth century, typically about 50–60 per 1000 people in the population. Anecdotal evidence suggests great fecundity in early colonial times—one soldier serving under the Marquis de Montcalm (1712–59) is said to have left 250 descendants when he died. Families of 15–20 children were not uncommon. Even though infant mortality was high, particularly from communicable diseases, the population grew quickly.

By 1770, the francophone population of Quebec had increased to 86 000. After 1759, all the growth of the French-Canadian population in Quebec was due to the natural excess of births over mortality, while much of the growth of the non-francophone population was due to immigration. By 1815, the francophone population of Quebec was 269 000 (there were also about 60 000 British colonists in Quebec at that time), and in 1885, there were 1.18 million (plus 0.25 million non-francophones).

During the nineteenth century, the average number of births in Catholic families in Quebec was about seven (this refers to all Catholics, but the great majority were French). This high fecundity is typical of populations at the beginning of their demographic transition. It should be pointed out, however, that high fecundity was not unique to Quebec—it was also typical of areas elsewhere in Canada, including Ontario.

In 1926, there were about 3 million francophones in Quebec, elsewhere in Canada, and in the United States. Almost all of these people were descendants of the original few hundred emigrants from France. At the present time, there are more than 6 million French Canadians. This includes about 5.6 million francophones living in Quebec, 0.4 million Acadians, and smaller numbers in other provinces. There are also hundreds of thousands of Americans of French descent, many of whom live in Louisiana and New England.

Since the mid-1980s, net immigration has contributed about half of Canada's population growth rate (the rest is due to natural growth; see Table 11.2). If sustained, the 0.75% per year rate of increase of 1991–2003 would result in the Canadian population doubling in only 93 years. This rate of population growth is similar to that of the United States and Australia, also relatively wealthy, industrialized countries with small natural growth rates but substantial rates of immigration. These three countries are exceptional in these respects. Most other industrialized countries, particularly those of Europe, have much smaller rates of population increase, in part because they do not permit

TABLE 11.2 | Population Growth Rates in Canada

Natural growth rates are calculated as births minus deaths, while the actual growth rate also accounts for net immigration (i.e., immigrants minus emigrants). The data are standardized per 1000 people in the population and are average annual rates.

TIME INTERVAL	NATURAL GROWTH RATE (%)	NET IMMIGRATION RATE(%)	ACTUAL GROWTH RATE (%)
1851–61	2.50	0.75	3.25
1861–71	1.89	−0.47	1.42
1871–81	1.87	−0.15	1.72
1881–91	1.51	−0.34	1.17
1891–1901	1.38	−0.27	1.11
1901–11	1.91	1.51	3.42
1911–21	1.76	0.43	2.19
1921–31	1.55	0.26	1.81
1931–41	1.18	−0.09	1.09
1941–51	1.71	0.15	1.86
1951–61	2.25	0.77	3.02
1961–71	1.43	0.40	1.83
1971–81	0.87	0.44	1.31
1981–91	0.39	0.24	0.63
1991–2001	0.52	0.55	1.07
2002	0.34	0.63	0.97

Sources: Data from Kalbach (1988) and Statistics Canada (2004)

much immigration (see Chapter 10). This can be attributed mainly to the differences in population density of European countries in comparison with Canada, the United States, and Australia.

Future Growth

Results of three models of future Canadian populations are summarized in Table 11.3. Scenario 1 is a low-growth model, involving lower rates of fertility and immigration than occur at present and resulting in population stabilization by about 2030. Scenarios 2 and 3 are moderate-growth models. Scenario 2 assumes that population growth will stabilize around 2040. Scenario 3 assumes a continuation of recent demographic parameters into the future and population growth that continues beyond 2040.

All three scenarios are realistic to some degree because they involve plausible outcomes of reasonable anticipated changes in two groups of factors: government policy regarding immigration and population issues, and reproductive choices made by individuals and families. Overall,

the models predict that the population of Canada will grow substantially from its 2005 value of about 32 million. The slow-growth projection suggests a population of about 35 million by 2040 (a 9% increase), compared with 50 million in the third scenario (a 65% increase), in which recent trends are extrapolated.

Population Structure

The age structure of the modern Canadian population is illustrated in Figure 11.2. In general, the pattern is typical of a population that has progressed most of the way through the demographic transition. Note, however, the anomalous bulge of numbers corresponding to the "baby boomers." Fecundity dropped dramatically in Canada after the baby boom, and once this bulge has worked its way through the population structure, the age distribution will assume a more vertical shape. As the baby boomers age and retire from work, they are expected to exert significant strain on Canada's capacity for providing social and medical care for its elderly citizens.

Although Canada has a population structure characteristic of a country that has almost completed its demo-

TABLE 11.3 | Projected Canadian Populations

Population projections are based on sets of assumptions about fertility, mortality, and net immigration. Scenario 1 is a low-growth model, suggesting lower rates of fertility and immigration than occur at present. Scenarios 2 and 3 are moderate-growth models, with Scenario 3 assuming that current trends will continue into the future.

YEAR	PREDICTED POPULATION (MILLIONS)		
	SCENARIO 1	SCENARIO 2	SCENARIO 3
1994	28.8	28.8	28.8
1996	29.5	29.6	29.6
2000	30.8	31.1	31.4
2005	32.1	33.0	33.8
2010	33.1	34.7	36.3
2015	33.9	36.4	38.9
2020	34.6	38.1	41.4
2025	35.2	39.6	43.8
2030	35.5	40.8	46.0
2035	35.5	41.8	48.0
2040	35.3	42.6	49.9

Source: Data from Statistics Canada (1994b)

FIGURE 11.2 | Age Structure of the Canadian Population

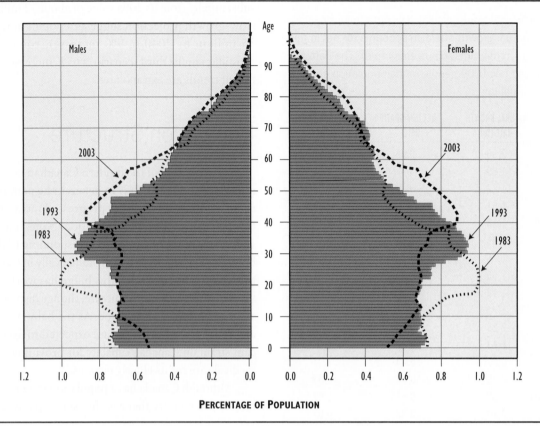

This diagram shows the relative numbers of people of various ages. The demographic "bump" of people who were 27–37 years old in 1983 and 36–46 years old in 2003 corresponds to a period of relatively high birth rates from the mid-1940s to mid-1960s, known as the "baby boom."

Source: Modified from Statistics Canada (2004)

graphic transition, the growth rate remains relatively high, even now approaching 1% per year. Much of the population growth is due to immigration. Although this factor is not closely related to age-class structure, it is notable that relatively young families and people of childbearing age are prominent among immigrants to Canada. This adds further inertia to population growth.

Regional Differences

All regions of Canada have experienced substantial population growth during the past century or more (Table 11.4). The increases have been less substantial in the Atlantic Provinces and most rapid in the western provinces of British Columbia and Alberta. In 1867, the Atlantic Provinces accounted for 21% of the Canadian population; Quebec, 32%, Ontario, 44%; and the rest of the country,

3%. At that time the western regions of Canada were largely unsettled, but tremendous population growth has occurred there since. By 2003, a much larger fraction of the Canadian population lived in western regions of the country: the Atlantic Provinces now account for 7% of the Canadian population; Quebec, 24%; Ontario, 39%; the Prairie Provinces, 17%; British Columbia, 13%; and the three territories, 0.3% (Table 11.5).

There is little variation in birth and death rates among the provinces and territories of Canada (Table 11.6). The major exception is Nunavut, which has by far the highest birth rate. First Nations communities, which tend to have relatively large families and a higher rate of population growth, make up a much larger proportion of the population of Nunavut (and to a lesser degree, NWT) than of any other province or territory. The territory also has a relatively low mortality rate, which is largely due to its comparatively young population. People younger than

TABLE 11.4	Regional Distribution of the Canadian Population

These data show the growth of the population of Canada and its regions since Confederation in 1867. Note that data for the Prairie Provinces prior to 1901 include only Manitoba. Data for Alberta, Saskatchewan, and Yukon were combined with the Northwest Territories until 1901, when they became separate political units. In 1949, Newfoundland joined Canada. Data are in thousands of people.

YEAR	CANADA	ATLANTIC PROVINCES	QUEBEC	ONTARIO	PRAIRIE PROVINCES	BRITISH COLUMBIA	YUKON, NWT, AND NUNAVUT
1867	3 466	726	1123	1 525	15	32	45
1881	4 325	871	1360	1 927	62	49	56
1891	4 833	880	1489	2 114	153	98	99
1901	5 371	894	1649	2 183	419	179	47
1911	7 207	938	2006	2 527	1327	393	16
1921	8 788	1001	2361	2 934	1955	525	12
1931	10 375	1008	2874	3 431	2354	694	14
1941	11 503	1130	3331	3 787	2421	817	17
1951	14 001	1618	4056	4 598	2549	1165	25
1961	18 238	1897	5259	6 236	3179	1629	38
1971	21 962	2083	6138	7 849	3597	2240	55
1981	24 820	2259	6548	8 811	4307	2824	71
1991	28 031	2370	7065	10 428	4705	3373	90
2001	31 021	2348	7397	11 898	5208	4078	99
2003	31 630	2344	7487	12 238	5311	4147	102

Source: Data from Statistics Canada (1992, 1995a, 1998, 2004)

15 years comprised 35% of the population of NU and 25% of NWT in 2003, compared with a national average of 18%. Overall, the natural rate of population growth in 2003 was 2.1% per year in NU and 1.0% per year in NWT,

TABLE 11.5	Population by Province and Territory in 2003

Data are in thousands of people.

PROVINCE	POPULATION	PERCENTAGE OF TOTAL
Canada	31 630	
Ontario	12 238	38.7 %
Quebec	7 487	23.7
British Columbia	4 147	13.1
Alberta	3 154	10.0
Manitoba	1 163	3.7
Saskatchewan	995	3.1
Nova Scotia	936	3.0
New Brunswick	751	2.4
Newfoundland and Labrador	520	1.6
Prince Edward Island	138	0.4
Northwest Territories and Nunavut	71	0.2
Yukon	31	0.1

Source: Data from Statistics Canada (2004)

equivalent to doubling times of 34 and 70 years, respectively. The age structure and growth rate are, in fact, typical of regions that are only beginning to pass through the demographic transition, and in that sense, are anomalous compared with the rest of Canada.

Alberta and Ontario have the fastest population growth rates among the provinces, 1.2–1.3% per year (2003), which is equivalent to a doubling time of only 54–58 years. This rapid rate of population increase occurs in spite of a 0.4–0.6% per year natural rate of population increase. Obviously, their populations are growing because of high rates of immigration from other countries and from other regions of Canada.

The smallest population growth rates occur in Saskatchewan (–0.06% per year), the four Atlantic Provinces (0.05–0.6% per year), Quebec (0.6% per year), and Manitoba (0.6% per year). Natural population growth in Saskatchewan is higher than the actual population increase, reflecting a net migration of people to other provinces (mostly Alberta) or other countries.

In general, the population of Canada is much denser in southern parts of the country. This pronounced spatial pattern reflects the distribution of economic opportunities in Canada, most of which are related to climate and suitability of the land for agriculture.

Canadian Focus 11.3

Immigrants and Refugees

In addition to descendants of its Aboriginal peoples, Canada is populated by immigrants and their offspring. Canada has a history of relatively open immigration policies and this continues today. For example, in 2003 Canada admitted 221 352 immigrants and 25 984 refugees, equivalent to about 0.8% of the national population (Citizenship and Immigration Canada, 2004). These newcomers constitute the largest component of population growth of Canada, which totalled about 0.97% in 2003. If not for its rather vigorous immigration rate, Canada would be close to a ZPG (zero population growth) condition.

In 2002, Parliament passed a new Immigration and Refugee Protection Act to replace the previous 25-year-old Immigration Act. The new act encourages the immigration of those with professional and technical skills, particularly if they are fluent in English and/or French. People with substantial amounts of investment capital are also encouraged to immigrate. (In 2005, the criteria for such investors included a net worth of at least $800 000 and a commitment to invest at least $400 000 in Canada.) Other favoured groups include people who have immediate family already in Canada and those nominated by specific provinces as being desirable immigrants. People in preferred "economic" categories (i.e., skilled workers, investors, and entrepreneurs) accounted for 53% of the immigrants to Canada in 2003. The top source countries were China (16.3% of the total), India (11.1%), Pakistan (5.6%), the Philippines (5.4%), South Korea (3.2%), the United States (2.7%), Iran (2.6%), and Romania (2.5%).

Canada also has one of the world's most open policies for accepting refugees, or persons with a well-founded fear of persecution or of cruel and unusual punishment in their home country. Canada has a Humanitarian Resettlement Program for people applying for refugee status while in another country, and an In-Canada Refugee Protection Process for those making a claim from within Canada (usually after coming ostensibly as a visitor). Canada's refugee policy is founded on both a long-standing humanitarian tradition and its obligations under the 1951 *Geneva Convention Relating to the Status of Refugees* and the subsequent *Protocol* of 1967. In 2003, there were 29 036 refugee claimants to Canada, about double the rate of five years previously. The top source countries were Pakistan (12.9% of the total), Mexico (8.4%), Colombia (6.6%), China (6.1%), Costa Rica (5.8%), Sri Lanka (4.4%), and India (4.1%).

Canada's immigration and refugee policies are not without controversy. Some longer-standing citizens protest that there are now "too many foreigners," perhaps forgetting that, except for Aboriginals, all Canadians are descended from immigrants. Other people believe that the newcomers place an excessive drain on social services, even though studies have shown that most quickly become self-supporting. There is also a widespread view that many people claiming refugee status are not truly fleeing persecution, but rather are economic migrants seeking opportunity. In this sense, Canada's rather open refugee system makes it easy for people to settle here, even if they do not fit the criteria of our immigration policy. In fact, about 60% of refugee claimants in 2001 entered Canada from the United States, where they were not at significant personal risk. (This fraction dropped precipitously in 2002 after the U.S. tightened its criteria for the entry of foreign nationals as a result of the terrorist actions of September 11, 2001 and again in late 2004 when Canada forbade people from making refugee claims after first landing in the U.S., which is considered a "Safe Third Country.") An additional reason for a stricter refugee-determination system is the desire to reduce the possibility of criminals or terrorists coming to Canada and using it as a base for illegal activities.

Some degree of controversy over immigration and refugee policies is common in all countries, not just Canada. It must be recognized, however, that newcomers have contributed enormously to the economic development and cultural diversity of Canada. They have been central in making our country an interesting and prosperous place to live. These great benefits must be balanced against some of the downsides of having relatively open immigration and refugee policies, including the contribution to rapid population growth.

Rural and Urban Populations

Until the latter half of the twentieth century, most Canadians lived in rural environments where they worked in agriculture and other country livelihoods. Since 1871, when the first data are available, the proportion of Canadians living in the countryside has steadily decreased, from 80% in 1871 to 20–24% since 1976 (Table 11.7).

In large part, this mass migration of people to urban areas has been caused by the mechanization of much of the routine labour in agriculture, forestry, mining, fishing, and

TABLE 11.6 | Demographic Parameters by Province and Territory in 2003

Data are per 1000 people in the population and are annual rates. Fertility rate is the average number of offspring per woman aged 15–49. Data for total increase include net immigration.

PROVINCE	BIRTH RATE	DEATH RATE	NATURAL INCREASE	NET MIGRATION	TOTAL INCREASE	TOTAL FERTILITY RATE
			(NO./1000 IN POPULATION)			
Canada	10.5	7.2	3.3	5.2	8.5	1.5
Ontario	10.8	7.1	3.7	7.9	11.6	1.5
Quebec	9.6	7.3	2.3	3.5	5.8	1.5
British Columbia	9.7	7.0	2.7	4.9	7.6	1.4
Alberta	12.2	6.0	6.2	6.4	12.6	1.7
Manitoba	11.9	8.7	3.2	3.0	6.2	1.8
Saskatchewan	12.2	9.0	3.2	−3.8	−0.6	1.9
Nova Scotia	9.3	8.8	0.5	1.2	1.7	1.4
New Brunswick	9.4	8.4	1.0	−0.4	0.6	1.4
Newfoundland	8.8	8.4	0.4	0.1	0.5	1.3
Prince Edward Island	10.1	8.8	1.3	4.5	5.8	1.5
Yukon	10.9	4.7	6.2	24.5	30.7	1.6
Northwest Territories	14.5	4.2	10.3	0.2	10.5	1.8
Nunavut	25.0	4.5	20.5	1.6	22.1	3.1

Source: Data from Statistics Canada (2004)

other typically rural industries. In earlier times, most of this work was performed by humans or draft animals, but this muscle power has largely been replaced by various kinds of mechanization. As a result, fewer Canadians are employed in rural economic sectors, even though the financial value

TABLE 11.7 | Rural and Urban Populations in Canada

Data are in millions of people.

YEAR	TOTAL POPULATION	% OF TOTAL	
		URBAN	RURAL
1871	3.7	19.6	80.4
1881	4.3	25.7	74.3
1891	4.8	31.8	68.2
1901	5.4	37.5	62.5
1911	7.2	45.4	54.6
1921	8.8	49.5	50.5
1931	10.4	53.7	46.3
1941	11.5	54.3	45.7
1951	14.0	56.7	43.3
1961	18.2	60.7	39.3
1971	21.6	76.1	33.9
1981	24.3	75.7	24.3
1991	27.3	76.6	23.4
2001	31.2	79.4	20.6

Sources: Data from Leacy (1983) and Statistics Canada (1994b, 1997b, 2000)

of the outputs from these sectors has increased greatly over time. The displaced rural people have moved to the towns and cities of Canada, where they earn their livelihoods in manufacturing, financial and service industries, commerce, government, and education.

As time passes, urban Canadians are living in larger centres of population. These cities are rapidly increasing in size. In 1871, only 2.9% of Canadians lived in centres with a population greater than 100 000 people. In 2004, 65% of Canadians lived in the 27 largest cities in the country (Table 11.8), even though these metropolitan areas account for only 0.7% of the country's landmass. In fact, 34% of Canadians live in the three largest cities.

Birth Control and Population Policy

Most government planners and politicians do not consider Canada to be overpopulated. In fact, many think that Canada is underpopulated and fully capable of comfortably absorbing population growth. This belief is debatable in view of the relatively intense lifestyles of Canadians (typical of people living in developed countries) and the corresponding large per capita environmental impact. Nevertheless, continuing the population-growth para-

TABLE 11.8 Cities of Canada

The populations of the 25 largest metropolitan areas of Canada, in decreasing order of population in 2004, as well as their population growth in recent decades.

| CITY | POPULATION (THOUSANDS) | | | | | % INCREASE |
	1971	1981	1991	2001	2004	1981–2004
Toronto, ON	2628	2999	3893	4881	5202	73
Montreal, QC	2743	2828	3127	3512	3607	28
Vancouver, BC	1082	1268	1603	2079	2173	71
Ottawa-Hull, ON-QC	603	718	921	1107	1146	60
Calgary, AB	403	593	754	972	1037	64
Edmonton, AB	496	657	840	956	1002	53
Quebec, QC	481	576	646	693	710	23
Hamilton, ON	499	542	600	681	710	31
Winnipeg, MB	540	585	652	685	702	20
London, ON	286	284	382	426	460	62
Kitchener, ON	227	288	356	432	450	56
St. Catharines, ON	303	304	365	393	395	30
Halifax, NS	223	278	321	359	380	37
Windsor, ON	259	246	262	314	331	35
Victoria, BC	196	234	288	319	330	41
Oshawa, ON	120	154	240	305	329	114
Saskatoon, SK	126	154	210	231	234	52
Regina, SK	140	164	192	198	199	21
St. John's, NF	132	155	172	176	180	16
Sherbrooke, QC	–	125	139	155	162	24
Sudbury, ON	155	150	158	157	161	7
Abbotsford, BC*					158	–
Kingston, ON*					157	–
Chicoutimi, QC	134	135	161	159	154	14
Trois Rivieres, QC	–	111	136	142	141	28
Saint John, NB	107	114	125	128	127	11
Thunder Bay, ON	112	121	124	125	127	5

* denotes new census area in 2001
Source: Data from Statistics Canada (1997b, 2002, 2004)

digm (model) is the predominant way of thinking among decision makers in Canadian governments. Consequently, Canada and its regions do not have well-developed population policies, other than those that establish targets and guidelines for the numbers and types of immigrants and refugees allowed into the country.

In addition, Canadian governments do not have a policy of encouraging other countries to develop their own population policies, particularly those that are less wealthy and have rapidly growing populations. Canadian governments also do not provide aid to those poorer countries to help them increase the availability of birth control. Our governments avoid high-profile controversy by not being directly involved in the population problems of poorer countries. This attitude contributes little to dealing with the global explosion of the human population.

Governments within Canada also lack policies to encourage their citizens to have small families as a means of slowing the growth rate of national or regional populations. In fact, some Canadian governments pursue policies that are distinctly pro-natalist. This has been particularly true of the government of Quebec, which in recent times has provided substantial cash payments to women based on the number of children they have—families with more than two children received proportionately larger payments than those with one or two. In addition, all provinces and the federal government provide income-tax breaks to parents based on the number of children they are supporting. Although these tax benefits are based on family income and are geared to lower-income families, this can still be interpreted as a pro-natalist aspect of the income-tax system.

Generally, governments in Canada permit their citizens to choose freely among a wide range of safe and effective birth control options. However, this is not to say that all birth control methods are freely available across the country. For example, the government of Prince Edward Island restricts access to abortion. Consequently, women must travel to another province to have access to abortion services. Similarly, reproductive and family planning education in schools varies considerably across Canada.

As discussed in Chapter 10, abortion is an extremely contentious issue in Canada and elsewhere. The controversy has resulted in public demonstrations and confrontations between pro-life and pro-choice groups. In a few instances, patrons and personnel of abortion clinics have been illegally harassed and physically assaulted, and clinics have been firebombed. A Vancouver doctor who had provided abortion services was shot in his home by a sniper, as was another doctor in Ancaster, Ontario.

Even though abortion and other means of birth control remain controversial issues, Canadians who desire to control the number and spacing of their children have relatively easy and inexpensive access to effective means of birth control. While most Canadians take advantage of this opportunity, it is not available to most of the world's peoples. Consequently, the natural rate of population increase in Canada is relatively small, while it is high in most poorer countries.

Conclusions

At the time of the "discovery" by European explorers, there were about 300 000 Aboriginal people living in what is now Canada. The Aboriginal population then collapsed due to the effects of introduced diseases, warfare, and social disruption, but it has now increased to about one million. The colonization of New France began in 1604 but totalled only a few thousand immigrants; however, the descendants of these people today number more than six million.

Photo 11.2   People living in wealthy countries, such as Canada, use resources intensively and therefore have a high per capita environmental impact.

Immigration of English and other Europeans also began in the seventeenth century and continued to the present, to be joined in the twentieth and twenty-first centuries by migrants from all parts of the world. Today, the population of Canada is about 32 million, and it continues to increase at a rate of almost 1% per year, sufficient to double in size in only another 70 years.

Key Terms

indigenous culture (First Nations)

virgin field

baby boom

population policy

Questions for Review

1. How did the populations of Aboriginal people in Canada differ before and after the European colonization?

2. How have recent trends in population and growth rates differed among the provinces and territories of Canada?

3. What is the relative importance of birth rate, death rate, immigration, and emigration to the population growth in the province or territory where you live?

Questions for Discussion

1. How has the growth of the Canadian population changed over time? Discuss the factors influencing growth during the past several decades and those that will influence it into the immediate future.

2. Compare the age-class structure of the Canadian population with that of a less developed country. Why do the differences exist?

3. What are the basic elements of the population policy of the government of Canada? Do you think they should be changed? How?

4. Do you consider Canada to be underpopulated or over-populated? Explain your reasons.

Exploring Issues

1. Assume that the government of Canada is worried about the "aging" population and is thinking about implementing pro-natalist policies (such as giving money to parents who have additional children) and doubling the rate of immigration. You are a prominent environmental scientist and have been asked to make a presentation to the House of Commons committee that is considering these issues. What arguments would you use to convince the politicians that a large increase in the rate of population growth of Canada is not desirable?

2. The decisions of whether to have children and how many to have are complex. Make a list of the "benefits and costs" of having children and how these change with increasing family size. Consider both the personal benefits and costs (e.g., the satisfaction of having and nurturing children, the cost of purchasing clothing) as well as those shared with society (e.g., medical and education costs).

References

Anonymous. 2002. *Registered Indian Population by Sex and Residence, 2001*. Ottawa: Department of Indian Affairs and Northern Development.

Bracq, J.C. 1926. *The Evolution of French Canada*. New York: Macmillan.

Burger, J. 1990. *The Gaia Atlas of First Peoples*. New York: Doubleday Dell.

Citizenship and Immigration Canada. Facts and Figures 2003: Immigration Overview. www.cis.gc.ca/english/pub/facts2003.index.html

Crosby, A.W. 1986. *Ecological Imperialism: The Biological Expansion of Europe, 900–1900*. London: Cambridge University Press.

Dumas, J. and A. Belanger. 1998. *Report on the Demographic Situation in Canada, 1997*. Ottawa: Statistics Canada.

Kalbach, W.E. 1988. Population. pp. 1719–22 in: *The Canadian Encyclopedia*. 2nd ed. Edmonton: Hurtig Publishers.

Law, B. 2002. *Scott's Canadian Sourcebook*. 37th ed. Toronto: Southam Inc.

Leacy, F.H. 1983. *Historical Statistics of Canada*. 2nd ed. Ottawa: Statistics Canada.

Ray, A. 1987. When two worlds meet. In: Brown, C. (ed.). *The Illustrated History of Canada*. Toronto: Lester. pp. 17–104.

Statistics Canada. 1992. *Postcensal Annual Estimates of Population by Marital Status, Age, Sex, and Components of Growth for Canada, Provinces, and Territories*. Ottawa: Statistics Canada.

Statistics Canada. 1994a. *Annual Demographic Statistics, 1994*. Ottawa: Statistics Canada.

Statistics Canada. 1994b. *Human Activity and the Environment 1994*. Ottawa: Statistics Canada.

Statistics Canada. 1995a. *Quarterly Demographic Statistics, 1995*. Ottawa: Statistics Canada.

Statistics Canada. 1995b. *Population Projections, 1993–2016*. Ottawa: Statistics Canada.

Statistics Canada. 1997a. *Annual Demographic Statistics, 1996*. Ottawa: Statistics Canada.

Statistics Canada. 1997b. *A National Overview—Population and Dwelling Counts*. Ottawa: Statistics Canada.

Statistics Canada. 1998. *Quarterly Demographic Statistics, July–Sept. 1998*. Ottawa: Statistics Canada.

Statistics Canada. 2001a. *Annual Demographic Statistics, 2000*. Ottawa: Statistics Canada.

Statistics Canada. 2001b. *Components of Population Growth, 2000*. Ottawa: Statistics Canada.

Statistics Canada. 2002. *Population of Census Metropolitan Areas, May 1, 2002*. Ottawa: Statistics Canada.

Statistics Canada. 2004. *Annual Demographic Statistics*. Ottawa: Statistics Canada.

Young, B. and J.A. Dickinson. 1988. *A Short History of Quebec: A Socio-Economic Perspective*. Toronto: Copp Clark Pitman.

Informative Websites

Canadian Women's Information Centre

www.womennet.ca/about.php

The Canadian Women's Information Centre and its website, womennet.ca, helps women respond to challenges and improve their quality of life, and it includes information and links related to reproductive health.

Planned Parenthood Federation of Canada.

www.ppfc.ca/ppfc/content.asp?cn=false

The Planned Parenthood Federation of Canada is a pro-choice, charitable organization dedicated to promoting sexual and reproductive health and rights in Canada and internationally. Its website provides information about relevant issues, as well as helpful links.

Statistics Canada. www.statcan.ca/

Statistics Canada provides a wealth of information related to the population and demographics of Canada and its regions. Cruise its website, in French or English, to discover a diversity of useful information.

CBC 🍁   **Canadian Case 2**

Birth Control and the Debate About Abortion

The human population has grown enormously during the past several hundred years—a phenomenal increase sometimes referred to as a "population explosion" (see Chapter 10). Today, more than six billion people are alive, and there could be as many as ten billion by the middle of this century. Humans and their mutualist species (i.e., domesticated animals and crop plants) have become the dominant organisms on Earth, and they are causing enormous environmental changes. Population growth and the associated industrialization of the human economy are the root causes of the environmental crisis.

The most important reason for the rapid growth of the human population has been a precipitous reduction of death rates, largely due to great improvements in sanitation and medical science. Although birth rates have also fallen, they have not been reduced as much as death rates. This has allowed populations to grow quickly. Clearly, the most desirable way to reduce population growth is to reduce the birth rate (it would never, of course, be acceptable to increase the death rate). Various family planning options are available to reduce birth rates (see Chapter 10), including abstinence, preventing conception during or after intercourse (by such means as birth-control pills, condoms, diaphragms, and intrauterine devices), steriliza-

tion (such as vasectomy of the male or tubal ligation of the female), and termination of pregnancies by medical abortion. All of these methods can result in safe and effective birth control, allowing parents to plan the size of their family and the spacing of the births of their children. Such choices generally result in a smaller family size, which contributes to a decreased rate of population growth.

However, all means of birth control are controversial to varying degrees (abstinence is an exception in this respect). Powerful interest groups, including religions, have steadfastly opposed the use of at least some of the most effective methods of birth control. This dispute represents a critical impediment to family planning and to the implementation of effective population policies.

Abortion is, by far, the most contentious method of birth control. Many people view an abortion as the taking of a human life, while others regard this medical procedure as a safe means by which a woman can choose to terminate an unwanted pregnancy. The situation is sometimes described as pitting the right to life of the fetus against the human rights of the mother to control her body and make decisions about her life. Although both positions may share a concern about preventing unwanted pregnancies, these polarized views on abortion are essentially irreconcilable and result in intense controversy. In Canada, although the medical procedure of abortion is no longer a crime, anti-abortion groups have picketed hospitals and private clinics where abortion services are provided. Most of these protest actions have been peaceful, although cases of extreme violence have occurred in both Canada and the United

States, including arson and bombing of clinics, and the assassination of doctors and other personnel involved with providing abortion as a medical service.

Henry Morgentaler is the most famous crusader for family planning and access to abortion services in Canada. In the past two decades he has been prosecuted several times by the government, under provisions of the Criminal Code of Canada that had effectively banned the provision of abortion services without the access decisions put in place in public hospitals (this required the consent of a committee of doctors before an abortion could be provided; some hospitals did not have such a committee, and some provinces did not allow their formation).

However, Morgentaler was never convicted by a jury in any of his four trials. Eventually, a majority of the Supreme Court of Canada, ruling in 1988 on an appeal by the Crown of one of Morgentaler's acquittals, struck down the criminal code provisions as contravening the *Charter of Rights and Freedoms*, based on the lack of access for many women in Canada to abortion services in hospitals. This decision effectively legalized the availability of abortions as a medical service in Canada. It may also have increased the frequency of abortion (69 000 abortions were reported in Canada in 1987, compared with 105 150 in 2002; however, prior to 1988 many unreported abortions occurred outside of hospitals).

A crucial aspect of the abortion debate is whether women, particularly those living in isolated regions and in poorer countries, are allowed to have ready access to effective means of family planning (i.e., to birth-control drugs, condoms, intrauterine devices, etc.). Many people believe that a successful population policy requires the education of women about health and reproductive issues, while ensuring that they have ready access to safe and effective means of birth control. Educating men to share responsibility for pregnancy is also crucial.

However, in most cultures and circumstances women have traditionally had the primary responsibility for pregnancy and childcare.

In addition to family planning, birth control, and abortion, other emerging issues related to human reproduction are also engendering great controversy. These include advances in reproductive technology leading to artificial insemination, test-tube babies, and cloning. Social changes, such as the increasing acceptability of same-sex couples, are also altering the traditional allocation of childcare responsibilities.

Population issues are volatile and uncomfortable for many people to discuss in an objective manner. Yet they are too important to ignore, because a sustainable economy will never be developed unless the population of humans on Earth is controlled.

Questions

1. Do you think that there are too many humans on Earth? What about Canada—is our national population too large in view of the relatively intensive lifestyles of typical Canadians?

2. Do you think that people should be allowed to make free choices about their own reproduction, including having ready access to medically safe and effective methods of birth control?

3. What is meant by "the empowerment of women"? Why is this considered to be an important component of an effective population policy?

Video Resource

Doctor's Dilemma," CBC The National, January 1998.

Selected References

Lifesite Canada. www.lifesite.net/ *(an anti-abortion website)*

Pro Choice Connection. www.prochoiceconnection.com *(a pro-choice website)*

United Nations Population Fund. www.unfpa.org/

Resources and Sustainable Development

12

CHAPTER OBJECTIVES

After completing this chapter, you will be able to

1. Outline the difference between renewable and non-renewable natural resources.
2. Discuss how appropriate management can increase the potential harvest of biological resources.
3. Describe at least two case studies of the degradation of potentially renewable resources and provide the reasons for those damages.
4. Distinguish between economic growth and economic development and outline the nature of a sustainable economy.

CHAPTER OUTLINE

Introduction

For about four decades now, we have been able to examine photographs of Earth as viewed from space. Images from that perspective show that Earth is a spherical mass, with a blue oceanic surface, brownish-green landmasses, and a clear atmosphere except where visibility is obscured by whitish clouds. Such images also reveal that beyond Earth and its atmosphere is the immense, black void of space—an extremely dilute, universal matrix. If we divert our attention from the compelling image of "**spaceship Earth**" and focus instead on the unimaginably larger abyss of space, we cannot fail to be stirred by the utter isolation of our planet, the only place in the cosmos known to sustain life and ecosystems.

With such a lucid image of spaceship Earth in mind, it is not difficult to understand that the resources necessary to sustain life are limited to those already contained on the planet, that is, with one critical exception—the electromagnetic radiation that is continuously emitted by the sun. A tiny fraction of that solar energy irradiates Earth, warms the planet, and drives photosynthesis. With the exception of sunlight, however, Earth's resources are self-contained and finite.

It is an undeniable reality that all organisms must have continuous access to resources obtained from their environment. Plants and algae, for example, require sunlight and inorganic nutrients, while heterotrophic animals and most microbes must feed on the living or dead biomass of other organisms. Ecosystems are similarly nourished by environmental capital. These resources must be available in at least the minimal amounts needed to sustain life, and in larger quantities in ecosystems that are increasing in biomass and complexity, as occurs during succession.

The same reality holds for individual humans, our societies, and our economic systems. All humans and their enterprises are subsidized by the harvesting of resources from the environment (including those taken from ecosystems). These must be available in the minimal quantities needed to sustain human life, and in much larger amounts in economic systems that are growing over time. An obvious conclusion is that *economic and ecological systems are inextricably linked*. Indeed, this is an undeniable fact.

The main connections between economic systems and the natural world involve flows of resources from ecosystems and the environment into the human economy, and flows of unused materials, by-products, and heat (all of which are sometimes referred to as "wastes") from the economy back to the environment. Associated with these interchanges of materials and energy are many kinds of damage caused to natural and managed ecosystems. These may be caused by disturbances associated with the harvesting of natural resources, by emissions of pollutants, or by other stressors related to economic systems and industrialized societies.

An ultimate goal of environmental science is to understand how resource use and environmental quality contribute to a **sustainable economic system** and to the quality of human life. Ultimately, a sustainable economy is one that runs forever and that operates without a net consumption of natural capital—the rates of resource use are equal to or smaller than the rates at which they are regenerated or recycled. This definition focuses on the resource-related aspects of sustainability. Also important are environmental damages that may be caused by the extraction and management of natural resources. The social context must also be considered, particularly how wealth is shared among the people who are participating in the economy.

In this chapter, we examine the broader issues related to the use of natural resources in economic systems. Initially, we examine the characteristics of non-renewable and renewable resources. Non-renewable resources are finite, do not regenerate, and are therefore diminished by use. In contrast, renewable resources can be managed to maintain or increase their productivity, and we describe practices that foster those goals. This is followed by a discussion of the reasons for a catastrophic but remarkably common phenomenon—the depletion of potentially renewable resources through excessive use. Finally, we consider the notion of sustainability, a topic that is critically important to the long-term health of both economic *and* ecological systems. This chapter deals with natural resources in a conceptual manner; Chapters 13 and 14 investigate the actual use of resources in international and Canadian economies.

Natural Resources

All natural resources (also known as natural capital) can be divided into two categories: non-renewable and renewable.

Non-renewables

Non-renewable resources are present in a finite quantity and do not regenerate after they are harvested and used. (If they do regenerate, it is so slowly as to be insignificant compared with the rate of use; see the section on fossil fuels in Chapter 13.) Consequently, as non-renewable

Global Focus 12.1

Easter Island as a Metaphor for Spaceship Earth

A prehistoric example of resource degradation occurred on Easter Island, a small (389 km^2), extremely isolated island in the southern Pacific Ocean (Jennings, 1979; Ponting, 1991; Diamond, 2004). Easter Island was first discovered by wandering Polynesians in about the ninth century. The only useful crops these people brought with them were chicken and sweet potato (the climate is too temperate for the tropical crops best known to prehistoric Polynesians, such as breadfruit, coconut, taro, and yam). Initially, the Easter Islanders could also hunt fish and porpoises in the rich, near-shore waters of their island, and on land they could hunt wild Polynesian rats, a species they had introduced.

Photo 12.1   A human-faced monolith on Easter Island.

Source: Phil Graham

By the sixteenth century, the Easter Islanders had developed a flourishing society, with a population estimated as large as 15 000. Because of food surpluses, the Easter Islanders had spare time to engage in a cultural activity that involved carving huge slabs of stone into human-faced monoliths, each erected on a great base of stone, at various places along the coast. The heavy monoliths (weighing up to 75 t) and their massive bases were carved at an inland quarry and then moved with enormous human effort (there being no draft animals) to their coastal sites by rolling them on logs cut from the island's forests.

Easter Island was quickly deforested by the aggressive cutting of trees to use as stone rollers and as timber to construct buildings and fishing boats. Unfortunately, once the forest resource was gone, the central enterprises of the Easter Islanders collapsed. Stone monoliths could no longer be moved, sturdy homes could not be built, and fishing and porpoise hunting became impossible without wooden boats. It also became difficult to cook food and keep warm because the only other fuels available were shrubs and herbaceous plants.

In other words, the deforestation of Easter Island caused the collapse of the economy of this prehistoric Polynesian society. The cultural and economic disintegrations were so great that, when Europeans first arrived at Easter Island in 1772, the inhabitants were not certain why the stone monoliths had been erected. These people were living in squalid conditions in caves and reed huts, were engaged in a perpetual state of warfare among rival clans, and were cannibals, possibly to supplement the meagre food available on their treeless island.

An obvious lesson of Easter Island is that even early human societies were capable of over-exploiting the vital ecological resources that they required for subsistence. Undoubtedly, some of the prehistoric Easter Islanders were keenly aware of their isolated and precarious circumstances—particularly the limited resources available to sustain their society on a small and isolated island. As these resources diminished, they likely discussed the need to conserve their resource base. Any such deliberations obviously came to naught, and there was an irretrievable collapse of the economy and culture of these people.

Easter Island is an obvious metaphor for Earth as a planetary "island." Earth, too, has limited stocks of energy, minerals, and biological resources to sustain human economies and natural ecosystems. Any of these natural resources can be rapidly depleted by excessive use. There was no alternate, resource-rich refuge to which the Easter Islanders could escape from their self-inflicted catastrophe. Likewise, as far as we know, there is no alternative to planet Earth.

Photo 12.2   Non-renewable resources can only be mined. This is an open-pit iron ore mine in Schefferville, Quebec.

resources are used, their remaining stocks in the environment become depleted. This means that non-renewable resources can never be used in a sustainable fashion—they can only be "mined." Examples of non-renewable resources include metal ores, petroleum, coal, and natural gas.

Photo 12.3   Renewable resources, such as timber and fish, are capable of regenerating after they are harvested. Provided they are not over-harvested or managed inappropriately, renewable resources can potentially be harvested in a sustainable fashion. This photo shows a load of timber harvested on Vancouver Island.

Although continuing exploration may discover "new" stocks of non-renewable resources, this does not change the fact that there is a finite quantity of these resources on Earth. For example, the discovery of large quantities of nickel and copper ore at Voisey's Bay in Labrador substantially increased the known, exploitable reserves of those metals. The discovery did not, however, affect the quantities of these metals present on Earth.

To some degree, metals can be recovered after their initial uses and recycled back into the economy, effectively extending the lifespan of their reserves. However, due to the growth and increasing industrialization of the human population, the demand for metals is accelerating. Because recycling cannot keep up with the increasing demands, additional metals must be mined from their known reserves in the environment.

Renewables

Renewable resources are capable of regenerating after harvesting, so potentially they can be utilized forever. Most renewable resources are biological, although some are non-biological.

Biological Renewable Resources:

- wild animals that are hunted as food, such as deer, moose, hare, ducks, fish, lobster, and seals
- forest biomass that is harvested for lumber, fibre, or energy
- wild plants that are gathered as sources of food
- plants cultivated as sources of food, medicine, materials, or energy
- the capability of soil to sustain the productivity of agricultural crops

Non-biological Renewable Resources:

- sunlight, of which there is a continuous input to Earth
- surface and ground waters, which are renewed through sunlight and the hydrologic cycle
- winds and waves, which are renewed through sunlight and Earth's heat-distribution system

Many renewable resources can be managed to increase their rates of recruitment and productivity and to decrease rates of mortality. In the following section we explain how management practices can be used to increase the productivity of biological resources.

Although a renewable resource can potentially regenerate after harvesting, it can also be degraded by excessive use or inappropriate management. These practices can damage a resource's ability to regenerate and may ultimately cause a collapse of its stocks. If this happens, the renewable resource is, in effect, being "mined" as if it were a non-renewable resource. As such, it becomes depleted by excessive use. For this reason, ecologists commonly use the qualified term **potentially renewable resources**.

Management of Renewable Resources

Potentially, populations of animals and plants, and their communities, can be harvested sustainably without depleting the stock size or capability for renewal. In all species, potential fecundity and productivity are greater than the actual recruitment, growth, and maturation of new individuals and biomass. Therefore, part of the excess of potential productivity minus actual survival and growth can be harvested and used to sustain humans and their economy. Moreover, the potential harvest can often be enhanced by management practices that increase the renewable yields of forest, fish, and agricultural ecosystems.

Ultimately, the potential productivity of individual organisms is limited by genetically determined factors that influence their fecundity, longevity, and growth rate. The same factors also constrain the potential productivity of populations. Sometimes, selective breeding of individuals with desirable traits can be used to alleviate genetically based constraints to productivity—ultimately, this may result in domesticated varieties of crops. In any case, however, the expression of these genetic factors is influenced by environmental variables, many of which restrict productivity (Figure 12.1).

FIGURE 12.1 | Factors Affecting the Yield of a Biological Resource

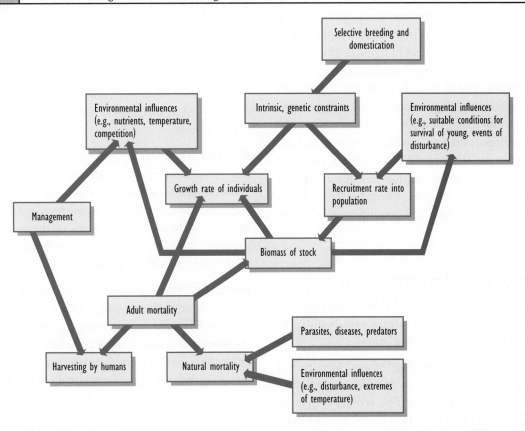

The biomass and productivity of a biological resource are determined by the recruitment of individuals into the population, by their growth rates, and by their rates of mortality through either harvesting or natural means. These factors are affected by both genetically determined and environmental influences. Often, environmental and biological factors can be managed to increase the productivity and size of the stock.

Source: Modified from Begon *et al.* (1990)

Therefore, in the real world of ecosystems, actual productivity is considerably less than potential productivity.

If resource managers understand the nature of environmental constraints on the productivity of biological resources, and can devise systems to reduce those influences, then the yield of harvested products can be increased. In any truly sustainable system of resource management, such increases in yield must be obtained without degrading the resource's capability for renewal (i.e., they cannot be obtained by over-harvesting the resource or by degrading the environment). Important practices used to increase the productivity of biological resources are briefly described below. (Note that this section illustrates commonly used practices to increase the productivity of biological resources. However, all management options cause some degree of ecological damage, as is discussed in other chapters.)

Selective Breeding

In all species, there is some degree of genetically based influence on such biological attributes as fecundity, longevity, and productivity of individuals. Plant and animal breeders deliberately select individuals that display traits that are considered desirable and use them in breeding programs intended to develop "improved" crops. This is the basis by which all domesticated species used in agriculture were developed, and selective breeding continues to be an important way in which crop varieties are produced (see also Chapter 14). In addition, since the 1980s, new methods for transferring genetic information from one species to another have been used to develop so-called "genetically modified" or "transgenic" crops (refer to In Detail 6.3).

Enhancement of Recruitment

The rate of recruitment of new individuals into exploited populations can be increased in various ways. Some commonly used methods are described below.

Planting: In intensively managed agricultural, forestry, and aquacultural systems, managers try to achieve an optimally spaced monoculture of the crop. This is done so that the productivity will not be limited by competition with non-crop species or by individuals of the crop growing too closely together. Recruitment of agricultural plants is often managed by sowing seeds under conditions that favour their germination and establishment, while optimizing crop density to minimize competition. Sometimes young plants are grown elsewhere and then out-planted—a prac-

tice used to cultivate paddy rice, develop fruit-tree orchards, and establish plantations in forestry.

Regeneration of Perennial Crops: Some management systems encourage perennial crops to regenerate by re-sprouting from surviving roots, rhizomes, or stumps after the above-ground biomass is harvested. This regeneration system is used with sugar cane and with stands of aspens, poplars, maples, and ashes in forestry. In some cases, the regenerating population may have to be thinned to optimize the density.

Stock Enhancement: Recruitment of many fishes, particularly species of salmon and trout, is often enhanced by stripping wild animals or hatchery stock of their eggs and milt (sperm). The eggs are fertilized under controlled conditions and incubated until hatching. The larval fish (called fry) are cultivated until they reach a fingerling size, when they are released to suitable habitat to supplement the natural recruitment of wild fish.

Site Preparation: Certain management practices favour the recruitment of economically desired tree species in forestry. For instance, some species of pine recruit well onto clear-cuts that have been site-prepared by burning, as long as a supply of seed is available. Seedlings of other tree species establish readily onto exposed mineral soil and are favoured by mechanical site preparation that exposes this substrate.

Managing Sex Ratios: Recruitment of some hunted animals can be maintained if only adult male animals are killed. For example, most species of deer are polygynous (i.e., males will mate with more than one female). Consequently, the hunt can be restricted to males, on the assumption that the surviving bucks will still be capable of impregnating all the females in the population.

Harvest Season: Recruitment of some animals can be managed by limiting the hunting season to particular times of the year. For example, restricting the hunt of waterfowl to the autumn allows ducks and geese to breed during the spring and summer so that recruitment can occur. Spring hunting interferes with this reproduction and is rarely permitted.

Enhancement of Growth Rate

As noted previously, the productivity of all plants and animals is constrained by environmental influences, which include inorganic factors such as nutrient availability and temperature and biological influences such as competition and disease. Often, management practices can be used to manipulate environmental conditions to reduce their limitation on growth rate, allowing an increased harvestable yield. Sometimes a **management system** is used, involving a variety of practices applied in a coordinated manner. Some examples follow.

Agricultural Systems: In intensive agricultural systems, high-yield varieties of crops are grown and managed to optimize their productivity. Management practices typically combine some or all of the following: fertilizer addition to enhance nutrient availability, irrigation to reduce the effects of drought, tillage (ploughing and harrowing the land) or herbicide use to decrease competition from weeds, fungicide use and other practices to control diseases, and insecticide use and other practices to lessen damage caused by insects and other animal pests.

Forestry: The intensity of management used in forestry varies greatly, but crop-tree productivity can be increased through silvicultural practices, such as thinning young stands to reduce competition among crop trees, using herbicide to control weeds, and using insecticide to cope with infestations of defoliating insects.

Aquaculture: In aquaculture, high-yield varieties of fish, crustaceans, or mollusks may be grown at high density in ponds or pens, where they are well fed and protected from diseases and parasites through the use of antibiotics and other chemicals.

Management of Mortality Rate

Mortality of juveniles and adults can seriously affect the sizes of plant and animal stocks. By thinning out the stock, mortality also influences the intensity of competition within the population and can increase the growth rates of the survivors. Mortality can be caused by natural influences such as predation, disease, or disturbance, or it can occur because humans have harvested some of the stock. Resource depletion occurs when the total rate of mortality (i.e., natural plus anthropogenic) exceeds the regenerative capability of the stock. Mortality associated with natural factors and harvesting can often be adjusted by management, as described below.

Natural Mortality

Mortality associated with natural predators, parasites, diseases, and accidents can be decreased in various ways.

Diseases, Parasites, and Herbivores: Mortality of crop plants caused by herbivorous insects may be managed by using insecticide or by changing the cultivation procedures to develop an ecosystem that is less favourable to the pest. Livestock are commonly affected by parasites, a problem that may also be reduced by using a pesticide. For example, sheep infested with ticks are dipped in chemical baths that kill the pests. Similarly, mortality caused by disease may be reduced by applying chemicals that manage the symptoms of disease, by administering antibiotics to deal with bacterial infections, or by changing cultivation systems to decrease vulnerability. All such practices allow diseases, parasites, and herbivores to be controlled over the short term, but none are long-term solutions to these causes of productivity loss and mortality.

Natural Predators: Coyote, wolf, cougar, and bears are rarely important predators of livestock, but many farmers still consider any losses to these natural predators to be unacceptable. Some hunters feel the same way about the mortality wild predators cause to hunted wildlife, such as deer, moose, and caribou. Consequently, these large predators have been relentlessly persecuted by shooting, trapping, and poisoning. Access of predators to livestock may be restricted by fences or by using guard animals such as dogs and donkeys.

Harvesting Mortality

Harvesting must also be managed to ensure that the total mortality (natural plus anthropogenic) stays below the threshold for depleting the resource. For an ideal population, the **maximum sustainable yield (MSY)** is the largest amount of harvest mortality that can occur without degrading the productivity of the stock. Theoretically, harvest rates less than MSY would leave a "surplus" of the stock to natural sources of mortality, while harvest rates greater than MSY would impair regeneration. Note that any harvest rate equal to or less than MSY would theoretically sustain the resource.

Harvest-related mortality is influenced by many factors, including the quantity and kinds of harvesting equipment and personnel and the amount of time that these units spend harvesting. Resource managers can adjust the rates of mortality by controlling the total harvesting *effort*, which is a function of both the *means* (e.g., the kinds of fishing boats and their gear) and the *intensity* (e.g., the number of boats and the amount of time each spends fishing) of harvesting.

Technology: This has a great influence on harvesting rate. Consider, for example, the various methods of catching fish, summarized in Figure 12.2. These technologies vary greatly in efficiency, which might be calculated as the quan-

FIGURE 12.2 | Fishing Technology

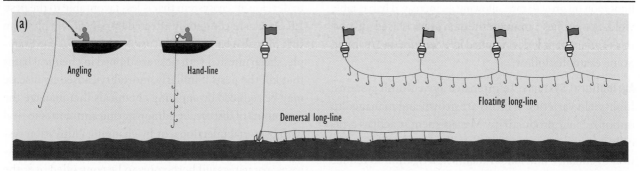

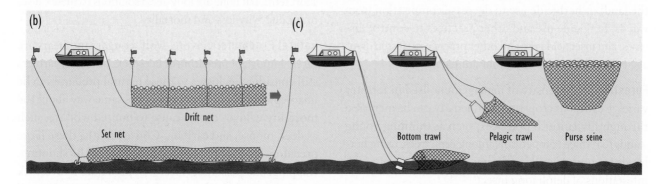

Methods of catching fish vary enormously in their efficiency and in the associated harvesting mortality. **(a)** Line methods range from hand-lines with one or more hooks to floating or bottom lines running for kilometres and having thousands of hooks. **(b)** Gill nets can be set on the bottom or attached to drifting buoys and can range up to tens of kilometres in length, catching fish and other animals as they try to swim through the mesh. **(c)** Trawls are open, broad-mouthed nets that are dragged along the bottom or through the water column, while purse seines are positioned around a school of fish swimming near the surface and then pulled shut with a bottom draw-line.

tity of fish caught per person fishing, per unit of energy expended, or per unit-value of investment in equipment. In general, much greater harvesting mortality is associated with the more intensive technologies, such as drift nets, trawls, and seines, compared with simpler methods such as hand-lines and long-lines. The more efficient methods may also have a much greater *by-catch* of species that are not the target of the fishery and are often thrown away. Similarly, hunters armed with rifles are more efficient than those using bows and arrows, and trees can be harvested more quickly using a feller-buncher than a chainsaw or an axe. (A feller-buncher is a large machine that cuts and de-limbs trees and stacks the logs into piles.)

Selection of Species and Sizes: The great variation in the selectivity of harvesting methods, with regards to both species and size, can be an important consideration in resource management. In a fishery, for example, a change in the net-mesh size directly influences the sizes of animals that are caught. Usually it is advantageous not to har-

vest smaller individuals, which may not yet have bred and often have a smaller value-per-unit-weight than larger animals. In forestry, size- or species-selective cutting might be used in preference to clear-cutting, perhaps to encourage regeneration of the most desirable tree species. This also reduces environmental damage, by keeping the physical structure of the forest relatively intact.

Number of Harvesting Units: An obvious way to manage mortality associated with harvesting is to limit the number of units participating in the harvest. In a fishery, for example, the government could limit the number of fishers by issuing only a certain number of licences. Usually, the kind of technology that may be used by the harvesters is also specified, for example, the number of boats using particular fishing gear.

Time Spent Harvesting: Harvesting effort is also influenced by the amount of time that each harvesting unit works. Because of the economic value of investments in machinery and personnel, there is strong pressure on regulators to allow harvesting to occur as long as possible. Even so, harvesting time is, in some cases, very closely regulated. For example, certain herring fisheries off western North America operate for as short as several hours per year.

To achieve control over harvesting effort (and therefore over the mortality associated with exploitation), managers often use legal and administrative tools. Relatively direct controls include licences that regulate the numbers of participants, the technology they may use, their resource quotas, and the times and places they may harvest. Indirect tools can be used to influence the profitability of different harvesting strategies. These tools include

- fines for non-compliance, which decrease profit by raising costs;

- taxes on more harmful harvesting methods or subsidies on less harmful ones, which influence profit by increasing or reducing costs, respectively; and

- buyouts of inappropriate or excess harvesting capacity (either equipment or licences), which increase profit for the remaining harvesters by increasing their relative allocation.

Maximum Sustainable Yield

Potentially, all management options (i.e., selective breeding, enhancement of growth and recruitment rates, and management of mortality rate) can result in larger yields of biological resources for use by humans. However, the factors that influence the size and productivity of stocks of potentially renewable resources are imperfectly understood. Consequently, the management systems advocated by foresters and fishery and agricultural scientists are also imperfect. Despite this caveat about uncertainty, enough is usually known about ecological factors affecting biological resources to design sustainable harvesting and management systems that will not degrade the capability for renewal.

At the very least, precautionary harvesting intensities small enough to avoid *over-exploitation* of the resource can be predicted, even though the harvest might be smaller than the potential maximum sustainable yield. Harvests of natural resources need not be as large as are potentially attainable. If resource managers cannot predict an accurate MSY, then it is ecologically prudent to harvest at rates known to be smaller than the MSY, but clearly sustainable. Of course, such strategies result in smaller harvests and less short-term profit. These are, however, more than off-

set by the long-term economic and ecological benefits of adopting prudent strategies of resource harvesting and management.

Moreover, the regional economic benefits of smaller (but sustainable) harvests can be enhanced by ensuring that the manufactured outputs of resource-dependent industries focus more on "value-added" products. In forestry, for example, exports of raw logs might be prohibited, while local manufacturing of such value-added products as lumber, furniture, and violins would be encouraged. Similarly, a regional fishing industry might focus on the production and export of higher-valued products, such as prepared foods, rather than unprocessed fish. These integrations of resource harvesting and manufacturing can optimize the regional economic benefits of resource-based industries, while allowing smaller, sustainable harvests of the resource.

Regrettably, however, non-sustainable rates of harvesting have been common in the real world of open, poorly regulated, bio-resource exploitation. This has happened even where so-called "scientific" management was being used. These facts become clear from the examples of resource degradation described in this chapter (and also in Chapters 14 and 26).

Unsustainable Use

Many potentially renewable resources have been used by humans in a non-sustainable fashion. Either these resources have been exploited excessively (a condition known as **over-harvesting** or **over-exploitation**), or their post-harvest regeneration has been managed inappropriately. Either of these can result in depletion or exhaustion of the resource by so-called "mining."

There are numerous examples of the unsustainable use of potentially renewable resources. Some species have even been made extinct by excessive hunting—for instance, the dodo, passenger pigeon, and great auk (the latter two used to occur in Canada; see Chapter 26). In other cases, seemingly abundant species were rendered endangered by over-harvesting, including American ginseng, Eskimo curlew, northern fur seal, plains bison, right whale, trumpeter swan, and various other species that were once common in parts of Canada (see Chapter 26). In fact, it is remarkably difficult to cite any examples of economically valuable, potentially renewable resources that have not been severely depleted at one time or another through excessive use or inappropriate management.

Additional examples of the mining of potentially renewable resources include the following:

- extensive deforestation of many parts of the world, resulting in losses of lumber and fuelwood resources as well as environmental damages such as erosion and regional changes in climate (Chapter 23)

- extensive degradation of the quality of agricultural soil, resulting in declining crop yields and sometimes the abandonment of previously arable land (Chapter 24)

- exhaustion of fisheries, such as those of cod and other groundfish off the Atlantic Provinces of Canada, and salmon and herring stocks off British Columbia (Chapter 14)

- depletion of many hunted resources—various species of Canadian fish, antelope, deer, furbearers, waterfowl, whales, and others (Chapter 14)

Not all cases of the mining of potentially renewable resources have occurred in modern times. Global Focus 12.1 and 12.2 describe examples that are ancient, even prehistoric. These well-known cases demonstrate that even relatively unsophisticated human societies with primitive technological capabilities have been able to cause enormous damage to their essential resource base.

In some cases, early depletions of potentially renewable resources were followed by vigorous efforts at **conservation** or improved management, which subsequently restored the depleted stocks (but not the extinct ones). (In the sense used here, "conservation" refers to the wise use of natural capital, including recycling and other means of efficient utilization, as well as ensuring that the harvest of renewable resources does not exceed their rate of regeneration.) For example, regulating the hunting of white-tailed deer in Canada has allowed that species to remain abundant in regions where habitat is suitable. Comparable successes have been achieved with other once-depleted animals, such as certain sport fish, ducks, and geese. Some examples of conservation achievements are described as case studies at the end of Chapter 26.

Overall, however, there is more bad news than good about future stocks and regeneration of many potentially renewable resources. Although some renewables are being used in a manner consistent with their future availability, many are not. If this situation does not change for the better in the near future, there will be grim consequences for human economies and for natural ecosystems and biodiversity.

Patterns of Over-exploitation

In cases of single-species resources, in which only a particular species is harvested, over-exploitation generally involves an excessive harvesting rate, occurring without adequate attention to regeneration. Under such conditions, the stocks are quickly mined, and they collapse to economic or biological extinction. Sometimes, a "virgin" or previously unexploited resource is dominated by large, old-growth individuals, which are harvested selectively during the initial stages of resource "development." This changes the structure of the resource to one dominated by smaller, younger individuals. Because younger individuals are often relatively fast growing, the productivity of the resource is not necessarily smaller than that of the original, old-growth stock, although the total biomass may be less. However, if this kind of resource degradation is taken too far, the population may collapse in both productivity and biomass. The collapse may be caused by inadequate recruitment into the harvested population because the fecundity of younger individuals is not sufficient to offset the harvesting mortality.

Patterns of resource degradation are more complicated in the case of mixed-species resources, which are often over-exploited in a sequential manner. At first, only certain species in the virgin, mixed-species resource may be considered desirable from the economic perspective. In addition, some individual organisms may be very large, especially in the case of old-growth resources. For instance, old-growth forest of coastal British Columbia is typically dominated by large individuals of valuable tree species, coexisting with many smaller individuals (see Chapter 23). Many pre-exploitation communities of fish, whales, and other species are also typically dominated by large individuals of desirable species.

The exploitation of a mixed-species resource usually involves a sequential harvest of commodities having increasingly smaller values (measured as value per individual, as well as per unit of biomass and of harvested area). Initially, the largest individuals of the most valuable species are harvested selectively and are rapidly depleted. In an old-growth forest, for example, the largest logs of the most desirable species have the highest value per unit of biomass. These can be used to manufacture large-dimension lumber of precious species or valuable veneer products. The intention of post-harvesting management is not to re-create another old-growth forest, because this would take too much time and would also involve an extended period of relatively low productivity (see Chapter 23). Instead, the site is typically converted into a second-growth forest.

Global Focus 12.2

Prehistoric Extinctions

Paleontologists have found clear evidence of various prehistoric mass extinctions of animal species, apparently caused by over-hunting by stone-age humans (Martin, 1967, 1984; Diamond, 1982, 2004; Freedman, 1995). The mass extinctions occurred at different times and places, but all coincided with the discovery and colonization of a landmass previously uninhabited by people. The extinct animals were naïve to predation by efficient groups of human hunters and were unable to adapt to the onslaught. These mass extinctions represent cases of unsustainable harvesting of wild-animal populations, which were potentially renewable sources of food for the neolithic hunters.

In North America, a wave of prehistoric extinctions began about 11 000 years ago, soon after humans colonized the continent by migrating across a land bridge from Siberia. (The land bridge existed because the sea level was lower than today, since so much water was tied up in glacial ice.) Within a relatively short time, at least 56 species of large mammals (i.e., weighing more than 44 kg), 21 species of smaller mammals, and several large birds had become extinct. The extinctions included 10 species of horses (genus *Equus*), the giant ground sloth (*Gryptotherium listai*), four species of camels (family Camelidae), two species of buffalo (genus *Bison*), a species of cow (genus *Bos*), the saiga antelope (*Saiga tatarica*), and four species in the elephant family, including the mastodon (*Mammut americanum*) and mammoth (*Mammuthus primigenius*). Predators and scavengers that depended on these large herbivores also became extinct, including the sabre-toothed tiger (*Smilodon fatalis*), the American lion (*Panthera leo atrox*), and a huge scavenging bird (*Terratornis merriami*). The best collection of fossil bones of many of the extinct animals has been excavated from natural tar pits in southern California. However, bones of many species are quite widespread and some have been found in various places in Canada. As colonizing humans spread in waves into Central America, and then into South America, extinctions of other vulnerable prey species occurred in those regions.

Similar events of mass extinction have occurred elsewhere, also coinciding with colonizations by prehistoric, stone-age hunters. In New Guinea and Australia, waves of extinction occurred about 50 000 years ago, following the discoveries of those islands by Melanesians spreading south from Asia. These mass extinctions involved the losses of many large species of marsupials, flightless birds, and tortoises.

In New Zealand, an extinction wave occurred less than 1000 years ago, following the discovery of those islands by Polynesians. This event swept away numerous species of large, flightless birds, including a 250-kg, 3-m-tall giant moa (*Dinornis maximus*), 26 other species of moa, a goose (*Cnemiornis calcitrans*), a swan (*Cygnus sumnerensis*), a giant coot (*Fulica chathamensis*), a pelican (*Pelecanus novaezealandiae*), and an eagle (*Harpagornis moorei*), plus fur seals and species of large lizards and frogs. The extinctions of the moas progressed as a wave sweeping from North Island to South Island over a two-century period following the Polynesian colonization. Great quantities of bones have been discovered at places where the moas had been herded and butchered. Some of these bone deposits were mined by early European colonists and processed into phosphate fertilizer.

The human colonization of Madagascar occurred about 1500 years ago. This also resulted in many extinctions, including the loss of 6–12 species of huge elephant birds, 14 species of lemurs, two giant tortoises, and various other large animals. Other prehistoric mass extinctions occurred in Hawaii, New Caledonia, Fiji, the West Indies, and other islands. All are believed to have resulted from over-hunting by newly colonizing humans.

Clearly, the unsustainable use of biological capital, resulting in irretrievable losses of species important to people as resources, is not only a modern phenomenon. Prehistoric humans could be as rapacious as their modern descendants, given appropriate opportunities in the form of naïve and edible species.

Next, smaller individuals of the most desired species might be harvested selectively, along with the largest individuals of secondarily desired species. In a forest, the economic products might involve smaller-dimension lumber. If management of the regenerating stand is intended to produce timber for manufacturing into lumber, the sub-

sequent harvests would be on a relatively long rotation, say 60–100 years, depending on growing conditions.

However, area-harvesting methods might then be used to harvest virtually all individuals of all species for manufacturing into bulk commodities. In the case of forestry, trees might be clear-cut for the production of

Photo 12.4   Ecologically rich old-growth forest in many tropical countries is being rapidly cleared to provide agricultural land. This ecological conversion results in the destruction of the forest (the mining of a potentially renewable resource), often to develop agricultural land that will probably not be productive for very long. This scene is from Sumatra, Indonesia.

pulp, industrial fuel, charcoal, or domestic fuelwood. Subsequent harvests for such purposes would be on a relatively short rotation, perhaps 30–50 years.

Sometimes the area-harvesting system is followed by management that regenerates a productive resource, although it has a different character from the original, natural ecosystem. In forestry, for example, natural mixed-species forest might be converted into a single-species plantation or perhaps into an agricultural ecosystem.

Intensive harvesting, sequential or otherwise, can also lead to a collapse of biological productivity and, therefore, to a huge loss of resource value. For instance, clear-cut forests sometimes regenerate into shrub-dominated ecosystems that resist the establishment of tree seedlings. This kind of severe resource degradation may require expensive management to restore another economically useful forest.

Reasons for Resource Abuse

To function over the longer term, economic systems depend on a sustained input of natural resources. Given this context, it would appear to be economically self-destructive to degrade renewable resources by over-harvesting or by inappropriate management. Nevertheless, this maladaptive behaviour has occurred frequently through human history—in fact, most uses of potentially renewable resources have been decidedly non-sustainable, causing stocks to become quickly depleted. The most important reasons for this foolish behaviour are outlined below.

The world's dominant cultures have developed an ethic that presumes that humans have the right to take whatever they want from nature for subsistence or economic benefits. This is an expression of the anthropocentric world view (Chapter 1). Particularly noteworthy is the so-called Judeo-Christian ethic (White, 1967). This ethic is based on the Biblical story of creation, in which God directed humans to "be fruitful, and multiply, and replenish the earth, and subdue it," and to "have dominion over the fish of the sea, and over the fowl of the air, and over the cattle, and over all the earth and over every creeping thing that creepeth upon the earth" (Genesis 1:28). From the purely ecological perspective, this is an arrogant attitude, but it is typical of the world's dominant cultures and religions. Modern technological ethics have developed from this commanding world view and are now used to legitimize the mining of many potentially renewable resources and the infliction of collateral ecological damage.

Individual people and their societies are intrinsically self-interested. This attitude is responsible for many cases of over-exploitation of resources in order to optimize short-term profit. At the same time, ecological damage associated with the resource degradation is discounted as being unimportant. This is readily done because, in most economic systems, the consequences of ecological damage are usually shared broadly across society, rather than being considered the responsibility of the persons or corporations who cause the damage.

In Detail 12.1

Investments in Renewable Resources

Consider a simple case: tree biomass in a forest is increasing at a rate of 5% per year, and interest rates (adjusted for inflation) on secure investments are 10% per year. Because the forest resource is growing at 5% per year, its value (i.e., its biomass) would double about every 14 years. If, however, the forest was harvested, the products sold, and the resulting money invested at an interest rate of 10% per year, the quantity of money would double in only 7 years, so profit would be made twice as quickly.

Obviously, this kind of investment strategy only works if

1. the objective is to gain short-term profit rather than achieve long-term resource sustainability;

2. the social perspective is that of individual people or corporations and not the welfare of society at large;

3. it is assumed that the natural resource has value only if it is harvested and converted into cash; and

4. only the costs of extraction are considered in the calculation of profit, while the costs of ecological damage and resource degradation are paid by society as a whole (i.e., in economic terms, they are treated as externalities).

Over the long term, the liquidation of potentially renewable resources is clearly a losing strategy for society and for future generations. For individuals, firms, and local economies, however, this can be a highly "profitable" strategy because wealth can be accumulated during a short period of time. Therefore, this tactic is often advocated and pursued by influential people. Consider the following statement in 1986 by Bill Vander Zalm, at the time the Premier of British Columbia, one of the world's greatest exporters of forest products: "Let's cut down the trees and create jobs."[1] This is what has been happening, more or less, to many potentially renewable resources in most parts of the world.

[1] Luinenberg, O. and S. Osborne, compilers. 1990. *The Little Green Book: Quotations on the Environment.* Vancouver: Pulp Press Publishers.

Natural resources are perceived as being boundless. Many people think that nature and its resources are unlimited in their extent, quantity, and productivity. This is referred to as the "frontier" or "cornucopian" world view (a cornucopia is the mythical "horn of plenty" that yields food in boundless amounts). In actual fact, Earth has limited stocks of resources available for use by humans, and most of these are being rapidly depleted by excessive use.

Investments of money in some sectors of the economy may accumulate profit faster than the growth rate of renewable resources. Consequently, apparent profit can be maximized over the shorter term by liquidating natural resources through over-exploitation and then investing the money earned in a faster-growing sector of the economy (see In Detail 12.1). The growth of many regional and national economies has been jump-started by economic "capital" gained through the unsustainable mining of ecological "capital."

Not all of the true costs of overexploitation are taken into account. The economic strategies suggested above only work if the ecological costs of over-exploitation are not paid for. In fact, some kinds of environmental damage can be interpreted as being "good" for the economy because they add to the **gross national product (GNP).** For example, the wreck of the *Exxon Valdez* in Alaska and the cleanup of the spilled petroleum were responsible for billions of dollars of growth in the GNP of the United States over several years (see Chapter 21). In actual fact, these environmental damages represent a depletion of ecological capital and are a sort of "natural debt." When apparent profit gained through over-exploitation is being calculated, **conventional economics** (i.e., economics as it is usually practised) does not properly account for costs associated with ecological damage and resource depletion. In theory, at least, this damage would be fully costed in a system of **ecological economics**, which is advocated by many enlightened economists and environmentalists.

Within an economic context involving free access to **common-property resources** (resources owned by all of society), the above factors inevitably lead to the over-harvesting of potentially renewable resources. In a highly influential essay, Garrett Hardin (1968) called this frequently observed phenomenon "the tragedy of the commons." He explained this economic misadventure using the analogy of a publicly owned pasture (the "commons"), to which all local farmers had free access for grazing their sheep. Individual, self-interested farmers believed that they would gain additional economic benefits by having as many of their own sheep as possible grazing the pasture. This led to an excessive aggregate use of the pasture, which damaged the forage resource. Hardin's major conclusion, that "freedom in a commons brings ruin to all," has generally been true of the ways in which many renewable resources have been abused.

Many nations are experiencing crises because of diminishing stocks of potentially renewable resources and the associated ecological damage caused by disturbance, pollution, and loss of biodiversity. Remarkably, many of these nations have not yet attempted to deal effectively with the resource degradation. With few exceptions, the design and implementation of intelligent strategies for using natural resources has proven to be beyond the capability of modern political and economic systems.

Nevertheless, humans are definitely capable of designing and implementing systems that would protect natural resources and the healthy ecosystems that are required to sustain economies. Solutions to resource-related predicaments require an integration of scientific knowledge and social change, along with the adoption of ecologically based economic policies that pursue true sustainability. Such solutions would be far preferable to unfettered economic growth based on the over-exploitation of resources.

Growth, Development, and Sustainability

To economists, growth and development are different phenomena. **Economic growth** is a feature of an economy that is increasing in size over time. It is usually associated with increases in both the numbers of people and their per capita use of resources. Particularly in developed countries, economic growth is achieved by the rapid consumption of natural resources. Non-renewable resources, such as metals and fossil fuels, are consumed in especially large quantities in a growing economy. Potentially renewable resources are also frequently mined, rather than being harvested on a sustainable basis.

At the present time, almost all national economies are growing quite rapidly. Moreover, most economic planners and politicians hope for additional increases in economic activity into the foreseeable future. Economic growth is

viewed as a means of generating more wealth for nations while providing a better life for their citizens.

Unfortunately, there are well-known limits to growth, which are related to the finite resources on planet Earth plus the laws of thermodynamics (Chapters 1 and 4). Consequently, unlimited economic growth can never be sustained over the longer term. In the perspectives of ecologists and ecologically minded economists, growth is not necessarily desirable: "Economic growth as it now goes on is more a disease of civilization than a cure for its woes" (Ehrlich, 1989).

Economic development is fundamentally different from growth. It implies an improving efficiency in the use of materials and energy and progress toward a sustainable economic system. In this sense, sustainable economic development involves the following actions:

- increasing the efficiency of use of non-renewable resources—for example, by recycling and re-using metals and other materials; by minimizing the use of energy for industrial, transportation, and space-heating purposes; and by improving designs of other materials and products

- increasing the use of renewable materials in the economy, such as products manufactured from trees or agricultural biomass

- rapid increases in the use of renewable sources of energy, such as electricity generated using hydro, solar, wind, or biomass technologies (see Chapter 13)

- increasing social equity, ultimately to such a degree that all citizens (and not just a minority of relatively wealthy people) have access to the necessities and amenities of life

Sustainable Development

The notion of **sustainable development** refers to making progress toward an economic system that uses natural resources in ways that do not deplete their capital or compromise their availability to future generations. In this sense, the present human economy is obviously non-sustainable because it involves rapid economic growth achieved by the vigorous mining of both non-renewable and potentially renewable resources.

Many politicians, economists, resource managers, and corporate spokespersons have publicly stated that they are

In Detail 12.2

Economics, Environment, and Ecology

"Conventional" economics is a social science that examines the allocation of scarce resources (i.e., of goods and services) among potential uses that are in competition with each other. A goal of economics is to understand and possibly manage the patterns of consumption of resources by individuals and sectors of society. In economics, the worth (or value) of goods and services is assessed on an anthropocentric basis, in terms of the direct or indirect usefulness to humans and their welfare. In large part, the value is determined by the supply of resources relative to the demand. When the supply is abundant, goods and services are relatively cheap, and when they are scarce they become more expensive, which stimulates efforts to increase the supply and/or find a cheaper substitute. Key assumptions of economics are that people seek to amplify their well-being and that corporations strive to maximize their profit. As a result, their choices can be used to reveal their valuations and investments in goods and services. Such valuations are usually made in units of tradable currency (such as dollars), and are routinely made for goods and services for which there are markets, such as:

- **manufactured goods**, such as buildings, clothing, computers, and vehicles
- **services**, such as those provided by entertainers, farmers, physicians, and teachers
- **natural resources** used in the economy, including non-renewable (e.g., metals and fossil fuels) and renewable ones (e.g., foodstuffs, fish, and timber)

However, conventional economics performs much less well in the valuation of resources for which there are no obvious markets. Such valuations require the use of surveys or the observation of behaviour (e.g., the numbers of people visiting a natural-area park, or those contributing money to an environmental charity). These sorts of valuations are difficult and somewhat controversial, but they are necessary if society is to implement a full-cost accounting system that acknowledges the fact that important environmental damage is associated with many economic activities. These kinds of valuations are made in the relatively new field of **environmental economics**, and they may involve finding the costs of:

- **the depletion of natural resources**, including longer-term implications for the survival of future generations
- **pollution** and its ecological and human health effects

- **disturbance** that causes damage to natural ecosystems
- **endangerment and extinction** of species
- **impairment of ecosystem services**, which are a major part of the life-support system of the planet
- **social effects of environmental damage**, including unacceptable economic disparities (including poverty) and the disenfranchisement of indigenous people or other cultural groups

These kinds of environmental damage are widely recognized as being important, and to some degree their value can be captured by conventional economics. This can allow the marketplace to account for environmental damage as a real cost of doing business and an expense to be reckoned when calculating profit. In environmental economics, it is argued that as long as these damages are properly costed, they can be objectively considered in cost–benefit analyses associated with decisions to undertake policies or engage in activities that carry risks for environmental quality (including any linkages with resource and ecological sustainability). This is a key part of the planning process known as environmental impact assessment (see Chapter 27), which is crucial in helping society to design and run its economy without causing unacceptable damage to the ecosystems that sustain humans and all other species.

The field of **ecological economics** goes even further than the valuation of environmental damage. Ecological economics arose as a conceptual fusion of economics and ecology (note that the names of these disciplines share the same root, "ecos," derived from the Greek word *oikos*, meaning household). The most important distinction of ecological economics is that it attempts to examine the relationships between ecosystems and economic systems in a non-anthropocentric manner (i.e., which goes beyond any known usefulness to humans and their welfare). In particular, ecological economics employs a variety of biophysical measures of scarcity and valuation. These include embodied energy content (i.e., a comprehensive life-cycle assessment of the energy used to manufacture, transport, and eventually discard of a product) and the ecological footprint (i.e., the land area needed to support the needs for energy and materials of an individual, city, or country; see Chapter 25). These approaches can yield compelling results that help us to understand the consequences of our economic activities and encourage individuals, corporations, and society at large to make choices that are less damaging to the environment.

in favour of sustainable development. However, most of these people are confusing genuine sustainable development with "sustained economic growth," which by definition is not possible.

The phrase "sustainable development" was first popularized in the widely acclaimed report *Our Common Future*, by the World Commission on Environment and Development, an agency of the United Nations. (The report, published in 1987, is sometimes referred to as the "Brundtland Report," after Gro Harlem Brundtland, the chairperson of the Commission at the time.) Even this report, however, obscured some important differences between economic growth and economic development. In fact, the Brundtland Report advocated a large expansion of the global economy: "It is...essential that the stagnant or declining growth trends of this decade [i.e., the 1980s] be reversed." The report suggested that economic growth, coupled with a more equitable distribution of wealth, was required to improve the living standards of poorer peoples of the world. Once society had achieved the socio-economic conditions required for stopping both population growth and the rampant depletion of natural resources, real progress could be made toward a no-growth, equilibrium economy.

One of the recommendations of the Brundtland Report was that the global average per capita income should grow by 3% per year (if maintained, this rate of increase would double per capita income every 23 years). However, because the global population was increasing at about 2% per year, the economic growth rate would have to compensate. Therefore, a 3% per year increase in per capita income would require a 5% per year increase in the total economy (resulting in a 14-year doubling time). Of course, in those regions where population growth is more rapid, such as much of Africa, south Asia, Latin America, and most cities (see Chapter 10), economic growth rates might have to be as high as 6% per year (doubling time of 12 years) or more in order to achieve a 3% per year increase in per capita income. Ultimately, the Brundtland Report estimated that a 5- to 10-fold expansion of the global human economy was required to set the stage for attaining a condition of sustainable development.

The authors of the Brundtland Report held that this growth would best be achieved through "policies that sustain and expand the environmental resource base." Such policies would include the advancement of efficient technologies that could help achieve economic growth while consuming fewer material and energy resources. In addition, a redistribution of some wealth from richer people and regions to poorer ones would be central to achieving the growth of per capita income that is championed in the Brundtland Report.

It is important to understand that the Brundtland Report was developed through a consensus-building process that involved wide-ranging consultations among diverse interested parties. Therefore, representatives of many nations and cultures had to agree on its content. Considering the diversity of the interests involved, it is not surprising that the report advocated enormous economic growth as a component of its "development" strategy. The growth-related aspects of the report make it easier for politicians and industry to support its recommendations.

From the ecological perspective, however, it is very doubtful that a 5- to 10-fold increase in the human economy could be sustained. Many have argued that it would be much more sensible to pursue solutions that aggressively attack both economic growth, as it is currently achieved, and population growth. These solutions would include vigorous actions toward population control, a more equitable distribution of wealth, reduced use of resources by richer peoples of the world, more equitable access for women to education and social empowerment, development and use of more efficient technologies, and rigorous conservation of natural resources. These sustainable solutions are more difficult and unpopular than the policies advocated by most mainstream politicians and economists, but they appear to be necessary.

Sustainable Economies

The proper definition of a **sustainable economy** is one that can be maintained over time without resulting in any depletion of its capital of natural resources. Ultimately, a sustainable economy can be supported only by the wise use of renewable resources, which would be harvested at rates equal to or less than their productivity. Therefore, "economic development" should refer only to progress toward a sustainable economic system. Unfortunately, there have been few substantial gains in this direction. This is because most actions undertaken by politicians, economists, and planners have supported rapid economic growth rather than sustainable economic development. In large part, they do this because they believe they are following the wishes of the public for greater access to wealth and employment.

Because non-renewable resources are always depleted by their use, they cannot provide the foundation of a sus-

Canadian Focus 12.1

Sustainable Development in Canada

A simple definition of sustainable development (SD), first articulated in a 1987 report by the World Commission on Environment and Development (also known as the Brundtland Report), is "development that meets the needs of the present without compromising the ability of future generations to meet their own needs." All levels of government and many private organizations in Canada have publicly committed to this meaning of sustainable development, and also to conserving the natural resources and biodiversity of Canada and the environmental health of Canadians. These organizations all claim to be striving to incorporate the principles of sustainable development into the core of their enterprises.

As we learned elsewhere in this chapter, however, a truly sustainable economy is fundamentally based on the wise use of renewable natural resources—ideally, with no net depletion of resources. Moreover, an ecologically sustainable economy would not cause unacceptable environmental damage, such as the endangerment or extinction of native species or natural ecosystems. Are these interpretations of sustainability at odds with those of government and most of the private sector?

Consider, for example, the following definition of sustainable development provided by a website of the federal Department of Finance: "long-term sustainable economic growth based on environmentally sound policies and practices." This meaning does not acknowledge that, from the environmental perspective, long-term economic growth can never be sustained. Moreover, recent experience has shown that the pursuit of unfettered economic growth leads to resource depletion and environmental damage. These facts are obvious to anyone who understands that Earth is an isolated planet with limited stocks of natural resources (except for sunlight). So, despite its avowed commitment to "environmentally sound policies and practices," the Department of Finance's notion of sustainability is seriously at odds with physical and ecological realities. The Department is not alone in its views, however, as most governments, private companies, and people also subscribe to this fallacious, continuous-growth model of sustainability.

Furthermore, examination of the condition of the Canadian economy leads to the inescapable conclusion that we are not making much progress toward sustainability. Some examples include the following:

- The consumption of resources, both non-renewable and renewable, is increasing rapidly.
- Only 17% of the consumption of energy involves renewable sources (Chapter 13).

- The reserve life of petroleum is only about 16 years, while that of natural gas is 9 years, copper is 12 years, and nickel 29 years (Chapter 13).
- The amount and quality of groundwater is being rapidly depleted in many regions (Chapter 12).
- Many stocks of marine and freshwater fishes have been degraded by excessive harvesting and habitat damage (Chapter 12).
- Our natural heritage of biodiversity is increasingly threatened by habitat loss and other stressors, and the number of species at risk is mounting (Chapter 26).
- Photochemical smog is becoming more severe over extensive areas of southern Canada (Chapter 16).
- Emissions of greenhouse gases continue to increase, while climate is warming and extreme weather events may be becoming more frequent (Chapter 17).

Clearly, in terms of making progress toward sustainability, Canada is moving in the wrong direction with these and many other indicators. It is important to recognize, however, that some other environmental indicators are more positive in tone, such as the following:

- The total extent and number of protected areas are increasing (Chapter 26).
- The abundance of some at-risk species has been increasing, including peregrine falcon, bald eagle, humpback whale, and grey whale (Chapter 26).
- Effective action has been taken against some pollutants, such as lead from gasoline (Chapter 18), substances that deplete stratospheric ozone (Chapter 17), phosphorus that causes eutrophication of freshwaters (Chapter 20), and certain pesticides (such as DDT and carbofuran) (Chapter 21).

In spite of these positive developments, however, any overall appraisal of the Canadian economy can only conclude that it is characterized by rapid economic growth. That growth is fuelled by a hasty depletion of critical non-renewable resources and of several renewable ones. At the same time, some kinds of pollution are becoming worse, and native biodiversity is increasingly threatened. These qualities do not suggest that much progress is being made in terms of truly sustainable development.

References

Department of Finance Canada. 2002. Sustainable Development Strategy: Planned Results for 2002–03. www.fin.gc.ca/toce/2002/susdevplane.html

Government of Canada. 2002. Sustaining the Environment and Resources for Canadians: Build on the Present; Secure the Future. http://environmentandresources.gc.ca/default.asp?Lang=En&nav=B3BE4E55-11

tainable economic system. However, non-renewable resources still have an important role to play in a sustainable economy. Their use should, however, be tied to improving the stocks of comparable renewable resources so that a net depletion of resources does not occur. For example, if people wanted to use non-renewable coal, they might act to provide a compensating increase in forest area and biomass. This could result in no net consumption of potential energy (since tree biomass and coal are both fuels), and no net increase in the concentration of atmospheric carbon dioxide or other pollutants (because trees absorb CO_2 as they grow, and mature forest can store carbon for a long time if not disturbed). Of course, any non-renewable materials already in use in the economy can continue to be used and should be recycled as efficiently as possible.

Symptoms of Non-sustainability

As was previously mentioned, the dominant trends of local, national, and global economies are mostly toward vigorous (but nonsustainable) economic growth, rather than toward sustainable development. The key indicators of these trends of non-sustainable growth are summarized below.

Rapid Growth of Economies: Because of increases in both population and per capita consumption of materials and energy, almost all economies are growing. This well-known fact is reflected by trends in many economic indicators, such as **gross domestic product** (**GDP**, the value of all goods and services produced by a nation in a year; GDP is equal to gross national product (GNP) minus net investment from foreign nations) and stock market and other indexes. For example, the Canadian economy grew by a factor of about 10 between 1947 and 2001, compared with a 2.7-fold increase in population during the same period (Figure 12.3).

Depletion of Non-renewable Resources: All stocks of metal ores, petroleum, natural gas, coal, and other non-renewable resources are finite, being limited to what is present on Earth. These resources are being consumed rapidly, and their exploitable reserves will eventually become depleted. Future discoveries of additional exploitable stocks will extend the economic lifetimes of non-renewable resources, as does efficient recycling. Nevertheless, global stocks of non-renewable resources are being depleted at accelerating rates.

Depletion of (Potentially) Renewable Resources: Around the globe there are crises of depletion of renewable resources. In many regions, for example, previously enormous fish stocks are collapsing, deforestation is proceeding rapidly, the fertility of agricultural soil is declining, supplies of surface and groundwaters are being depleted and polluted, and hunted animals are becoming scarcer. Not all stocks of renewable resources are severely depleted, but the declines are becoming much more common and widespread.

Depletion of Non-economic, Environmental Resources: Some resources that are necessary for the health of economic systems are not assigned value (or "traded") in the marketplace—that is, they are not valuated in dollars. Nevertheless, these resources are important to the health of the ecosystems that sustain the human economy. Examples of such non-valuated, environmental resources include the ability of ecosystems to cleanse the environment of toxic pollutants associated with human activities,

| FIGURE 12.3 | Growth of the Canadian Economy and Population, 1943–2003 |

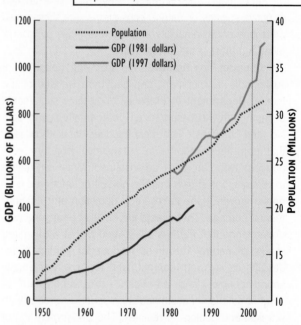

Gross domestic product (GDP) is an economic indicator related to the total size of a national economy. Because these data for Canadian GDP are standardized to either constant 1981 or constant 1997 dollars, the pattern of steady economic growth is not due to inflation. Compare the growth of GDP with the growth of the Canadian population.

Sources: GDP data from Statistics Canada (1989, 1995, 2005), and population data from Figure 11.1

such as sulphur dioxide and ozone; ecological services such as the production of atmospheric O_2 and consumption of CO_2 (the latter being an important pollutant associated with the economy); and ecological functions that support the productivity of conventional resources, such as the plant and algal productivity that ultimately allows the growth of stocks of hunted deer, fish, and other animals.

Depletions of Other Ecological Values: Some ecological values are not directly or indirectly important in the human economy, but still have intrinsic (or existence) worth. This makes these values significant, regardless of any real or perceived importance to human welfare (see also Chapter 1). The most important examples of these ecological values are associated with biodiversity, especially the many species and natural ecosystems that are indigenous to different regions. These biodiversity values are increasingly being threatened and lost in virtually all regions of the globe (Chapter 26). Such losses would never be tolerated in an **ecologically sustainable economic system** (i.e., an economy in which renewable resources are used in ways that do not compromise their future availability and do not endanger species or natural ecosystems; Chapter 27).

Modern economies deliver great benefits to those who are wealthy enough to purchase a happy and healthy lifestyle, replete with sufficient food, shelter, material goods, and recreational opportunities. For less wealthy people, however, current economic systems may allow only minimal access to the most fundamental basics of subsistence. If a fairer, more equitable delivery of economic benefits to the poorer people of the world is to be achieved, either unsustainable economic growth or a substantial redistribution of some of the existing wealth will be required.

Ultimately, the global scale and long-term sustainability of the human economy will be limited by the ability of the biosphere to deliver renewable resources. The limits of many potentially renewable resources have already been reached or exceeded, resulting in stock declines or collapses. These well-documented damages should be regarded as warnings of the likely future of the human enterprise (assuming that resource-use systems do not improve). If critical resources are no longer available to support economic activity, the nonsustainable economy will be forced to contract in size, and may in fact collapse.

It must be recognized that ecologically sustainable economic systems might not be very popular among the public, politicians, government administrators, or industrial interests. All of these stakeholders would experience short-term pain (likely felt over decades) to achieve long-term, sustainable, societal gains. The pain would be associated with a less-intensive use of natural resources, the abandonment of the economic-growth paradigm, and the rapid stabilization—and perhaps downsizing—of the human population. The gains would be associated with a sustainable economic system that could support human society for a very long time.

As we have repeatedly observed, humans rely on natural resources to sustain their enterprises. Throughout history, resources essential to economies have, technological capabilities permitting, been consumed to exhaustion. It is clear that better, more sustainable systems must be found that allow us to use renewable resources without depleting them and without degrading environmental quality. Human societies desperately require these sustainable systems. It remains to be seen, however, whether these essential systems will ever be designed and implemented.

Conclusions

The human economy can function only if it has access to a continuous input of natural resources, of which there are two kinds: non-renewable and renewable. Non-renewable resources cannot regenerate, so they become depleted as they are used. In contrast, renewable resources are capable of regeneration, so they can potentially be available forever. Nevertheless, excessive harvesting or inappropriate management can degrade potentially renewable resources, causing them to become diminished or even disappear. The human economy has been growing rapidly, and this has been achieved by the vigorous consumption and depletion of both non-renewable and potentially renewable resources. However, this process is clearly non-sustainable because it has relied on such rapid resource depletion, while also causing other damage, for example, to biodiversity. Ultimately, a sustainable human economy must be fundamentally based on the wise use of renewable resources, that is, use that does not compromise their availability in the future. In addition, an ecologically sustainable economy would not cause unacceptable collateral damage to other parts of Earth's ecosystem, such as putting other species and natural ecosystems at risk of extinction.

Key Terms

spaceship Earth

sustainable economic system

non-renewable resource

renewable resource

potentially renewable resource

management system

maximum sustainable yield (MSY)

over-harvesting (over-exploitation)

conservation

gross national product (GNP)

conventional economics

ecological economics

common-property resource

economic growth

economic development

sustainable development

environmental economics

ecological economics

sustainable economy

gross domestic product (GDP)

ecologically sustainable economic system

Questions for Review

1. What are the differences between non-renewable and (potentially) renewable natural resources? Give examples of each.

2. How can the productivity of biological resources be increased through management?

3. Describe three cases of the "mining" of (potentially) renewable natural resources. Why did the over-exploitation occur in each case?

4. What are the key differences between conventional economics and ecological (environmental) economics?

Questions for Discussion

1. What are the differences between economic growth and development? Relate economic growth and development to the notion of sustainable development. Do you believe that the Canadian economy is making much progress toward sustainable development? Explain your answer.

2. Can you think of any examples of economically valuable, potentially renewable resources that have not been severely depleted through excessive use or inappropriate management? Explain your answer.

3. List several environmental values that do not directly contribute to the human economy, but are nevertheless important to the healthy functioning of ecosystems and the biosphere. Should these environmental services be valued and measured in dollars to allow their degradation to be considered a true "cost" of doing business? What would be the benefits of such an ecological cost-accounting?

4. In this chapter, we defined sustainable development as "progress toward an economic system based on the use of natural resources in a manner that does not deplete their stocks nor compromise their availability for use by future generations of humans." We also defined ecologically sustainable development as "considering the human need for resources within an ecological context, and including the need to sustain all species and all components of Earth's life-support system." Discuss the key similarities and differences in these two kinds of economic sustainability.

Exploring Issues

1. Show how natural resources are important in your life by making a list of resources you use daily for energy, food, or as materials in manufactured products.

2. You have been asked to help develop a plan for sustainable forest management on a large area of land. What practices would you recommend to ensure that the timber harvesting does not deplete the resource? What about other economic resources, such as fish, hunted animals, and opportunities for outdoor recreation? How would your plan accommodate the need to sustain indigenous species and natural ecosystems?

References

Brown, L.R. 2001. *Eco-Economy: Building an Economy for the Earth*. New York: W.W. Norton and Company.

Brown, L.R. 2003. *Plan C: Rescuing a Planet Under Stress and a Civilization in Trouble*. New York: W.W. Norton and Company.

Burton, P.S. 1993. Intertemporal preferences and intergenerational equity considerations in optimal resource harvesting. *J. Environ. Economics & Manage.*, **24**: 119–32.

Chambers, N., C. Simmons, and N. Wackernagel. 2001. *Sharing Nature's Interest: Ecological Footprints as an Indicator of Sustainability*. London, UK: Earthscan Publications.

Chiras, D.D., J.P. Reganold, and O.S. Owen. 2001. *Natural Resource Conservation: Management for a Sustainable Future*. 8th ed. Upper Saddle River, NJ: Prentice Hall.

Clark, W.C. 1989. Clear-cut economies: Should we harvest everything now? *The Sciences*, Jan./Feb.: 16–19.

Clark, W.C. and R.E. Munn (eds.). 1986. *Sustainable Development of the Biosphere*. New York: Cambridge University Press.

Costanza, R. 1991. *Ecological Economics: The Science and Management of Sustainability*. New York: Columbia University Press.

Costanza, R. and H.E. Daly. 1992. Natural capital and sustainable development. *Conserv. Biol.*, **6**: 37–46.

Cushing, D.H. 1988. *The Provident Sea*. Cambridge: Cambridge University Press.

Daly, H.E. 1997. *Beyond Growth: The Economics of Sustainable Development*. Boston: Beacon Press.

Diamond, J.M. 1982. Man the exterminator. *Nature*, **298**: 787–89.

Diamond, J. 2004. *Collapse: How Societies Choose to Fail or Succeed*. East Rutherford, NJ: Viking.

Faber, M.M., R. Manstetter, and J. Proops. 1996. *Ecological Economics: Concepts and Methods*. New York: Edward Elgar Publishers.

Farley, J. and H.E. Daly. 2003. *Ecological Economics: Principles and Applications*. Washington, DC: Island Press.

Freedman, B. 1995. *Environmental Ecology*. 2nd ed. San Diego, CA: Academic.

Hardin, G. 1968. The tragedy of the commons. *Science*, **162**: 1243–48.

Holechek, J.L., R.A. Cole, J.T. Fisher, and R. Valdez. 2002. *Natural Resources: Ecology, Economics, and Policy*. 2nd ed. East Rutherford, NJ: Prentice Hall.

Martin, P.S. 1984. Catastrophic extinctions and late Pleistocene blitzkrieg: two radiocarbon tests. In: *Extinctions* (M.H. Nitecki, ed.). Chicago: University of Chicago Press. pp. 153–89.

Martin, P.S. and H.E. Wright (eds.). 1967. *Pleistocene Extinctions: The Search for a Cause*. New Haven, CT: Yale University Press.

Meadows, D.H., D.L. Meadows, and J. Randers. 1992. *Beyond the Limits: Global Collapse or a Sustainable Future*. 1992. London: Earthscan.

Meadows, D.H., J. Randers, and D.L. Meadows. 2003. *Limits to Growth: The 30-Year Update*. White River Junction, VT: Chelsea Green Publishing Co.

Mowat, F. 1984. *Sea of Slaughter*. Toronto: McClelland & Stewart.

Owen, O.S., D.D. Chiras, and J.P. Reganold. 1998. *Natural Resource Conservation: Management for a Sustainable Future*. 7th ed. Upper Saddle River, NJ: Prentice Hall.

Ponting, C. 1991. *A Green History of the World*. Middlesex, U.K.: Penguin.

Rees, W.E. 1990. The ecology of sustainable development. *Ecologist*, **20(1)**: 18–23.

Statistics Canada. 2005. *Gross Domestic Product (GDP), Expenditure-Based, Canada, 1997 Constant Prices, Seasonally Adjusted; At Market Prices*. http://dc2.chass.utoronto. ca/cgi-bin/cansim2/getSeries.pl?s=V1992259

Thirgood, J.V. 1981. *Man and the Mediterranean Forest: A History of Resource Depletion*. New York: Academic.

Tietenberg, T. 2002. *Environmental and Natural Resource Economics*. 6th ed. Boston, MA: Addison Wesley.

Townsend, C.R., M. Begon, and J.L. Harper. 2002. *Essentials of Ecology*. 2nd ed. Cambridge, UK: Blackwell Publishers.

Tristram, H.B. 1873. *The Natural History of the Bible*. London: Society for Promoting Christian Knowledge.

White, L. 1967. The historical roots of our ecological crisis. *Science*, **155**: 1203–07.

World Commission on Environment and Development (WCED). 1987. *Our Common Future*. Oxford: WCED, Oxford University Press.

World Resources Institute. 2005. *Earth Trends. The Environmental Information Portal*. Washington, DC: WRI.

Informative Websites

Canadian Resource and Environmental Economics Study Group (CREE). http://socserv.socsci.mcmaster.ca/~cree/

This is the website of an informal group of Canadian economists interested in natural-resource and environmental economics.

Canadian Society for Ecological Economics (CSEE). www.cansee.org/

CSEE is the Canadian chapter of the International Society for Ecological Economics. ISEE and CSEE endeavour to facilitate understanding between economists and ecologists in pursuit of a vision of a sustainable future, through transdisciplinary research and dialogue.

Economics. www.enviroliteracy.org/subcategory.php/12.html

Economics and how it affects the environment is the focus of this website. Links to related sites such as a quiz on basic economic concepts, economic explanations of current news items, and others are also included.

International Institute for Sustainable Development (IISD). www.iisd.org/

The IISD is a Canadian-centred international organization whose mission is to champion innovation, enabling societies to live sustainably.

The International Society for Ecological Economics. www.ecoeco.org/

This website explains the field of ecological economics and provides useful links.

Linkages: A Multimedia Resource for Environment and Development Policy Makers. www.iisd.ca/

This comprehensive site is designed to be an electronic clearing house for information on past and upcoming international meetings that are related to environment and development policy.

Resources for the Future. www.rff.org/

Searching for predictions on our environmental future? Visit this American site to find out what the latest theories are from the EPA, World Bank, and the RFF.

World Resources Institute. EarthTrends. The Environmental Information Portal. http://earthtrends.wri.org/

The WRI is a leading environmental organization that provides excellent information about resource issues.

World Resources Institute Research Topics. www.wri.org/wrisites.cfm

From the genetic diversity of agriculture to zoological parks, this site provides links to everything resource-related.

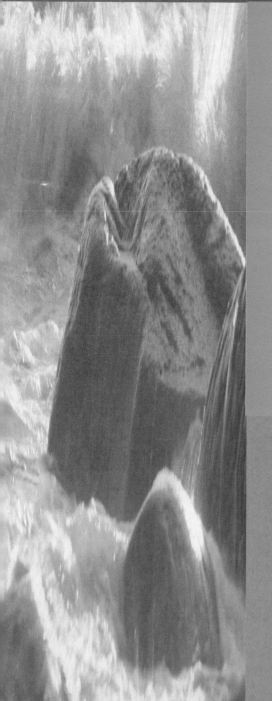

13 Non-renewable Resources

CHAPTER OBJECTIVES

After completing this chapter, you will be able to

1. Describe the global and Canadian production and use of metals, fossil fuels, and other non-renewable resources.
2. Discuss the reliance of industrialized economies on non-renewable resources, and predict whether these essential sources of materials and energy will continue to be available into the foreseeable future.
3. Outline five major sources of energy available for use in industrialized countries and describe the potential roles of these in a sustainable economy.

CHAPTER OUTLINE

Introduction

As we noted in Chapter 12, reserves of **non-renewable resources** are inexorably diminished as they are used. This is because non-renewable resources are finite in quantity and their reserves do not regenerate after they are mined from the environment. Note that the word "**reserve**" has a specific meaning here: to denote known quantities of material that can be *economically* recovered from the environment (i.e., while making a profit).

Of course, continuing exploration may discover exploitable, previously unknown deposits of non-renewable resources, resulting in increases in the known reserves. For example, the world's known reserves of nickel and copper were increased recently because of the discovery of rich deposits of those metals in northern Quebec and Labrador. There are, however, limits to the number of "new" discoveries of non-renewable resources that can be made on planet Earth.

Changes in the value of non-renewable commodities can also affect the sizes of their economically recoverable reserves. For example, an increase in the market value of gold can make it profitable to mine previously non-economic ores, to engage in exploration in remote places, or to reprocess "waste" materials containing small quantities of this valuable metal. A change in technology can have the same effect—for instance, by making it profitable to recover and process lower-grade ores.

In addition, the useful lifecycle of some non-renewable resources, particularly metals, can be extended by **recycling**. This involves processing disused industrial and household products (sometimes referred to as "wastes") to recover reusable materials. However, thermodynamic and economic limits mean that recycling cannot be 100% efficient. Furthermore, the demand for non-renewable resources is increasing rapidly because of population growth, spreading industrialization, and enhanced living standards and associated per capita consumption. This accelerating demand must be satisfied by mining additional quantities from the environment.

The most important classes of non-renewable resources are metals, fossil fuels, and certain other minerals such as gypsum and potash. The production and uses of these important resources are described in the following sections.

Metals

Metals are materials with a wide range of useful physical and chemical properties. They can be used as pure elemental substances, as alloys (mixtures) of various kinds of metals, and as compounds that also contain non-metals. Metals are used to manufacture tools, machines, and electricity-conducting wires; to construct buildings and other structures; and for many other purposes.

The most prominent metals in industrial use are aluminum (Al), chromium (Cr), cobalt (Co), copper (Cu), iron (Fe), lead (Pb), manganese (Mn), mercury (Hg), nickel (Ni), tin (Sn), uranium (U), and zinc (Zn). The extremely valuable metals gold (Au), platinum (Pt), and silver (Ag) have some industrial uses (e.g., as conductors in computers and other electronics), but they are valued mostly for aesthetic reasons, particularly the manufacturing of jewellery. Some of the more common alloys are brass (containing at least 50% Cu, plus Zn), bronze (mostly Cu, plus Sn, and sometimes Zn and Pb), and steel (mostly Fe, but also containing carbon, Cr, Mn, and/or Ni).

Metals are mined from the environment, usually as minerals that also contain sulphur or oxygen. Deposits of metal-bearing minerals that are economically extractable contribute to the known reserves of the metal. Ores are mixtures of minerals that are mined and processed to manufacture pure metals. The stages in metal processing, manufacturing, and recycling are summarized in Figure 13.1.

The initial step is ore extraction by mining, which may be conducted in surface pits or strip mines, or in shaft mines that can penetrate kilometres underground. In an industrial facility called a mill, ore is crushed to a fine powder by heavy steel balls or rods in huge, rotating tumblers. The ground ore is then separated into a metal-rich fraction and a waste known as tailings. Depending on local geography, the tailings may be discarded onto a contained area on land, into a waterbody, or into the ocean (see also Chapter 18).

If the metal-rich fraction contains sulphide minerals, it is concentrated in a smelter by roasting at high temperature in the presence of oxygen. This releases gaseous sulphur dioxide (SO_2) while leaving the metals behind. The smelter concentrate is subsequently processed into pure metal in a refinery. The pure metal is then used to manufacture industrial and consumer products. The SO_2 may be processed into useful sulphur or sulphuric acid or emitted into the environment as a pollutant.

After their useful lifespan, manufactured products can be recycled back into the refining and manufacturing processes, or they may be discarded into a landfill.

High-quality ores are geologically uncommon. Deposits that are most economic for mining are located fairly close to the surface, and the ores have relatively high concentrations of metals. This varies, however, depend-

FIGURE 13.1 | Metal Mining and Use

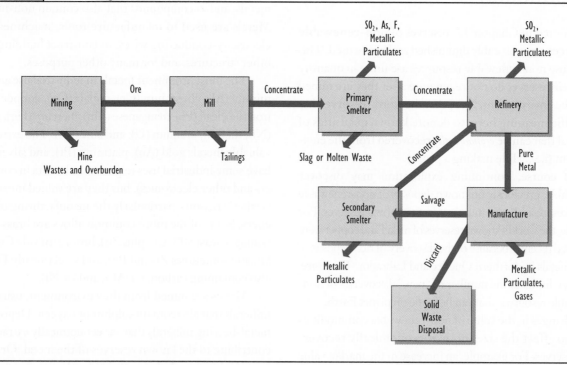

This diagram shows major stages of the mining, manufacturing, use, and re-use of metals, as well as the associated emissions of waste gases (particularly sulphur dioxide) and particulates to the environment. Overall, the system is a flow-through, with some recycling to extend the lifetime of metals within the economic system.

Source: Modified from Freedman (1995)

ing on the value of the metal being processed. Because gold and platinum are extremely valuable metals (on a unit-weight basis), ores with very small concentrations can be economically mined and processed. In contrast, less valuable aluminum and iron must be mined as richer ores, in which the metals are present in high concentrations.

Data showing the global production of industrially important metals are given in Table 13.1. Note that for most metals the amounts consumed are somewhat larger than the annual production: this indicates that some of the consumption involves recycled metal that has been reclaimed from previous uses. Also note the large increase in production of most metals between 1977 and 2003.

Iron and aluminum are the two metals produced and used in the largest quantities. The **life index** (or production life, calculated as the known reserves divided by the annual rate of production) of aluminum is only about 160 years, and for iron ore it is 134 years. Life indexes for most other metals listed in Table 13.2 are much less, suggesting that their known reserves are being depleted quickly. It is important to remember, however, that known reserves

are increased by new discoveries, changes in technology, and more favourable economics for the resource.

As depletion occurs, the specific value (i.e., the per-tonne value) of the remaining reserves will increase in an open marketplace. The increasing value of diminishing supplies of metals stimulates more exploration, the exploitation of previously discovered deposits which may be of relatively low quality, more efficient recycling of metals from discarded products, and the substitution of less expensive alternative materials. For example, water-conducting pipes manufactured from polyvinyl chloride and other plastics have largely replaced copper piping because the metal has become relatively expensive.

The mining and processing of metals is big business in Canada, with a production value of $10.5 billion in 2004 (Statistics Canada, 2005). In terms of quantities produced, the leading metals in Canada are iron, aluminum, zinc, copper, lead, and nickel (Table 13.2). In terms of value, however, the leading metals are gold, copper, zinc, nickel, and iron ore (Table 13.3). Regional Canadian production of these most valuable metals is also described in

TABLE 13.1	Global Production, Consumption, and Reserves of Selected Metals			
METAL	**PRODUCTION** (10^6 tonne/year)		**RESERVES 2003** (10^6 t)	
	1977	**2003**	**KNOWN**	**LIKELY**
Aluminum	13.1	27.3	23 000	33 000
Cadmium	0.017	0.015	0.60	1.80
Copper	7.7	12.6	427	855
Iron (ore)	831	1120	136 000	300 000
Lead	3.4	2.8	67	140
Mercury	0.007	0.002	0.12	0.24
Nickel	0.77	1.40	62	140
Tin	0.23	0.27	6.1	11.0
Zinc	6.1	8.5	220	460
Steel (crude)	673	924	–	–

Sources: Data from World Resources Institute (1996) and U.S. Geological Service (2005)

Table 13.3. Note that aluminum is not mined in Canada, but huge quantities of its bauxite ore are imported for processing into pure metal. Most aluminum smelters are in Quebec and British Columbia because these facilities require relatively inexpensive and abundant hydroelectric energy.

Canada is one of the world's leading producers of metals, accounting for 11% of the global production of nickel in 2003, 9% of global zinc production, 5% of cadmium, 4% of copper, 3% of lead, and 3% of iron ore (see Tables 13.1 and 13.2). Most metal production in Canada is intended for export. Domestic consumption is about 30% of the value of production of all metals (see also Table 13.2).

The reserve life (life index) of known Canadian reserves of metals is similar to or shorter than their global values (see Table 13.2). Canadian reserves make up 75% of the global reserves of uranium and 5–9% of those of cadmium, nickel, silver, and zinc.

TABLE 13.2	Reserves, Production, and Consumption of Selected Metals in Canada, 2003				
METAL	**LIFE INDEX (years)**		**CANADIAN RESERVES** (% OF GLOBAL)	**CANADIAN PRODUCTION** (10^3 tonne)	**CANADIAN CONSUMPTION** (10^3 tonne)
	CANADIAN	**GLOBAL**			
Aluminum[1]	–	160	0	2 792	1020
Cadmium	61	40	9.1	0.70	0.209
Cobalt	19	149	1.3	1.74	0.092
Copper	12	34	2.1	534	274
Gold	8	17	3.0	0.141	0.042
Iron ore	53	134	1.1	32 960	13 355
Lead	25	24	3.0	77	66.6
Molybdenum	60	68	5.2	9.30	2.66
Nickel	29	44	8.4	155	19.0
Platinum group	17	198	0.4	0.019	–
Silver	13	14	5.9	1.26	0.31
Uranium	45	62	75	10.3	1.7
Zinc	11	29	5.0	744	150

[1] Aluminum is not mined in Canada, but bauxite ore is imported for processing.

Sources: Based on information from Natural Resources Canada (1994a, 2004a, b) and U.S. Geological Service (2005)

TABLE 13.3	Provincial Production of Selected Metals in Canada, 2003				
REGION	GOLD (tonne/year)	COPPER (10^3 t/y)	ZINC (10^3 t/y)	NICKEL (10^3 t/y)	IRON ORE (10^6 t/y)
Newfoundland	1.2	–	–	–	19.9
Prince Edward Island	–	–	–	–	–
Nova Scotia	–	–	–	–	–
New Brunswick	0.24	9.3	278	–	–
Quebec	28.0	80.1	253	25	13.3
Ontario	76.2	165	72	92	–
Manitoba	3.9	28.9	83	38	–
Saskatchewan	2.1	12.2	5.4	–	–
Alberta	0.07	–	–	–	–
British Columbia	22.9	246	66	–	–
Yukon	1.6	–	–	–	–
Northwest Territories	2.6	–			
Nunavut	2.1	–			–
NATIONAL TOTAL	141	541	757	155	33.3
Value ($$10^6$)	2307	1300	883	2136	1281

Source: Based on information from Natural Resources Canada (2004b)

Fossil Fuels

Fossil fuels include coal, petroleum, natural gas, oil sand, and oil shale. All of these materials are derived from the partially decomposed biomass of dead plants and other organisms that lived many millions of years ago. The ancient biomass became entombed in sediment, which later was buried and lithified into sedimentary rocks such as shale and sandstone. Deep within the geological formations, under conditions of high pressure, high temperature, and low oxygen, the biomass transformed extremely slowly into hydrocarbons (composed entirely of carbon and hydrogen) and other organic compounds. In some respects, fossil fuels can be considered to be stored solar energy—sunlight fixed by plants into organic matter and then stored geologically.

Fossil fuels are still being produced today, by the same geological processes involving biomass subjected to high pressure and temperature. Because the natural production of fossil fuels continues, it might be argued that these materials are renewable resources. However, fossil fuels are being used at a rate that is enormously faster than their extremely slow rate of natural regeneration. Under such circumstances, fossil fuels can only be regarded as being non-renewable.

Hydrocarbons are the most abundant chemical compounds in fossil fuels. These fuels may also contain many other kinds of organic compounds, incorporating sulphur, nitrogen, and other elements. Coal is often contaminated with many inorganic minerals, such as shales and pyrites.

The most important use of fossil fuels is as a source of energy. They are combusted in vehicle engines, power

Photo 13.1 Because petroleum and other fossil fuels are non-renewable resources, their future reserves are diminished by mining. These are oil pumps near Taber, Alberta.

Source: Victor Last/Geographical Visual Aids

plants, and other machines to produce the energy needed to perform work in industry, for transportation, and for household use. Fossil fuels are also combusted to produce energy to heat indoor spaces, an important use in countries with a seasonally cold climate. Another key use of fossil fuels is for manufacturing synthetic substances, including most types of plastics. Asphaltic materials obtained from fossil fuels are used in road construction and to manufacture roofing shingles and siding for buildings.

Coal is a solid material that can vary greatly in character. The highest quality coals are anthracite and bituminous, which are hard, shiny, black minerals with a high energy density. Lignite, a poorer grade of coal, is a softer, flaky material with a lower energy density. Coal is mined in various ways. If coal deposits occur close to the surface, they are typically quarried using a strip-mining technique. This involves the use of huge shovels known as draglines to uncover and collect the coal-bearing strata. Deeper deposits of coal are mined from underground shafts and tunnels, which may follow seams kilometres into the ground. Most coal in North America is mined by strip-mining.

After mining, industrial coal may be washed to remove some of the impurities and then ground into a powder. Most coal is combusted directly in large industrial facilities, such as coal-fired generating stations, a use that accounts for about half of the global use of coal and 70% in Canada. In addition, about 75% of the world's steel is manufactured using coal as an energy source, often as a concentrated material known as coke. Coal can also be manufactured into synthetic petroleum.

Petroleum (crude oil) is a fluid mixture of hydrocarbons with some impurities, including organic compounds containing sulphur, nitrogen, and vanadium. Petroleums from different places vary greatly in their physical and chemical qualities, from heavy, tarry materials that must be heated before they will flow, to extremely light liquids that quickly volatilize into the atmosphere. Petroleum is mined using wells drilled to various depths, from which the liquid mineral is forced to the surface by geological pressure. Often, this natural pressure is supplemented by pumping. Petroleum is also produced by mining and refining oil sand, which is strip-mined in large quantities in northern Alberta.

Mined petroleum is transported by overland pipelines, trucks, trains, and ships to industrial facilities known as refineries, where the crude material is separated into various constituents. The petroleum fractions may be used as liquid fuels, or they can be manufactured into many kinds of useful materials, such as plastics and pigments. The refined fractions include

- a relatively light hydrocarbon fraction known as gasoline, which is used to fuel automobiles;
- slightly heavier fractions, such as diesel fuel for trucks and trains and home-heating fuel;
- kerosene, used for heating and cooking and as a fuel for airplanes;
- dense residual oils, used in oil-fired power plants and as a ship fuel; and
- tarry, semi-solid asphalts used to pave roads and manufacture roofing material.

Natural gas is likewise mined with drilled wells. Methane is the dominant hydrocarbon in natural gas. Other gaseous hydrocarbons such as ethane, propane, and butane are also present, as are sulphurous gases such as hydrogen sulphide. Most natural gas is transported in pipelines from the well sites to distant markets. Sometimes it is liquefied under pressure for transportation, particularly by ships. In Canada, however, it is distributed mostly through an extensive network of steel pipelines. Natural gas is used to generate electricity, to heat buildings, to cook food, to power light vehicles, and to manufacture nitrogen fertilizer.

Production, Reserves, and Consumption

Table 13.4 shows the global production and reserves of fossil fuels. The production of petroleum and natural gas increased 16% from 1993 to 2003, and natural gas by 26%. There is active exploration for all of these fuels, and additional reserves are being discovered in various regions of the world. Fossil fuels are, however, being consumed extremely rapidly, particularly in industrial economies. Consequently, the expected lifetimes of the known reserves are alarmingly short, equivalent to 200 years for coal and only a few decades for natural gas and petroleum. These specific numbers must not be interpreted too literally, however, because continuing exploration for fossil fuels is discovering additional deposits, which add to the known reserves. Nevertheless, the discoveries will be limited by the finite amount present on Earth, so the fact remains that the stocks of these non-renewable resources are being depleted rapidly.

At the present time, petroleum is the world's most important hydrocarbon resource, largely because it can eas-

TABLE 13.4 | Global Production and Reserves of Fossil Fuels, 2004

"Proven" reserves are the total amounts of the commodity known to exist on Earth; reserve life is reserves divided by the annual rate of production.

FOSSIL FUEL	PROVEN $10^9 t$	RESERVES (10^9 t) $10^9 toe$ [2]	PRODUCTION $10^9 t$	$10^6 toe$	RESERVE LIFE (y)
Hard coals	478.8	320.5	–	–	–
Soft coals	430.3	164.6	–	–	–
Total coals	908.1	462.8	5.54	2.73	164
Crude oil	161.9	161.9	3.87	3.87	41
Natural gas[1]	179.5	161.5	2.81	2.81	67

[1] Reserves of natural gas are given in $10^{12} m^3$.
[2] toe = tonnes of oil equivalent

Source: Data from British Petroleum (2004)

ily be refined into portable, liquid fuels that are readily used as a source of energy for industrial and domestic purposes. In addition, petroleum is the major feedstock used to manufacture plastics and other synthetic materials.

About 53% of the world's proven recoverable reserves of petroleum occur in the Middle East (Table 13.5). This fact underscores the strategic importance of that region to the world's industrial economies. Saudi Arabia alone has 23% of the world's petroleum reserves, followed by Iraq, Kuwait, and Iran, each with 8–10%. The world's most industrialized countries are in Europe, North America, and eastern Asia, and these depend heavily on petroleum imports from the Middle East, Russia, and Venezuela to maintain their consumption levels. The world's best-endowed country in terms of total hydrocarbon resources is Russia, which has the bulk of the proven reserves of natural gas, as well as enormous reserves of coal and petroleum (see Table 13.5).

The production lives of proven recoverable Canadian reserves of fossil fuels are shown in Table 13.6. It must be remembered, however, that new reserves are still being discovered, which extend these production lives. Most reserves of fossil fuels in Canada occur in the western provinces, as does most production (Table 13.7). In the western provinces, coal is generally extracted using open-pit and strip mines, while coal in the eastern provinces is also mined underground. In addition to crude oil, Canada also has a huge resource of oil sand, which is used to manufacture petroleum (see Canadian Focus 13.1). There are

Photo 13.2 Continued exploration for non-renewable resources can discover new reserves. Because Earth is finite, however, there are limits to these discoveries, which are being approached rapidly. This enormous off-shore production platform was constructed to develop the Hibernia petroleum deposit on the Grand Banks off Newfoundland.

Source: Greg Locke/Straylight Photographic Services

TABLE 13.5 | Reserves of Fossil Fuels in Selected Countries

Countries are listed in order of decreasing reserves of petroleum (crude oil) in 2004. Data are proved recoverable reserves.

COUNTRY	PETROLEUM (10^9 tonne)	HARD COAL (10^9 t)	SOFT COAL (10^9 t)	NATURAL GAS (10^{12} metre^3)
Saudi Arabia	36.1	–	–	6.75
Iran	18.2	0.19	2.30	27.6
Iraq	15.5	–	–	3.17
Kuwait	13.6	–	–	1.57
United Arab Emirates	13.0	–	–	6.75
Venezuela	11.1	0.48	–	4.22
Russian Fed.	9.9	49.2	107.9	48.0
Kazakhstan	5.4	28.2	3.12	3.00
Libya	5.1	–	–	1.49
Nigeria	4.8	–	–	5.00
United States	3.6	111.3	135.3	5.29
China	2.3	62.2	52.3	2.23
Canada	*2.4*	*3.47*	*3.11*	*1.60*
Mexico	2.0	0.86	0.35	0.42
Qatar	2.0	–	–	25.8
Brazil	1.5	–	10.1	0.25
Algeria	1.5	–	–	4.55
Norway	1.3	–	0.04	2.46
India	0.7	90.1	2.36	0.85
Indonesia	0.7	0.79	4.22	2.56
United Kingdom	0.6	0.22	0.50	0.59
Australia	0.5	38.6	39.9	2.46
Germany	0.05	23.0	43.0	0.21
Japan	<0.01	0.77	0.02	0.03

Source: Data from British Petroleum (2005)

| TABLE 13.6 | Production, Consumption, and Reserves of Fossil Fuels in Canada, 2004 |

Percentage consumption refers to the fraction of production that is used in Canada. Reserve life is reserves divided by annual production.

FOSSIL FUEL	CANADIAN PRODUCTION	CANADIAN CONSUMPTION	PERCENTAGE CONSUMPTION	PROVED RESERVES	RESERVE LIFE (years)
Coal (10^6 t)	66.0	57.7	86	6578	100
Petroleum (10^6 t)	147.6	99.6	67	2400	15
Natural gas (10^9 m^3)	164.5	80.5	49	1600	9

Source: Data from British Petroleum (2005)

about 14 million hectares of oil sand deposits in northern Alberta, which can potentially yield about 42 billion tonnes of synthetic oil.

About half of the Canadian production of natural gas is consumed domestically, the rest being exported to the U.S. (see Table 13.6). In contrast, about 86% of Canada's net production of coal and 67% of petroleum is used domestically. (Actually, a large fraction of the petroleum mined in western Canada is exported to the U.S., but this is offset by a substantial import of foreign petroleum to the eastern provinces. The 67% figure is a net value.)

The mining of oil and gas is an extremely important economic sector in Canada, with a production value of $23 billion in 2003. Canada produces about 7% of the global production of natural gas, 4% of the petroleum, and

1% of the coal. These are much larger than the 0.5% of global population that lives in Canada.

Other Mined Minerals

Other materials that are mined in large quantities in Canada include asbestos, diamonds, gypsum, limestone, potash, salt, sulphur, aggregates, and peat. Except for diamonds, these materials have a relatively small commodity value (i.e., value per tonne) compared with metals and fossil fuels. Global or Canadian shortages of these materials are not imminent.

Asbestos is a group of tough, fibrous, incombustible, silicate minerals used for manufacturing fireproof insulation, cement additives, brake linings, and many other products. Certain kinds of asbestos minerals have been linked to human health problems, particularly the development of lung diseases. These health hazards have greatly reduced the market for this otherwise extremely useful mineral. Still, about 0.24 million tonnes of asbestos were mined in Canada in 2003, with an economic value of $98 million (Natural Resources Canada, 2004). Almost all of the asbestos mining in Canada occurs in Quebec.

Diamonds are relatively new on the mining scene in Canada, with the first major discoveries being made in the 1990s. About 4900 carats of diamonds were mined in Canada in 2003, with an economic value of $792 million. Almost all of the mining occurs in the Northwest Territories, although exploration is also occurring elsewhere on the Canadian Shield.

Gypsum, a mineral composed of calcium sulphate, is used mainly to manufacture plaster and wallboard for the construction industry. About 8.8 million tonnes of gypsum were mined in Canada in 2003, with an economic value of $105 million. About 75% of gypsum mining occurs in Nova Scotia, with the rest in Ontario, British Columbia, and Newfoundland.

| TABLE 13.7 | Provincial Production of Fossil Fuels, 2003 |

Data for natural gas include byproducts.

REGION	PETROLEUM (10^6 metre^3/year)	NATURAL GAS (10^9 m^3/y)	COAL (10^6 tonne/year)
Newfoundland	19.6	3.6	–
Prince Edward Island	–	–	–
Nova Scotia	–	4.7	1.08
New Brunswick	–	–	0.14
Quebec	–	–	–
Ontario	0.20	0.30	–
Manitoba	0.63	–	–
Saskatchewan	24.3	8.5	11.3
Alberta	86.6	165.5	28.2
British Columbia	2.2	29.5	23.1
Yukon	–	0.25	–
Northwest Territories	1.3	0.98	–
Nunavut	–	–	–
NATIONAL TOTAL	134.7	213.2	62.1

Source: Data from Statistics Canada (2004)

Canadian Focus 13.1

The Oil Sands

Oil sands (tar sands) are a fossil-fuel resource that consists of a mixture of sand and clay with interstitial bitumen at a typical concentration of 10–12%. Oil sands occur over a 140 000-km^2 region of northern Alberta and, to a much lesser degree, in Saskatchewan. Deposits also occur elsewhere, particularly in Venezuela.

The oil sand resource of Alberta is immense. The total reserve is about 230×10^9 t of petroleum equivalent (or 1600×10^9 t barrels), but the economically recoverable stocks are 24×10^9 t (175×10^9 bbl; note that improvements in technology could increase this to as much as 42×10^9 t or 311×10^9 bbl). For comparison, Saudi Arabian reserves of conventional petroleum, the largest in the world, are about 36×10^9 t.

In 2003, the production of oil sand bitumen in Alberta was 48.1×10^3 t. About 67% of this was used to produce 26.6×10^3 t of synthetic petroleum for refining into gasoline, diesel, and other fuels. The rest was sold as bitumen for use in asphalt to build roads and to manufacture roofing products. The 2003 oil sand production was equivalent to 54% of the total petroleum output of Alberta; 39% of Canada, and 9% of North America.

Development of the oil sand resource has been proceeding quickly since the first significant activity began in the late 1960s. Investments up to 1995 totalled several billion dollars, but then accelerated so that between 1996 and 2003 a total of $28 billion was invested in new and ongoing projects. Moreover, it has been estimated that additional investments of up to $75 billion may be made between 2004 and 2013, particularly if crude-oil prices remain high. (In 1999, the value of petroleum was as low as US$12 per standard barrel, but between 2000 and 2005 it has typically been US$25–$35 and has exceeded US$70 per barrel for short periods.) Most of the frenetic oil sand development is occurring in the vicinity of Fort McMurray, which has rapidly grown from a village of several thousand people in the 1960s, to 56 000 in 2004, and a projected 75 000 in 2010.

Deposits of oil sand that occur near the surface (<75 m deep) are strip-mined using immense draglines—these huge shovels, and the trucks they load, are the largest such machines in the world. The raw oil sand is processed using heat and steam to yield a viscous bitumen (with a room-temperature consistency similar to molasses), which is then modified with light

Photo 13.3   A view of a facility in northern Alberta that processes mined oil sand into liquid bitumen.

hydrocarbon additives to reduce its viscosity so that it can flow easily and be transported in a pipeline. The typical yield from mined oil sand is about 1 t of synthetic petroleum from 15 t of raw resource. About 75–90% of the bitumen present is actually recovered; the remainder, along with massive amounts of processed sand and clay (known as tailings), is back-filled into the huge open-pit quarries. The back-filled areas are then contoured, top-dressed with previously stockpiled overburden (gravel, sand, clay, and organic muck from muskeg), and planted to restore the land-use to pasture or forest. The industry is required to rehabilitate mined sites to a level of productivity at least that of the pre-existing ecosystem. In 2003, about two-thirds of the production of oil sand bitumen was from surface mines.

The other one-third of oil sand bitumen production was from in situ ("in place") extraction of deposits occurring deeper than about 75 m. This can be done in various ways, such as injecting steam into the deposit and then pumping the liquefied bitumen to the surface for further processing. Alternative extraction methods include the passive collection of flowable bitumen from lower-viscosity deposits and the use of injected solvents.

Oil sand mining and processing are energy-intensive activities that take place in immense industrial facilities. The energy to run machinery and processing facilities is obtained by burning fossil fuels, so the industry is a major contributor to Canada's emissions of greenhouse gases. The oil sand industry has voluntarily committed to major investments in improved technology to decrease their energy use and CO_2 emissions, and to thereby contribute to Canada's goal of reducing emissions of green-

house gases (GHGs) under the Kyoto Protocol. (Canada's commitment, ratified in 2002, is to achieve a 6% reduction in national emissions of GHGs from 1990 levels by 2008–12; see Canadian Focus 17.1.) The industry's pledge is to achieve a 45% reduction in CO_2 emissions per tonne of synthetic petroleum produced by 2010, compared to 1990 levels. This is an impressive promise to achieve increased efficiency. Nevertheless, it must be borne in mind that because of huge increases in industrial capacity to mine and process oil sand since 1990, the total CO_2 emissions by this industrial sector will actually be much larger during 2008–12.

There are other important environmental effects of the mining and processing of oil sands. They include pollution of the atmosphere, groundwater, and surface water, the extensive destruction of natural habitats, and socio-economic disruptions of rural and Aboriginal communities. In the larger context, however, these important environmental damages must be viewed as an inevitable result of the enthusiasm of Canadian society, politicians, and business interests to mine, sell, and use fossil-fuel resources at rapid (and non-sustainable) rates. This is happening because of the importance of these activities to the domestic and export economies of Canada.

References and Additional Information
Alberta Energy. 2003. *Alberta's Oil Sands.*
   www.energy.gov.ab.ca/docs/oilsands/pdfs/osgenbrf.pdf
Nichols Applied Management. 2004. *Oil Sands Industry Update.* Alberta Economic Development.
   www.alberta-canada.com/oandg/pdf/oilsands_
   sept04_revised.pdf

Limestone is a rock composed of calcium carbonate. Limestone is used to manufacture cement, as well as lime for making plaster. In addition, some limestone, and the related metamorphic rock known as marble, is quarried for use as building stone and facings. About 13.0 million tonnes of cement were manufactured in Canada in 2003, with an economic value of $1.5 billion. Another 2.3 million tonnes of lime were manufactured, with a value of $221 million. Ontario, Quebec, and British Columbia have the largest cement manufacturing industries, and Ontario has the largest lime-making capacity.

Potash is a rock formed from the mineral potash feldspar, and it is mined to manufacture potassium-containing fertilizers. About 8.4 million tonnes of potash (expressed as

K_2O) were mined in Canada in 2003, with an economic value of $1.6 billion. Potash is mined in Saskatchewan and New Brunswick.

Salt, or sodium chloride, is used in the chemical manufacturing industry, for de-icing roads, as "table salt," and as a food additive and flavouring. About 12.7 million tonnes of salt were mined in Canada in 2003, with an economic value of $419 million. The largest salt mines are in Ontario, Alberta, Saskatchewan, and Nova Scotia.

Sulphur is manufactured from hydrogen sulphide obtained from sour-gas wells (i.e., gas wells rich in H_2S), from pollution-control "scrubbers" (for sulphur dioxide) at metal smelters, and from deposits of "native sulphur." Sulphur is used mostly in the chemical manufacturing industries and to make fertilizers. About 7.7 million tonnes of sulphur were produced in Canada in 2003, with an economic value of $77 million. About 90% of the sulphur production is obtained from sour-gas wells in Alberta and Saskatchewan.

Aggregates include sand, gravel, and other materials that are mined for use in road construction and as fillers for concrete in the construction industry. Aggregates are a low-grade resource, having relatively little value per tonne. Close to large cities, however, these materials may be available only in small quantities, leading to local shortages. About 238 million tonnes of sand and gravel were quarried in Canada in 2003, with an economic value of $1.05 billion. These materials are mined in all provinces and territories, at rates more or less determined by the local construction activity.

Peat, another mined commodity, is a sub-fossil material developed from dead plant biomass that is hundreds to thousands of years old. It accumulates in wetland bogs where it becomes partially decomposed (humified). Peat is sometimes dried and burned as a source of energy, an important use in Ireland, parts of northern Europe, and Russia. In Canada, however, most peat is mined for use as a horticultural material and to produce highly absorbent hygienic products such as diapers and sanitary napkins. About 1.4 million tonnes of peat were mined in Canada in 2003, with an economic value of $195 million. About 37% of peat mining occurs in Quebec, 33% in New Brunswick, and the rest in Alberta, Ontario, and other provinces.

Energy Use

Having ready access to relatively inexpensive and accessible energy is critical to any economy. The use of large quantities of energy is particularly characteristic of highly industrialized nations, such as Canada. As has been discussed previously, relatively wealthy, developed countries use much more energy (on a per capita basis) than do poorer, less developed countries.

Ever since the mastery of fire, people have used fuels for subsistence purposes, that is, to cook food and to keep warm. Initially, the fuels used for those purposes were locally collected wood and other plant biomass. When fire was first domesticated, perhaps only one million people were alive, and their per capita energy usage was small. Consequently, biomass fuels were a renewable source of energy because the rate at which they were being used was much smaller than the rate at which new biomass was being produced by vegetation.

The human population in modern times, however, is much larger than it was when fire was first put to work. Moreover, many countries now have intensely industrialized economies in which per capita energy usage is extremely high. The combination of population growth and increased per capita energy use means that enormous quantities of energy are used in these developed countries. The energy is needed to fuel industrial processes, to manufacture and run machines, to keep warm in winter and cool in summer, and to prepare food.

Most industrial energy supplies are based on the use of non-renewable resources, although some renewable sources are also important. For comprehensiveness, both non-renewable and renewable energy sources are discussed together in this section.

Sources of Energy

The world's major sources of industrial energy are fossil fuels and nuclear fuels, both of which are non-renewable. Hydroelectric power, generated using the renewable energy of flowing water, is also important in some regions, including much of Canada. Relatively minor energy sources, often called "alternative energy sources," include solar power, geothermal power, wind, waves, and biomass, all of which are potentially renewable.

All of the above sources can be used to drive a turbine, which spins an electrical generator that converts the kinetic energy of motion into electrical energy. Solar energy can also be used to generate electricity more directly, through photovoltaic technology (see below). One of the most important kinds of energy used in industrial societies, electricity is widely distributed to industries and homes through a network of transmission lines.

The following sections briefly describe how these various energy sources are used.

Fossil Fuels

Coal, petroleum, natural gas, and their various refined products can be combusted in power plants, where the potential energy of these fuels is harnessed to generate electricity. Fossil fuels are also used to power machines directly, particularly in transportation, in which gasoline, diesel, liquefied natural gas, and other "portable" fuels power automobiles, trucks, airplanes, trains, and ships. Fossil fuels are also combusted in the furnaces of many homes and larger

Photo 13.4   Electricity generated by burning coal, oil, or natural gas uses non-renewable sources of energy. This is a generating station at Shawinigan, Quebec.

buildings to provide warmth during colder times of the year. The burning of fossil fuels has many environmental drawbacks, including large emissions of greenhouse gases, sulphur dioxide, and other pollutants into the atmosphere.

Nuclear Fuels

Nuclear fuels contain unstable isotopes of the heavy elements uranium and plutonium (^{235}U and ^{239}Pu, respectively). These can decay through a process known as *fission*, which produces lighter elements while releasing two or three neutrons and enormous quantities of energy. The emitted neutrons may be absorbed by other atoms of ^{235}U or ^{239}Pu, causing them to become unstable and undergo fission themselves in a process known as a *chain reaction*. Uncontrolled chain reactions can result in a nuclear explosion. In a nuclear reactor, however, the flux of neutrons is carefully regulated, allowing electricity to be produced

safely and continuously.

Nuclear reactions are fundamentally different from conventional chemical reactions, in which atoms recombine into different compounds without changing their internal structure. In nuclear fission reactions, atomic structure is fundamentally altered, and small amounts of matter are transformed into immense quantities of energy.

Most of the energy liberated by nuclear fission is released as heat. In a nuclear power plant, some of the heat is used to boil water. The resulting steam drives a turbine, which generates electricity. Most nuclear-fuelled power plants are huge commercial reactors that produce electricity for industrial and residential use in large urban areas. Smaller reactors are sometimes used to power military ships and submarines.

^{235}Uranium is the element used in conventional nuclear reactors, such as the CANDU system developed and used in Canada (see Canadian Focus 13.1). ^{235}Uranium

Canadian Focus 13.2

The CANDU System

The Canadian system for generating electricity using controlled nuclear fission, called CANDU (CANada Deuterium Uranium), was developed by Atomic Energy of Canada Limited (AECL), a federal Crown corporation, and Ontario Hydro, a provincial utility (now Ontario Power). The CANDU reactor design uses a heavy-water technology to enable the use of natural uranium as fuel. (Heavy water contains deuterium, an isotope of hydrogen.) The heavy water moderates, or slows down to lower energy levels, the high-energy or "fast" neutrons emitted by the fissioning ^{235}U fuel. This increases the proportion of "thermal neutrons," which have a higher probability of hitting and fissioning the ^{235}U atoms than fast neutrons (^{235}U is an isotope with an atomic weight of 235), and sustains the nuclear chain reaction. Heavy water is also used as the thermal-transport fluid, which removes heat from the fuel and transfers it in a high-temperature, high-pressure condition to exchangers that produce light-water steam.

Uranium fuel for CANDU reactors—natural uranium oxide (UO_2)—is placed into 50-cm-long tubes of zirconium alloy, which are welded shut at both ends. One fuel bundle is made up of 37 of these tubes. A pressure tube contains 12 or 13 fuel bundles arranged end-to-end and surrounded by the high-pressure, heat-transporting heavy water. The combination of pressure tube, heavy-water coolant, and supports and associated fittings is called a fuel channel. There are several hundred fuel channels in the core of the reactor, along with the low-temperature, low-pressure, heavy-water moderator. The core is constructed of alloys of zirconium, which do not absorb neutrons well. The arrangement of the fuel channels and the presence of heavy water ensure optimum conditions for a controlled fission reaction. If these conditions are upset in a severe core accident, the nuclear chain reactions cease automatically, an important safety feature of the CANDU design.

Each CANDU reactor is heavily shielded with reinforced concrete about 1 m thick. The shield prevents the emission of extremely energetic gamma and neutron radiation, which would be a hazard to people working at the station. In addition, the reactor and its heavy-water transport system are encased within a massive containment building made of concrete. This outermost structure is intended to prevent any emissions of radioactivity

The CANDU System of Generating Electricity

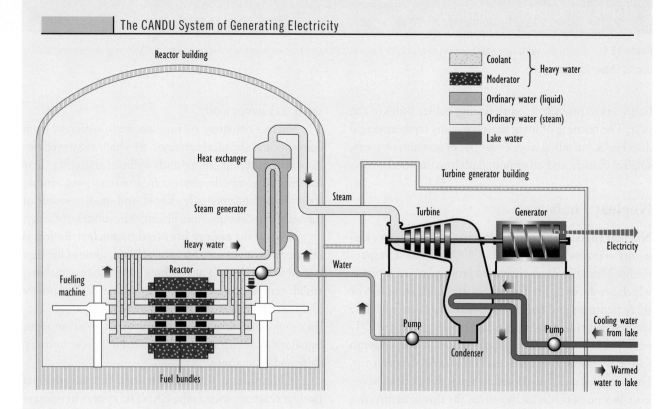

into the environment from normal operation or in the unlikely event of a reactor system failure.

The pressurized heavy-water coolant circulates through the fuel channels in a closed system, carrying thermal energy to large heat exchangers. Ordinary or "light" water is heated in the exchanger and the generated steam drives a turbine, which spins a generator that produces electricity (see Figure). The technology used to generate electricity from steam is not unique to nuclear power—essentially the same technology is used in fossil-fuelled generating stations.

A single fuel bundle in a CANDU reactor produces as much energy as about 500 t of coal or 450 000 L of petroleum. About 1600 t of uranium fuel is used annually in Canadian reactors. Canada's reactors have a total of 15 857 MW of electricity generating capacity, about 15% of the total capacity in the country (Canadian Nuclear Association, 2005). Ontario has 20 large reactors, which account for about 91% of Canada's nuclear generating capacity. Quebec and New Brunswick each have one reactor.

In the short term, the CANDU nuclear reaction is controlled by inserting or removing materials from the core (i.e., the moderator) that absorb neutrons and slow the reaction. This control process allows the operator to precisely manage the rate of the nuclear reaction and to quickly shut down the reactor if necessary.

The design of the CANDU reactors allows them to be refuelled while still operating. This feature minimizes shutdowns and contributes to the efficiency of operation. A fuel bundle stays in the core for 9 to 15 months, after which it is removed from the fuel channels by a remotely operated machine. It is then stored in a light-water pool for several years, where the residual decay heat is dissipated and emitted radiation is absorbed.

Natural uranium contains about 0.7% fissile material as ^{235}U. The remainder is ^{238}U. In a CANDU reactor, fissioning initially occurs with the ^{235}U. However, the neutron flux produced by this fissioning causes some of the ^{238}U to be transformed into ^{239}Pu (^{239}plutonium). The subsequent fissioning of the ^{239}Pu produces about 50% of the heat released by the fuel. When a CANDU fuel bundle is removed from a reactor, it still contains about 0.5% fissile material, made up of 0.25% ^{235}U and 0.25% ^{239}Pu. When sufficiently cooled, the spent fuel could theoretically be processed to reclaim the fissile material for use as fuel. However, it is not considered economical to do this, and Canadian government policy

requires the spent fuel to be stored and not reprocessed. It is possible and more realistic to reprocess spent light-water reactor fuel, which contains about 1.2% fissile material, and to use the reclaimed material as fuel in CANDU reactors. However, even this is not economical compared to the use of natural uranium fuel.

Initially, fuel bundles are highly radioactive and can be handled only remotely; however, the radioactivity decays. After about 500 years it is reduced by a factor of 20, and after 1000 years, by a factor of 100. Handling it then will be much less hazardous and storage requirements, less onerous. Together with high-level wastes from reactors that produce medical isotopes, disused nuclear research technology, and old reactor parts, the spent fuel must be stored safely for a long time. To avoid environmental damage, such high-level wastes must be permanently managed in a safe, fully-contained manner. Canada has not yet implemented a system for the long-term disposal of high-level nuclear wastes. However, a concept developed by AECL, involving deep geological disposal into 500-m-deep chambers mined into extremely stable granitic masses (known as plutons) in the Canadian Shield, has been reviewed by a federal task force and found to be technically acceptable. Although the concept has not yet received public acceptance, the intent is to proceed along the lines proposed, managed by an organization formed and funded by the nuclear utilities. The disposal site, probably to be located in northwestern Ontario, must be capable of safely containing the nuclear wastes for many thousands of years.

In recent years, problems with pressure tubes and heat exchangers have necessitated shutting down some of the CANDU reactors for repairs and rehabilitation. Such technical problems are resolvable but expensive, and they can involve some loss of confidence in the technology by the public. In addition, the management and maintenance of reactors, including training and planning, must be improved to achieve the technical performance and returns on investment inherent in the facilities. Without such attention, the safety margins for operation of CANDU reactors could decrease. Such problems are not restricted to CANDU reactors; they are also apparent in light-water reactors. These problems must be resolved if nuclear technology is to meet its economic targets as well as help in the solution to greenhouse gas emissions and atmospheric pollution from the burning of fossil fuels.

is obtained from uranium ore, which is mined in various places in the world. (Canada is a major player in uranium mining, most of which is exported; see Table 13.2.) Uranium metal produced by refining ore typically consists of about 99.3% non-fissile ^{238}U and only 0.7% ^{235}U. Most commercial reactors require a fuel that has been further refined to enrich the ^{235}U concentration to about 3%. However, the Canadian-designed CANDU reactors can use non-enriched uranium as fuel.

Various elements, most of which are also radioactive (e.g., radon gas), are produced during fission and other nuclear reactions. One of these, ^{239}plutonium (^{239}Pu), can also be used as a component of nuclear fuel in power plants. To obtain ^{239}Pu for this purpose (or for use in manufacturing nuclear weapons), spent fuel from nuclear generating stations is reprocessed. Other transuranium elements and any remaining ^{235}U (as well as non-fissile ^{238}U) can also be recovered; these can be used to manufacture new fuel for reactors. So-called "fast" breeder reactors are designed to optimize the production of ^{239}Pu (which occurs when an atom of ^{238}U absorbs a neutron to produce ^{239}U, which then forms ^{239}Pu by the emission of two beta electrons). Although fast-breeder reactors have been demonstrated, they have not been commercially developed to any great extent. Even though breeder reactors produce "new" nuclear fuel (by producing plutonium) and thereby help to optimize use of the uranium resource, there are limits to the process because the original quantity of ^{238}U is eventually depleted. Therefore, both ^{235}U and ^{239}Pu should be considered non-renewable resources.

A number of important environmental problems are associated with nuclear power. These include the small but real possibility of catastrophic accidents such as a meltdown of the reactor core, which can result in the emission of large amounts of radioactive materials into the environment (as happened at the Chernobyl reactor in Ukraine in 1986). Nuclear reactions also produce extremely toxic, long-lived radioactive byproducts (such as plutonium), which must be safely managed for very long periods of time (i.e., tens of thousands of years). Enormous quantities of these "high-level" nuclear wastes are stockpiled in Canada and in other countries that use nuclear power, but so far there are no solutions to the problem of their long-term management. Another problem is the emission of toxic radon gas and radioactivity from "low-level" wastes associated with uranium mines, structural elements of nuclear power plants, and other sources.

Another kind of energy-producing nuclear reaction is known as *fusion*. This process occurs when light nuclei are forced to combine under conditions of extremely high temperature (millions of degrees) and pressure, resulting in an enormous release of energy. Fusion usually involves the combining of hydrogen isotopes. The most common fusion reaction involves two protons (i.e., two hydrogen nuclei, ^1H) fusing to form a deuterium nucleus (composed of one proton and one neutron, ^2H), while also emitting a beta electron and an extremely large amount of energy.

Fusion reactions occur naturally in the interior of the sun and other stars and can also be initiated by exposing hydrogen to the enormous heat and pressure generated by a fission nuclear explosion, as occurs in so-called hydrogen bombs. Nuclear technologists have not, however, designed a system that can control fusion reactions to the degree necessary to generate electricity. If this technology is ever developed, it would be an enormous benefit to industrial society. Essentially unlimited supplies of hydrogen fuel for fusion reactors could be extracted from the oceans, virtually eliminating the constraints on energy use by humans. So far, however, controlled fusion reactions remain the stuff of science fiction.

Hydroelectric Energy

Hydroelectric energy involves harnessing the kinetic energy of flowing water to drive turbines that generate electricity. Because the energy of flowing water develops naturally through the hydrologic cycle, hydroelectricity can be viewed as a renewable source of energy. There are two classes of technologies for the generation of hydroelectricity:

Run-of-the-river hydroelectricity involves tapping part of the natural flow of watercourses without developing a large storage reservoir. Consequently, this electricity generation depends on the natural patterns of river flow and is highly seasonal.

Reservoir-generated hydroelectricity involves the construction of dams to store huge quantities of water. The reservoir accumulates part of the seasonal high flow of water so that generation can occur relatively continuously throughout the year. Some enormous reservoirs have been developed by flooding extensive areas of land that previously were covered by forest and wetlands—for example, in northern Quebec, Labrador, Manitoba, and British Columbia.

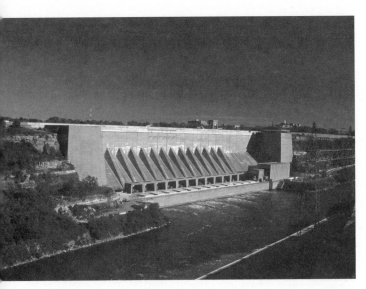

Photo 13.5 Hydroelectricity is a renewable source of energy. This facility taps part of the flow of the Niagara River to generate electricity.

Canada's largest hydroelectric stations are Churchill Falls in Labrador, with a capacity of 5429 MW; La Grande 2 in northern Quebec, with 5328 MW; G.M. Shrum in British Columbia, with 2730 MW; and La Grande 4 and 3 in Quebec, with 2651 and 2304 MW, respectively.

Although hydroelectric energy is renewable, important environmental impacts are associated with the technology. Changes in the amount and timing of water flow in rivers cause important ecological damage, as does the extensive flooding involved in the development of a reservoir (see Chapter 20).

Solar Energy

Solar energy is continuously available, although only during the day at any particular location. Solar energy can be tapped in various ways as a renewable source of energy. For example, it is stored by growing plants, the biomass of which can be harvested and combusted to release its potential energy (see Biomass Energy, below).

Solar energy can also be trapped within a glass-enclosed space. This happens because glass is transparent to visible wavelengths of sunlight, but not to most of the infrared. This allows the use of passive solar or "green-house" designs to heat buildings. Solar energy can also be captured using black, highly absorptive surfaces to heat

enclosed water, which can then be distributed through piping to warm the interior of a building.

Solar energy can also be used to generate electricity through photovoltaic technology (solar cells), which converts electromagnetic energy directly into electricity. In another technology, large, extremely reflective, parabolic mirrors are used to focus sunlight onto a small, enclosed space containing water or some other fluid, which becomes heated and generates steam, driving a turbine to generate electricity.

Geothermal Energy

Geothermal energy can be tapped in the few places where magma from Earth's mantle occurs relatively close to the surface and heats water. Boiling-hot water can be piped to the surface, where its heat content can be used to warm buildings or generate electricity. The energy of less-hot water can be utilized by heat-pump technology, mostly for space heating or to provide warm water for a manufacturing process. Geothermal energy can be a renewable source as long as the supply of groundwater available to be geothermally heated is not depleted.

Wind Energy

Wind energy, the kinetic energy of moving air masses, can be tapped and used in various ways. Sailboats use wind energy to travel through the water, and windmills can be designed to lift water in wells or to generate electricity. Extensive wind farms, consisting of arrays of highly efficient wind-driven turbines, have been constructed to generate electricity in a few consistently windy places—for example, in northern California, in southeastern Quebec, in southeastern Alberta, and in Nova Scotia. In 2004, Canada had 552 MW of installed wind-power capacity, and this is expected to increase to 4000 MW by 2010 (Natural Resources Canada, 2005).

Tidal Energy

Tidal cycles develop because of the gravitational attraction between the Earth and the Moon. In a few coastal places, **tidal energy**, the kinetic energy of tidal flows, can be harnessed to drive turbines and generate electricity. The Bay of Fundy in eastern Canada has enormous tides, which can exceed 16 m at the head of the bay. A medium-scale (20 MW), tidal-power facility has been developed at

Photo 13.6 Wind is increasingly being used as a source of commercial energy in Canada. This windmill is operating in southwestern Nova Scotia.

Annapolis Royal in Nova Scotia. There is potential for much more tidal power development within the Bay of Fundy, although the technological challenges are great. Also, the construction and operation of the required dams would cause enormous environmental damage.

Wave Energy

Waves on the ocean surface are another manifestation of kinetic energy. **Wave energy** can be harnessed using specially designed buoys that generate electricity as they bob up and down, although this has not yet been done commercially.

Biomass Energy

The biomass of trees and other plants contains chemical potential energy. This **biomass energy** is actually solar energy that has been fixed through photosynthesis. Peat, mined from bogs, is a kind of sub-fossil biomass.

Like hydrocarbon fuels, biomass can be combusted to provide thermal energy for industrial purposes and to heat homes and other buildings. Biomass can also be combusted in industrial-scale generating stations, usually to generate steam, which may be used to drive a turbine that generates electricity. Biomass can also be used to manufacture methanol, which can be used as a liquid fuel in vehicles and for other purposes.

If the ecosystems from which biomass is harvested are managed to allow post-harvest regeneration of the vegetation, this source of energy can be considered a renewable resource. Peat, however, is always mined faster than the slow rate at which it accumulates in bogs and other wetlands, so it is not a renewable source of biomass energy.

Energy Consumption

Energy consumption varies greatly among the world's countries, largely depending on differences in their populations and degree of development and industrialization (Table 13.8 and Appendix C). In general, per capita rates of energy consumption in less developed countries are less than about 20 gigajoules per person per year (i.e., 20×10^9 J/person-year). Most energy consumption in the least developed countries involves "traditional" fuels, such as wood, charcoal, dried animal manure, or food-processing residues such as coconut shells or bagasse (a residue of sugarcane pressing).

Countries that are developing rapidly are intermediate in their per capita energy consumption. Their rates of energy use are, however, increasing rapidly due to their accelerating industrialization. In Malaysia, for example, the national consumption of energy increased by 130% between 1990 and 2001, while in South Korea it increased by 104%; in Thailand, by 75%; in Indonesia, by 64%; in India, by 46%; and in Brazil, by 31%. While the use of energy has grown in these countries, reliance on traditional fuels has dropped. This happens because traditional fuels are relatively bulky, smoky, and less convenient to use than electricity or hydrocarbon fuels, particularly in the urban environments where people are living in increasingly large numbers. In addition, supplies of wood, charcoal, and other traditional fuels have become severely depleted in most rapidly developing countries, particularly near urban regions and other densely populated areas.

Relatively industrialized countries have very high per capita consumptions of energy (see Table 13.8). Their energy use is typically more than about 150 GJ/person-y and almost entirely involves "commercial" sources such as electricity and hydrocarbon fuels. The world's most energy-intensive economies are those of Canada and the U.S.

In terms of the total amounts, the world's largest consumers of energy are the U.S., China, and Russia, using 95×10^{18} J, 46×10^{18} J, and 25×10^{18} J, respectively (in 2001). Canada is also a highly industrialized country, but

TABLE 13.8	Energy Consumption in Selected Countries, 2001

"Commercial energy" includes hydrocarbon fuels and the electricity produced by public and/or private utilities and in large industrial facilities. National energy consumption reflects the size of a country's economy and its population, while per capita data allow a comparison of the lifestyles of average citizens; percentage renewable refers to the energy consumption derived from renewable sources. Countries are arranged within groups in order of total per capita energy use. See Appendix C, Table 4 for additional country data of this type.

COUNTRY	TOTAL ENERGY USE		USE OF COMMERCIAL ENERGY		PERCENTAGE RENEWABLE
	NATIONAL (10^{18} joule)	PER CAPITA (10^9 J)	NATIONAL (10^{18} J)	PER CAPITA (10^9 J)	
RELATIVELY UNDEVELOPED COUNTRIES					
Afghanistan	0.08	4	0.02	1	75
Tanzania	0.63	18	0.04	1	95
RAPIDLY DEVELOPING COUNTRIES					
China	45.6	36	36.7	28	21
Brazil	7.5	45	5.6	31	38
DEVELOPED COUNTRIES					
Japan	22.0	170	21.6	166	3
Canada	*10.1*	*332*	*9.8*	*305*	*17*
United States	95.0	339	90.9	309	5

Source: Data from World Resources Institute (2005)

because of its relatively small population and moderate-sized economy, it uses much less energy in total—about 10×10^{18} J. However, if calculated on a per capita basis, Canadians and Americans are the world's most intensive consumers of energy (332 GJ/person-y and 339 GJ/person-y in 2001, respectively). This is more than 30 times the per capita usage by people living in the world's least developed economies. Also, about 99% of Canada's total energy consumption comes from commercial sources, such as electricity and fossil fuels.

Canada's energy consumption increased by 330% between 1958 and 1997, and by 19% between 1990 and 2001, while per capita consumption increased by 91% and 6% during the same periods, respectively (Table 13.9). Because per capita energy consumption increased much less quickly than national usage, the data suggest that Canadians became somewhat more efficient in their use of energy during those times. More small automobiles, improved gas economy of vehicles, better insulation of residences and commercial buildings, and the use of more efficient industrial processes have all contributed to this increased efficiency. Although substantial, these gains in efficiency have been more than offset by growth in the per capita ownership and use of automobiles, consumer electronics, and other energy-demanding products and technologies.

The intensive energy usage by Canadians reflects the high degree of industrialization of their national economy. Also significant is the relative affluence of average Canadians (compared to the global average). Wealth allows people to lead a relatively luxurious lifestyle, with ready access to energy-consuming amenities such as automobiles, home appliances, space heating, and air conditioning. Canada is also a large country, so energy expenditures for travel are relatively high. In addition, Canada's cold climate means that people use a great deal of energy to keep warm.

TABLE 13.9	Recent Trends in Consumption of Commercial Energy in Canada

YEAR	NATIONAL CONSUMPTION (10^{15} joules)	PER CAPITA CONSUMPTION (10^9 J)
1960	3 134	175
1970	5 545	260
1980	7 929	322
1990	8 738	314
2001	10 124	332

Sources: Data from Statistics Canada (1994b) and World Resources Institute (2005)

TABLE 13.10	Energy Consumption in Selected Industrialized Countries, 2001

Data are in units of 10^6 tonnes of oil equivalent (1 toe = 41.9×10^9 J).

COUNTRY	TOTAL CONSUMPTION	COAL	PETROLEUM	GAS	GEOTHERMAL AND WIND	HYDRO	NUCLEAR	BIOMASS
Sweden	51	2.8	14.1	0.8	0.1	6.8	18.8	7.6
Belgium	59	7.7	24.3	13.2	<0.1	0.1	12.1	0.4
Netherlands	77	8.3	1.4	35.5	0.1	<0.1	1.0	0.5
Australia	116	55.4	33.2	20.3	0.1	1.4	0.0	4.8
Spain	127	18.7	67.1	16.4	0.7	3.5	16.6	3.7
Italy	172	13.4	86.5	58.1	3.4	4.0	0.0	1.7
United Kingdom	235	39.8	81.5	86.8	0.1	0.4	23.5	0.9
Canada	248	30.7	88.8	71.5	0.1	28.6	20.0	10.5
France	266	12.7	93.8	36.7	0.2	6.4	109.7	9.6
Germany	351	85.1	134.5	75.6	1.1	1.8	44.6	4.6
Japan	521	100.2	256.1	64.8	3.8	7.2	83.4	3.8
India	532	179	112	23.2	0.2	6.4	5.0	205
Russia	621	106.6	133.0	325.2	0.1	15.0	36.1	3.8
China	1 139	637	227	31.4	<0.1	23.9	4.6	215
United States	2 281	544.7	903.7	517.4	14.8	17.3	210.6	52.9
WORLD	10 029	2 341	3 507	2 122	50.6	222	692	1 046
Average distribution	100%	20.0%	37.4%	25.8%	0.5%	1.8%	11.2%	2.0%

Source: Data from World Resources Institute (2005)

Energy Production

As was discussed in Chapter 12, truly sustainable enterprises are not supported mostly by the mining of non-renewable sources of energy or other resources. Therefore, a sustainable economy must be based on the use of renewable sources of energy.

However, most energy production in industrialized countries is based on non-renewable sources. Averaged across the 13 developed countries shown in Table 13.10, natural gas accounts for 26% of energy consumption; coal, for 20%; petroleum, for 37%; and nuclear reactors, for 11%. In total, these and other non-renewable sources of energy account for 96% of the total use of energy in those countries. Renewable sources, such as hydroelectric, geothermal, and wind power, account for only about 4%. These are sobering data. Considering the rapid rate at which reserves of non-renewable energy resources are being depleted by mining and use, one wonders how long the energy-intensive economies of developed nations can be maintained.

Of Canada's consumption of energy, 29% comes from natural gas; 36%, from petroleum; 12%, from coal; and 8%, from nuclear energy. These non-renewable energy sources account for 85% of the total energy use in Canada. Most of the remaining production comes from hydro-electricity (11%), which is renewable (although it can cause substantial environmental damage through flooding to create reservoirs, and can require large quantities of non-renewable resources for the construction of dams, transmission lines, and related infrastructure; see Chapter 20). Another 4% involves the use of biomass as energy. There are also, of course, environmental impacts of the harvesting of trees and other kinds of biomass for use as fuel (see Chapter 23).

Electricity produced by public or private utilities accounts for much of the energy used by industry, institutions, and residences in Canada. About 59% of the 561×10^6 MW-hr of electricity produced in Canada in 2003 was generated from hydroelectric sources; 28%, from fossil fuels; and 13%, by nuclear technology (Statistics Canada, 2005).

Conclusions

Non-renewable resources are inexorably diminished as they are used. Although non-renewables can be used with great enthusiasm to achieve economic growth, they cannot be the basis of a sustainable economy. Only renewable resources can play that fundamental role. In this chapter we learned that the non-renewable resources that are key to the functioning of modern "advanced" economies, such as that of Canada, are being rapidly depleted. For instance, the life index of the global reserves of copper is only about 34 years, while that of lead is 24 years, and zinc, 29 years. Among fossil fuels, the life index of petroleum's global reserves is about 41 years, while that of natural gas is 67 years, and coal, 164 years. While it is true that continuing exploration will find additional reserves of these and other non-renewable resources, there are limits to further discoveries. In addition, about 85% of energy consumption in Canada is based on non-renewable sources, as is 41% of electricity generation. Reserves of all non-renewable resources are being depleted rapidly, both in Canada and around the world. Consequently, the long-term sustainability of the energy-intensive economies of developed countries, such as Canada, and the lifestyles of their citizens, is highly doubtful.

Key Terms

non-renewable resource

reserve

recycling

metal

life index

fossil fuel

coal

petroleum (crude oil)

natural gas

nuclear fuel

hydroelectric energy

solar energy

geothermal energy

wind energy

tidal energy

wave energy

biomass energy

Questions for Review

1. Describe the Canadian and global production and use of non-renewable resources using information from this chapter.

2. Show how industrialized countries rely mostly on non-renewable resources to sustain their economies. Will this kind of resource use be able to continue for very long? Why or why not?

3. What are the various non-renewable and renewable sources of energy available for use in industrialized countries? What are the future prospects for increasing the use of renewable sources?

4. What are the key sources of energy and materials that are ultimately based on sunlight? Which of these resources would you consider to be renewable, and which not?

Questions for Discussion

1. Outline the ways in which you use energy, both directly and indirectly. For each of your major uses, how could you decrease your energy consumption? How would a decrease in your energy consumption affect your lifestyle?

2. What are the apparent barriers to the widespread adoption of renewable sources of materials and energy in advanced economies (such as Canada)?

3. What are the roles of non-renewable and renewable resources in a sustainable economy?

4. Biomass, wind, and hydroelectricity are all examples of potentially renewable sources of energy. Examine the energy-source distributions for several countries in Table 13.10 and discuss why they are apparently not relying more on renewable sources of energy production.

5. Make lists of the apparent "benefits" and "risks" associated with nuclear power. Focus on resource and environmental issues, such as the depletion of fossil fuels, emissions of greenhouse gases, and the long-term disposal of toxic and hazardous wastes.

Exploring Issues

1. A committee of the House of Commons is examining the sustainability of the Canadian economy. You are an environmental scientist, and the committee has asked you to advise them on improving the sustainability of the use of materials and energy. What would you tell them about the sustainability of present use in Canada? What improvements would you recommend?

References

British Petroleum. 2005. *Statistical Review of World Energy, 2004.* www.bp.com/genericssection.do?categoryId=93&content Id=7005893

Canadian Nuclear Association. 2005. Nuclear Energy. www.cna.ca/english/Nuclear_Facts/Clean_Electricity_ August_8x11.pdf

Chiras, D.D., J.P. Reganold, and O.S. Owen. 2001. *Natural Resource Conservation: Management for a Sustainable Future.* 8th ed. Upper Saddle River, NJ: Prentice Hall.

Craig, J.R., D.J. Vaughan, B.J. Skinner, and D. Vaughan. 2001. *Resources of the Earth: Origin, Use, and Environmental Impact.* 3rd ed. Upper Saddle River, NJ: Prentice Hall.

Ehrlich, P.R., A.H. Ehrlich, and J.P. Holdren. 1977. *Ecoscience: Population, Resources, Environment.* San Francisco: W.H. Freeman.

Freedman, B. 1995. *Environmental Ecology*, 2nd ed. San Diego: Academic.

Holechek, J.L., R.A. Cole, J.T. Fisher, and R. Valdez. 2002. *Natural Resources: Ecology, Economics, and Policy*. 2nd ed. East Rutherford, NJ: Prentice Hall.

Kesler, S.E. 1994. *Mineral Resources, Economics, and Environment*. New York: Macmillan.

Miller, G.T. 1990. *Resource Conservation and Management*. Belmont, CA: Wadsworth.

Mitchell, B. (ed.). 1991. *Resource Management and Development*. Toronto: University of Toronto Press.

Natural Resources Canada. 2004a. *Canadian Minerals Yearbook 2003*. Ottawa: NRC.

Natural Resources Canada. 2004b. *Mineral Production of Canada, by Province and Territory*. Ottawa: NRC. http://mmsd1.mms.nrcan.gc.ca/mmsd/production/production_e.asp

Natural Resources Canada. 2005. *Canada's Wind Power Capacity*. Ottawa: NRC. http://www.nrcan-rncan.gc.ca/media/newsreleases/2005/200512_e.htm

Priest, J. 1991. *Energy*. New York: Addison-Wesley.

Ripley, E.A., R.E. Redmann, and A.A. Crowder. 1996. *Environmental Effects of Mining*. Delray Beach, FL: St. Lucie.

Robertson, J.A.L. 1988. Nuclear energy and nuclear power plants. In: *The Canadian Encyclopedia*, 2nd ed. Edmonton: Hurtig. pp. 1543–46.

Statistics Canada. 1994. *Human Activity and the Environment 1994*. Ottawa: Statistics Canada.

Statistics Canada. 2000. *Human Activity and the Environment*. Environment and Statistical Division, System of National Accounts. Ottawa: Statistics Canada.

Statistics Canada. 2002. *Geography*. www.statcan.ca/english/Pgdb/geogra.htm

Statistics Canada. 2004. Tables 126-0001, 131-0001, and 303-0016—Supply and disposition of crude oil and natural gas and coal and coke statistics. http://estat.statcan.ca/cgi-win/CNSMCGI.EXE?CANSIM2=1&DrillIndex=1741&SDDSLOC=//www.statcan.ca/english/sdds/*.htm&ROOTDIR=ESTAT/&C2DB=EST&DrillAction=0&Lang=E&ESTATTEMPLATE=ESTAT/CII_FLST

Statistics Canada. 2005a. *Gross Domestic Product at Basic Prices, Primary Industries*. Ottawa: Statistics Canada.

Statistics Canada. 2005b. Table 128-0002—Supply and demand of primary and secondary energy; Table 127-0001—Electric power statistics. http://cansim2.statcan.ca/cgi-win/cnsmcgi.exe?Lang=E&RootDir=CII/&ResultTemplate=CII/CII_pick&Array_Pick=1&ArrayId=1280002

Tietenberg, T. 2002. *Environmental and Natural Resource Economics*. 6th ed. Boston, MS: Addison Wesley.

United States Geological Service. 2005. *Mineral Commodity Summaries 2004*. http://minerals.er.usgs.gov/minerals/pubs/mcs/2004/mcs2004.pdf

World Resources Institute (WRI). 1996. *World Resources 1996–97: A Guide to the Global Environment: The Urban Environment*. New York: Oxford University Press.

World Resources Institute. 2005. *Earth Trends. The Environmental Information Portal*. Washington, DC: WRI.

Informative Websites

American Petroleum Institute. http://api-ec.api.org/newsplashpage/index.cfm

Greenhouse emissions, OPEC, heating oil, and energy bills are all hot topics at this searchable website.

Atomic Energy of Canada Ltd. www.aecl.ca/

If you have questions about the CANDU nuclear reactor or nuclear energy in general this site is for you. A glossary, some statistics, and a list of environmental effects are available here.

British Petroleum. Statistical Review of World Energy 2005. http://www.bp.com/subsection.do?categoryId=95&contentId=2006480

This website of British Petroleum is an excellent source of information about energy production, consumption, and reserves.

Energy. www.enviroliteracy.org/category.php/4.html

This site from the Environmental Literacy Council covers sources of energy, including fossil fuels, nuclear, renewable, cogeneration, and hydrogen.

Environmental Literacy Council. www.enviroliteracy.org/

This organization provides a rich array of materials about natural resources.

Energy Information Administration. http://eia.doe.gov/

An assessment of international energy markets with projections of worldwide energy consumption by fuel type and carbon emissions by region to the year 2020 exists at this site, as well as information on natural gas, coal, nuclear energy, and electricity.

EPRI (Electric Power Research Institute). www.epri.com/

The EPRI offers help in solving energy questions. The environment, power generation, nuclear power, and transmission systems are some of the areas where the EPRI provides expertise.

International Atomic Energy Agency. www.iaea.org/worldatom/

The IAEA is the world's central intergovernmental forum for scientific and technical cooperation in the nuclear field. Safety of nuclear energy production and waste disposal is emphasized.

International Institute for Sustainable Development (IISD). www.iisd.org/

The IISD is a Canadian-centred international organization whose mission is to champion innovation, enabling societies to live sustainably.

Natural Resources Canada. Office of Energy Efficiency. http://oee.nrcan.gc.ca/english/

A division of Natural Resources Canada, the Office of Energy Efficiency suggests how to save energy at home, at work, and on the road.

U.S. Department of Energy. Energy Efficiency and Renewable Energy. www.eere.energy.gov/

The U.S. Department of Energy provides information on many energy issues.

Worldwatch Institute. www.worldwatch.org/

This international organization provides useful information on a wide range of topics, including the depletion of non-renewable resources.

World Resources Institute (WRI). EarthTrends. The Environmental Information Portal. http://earthtrends. wri.org/

The WRI is a leading environmental organization that provides excellent information about resource issues.

14 Renewable Resources

Introduction

Renewable resources are capable of regenerating after harvesting, so their use can potentially be sustained forever. For this to happen, however, the rate of usage must be equal to or less than the rate of regeneration; otherwise, (potentially) renewable resources are "mined"—that is, they are used as if they were non-renewable resources.

The most important classes of renewable resources are surface water and groundwater, agricultural site capability, forests, and hunted animals such as fish, deer, and waterfowl. In the following sections we examine the use and abuse of these potentially renewable resources. (Renewable sources of energy—for example, hydro, solar power, wind, and biomass—were described in Chapter 13.)

Fresh Waters

Surface Waters

Surface waters comprise lakes, ponds, streams, and rivers. They can be used as sources of drinking water, for irrigation, to generate hydroelectricity, for industrial purposes such as cooling, and for recreation. Surface waters are abundant in regions with a climate characterized by more precipitation than evapotranspiration, allowing the resource to be recharged (see Chapter 3). In drier regions, surface waters may be uncommon or rare, which can present a natural constraint on ecological and economic development.

In regions with a low rate of recharge, the excessive use of surface waters for irrigation or industrial or municipal requirements (e.g., drinking, washing, and toilet flushing) can greatly deplete the quantity of the resource. Shortages of surface waters in arid places can lead to conflicts between local areas, and even between countries. Each region wants as much water as possible to conduct its agricultural and industrial activities and to service its urban areas. Severe competition for surface water is a chronic problem in some parts of the world, particularly the Middle East, much of Africa, and parts of southwestern North America.

For example, in the Middle East, the watershed of the Jordan River is shared by Israel, Jordan, Lebanon, and Syria. All of these countries have a semiarid climate, and all demand a share of the critical water resource. Also in the Middle East, the watersheds of the Tigris and Euphrates Rivers originate in Turkey, while Iraq and, to a lesser degree, Syria are highly dependent *downstream* users that are threatened by hydroelectric and other diversion schemes in Turkey. In northern Africa, the watershed of the Nile River encompasses territory in nine countries: Egypt, Ethiopia, Sudan, Rwanda, Burundi, Democratic Republic of Congo, Tanzania, Kenya, and Uganda.

In North America, contentious water use conflicts involve the Colorado River and the Rio Grande, which are shared by the U.S. and Mexico. Use of water from these rivers is extremely intensive, particularly for irrigated agriculture. In fact, virtually all the flow of the Colorado River can potentially be used in the U.S. before it even reaches northern Mexico, where there is also significant demand. In addition, water quality is degraded by inputs of dissolved salts from agricultural use in the U.S., a factor that severely reduces the potential use of any remaining river-water flow in Mexico. Because this binational problem is important, the two federal governments have negotiated a treaty that guarantees a minimum flow quantity and water quality where the Colorado River crosses the international boundary. The Rio Grande has a similar problem, which has likewise been dealt with by a treaty between the two countries.

Even where surface waters are relatively abundant, their quality can be degraded by pollution. They can be contaminated by nutrients, hydrocarbons, pesticides, metals, or oxygen-consuming organic matter. Excessive nutrients can increase the productivity of surface waters, causing a problem known as *eutrophication* (see Chapter 20). Biological contamination by bacteria, viruses, and parasites from fecal matter of humans, pets, or livestock can render the water unfit for drinking or even for recreation. Thermal pollution, due to the release of excess heat from power plants or factories, can also cause ecological damage in receiving waterbodies.

Groundwater

Groundwater consists of underground reservoirs of water. Groundwater resources are known as **aquifers**, and they occur in the interstitial spaces and cracks of overburden and porous bedrock, such as sandstone, limestone, and other rocks. Groundwater can be an extremely valuable natural resource, especially in regions where lakes and rivers are not abundant. It is typically accessed by drilling and pumping to the surface.

Groundwater stores are recharged through the hydrologic cycle. This happens as water from precipitation slowly percolates downward through surface overburden and bedrock in a sometimes extensive area known as a recharge zone. In humid regions, where the quantity of precipitation is larger than the amounts of water dissipated by evapotranspiration and surface flows, the excess serves to recharge groundwater. Such rapidly recharging aquifers can sustain a high rate of groundwater pumping and can be managed as a renewable resource.

In drier environments, however, the quantity of precipitation available to recharge groundwater is much smaller. Aquifers that recharge extremely slowly are essentially filled with old, "fossil" water that has accumulated over thousands of years or more. These aquifers have little capability of recharging if their groundwater is used rapidly, so their stores are easily depleted. Slowly recharging aquifers are essentially non-renewable resources, whose reserves are mined by excessive use.

The world's largest aquifer, known as the Ogalalla, occurs beneath about 572 000 km^2 of arid land in the southwestern United States. The Ogalalla aquifer is recharged very slowly by underground seepage that originates from precipitation falling on distant mountains. Most of the groundwater in the Ogalalla is fossil water, accumulated during tens of thousands of years of slow infiltration. Although the Ogalalla aquifer is enormous (containing about 2.5 billion litres), it is being depleted rapidly by pumping at more than 150 000 drilled wells. Most wells withdraw water for irrigation and a few, for drinking and other household purposes. The level of the Ogalalla aquifer is decreasing by as much as 1 m/y in zones of intensive use, while the annual recharge rate is only about 1 mm/y. Clearly, the Ogalalla aquifer is being rapidly mined. Once it is effectively drained—as is likely to occur within several decades—irrigated agriculture in much of the southwestern U.S. may fail.

Groundwater resources are also threatened by pollution when chemicals are accidentally or deliberately discarded into the ground. For instance, groundwater may be polluted by gasoline leaking from underground storage tanks at service stations, degraded by agricultural fertilizer and pesticides, and contaminated by bacteria and nutrients seeping from septic fields. Badly contaminated groundwater may not be usable as a source of drinking water, and may not even be suitable for irrigation of crops.

Groundwater can also be degraded through intrusions of salt water, which can render the resource unfit for drinking or irrigation. In areas close to an ocean, deeper saline groundwater is overlain by a surficial layer of fresh water (which is less dense than salt water and therefore "floats" above it). If fresh groundwater is withdrawn at a rate faster than the recharge capability of the aquifer, the deeper salt water will rise. Once this happens, it is extremely difficult to displace the salt water, and the ability of the aquifer to supply fresh water is destroyed.

Use of Water Resources

Water Supply

The regions of the world with the smallest per capita water resources are Asia, Africa, and Europe—a pattern that reflects the high population densities of those continents (Table 14.1). In general, Canada has abundant supplies of both surface water and groundwater. Water is scarce only in relatively arid regions of the country, such as southern parts of the Prairie Provinces and southeastern British

| TABLE 14.1 | Water Availability and Use in Major Regions of the World |

The per capita resources are standardized to 2000 populations. The number in parentheses following total annual use refers to the percentage of the total resource that is used annually.

REGION	RENEWABLE RESOURCE (2004)		ANNUAL USE (2000)		SECTORAL USE (%)		
	TOTAL (10^3 kilometre^3)	PER CAPITA (10^3 metre^3)	TOTAL (km^3/y)	PER CAPITA (10^3 m^3/y)	DOMESTIC	INDUSTRY	AGRICULTURE
Asia	13.5	4.1	2148 (16)	0.63	7	12	81
South America	12.0	47.0	164 (1)	0.47	19	13	68
North America	6.7	20.0	525 (8)	1.66	14	48	38
Africa	4.1	6.3	438 (11)	0.31	9	3	88
Europe	6.6	10.7	400 (6)	0.58	15	52	33
Oceania	2.4	54.6	26 (1)	0.90	18	10	72
World	42.7	8.5	3802 (9)	0.63	10	20	70

Source: Data from World Resources Institute (2005)

Columbia. There, the shortage of water for irrigation is a constraint on agricultural development, a problem that may intensify in the future.

Groundwater is an important resource in some regions of Canada, particularly where surface water is not abundant or its chemical quality is poor. Often, groundwater is naturally cleaner than surface water and is therefore better suited for many purposes, especially household use. Sometimes, however, groundwater quality is impaired through naturally high concentrations of calcium, iron, and other chemicals.

Water Use

North America has the world's highest per capita water usage, mostly to meet the demands for irrigation and industry. The world's least developed regions have the smallest per capita water usage, as is seen in most countries of Africa, South America, and Asia (see Table 14.1).

National patterns of water use are influenced by the degree of economic development, the population size, and the humidity of the climate (Table 14.2). Among the arid, less developed nations, several depend on irrigation for much of their agricultural production. Their per capita water use is relatively heavy, with agriculture accounting for more than 85% of the total. Other relatively poor, arid countries, such as Ethiopia, Kenya, Somalia, and Tanzania, would benefit greatly from having more irrigated agriculture. However, these countries do not have access to sufficient water for this kind of management, so per capita water use, while largely agricultural, remains small.

The patterns of water use in humid, less developed countries are also complex. Some countries, such as those in southeast Asia, cultivate rice extensively in irrigated fields, so their water use is relatively high. Other countries do not grow paddy rice or other irrigated crops, so their per capita water use is less, although most of their national water use still goes to agriculture. For example, Haiti would benefit from more extensive development of irrigated agriculture. Unfortunately, Haiti is too impoverished to invest in the infrastructure needed for irrigation.

Some developed countries have rather high per capita water use. Canada and the U.S., for example, use much of their surface water for generating hydroelectricity. In addition, the western U.S. has invested heavily in irrigated agriculture (see Table 14.2 and Appendix C, Table 5).

Canadians use about 5.4 billion m^3/y of water from both surface water and groundwater sources. Only about 4% of that total water usage is groundwater. However, about

11% of the total water used by municipalities is derived from groundwater, and overall, about 30% of Canadians rely on groundwater for domestic use (Table 14.3).

Water is used for myriad purposes in Canada, by all individuals as well as municipal, institutional, and industrial users. Averaged across the country, about 64% of the total water use is to cool thermal electric plants (these are fuelled by either fossil fuels or nuclear power); 14%, for manufacturing purposes; 10%, in municipalities (including urban residential use); 9%, in agriculture (mostly for irrigation); 2%, for rural households and businesses; and 1%, in the mining industry (Table 14.4). Within the home, about 35% of the total water use is typically for showers and baths; 30%, to flush toilets; 20%, to do laundry; 10%, for drinking; and 5%, for cleaning (Environment Canada, 2005). As was noted earlier, the water returned to the environment after these various uses is typically severely degraded in quality.

On average, 12% of the water used is *consumed* during the process—that is, it evaporates into the atmosphere so that the discharge of used water is smaller than the quantity initially withdrawn. This is particularly true of heavy agricultural use, in which much of the applied water evaporates. This is a reason why about 58% of the water used in the Prairie Provinces is consumed during the process (see Table 14.4). In comparison, only about 2% of the water used in Ontario is consumed during the process; most of the rest is for flow-through cooling in industry.

TABLE 14.2	Water Use in Selected Countries (2000)		

See Appendix C, Table 5 for additional country data of this type.

COUNTRY	PER CAPITA USE (m^3/year)	SECTORAL USE (%)		
		DOMESTIC	INDUSTRY	AGRICULTURE
ARID, LESS DEVELOPED COUNTRIES				
Tanzania	57	6	1	93
India	535	8	4	86
Pakistan	1187	2	2	96
HUMID, LESS DEVELOPED COUNTRIES				
Indonesia	391	8	1	91
Mexico	791	17	6	77
DEVELOPED COUNTRIES				
Japan	696	20	18	62
Canada	*1494*	*20*	*68*	*12*
United States	1682	13	46	41

Source: Data from World Resources Institute (2005)

TABLE 14.3	Use of Water for Municipal Purposes in Canada, 2001	
	PERCENTAGE OF FLOW FROM GROUNDWATER (%)	AVERAGE MUNICIPAL USE (L/PERSON.DAY)
British Columbia	15	651
Alberta	6	519
Saskatchewan	12	517
Manitoba	18	410
Ontario	12	533
Quebec	7	777
New Brunswick	20	1314
Prince Edward Island	100	529
Nova Scotia	9	667
Newfoundland & Labrador	5	971
Yukon	31	803
Northwest Territories	0	424
Nunavut	0	105
CANADA	11	622

Source: Environment Canada (2004, 2005b)

Canada manages the flow of tremendous quantities of surface water using dams and reservoirs. This is done to control flooding, to accumulate water for irrigation, to develop municipal reservoirs, and to generate hydroelectricity. Canada has about 650 large dams, of which 86% are used to provide hydroelectricity; 9%, for irrigation; and 7%, for storing municipal water (Table 14.5).

An important use of groundwater in Canada is as a source of domestic water in rural areas. Many rural homeowners tap into the resource using drilled wells or shallow dug wells. About 82% of rural domestic water use in Canada comes from groundwater accessed through wells. Groundwater is also an important source of irrigation water in some areas and is sometimes used for industrial purposes.

Agricultural Resources

The total production of an agricultural crop is related to several factors, including the amount of land under cultivation and the productivity of the crop. Productivity is related to the management system and an important quality of the land known as *site capability*. (Recall that, in Chapter 4, ecological **production** was defined as the total yield of biomass, while **productivity** is standardized per unit area and unit time. For example, the global *production* of a crop such as wheat is measured in millions of tonnes, while the average *productivity* of a wheat field is expressed as tonnes per hectare per year.)

Ultimately, the agricultural land in any region, and on Earth, is a limited resource with a constrained area. To some degree, the area of land suitable for cultivating crops can be increased by clearing forest and grassland growing on fertile sites and by draining certain kinds of wetlands. There are, however, finite areas of natural ecosystems suitable for *conversion* into arable land. Only about 30% of Earth's surface is terrestrial, and most of that land is too

TABLE 14.4	Use of Surface Water in Regions of Canada, 1996						

Data on the use of surface waters for hydroelectricity are not included. Data are in 10^6 m³/y; information for B.C. incorporates the Yukon, Northwest Territories, and Nunavut.

SECTOR	ATLANTIC PROVINCES	QUEBEC	ONTARIO	PRAIRIE PROVINCES	BRITISH COLUMBIA	CANADA	% OF TOTAL
Agriculture	14	103	173	3030	778	4098	9
Mining	206	38	56	61	158	519	1
Manufacturing	480	1173	3011	368	1008	6040	14
Thermal cooling	2372	809	23228	2337	4	28 750	64
Municipal	285	1351	1496	534	668	4334	10
Rural	134	278	291	141	135	979	2
Total	3491	3752	28 225	6471	2751	44 720	100
% increase 1981–96	+11%	−10	+35	+17	−38	+21	
Consumption as % of withdrawal	3.7	8.5	1.8	58.4	26.7	11.9	

Source: Data from Statistics Canada (2005)

Canadian Focus 14.1

The Walkerton Tragedy

In 2000, the town of Walkerton in southern Ontario suffered a widespread outbreak of water-borne disease caused by contamination of the town's improperly treated water-supply system. After using tap water, hundreds of people suffered the debilitating symptoms of poisoning by toxic *E. coli* bacteria, and seven people died.

Like many towns and cities, Walkerton supplies its citizens with drinking water using a system of drilled wells. Unfortunately, *E. coli* polluted the groundwater in one of the wellfields. This was likely caused by livestock manure that had been spread on the surface of nearby agricultural fields. This practice is commonly used to discard the enormous amounts of fecal waste generated by livestock in Canada.

A subsequent inquiry discovered an astonishing combination of irresponsibility and incompetence on the part of town officials. Initially, the bacterial pollution was not detected by water-quality monitoring and, when it was discovered, sensible and effective action was not immediately taken to deal with the problem. According to the local Medical Officer of Health, officials in the Walkerton Public Utilities Commission knew about the

E. coli pollution for several days before they informed the public. Meanwhile, people continued to drink the water, so that hundreds became ill and seven eventually died from bacterial poisoning.

A study released in 2001 reported that the Walkerton tragedy caused direct economic damage of about $6.9 million to the citizens and businesses of the town and decreased property values by $1.1 million. Additional economic costs included more than $9 million to fix the water system and $3.5 million spent on legal fees by the Government of Ontario. However, if the indirect costs of illness and suffering are also considered, the incident may have caused damages equivalent to $65–155 million.

Obvious lessons to be learned from the Walkerton tragedy include the need for (a) effective local maintenance and monitoring of public water supplies; (b) oversight of the local agencies by higher authorities (in this case, the Provincial Government); and (c) sensible regulation and close monitoring of the disposal and environmental effects of the enormous quantities of improperly treated livestock sewage that are produced in Canada.

cold, hot, dry, wet, rocky, or infertile to be converted into agricultural land-use.

Some countries still have substantial areas of natural ecosystems that are suitable for conversion. In most cases, this means of economic development is being actively pursued, particularly in countries that also have a rapidly growing population. Prominent examples include parts of Brazil and Vietnam. These countries have been substantially increasing their areas of cultivated land, mostly by clearing natural tropical rainforest, savannah, and wetland (see Table 14.6 and Appendix C, Table 6 for percentage change between 1992 and 2002). Other less developed countries have few remaining areas of natural land that are suitable for agricultural development. In spite of their rapidly growing populations, these countries have not managed to create much additional cropland since about 1980. This is the situation of Bangladesh, Malaysia, Nigeria, and Tanzania (Table 14.6).

Most of the world's wealthier countries are not developing much additional arable land, largely because their areas with good site capability for agriculture are already

Photo 14.1   Agricultural production relies on rainfall and soil capability, which supply moisture, nutrients, and other factors crucial to plant growth. This is a view of a hayfield on Prince Edward Island.

TABLE 14.5	Numbers of Large Dams in Canada	

A "large dam" is defined as being higher than 15 m, with a capacity greater than 1 million m^3, and maximum discharge rate greater than 2000 m^3/s.

PROVINCE	1969	1994
Newfoundland	15	86
Prince Edward Island	–	–
Nova Scotia	27	35
New Brunswick	16	16
Quebec	103	203
Ontario	74	81
Manitoba	24	34
Saskatchewan	34	43
Alberta	44	57
British Columbia	80	89
Yukon	3	3
Northwest Territories and Nunavut	3	3
Canada	423	650
Hydroelectric	267	557
Irrigation	48	55
Municipal	38	43
Flood control	18	22
Other	52	58

Source: Data from Statistics Canada (2000)

TABLE 14.6	Agricultural Land in Selected Countries			

Land areas are for 1997; % refers to percentage change of 2002 relative to 1992. (A positive value indicates an increase.) See Appendix C, Table 6 for additional country data of this type.

COUNTRY	CROPLAND		PASTURE	
	(10^6 hectare)	%	(10^6 hectare)	%
RELATIVELY UNDEVELOPED COUNTRIES				
Bangladesh	8.4	1	0.6	0
Nigeria	33.0	2	39.2	–2
Tanzania	5.1	13	35.0	0
Vietnam	8.9	33	0.6	94
RAPIDLY DEVELOPING COUNTRIES				
Brazil	66.6	13	197.0	5
China	154.0	16	400.0	0
Malaysia	7.4	–3	0.3	2
DEVELOPED COUNTRIES				
Canada	*45.9*	*1*	*29.0*	*0*
France	19.6	2	10.0	–10
United States	178.1	–4	233.8	–2

Source: Data from World Resources Institute (2005)

being used. In fact, many developed countries have taken a great deal of land out of agricultural use since about 1980 (Table 14.6). The land withdrawals have occurred for two major reasons: (1) to reduce the production of certain crops, which keeps prices relatively high; and (2) to conserve environmental quality through less intensive use of marginal land that is prone to erosion and other kinds of degradation. In addition, some high-quality agricultural land has been lost to urbanization in many developed countries, including Canada.

Agricultural Site Capability

Agricultural site capability (site quality) can be defined as the potential of an area of land to sustain the productivity of agricultural crops. Site capability is a complex ecological quality that depends on the maintenance of soil fertility, organic matter, drainage, and other factors that influence crop productivity. These factors are influenced by climate and drainage, by the vigour of ecological functions such as decomposition and nutrient cycling, and by the nature of the plant and microbial communities.

Site capability is critically important to the productivity of agricultural systems and therefore to the production and availability of food. Because the beneficial qualities of cultivated land can be maintained and even improved by appropriate management practices, agricultural site capability represents a potentially renewable resource. It can also, however, be degraded by some agricultural practices (see also Chapter 24).

Ultimately, site capability for agriculture depends on seven interrelated factors: soil fertility, soil organic matter, bulk density of soil (including compaction), resistance to erosion, moisture status, salinization, and prevalence of weeds. We will now examine each of these in turn.

Soil Fertility

Soil fertility is related to the ability of the ecosystem to supply the nutrients required to sustain crop productivity. Especially important are sources of inorganic nitrogen, particularly ammonium and nitrate, as well as phosphate, potassium, calcium, magnesium, and sulphur. Soil fertility is influenced not only by the quantities of these nutrients, but also by factors such as the following, which affect their availability to plants:

- cation exchange capacity, or the degree to which positively charged ions of such nutrients as ammonium (NH_4^+), potassium (K^+), and calcium (Ca^{2+}) are bound by soil

- anion exchange capacity, which is related to the binding of negatively charged ions such as nitrate (NO_3^-), phosphate (PO_4^{3-}), and sulphate (SO_4^{2-})

- soil acidity or alkalinity, usually measured as pH, which affects the solubility of many nutrients and aspects of microbial activity

- rates of oxidation of organically bound nutrients into inorganic compounds that plants can take up and use more effectively

- nutrient addition to the land by agricultural fertilization

For example, consider nitrification (see Chapter 5), an important process performed by certain species of bacteria that transform ammonium into nitrate. The rate of nitrification is greatly decreased in acidic or waterlogged soils, resulting in less nitrate availability to crops. Soil fertility can also be degraded by removing excessive quantities of nutrients with the harvested crops, as well as by compaction, depletion of soil organic matter, waterlogging, and acidification.

Soil Organic Matter

Soil organic matter consists of plant debris and humified organic material. Organic matter contributes to the ability of soil to form a loose, crumbly structure called **tilth**. Soil with good tilth is well aerated, allows plant roots to grow freely, and retains moisture—all of which are factors critical to crop growth.

Some nutrients are components of soil organic matter. Organically bound nutrients can be slowly released for plant uptake through the process of decomposition, which, in this respect, can be viewed as a natural, slow-release, organic fertilization. Organic matter also helps the soil to retain ionic forms of nutrients through cation and anion exchange capacity. Intensive cropping with insufficient return of crop residues commonly leads to losses of soil organic matter and degradation of the valuable services it provides.

Bulk Density of Soil

A low bulk density of soil (i.e., its weight per unit volume) is preferred for soil tilth and drainage. Bulk density can be degraded by losses of soil organic matter and by excessive compaction from the repeated passage of heavy machinery, especially when fields are wet. Soil degraded by compaction may become wetter, may be lacking in oxygen, and may have impaired nutrient cycling and poor growth of plant roots. These changes can result in substantial decreases in crop productivity.

Resistance to Erosion

Soil mass can be lost by erosion, which is caused by particles being carried away by the forces of wind or running water. Any agricultural practices that increase the rate of erosion should be viewed as a mining of soil capital. In severe cases, erosion can strip away the relatively fertile, surface horizons of soil. In the worst cases, bedrock may be exposed.

Erosion is encouraged when soil is left without a cover of vegetation or crop residues during the winter, when contour ploughing is not practised (i.e., when cultivation runs down a slope rather than along it), and when steep terrain is tilled. Sites are relatively resistant to erosion if they are well vegetated, their soil has good tilth, they are flat, and the climate is not excessively wet or windy.

Moisture Status

Moisture status is another important aspect of site capability. In general, an intermediate moisture status (referred to as *mesic*) is preferred for the growth of most crops. Excessively dry (*xeric*) sites will produce small yields, and crops may even die from extreme drought. In contrast, excessively wet (*hydric*) sites tend to have cool soil with little or no oxygen present, conditions that are stressful to almost all crops.

The moisture status of most sites is largely affected by climatic factors, especially the rates of precipitation and evapotranspiration. Soil moisture is also affected by drainage characteristics—coarse-grained soils may drain too rapidly and have little ability to hold moisture, while heavy clay soils may not drain well enough, retaining water close to the surface. Soils with good tilth tend to have a degree of drainage midway between these extremes.

Salinization

Salinization refers to the accumulation of salts in soil, particularly excessive concentrations of sodium, magnesium, potassium, chloride, or sulphate. These and other salts are present in irrigation water and in certain fertilizers and remain behind when water evaporates to the atmosphere. Salinization is a common problem in sites that are irrigated but do not have enough drainage to carry the salts away, causing them to accumulate in the surface soil.

Prevalence of Weeds

Weeds can be broadly defined as plants that are judged to be interfering with some human purpose (see Chapter 21). Weeds are considered a problem in agriculture if they present crop species with undue competition. Continuous cultivation of the same species of crop can result in an increased abundance of weeds, which may interfere with crop productivity. This problem is commonly managed by tillage and/or the use of herbicides. Often, however, the buildup of weed populations can be avoided by rotating crops and using other management practices that provide less favourable conditions for the unwanted plants.

Degradation of Site Capability

In the long term, intensive agricultural management can degrade site capability. When this happens, the productivity of crops decreases, and in severe cases, the land may no longer be suitable for agricultural use. Such damage can often be avoided or mitigated by changing the management system. For example, inorganic fertilizer may be applied to the soil in an attempt to compensate for declining fertility. Organic soil conditioners, such as compost and manure, can also be added to mitigate losses of organic matter, thereby helping to maintain the fertility and tilth of soil. In other cases, pesticides may be used to try to manage weeds and other pests. These management options are, however, intensive in their use of material and energy resources, and they may cause additional damage to the site and nearby ecosystems. Ultimately, truly sustainable agricultural systems involve management strategies that *conserve* site capability while minimizing the use of nutrients, pesticides, and non-renewable sources of energy.

Production and Management

The number of people and domestic animals that can be supported depends on the production of agricultural crops. In addition to the 6.4 billion humans that had to be fed in 2005, there were about 1.3 billion cows, 4 billion sheep and goats, 0.95 billion pigs, 0.17 billion camels and water buffaloes, 0.20 billion horses and asses, and 18 billion chickens (see Chapter 10). Most of the domestic livestock forage extensively on wild plants, but many are fed crops grown in agriculture. In fact, about 40% of the global production of grain is fed to livestock. Eventually, food products derived from the livestock are eaten by humans, who are secondary consumers (and top predators) in the agricultural food chain.

Countries with an excess of agricultural production over domestic consumption have a surplus available for export, while nations with a deficit must import some of their food (Table 14.7). In general, the world's greatest food-exporting nations have relatively developed economies. Many poor countries export such foods as sugar, coffee, tea, palm oil, and other cash crops. Overall, however, most of the less developed countries have food deficits or are only marginally self-sufficient. The food deficits must be made up by expensive purchases of food grown elsewhere or by donations from wealthier nations (see Table 14.7 and Appendix C, Table 7).

The world's most important crops are cereals, such as wheat, rice, maize, sorghum, and barley. Of secondary importance are tuber crops, such as potato, cassava, sweet potato, and turnip. In any country, the total production of cereals and other crops is a function of the amount of land

TABLE 14.7	International Trade of Agricultural Produce

Net trade is calculated as exports minus imports. Positive numbers are net exports, while negative numbers are net imports. Cereals include maize, rice, sorghum, and wheat. Pulses are seeds in the legume family, such as peas, beans, and soybeans. Data are for 2002 and are in 10^6 tonnes per year. See Appendix C, Table 7 for additional country data of this type.

	CEREALS			PULSES		
	EXPORTS	IMPORTS	NET TRADE	EXPORTS	IMPORTS	NET TRADE
REGION						
North America	96.9	9.6	87.3	1.97	0.35	1.62
Europe	89.6	61.0	28.6	2.06	2.02	0.04
Oceania	19.4	1.2	18.2	1.03	0.03	1.00
South America	21.1	19.0	2.1	0.34	0.48	−0.14
Central America	0.9	22.9	−22.0	0.22	0.41	−0.19
Africa*	5.4	79.3	−73.9	0.70	1.35	−0.65
Asia	46.3	80.0	−33.7	2.35	3.96	−1.61
LEADING EXPORTERS						
United States	82.2	5.0	77.2	0.55	0.26	0.29
France	27.9	1.6	26.3	0.99	0.12	0.87
Canada	*14.7*	*4.6*	*10.1*	*1.41*	*0.01*	*1.40*
LEADING IMPORTERS						
Japan	0.5	26.6	−26.1	0.00	0.16	−0.15
Korea, Rep.	<0.1	13.4	−13.4	0.00	0.06	−0.06
Egypt	0.5	10.3	−9.8	0.03	0.41	−0.38

*includes Middle East

Source: Data from World Resources Institute (2005)

devoted to the cultivation of those species, multiplied by the average productivity.

Productivity reflects the combined influences of site capability and the intensity of management. In agriculture, *management* is intended largely to mitigate some of the constraints associated with site quality, as well as the yield-reducing influences of inclement weather, insect infestations, weeds, and crop diseases. The productivity of cereals and other crops varies among countries, being relatively low in less developed countries and higher in more developed ones (Table 14.8 and Appendix C, Table 8). In general, this difference reflects the use of highly mechanized agricultural systems in wealthier countries, including intensive applications of fertilizer and pesticides and a great expenditure of fossil-fuel energy.

The index of food production shown in Table 14.8 is a composite indicator that takes into account the production of all important crop species. The 1999–2000 value of the index of food production was assigned a value of 100, and other years are relative to that number. The index shows whether agricultural production has increased (>100) or decreased (<100) during the time period, both on a total and per capita basis.

It is important to understand that the high yields from intensive agricultural systems are heavily subsidized by large inputs of non-renewable resources. For example, the most important agricultural fertilizers are inorganic compounds of nitrogen, such as urea or ammonium nitrate, both of which are manufactured using natural gas. The second- and third-most-important fertilizer nutrients are compounds of phosphate and potassium, which are manufactured from mined minerals. In addition, most pesticides are manufactured from petrochemicals, using energy-intensive technologies. Moreover, the mechanization of agricultural systems involves the use of large tractors pulling heavy equipment for tilling, harvesting, and other purposes. The manufacture of these machines requires large quantities of non-renewable energy and materials, such as metals and plastics. Furthermore, the machines run on non-renewable fuels, such as gasoline or diesel.

Therefore, the high productivity of the intensively managed agricultural systems used in developed countries is achieved mainly through the use of large amounts of non-renewable resources. This fact is indicated by data that show much larger rates of fertilizer use and numbers of tractors in these countries, compared with less wealthy nations (Table 14.9 and Appendix C, Table 9).

Some agricultural systems used in less developed countries are also quite intensive and result in high yields. For example, in many humid tropical countries, rice is cultivated using a system known (in parts of Asia) as paddy. Water buffalo are used to plough and till the dyked, flooded

TABLE 14.8	Indexes of Agricultural Production in Selected Countries

Data are for 2003; % refers to percentage change between 1993 and 2003. The 1999–2001 value of the index of food production was assigned a value of 100, and the 2003 data are shown relative to that number. See Appendix C, Table 8 for additional country data of this type.

COUNTRY	CEREALS			ROOTS & TUBERS			INDEX OF FOOD PRODUCTION	
	PRODUCTION (10^6 tonne)	YIELD (tonne/hectare·year)	%	PRODUCTION (10^6 tonne)	YIELD (tonne/hectare·year)	%	TOTAL	PER CAPITA
RELATIVELY UNDEVELOPED COUNTRIES								
Bangladesh	39.7	3.3	25	3.7	13.2	26	104	98
Nigeria	24.5	1.1	–8	66.6	8.4	–20	105	97
RAPIDLY DEVELOPING COUNTRIES								
Brazil	66.4	3.4	42	26.0	13.8	13	119	114
China	377.5	4.8	6	172.5	17.0	0	112	109
Mexico	30.6	2.8	7	1.9	24.9	42	105	101
DEVELOPED COUNTRIES								
Canada	50.2	2.7	4	5.3	29.4	11	98	95
France	54.9	6.1	–6	6.2	39.9	12	94	93
United States	348.6	7.0	40	21.6	39.6	12	101	98

Source: Data from World Resources Institute (2005)

TABLE 14.9	Intensity of Agricultural Management in Selected Countries (2001)

See Appendix C, Table 9 for additional country data of this type.

| COUNTRY | CROPLAND | | | FERTILIZER USE (kilogram/hectare of cropland) | NUMBER OF TRACTORS (ha/tractors) |
	AREA (10^6 hectare)	PER CAPITA (ha/person)	% IRRIGATED		
RELATIVELY UNDEVELOPED COUNTRIES					
Bangladesh	9.4	0.06	47	171	1534
Nigeria	30.7	0.03	1	7	1040
RAPIDLY DEVELOPING COUNTRIES					
Brazil	58.4	0.32	4	103	83
China	175.3	0.13	20	228	140
Mexico	19.4	0.18	24	68	84
DEVELOPED COUNTRIES					
Canada	29.0	0.91	2	54	63
France	40.0	0.66	11	213	16
United States	114.7	0.39	13	111	37

Source: Data from World Resources Institute (2005)

fields. People then hand-transplant the young rice plants, weed the crop with hoes, and eventually harvest by hand-scything. In places with evenly spaced precipitation and naturally fertile soil, such as parts of Java, Sumatra, and the Philippines, as many as three rice crops can be grown each year. The paddy system, typically used by families working small plots of land, can achieve high yields with relatively small inputs of inorganic fertilizer or pesticides.

Other agricultural systems used in less developed countries are much less productive than paddy rice, generally because of suboptimal rainfall and less fertile soil. The least productive systems are used in semiarid regions. Under such conditions, it is not possible to cultivate many plant crops. However, livestock such as cows, camels, goats, and sheep can forage extensively over the landscape, harvesting the sparse production of native forage. The dispersed plant biomass of semiarid ecosystems is too small in quantity and too poor in nutritional quality for direct harvesting and use by humans. Grazing livestock can, however, convert the poor-quality forage into a form (such as meat or milk) that humans can utilize as food.

Increasingly, the agricultural systems used in less developed countries are becoming more intensive in their management. In this sense, they are proceeding toward the kinds of systems used in developed countries. Indicators of this change include increasing use of fertilizer, pesticides, and mechanization. This has resulted in the increasing yields seen in many less developed countries since about

1980 (see Table 14.8). For example, the productivity of cereal crops in Bangladesh, China, India, Iran, and Vietnam has increased by more than 60% since about 1980. This is largely due to the adoption of more intensive agricultural practices, particularly fertilization, pesticide use, and increased mechanization.

The industrialization of agricultural production in these countries also results in important social changes. Of particular importance is the rapid amalgamation of small family farms into larger industrial units. This results in the displacement of many poor people from agricultural livelihoods. These economic refugees then migrate to towns and cities, resulting in an increase of the urbanization rate far beyond that expected from population growth alone.

Agriculture in Canada

Plant Crops

Canada is one of the world's great agricultural nations and a major contributor to the international trade in food. Canada's 29 million hectares of cropland represent 2% of the global total. Canada's grain production of 50 million t/y in 2003 ranked seventh in the world (see Appendix C, Table 8). In 2003, Canada exported 15×10^6t of grain (as trade plus aid shipments), which ranked fifth in the world.

Canadian exports of agricultural products in 2004 had a value of $26.8 billion, including $4.6 billion of livestock and meat products, and $22.2 billion of all other commodities, mostly grains (Statistics Canada, 2005). These exports were largely offset by imports of $21.4 billion, for a net trade surplus of $5.4 billion for the agricultural sector.

At the beginning of the twentieth century, more than 80% of the Canadian labour force was employed in agriculture. Farming mostly relied on animal and human labour as sources of energy for cultivation and harvesting. Most farms were relatively small, family-operated enterprises, run mainly as subsistence operations to produce food and other crops for use by the family. Any surplus production was traded in local markets for cash or manufactured goods. The agricultural surplus was eventually sold in Canadian cities or exchanged internationally by traders. Much of today's agricultural activity in less developed countries still has this socio-economic character.

Today, most Canadian agriculture involves highly mechanized, industrial operations. Only about 3% of the national workforce is employed in farming (about 330 000 people in 2005). Virtually all cultivation, harvesting, and processing is accomplished by large, fossil-fuelled machines. Tractors haul cultivating, seeding, and spraying machines, and self-contained harvesters harvest and process crops. Canadian farmers used 460 000 tractors in 2005.

Canada has an immense land base, some 10 million km^2, making it the second-largest country in the world (after Russia). However, the area suitable for agriculture is quite limited and is largely restricted to the southern parts of the country. The ability of land to support agricultural uses is categorized by a system known as the Canada Land Inventory (see Canadian Focus 14.2). The distribution of the most productive lands for agriculture in Canada is shown in Table 14.10.

Most of the highest capability land is located in southern parts of Canada, in regions where the growing season is relatively long and moist, and on sites with relatively fertile soil and flat terrain. Southern Ontario, for example, has 52% of the class 1 land in Canada, while Saskatchewan has 24%; Alberta, 19%; and Manitoba, 4%. Unfortunately, some of the best land in southern Ontario is being destroyed rapidly through conversion to residential and industrial land-uses, particularly in the greater Toronto area and the Niagara Peninsula. Excellent agricultural land is likewise being lost to urbanization in the delta of the Fraser River and the Okanagan Valley in southern British Columbia. These depletions of high-quality land directly affect the overall production of foodstuffs in Canada.

| **TABLE 14.10** | Distribution of Class 1–3 Land in Canada |

Soil capability classes 1–3 are suitable for the cultivation of crop species. Classes 4 and 5, used for pasture or rough grazing, are not reported here. Not all of the high-quality land is used for agriculture—some has been converted to urban and suburban land-uses. Data are expressed in 10^3 km^2.

PROVINCE	TOTAL LAND	CAPABILITY CLASS		
		1	2	3
Newfoundland	373.9	–	–	0.02
Prince Edward Island	5.7	–	2.5	1.4
Nova Scotia	53.3	–	1.7	9.8
New Brunswick	71.5	–	1.6	11.5
Quebec	1365.1	0.2	9.1	12.8
Ontario	917.7	21.6	22.2	29.1
Manitoba	553.6	1.6	25.3	24.4
Saskatchewan	591.7	10.0	58.7	94.2
Alberta	642.3	7.9	38.4	61.1
British Columbia	925.2	0.2	2.4	6.9
Yukon	474.4	–	–	–
NWT	1183.1	–	–	–
Nunavut	1936.1	–	–	–
Canada total	9094.0	41.5	161.8	251.3

Source: Data from Statistics Canada (1994, 2005)

As previously noted, the quality of land for agriculture is strongly influenced by such factors as soil fertility, organic matter concentration, drainage, and weed populations. All of these qualities can be degraded through inappropriate management of the land. It is important to monitor changes in these site factors over time, in order to track changes in the sustainability of Canadian agriculture. Unfortunately, suitable monitoring data do not yet exist in most areas, although programs are being designed.

There are, however, some general indications that soil fertility and other site factors are declining in quality over much of the agricultural landbase of Canada. For example, in order to maintain the productivity of many Canadian agroecosystems, large quantities of fertilizer and soil conditioners must be added to the system. Similarly, herbicide, insecticide, fungicide, and other pesticides must be used to manage pest problems (see Chapter 22). The pressing need to use intensive management practices to maintain productivity could, in itself, be considered a symptom of unsustainable stress on the agroecosystem. Moreover, most fertilizers, pesticides, and their mechanized application systems are based on the mining and use of non-renewable

Canadian Focus 14.2

Canada Land Inventory

The ability of land in Canada to support agricultural uses is classified according to a system known as the *Canada Land Inventory*. Lands in classes 1, 2, and 3 have the highest capability and account for almost all of the crop production in Canada. Lands in classes 4 and 5 are generally unsuitable for plant crops but may be suitable as rough pasture for livestock.

Class 1. The best agricultural land, class 1, has no significant limitations for the growth of crops. These lands have deep soil, gentle or no slope, good drainage, and sufficient organic matter to retain water and nutrients well. These lands are fertile, do not erode easily, and sustain a high productivity of crop plants suited to the local climate.

Class 2. This land either has moderate limitations that restrict the productivity of at least some species of crop

plants, or it requires moderately intense management for conservation purposes. Limitations of these sites are generally associated with a mildly adverse local climate, moderate erosion, poor soil structure, imperfect drainage, acidic soil, moderate slope, and seasonal wetness. Class 2 soils can, however, sustain a good productivity of a wide range of crop species.

Class 3. This land has moderately severe limitations for crop productivity or requires special conservation practices to maintain site quality. Limitations of class 3 land include the same factors that restrict class 2 land, that is, climate, relatively steep slopes with high erosion potential, poor fertility, poor drainage or poor water-holding capacity, and sometimes salinity. However, if properly managed for carefully selected crops, class 3 land can achieve a moderate to fair agricultural productivity.

---

resources, representing another element of non-sustainability (see also Chapter 24).

Huge amounts of fertilizer are used to increase crop productivity in Canada. In 2001, fertilizer was applied to 24 million ha of farmland, more than a 3-fold increase over 1971 (Table 14.11). In 1997, agricultural land was fertilized with 1.3 million t of nitrogen and 0.7 million t of phosphate (Statistics Canada, 1998). Compared with rates of fertilizer use in 1970, these represented increases of about 5-fold and 2.4-fold, respectively.

The use of pesticides to deal with insect pests, weeds, and fungal pathogens is also intensive in Canadian agriculture. In 2001, herbicide was applied to 26 million ha of farmland, representing a 3-fold increase over 1971 (Table 14.11). Insecticides and fungicides were applied to 4.8 million ha in 2001, a 5-fold increase over 1971. A total of 29 400 t of pesticides was applied in 1996.

Canadian agricultural systems also utilize crop varieties that have been selectively bred to increase their potential productivity and resistance to important pests and pathogens, to respond vigorously to fertilization and other intensive management practices, and to grow well under regional climatic regimes. This is not to say that these varieties are optimally adapted to intensively managed agroecosystems. New pests and diseases often develop, so the crop-breeding industry must continuously respond to changing environmental and ecological conditions.

The intensification of industrial agriculture in Canada has greatly increased crop production (see Figure 14.1). Similarly large increases in agricultural production have been accomplished in other countries that have adopted

TABLE 14.11	Agricultural Land-Use and Crops in Canada				
LAND USE **(10^6 hectare)**	**1971**	**1981**	**1991**	**2001**	**2004**
Farmed area	68.66	65.89	67.75	67.50	67.50
Land in crops	27.83	30.97	33.51	36.39	36.40
Summerfallow	10.82	9.70	7.92	4.68	3.40
Improved pasture	4.14	4.40	4.14	4.80	4.80
Rough pasture	25.87	20.82	22.18	21.63	15.39
Grains: total	20.78	22.86	22.84	18.75	19.26
Wheat	7.85	12.45	14.16	10.86	10.40
Oats	6.70	3.81	3.05	1.89	1.99
Barley	5.66	5.46	4.52	4.70	4.68
Corn	0.57	1.14	1.11	1.30	1.18
Fodder crops	6.08	6.25	6.47	2.80	7.72
Soybean	0.15	0.28	0.60	1.08	1.25
Oilseeds	3.13	2.28	4.32	3.80	5.32
Fertilizer application	6.93	18.51	21.56	24.01	–
Herbicide application	8.57	15.22	21.60	25.90	–
Insecticide or fungicide	0.91	1.65	2.77	4.79	–

Source: Data from Statistics Canada (2005)

FIGURE 14.1 | Changes in Agricultural Activity in Canada

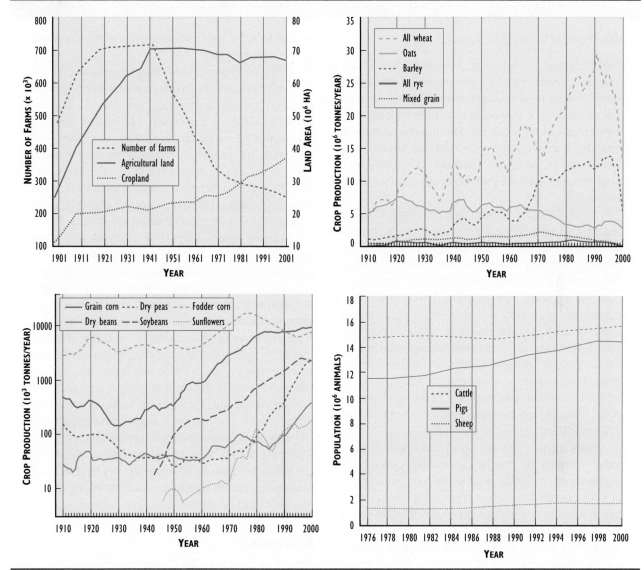

(a) Number of farms and cultivated area; (b) production of small grains, 1911 to 2001 (5-year running averages); (c) production of other crops, 1911 to 2001 (5-year averages; note the logarithmic scale); (d) livestock populations.

Source: Modified from Statistics Canada (2004)

intensive and mechanized agricultural systems. This includes the U.S., most countries of western Europe, and—increasingly—China, India, Russia, Ukraine, and other rapidly developing countries. The increases in agricultural production have been accomplished mainly through intensified management and the cultivation of improved crop varieties, rather than by increasing the areas of cultivated land.

About 67.5×10^6 ha of land are cultivated on 247 000 farms in Canada (Table 14.11). This area is equivalent to about 7% of Canada's landmass. Compared with 1971, this represents a 1.7% decrease in the cultivated area,

a 36% decrease in the numbers of farms, and a 35% increase in the average farm size. Of the total cultivated area, 54% was actively managed for crops, 7% was in summer fallow, 7% was in improved pasture, and 32% was natural grazing land, mostly in the western provinces. The area of cultivated crops increased by 31% between 1971 and 2001, while the area of other agricultural land-uses decreased by 24%. Wheat is by far the most extensively grown crop in Canada, accounting for 70% of the area sown to grains, and increasing by 33% between 1971 and 2004 in response to expanding export opportunities (see Table 14.11).

Canadian Focus 14.3

Weather Extremes and Agriculture

Climatic factors, such as heat, wind, and soil moisture, have an important influence on agricultural production. When they are present at moderate intensities, harvests can be bountiful. If they occur at an extreme level, however, crops can be wiped out. For instance, periods of extended dry conditions, or drought, are an important factor in the Prairie region, where large areas have marginal moisture availability for key crops such as wheat and canola.

During 2001, for example, much of western Canada experienced some of the driest growing conditions ever recorded in the region. Large areas had below-average moisture, and parts of Saskatchewan, British Columbia, and southern Alberta had severe drought and record-low precipitation. There were widespread decreases of production and even crop failures in the drought-stricken areas. Drought was also severe in 2002, although the most severely stricken areas were further north, in central Alberta and nearby Saskatchewan. In the southernmost Prairie Provinces, where drought was most severe in 2001, moisture was generally normal or better in 2002. Drought was generally less of a problem from 2003 to 2005.

Years of severe drought have had a hugely destabilizing influence on the agricultural economy of the Prairie region. In 2002, owing to the cumulative effects of three consecutive years of poor spring runoff (due to below-average snowfall) and sparse precipitation during the growing season, the amount of forage available in drought-stricken areas was critically low. Many ranchers had to sell off most or all of their cattle, including vital breeding stock, because they were unable to grow enough forage to service their animals or to pay the high cost of importing feed.

The production of annual crops was also hard hit. The national production of non-durum wheat, which is mostly grown in the Prairie Provinces, was only 11.8 million tonnes in 2002, compared with 17.6 million tonnes in 2001 and 21.2 million tonnes in 2000 (an overall 44% decrease). The production of canola was also markedly down, from 7.1 million tonnes in 2000 to 4.9 million tonnes in 2001, and 3.2 million tonnes in 2002 (a 55% decrease). Although Canada is normally an exporter of grain to global markets, in 2002 we imported wheat from Russia.

Farmers have a number of management options available to them during periods of drought. For instance, they can practise summerfallow, a practice in which the land is not cultivated in some years in order to conserve vital soil moisture. Farmers can also choose to grow drought-tolerant crops, such as field pea or wheat. If surface water or groundwater are available, irrigation may be an option. The practice of agriculture has always been somewhat risky in the Prairie region, and farmers can suffer terribly from the economic and emotional damage of drought. During such times, it is essential that affordable crop insurance and other means of financial support be available to the agricultural community. This must, in fact, be a national priority—all Canadians are fed by the produce grown by farmers, and we must share with them the consequences of the ecological and economic risks inherent in their agricultural enterprise.

References

Agriculture Canada. 2005. *Drought watch.* www.agr.gc.ca/pfra/drought/default.htm

Livestock

Animal husbandry has also become intensive in Canada. Most production of chickens, cows, and pigs now occurs on so-called "factory farms." This is an industrial system that involves raising livestock indoors under densely crowded conditions. The livestock are fed to satiation with nutritionally optimized diets, while diseases are managed with antibiotics and other medicines. Productivity may be enhanced with growth hormones (Chapter 24).

In 2003, 611 million chickens were raised for their meat and eggs on Canadian farms, most of them in operations of an industrial scale and intensity (Statistics Canada, 2005). This represented a 4.3-fold increase in chickens since 1971. The 2003 production of chicken eggs was 7.6 billion, equivalent to a 26% increase since 1971. As well, 20.6 million turkeys were raised, again mostly on factory farms.

Larger livestock in 2003 included 14.7 million cows (of which 1.7 million were milk cows), 29.9 million pigs, 0.8 million sheep, and 0.9 million horses. Dairy cows and pigs are raised mostly on factory farms. Most beef cows spend part of their lives grazing outdoors in pastures or on semi-natural prairie. However, prior to slaughter, most are rounded up and kept in densely crowded feedlots, where they are well fed so that they can gain weight rapidly. Sheep, goats, and horses are raised under less intensive conditions.

Overview

The twentieth century witnessed enormous increases in agricultural production. This has fed the similarly rapid increases in the global populations of humans and domestic animals. The rapid intensification of agriculture is, however, substantially dependent on non-renewable sources of energy and materials, a fact that makes the sustainability of the overall production systems highly questionable. Moreover, intensive agricultural systems cause important damages to the environment, many of which are described in later chapters.

Forest Resources

Forests of various kinds are extremely important terrestrial ecosystems. They cover extensive areas of Earth's surface, fixing and storing large quantities of biomass. Earth's cover of closed forests (i.e., with >50% canopy cover) is about 3.14 billion ha (in 2000), of which 56% is in temperate and boreal regions and 44% in tropical ones (World Resources Institute, 2005). The present forest area is about 53% of what it was before humans began to cause deforestation, mostly to develop additional agricultural land. Although temperate and boreal forests now cover an area comparable to the tropical forest, their production is only about one-half as large, and they store only 61% as much biomass. There are also another 3.39 billion ha of more open woodlands and savannahs. The most heavily forested regions are in North and South America, Europe, and Russia, all of which have more than 30% forest cover.

Worldwide, an immense area of about 25 million ha of forest is cleared or harvested each year. Tree biomass is harvested for three major reasons:

1. as a fuel for subsistence purposes, that is, to burn as a source of energy for cooking and warmth

2. as an industrial fuel, used to generate electricity or to produce steam or heat for a manufacturing process

3. as a raw material for the manufacture of lumber; paper; composite materials such as plywood, masonite, or waferboards; and other products, such as the synthetic fabrics rayon and celluloid

In addition, forests may be cleared not so much for their biomass, but to create new agricultural or urbanized

Photo 14.2 Clear-cutting is the most common method of harvesting forests in Canada. Mechanized harvesting systems are used in most areas, such as this machinery that fells and de-limbs trees, cuts them into convenient lengths, and hauls the wood to a roadside.

land. These longer-term **ecological conversions** result in a permanent loss of forest cover (**deforestation**).

The net primary production of global forests has been estimated to be 48.7 billion t/y, of which an extraordinary 28% is used by humans (Vitousek *et al.*, 1986). Human use can be divided into the following categories:

- short-term clearing of forests for shifting cultivation in less developed countries (45%)
- more permanent conversion of forests to agricultural land-uses (18%)
- harvesting of tree biomass (16%)
- productivity of trees in plantations (12%)
- loss during harvest (9%)

Changes in Forest Cover

Forest resources in many countries are being depleted rapidly by high rates of clearing. This is particularly true in many tropical countries, where deforestation is largely driven by increasing populations and the resulting need for more agricultural land and wood fuels. Also important are the economic and industrial demands for tree biomass to manufacture into charcoal and products for international trade.

The global rate of deforestation was 9.4 million ha/y between 1990 and 2005, considerably less than the

15.5 million ha/y lost between 1980 and 1990 (WRI, 2005). However, these are still extremely high rates of forest loss, and they may have increased again since the late 1990s. Satellite data for Amazonia, for example, suggest that clearing may have increased by 50% in 1996–97, which was a relatively dry year that was favourable for removing tropical forest by burning.

Rates of deforestation of some less developed and rapidly developing countries are listed in Table 14.12. Recently, some of these countries have been losing their forests at extraordinary rates. For instance, deforestation is occurring at 2.3%/y in the Philippines, for a half-life of only about 30 years. Moreover, many tropical countries have been increasing their rates of deforestation—for example, by 80% in Myanmar between 1992 and 2002, by 33% in Congo, and by 25% in Angola (Table 14.12 and Appendix C, Table 10).

The rapid deforestation in most developing countries represents the mining of a potentially renewable natural resource. In addition to the loss of timber resources, deforestation in the tropics and subtropics has terrible ecological costs, such as extinctions of indigenous biodiversity. These topics are discussed in Chapters 23 and 26.

In contrast to the rapid deforestation in most less developed countries, the forest cover of many developed countries is relatively stable or even increasing (Table 14.12). This is happening in spite of industrial harvesting of forest resources in many of those countries, largely to manufacture lumber and paper. In the industrial forestry that is typically pursued in Canada, the U.S., and western Europe, another forest is allowed or encouraged to regenerate on harvested sites. Consequently, deforestation does not occur—appropriate management can ensure that the forest resource does not become depleted by harvesting.

This does not, however, mean that forestry is ecologically benign in developed countries. Industrial forestry results in substantial changes in the character of the ecosystem, with important consequences for biodiversity and other ecological values (see Chapter 23).

Although most developed countries currently have a stable forest cover, this has not always been the case. Many of these countries were being actively deforested as recently as the beginning of the twentieth century. Most of the early deforestation occurred in order to develop land for agriculture. For instance, most of western Europe was still forested as recently as the Middle Ages (up until about 1500), as was eastern North America up until one to three centuries ago. Parts of these regions are now largely devoid of forest cover, which has been replaced by agroecosystems and urbanized land.

TABLE 14.12	Forest Resources and Forestry Production in Selected Countries

Forest cover data are for 2000; deforestation is the change in natural forest between 1990 and 2000 (a positive value means the forest increased); net deforestation is the percentage of original area of natural forest that remains; harvesting data are for 2002; percentage increase refers to the increase of total harvest between 1992 and 2002. See Appendix C, Table 10 for additional country data of this type.

COUNTRY	FORESTS (10^6 hectare)	DEFORESTATION RATE (%/year)	DEFORESTATION NET (%)	FOREST HARVESTING TOTAL (10^6 metre^3/y)	FOREST HARVESTING FUEL (10^6 m^3/y)	FOREST HARVESTING INDUSTRIAL (10^6 m^3/y)	PERCENTAGE INCREASE
RELATIVELY UNDEVELOPED COUNTRIES							
Myanmar	34.4	−13	41	39.8	35.4	5.9	80
Zambia	31.2	−21	70	8.1	7.2	1.0	5
RAPIDLY DEVELOPING COUNTRIES							
Brazil	543.9	−4	66	235.3	134.5	130.5	5
Malaysia	19.3	−11	64	61.2	3.3	29.3	−1
DEVELOPED COUNTRIES							
Canada	*244.6*	*0*	*91*	*229.4*	*3.0*	*271.2*	*−1*
Japan	24.1	0	58	62.8	0.1	34.4	0
United States	226.0	2	60	615.3	73.1	615.3	−3
WORLD	3869	−2.4	47	3385	1797	1588	5.7

Source: Data from World Resources Institute (2005)

This process of deforestation largely stopped around 1920 to 1930. At that time, forested areas began to increase in many developed countries. This happened because many small farms of marginal agricultural capability were abandoned, and their inhabitants migrated to urban areas to seek work. Over time, the land reverted to forest. For example, because of these socio-economic and ecological dynamics, the area of forest in much of the Maritime Provinces has approximately doubled since the beginning of the twentieth century. Similar changes have occurred in other developed regions of the world.

Harvesting and Managing Forests

Globally, however, the net trend is one of accelerating deforestation. During the past decade, about 25 million ha/y of forest were cleared around the world, compared with 20 million ha in 1978, 16 million ha in 1950, 10 million ha in 1900, and 6 million ha in 1800 (Freedman, 1995; World Resources Institute, 2005). Most of this aggressive deforestation is associated with the conversion of tropical forest into agricultural land, but the harvesting of forest products is also important in some regions.

During 2002, the global consumption of wood averaged 3.4 billion m^3/y, representing a 6% increase from a decade earlier (Table 14.12). The wood consumption included

- 0.39 billion m^3/y of sawn timber (an 11% decrease from 1992);

- 0.20 billion m^3/y of wood panels such as plywood (a 60% increase);

- 1.59 billion m^3/y of industrial roundwood (a 7% increase; mostly used to manufacture paper); and

- 1.80 billion m^3/y of fuelwood and charcoal (a 5% increase; about 85% of the fuelwood was consumed in less developed countries).

In Canada, an enormous industrial complex depends on the harvesting of forest biomass, largely for manufacture into lumber; composite materials such as plywood and waferboard; and pulp and paper. The total value of Canadian forest products in 2004 was $71 billion (Statistics Canada, 2005); see Table 14.13.

Most of Canada's production of forest products is intended for export, providing foreign earnings that are crucial to maintaining a positive balance of trade. In 2004, Canadian exports of forest products had a value of $39.2 billion and contributed $36.0 billion to the country's international balance of trade of $67.2 billion (calculated as $39.2 billion of exports, minus $3.2 billion of forest product imports, for a net value of $36.0 billion; Statistics Canada, 2005). In terms of dollar value, Canada is the world's leading exporter of forest products.

In fact, the net earnings from the export of forest products ($36.0 billion) approximated the total of the net earnings for all other economic sectors in Canada ($31.2 billion), underscoring the importance of forest product exports to the national economy. (The net earnings from trade of energy commodities in 2004 were $40.3 billion, while automotive products earned $13.0 billion, agricultural and fishery products $8.3 billion, and industrial goods $4.1 billion. Other sectors had a negative balance of trade: machinery, equipment, and automotive products, –$11.9 billion; and other consumer goods, –$30.4 billion.)

Of course, to achieve the great economic benefits of forestry, large areas of mature forest must be harvested each year. In 2002, 0.97 million ha of mature forest were harvested in Canada, of which 91% was due to clear-cutting (Canadian Council of Forest Ministers, 2005). The total volume of the industrial harvest was equivalent to 189 million m^3 of stem biomass, of which 82% was from conifer trees ("softwoods") and 18% from broad-leafed trees ("hardwoods"). The area of forest harvested in 2002 was equivalent to about 0.2% of the total area of Canadian forests and 0.4% of the area of "productive" forests. Economically "productive" forests are relatively productive and well stocked and are most widespread in more southern regions of Canada.

Almost all of the industrially harvested area in Canada is allowed to regenerate to forest. Conversions to agricultural or urbanized land-uses are relatively uncommon. The rate of net deforestation in Canada is consequently close to zero (Table 14.12), in spite of the annual harvesting of about 1 million ha of forest. However, it must be understood that much of the harvested forest in Canada is not regenerating well and is considered poorly stocked with commercially valuable tree species. For example, about 15% (2.1 million ha) of Crown land harvested in Canada between 1975 and 2001 is considered to be currently understocked (Canadian Council of Forest Ministers, 2005).

Moreover, regeneration (reforestation) on most of the harvested area is actively encouraged by planting and other aspects of **silvicultural management**, such as thinning and herbicide and insecticide applications. In 2002, 428 400 ha of harvested forest (or 44% of the total) were planted with 634 million tree seedlings. Some of the planted areas are managed quite intensively, developing tree **plantations**. This represents the application of an agricultural model to the cultivation of trees, also known as **agroforestry**. Tree farms are generally more productive of biomass than natural forest, but they lack many elements of indigenous biodiversity and other ecological and aesthetic values (Chapter 23).

Almost all the non-planted part of the harvested area in Canada (56% of the total) also reverts to forest. However, this occurs through a relatively "natural" regeneration of tree species. Natural regeneration may involve seedlings that existed on the site prior to harvesting and survived the disturbance (this is known as

TABLE 14.13	Forest Resources and Forestry Production in Canada

Land classified as "productive" of timber has a sufficiently high productivity and stocking of trees to be economically exploitable, while "non-productive" forest is considered uneconomical. Harvest data are for 2002, with percentage increases calculated from 1990.

PROVINCE	FOREST LAND (10^6 hectare)			HARVEST	
	TOTAL	PRODUCTIVE	NON-PROD.	(10^3 ha)	% INCREASE
Newfoundland	20.1	11.2	8.9	22.0	27
Prince Edward Island	0.3	<0.1	0.3	4.9	−2
Nova Scotia	4.3	3.7	0.6	50.0	24
New Brunswick	6.2	6.0	0.2	105.8	4
Quebec	84.6	54.0	30.6	309.2	46
Ontario	68.3	42.0	26.3	184.3	14
Manitoba	36.3	14.9	21.4	15.0	−5
Saskatchewan	24.3	12.2	12.1	23.2	31
Alberta	36.4	23.7	12.6	68.4	18
British Columbia	64.1	51.3	12.8	189.3	3
Yukon	22.8	7.4	15.4	<0.1	–
Northwest Territories	33.3	12.0	21.3	0.1	–
Nunavut	0.9	<0.1	0.9	<0.1	–
CANADA TOTAL	401.9	238.0	63.9	974	14

Source: Data from Canadian Council of Forest Ministers (2005)

"advance regeneration"); seedlings that established from seeds dispersed onto the site from nearby forest; or seeds dispersed by mature "seed-trees" left on the site.

Overall, from the industrial perspective, forestry as it is practised in Canada appears to be conserving its primary economic resource—the area of forest and the productivity of tree biomass. Supporting this bold statement are three facts: (1) the rate of net deforestation is small in Canada; (2) almost all harvested sites eventually regenerate back to forest, which will be available for harvesting again once the trees grow to an appropriate size; and (3) except in some local areas, for short periods of time, the amount of harvesting of forest biomass does not exceed the landscape-scale forest productivity. Of course, not all considerations are so positive. As previously noted, natural regeneration has resulted in extensive areas that are, from the economic perspective, understocked with valuable tree species.

Moreover, there are additional environmental considerations that must be weighed before Canadian industrial forestry can be considered ecologically sustainable (in the sense explained in Chapter 12). These issues, to be examined in Chapter 23, include the following:

■ long-term effects of harvesting and management on site capability, which may become degraded by nutrient losses and erosion

■ effects of forestry on populations of fish, deer, and other hunted species, which also represent an economic "resource"

■ effects on indigenous biodiversity, including all native species and naturally occurring ecosystems (such as old-growth forest)

■ effects on hydrology and aquatic ecosystems

■ implications of forestry for carbon storage (this is important in the light of anthropogenic influences on the greenhouse effect; see Chapter 17)

These ecological values can be severely degraded by forestry, and this detracts from the ecological sustainability of this industrial activity.

Fish Resources

Wild populations of fish have long been exploited as food. In recent decades, the rate of harvesting wild fish has increased enormously, as has the cultivation of certain species in semi-domestication—a practice known as **aquaculture**. Like crop plants, livestock, and forests, populations of fish can be harvested in a sustainable manner, which would allow yields to be maintained over time. Fish stocks can also, however, be over-harvested to the degree that regeneration is impaired. When this happens, productivity declines and the resource can collapse disastrously. Regrettably, the recent history of almost all of the world's major fisheries provides abundant examples of over-exploitation causing rapid declines in resources.

The global harvest of fish and shellfish during 1999–2001 was about 130 million t/y. This included 85 million t/y of marine fish (representing a 6% increase over 1989–91), 6.9 million t of freshwater fish (a 38% increase), and 36 million t of fish grown in aquaculture (Table 14.14).

Canada is a major fishing nation, with an annual harvest of 1.07 million t of marine fish in 2003 (Table 14.15). Canadian exports of raw and processed fish products in 2004 had a value of $3.95 billion. These exports were partly offset by fish imports of $1.81 billion, for a net trade balance of $2.14 billion in this economic sector.

There is also a substantial harvest of freshwater fish in Canada, which in 2003 was equivalent to 38 700 tonnes and had a value of $77.7 million (Fisheries and Oceans, 2005a). The largest harvests are of whitefish (*Coregonus* spp.; about 9200 t), yellow pickerel (*Stizostedion vitreum*; 7800 t), sucker (*Catastomus* spp.; 3900 t), yellow perch (*Perca flavescens*; 2700 t), and pike (*Esox lucius*; 2500 t).

Aquaculture is also becoming increasingly important in Canada. The total harvest of fish in 2003 was 119 700 t, with a value of $512 million (Fisheries and Oceans, 2005). The total harvest of shellfish was 35 500 tonnes, with a value of $63.6 million. By far the largest harvests are of Atlantic salmon (*Salmo salar*; 105 000 t; $434 million).

The most important marine species harvested in Canada are summarized in Table 14.15. Note that these data are for Canadian landings only. Some foreign nations also fish waters within Canada's

Photo 14.3   Trawling is a technology used to harvest fish from large volumes of water and is the marine equivalent of clear-cutting a forest. This scene illustrates a trawl for cod off Newfoundland.

Source: Department of Fisheries and Oceans

TABLE 14.14   Fish Catches & Aquaculture in Selected Countries

Data are in 10^6 t/y, averaged for 1999–2001, with percentage increase since 1989–91 given in parentheses. Countries are listed in order of decreasing catches of marine fish. Diadromous fish migrate between salt and fresh water. See Appendix C, Table 11 for additional country data of this type.

COUNTRY	MARINE FISH	FRESHWATER FISH	AQUACULTURE MARINE FISH	AQUACULTURE FRESHWATER FISH
Global	85.2 (6)	8.7 (38)	14.2 (184)	21.4 (166)
China	14.7 (3)	2.2 (148)	9.4 (356)	15.1 (242)
Peru	9.0 (31)	0.04 (0)	<0.1	<0.01
Japan	4.9 (–48)	0.07 (–37)	0.71 (2)	0.10
United States	4.8 (–10)	0.03 (–28)	0.12 (15)	0.24 (–27)
Canada	*1.0 (–35)*	*0.04 (–13)*	*0.04 (237)*	*0.01*

Source: Data from World Resources Institute (2005)

TABLE 14.15   Catches of Marine Fish in Canada

Catch biomass is in 10^3 tonne/year, and economic value of the catch is in millions of dollars. Data are for 2003. See Appendix C, Table 12 for species data.

SPECIES	ATLANTIC COAST QUANTITY	VALUE	PACIFIC COAST QUANTITY	VALUE	CANADA QUANTITY	VALUE
Groundfish	129.1	157	1278	127	256.9	284
Pelagic fish	277.3	87	70.2	94	347.5	181
Shellfish	443.8	1592	19.7	120	463.5	1712
Total	850.3	1835	217.6	341	1067	2177

Source: Data from Fisheries and Oceans Canada (2005a)

Canadian Focus 14.4

Mining the Cod in the Northwest Atlantic Ocean

In 1497, John Cabot explored waters around New-foundland on behalf of the English Crown. On his return, he wrote with enthusiasm that the Grand Banks were so "swarming with fish [that they] could be taken not only with a net but in baskets let down [and weighted] with a stone."

At that time, cod (*Gadus morhua*) was a bountiful resource on the Grand Banks, a marine ecosystem of 25 million ha. Important cod stocks also occurred off Labrador, Nova Scotia, the Gulf of St. Lawrence, and New England.

By 1550, hundreds of ships were sailing from western Europe, catching cod and preserving it by drying or salting to sell in the hungry markets of Europe. By 1600, about 650 ships were fishing off Newfoundland, and by 1800, about 1600 vessels were doing so. Between 1750 and 1800, the average landings were 190 000 t/y, increasing to 400 000–460 000 t/y during 1800–1900, and to almost 1 million t/y between 1899 and 1904 (Mowat, 1984; Cushing, 1988).

The cod were harvested using hand-lines, long lines, traps, and seines. Many men fished from small dories, often launched from a larger mother ship, such as a celebrated fishing schooner sailing from Newfoundland or Nova Scotia. Although this technology was inefficient, the total fishing effort was large and so was the catch. Consequently, some near-shore cod stocks became depleted, although not those of the offshore banks.

The fishery greatly intensified during the twentieth century because of such technological innovations as

- the development of more efficient netting technologies, particularly trawls and monofilament gill-nets;
- the use of sonar equipment to locate schools of fish; and
- increases in ship-borne capacity to store and process fish, which allowed vessels to stay at sea for a longer time.

The improved technology allowed enormous catches to be made in the northwest Atlantic, particularly in the 1960s when the fishery was essentially an unregulated, open-access enterprise. By this time, unsustainably high catches in the region were causing cod stocks to collapse (see Figure).

In response to an economic crisis caused by the declining stocks of cod, the Government of Canada

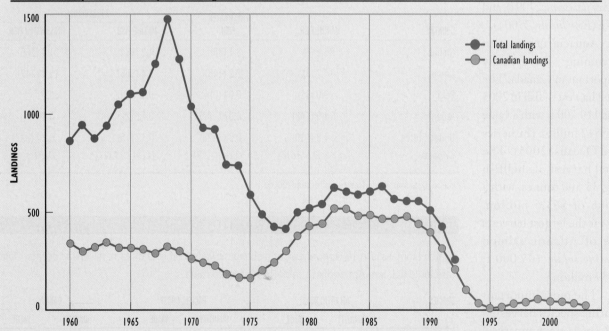

| Recent History of Landings of Cod off Eastern Canada

Note the large decrease in overall landings and the increasing proportion of Canadian landings after the declaration of the 320-km management zone in 1977. A moratorium on cod fishing was declared in 1992, but there has been some bycatch and sporadic quotas since then. Data are in thousands of tonnes.

Sources: Statistics Canada (1994) and Fisheries and Oceans Canada (2005a)

declared a 320-km-wide fisheries-management zone in 1977 and began to control and allocate quotas of fish. The conservation actions resulted in short-lived increases in cod stocks and landings. However, exploitation levels were still too high, and the fishery experienced an even more serious collapse. In 1992, the federal government declared an outright moratorium on commercial fishing for cod, a ban that was still largely in force in 2005 (when this was written). Because only small populations of adult cod are available for spawning, the recovery of the stocks has been slow. However, if allowed, the cod population may eventually recover to the point where it can again be a bounteous resource.

There are several proposed explanations for the collapse of cod stocks in the northwest Atlantic, each based on more or less convincing logic and information. The most important of these are discussed below (Freedman, 1995; Hutchings and Myers, 1995).

The hypothesis of *over-exploitation* suggests that the cod resource was exploited faster than it could regenerate, which caused a decline that became especially acute from the 1970s to early 1990s. The excessive harvesting was caused by several factors. Over the years, scientists had estimated the size and productivity of cod stocks and their maximum sustainable yield (MSY). The *scientific information* was, however, imperfect. First, it is extremely difficult to estimate the abundance of fish in the open ocean. Then, in the late 1980s, an error was discovered in a population model being used to determine stock size and to set quotas. This error caused an over-estimation of cod biomass and MSY, resulting in excessive fishing quotas.

Moreover, politicians and other decision makers in Canada (and everywhere else) are influenced by various *socio-economic considerations* in addition to the advice of scientists. In the context of cod, these pressures come from individual fishers, their associations, and fish companies. These interest groups all need cash flows and livelihoods, in a context where there are few alternatives to fishing for employment and revenue generation. These powerful socio-economic influences can lead to decisions to set quotas larger than those recommended by fishery scientists, a factor that has contributed to the mismanagement of cod stocks and many other resources.

Most of the Grand Banks falls within Canada's 320-km management zone. Some parts, however, extend into international waters, where, until 1995, there was an unregulated multinational fishery. Because cod and most other marine species are mobile and do not recognize the boundaries of management zones, *foreign overfishing* in international waters compromised efforts to conserve the stocks. However, between 1977 and 1991,

Photo 14.4   Before the stocks of cod were heavily exploited, individual fish were much larger than they are today. Immense "mother cod" are now exceedingly rare. This is unfortunate because they have much greater spawning capacity than smaller cod. This photo was taken in Battle Harbour, Labrador in the 1890s.

Source: National Archives of Canada

Canadians landed about 85% of the cod caught in the northwest Atlantic, and their fishery was being regulated.

Humans are not the only predators of marine resources. The *harp seal (Phoca groenlandica)* is the most abundant marine mammal in the northwest Atlantic (about 5 million). The seal population consumes about 1 million t/y of food. However, this seal's prey consists of a wide variety of species, especially crustaceans and small fish such as capelin (*Mallotus villosus*) and arctic cod (*Boreogadus saida*). Even though the cod stocks collapsed at the same time that the seal population was increasing, the minor role of cod in their diet makes it unlikely that seals were an important cause.

Finally, some people believe that the recruitment of cod may have been somehow impaired by *environmental changes*, including several years of cold surface-water temperatures in parts of the Northwest Atlantic. However, there is no direct evidence to support such an environment-related cause of the collapse of the cod stocks.

The simplest and most compelling hypothesis offered to explain the collapse of cod stocks is this: the valuable resource was exploited at an intensity that exceeded its capability for renewal. That is, the cod stocks of Atlantic, one of the world's greatest potentially renewable resources, were fished to *commercial extinction*.

320-km management jurisdiction, but their landings are not included in Table 14.15.

In 1992, the total catch of cod in Atlantic Canada was 239 000 t, of which 80% was landed by Canadian vessels and 20% by the foreign fleet working within the 320-km management zone (Statistics Canada, 1994). The 1992 catch was, however, much smaller than had been attained in recent decades, which averaged as much as 598 000 t during 1982–86 (81% of this was Canadian landings). In fact, the declining harvest reflects a collapse of the cod stocks over most eastern Canadian waters, a resource calamity that resulted in the closure of virtually the entire fishery in 1992 and 1993. The cod stocks were still largely closed to commercial exploitation in 2005, and will likely remain so for several years. In 2003, the cod landings in the Atlantic region were 23 500 t/y, only 10% of the catch in 1992 (Fisheries and Oceans Canada, 2005). The devastation of cod stocks in the northwestern Atlantic Ocean, mostly caused by Canadian overfishing, is a clear example of the mining of a potentially renewable natural resource (see Canadian Focus 14.4).

Other Hunted Animals

Marine Mammals

Marine mammals have also been subjected to intensive commercial hunting in many parts of the world. These animals were initially hunted as a source of oil, which in pre-petroleum times was an extremely valuable commodity used as a fuel in lamps and for cooking. A few species of marine mammals, including Steller's sea cow, the Caribbean monk seal, and the Atlantic grey whale, became extinct from overhunting (see Chapter 26). Many other species or populations of marine mammals became endangered by over-harvesting. Among the best known commercial hunts of marine mammals are those of the great whales of all oceans of the world and the harp seal of eastern Canada.

Whaling: Mining Marine Megamammals

Humans have been hunting whales for centuries. The first species of whale to be commercially hunted was the northern right whale (*Balaena glacialis*), considered the "right" whale to kill because it swims slowly and close to shore and floats when dead. Early records tell of hunts in the Bay of Biscay. Men would row or sail near a right whale, harpoon it, allow it to tow their boat until exhausted, and then repeatedly lance the animal until it bled to death. The carcass was towed to shore and butchered, and its blubber boiled and rendered into valuable oil. Even this crude hunt was enough to eliminate the right whale from European waters.

The development of steam ships made it possible to hunt swifter whales, such as the blue, fin, sei, and minke. The invention of the harpoon gun in 1873, and later the exploding-head harpoon, made it easy to kill even the largest whales. By 1925, giant factory ships could spend months or years in remote waters, processing whales killed by a small fleet of catcher-killer boats, sometimes guided to their prey by spotter aircraft. Whales of all species and sizes could be efficiently located, killed, and processed. This onslaught resulted in a rapid, and profitable, depletion of whale stocks.

With only a few exceptions, whale populations were not over-harvested to extirpation, but rather to **commercial extinction**, or to a small population that was no longer profitable to find and kill. The sequential exploitation of a whale community is best illustrated by the hunt in Antarctic waters, where five species initially co-existed in great abundance (Figure 14.2).

In response to concerns about declining populations of whales, the International Whaling Commission (IWC) was established in 1949. The IWC was given a mandate to develop and implement conservation-related controls over the multinational, fiercely competitive, highly capitalized, and profitable whaling industry. Unfortunately, the initial efforts of the IWC were not very successful, mainly because it is extremely difficult to estimate whale stock sizes and recruitment rates and to determine accurate sustainable yields. In addition, the whaling nations were not particularly cooperative, and the IWC was not aggressive in setting and enforcing quotas small enough to ensure that whale populations would not be depleted. These problems are to be expected whenever a for-profit enterprise is allowed to regulate and police itself. According to J.L. McHugh, a former commissioner and chairperson of the IWC, "From the time of the first meeting of the Commission...almost all major actions or failures to act were governed by short-range economic considerations rather than by the requirements of conservation" (cited in Ellis, 1991).

Because of its enormous size, reaching 32 m and 136 t for the largest male animals, the blue whale (*Balaenoptera musculus*) was initially the most profitable species in the Antarctic seas. The original population was about 180 000 blue whales, and as many as 29 000 animals were killed in a single year (Figure 14.2; note that during the Second World War, as few as 59 animals were har-

FIGURE 14.2 | Whaling in Antarctic Waters

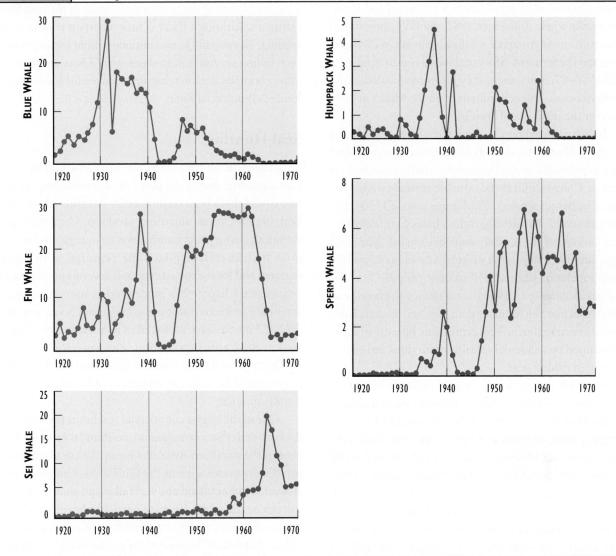

Annual catches in thousands of whales.

Source: Data from Ellis (1991)

vested in a year). Between 1955 and 1962, declining stocks of blue whales meant an annual harvest of only 1000–2000. After 1965, killing this species was prohibited by the IWC. In total, about 331 000 blue whales were killed in Antarctic waters between 1920 and 1965. The present Antarctic population of blue whales is fewer than 2000, only about 1% of their initial abundance. The global population is less than 10 000 individuals.

As blue whales became depleted, the fin whale (*B. physalus*) became the favoured species of the Antarctic hunt. This is the second-largest species, up to 21 m long. As many as 29 000 animals were harvested in a year, causing this species to decline, though not to commercial

extinction. More than 704 000 fin whales were killed in this region. The present population is less than 85 000 animals, about 21% of the original abundance.

As the largest species became difficult to harvest because of their increasing rarity, initially "less desirable" species were hunted. These were the sei whale (*B. borealis*), humpback whale (*Megaptera novaeangliae*), sperm whale (*Physeter macrocephalus*), and minke whale (*B. acutorostrata*). These smaller species were also over-harvested, and their populations declined markedly (Figure 14.2).

Toward the end of the hunt in the Antarctic Ocean, the population of blue whales had been reduced by about 99%, humpback whales by 97%, sei whales by 82%, and fin whales by 79%. By the early 1980s, whalers were killing mostly the relatively small (up to 9.1 m long) and abundant minke whale. Finally, in 1982, the IWC announced a moratorium on Antarctic whaling, to begin in 1985–86. Japan and the former USSR continued a commercial hunt until 1986–87. Since then, only Japan has whaled in the southern ocean, killing hundreds of minke whales in most years for the purposes of "research."

Industrial whaling also depleted whale stocks in the Northern Hemisphere. Early European explorers found large populations of northern right whales in waters off Atlantic Canada, and these valuable animals were soon hunted by Basque whalers. The Basque hunt of 1530–1610 killed about 25 000–40 000 right whales (but few afterward because of the severely depleted stocks). The right whale survives today in the western Atlantic as an endangered population of about 350 animals, only 3–4% of the original abundance. Although this species has been protected from hunting for more than 50 years, its abundance is not increasing much. This is probably because of mortality caused by accidental collisions with ships and entanglement in fishing gear.

Soon after right whales were depleted off eastern North America, more northerly populations of bowhead whales (*Balaena mysticetus*) were discovered in arctic Canada, Alaska, and eastern Siberia. Like right whales, the slow-swimming bowhead could be easily overtaken by whaling boats and killed. The population of about 55 000 bowheads in the western Arctic was soon depleted. Bowhead whales are now rare, although their populations are slowly increasing. These animals are no longer hunted commercially, although a hunt by Inuit in northern Alaska kills 20–40 animals per year. In 1996, Canadian Inuit were allowed to again hunt a few bowhead whales, a practice that is permitted because of the importance of this species in their culture.

A final example of depletion of a whale stock involves the grey whale (*Eschrichtius robustus*) of western North America. This species winters and breeds in warm waters off Mexico and migrates up the Pacific coast to summer in the western Arctic Ocean. Commercial hunting of grey whales began in 1845 and largely ended by 1900 because the stock had been reduced to an endangered several thousand animals. These were protected from further hunting, and the grey whale has since increased to approximately its pre-exploitation abundance of about 24 000 animals off western North America. However, the species remains extirpated off western Europe and is critically endangered in eastern Asia.

In total, more than 2.5 million whales of all species were killed during the commercial hunts of the past four centuries. Although there is now a ban on commercial whaling, Norway and Japan continue to hunt minke whales, each killing several hundred per year. These and several other countries are lobbying aggressively for a return to a limited commercial hunt.

Seal Hunting

Seals breed on land or sea ice, often in dense populations. Consequently, during the past few centuries, huge numbers of seals have been commercially slaughtered for their skin, blubber, meat, and other products. Until the mid-twentieth century, seal hunting was an unregulated enterprise that severely depleted the resource, with many regional and local extirpations, and several species made extinct (see Chapter 26). Since then, conservation measures have protected most seal populations. Some severely depleted species have managed to increase in abundance, such as the California sea lion (*Zalophus californianus*), northern fur seal (*Callorhinus ursinus*), and northern elephant seal (*Mirounga angustirostris*) of Pacific waters of North America.

One of the largest commercial seal hunts has involved the harp seal (*Phoca groenlandica*), an abundant species that lives in the northern Atlantic Ocean. These seals breed prolifically on pack ice in the Gulf of St. Lawrence and around Newfoundland and Labrador and summer in the eastern Arctic. Harp seals are particularly vulnerable to hunters in April, when large numbers of newborn pups, called "whitecoats" because of the colour of their birth fur, lie about on the pack ice. Because they are not yet aquatic, the pups can easily be approached and killed. Adults are also concentrated at that time and can be caught in nets, shot on the ice, or clubbed if they try to defend their young. The skins of harp seals are a valuable commodity, and many people enjoy eating their meat.

Historically, the largest hunts were by Newfoundlanders, but hunters from Labrador, Nova Scotia, Prince Edward Island, and Quebec have also been active. The numbers of seals harvested in any year mostly depended on ice conditions, which affect how close sealers can get to the whelping aggregations of seals. During the heyday of this enterprise, more than 600 000 animals were harvested annually, as occurred in 1831, 1840, 1843, and 1844 (Busch, 1985). Overall, about 21 million harp seals were taken between 1800 and 1914. This vast slaughter of a large wild animal has only a few parallels, including the massacre of bison in the nineteenth century (Chapter 26), the modern hunt of kangaroos in Australia, and that of deer in the Americas.

Another 12 million harp seals were taken between 1915 and 1982, up to 380 000 in one year (1956). Since then, the harvests have been smaller, mostly because of controversy about a commercial harvest of wild-animal babies and the consequently diminished market for seal products. For instance, in 1984, the European Union (EU) banned the import of whitecoat pelts, which resulted in reduced harvests in Canada, from 190 000/y in 1981–82 to 19 000–80 000/y during 1983–90. (Note that young harp seals are not called "whitecoats" after they are 9–10 days old, when they begin to shed their white fur. Older young can still be legally imported to the EU, but the most lucrative market was for whitecoats.)

In recent decades, animal-rights and conservation advocates, and elements of the popular media, have engaged in sensationalized reporting of the hunting of harp seals in Atlantic Canada. This has resulted in seal hunting being popularly regarded as a cruel and barbaric enterprise, mostly because baby seals, which are extremely attractive animals, are the objects of the hunt. The young seals are killed by clubbing or shooting, which are humane methods of slaughter. Unfortunately, some sealers are not competent in these killing methods, and videos have shown that during the rush to harvest young seals, animals might be inadequately clubbed and then skinned while apparently "alive" (or at least still twitching—the seals are likely brain dead). Video images like this are extremely upsetting to most people, and they have been widely publicized by well-organized opponents of the Canadian hunt of harp seals.

Many people, however, do not agree with the portrayal of the seal hunt as being unusually "cruel and brutal." They contend that the commercial harvesting of wild seals is no more brutal than the slaughter of domestic livestock. For example, earlier in this chapter, we learned that about 34 million large mammals and 600 million chickens are raised and slaughtered annually in Canada, often under cruel conditions, to provide meat and other products (see also Chapter 24). Clearly, there are elements of cruelty in the commercial slaughter of both wild animals and livestock. An analysis of the ethics of killing animals should also, however, recognize that seals are wild creatures while livestock are specifically bred, raised, and killed for consumption by humans. It is up to philosophers, and to individual consumers of animal products, to determine which of these commercial slaughters of animals, if either, is the greater moral outrage.

Although the intense hunting caused harp seals to decrease in abundance, the species was never depleted to biological or commercial endangerment. This was not a result of a conservation ethic by the sealers or their industry. In fact, sealers typically killed as many harp seals as possible that were encountered, particularly before 1970 when the Canadian government began to regulate the hunt through a quota system. In general, only the physical difficulty of hunting in treacherous pack ice limited the numbers of seals that could be found and killed, and so prevented a severe depletion of their population.

When the commercial hunt was reduced in the late 1980s, the global abundance of harp seals was about 3 million animals, including 2 million in Canadian waters. Even then, the harp seal was among the world's most populous large wild animals. In 2005, its abundance in Canadian waters was about 5 million (Fisheries and Oceans Canada, 2005b). In fact, the rapidly increasing harp seal population is alarming some people, who are concerned that the seals are "eating too many fish" (although there is little evidence to support this idea; see Canadian Focus 14.4 on page 254). In any event, harp seals are again being harvested in large numbers. This harvest is intended to cull the seal population somewhat, while providing economic benefits through the sale of meat, hides, and other products (including penises, for which there is a recently emerged market in eastern Asia). The most recent quota allows the harvest of 975 000 harp seals over three years (2003–05), including adults and recently moulted young seals (but not whitecoats). The 2004 commercial hunt resulted in direct product sales of $16.5 million, compared with $13 million in 2003 and $21 million in 2002. A nominal goal of the management plan is to reduce the abundance of harp seals to about 70% of the present abundance (to 3.85 million), where it would likely be maintained.

Terrestrial Hunting

Many terrestrial animals are also hunted in large numbers, including large mammals such as deer, antelope, bears, pigs, and kangaroos. Many birds are also hunted, particularly waterfowl, grouse, pheasants, and shorebirds. Much hunting of wild animals is undertaken for subsistence purposes, but sport hunting is also important in some regions.

Hunting is a popular activity in Canada. Many Canadians hunt, whether for subsistence, as a blood sport, or for both reasons. The most commonly hunted large mammals are species in the deer family, but other animals are also taken. The most important big-game species in

Photo 14.5 About 270 000 white-tailed and mule deer (*Odocoileus virginianus* and *O. hemionus,* respectively) are harvested by hunters each year in Canada. This mule deer was photographed in Jasper National Park, Alberta.

Canada (harvested during the 2003 hunt; these are rounded numbers) are the following:

white-tailed deer (*Odocoileus virginianus*)	278 200 harvested
moose (*Alces alces*)	72 750
mule deer (*Odocoileus hemionus*)	58 050
caribou (*Rangifer tarandus*)	43 750
black bear (*Ursus americanus*)	21 900
elk (*Cervus canadensis*)	10 450
pronghorn antelope (*Antilocapra americanus*)	460
wolf (*Canis lupus*)	1 200
mountain sheep (*Ovis canadensis*)	575
mountain goat (*Oreamnos americanus*)	642
cougar (*Felis concolor*)	300
grizzly bear (*Ursus arctos*)	290

(These data were compiled from information provided by provincial and territorial governments. However, the data are incomplete in that they are based on reports by hunters; kills due to poaching, i.e., illegal hunting, are not included. In addition, hunting by Aboriginal Canadians is not usually reported or is considered proprietary information, particularly in northern Canada.)

Although the demand for wild furs has declined significantly in recent decades, fur-bearing animals are still trapped in large numbers in Canada. In 2002, about 1.02 million furbearers were trapped, including 280 100

muskrat, 254 400 beaver, 112 600 lynx, 76 900 squirrels, 58 600 raccoons, 55 200 coyotes, and 48 200 fox (Statistics Canada, 2004). An additional 1.13 million mink were raised and harvested on fur farms.

Waterfowl are also harvested in large numbers in Canada. In total, about 1.4 million ducks were taken by hunters in 2002, along with 875 000 geese (Canadian Wildlife Service, 2005). This is considerably smaller than the U.S. harvest from this essentially same population of migratory waterfowl, which totalled about 7 million ducks and 3.2 million geese. The most commonly hunted game birds in Canada (2002 data) are the following:

mallard (*Anas platyrhynchos*)	547 000 harvested
black duck (*Anas rubripes*)	123 000
green-winged teal (*Anas crecca*)	132 000
wood duck (*Aix sponsa*)	121 000
ring-necked duck (*Aythya collaris*)	95 000
lesser scaup (*Aythya affinis*)	33 000
another 22 duck species	349 000
Canada goose (*Branta canadensis*)	650 000
snow goose (*Chen caerulescens*)	172 000
white-fronted goose (*Anser albifrons*)	52 000
murres (*Uria lomvia & U. aalge*)	158 000
woodcock (*Scolopax minor*)	49 500
snipe (*Gallinago gallinago*)	14 000
sandhill crane (*Grus canadensis*)	7 900
coot (*Fulica americana*)	2 000

Photo 14.6 More than 800 000 geese are harvested by hunters each year in Canada. This snow goose (*Chen caerulescens*) was photographed on Ellesmere Island.

Conclusions

Renewable resources are the fundamental basis of a sustainable economy. In this chapter, we learned that the most important kinds of renewable resources harvested in Canada and the rest of the world are freshwater, agricultural products, forest biomass, fish, and hunted birds and mammals (renewable sources of energy were described in Chapter 13). Some of these are wild resources that are harvested from natural ecosystems, while others are managed in agricultural systems to achieve higher yields (including agroforestry and aquaculture). In general, Canada is a country rich in renewable resources, with a bountiful surplus available to export to other countries. Nevertheless, there are many examples of the depletion of potentially renewable resources by excessive harvesting or inadequate management of the regeneration.

Key Terms

renewable resource	ecological conversion
surface water	deforestation
groundwater	silvicultural management
aquifer	plantation
production	agroforestry
productivity	aquaculture
agricultural site capability	commercial extinction
tilth	

Questions for Review

1. What is meant by a renewable natural resource? Illustrate the principle by referring to one of the following: surface water and groundwater, agricultural site capability, timber, or a hunted wild animal.

2. What are the most important renewable resources in Canada? Indicate, giving reasons, whether you think those resources are being used in a sustainable manner.

3. Use the data on resources in Chapters 13 and 14 to develop a "resource profile" for the province or territory where you live. Consider the relative importance of non-renewable and renewable resources in the economy and the implications for longer-term sustainability.

4. What are the criteria for ecological sustainability?

Questions for Discussion

1. Identify a potentially renewable natural resource that has been over-harvested and depleted in your region. What reasons are there for the unsustainable use of the resource?

2. Should relatively abundant species of whales (e.g., minke) or harp seals be hunted? Your answer should consider whether the species can be harvested in a sustainable manner and should also address the ethics of hunting.

3. What are the political and economic problems of sharing water resources between countries or regions?

4. Although food can be purchased in a store, it does not really come from there—it is harvested from wild ecosystems or is cultivated in agriculture. Consider the food you eat and the ethical and environmental issues associated with its production. You may find this question to be particularly interesting if you focus on meat, which is lethally harvested from millions of animals each year in Canada.

Exploring Issues

1. The Minister of the federal Department of Fisheries and Oceans has been asked to allow the resumption of whale hunting in Canada. The minister asks for your advice on the matter, and you decide to develop lists of benefits and damages that would occur if it were allowed. Prepare these lists and describe how each item relates to the ecological sustainability of a potential whale harvest.

References

Bolen, E.G. and W.L. Robinson. 2002. *Wildlife Ecology and Management*. 5th ed. Upper Saddle River, NJ: Prentice Hall.

Busch, B.C. 1985. *The War Against the Seals: A History of the North American Seal Fishery*. Kingston, ON: McGill-Queen's University Press.

Canadian Council of Forest Ministers (CCRM). 2005. *Compendium of Canadian Forestry Statistics*. Ottawa, ON: CCRM. http://nfdp.ccfm.org/compendium/index_e.php

Canadian Wildlife Service. 2003. *Population Status of Migratory Game Birds in Canada, 2003*. www.cws.ec.gc.ca/publications/status/nov03/index_e.cfm

Chiras, D.D., J.P. Reganold, and O.S. Owen. 2001. *Natural Resource Conservation: Management for a Sustainable Future*. 8th ed. Upper Saddle River, NJ: Prentice Hall.

Craig, J.R., D.J. Vaughan, B.J. Skinner, and D. Vaughan. 2001. *Resources of the Earth: Origin, Use, and Environmental Impact*. 3rd ed. Upper Saddle River, NJ: Prentice Hall.

Cushing, D.H. 1988. *The Provident Sea*. Cambridge: Cambridge University Press.

Ehrlich, P.R., A.H. Ehrlich, and J.P. Holdren. 1977. *Ecoscience: Population, Resources, Environment.* San Francisco: W.H. Freeman.

Ellis, R. 1991. *Men and Whales.* New York: Knopf.

Environment Canada. 2004. *Municipal Water Use Report.* www.ec.gc.ca/water/en/info/pubs/sss/e_mun2001.htm

Environment Canada. 2005a. *Water Use.* www.ec.gc.ca/water/en/manage/use/e_use.htm

Environment Canada. 2005b. *The Nature of Water.* www.ec.gc.ca/water/en/nature/e_nature.htm

Fisheries and Oceans Canada. 2005a. *Landings.* www.dfo-mpo.gc.ca/communic/statistics/main_e.htm

Fisheries and Oceans Canada. 2005b. *Technical Briefing on the Harp Seal Hunt in Atlantic Canada.* www.dfo-mpo.gc.ca/misc/seal_briefing_e.htm

Freedman, B. 1995. *Environmental Ecology.* 2nd ed. San Diego, CA: Academic.

Holechek, J.L., R.A. Cole, J.T. Fisher, and R. Valdez. 2002. *Natural Resources: Ecology, Economics, and Policy.* 2nd ed. East Rutherford, NJ: Prentice Hall.

Hutchings, J.A. and R.A. Myers. 1993. What can be learned from the collapse of a "renewable" resource? *Atlantic cod, Gadus morhua, of Newfoundland and Labrador.* St. John's, NF: Department of Fisheries and Oceans, Science Branch.

Hutchings, J.A. and R.A. Myers. 1995. The biological collapse of Atlantic cod off Newfoundland and Labrador: An exploration of historical changes in exploitation, harvesting technology, and management. In: *The North Atlantic Fisheries: Successes, Failures, and Challenges.* Charlottetown, PEI: Institute of Island Studies. pp. 39–93.

Martin, E.M. and P.I. Padding. 2002. *Preliminary Estimates of waterfowl harvest and hunter activity during the 2001 hunting season.* Laurel, MD: U.S. Fish and Wildlife Service. www.fws.gov/migratorybirds/reports/whs/water-fowl%20harvest%20report%202002.pdf

Miller, G.T. 1990. *Resource Conservation and Management.* Belmont, CA: Wadsworth.

Mowat, F. 1984. *Sea of Slaughter.* Toronto: McClelland & Stewart.

National Marine Fisheries Service (NMFS). 1991. *Endangered Whales: Status Update.* Silver Spring, MD: U.S. Dept. of Commerce, National Oceanic and Atmospheric Administration, NMFS.

Natural Resources Canada. 2005. *The State of Canada's Forests, 2003–2004.* www.nrcan-rncan.gc.ca/cfs-scf/national/what-quoi/sof/latest_e.html

Statistics Canada. 1994. *Human Activity and the Environment 1994.* Ottawa: Statistics Canada.

Statistics Canada. 2000. *Human Activity and the Environment.* Ottawa: Environment Accounts and Statistics Division.

Statistics Canada. 2004. *Human Activity and the Environment, Annual Statistics 2004.* http://estat.statcan.ca/content/english/articles/other/0000416-201-XIE.pdf

Statistics Canada. 2005. *E-Stat.* http://estat.statcan.ca/content/english/over.shtml

Tietenberg, T. 2002. *Environmental and Natural Resource Economics.* 6th ed. Boston, MS: Addison Wesley.

Vitousek, P.M., P.R. Ehrlich, A.H. Ehrlich, and P.A. Matson. 1986. Human appropriation of the products of photosynthesis. *Bioscience,* **36**: 368–73.

World Resources Institute (WRI). 1998. *World Resources 1998–99: A Guide to the Global Environment: Environmental Change and Human Health.* New York: Oxford University Press.

World Resources Institute (WRI). 2000. *World Resources 2000–01: People and Ecosystems, The Fraying Web of Life.* Washington, DC: WRI.

World Resources Institute. 2005. *Earth Trends. The Environmental Information Portal.* Washington, DC: WRI.

Informative Websites

Bioenergy Information Network. http://bioenergy.ornl.gov/

Visit this site to discover facts about fast-growing trees, grasses, and residues and how they are used for fuel and power.

Ecological Society of America (ESA). *Effects of Aquaculture on World Fish Supplies.* www.esa.org/Science/Issues/FileEnglish/issue8.pdf

This publication of the ESA explains how aquaculture can increase the amount of protein available to be harvested from the oceans and discusses the environmental risks to be managed.

Environmental Literacy Council. www.enviroliteracy.org/

This organization provides a rich array of materials about agricultural crops, forests, water, and other renewable resources.

FAOSTAT. FAO Statistical Databases. http://faostat.fao.org/

The Food and Agricultural Organization of the United Nations (FAO) is an international organization that focuses on agricultural development and production. This website provides access to a wide range of useful information about agriculture, forestry, and fisheries.

Fisheries and Oceans Canada. www.dfo-mpo.gc.ca

Departmental publications, fisheries statistics, and related links are just a few of the resources available at this site.

Fisheries and Oceans Canada. www.dfo-mpo.gc.ca/communic/statistics/main_e.htm

The Statistical Services Unit of the Department of Fisheries and Oceans reports on a wide range of fisheries data.

International Institute for Sustainable Development (IISD). www.iisd.org/

The IISD is a Canadian-centred international organization whose mission is to champion innovation, enabling societies to live sustainably.

Soils of Canada.
http://web.unbc.ca/~quarles/nres/soc/soc.htm

This page is a collection of selected soil profiles representing the great groups within the Canadian System of Soil Classification.

Solstice. http://sol.crest.org/

Solstice is the Internet information service of the Renewable Energy Policy Project and the Center for Renewable Energy and Sustainable Technology (REPP-CREST). This site also has discussion groups, related links, and documents and databases.

Statistics Canada. www.statcan.ca

Statistics Canada is the country's national statistical agency and has programs organized into three broad subject areas: demographic and social, socio-economic, and economic. Take a quiz and test your knowledge of Canada here.

Trade Services Agri-Food Industry.
http://ats-sea.agr.ca/supply/factsheet-e.htm

Click on any of the html files at this website to find information about Canada's food industries.

Worldwatch Institute. www.worldwatch.org/

This international organization provides useful information on a wide range of topics, including the environmental impacts of agriculture, sustainability of agriculture, and food security.

World Resources Institute. Earth Trends. The Environmental Information Portal.
http://earthtrends.wri.org/

The WRI is a leading environmental organization that provides excellent information about resource issues.

CBC ⬤   # Canadian Case 3

Fished Out

It is becoming increasingly obvious that the condition of the world's fisheries tells a grim and sad story. In region after region throughout the world, marine scientists are finding evidence of a severe depletion of previously abundant stocks of marine fishes. In all cases the damage has been caused by the insatiable over-exploitation of this potentially renewable resource. Usually, the worst offenders are industrial-scale fishing industries bent on maximizing their catches with little attention paid to the sustainability of their enterprise.

The over-fishing has occurred throughout the high seas of the world—in poorly regulated waters beyond the jurisdictions of nearby coastal nations. In many other cases, however, the damage has occurred in regulated fisheries, in which the catch levels were being set by governmental agencies. The problem has been that the regulations were inadequately enforced and were therefore ignored by the fishers, and/or the quotas were set at too high a level to be sustainable.

Over-fishing has been the case for most stocks of medium-sized fishes, including many populations of Pacific salmon that utilize the coastal waters and rivers of British Columbia, as well as cod and other groundfish of eastern Canada found in the coastal waters of Newfoundland and Labrador, New Brunswick, Nova Scotia, Prince Edward Island, and Quebec. Over-fishing is also a terrible problem for stocks of the largest fish species, such as the bluefin tuna, swordfish, and various species of sharks in oceans all around the world. The voracious harvesting of these top predators, as well as most other commercially valuable species, has depleted their once-plentiful stocks to the degree that it is no longer profitable to fish them—a situation known as economic extinction. The effects of this damage can be seen in marine food resources in coastal waters throughout the world, and also in open-ocean ecosystems far from the continental shores.

It is appalling that our national governments and international organizations (such as the United Nations) have allowed such damage to be caused to potentially renewable marine resources. In many cases, however, there is still time to repair the damage. In the worst cases, there must be strict moratoriums during which no fishing is allowed, a drastic action that may allow the depleted stocks to recover in abundance. In cases where the stocks are still large enough to allow for some harvesting, precautionary limits must be determined and set on the fishing effort. These actions must be strictly enforced in the coastal waters of Canada and other countries and also on the high seas where international cooperation and action are required.

There is also a critical role for marine protected areas or regions where no fishing or other industrial activities are allowed in the conservation of fish stocks. Protected areas provide a crucial service by enhancing the regeneration of fish stocks in surrounding areas where fishing is still permitted. Protected areas also allow natural ecological communities to exist on at least some of the seascape.

These issues are explored from a Canadian context in the accompanying CBC video resource.

Questions

1. What has caused the collapse of so many initially abundant stocks of marine fishes? Clearly, these animals comprise a potentially renewable natural resource. What went wrong?

2. Do you think that it would be sensible to have a system of marine protected areas? What would the likely ecological and economic benefits be?

Video Resource

"Fished Out," CBC The National, May 14, 2003.

Selected References

Fisheries and Oceans Canada. 2005.
http://www.dfo-mpo.gc.ca/home-accueil_e.htm
Greenpeace. 2005. Canadian Atlantic Fisheries Collapse.
http://archive.greenpeace.org/comms/cbio/
cancod.html

Pollution and Disturbance as Environmental Stressors

15

CHAPTER OBJECTIVES

After completing this chapter, you will be able to

1. Describe the nature and causes of environmental stress and explain how ecosystems respond to changes in its intensity.
2. Compare and contrast contamination and pollution.
3. Identify examples of naturally occurring pollution and disturbance, and discuss how knowledge of these phenomena can contribute to understanding the effects of anthropogenic stressors.
4. Outline the differences between toxicology and ecotoxicology.
5. Compare voluntary and involuntary risks.
6. Identify the typical steps in a risk assessment of a predicted exposure to a toxic chemical.

CHAPTER OUTLINE

- Environmental Stressors
- Contamination and Pollution
- Disturbance
- Ecotoxicology
- Environmental Risks
- Conclusions

Environmental Stressors

Environmental stressors are factors that can constrain productivity, reproductive success, and ecological development (see Chapter 9). To some degree, environmental stressors affect all organisms as well as their populations, communities, and ecoscapes (landscapes and seascapes). Many stressors are natural in origin, being associated with such environmental factors as

- competition, predation, disease, and other interactions among organisms;
- constraints related to climate or to inadequate or excessive nutrients, moisture, or space; and
- disturbances such as wildfire and windstorms.

The effects of natural stressors are not always negative. Some individuals, populations, and communities may benefit from the ecological effects of natural stress, even while others suffer.

Increasingly, however, stressors associated with human activities are critically influencing Earth's species and ecosystems. In too many cases, these anthropogenic stressors are causing important damage to resources needed to sustain humans and their economy, and also to Earth's natural biodiversity and ecosystems, more generally.

Photo 15.1 Wildfire, windstorms, and insect outbreaks can result in extensive disturbances affecting entire landscapes. This photo shows an area of eastern hemlock (*Tsuga canadensis*) trees that have been killed by several years of intense defoliation by the pale-winged grey moth (*Iridopsis ephyraria*) in Nova Scotia.

| **FIGURE 15.1** | The Relationship between Environmental Stressors and Responses |

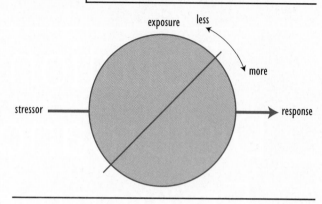

This is a diagrammatic representation of the relationship between stressors and biological/ecological responses. Stressors are environmental factors that affect organisms and ecosystems. They can exist at varying exposures, as is suggested by the graphical dial, which can be turned to change the intensity of the stressor, much like a volume knob of a radio can be used to increase or decrease the sound level. If a threshold for biological or ecological tolerance is exceeded, then a response will occur.

Source: Modified from Freedman (2005)

Environmental stressors can occur as intense, short-lived events of destruction, also known as **disturbances**. Alternatively, stressors may exert their influence over an extended period of time—that is, in a *chronic* manner. The interaction of organisms with an environmental stressor at a particular place and time is called **exposure**. Exposure can be instantaneous or it may accumulate over time. If an exposure is intense enough, it will cause some sort of biological or ecological change, called a **response**. It is important to understand, however, that individuals, populations, communities, and ecosystems are capable of tolerating a range of intensities of environmental stressors without suffering any significant damage. In other words, *thresholds* of biological or ecological *tolerance* must be exceeded before damage is caused (Figure 15.1).

Damage occurs when stressors elicit responses that result in a degradation of environmental quality. Such responses include, for example, illness or death caused by pesticide exposure of wild animals, reduced productivity of ecosystems, and the endangerment of elements of biodiversity. In this chapter we examine a conceptual framework for the study of damage caused by environmental stressors. In the following 11 chapters, we will deal with specific groups of stressors and examine many examples and case studies of environmental damage.

Kinds of Environmental Stressors

The diverse kinds of environmental stressors can be grouped into several classes, although they are not all mutually exclusive.

Physical stress is a type of disturbance that involves an intense exposure to kinetic energy, which damages habitats and ecosystems. Physical stress includes such disruptive events as a hurricane or tornado, a seismic sea wave (tsunami), the blast of a volcanic eruption, an explosion, or trampling by heavy machinery or hikers.

Wildfire is another disturbance, involving the uncontrolled combustion of the biomass of an ecosystem. Wildfires can be ignited by humans or naturally by lightning or lava flows. Severe fires consume much of the biomass of an ecosystem, particularly trees, but even less severe wildfires can kill many organisms by scorching and toxic-gas poisoning.

Chemical pollution occurs when one or more substances occur in concentrations high enough to elicit physiological responses in organisms, potentially causing toxicity and ecological change. Chemical stressors include pesticides, gases such as sulphur dioxide and ozone, and toxic elements such as mercury, lead, and arsenic. Pollution can also result from excessive nutrients, which can distort productivity and other ecological functions. Note that the presence of a potentially toxic agent in the environment does not necessarily cause pollution. (We examine the distinction between contamination and pollution later in this chapter.)

Thermal pollution is caused by the release of heat (thermal energy) into the environment, resulting in ecological stress because species vary in their tolerance of temperature extremes. Thermal stress may occur at natural springs and submarine vents where geologically heated water is emitted. It is also associated with discharges of hot water from power plants and other industrial facilities.

Radiation stress is caused by excessive exposure to ionizing energy. The radiation can be emitted by nuclear wastes or explosions, or it can be diagnostic X-rays or solar ultraviolet energy.

Climatic stress is associated with insufficient or excessive regimes of temperature, moisture, solar radiation, wind, or combinations of these.

Biological stressors are associated with interactions among organisms, such as competition, herbivory, predation, parasitism, and disease (see Chapter 9). For example, individuals of the same or different species may compete for essential resources that are limited in supply. Herbivory,

Photo 15.2 "Biological pollution" is caused when humans introduce species beyond their natural range, where they may cause ecological damage. This non-native lupine (*Lupinus polyphyllus*) has been introduced widely to eastern Canada, where it thrives in gardens and along roadsides. Although it is an attractive wildflower, it displaces indigenous plants and is not eaten by many native animals.

predation, parasitism, and disease are *trophic* interactions, in which one species exploits another. Exploitation can be anthropogenic, as when wild animals or trees are harvested, or it can be natural, perhaps associated with defoliating insects or disease-causing pathogens.

Biological pollution can occur when humans change ecological conditions by releasing organisms beyond their natural ranges. This might involve intentional or unintentional introductions of alien species that invade and alter natural ecosystems, or it may be the release of pathogens into the environment through discharges of raw sewage.

Ecological Responses to Changes in Environmental Stress

An ecosystem that is disrupted by a disturbance (i.e., an intense, short-lived event) typically suffers mortality among its species, along with various damages to its structural (e.g., species composition, biomass distribution) and functional properties (e.g., productivity and nutrient cycling). Once the disturbance is over, a process of recovery through succession begins. If succession proceeds for a long enough time, it will eventually restore another mature ecosystem, perhaps one similar to that existing before the disturbance.

Chronic stressors, which operate over longer periods of time, include ionizing radiation and many types of chemical and thermal pollution. Depending on the intensity of exposure to the chronic stressor, organisms may suffer acute toxicity resulting in tissue damage or death, or chronic toxicity resulting in decreased productivity.

Increased exposure to environmental stressors can result in evolutionary changes within populations if individual organisms vary in their tolerance to the stressors and those differences are genetically based. Under such conditions, natural selection in favour of tolerant individuals will eventually result in increased tolerance at the population level. At the community level, relatively vulnerable species will be reduced in abundance or eliminated from sites if the intensity of stress increases markedly. The niches of those species may then be occupied by more tolerant members of the community or by invading species that are capable of exploiting a stressful but weakly competitive habitat.

Long-term ecological change will result from a prolonged intensification of stress. Consider, for example, a new smelter that causes chronic pollution in a forested landscape. The intense toxic stress can damage the tree-sized plants of the original forest and may eventually make them give way to shrub-sized and herbaceous vegetation. If the long-term toxic stress is extremely severe, the landscape may lose its vegetation entirely. This type of ecological damage has actually occurred around some Canadian smelters, such as those near Sudbury, Ontario (Chapter 16).

These kinds of ecological damage involve changes in the composition and dominance of species in communities, in the spatial distribution of biomass, and in functions such as productivity, litter decomposition, and nutrient cycling. Because a smelter is a discrete, point source of environmental stress, the ecological responses will eventually stabilize as *gradients* of community change that radiate outward, in a downstream or downwind direction, from the source of pollution.

Occasionally, the intensity of an environmental stress decreases in time and space. When this happens, the ecological responses are, in many respects, the reverse of the degradation seen when the stress intensifies. These changes represent a process of recovery through succession. In the case of the Sudbury smelters, emissions of pollutants have decreased greatly since the installation of pollution-control technology. This resulted in decreased toxic stress in the surrounding environment, which allowed some ecological recovery to occur (Chapters 16 and 18).

Ecologists have described the general attributes of ecosystems that have been subjected to severe stress for different periods of time. As environmental stress intensifies significantly (e.g., by increasing pollution), the following changes are commonly observed:

1. Rates of mortality increase.

2. Species richness decreases.

3. Nutrients and biomass are depleted.

4. Rates of community respiration exceed production, so net production becomes negative.

5. Sensitive species are replaced by more tolerant ones.

6. Top predators and large-bodied species are lost from the ecosystem.

7. Previously self-maintaining ecosystems may have to be managed by humans in order to maintain their desirable attributes; for example, action may be needed to enhance the declining population of rare or economically valuable species that have become threatened by anthropogenic stressors.

Ecosystems that are chronically subjected to intense stress (e.g., climate-stressed tundra) eventually stabilize. Typically, the stable ecosystems are low in species richness, simple in structure and function, and dominated by relatively small, long-lived species. As well, they have low rates of productivity, decomposition, and nutrient cycling.

Note that these sorts of ecological change are often considered to represent damage and are viewed as a degradation of *ecological integrity* and *environmental quality* (see Chapter 27 and In Detail 27.2).

Contamination and Pollution

Pollution is caused by exposure to chemicals or energy at an intensity that exceeds the tolerance of organisms. As such, pollution is judged to occur when toxicity to organisms, or other kinds of ecological damage, can be demonstrated. Pollution can affect humans and other species, as well as communities and larger ecosystems.

Pollution is often caused by exposure to toxic chemicals in concentrations large enough to poison at least some organisms. Pollution can also be caused by non-toxic exposures to environmental stressors—for example, the excessive fertilization of water (which causes eutrophication; see Chapter 20), the release of waste heat into the environment, or the discharge of raw sewage containing microbial pathogens.

Contamination refers to those much more common situations in which potentially damaging stressors are present in the environment, but at intensities too low to cause detrimental effects. For example, a certain chemical may occur in a higher concentration than is normally encountered in the environment. However, if its concentration is too low to cause measurable toxicity to organisms, or to affect other ecological components or processes, the chemical is contaminating, not polluting.

For example, metals such as aluminum, cadmium, copper, lead, mercury, nickel, and zinc are present in all parts of the environment, including all organisms, in at least trace concentrations. If the detection limits of the available analytical chemistry are sensitive enough, this universal contamination by metals can be demonstrated. Potentially, all metals are toxic. However, metals (and any other chemicals) must be present in a high enough concentration for a long enough period of time to actually poison organisms and cause ecological damage. In other words, the exposure must exceed biological tolerances before damage is caused and pollution can be said to occur.

Pollution and contamination are often judged from a human-focused bias. People decide whether pollution is causing damage at some place and time, and how important the damage might be. This anthropocentric bias tends, quite naturally, to favour humans. It also favours those species, communities, and ecological functions that are recognized as supporting human welfare or that may be appreciated for other reasons, such as aesthetics.

Interestingly, some species, communities, and ecological processes actually benefit from many types of pollution. For example, certain species may take advantage of ecological opportunities made available when pollution reduces the numbers of a previously dominant species. Many of the case studies described in following chapters involve situations in which *opportunistic* species of plants, animals, and microorganisms have benefited from ecological changes caused by pollution.

Pollution Can Be Natural

Pollution is not only caused by human activities—in some cases, it is a wholly natural phenomenon. Natural sources of pollution include emissions of particulates and gases, such as sulphur dioxide, from volcanoes; oil seeps on the

Photo 15.3 Natural disturbances such as wildfire initiate a process of ecological recovery known as succession. This photo shows a seven-year-old burn of boreal forest near Inuvik in the Northwest Territories. The community at this early stage of succession is dominated by a herbaceous plant known as fireweed (*Epilobium angustifolium*).

ocean floor; high metal concentrations in some soils and rocks; and the heat of geothermal springs. "Natural" pollution can cause severe ecological changes (which humans may view as damage). The damage can be as intense as that resulting from anthropogenic pollution, although the effects of natural emissions are usually more localized. The fact of natural pollution is interesting and well recognized, but it does not justify human activities that cause similar kinds of damage.

Studies of the ecological effects of natural pollution can yield useful insights into the potential long-term effects of anthropogenic emissions. This is because many examples of natural pollution are ancient, and their patterns of ecological damage may be similar to those caused by anthropogenic emissions.

One interesting example occurs at the Smoking Hills in the Northwest Territories. This is a remote wilderness, little influenced by humans. At several places along the seacoast, erosion has exposed deposits of bituminous shale. These carbon-rich deposits have spontaneously ignited and have been smouldering for centuries, fumigating the nearby tundra with sulphur dioxide. The SO_2 is toxic to vegetation and causes intense acidification of soil and water. The natural pollution at the Smoking Hills has severely damaged both terrestrial and aquatic communities of the tundra (see Chapter 16).

Another kind of natural pollution occurs when metal-rich minerals occur close to the ground surface, resulting in toxic conditions for vegetation. For example, plant ecologists have studied soil containing "serpentine" minerals, which are rich in nickel and cobalt. In high concentrations, these metals are toxic to most plants. Habitats containing serpentine minerals develop a distinctive plant community, dominated by low-growing species that can tolerate the toxic stress of the metal-rich soil (see Chapter 18).

An additional case of natural pollution involves certain species of marine phytoplankton that occasionally become abundant and cause ecological damage. In events called "toxic blooms," these algae release biochemicals that are poisonous to a broad range of animals exposed to them through the food web. In 1985, 14 humpback whales died at sea off Massachusetts after eating fish polluted with saxitoxin, a potent neurotoxin synthesized by dinoflagellate algae. Likewise, in 1987, some Canadians became ill after eating mussels containing domoic acid, which had originated in diatoms in Atlantic coastal waters.

Research and discussion of naturally occurring pollution is useful and informative in environmental science. However, in this book we emphasize pollution caused by human activities and its resulting damage. This emphasis is sensible because anthropogenic pollution is increasing rapidly in many countries, including Canada. There is a pressing need to avoid or manage the damage that affects both people and natural ecosystems.

Anthropogenic Pollution

In the modern world, an enormous amount of pollution is associated with human activities. This has caused important damage to ecosystems and sometimes to human health. Humans cause pollution in diverse ways, and we exam-

ine these in detail in following chapters of this book. Most commonly, anthropogenic pollution is associated with the following activities:

- accidental or deliberate emissions of chemicals, such as sulphur dioxide, metals, pesticides, and petroleum, into the environment
- releases of substances that react in the environment to synthesize chemicals of greater potential toxicity, known as "secondary pollution" (as occurs when ozone is synthesized by photochemical reactions in the atmosphere)
- emissions of chemicals that degrade stratospheric ozone, such as chlorofluorocarbons
- releases of waste industrial heat, as when a power plant discharges hot water into a river or lake
- discharges of nutrient-laden sewage or fertilizer into waterbodies

Disturbance

A disturbance is an episodic but intense influence that causes severe biological and ecological damage (see also Chapter 9). Events of disturbance are followed by a sometimes protracted period of ecological recovery through the process known as succession. There are two broad types of disturbances, **community-replacing disturbances** and **microdisturbances**.

Community-replacing disturbances are relatively extensive in scale and result in a catastrophic destruction of the original community. Natural examples of community-replacing disturbances include wildfires, severe windstorms, avalanches, and glaciation, while anthropogenic ones include clear-cutting, ploughing, and conversions of natural ecosystems into agroecosystems. A community-replacing disturbance may be followed by successional recovery that eventually regenerates a community similar to what was destroyed. Younger communities in the successional sequence (or *sere*) have relatively dynamic rates of change in their structural and functional properties. Younger communities are typically dominated by species that are abundant only during the initial period of recovery, when competition is not intense. Community change in later stages is much less dynamic.

Microdisturbance involves local disruptions that affect small areas within an otherwise intact community. Anthropogenic microdisturbances include the selective harvesting of individual large trees or animals while leaving the community otherwise intact. Ecological changes are relatively rapid within the habitat patch affected by a recent microdisturbance, but at the stand level the community is stable. So-called patch- or gap-phase successional dynamics occur in all natural forests but are particularly important during later stages of succession. This is especially the case in older-growth forests, where individual trees might die from disease, insect attack, or a lightning strike, creating a gap in the canopy.

Natural Disturbance

Disturbance is a natural force that affects all ecosystems. An example of a natural disturbance is wildfire, which may kill mature trees over large areas, followed by regeneration through succession. Fire is common in the boreal forest and in drought-prone ecosystems such as prairie and savannah. On average, about three million hectares of forest burns each year in Canada, mostly in fires started by lightning. Wildfire transforms habitat conditions and causes pollution by the emission of particulates and gases such as carbon dioxide and nitrogen oxides to the atmosphere.

Hurricanes, tornadoes, flooding, and glaciation (over geologically long periods of time) also cause extensive ecological damage, which is followed by successional recovery. After glaciation, which involves prolonged burial and abrasion of the land by an enormous mass of ice, the post-melting recovery requires recolonization of the landscape by immigrating organisms (i.e., primary succession).

Volcanic eruptions and earthquakes can generate devastating oceanic waves or tsunamis. In 1883, the cataclysmic eruption of Krakatau in Indonesia initiated a 30-m-high sea wave that killed about 36 000 people. In 2004, about 300 000 people were killed by a tsunami in the Indian Ocean (see Global Focus 3.1).

The blast and heat of a volcanic eruption can also damage ecosystems, as occurred in 1980 when Mount St. Helens in Washington erupted more or less sideways. The blast blew down 21 000 ha of conifer forest, killed another 10 000 ha by heat injury, and otherwise damaged an additional 30 000 ha. Devastating mudslides also occurred, and a huge area was covered in particulate ejecta (known as tephra) that settled from the atmosphere up to 50 cm deep.

Volcanic eruptions can also emit huge quantities of sulphur dioxide, particulates, and other pollutants into the atmosphere. Quantities of SO_2 amounting to about 2–5 million t (expressed as the sulphur content, or SO_2-S) are typically emitted by volcanoes each year, and an individual eruption may emit more than 1 million t. This natural SO_2 contributes to the acidification of precipitation and to other environmental damage (Chapter 19).

Natural population outbreaks (irruptions) of herbivores, predators, or pathogens can result in intense damage to natural habitats. For instance, spruce budworm (*Choristoneura fumiferana*) periodically defoliates huge areas of conifer forest in eastern Canada (more than 55 million ha in 1975). This causes extensive mortality of fir and spruce trees and other ecological changes (see Chapter 21). The mountain pine-beetle (*Dendroctonus ponderosae*) causes similar damage to pine forest in western Canada. A marine example involves the green sea urchin (*Strongylocentrotus droebachiensis*), which occasionally irrupts in rocky, subtidal habitats off Nova Scotia. These invertebrates can overgraze mature "forests" of the kelps *Laminaria* and *Agarum*, resulting in a "barren ground" with much less productivity and biomass. After the population of sea urchins collapses, the kelp forest quickly re-establishes.

In addition to community-replacing disturbances, microdisturbances also occur in natural ecosystems. Examples of these smaller-scale disturbances include the deaths of individual large trees or small groups of trees within an otherwise intact forest, perhaps caused by disease or an accident (such as a lightning strike). This creates a natural gap in the forest canopy, beneath which a microsuccession occurs as plants compete to take advantage of temporary resource opportunities such as extra light. The foliage of mature trees eventually fills the gap. Similarly, the deaths of individual coral heads within an otherwise intact reef initiate a microsuccession within that marine ecosystem.

Ecologists try to understand the effects of natural disturbances. They may use this knowledge to help them design management systems that allow resources to be harvested or otherwise used while controlling the ecological damage as much as possible. For example, understanding the characteristics of gap-phase disturbances in an old-growth forest can aid in the design of a selective harvesting system that emulates the natural disturbance regime. Using such a system would leave the physical and ecological integrity of the forest substantially intact, even while individual trees are periodically harvested for industrial use. These individuals would be replaced by natural regeneration. In view of the natural, gap-phase disturbance dynamics of old-growth forest, clear-cutting followed by planting of tree seedlings might be considered a less "natural" management system. However, clear-cutting might be an appropriate practice to use when harvesting forest that is adapted to community-replacing disturbances, such as wildfire or insect outbreaks (see Chapters 21 and 23).

Anthropogenic Disturbance

Humans also disturb ecosystems in diverse ways, many examples of which are described in the following chapters. Anthropogenic disturbances are associated with many human activities: harvesting, conversion, species introductions, and war.

The harvesting of both renewable and non-renewable resources often causes disturbances to ecosystems. So does the post-harvest management of renewable resources. For instance, intense disturbance is caused by strip-mining the surface for coal or oil sand. Similarly, harvesting a forest by clear-cutting represents a community-replacing disturbance, which is followed by regeneration through succession. Additional disturbances may be associated with silvicultural management, such as scarification of the site to prepare it for planting tree seedlings or herbicide spraying to decrease the abundance of weeds. Harvesting may also be selective, as when particular species or sizes of trees or fish are targeted for harvesting. This may represent a kind of gap-phase disturbance.

The conversion of natural ecosystems to agricultural or urbanized land-uses also represents a severe disturbance. In these cases, the successional recovery is intensively managed to foster the development of an anthropogenic ecosystem. Usually, these ecosystems are dominated by introduced species of plants and animals and, sometimes, by the bricks and concrete of the built environment. The conversion consequently displaces or eliminates indigenous species and natural ecosystems.

Humans have deliberately or accidentally introduced many species beyond their natural ranges. Often, the introduced species become invasive of natural communities, displacing native species and causing other kinds of ecological damage. North American examples include the introduction of zebra mussels (*Dreissena polymorpha*) into the Great Lakes; purple loosestrife (*Lythrum salicaria*) into wetlands; and starlings (*Sturnus vulgaris*), house sparrows (*Passer domesticus*), and domestic pigeons (rock doves, *Columba livia*) into urban areas.

Warfare also produces a wide range of community-replacing and microdisturbances through explosions, the movement of heavy machinery over the landscape, spills of fuel and other toxic chemicals, hunting to provide food for large numbers of soldiers, and even—as occurred during the Vietnam War—extensive spraying of herbicide onto forests and agricultural areas.

Anthropogenic Pollution and Disturbance in Context

To summarize, pollution and disturbance can be natural phenomena. Since life began, both of these kinds of environmental stress have affected the structure and function of ecosystems. In modern times, however, pollution and disturbance associated with human activities are becoming increasingly important causes of ecological damage. The prevention of anthropogenic pollution and disturbance and the management of the damage already caused are among the most important challenges of the global environmental crisis.

Ecotoxicology

Toxicology is the science of the study of poisons. It examines their chemical nature and their effects on the physiology of organisms. If the dose (exposure) is large enough, any chemical, even water, is potentially toxic (see In Detail 15.1).

Environmental toxicology is a somewhat broader field than conventional toxicology. It also examines the environmental factors that can influence the exposure of organisms to potentially toxic levels of chemicals. Important topics in environmental toxicology are the following:

1. the cycling and transport of potentially toxic chemicals

2. their transformation into other substances (which may be more or less poisonous than their precursors)

3. the determination of "sinks" where chemicals may accumulate in especially high concentrations, including within the bodies of organisms

Ecotoxicology has an even broader domain, because it studies both the direct poisonous effects of chemicals and their indirect effects. Examples of indirect ecological effects include changes in habitat or in the abundance of food. For instance, the use of a herbicide in forestry or agriculture will change the biomass and species composition of the vegetation. These are important changes in the habitats of animals. Even if the herbicide does not poison animals directly, they may be affected by changes in their habitat.

A complex of factors influences the ecotoxicological risks associated with exposure to chemicals in the environment. The most important factors are biological sensitivity, the intrinsic toxicity of the chemical being

In Detail 15.1

What Is Toxicity?

In the biological sense, a chemical can poison an organism if it detrimentally affects some aspect of its metabolism. This effect is called *toxicity*. The toxic chemical may, for example, disrupt the function of an enzyme system or interfere with cellular division. However, the legal definition of *toxic substance*, as stated by the Canadian Environmental Protection Act, is as follows:

A substance is defined as toxic if it enters or may enter the environment in a quantity or concentration or under conditions that: (1) have or may have an immediate or long-term harmful effect on the environment; (2) constitute or may constitute a danger to the environment on which human life

depends; or (3) constitute or may constitute a danger in Canada to human life or health.

This definition has legal standing in Canada and is used in the management and regulation of certain chemicals.

However, this definition is inadequate in some important respects, particularly because it deals only with extremely toxic chemicals, under conditions in which they occur in high concentrations. Substances of less acute toxicity may cause subtle, long-term damage to people, to other species, or to important ecological values. These kinds of exposures are not dealt with by this definition.

considered, the intensity of the exposure, and any indirect effects that might be caused.

Biological Sensitivity

Sensitivity to chemical exposures varies greatly among individual organisms and species. Toxicology studies, conducted under controlled laboratory conditions, compare the susceptibilities of organisms to toxic substances. **Acute toxicity** is defined as a short-term exposure to a chemical in a high enough concentration to cause measurable biochemical or anatomical damages or even death (a common acute *endpoint*). **Chronic toxicity** involves long-term exposure to low to moderate concentrations of a chemical. Over time, chronic exposures may cause biochemical or anatomical damage, or perhaps a lethal condition such as cancer.

Data in Table 15.1 illustrate the sensitivities of several species to the extremely toxic chemical TCDD (2,3,7,8-tetrachlorodibenzo-*p*-dioxin). (TCDD has no industrial or medicinal use. It is, however, incidentally synthesized during high-temperature combustions in incinerators and fossil-fuelled power plants, during forest fires, in the chlorine bleach whitening process for wood pulp, and in the manufacture of certain industrial chemicals, particularly trichlorophenol, used to produce the herbicide 2,4,5-T and the antibacterial agent hexachlorophene. These various syntheses can result in the emission of TCDD into the environment, where humans and other organisms may be exposed.)

| TABLE 15.1 | Acute Toxicity of TCDD to Various Animals |

Animals were exposed to TCDD in controlled tests under laboratory conditions. Oral exposure occurs by ingestion into the stomach; dermal exposure involves absorption through the skin; intraperitoneal exposure involves injection into the abdominal cavity. LD_{50} (lethal dose for 50%) is the dose of chemical required to kill one-half of a population of experimental animals. LD_{50} is measured in units of amount of chemical per unit of body weight of the animals (e.g., μg/kg).

SPECIES	ROUTE OF EXPOSURE	LD_{50} (μg/kg)
Guinea pig (male)	oral	0.8
Guinea pig (female)	oral	2.1
Rabbit (male and female)	oral	115
Rabbit (male and female)	dermal	275
Rabbit (male and female)	intraperitoneal	252–500
Monkey (female)	oral	<70
Rat (male)	oral	22
Rat (female)	oral	45–500
Mouse (male)	oral	<150
Mouse (male)	intraperitoneal	120
Dog (male)	oral	30–300
Dog (female)	oral	>100
Hamster (male and female)	oral	1157
Hamster (male and female)	intraperitoneal	3000
Frog	oral	1000

Source: Data from Tschirley (1986)

The data in Table 15.1 suggest that species vary greatly in their sensitivity to TCDD. Guinea pigs are extremely vulnerable, while hamsters and frogs are much less so. Sensitivity to toxic chemicals also varies with the route of exposure and with the sex and age of the animals.

Data showing acute and chronic toxicities are presented in Table 15.2. The chemical illustrated here is glyphosate, a herbicide widely used in agriculture, forestry, and horticulture (see Chapter 22). The data suggest that, if the concentration of glyphosate is large enough, it will cause acute toxicity. However, long-term tests of chronic toxicity did not demonstrate any observable effects at the examined levels of exposure. (Note that the doses required to cause acute toxicity, and those tested for chronic toxicity, are much higher than exposures that would be encountered during the routine use of glyphosate as a herbicide.)

Intrinsic Toxicity of the Chemical

Chemicals vary enormously in their intrinsic, or relative, toxicity. In other words, some chemicals are extremely toxic even in minute doses, while others will only cause poisoning at much higher doses (i.e., exposures). This is illustrated by Table 15.3, which compares the acute toxicity (to rats) of a wide range of chemicals. There are two central messages in Table 15.3:

1. Chemicals vary enormously in their relative toxicity.
2. At large enough doses, any chemical may be toxic.

Exposure

Exposure has a fundamental influence on toxicity. It is defined as the dose of chemical that any individual or group of organisms receives per unit time. An exposure to any potentially toxic chemical is affected by many factors, including environmental influences. For example, the exposure of, say, a mouse in an agricultural field sprayed with an insecticide could be affected by such factors as the spray rate, the types of equipment being used, the weather, the persistence of the chemical (i.e., how long it remains active), and the mouse's behaviour and choices of food and habitat. If toxicologists were evaluating exposures of humans to potentially toxic chemicals, they would consider the amounts ingested with solid and liquid food, the intake while breathing, and the amounts found in both working and ambient (i.e., non-occupational) environments.

TABLE 15.2   **Acute and Chronic Toxicity of Glyphosate**

Toxicity to rats and mice is indicated by data from controlled tests under laboratory conditions. Acute toxicity is measured by oral LD_{50}, while chronic exposures are from long-term feeding experiments. The data given for chronic exposure are no-effect levels—that is, doses at (and below) which there is no observable effect.

SPECIES	TYPE OF EXPOSURE	
Rat	acute:	oral LD_{50}: 5600 mg/kg
	chronic:	fed for 90 days with food containing 2000 mg/kg; no observable effects
	chronic:	fed for 2 years with food containing 100 mg/kg; no observable effects
	chronic:	3 generations fed food containing 300 mg/kg; no observable effects
Mouse	acute:	oral LD_{50}: 1570 mg/kg
	chronic:	fed for 18 months with food containing 300 mg/kg; no observable effects

Source: Modified from Freedman (1991)

TABLE 15.3   **Acute Toxicities of Various Chemicals**

Toxicity to rats is indicated by oral LD_{50} data from controlled laboratory tests.

CHEMICAL	ORAL LD_{50} (milligram/kilogram)
TCDD (dioxin isomer)	0.01
tetrodotoxin (globefish toxin)	0.01
saxitoxin (paralytic shellfish neurotoxin)	0.3
carbofuran (insecticide)	10
strychnine (rodenticide)	30
nicotine (alkaloid in tobacco)	50
caffeine (alkaloid in coffee, tea)	200
DDT (insecticide)	200
fenitrothion (insecticide)	250
2,4-D (herbicide)	370
2,4,5-T (herbicide)	500
acetylsalicylic acid (Aspirin)	1 700
sodium hypochlorite (household bleach)	2 000
sodium chloride (table salt)	3 750
glyphosate (herbicide)	5 600
ethanol (drinking alcohol)	13 700
sucrose (table sugar)	30 000
distilled water	44 000[1]
isotonic saline	68 000[1]

(1) These data are for the house mouse, with the substance given intravenously rather than by oral ingestion. From Balazs (1970).

Source: Data from Freedman (1995)

Indirect Effects

Also important in ecotoxicology are the indirect effects of toxic chemicals—that is, effects other than the direct poisoning of organisms. Indirect effects are most commonly associated with changes in habitat or in the condition of an organism's immune system. In some cases, indirect damage is worse than the direct, toxic effects of chemicals. For instance, the use of a herbicide in forestry causes changes in vegetation, affecting the animals that live in the habitat, even if the herbicide itself is not directly toxic to them.

Potentially, Any Chemical Is Poisonous

The above discussion suggests that, if an exposure is intense enough, even routinely encountered chemicals may be poisonous. For example, poisoning can even be caused by water if a person drinks enough in a short period of time. The physiological capacity for regulating the concentration of dissolved salts in the blood plasma can be overwhelmed by drinking too much water too quickly causing a toxic syndrome called hyponatremia. Depending on body weight, the lethal dose for an average adult is about 5 L, ingested over about an hour. Similarly, if the dose is large enough, carbon dioxide, table sugar, table salt, Aspirin, ethanol (drinking alcohol), and other routinely ingested chemicals can cause poisoning (Table 15.3).

This fundamental rule of toxicology was first emphasized by Paracelsus (1493–1541), a Swiss physician and alchemist who is considered to be the father of "modern" toxicology. One of Paracelsus's most famous conclusions can be paraphrased as "Dosage determines poisoning."

In perhaps all cases there are thresholds of tolerance to potentially toxic chemicals. Tolerance occurs because organisms have physiological mechanisms to excrete toxins from the body, to metabolize them into less toxic chemicals, or to sequester (store) them in certain body tissues where they will not cause damage. Organisms also have mechanisms to repair damage to tissues or biochemical systems, providing that chemical exposures are not too high and excessively damaging. For the chemical to cause toxicity, the capacities of these physiological systems must be overwhelmed.

Interpretation of Damage

The notion of physiological thresholds of tolerance helps define the difference between contamination and pollution, which we examined previously. The notion of thresh-olds also indicates why it is best to couch the discussion in terms of *potentially* toxic levels—particularly when the actual environmental exposure to chemicals is not known, and when the biological risks of extremely small doses are not sufficiently understood.

However, the notion of biological thresholds of tolerance is controversial, and some toxicologists do not agree with the explanation just given. These scientists believe that exposure to even one or a few molecules of certain chemicals may be of toxicological importance. This is particularly true in the case of chemicals believed to be carcinogenic at extremely small exposures, and also in the case of radionuclides and highly energetic forms of ionizing energy, such as X-rays and gamma radiation.

Often, the risks to humans exposed to chemicals are interpreted differently from those of other species, particularly wild animals and plants. This is because prevailing cultural attitudes place much greater value on the life and health of individual people than on those of other species. As such, there is a special reluctance, both social and regulatory, to permit human exposures to potentially toxic chemicals.

However, regulations and guidelines tend to be considerably less strict for human exposures in the workplace compared with non-occupational exposures. This recognizes the fact that considerable risks are inherent in the normal activities and environmental conditions of many occupations. Particularly significant hazards confront firefighters, police officers, members of the armed forces, operators of heavy equipment in construction and agriculture, and workers in chemical industries. Within limits, chemical exposures associated with earning a living are generally interpreted as a "cost of doing business" and may, therefore, be judged acceptable.

Such attitudes can, however, change markedly over time. Certain occupational hazards that were once considered routine and tolerable are now viewed as unacceptable. For instance, when synthetic organic insecticides, such as DDT, were first introduced in the mid-1940s and 1950s, people were remarkably cavalier about using them in agriculture, forestry, and public sanitation. Workers often applied these insecticides with only minimal attention to avoiding exposure to themselves and others. Such poorly controlled usages would be unthinkable today, at least in relatively well-regulated countries such as Canada.

In addition, many people willingly choose to expose themselves to toxicologically significant doses of certain chemicals. These choices include taking up hazardous occupations, smoking cigarettes, and ingesting medicines and recreational drugs. The consequences of "voluntary" chemical exposures are interpreted using criteria different from those applied to "involuntary" exposures.

If chemicals cause toxicity to species other than humans, the importance is interpreted on the basis of the following considerations.

Are measurable changes seen in the populations of affected species? From the ecological perspective, population-level damage is the most important consideration (even while it is acknowledged that the death of an individual organism is regrettable). Populations of all species have a certain degree of resilience and can tolerate some mortality caused by toxic chemicals without suffering an overall decline.

Are affected species important in maintaining the integrity of their community? Ecological philosophies suggest that all species have intrinsic value. Nevertheless, species vary greatly in their contributions to the functioning and structure of their community. So-called "keystone" species have a dominant influence on their community (Chapter 9). Substantial changes in their abundance should be judged as relatively important compared with damage inflicted on more minor species.

Is the damage of economic importance? This consideration involves damage to resources that are needed by humans and therefore have economic value. In this sense, damage is judged relatively important if it is caused to hunted animals such as deer or trout, to trees that can be harvested to manufacture pulp or lumber, or to important ecological services such as the provision of clean water and air. From the purely utilitarian perspective, damage caused to non-economic values, both species and services, is viewed as being less important.

Other considerations, less tangible than those just mentioned, involve appraising damage in aesthetic or ethical terms. These considerations are important. They are, however, difficult to interpret in terms of risks or benefits to human welfare or in economic terms. As a result, aesthetic or ethical considerations are rarely reflected in regulatory criteria or in the management of potentially toxic chemicals in the environment.

Environmental Risks

Broadly interpreted, **environmental risks** are hazards—the probabilities of suffering damage or misfortune as a result of exposure to some environmental circumstance. Risks are associated with driving an automobile, flying in an airplane, participating in sports, hiking in the wilderness, exposing oneself to toxic chemicals, and getting out of bed in the morning. Environmental risks interact with biological factors to determine the likelihood of experiencing some damage, such as developing a cancer or suffering an accident.

Statisticians assign reasonable probability values to many kinds of risks using data based on previous experience, such as the frequency of automobile accidents or cases of poisoning with a specific chemical such as a medicine. This is illustrated in Table 15.4, which summarizes the recent causes of mortality in Canada. These data suggest that the average Canadian has an annual risk of dying of about 0.7% (calculated as the total annual mortality divided by the national population).

Data concerning less common environmental risks are more difficult to acquire. Usually they must be developed from models based on knowledge about medical science and likely exposures to environmental influences. However,

TABLE 15.4	Causes of Mortality in Canada	
These data for 2001 summarize the most important attributed causes of deaths among Canadians.		
RISK FACTOR	**NUMBER OF DEATHS**	**% OF TOTAL**
All causes of mortality	219 538	100
MEDICAL CAUSES		
Diseases of circulatory system	74 824	34.1
Cancers (all malignancies)	63 774	29.1
Respiratory diseases	17 585	8.0
Diseases of nervous system	10 182	4.6
Diabetes	7097	3.2
Infectious and parasitic diseases	3044	1.4
Liver diseases	2741	1.2
Congenital abnormalities	893	0.4
Perinatal (just before or after birth)	936	0.4
ACCIDENTS AND RELATED CAUSES		
Suicide	3688	1.7
Motor vehicle accidents	3032	1.4
Other accidental deaths	5369	2.4
Accidental falls	1727	0.8
Homicide	463	0.2
All other causes of death	24 143	11.1

Source: Data from Statistics Canada (2005)

Canadian Focus 15.1

Environmental Stressors and the Health of Children

Many environmental factors can potentially affect human health. Children may be particularly vulnerable to many of these risks because of rapid body growth and development, an incomplete immune system, and inexperience in avoiding hazards. Although there is controversy about the degree of risk, many scientists and medical practitioners believe that children are subjected to unnecessary exposures to environmental stressors that threaten their health.

Some hazards involve obvious safety issues, such as the risks of crossing busy roads in urban areas, of being attacked by unleashed dogs, or being near an unsecured construction site. Other hazards, however, involve exposure to chemicals and other environmental factors that may pose significant risks to both body and reproductive development or to proper functioning of the endocrine system.

According to the Canadian Association of Physicians for the Environment (CAPE, 2005), there is evidence that exposure to certain chemicals at levels likely to be encountered in the environment can adversely affect children. These chemicals include pesticides, plasticizers, metals, and organic solvents (see also In Detail 15.1). Children may be exposed to these chemicals during prenatal development, through breast milk, and via food, water, and air. They may also be affected via parental exposures that result in mutagenic effects on gametes. The chemicals are believed to pose risks to children by causing congenital anomalies (birth defects), by influencing reproductive development, or by affecting the endocrine system. There has been particular concern over the potential effects of exposure to low levels of hormonally active agents, which may disrupt healthy endocrine functioning.

Although a considerable body of scientific evidence shows reproductive toxicity and other health effects of many of these chemicals, it is largely based on work with other species or on occupational exposures of humans to relatively high doses. There is still a great deal of uncertainty about the potential effects of lower-level exposure to reproductive toxicants and endocrine disruptors on children and adults. Despite the uncertainly, CAPE argues that it is prudent and precautionary to reduce the chemical exposures of children as much as possible. To this end, government must adopt stricter regulations about emissions of certain chemicals and their residues in foods. In addition, parents should avoid exposing their children to some foods, such as larger species of fish, meat of marine mammals, and perhaps even fatty animal tissues in general. Other potential sources of exposure to harmful chemicals are foods microwaved in plastic containers, pesticide-treated lawns, and cigarette smoke.

Reference

Canadian Association of Physicians for the Environment (CAPE). 2005. *Children's Environmental Health.* http://cape.ca/children.html

both of these kinds of information are imperfect because they are based on an incomplete understanding of interactions between environmental factors and biological responses. Consequently, the calculated risk factors are inaccurate and often controversial. These issues are particularly important for diseases, such as cancers, that have an extended latency period between exposure and development.

Cancers are a leading cause of mortality in Canada and many other relatively wealthy countries. Remarkably little is known, however, about the specific environmental and biological factors that predispose organisms to developing various types of cancer. Table 15.5 summarizes data from a study that estimated the risks of dying from cancers that are associated with several potentially contributing factors. Of the approximately 0.5 million cancer deaths that occur each year in the U.S., dietary factors are believed to be the most important predisposing factor, accounting for about 35% of the mortality, followed by tobacco smoking (30%), infections (10%), and reproductive and sexual behaviour (7%). Of the various risks of developing cancer, smoking is most preventable—this voluntary exposure is responsible for about 86% of lung cancers, as well as other diseases (Canadian Cancer Society, 2005). About half of Canadian smokers will die from a smoking-related ailment, most before the age of 70.

The population of Canada is 10.8% that of the U.S., while the number of cancer-related mortalities in Canada is 11.3% that of the United States. These similar proportions, along with the comparable lifestyles of Canadians and Americans, suggest that the estimated risks in Table 15.5 are also relevant to Canadians.

TABLE 15.5   Estimated Risks of Cancer Mortality

Cancers are grouped by their possible causes, in terms of environmental exposures. The data are the best estimates for the U.S. population, with the range of estimates in brackets.

RISK FACTOR	RELATIVE CAUSE OF CANCER MORTALITY (% OF TOTAL)	
Diet factors	35 (10–70)	
Smoking tobacco	30 (25–40)	
Infections	10 (1–?)	
Reproductive and sexual behaviour	7 (1–13)	
Occupational exposures	4 (<2–8)	
radiation in workplace		0.01
pesticide application		<0.02
chemicals in workplace		<0.06
Geophysical factors	3 (2–4)	
sunlight exposures		2
indoor radon		2 (1–4)
Alcohol consumption	3 (2–4)	
Exposure to pollution	2 (<1–5)	
secondary tobacco smoke		1.0
indoor organic chemicals		0.3
pesticides on food		0.9 (0.6–1.2)
hazardous toxic air pollutants		0.3 (0.2–0.4)
chemicals in drinking water		<0.1 (0.04–0.09)
other pesticide exposures		0.02 (0.02–0.03)
Medicines and medical procedures	1 (<1–3)	
Exposures to food additives	<1 (-5–2)	
Exposures from consumer products	<1	

Sources: Modified from Gough (1989) and Canadian Cancer Society (2005)

In spite of excellent data (and common sense) about the known risks of many activities, people often choose to expose themselves to obvious high risks of injury or disease. Examples of such risky activities include skiing down steep slopes, bungee jumping, smoking cigarettes, and drinking alcohol. Moreover, people are also exposed to hazards over which they have little control—that is, to involuntary risks, such as crime, polluted outdoor air, and pesticides in food.

Perceptions of risk are an important consideration. One survey of Canadians indicated that people are aware of, and concerned about, a wide range of risks to their health and well-being (Table 15.6). People are especially concerned about health-related risks associated with lifestyle choices, such as smoking cigarettes, using recreational drugs or alcohol, and behaviour involving exposure to HIV. People are also concerned about exposures to potentially toxic levels of chemicals in the atmosphere, drinking water, and foods.

Obviously, people understand that environmental factors pose risks to human health. Often, however, they have little understanding of the *actual* risks, as opposed to the *perceived* risks. Sometimes, people view high risks to be inconsequential while considering much smaller risks as unduly important. Nevertheless, public perceptions of risks have an extremely important influence on politicians, policy makers, and bureaucrats in government and industry, and on their decisions concerning the management and regulation of environmental and health hazards.

Environmental Risk Assessment

Environmental risk assessments are evaluations of the risks associated with some sort of hazard in the environment. Risk assessments quantify these threats to humans, as well as to other species and to broader ecological values. A risk assessment requires knowledge of three factors:

1. the likelihood of encountering the hazard
2. the likely intensity of the hazard
3. the biological damage that is likely to result from the predicted exposure

Meteorologists, for example, may predict the probability that a particular place will be struck by lightning under various weather conditions. Such probabilities are much greater during a thunderstorm than during sunny conditions and are greater beneath a large tree in an open field than beside a shrub in a ditch. The energy content of a typical lightning strike is also known, as is the biological damage to a human who might be struck. With this information, it is relatively straightforward to model the risks of a lightning-caused injury associated with standing in the middle of an open field, or under a tree in that same field, on a sunny day or during a thunderstorm. This is a simple example of an environmental risk assessment.

Risk assessments for potentially toxic exposures to chemicals can be conducted for individual organisms, for populations, or for broader ecological functions such as productivity, decomposition, and nutrient cycling. To assess the risks associated with exposure to chemicals, one requires knowledge of two factors: the intensity of expo-

TABLE 15.6	Public Perception of Risks of Various Environmental and Medical Hazards

The data, based on a national survey of 1500 Canadians in 1992, indicate the percentage of the survey group that chose the designated category. The totals do not add to 100% because some respondents said they "didn't know."

RISK FACTOR	PERCEIVED RISK (% RESPONSE)			
	HIGH	MODERATE	SLIGHT	NONE
Smoking cigarettes	61	31	7	1
Use of silicone breast implants	61	25	10	6
Depletion of stratospheric ozone	58	28	9	1
Recreational drugs	57	32	9	1
Emotional and physical stress	54	29	9	2
Pollution by chemicals	54	35	10	1
Crime and civil violence	53	35	10	1
Suntanning	52	33	12	2
AIDS virus	49	39	10	2
Motor-vehicle accidents	48	30	10	2
Nuclear wastes	48	22	16	7
Use of alcohol during pregnancy	41	41	14	2
PCBs and dioxins	39	33	17	4
Pesticides in foods	37	38	19	3
Additives in foods	36	39	19	4
Consumption of alcohol	34	48	15	2
Nuclear power plants	31	34	23	10
Effects of climate change	28	39	22	7
Use of non-prescription medicines	26	36	28	9
Exposure to asbestos	26	32	28	7
Municipal incinerators	23	37	23	11
Effects of malnutrition	23	43	25	6
High-voltage power lines	21	30	30	15
Consumption of irradiated foods	21	32	31	10
Use of prescription medicines	19	43	27	10
Genetically engineered bacteria	18	34	25	6
Outdoor air quality	18	47	27	7
Pathogenic bacteria in food	18	38	35	8
Fungi and moulds in food	16	27	39	12
Mercury in dental fillings	13	30	29	16
Consumption of tap water	12	38	35	13
Exposure to medical X-rays	12	40	39	13
Indoor air quality	11	43	32	11
Video display monitors	10	36	26	8
Use of contraceptives	10	31	40	20
Use of a heart pacemaker	6	26	39	26
Consumption of bottled water	5	17	35	39
Use of contact lenses	4	17	45	34

Source: Modified from Krewski *et al.* (1994)

sure (i.e., the anticipated dose) and the biological damage that is likely to be caused by the predicted exposure. The integration of these two types of information is known as a **dose-response relationship** (Figure 15.2).

Dose-response relationships can be determined by conducting experiments in which, for example, populations of organisms are exposed to various amounts of a chemical. Results of simple dose-response experiments involving several herbicides are shown in Figure 15.3.

It is sometimes possible to infer dose-response relationships by studying patterns of damage in the real world. For instance, the intensity of pollution can be determined at various distances from a large point source of emissions, such as a power plant or smelter. The exposure to pollution can then be related to the pattern of ecological damage that occurs along that gradient of toxic stress. Patterns of pollution and ecological damage around a large smelter near Sudbury is one example of such a relationship (see Chapters 16 and 18).

An **exposure assessment** investigates all of the ways in which organisms may encounter a potentially toxic level of a chemical. For example, humans may be exposed to mercury through various pathways, each of which can be quantified (i.e.,

FIGURE 15.2 | Conceptual Models of Dose-Response Relationships

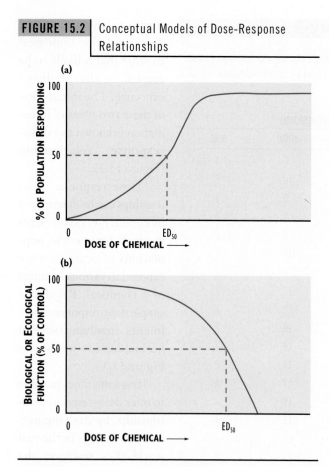

(a)

(b)

FIGURE 15.3 | Examples of Dose-Response Curves

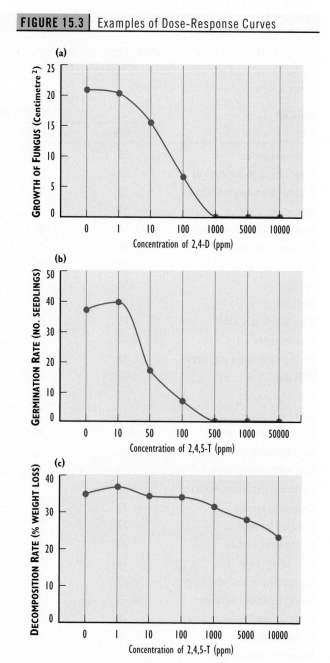

(a)

(b)

(c)

Model (a) suggests that the larger the dose encountered, the greater the proportion of the population that is affected. ED_{50} represents the dose that affects 50% of the test population (effective dose). If the biological response being measured is death, the term LD_{50} is used, or the dose killing 50% of the population (lethal dose). **Model (b)** suggests that larger doses have a more pronounced effect on physiology (or on an ecological function). In this case, the rate of a biological function is plotted versus the chemical exposure, and the data are expressed as a percentage of the control rate (i.e., the rate occurring in the absence of the chemical). In this curve, ED_{50} represents the dose needed to decrease the rate of the function by 50%.

Note the extremely wide ranges of doses that were examined in these experiments. Each experiment includes a control treatment involving a zero dose of the chemical being tested.
Graph (a) describes the effects of the herbicide 2,4-D on the growth rate of a mycorrhizal fungus, *Hebeloma longicaudum*.
Graph (b) illustrates the effects of the herbicide 2,4,5-T on the germination of seeds from the surface organic mat of a young clear-cut. **Graph (c)** shows the effects of 2,4,5-T on the decomposition of leaf litter, an ecological function.

Sources: Data from Estok *et al.* (1989), Fletcher and Freedman (1989), and Morash and Freedman (1989)

measured or calculated). The principal avenues of exposure include inhaling mercury vapour or particulates in the atmosphere, ingesting dissolved mercury in drinking water, and ingesting the metal in foodstuffs, especially in certain kinds of fish and animal organs. Also included among the principal avenues of exposure are such miscellaneous sources as mercury-amalgam dental fillings and certain pigments used in ceramics and paints.

The assimilation rate of a chemical into the bloodstream and organs varies greatly among the exposure path-

In Detail 15.2

Environmental Mutagens, Teratogens, and Hormonally Active Substances

Environmental mutagens, teratogens, and hormonally active substances are trace chemicals and other agents that are present in the environment and have the potential to affect the genetics or metabolism of animals in even extremely small concentrations. They may be naturally present or associated with anthropogenic emissions. Relatively intense exposures of wild animals to these agents may occur in areas affected by effluent from factories, in wetlands receiving drainage from pesticide-treated fields, and in places where sewage is dumped. Human exposures are associated with smoking (including involuntary exposures), eating fatty meats (especially if barbequed) and some other foods, and living in a polluted urban environment.

Environmental mutagens: A **mutagen** is a substance or agent that induces a genetic mutation (i.e., a change in the coding sequence of nucleic acids in DNA). Exposure to mutagens may result in numerous mutations that are "harmless," meaning that the genetic change is not known to result in serious biochemical damage. In other cases, however, a mutation may result the development of a deformity or a disease, such as many kinds of cancer. Cancer can be an endpoint of mutations occurring in body (somatic) cells, while mutations of sperm and egg cells can result in changes that can potentially be passed to offspring.

Incidents of genotoxicity have been observed in wild animals—for example, epidemics of fish tumours and frogs born with excess limbs. In humans, genotoxicity may be associated with some kinds of cancer and also with increases in the incidence of congenital birth defects, which normally occur at a frequency of about 3% of births.

Genotoxicity is caused by exposure to various chemicals and other agents. Two especially potent mutagens that are used in biomedical research include ethyl-methanesulfonate and nitrosoguanidine. Other sources of laboratory and environmental genotoxicity include the following:

- highly energetic (ionizing) radiation associated with ultraviolet-B, X-rays, and gamma radiation
- polycyclic aromatic hydrocarbons (PAHs), such as benzo(a)pyrene
- polychlorinated biphenyls (PCBs) and some pesticides
- methyl mercury and some other metals
- aflatoxin present in mouldy nuts and grains
- dimethyl nitrosamine present in some nitrite-treated foods
- diesel exhaust
- effluent from pulp mills
- tobacco and barbecue smoke

Environmental teratogens: A **teratogen** is an agent that induces abnormal development of an embryo or fetus. It may act through mutagenicity or by some other means, such as physical irritation of cells or developing tissues. One of the most famous examples of teratogenic damage involves thalidomide, which was prescribed as a sedative to pregnant women from 1950–61. Thalidomide proved capable of crossing the placenta and caused devastating limb abnormalities (extreme shortening or absence of limbs) in the developing fetus, resulting in a multi-year epidemic of seriously deformed children. Another well-known teratogen is ethyl (or drinking) alcohol, which, if taken in excess during pregnancy, can cause fetal alcohol syndrome. Exposure to rubella virus during pregnancy can also lead to severe deformity of the fetus. Environmental exposures to teratogens have also caused an increased incidence of deformities of wild animals, including mollusks, fish, and amphibians.

Hormonally active substances: The endocrine system of animals consists of various glands (e.g., adrenal gland, ovaries, pancreas, pituitary gland, testes, and thyroid gland) that secrete chemicals known as **hormones**. Hormones are chemical messengers that travel through the circulatory system until they reach specific receptor cells in target organs, where they regulate physiological functions. Hormones help to regulate growth, development, metabolism, fat deposition, maintenance of the electrolyte balance of fluids, sexuality, and behavioural responses to external stimuli (e.g., excitement and fright). Examples of hormones produced naturally by animals include the following:

- adrenaline (epinephrine) and noradrenaline (norepinephrine), two adrenal hormones that stimulate the body to react to a stressful condition by increasing blood pressure, blood sugar levels, and heart rate (this is sometimes known as a "flight or fight" response)
- estrogen, a female sex hormone produced by the ovaries, and androgens, male hormones produced by the testes

▶

■ insulin, formed by the pancreas to regulate the use and storage of carbohydrates (including blood sugar)

■ thyroid hormone, which influences the growth and metabolism of virtually all body cells

Because hormones are necessary for healthy physiology, development, and behaviour, any serious disruption of their activity can have severe consequences. Chemicals in the environment, including some that are natural and others that are anthropogenic, can cause such interference. Certain plants, for example, contain so-called phytoestrogen chemicals, which can affect the hormone physiology of animals feeding upon them. Examples of plants with relatively high levels of phytoestrogens include soybean *(Glycine max)*, red clover *(Trifolium pratense)*, flax *(Linum vulgare)*, and black cohosh *(Cimicifuga racemosa)*. Some women use herbal preparations of these plants to relieve symptoms of menopause. Other natural phytoestrogens have been used in birth-control pills to control human fertility.

Many other substances present in the environment are also hormonally active, including a wide array of contaminants emitted by human activities. Even at extremely small levels of exposure, they may mimic or block the action of certain hormones, resulting in a physiological change. This may have detrimental effects on wild and domestic animals and also on humans. Anthropogenic chemicals thought to be hormonally active through environmental exposures include

■ organochlorines, including dioxins (e.g., TCDD), polychlorinated biphenyls (PCBs), and the insecticides DDT, dieldrin, and lindane;

■ other pesticides, including atrazine, permethrin, and trifluralin;

■ tributyltin, used as a marine antifoulant;

■ alkylphenols used as surfactants, such as nonylphenol;

■ certain placticizers, such as dibutyl phthalate and butylbenzyl phthalate;

■ natural hormones produced by animals and synthetic steroids from contraceptives that are emitted to the environment with sewage or occur as residues in food, including estradiol, estrone, and testosterone; and

■ phytoestrogens in pulp-mill effluents, including isoflavones, lignans, and coumestans.

The biological effects of environmental mutagens, teratogens, and hormonally active substances are not yet well understood. Although the presence of many of these agents in the environment has been widely noted, scientists do not yet know the level of contamination required to cause an unacceptable amount of biological damage. This has resulted in controversy about the potential effects of these bioactive chemicals on wild animals and humans—some people recommend a highly precautionary approach, while others believe that more evidence of damage is necessary before more stringent control practices are implemented. Although there are observations of some local populations of wild animals suffering significant damage, there is not yet convincing evidence of the effects on humans from environmental exposures to these agents. Of course, any significant level of genetic or developmental damage to humans would be deemed unacceptable.

References

Environment Canada. 2002. Endocrine disrupting substances in the environment. www.ec.gc.ca/eds/fact/

McLachlan, J.A. and L.J. Guillette (eds.). 2002. *Environmental Hormones: The Scientific Basis of Endocrine Disruption*. Annals N.Y. Academy of Sciences, 948.

Phillips, D.H. and S. Venitt (eds.). 1995. *Environmental Mutagenesis*. San Diego, CA: Academic Press.

World Resources Institute. 2003. *Are Hormone Mimics Affecting Our Health?* www.wri.org/pubs_content_text.cfm?ContentD=1319

ways. Assimilation depends on several factors, including the specific metabolic characteristics of the organ into which the chemical is being absorbed—for example, the lungs, the gastrointestinal tract, or the skin. The physical-chemical form of the substance also affects uptake dynam-ics. For instance, mercury can occur as an elemental vapour or liquid, as inorganic compounds such as mercuric chloride, and as organomercurial complexes such as methylmercury (an extremely bioavailable and poisonous compound). The total exposure for a person is the sum of the chemi-

Photo 15.4 Many human activities result in emissions of pollutants into the environment. This image shows a 380-metre-tall smokestack at a metal smelter near Sudbury, Ontario.

cal assimilated through all pathways, which typically vary greatly in their effect.

The relative importance of various sources of a chemical depends to some extent on a person's lifestyle and occupation. These influence how often and to what degree the various sources are encountered. Dental workers, for example, commonly come into contact with mercury vapours because this metal is used to make fillings. In addition, a diet rich in certain species of large oceanic fish, such as halibut, shark, swordfish, and tuna, is relatively rich in mercury (see Chapter 18). Therefore, both dental workers and fish consumers may have a higher risk of mercury exposure.

Once an exposure assessment has been performed, the biological hazards can be predicted on the basis of known dose-response relationships. Unfortunately, dose-response information is often incomplete, or even totally lacking. For instance, most hypotheses about potential dose-response relationships in humans are actually inferred from research conducted in laboratories using other species of mammals, such as mice, rats, dogs, pigs, and monkeys. These species have physiological, anatomical, and behavioural characteristics that are broadly similar to those of humans, but they are also different in many important respects. Consequently, most assessments of human exposure to trace levels of environmental chemicals are inaccurate.

In addition, the information about dose-response relationships is almost non-existent for wild species, as well as for community-level ecological functions such as productivity and nutrient cycling. As with human-focused assessments, it is common to use data for "surrogate" species, which are believed to be typical in their dose responses.

Consider, for example, an attempt to predict the potential effects of chemical inputs to a particular lake. It is highly unlikely that relevant dose-response data will be available for the species of fish in the ecosystem. Consequently, predictions will typically be made using information for surrogate species, such as rainbow trout (*Salvelinus gairdneri*) and fathead minnow (*Pimephales promelas*). These two species have been well studied in toxicological laboratories and are widely used as indicators. Similarly, the potential effects on the community of zooplankton might be predicted using information available for well-studied species, such as the water fleas *Daphnia magna* and *Ceriodaphnia dubia*, while the risk assessment for phytoplankton might use data for the unicellular algae *Selenastrum capricornutum* and *Chlorella vulgaris*.

The results of risk assessments for an ecological community, based on laboratory studies of surrogate species, are always uncertain. This is especially true if the potential effects of chemical exposures in natural, ecological contexts are being predicted. Such risk assessments are, however, the best that can be done under most circumstances because there is rarely enough funding or time to do better. Nevertheless, because these methods deliberately overestimate the potential risks, they provide conservative guidance for management purposes.

Conclusions

Environmental stressors are factors that can constrain the productivity and reproduction of organisms and the development of ecosystems. The stressors can be natural or anthropogenic and may operate over the short term (acute) or long term (chronic). Stressors may cause physical disruption, as when a forest is affected by a severe windstorm, wildfire, or timber harvest. Other stressors operate by causing toxicity, as when organisms are exposed to solar ultraviolet radiation or to pesticides. Environmental risks are associated with exposure to a wide variety of factors in the environment. A major activity in environmental science is the study of these risks and the prediction of their effects on people, other species, and ecosystems.

Photo 15.5 Smoking entails a voluntary exposure to a wide range of chemicals that are known to be toxic. In addition, non-smokers are involuntarily exposed to "sidestream smoke" as a result of sharing space with smokers in restaurants, taverns, or their home.

Source: CP/Fred Chartrand

Key Terms

environmental stressor
disturbance
exposure
response
pollution
contamination
community-replacing
  disturbance
microdisturbance
toxicology
environmental toxicology

ecotoxicology
acute toxicity
chronic toxicity
environmental risk
environmental risk
  assessment
dose-response relationship
exposure assessment
mutagen
teratogen
hormone

Questions for Review

1. What are the various kinds of environmental stressors? Give examples of each.
2. What is the difference between pollution and contamination?

3. How do toxicology, environmental toxicology, and ecotoxicology differ?
4. Use the data in Table 15.4 as the basis of a short essay about the risks of death in Canada. Make sure that you relate the risks to environmental exposures, where appropriate.

Questions for Discussion

1. Identify several examples of naturally occurring pollution and disturbance in the region where you live.
2. Compare the ecological effects of community-replacing disturbances and gap-phase microdisturbances. How is the knowledge of these effects useful for designing ecologically appropriate practices for resource harvesting and management? Use old-growth forest as an example.
3. What do you consider to be the most important risks to your health? Compare your list with the data in Tables 15.4 and 15.5. What are the similarities and differences? Why do these exist?
4. If all chemicals are potentially toxic, should society allow any exposure to these potential health risks? Discuss this statement and its conceptual fallacy.

Exploring Issues

1. How could the data presented in Table 15.2 for the herbicide glyphosate be used to assess the probability of people or animals suffering toxicity when this chemical is used in agriculture, forestry, or around the home (these are all common uses of glyphosate)? What additional information would you need to perform a comprehensive risk assessment for this chemical? What about the indirect effects of glyphosate on wild animals caused by changes in the amount and species composition of vegetation in treated areas?

References

Barrett, G.W. and R. Rosenberg (eds.). 1981. *Stress Effects on Natural Ecosystems*. New York: Wiley.

Canadian Cancer Society. 2005. *Canadian Cancer Encyclopedia*. Regina, SK: Canadian Cancer Society.

Clarke, L.B. 1989. *Acceptable Risk? Making Decisions in a Toxic Environment*. Berkeley, CA: University of California Press.

Cote, R.P. and P.G. Wells. 1991. *Controlling Chemical Hazards: Fundamentals of the Management of Toxic Chemicals*. London: Unwin Hyman.

Estok, D., B. Freedman, and D. Boyle. 1989. Effects of the herbicides 2,4-D, glyphosate, hexazinone, and triclopyr on the growth of three species of ectomycorrhizal fungi. *Bull. Environm. Contam. & Toxicol.*, **42**: 835–839.

Fletcher, K. and B. Freedman. 1986. Effects of several herbicides used in forestry on litter decomposition. *Can. J. For. Res.*, **16**: 6–10.

Forbes, V.E. and T.L. Forbes. 1994. *Ecotoxicology in Theory and Practice*. New York: Chapman & Hall.

Freedman, B. 1991. Controversy over the use of herbicides in forestry, with particular reference to glyphosate usage. *J. Envir. Sci. & Health*, **C8**: 277–286.

Freedman, B. 1995. *Environmental Ecology*. 2nd ed. San Diego, CA: Academic.

Gough, M. 1989. Estimating cancer mortality. *Environ. Sci. & Technol.*, **23**: 925–930.

Hodge, R.A., P.R. West, and R. Gregory-Eaves. 1996. Toxic substances. Chapter in: *1996 State-of-the-Environment Report for Canada*. Ottawa: Environment Canada.

Kolluru, R.V., S.M. Bartell, R.M. Pitbaldo, and S. Stricoff (eds.). 1996. *Risk Assessment and Management Handbook for Environmental, Health, and Safety Professionals*. New York: McGraw Hill.

Krewski, D., P. Slovic, S. Bartlett, J. Flynn, and C. Mertz. 1994. *Health Risk Perception in Canada*. Calgary: University of Calgary. Environmental Risk Management Working Paper ERC 94-4, EcoResearch Chair.

Landis, W.G. and M-H. Yu. 2004. *Introduction to Environmental Toxicology: Impacts of Chemicals Upon Ecological Systems*. 3rd ed. Boca Rotan, FL: CRC Press.

Levin, S.A, M.A. Harwell, J.R. Kelly, and K.D. Kimball (eds.). 1989. *Ecotoxicology: Problems and Approaches*. New York: Springer.

Morash, R. and B. Freedman. 1989. Effects of several herbicides on the germination of seeds in the forest floor. *Can. J. For. Res.*, **19**: 347–350.

Moriarty, F. 1999. *Ecotoxicology: The Study of Pollutants in Ecosystems*. 3rd ed. San Diego, CA: Academic Press.

Newman, M.C. and M.A. Unger. 2002. *Fundamentals of Ecotoxicology*. 2nd ed. Boca Raton, FL: CRC Press.

Odum, E.P. 1985. Trends expected in stressed ecosystems. *BioScience*, **35**: 419–422.

Odum, E.P. and G.W. Barrett. 2004. *Fundamentals of Ecology*. Florence, KY: Brooks Cole.

Schindler, D.W. 1987. Detecting ecosystem responses to anthropogenic stress. *Can. J. Fish. Aquat. Sci.*, **44**: 6–25.

Smith, W.H. 1984. Ecosystem pathology: A new perspective for phytopathology. *For. Ecol. Manage.*, **9**: 193–219.

Statistics Canada. 2005. Table 102-0540. Deaths, by Cause: External causes of morbidity and mortality in Canada. http://estat.statcan.ca/cgi-win/CNSMCGI.EXE

Suter, G.W., L.W. Barnthouse, S.M. Bartell, T. Mill, and S. Paterson. 1993. *Ecological Risk Assessment*. Boca Raton, FL: CRC Press.

Thomas, S.P. and S.E. Hrudey. 1997. *Risk of Death in Canada: What We Know and How We Know It*. Edmonton: University of Alberta Press.

Townsend, C.R., M. Begon, and J.L. Harper. 2002. *Essentials of Ecology*. 2nd ed. Cambridge, UK: Blackwell Publishers.

Tschirley, F.H. 1986. Dioxin. *Sci. Amer.*, **254** (2): 29–35.

Walker, C.H., S.P. Hopkin, R.M. Sibley, and D.B. Peakall. 2001. *Principles of Ecotoxicology*. Boca Rotan, FL: CRC Press.

Informative Websites

Canadian Centre for Occupational Health and Safety.
www.ccohs.ca/

The Canadian Centre for Occupational Health and Safety promotes a safe and healthy working environment by providing information and advice about occupational health and safety. This site discusses issues such as hepatitis B, forklift safety, and workers' compensation.

Environmental Literacy Council. Risk.
www.enviroliteracy.org/article.php/415.html

Read articles about how the public generally rates as more risky those things over which they have no control than behaviours that are actually more likely to result in harm but are voluntarily undertaken.

RiskWorld. www.riskworld.com/

RiskWorld, a newsletter of the Society for Risk Analysis, provides newspaper articles, reports, and papers that introduce many issues concerning risk and risk management.

Statistics Canada. Health.
www.statcan.ca/english/Pgdb/health.htm

This Statistics Canada website contains data on risk and health in Canada and its regions.

World Resources Institute. Characterizing Environmental Hazards.
http://pubs.wri.org/pubs_content_text.cfm?ContentID=1295

This article, written by the World Resources Institute, focuses on biological and chemical hazards in the environment.

World Resources Institute. Smoking-Related Deaths.
http://pubs.wri.org/pubs_content_text.cfm?ContentID=1313

The World Resources Institute published this article about tobacco-related illnesses.

World Resources Institute. EarthTrends. The Environmental Information Portal.
http://earthtrends.wri.org/index.cfm

This website contains interesting data about health, environmental quality, and effects of environmental stressors.

Gaseous Air Pollution

16

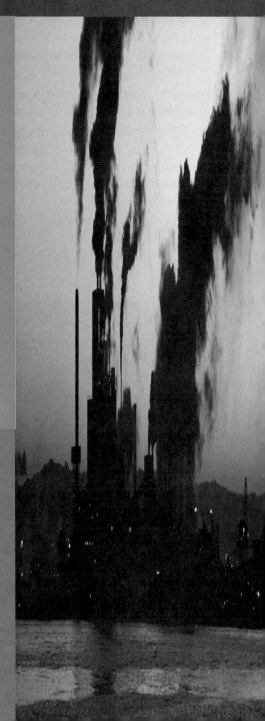

CHAPTER OBJECTIVES

After completing this chapter, you will be able to

1. Outline the major sources of emission of air pollutants associated with sulphur, nitrogen, and hydrocarbons.
2. Explain the difference between primary and secondary pollutants.
3. Contrast the environmental problems associated with stratospheric and tropospheric ozone.
4. Examine the importance of air pollutants to ecosystems and to human health.
5. Outline the lessons to be learned from air pollution at the Smoking Hills.
6. Describe the patterns of pollution and ecological damage near point sources of air pollution.

CHAPTER OUTLINE

Introduction

Gaseous air pollutants are emitted from various natural sources, such as volcanoes, forest fires, and wetlands. In fact, the natural emissions of some gases exceed those due to human activities. However, anthropogenic emissions of other gases are larger than the natural ones, and are increasing because of the growth of the human population and its degree of industrialization.

In ancient times, people were responsible for very little atmospheric pollution. Even then, however, there were local problems—smoky wood fires, commonly used for cooking and warmth, likely resulted in poor-quality air inside of badly ventilated dwellings. Hunting cultures often used fire to drive game animals and to increase the abundance of prey species by improving local forage availability. These burns would have resulted in substantial emissions of particulate carbon (soot), carbon dioxide, and other gases and would have temporarily impaired air quality. Still, these effects would have been rather minor.

As humans became more numerous and industrialized, air pollution developed into a much more extensive problem. Because coal was the major fuel used to generate heat and energy for machines, severe air pollution became especially common at the beginning of the Industrial Revolution in the early 1800s. The widespread use of coal led to severe pollution by sulphur dioxide (SO_2)

and soot in the industrial cities and towns of Europe and the Americas. Since 1900, spreading industrialization and new technologies such as power plants and automobiles have further increased the emissions of pollutants.

Air pollution can be especially severe when the lower atmosphere is unusually stable and calm. These conditions often occur beneath **atmospheric inversions**, which are characterized by cool air being trapped beneath a layer of warmer air. This stable condition prevents the mixing of polluted, ground-level air with cleaner air from higher altitudes (see In Detail 16.1). If an atmospheric inversion is accompanied by fog, the air pollution is known as "**smog**" (a composite word derived from "smoke" and "fog"). As recently as the 1950s, "killer smogs" rich in sulphur dioxide and soot caused the deaths of thousands of people, and many more suffered from acute respiratory distress. Smogs rich in sulphur dioxide are also called "reducing smogs." The most famous killer smogs occurred in London, Glasgow, some other industrial centres of Europe, and near Pittsburgh in the United States (these are described later).

Once the severe damage inflicted by air pollution was recognized, governments passed laws to decrease the emissions. Pollution control became particularly vigorous after medical researchers discovered convincing evidence of linkages between air pollution and increases in human diseases and deaths. Particular attention was paid to air quality

In Detail 16.1

Atmospheric Inversions

Normally, the temperature of the atmosphere decreases with increasing altitude. Under certain conditions, however, a layer of relatively cool air may become trapped under a layer of warmer air, a phenomenon known as an *atmospheric inversion* (or temperature inversion).

Atmospheric inversions can develop on clear, cloudless nights. Under such conditions, the ground surface cools quickly as it radiates the heat that was absorbed during the day. This can result in a layer of cool air occurring beneath a layer of warmer air. Hilly terrain is particularly vulnerable to developing atmospheric inversions because relatively dense cool air can drain from slopes and hilltops and accumulate in valleys. Sometimes during the summer, stable atmospheric conditions

may develop at higher altitude, capping a still-mixing air mass at ground level.

Atmospheric inversions can be rather stable. Until they are dispersed by vigorous winds, they can trap and accumulate air pollutants emitted during the inversion event. Severe episodes of air pollution can occur when stable inversions develop and are maintained for several days.

Some places regularly develop less persistent inversions. This occurs in the Los Angeles basin, around Mexico City, and in the Greater Vancouver area. In these places, the inversions develop in the morning but are typically dispersed during the afternoon. In the meantime, however, large concentrations of oxidizing air pollutants such as ozone can accumulate into a photochemical smog.

in urban environments, where the killer smogs were most frequent. The most important control actions have typically included the following:

- switching from coal, which is a relatively "dirty" fossil fuel, to "cleaner" fuels such as natural gas or oil or to alternative technologies such as nuclear power or hydroelectricity
- constructing tall smokestacks to spread emissions over a wider area so that ground-level exposures become less common and less intense—this tactic is known as the "dilution solution to pollution"
- centralizing energy production in large power plants to replace much of the relatively dirty coal burning in home fireplaces and furnaces, and so allowing better control of emissions and less overall energy use
- treating waste gases to remove some of their pollutant content, thereby reducing emissions into the atmosphere

Because of these helpful measures, so-called "oxidizing smogs" have supplanted the SO_2-rich reducing smogs in many regions. Oxidizing smog develops in the atmosphere through complex photochemical reactions in which hydrocarbons and nitrogen oxides are transformed into other gases and ozone (O_3) is produced. Ozone and other oxidizing gases harm vegetation and irritate the respiratory system and eyes of people. Oxidizing smog develops under sunny conditions if hydrocarbons and nitrogen oxides are present from automobile and industrial emissions, and particularly if atmospheric temperature inversions reduce dispersion.

In this chapter we examine the most important types of gaseous air pollutants. Their emission sources, chemical transformations, and toxicity are described, and Canadian case studies are used to demonstrate the ecological damages that may be caused.[1]

Sulphur Gases

Emissions and Transformations

Sulphur dioxide (SO_2) is one of the most important of the gaseous air pollutants. SO_2 is a colourless but pungent gas. Humans can detect the bitter taste of SO_2 at a concentra-

tion of only 0.3–1 ppm (parts per million). Hydrogen sulphide (H_2S), another sulphur gas, can be detected as a foul odour, reminiscent of rotten eggs, at concentrations lower than 1 ppb (parts per billion).

After they are emitted to the atmosphere, SO_2 and H_2S become oxidized to other compounds, and ultimately to sulphate (SO_4^{2-}; see In Detail 16.2). The sulphate ion carries negative charges and is, therefore, an anion (see In Detail 16.3). Because H_2S is rather quickly oxidized to SO_2, its atmospheric residence time is less than one day. SO_2 oxidizes more slowly, at a rate of <1–5% per hour, depending on sunlight, humidity, the concentration of strong oxidants such as ozone, and the presence of metal-containing particulates that can serve as catalysts. A typical residence time of SO_2 in the atmosphere is about four days. Consequently, SO_2 may disperse a long distance from its point of emission before it becomes oxidized or is deposited to a terrestrial or aquatic surface. This dispersal is referred to as long-range transportation of air pollution, or LRTAP.

Atmospheric sulphate, formed by the oxidation of SO_2 and H_2S, can combine with positively charged ions (cations) to form various compounds. Most atmospheric sulphates occur as tiny particulates, especially as ammonium sulphate (($NH_4)_2SO_4$). Ammonium sulphate is the most prominent component, along with ammonium nitrate (NH_4NO_3), of the particulate haze that often impairs visibility in cities. Haze is also seen in some rural areas where air pollutants have been transported from emission sources elsewhere (i.e., by LRTAP). Other cations that combine with sulphate include calcium (Ca^{2+}), magnesium (Mg^{2+}), and sodium (Na^+). Often, however, there is not enough of these cations (i.e., NH_4^+, Ca^{2+}, Mg^{2+}, or Na^+) to balance all of the negative charges of the sulphate (SO_4^{2-}) present. Under such conditions, hydrogen ions (H^+) serve to balance some of the negative charges of SO_4^{2-}. This results in an aerosol containing sulphuric acid (H_2SO_4), the most important component of acidic precipitation (see Chapter 19).

Sources of SO_2 Emissions

Volcanoes are natural sources of emission of atmospheric sulphur gases. On average, volcanoes emit about 12 million t/y of sulphur gases, of which 90% is SO_2 and 10%, H_2S. However, the enormous 1991 eruption of Mount Pinatubo in the Philippines emitted about 7–10 million t of SO_2 (expressed as the sulphur content, or SO_2-S). The much smaller eruption of Mount St. Helens in

---

[1] Unless otherwise indicated, specific data cited in this and other chapters in this section on environmental damages are from Freedman (1995).

In Detail 16.2

Air Pollution Chemistry

Air pollutants are emitted as particular chemicals, which may become transformed into other compounds through chemical reactions occurring in the atmosphere. Several examples follow.

Oxidation of SO_2

$$SO_2 + OH \rightarrow HO \cdot SO_2 \tag{1}$$
$$HO \cdot SO_2 + O_2 \rightarrow HO_2 + SO_3 \tag{2}$$
$$SO_3 + H_2O \rightarrow H_2SO_4 \tag{3}$$
$$H_2SO_4 \rightarrow 2H^+ + SO_4^{2-} \text{ (in aqueous solution)} \tag{4}$$

Note that the SO_4^{2-} produced is important as a constituent of acid rain and as particulate ammonium sulphate, both of which are prominent air pollutants.

Oxidation of NO

$$NO + HO_2 \rightarrow NO_2 + OH \tag{5}$$
$$NO_2 + OH \rightarrow HNO_3 \tag{6}$$
$$HNO_3 \rightarrow H^+ + NO_3^- \text{ (in aqueous solution)} \tag{7}$$

Similarly, the NO_3^- produced is important as a constituent of acid rain and as particulate ammonium nitrate.

Formation and Destruction of Stratospheric O_3

$$O_2 + UV \text{ radiation} \rightarrow O + O \tag{8}$$
$$O + O \rightarrow O_2 \tag{9}$$

$$O + O_2 \rightarrow O_3 \tag{10}$$
$$O_3 + UV \text{ radiation} \rightarrow O_2 + O \tag{11}$$

Reaction 11 is an ultraviolet photodissociation of O_3. Ozone can also be consumed by reactions with NO, NO_2, or N_2O or with ions or simple molecules of chlorine (especially ClO), bromine, and fluorine. These latter reactions are too complex to describe here (see Freedman, 1995).

Formation and Destruction of Ground-Level O_3

$$O + O_2 \rightarrow O_3 \tag{10}$$
$$NO_2 + UV \text{ radiation} \rightarrow NO + O \tag{12}$$
$$NO + O_3 \rightarrow NO_2 + O_2 \tag{13}$$
$$NO + RO_2 \rightarrow NO_2 + RO \tag{14}$$

The formation of O_3 (reaction 10) requires atomic O, formed by the photodissociation of NO_2 (reaction 12). Ozone can be consumed by reaction with NO (an emitted gas), which regenerates NO_2 (reaction 13). Atmospheric O_3 can, however, accumulate if other reactions (such as reaction 14) convert NO to NO_2, because these operate in competition with reaction 13 for NO. (The species RO_2 in reaction 14 includes various chemicals known as peroxy radicals, formed by the degradation of organic molecules through reaction with hydroxyl radicals, followed by the addition of molecular O_2. RO is the chemically reduced form of RO_2.)

Washington State in 1980 vented about 0.2 million t of SO_2-S. Natural emissions of SO_2 also occur when biomass burns during wildfires.

The global anthropogenic emissions of SO_2 are about 63–72 million t/y, about double the natural emissions (Table 16.1). Fossil-fuel combustion accounts for 54% of the anthropogenic emissions. Coal and petroleum contain mineral compounds of sulphur, such as pyrite (FeS_2), as well as many organic sulphur compounds. When these fuels are burned, the sulphur is oxidized to gaseous SO_2,

In Detail 16.3

Cations and Anions

Cations and anions are ions, atoms or molecules that carry an electrical charge. Cations have one or more positive charges, and anions have one or more negative charges. Common examples of cations include Na^+ (sodium ion), Ca^{2+} (calcium ion), and Al^{3+} (aluminum ion),

having one, two, and three positive charges, respectively. Some anions include NO_3^- (nitrate), SO_4^{2-} (sulphate), and PO_4^{3-} (phosphate), with one, two, and three negative charges, respectively. See also In Detail 19.2 in Chapter 19 for a description of the *conservation of electrochemical neutrality*.

TABLE 16.1	Global Emissions and Other Characteristics of Important Air Pollutants

Emission data are for 1995.

POLLUTANT	NATURAL EMISSIONS (10^6 tonne/year)	ANTHROPOGENIC EMISSIONS (10^6 t/y)	TYPICAL CONCENTRATION		ATMOSPHERIC RESIDENCE TIME
			BACKGROUND (ppm)	POLLUTED AIR (ppm)	
SO_2	40	142	0.0002	0.2	4 days
H_2S	100	3	0.0002	–	<1 day
CO	33	852	0.1	40–70	<3 years
NO_X (as NO)	430	65	<0.002	–	5 days
NO_X (as NO_2)	658	99	<0.004	0.2	–
NH_3	1160	4	0.01	0.02	7 days
N_2O	18	6	0.31	–	4 years
Hydrocarbons	200	160	<0.001	–	?
CH_4	1600	–	1.7	2.5	4 years
Particulates	3700	3900	–	–	–
O_3	–	–	0.03	0.08	–

Sources: Modified from Freedman (1995) and World Resources Institute (2005)

which is usually vented to the atmosphere. Hard coals mined in eastern North America contain 1–12% sulphur; softer coals from western regions have <0.3–1.5%; crude oil has 0.8–1.0%, residual fuel oils such as bunker-C have 0.3–0.4%, and motor fuels such as diesel and gasoline have 0.04–0.05%. Other important sources of SO_2 emissions are manufacturing processes (accounting for 23% of global emissions) and the smelting of metal ores (accounting for 7%).

Anthropogenic emissions of SO_2 have increased enormously since the beginning of the Industrial Revolution. Emissions in 1860 were about 5 million t, compared with about 142 million t in 1995. Since then, most wealthier countries have invested in clean-air technologies for power plants and for other industrial users of coal and oil in order to reduce emissions of damaging SO_2 to the atmosphere. The clean air actions include the following:

- installation of technologies to capture SO_2 from post-combustion waste gases (also known as flue-gas desulphurization or "scrubbing")
- removal of some of the sulphur content of fuels (also known as fuel desulphurization or "coal washing")
- installation of particulate-control devices (such as electrostatic precipitators) to greatly reduce emissions of particulates (although this has little effect on SO_2 emissions)
- switching to low- or no-sulphur fuels such as natural gas, or to no-sulphur energy technologies such as hydroelectricity and nuclear power

- energy conservation to reduce the overall demand for fuel and associated emissions of air pollutants
- building taller smokestacks to disperse emissions of SO_2 more widely, which helps to decrease local, ground-level pollution

However, future global emissions are bound to increase. China, India, and other rapidly industrializing countries supply much of their burgeoning energy needs by burning coal and petroleum fuels. In China, for example, coal is the major source of industrial energy, accounting for 78% of the energy supply (in 1995). Due to increasing industrialization, emissions of SO_2 in China increased from 10 million t in 1980 to 34 million t in 1995, a 340% increase in only 16 years.

The quantities of SO_2 emissions differ greatly among nations, depending on their populations, the nature of their industrialization, and the types of fuels they use. For instance, Canadian emissions of SO_2 are about 16% of those of the U.S. (Table 16.2). However, the population of Canada is only about 11% that of the U.S. (Chapter 10). Therefore, per capita emissions of SO_2 are about 45% larger in Canada.

About 67% of Canadian emissions of SO_2 are from large industrial sources, particularly metal smelters, while 29% are from "fuel combustion," which is mostly fossil-fuelled power plants. In comparison, 86% of U.S. emissions are from power plants, and 9% from industrial sources. Most of this difference is due to two factors: a relatively large proportion of electricity generation in

TABLE 16.2	Comparison of Emissions of Air Pollutants in Canada and the United States					

Data are for 2002, in units of millions of tonnes per year. Percent refers to the percentage of total emissions by country.

SOURCE OF EMISSIONS	SO_2		NO_x (AS NO_2)		CO	
	(10^6 t/y)	%	(10^6 t/y)	%	(10^6 t/y)	%
CANADA						
Transportation	0.08	3	1.55	59	8.4	74
Industrial processes	1.59	67	0.64	25	1.3	12
Fuel combustion	0.68	29	0.38	15	0.7	6
Miscellaneous	0.01	1	0.03	1	0.9	8
Total	2.36		2.60		11.3	
UNITED STATES						
Transportation	0.70	5	11.5	56	79.3	83
Industrial processes	1.20	9	1.0	5	4.8	5
Fuel combustion	12.40	86	7.6	37	3.8	4
Miscellaneous	0.30	<1	0.4	2	7.6	8
Total	14.60		20.5		95.5	

Sources: Modified from Environmental Protection Agency (2005) and Environment Canada (2005)

Canada is from nuclear and hydro technologies, which do not emit SO_2, and SO_2-emitting metal smelting is a major Canadian industry.

Because of human-health and environmental damages associated with SO_2 and other air pollutants, most industrialized nations have taken measures to reduce their emissions. In Canada, for example, total emissions of SO_2 were reduced by about 30% between 1985 and 2002, compared with a 24% reduction in the U.S. during the same period. In both countries the reductions have been achieved by

- switching to low- or no-sulphur fuels for some major uses, especially for electricity generation;
- removing sulphur from some fuels prior to combustion, mostly by coal washing;
- reducing energy demands by conservation; and
- installing scrubbers to remove SO_2 from post-combustion waste gases before they are vented to the atmosphere.

Sources of Sulphide Emissions

In contrast to SO_2, most global emissions of sulphide gases are from natural sources (see Table 16.1). The most important sources are H_2S emitted from oxygen-poor sediment in shallow marine and inland waters, and dimethyl sul-

phide (($CH_3)_2S$) produced by marine phytoplankton and out-gassed from oceanic waters. The natural emission of H_2S is about 100 million t/y and dimethyl sulphide, about 15 million t/y (both expressed as "sulphur equivalent"; that is, as tonnes of S). Anthropogenic emissions of H_2S are much smaller, about 3 million t/y, mostly associated with chemical industries, sewage-treatment plants, and live-stock manure.

The global emission of all sulphur-containing gases is equivalent to about 285 million t/y of sulphur. About half of this global emission is from anthropogenic sources.

Clean air typically contains less than 0.2 ppb of SO_2 or H_2S. Concentrations of SO_2 and H_2S in air polluted by emissions are highly variable. However, they are typically about 0.2 ppm in urban atmospheres and can exceed 3 ppm close to large emission sources.

Toxicity of Sulphur Gases

Concentrations of H_2S in the environment are rarely high enough to be toxic to plants. However, accidental emissions from sour-gas plants may cause local vegetation damage. In contrast, concentrations of SO_2 in cities and near industrial sources are often high enough to injure wild and cultivated plants. Near smelters, vegetation has been severely damaged, as we examine later.

An exposure to 0.7 ppm SO_2 for one hour will result in acute injury to most plant species, as will an exposure to 0.2 ppm over an eight-hour period. It is important to note, however, that some species of plants are particularly sensitive to SO_2 exposures (i.e., they are **hypersensitive**) and can suffer acute injuries at SO_2 concentrations lower than those just noted.

In addition, plants often exhibit reductions in yield when exposed to concentrations of SO_2 lower than those required to cause an acute injury. This type of response, occurring without symptoms of acute tissue damage, is referred to as "**hidden injury**." Hidden injuries to wild and agricultural vegetation have been documented by enclosing plants in chambers and exposing them either to ambient concentrations of SO_2 or to air that has been filtered through charcoal, which removes this gas. If the plant productivity is greater in the filtered air, it follows that ambient SO_2 is sufficient to cause a hidden injury. Studies of pasture grasses in England, for example, have found that exposure to SO_2 concentrations averaging only 0.04 ppm causes hidden injuries, manifested by reductions in yield.

Interestingly, the Canadian air-quality guideline for ambient SO_2 in the atmosphere is a maximum of 0.34 ppm over a one-hour exposure (Table 16.3). This guideline is based on the concentration of SO_2 that causes acute foliar (leaf) injuries to most agricultural plants. Although regions meeting this guideline would not have much acute damage to vegetation, relatively sensitive species might be affected through hidden injuries, possibly resulting in significant losses of yield.

Humans and most other animals are much less sensitive to SO_2 than plants are. Guidelines for allowable exposures of humans to SO_2 and other potentially toxic gases accommodate the fact that, in terms of dose received, longer-term exposures to low concentrations can be as important as higher acute exposures.

Guidelines for occupational exposures to air pollutants are frequently greater than those for ambient exposures. In North America, it is recommended that occupational exposures to SO_2 be no higher than 2 ppm over the long term, and no higher than 5 ppm for shorter exposures. However, some people are relatively sensitive to SO_2, and concentrations less than 1 ppm can cause them to develop acute asthma or other distresses related to impaired pulmonary function. In addition, some studies have suggested that long-term exposures of large human populations to sulphate particulate aerosols (which are ultimately derived from gaseous SO_2) in cities may negatively affect health. The studies have found small increases in the incidence of diseases of the respiratory and circulatory systems, most probably in hypersensitive people.

| TABLE 16.3 | Canadian Guidelines for Permissible Exposures to Several Air Pollutants |

Note that, in terms of the dose received by an organism, longer-term exposures to lower concentrations of chemicals can be equivalent to shorter-term exposures to higher concentrations. Data are in ppm (except O_3, in ppb).

POLLUTANT	AVERAGING TIME	MAXIMUM DESIRABLE CONCENTRATION	MAXIMUM ACCEPTABLE CONCENTRATION	MAXIMUM TOLERABLE CONCENTRATION
Sulphur dioxide	annual	0.01	0.02	–
	24 h	0.06	0.12	0.31
	1 h	0.17	0.34	–
Nitrogen oxide	annual	0.03	0.05	–
	24 h	–	0.11	0.16
	1 h	–	0.21	0.53
Carbon monoxide	8 h	5	13	17
	1 h	13	31	–
Ozone (ppb)	annual	–	15	–
	1 h	50	82	153

Source: Modified from Furmanczyk (1994)

Nitrogen Gases

Emissions and Transformations

The most important of the nitrogen-containing gases are nitric oxide (NO), nitrogen dioxide (NO_2), nitrous oxide (N_2O), and ammonia (NH_3). NO and NO_2 are often considered together as a complex, referred to as NO_x.

Ammonia, a colourless gas, is emitted mostly from wetlands, where it is produced during anaerobic decomposition of dead biomass. Natural emissions of NH_3 are about 1 billion t/y (see Table 16.1). Sources of anthropogenic emissions include fossil-fuel combustion (4 million t/y) and animal husbandry (0.2 million t/y). The residence time of NH_3 in the atmosphere is about 7 days (the NH_3 is eventually oxidized to nitrate).

Nitrous oxide (N_2O) is a colourless, non-toxic gas that produces a mild euphoria when inhaled. This gas is also known as "laughing gas" and is used as a mild anaesthetic in medicine, and sometimes as a recreational drug. Because N_2O is a rather unreactive compound, it has a long residence time in the atmosphere, about four years. Most N_2O emissions are associated with microbial denitrification in soil and water. These are equivalent to about 18 million t/y, while industrial emissions amount to about 6 million t/y. Agricultural soil fertilized with nitrate can have quite high rates of N_2O emission, and modern agricultural practices are thought to have increased global emissions of N_2O by about 40%.

Nitric oxide is a colourless and odourless gas, while nitrogen dioxide is reddish, pungent, and irritating to respiratory and eye membranes. Natural emissions of NO_x are about 430 million t/y (expressed as NO; the same emissions expressed as NO_2 are 658 million t/y). The most important natural emissions of NO_x are due to bacterial denitrification of nitrate in soils, fixation of atmospheric nitrogen gas (N_2) by lightning, and oxidation of biomass nitrogen during fires (see also Chapter 5).

Anthropogenic emissions of NO_x, about 65 million t/y (expressed as NO), result mostly from the combustion of fossil fuels, especially in automobiles and power plants (see Table 16.1). These emissions are mostly NO, which is secondarily oxidized to NO_2 by reactions in the atmosphere. Ultimately, most atmospheric NO_x gases become oxidized to nitrate (NO_3^-), an ion that is important in the acidification of precipitation and ecosystems (see Chapter 18).

Toxicity of Nitrogen Gases

It is rare that concentrations of NH_3 or NO_x gases are high enough to injure vegetation. The environmental damage associated with NO_x gases includes the photochemical reactions by which ozone, a much more toxic chemical, is produced (see below), and also the acidification of precipitation and ecosystems.

Ambient concentrations of NH_3 and NO_x are rarely high enough to bother humans. Guidelines for long-term exposures in an occupational setting are 25 ppm for NO and 5 ppm for NO_2. Occupational guidelines for short-term exposures are 35 ppm and 5 ppm, respectively. Intense occupational exposures to NO_x can cause impaired pulmonary function in humans.

Organic Gases and Vapours

Emissions and Transformations

Hydrocarbons are a diverse group of chemicals with molecular structures containing various combinations of hydrogen and carbon. The simplest hydrocarbon is methane (CH_4), a gas. Hydrocarbons with larger weights and more complex structures may occur as vapours, liquids, or solids (see Chapter 22). Other volatile organic compounds (VOCs) may contain oxygen, nitrogen, and other light elements in addition to carbon and hydrogen, and include such groups as aldehydes, alcohols, and phenols.

The background concentration of methane in the atmosphere is about 1.5 ppm, while all other hydrocarbons and volatile organics together amount to less than 1 ppb (see Table 16.1). Most emissions of CH_4 are natural and are associated with the fermentation of organic matter by microbes in anaerobic wetlands. Smaller amounts of CH_4 are out-gassed from fossil-fuel deposits and during wildfires, and to some degree, from ruminant animals (such as cows and sheep) and termites, which produce CH_4 as they digest their plant foods. The global emissions of CH_4 are estimated to be about 1.6 billion t/y.

Atmospheric hydrocarbons other than CH_4 are referred to as *non-methane hydrocarbons*. Natural emissions of these and many organics occur mainly as gases and vapours evaporated from living vegetation, along with smaller quantities out-gassed from deposits of fossil fuels. The largest emissions from forests typically occur during hot, sunny days. Natural emissions of non-methane hydrocarbons are estimated to be about 200 million t/y, compared with anthropogenic emissions of 160 million t/y (see Table 16.1). The most important anthropogenic sources involve unburned fuel emitted from vehicles and aircraft, releases during fossil-fuel mining and refining, and evaporation of solvents and oil-based paints.

Toxicity of Organic Gases and Vapours

Organic gases and vapours can be toxic, but atmospheric concentrations are rarely high enough to damage vegetation or animals. The environmental importance of these gases and vapours lies mainly in their role in the photochemical reactions that produce toxic ozone. In addition, CH_4 is an important greenhouse gas (Chapter 17). In some workplaces, however, relatively toxic organics such as benzene and formaldehyde may be important pollutants.

Ozone and Other Photochemical Pollutants

There are two quite different ozone-related environmental issues: O_3 in the troposphere (ground-level ozone) and O_3 in the stratosphere. High concentrations of ozone are naturally present in the upper-atmospheric layer known as the stratosphere, which begins at about 8–17 km above the Earth's surface, depending on latitude and season. Stratospheric O_3 causes no direct damage and is not an air pollutant. Rather, by absorbing solar ultraviolet radiation, stratospheric O_3 helps to protect organisms on Earth's surface from many damaging effects of exposure to this harmful part of the electromagnetic spectrum (see below). In contrast, O_3 in the lower atmosphere (i.e., the troposphere) is an important air pollutant, known to cause extensive damage to vegetation, materials, and human health. Ozone is removed from the atmosphere by interactions with other gases, organic vapours, and terrestrial and aquatic surfaces (including vegetation).

Ground-Level Ozone

Ground-level ozone (O_3) is the most damaging of the so-called **photochemical air pollutants**. Less important are peroxyacetyl nitrate (PAN), hydrogen peroxide (H_2O_2),

and other oxidant gases. **Oxidizing smog** is rich in O_3 and these other oxidant gases. These chemicals are all called **secondary pollutants**, meaning that they are not actually emitted to the atmosphere (as are **primary pollutants** such as SO_2 and NO_x). Instead, they are synthesized within the atmosphere by photochemical reactions (chemical reactions requiring light). These proceed at faster rates (resulting in a buildup of O_3 in the lower atmosphere) if NO_x and hydrocarbons are present in high concentrations—a condition typically due to anthropogenic emissions.

Some localities tend to develop a weak atmospheric inversion in the morning (see In Detail 16.1). Because inversions are relatively stable and resist the in-mixing of cleaner, ambient air, they encourage the development of oxidizing smog during the morning and early afternoon. Later in the day, the inversion is broken up by stronger winds, and the air pollution is dispersed. Such inversions and their ozone-rich smog are common phenomena around Vancouver, the Los Angeles basin, Mexico City, and some other places.

The concentrations of ambient, ground-level O_3 vary greatly among different regions of North America. Average concentrations in the southwestern U.S. are relatively high, at about 100 ppb, and they generally range from 40–60 ppb in other regions of the U.S. and in southern Canada.

Canada, the U.S., and other countries have developed air-quality standards for O_3. These are intended to reflect concentrations that would prevent severe damage to agricultural and wild vegetation. For some time, the American O_3 standard was 80 ppb (for an average one-hour exposure), but in 1979 this was relaxed to 120 ppb. The authorities made the change because the original standard (i.e., 80 ppb) was frequently exceeded over large regions and was therefore essentially unenforceable. In fact, even the 120 ppb criterion is commonly exceeded in some regions, particularly in the southwestern United States.

The Los Angeles basin suffers especially intense photochemical air pollution. Concentrations of O_3 can exceed 500 ppb (one-hour average), and they typically exceed 100 ppb for more than 15 days during the summer. Maximum O_3 concentrations are lower in other cities of North America, typically reaching up to 150–250 ppb (one-hour average). These concentrations are well within the range at which O_3 can cause acute injuries to plants, which is why O_3 is considered such an important air pollutant. The emissions of ozone precursors (NO_x and hydrocarbons) occur mainly in cities, but extensive ecological damage is caused when polluted air masses are transported to rural areas covered with agricultural or natural vegetation.

In Canada, the regions that most often experience ozone pollution are the lower Fraser Valley in southwestern British Columbia, the Windsor–Quebec City corridor, and the southern Maritimes (Environment Canada, 1999). The lower Fraser Valley, a coastal lowland bounded by mountains to the east, is frequently subject to atmospheric inversions and receives large emissions of ozone precursors from the Greater Vancouver area to the west. Some places in the lower Fraser Valley have maximum O_3 concentrations of about 100 ppb.

The Windsor–Quebec City corridor likewise has local emissions associated with people and industries (about 60% of the Canadian population lives in the region), but this area also receives ozone and its precursors in air masses blowing from industrial regions in the northeastern United States. Many places in the corridor have maximum O_3 concentrations of about 110–160 ppb, and values of 190 ppb have been measured.

The southern Maritime region has a moderately large population, but it is affected mainly by ozone-rich air masses blowing in from industrial parts of southern Ontario, Quebec, and the northeastern United States. Some places in southern New Brunswick and western Nova Scotia have maximum O_3 concentrations of about 90–110 ppb.

Toxicity of Ozone

Humans and some animals are rather sensitive to O_3 exposures, which can irritate and damage membranes of the eyes and respiratory system and cause some loss of pulmonary function. The guideline for long-term exposure to O_3 in an occupational setting is 100 ppb, and it is 300 ppb for short-term exposures. Sensitive people can, however, be severely affected by O_3-related symptoms at lower concentrations. Exposure to O_3 can result in asthmatic attacks and can exacerbate bronchitis and emphysema.

Ozone causes important damage to wild and agricultural plants over widespread areas. Distinctive foliar injuries diminish the photosynthetic capacity of plants and therefore reduce their productivity. Acute injuries are caused to most species by two to four-hour exposures to 200–300 ppb O_3, while long-term exposures to only 40–100 ppb may cause hidden injuries (and reduced yield). However, many species of plants are more sensitive than this and suffer acute and hidden injuries at lower concentrations. Some varieties of tobacco (*Nicotiana tobacco*), for example, can suffer acute foliar injuries from a two- to three-hour exposure to only

50–60 ppb, and spinach (*Spinacea oleracea*), from one to two hours at 60–80 ppb. Sensitive species of conifer trees may suffer acute injuries from exposures to 80 ppb O_3 over 12 hours.

Researchers have grown agricultural plants in chambers receiving ambient air, or in chambers with air filtered through charcoal, which removes O_3. These studies have been extremely useful in defining the extent of the damage caused to agricultural crops by exposure to ambient O_3. One series of field experiments demonstrated that crop yields were reduced in all regions of the United States. The worst damage occurred in the southwest, where sunny conditions and large emissions of NO_x and hydrocarbons result in especially high O_3 concentrations. That study estimated that crop damage due to O_3 was equivalent to 2–4% of the total agricultural yield in the U.S., with economic losses equivalent to more than $5 billion/y. Because O_3-related damage to vegetation occurs over extensive areas of North America, O_3 is by far the most important air pollutant in agriculture. It is probably also the leading air pollutant causing damage to forests and other natural ecosystems.

Stratospheric Ozone

In contrast, ozone in the stratosphere protects life on Earth. The fact that stratospheric ozone is being destroyed by anthropogenic emissions of pollutants is cause for alarm.

Ozone is produced in the stratosphere by natural reactions. These involve the absorption of solar ultraviolet radiation by oxygen molecules (O_2), forming highly reactive oxygen atoms (O) that join with other O_2 molecules to form O_3 (see In Detail 16.2). These reactions proceed relatively quickly in the stratosphere because high-energy ultraviolet radiation is abundant there. As a result, O_3 concentrations are typically 200–300 ppb in the stratosphere, about 10 times higher than in the ambient troposphere.

Stratospheric O_3 provides a critical environmental service. It efficiently absorbs most high-energy ultraviolet (UV) radiation, which, if intense, can be extremely damaging to organisms. In particular, DNA (deoxyribonucleic acid) is a strong absorber of UV and can be damaged by this radiation. This can increase the risk of developing skin cancers, including melanoma, an often-fatal disease. Other health risks from UV exposure include the development of cataracts in the eyes and suppression of the immune system. UV radiation also damages plants, in part because chlorophyll (the major photosynthetic pigment) can be degraded by UV absorption, leading to decreases in productivity. The waxy covering of the cuticle of foliage can also be damaged by UV radiation.

Stratospheric O_3 can be destroyed by various processes, including reactions with the trace gases NO_x and N_2O and with reactive ions of chlorine, bromine, and fluorine. Because of anthropogenic emissions, the concentrations of some of these O_3-consuming chemicals have been increasing in the stratosphere, leading to concerns about the depletion of stratospheric O_3. It is widely believed that emissions of chlorofluorocarbons (CFCs), particularly the industrial

gases known as "freons," have been especially important in this regard. Because CFCs are extremely unreactive in the troposphere, they eventually migrate up to the stratosphere, where they are bombarded with ultraviolet radiation and slowly degrade (photodissociate) to release free chlorine. The chlorine efficiently reacts with and destroys O_3.

The O_3-destroying reactions proceed most effectively under extremely cold and stagnant conditions in the stratosphere, such as those occurring above polar latitudes at the end of the antarctic or arctic winters. These polar-

Global Focus 16.1

A Success Story in Pollution Control: The Montreal Protocol

Soon after it became widely recognized that emissions of chlorofluorocarbons (CFCs) and other chemicals were degrading the stratospheric ozone layer, world governments took action to deal with the problem. In 1987, the United Nations Environment Program (UNEP) organized an international meeting in Montreal, where intense negotiations led to a treaty known as *The Montreal Protocol on Substances That Deplete the Ozone Layer.* The Montreal Protocol is an international agreement committing each party (signatory nation) to a schedule for phasing out the production and use of CFCs and other substances harmful to the ozone layer. It required the signatory nations to freeze their production and consumption of CFCs at 1986 levels by 1989, and to further reduce them to 50% of 1986 levels by 1998.

However, the governments of many countries found it difficult to ratify the protocol because they did not want to impose strict controls on the manufacturing and use of chemicals believed necessary for the functioning of their economies. This was particularly true for nations of the European Community, the former Soviet Union, and Japan. However, Canada, the U.S., Norway, Sweden, and several other countries strongly advocated control measures, and they managed to convince the reluctant nations to phase out their use of ozone-depleting substances. The Montreal Protocol came into force on January 1, 1989, and was then ratified by 40 countries, which accounted for about 82% of the global use of CFCs.

The Montreal Protocol was subsequently amended to eliminate the use of halons by 1994; of CFCs, methyl chloroform, HBFCs (hydrobromofluorocarbons), and carbon tetrachloride by 1996; of methyl bromide by

2010; and of HCFCs (hydrochlorofluorocarbons) by 2030. The amended protocol was ratified by many additional countries, including China and India, huge nations that had not participated in the initial negotiations. In 2005, 189 countries were parties to the Montreal Protocol, representing about 98% of the global population. The amendments also established the *Montreal Protocol Multilateral Fund* to provide financial support to help developing nations become less dependent on ozone-depleting chemicals.

The Montreal Protocol and its subsequent amendments have been called a "success story" in pollution control. Many developed countries (including Canada) have accelerated and surpassed the original reduction targets, and less developed countries have committed to not develop the use of ozone-depleting substances in their economies. This success was achieved because

1. there was international recognition of a clear threat to the global environment;

2. the threat was associated with certain chemicals that could be easily controlled, as they were being manufactured in only a few places and were used for relatively discrete purposes; and

3. economically acceptable substitutes were quickly developed to replace the uses of ozone-depleting substances.

In summary, scientifically rigorous information, effective international and national institutions, a spirit of co-operation, effective leadership by inspired individuals, and the availability of alternative technologies combined to bridge political differences in favour of the pursuit of a common environmental interest. This is why the Montreal Protocol and its implementation are regarded as a success story of environmental action.

focused O_3 depletions result in the development of so-called "ozone holes" during the early spring. These phenomena have been observed regularly since the early 1980s. The O_3 holes over Antarctica are particularly extensive and typically involve decreases of total O_3 concentration of 30–50% during the spring. Smaller depletions of O_3 occur above the Arctic, including northern Canada. The affected areas in the Northern Hemisphere are less extensive than their counterparts in Antarctica.

The sizes of the ozone holes vary from year to year. Between 1991 and 2005, the ozone holes exceeded 20 million km^2 each year, compared with 2–3 million km^2 between 1979 and 1982. In 2000, Antarctica had its largest-ever ozone hole, covering an area of about 30 million km^2, and in 2004, it was 28 million km^2. Although the seasonal depletions of stratospheric O_3 occur only over polar regions, lower latitudes may be affected when O_3-depleted polar air becomes dispersed during the breakup of the ozone holes. This may temporarily reduce stratospheric O_3 concentrations throughout the hemisphere.

In summary, stratospheric O_3 provides a critical UV shield that helps protect organisms on Earth's surface from damage caused by ultraviolet radiation. This function is impaired by the development of O_3 holes above the polar regions, particularly over Antarctica. This phenomenon is caused largely by emissions of CFCs and other pollutants such as NO_x and N_2O into the atmosphere.

Air Pollution and Human Health

An extraordinary case of a natural emission of gas causing human deaths involved the release of a large volume of CO_2 from a lake in Cameroon, West Africa. Lake Nyos is a 200-m-deep volcanic lake in which the deep waters are naturally supersaturated with CO_2, similar to bottled soda water. One night in 1986, a large slump of sediment apparently eroded into the steep-sided lake, causing bottom water to churn to the surface. The water de-gassed its CO_2 content into a dense, ground-level air mass, which then flowed into low areas in the surrounding landscape. The CO_2-rich air mass asphyxiated about 2000 sleeping people living as far as 25 km from the lake, plus thousands of cattle and uncounted numbers of wild animals. Plants are much less vulnerable to CO_2 toxicity, so no vegetation was damaged by this rare and astonishing natural event.

Anthropogenic emissions of gaseous pollutants have frequently caused increases in human mortality and dis-

eases. Some people, especially those with chronic respiratory or heart diseases, are particularly vulnerable to the effects of air pollution. Exposures of people to toxic gases can occur within several contexts, including the following.

The ambient environment: The urban atmosphere typically contains relatively high concentrations of potentially toxic chemicals. This is true in general, but air quality is especially bad during smog events, often caused by poor dispersion during an atmospheric inversion. Consequently, city people living their normal urban lives are routinely exposed to higher concentrations of air pollutants than those living in cleaner, rural environments.

The working environment: Many people are exposed to high concentrations of pollutants as a consequence of their occupation. Of course, the specific exposures depend on the job—workers in metal smelters may be exposed to sulphur dioxide and metallic particulates, auto mechanics may be affected by exhaust fumes containing carbon monoxide and hydrocarbons, and dental workers may inhale mercury vapours.

The indoor environment is often contaminated by various gases and fumes. For example, space heaters, furnaces, and fireplaces burning wood, kerosene, or fuel oil may emit carbon monoxide into the indoor environment. All high-temperature combustions emit nitric oxide, and many synthetic materials and fabrics vent formaldehyde and other organic vapours. These chemicals can accumulate if indoor air is not exchanged frequently with cleaner, outdoor air.

The smoking of tobacco is the leading source of easily avoidable air pollution. Smoking is also the most important cause of preventable diseases, particularly lung cancer and heart disease (see Chapter 15). People directly inhale a great variety of toxic gases and fumes when they smoke tobacco (and also marijuana) in cigarettes, cigars, or pipes. In addition, non-smokers are indirectly exposed to lower concentrations of all of those chemicals because of the lingering residues of so-called "sidestream" and "secondhand" smoke that occur in indoor atmospheres.

All of these exposures to air pollutants have important implications for human health. However, only the pollution of the ambient, urban environment is discussed in the following paragraphs.

Since the beginning of the Industrial Revolution in western Europe in the early nineteenth century, people living in cities and working in certain types of factories have been exposed to high concentrations of air pollutants.

Canadian Focus 16.1

Smog in Canadian Cities

Smog is a serious problem in many cities and also in some rural areas because of LRTAP from urban areas. Smog is typically characterized as a noxious mixture of pollutants visible as a brownish-yellow or greyish-white haze. The key components are:

- O_3 gas, along with SO_2 and NO_x;
- organic vapours; and
- fine particulates (<10 μm diameter), including acidic droplets of H_2SO_4 and HNO_3, particulate NH_4NO_3 and $(NH_4)_2SO_4$, and organics from diesel exhaust and other combustion sources.

Smog is widely regarded as a major cause of environmental damage, including toxicity caused to vegetation and the deterioration of building surfaces and other materials. Smog is also known to cause disease and discomfort in people. The elderly and children are particularly vulnerable, as are people with existing heart or lung disease (especially asthma, bronchitis, and emphysema). Even healthy adults, however, may be affected on days with severe smog. The key causes of toxicity are ozone, other gases, and the finest particulates (<2.5 μm), which can penetrate into the smallest lung cavities (known as alveoli) and cause irritation and other problems.

It must be recognized, however, that the data showing an association of smog and human diseases are epidemiological in nature—they involve discovering statistical relationships between smog intensity and the prevalence of certain maladies. In southern Ontario, for example, there is a predictable increase in hospital admissions of people suffering from respiratory ailments at times during the summer when concentrations of ozone and/or sulphate particulates are high. Although it is rarely possible to link a specific disease in a particular person to exposure to air pollution, one statistical estimate by the Ontario Medical Association suggested that smog is annually responsible for about 1900 premature deaths and $1 billion in health-related costs in Ontario alone.

Because of the importance of smog as a stressor of urban Canadians, governments have initiated programs to monitor air pollutants and predict their future concentrations so that "smog alerts" can be issued to the public. Environment Canada, for example, in partnership with provincial and municipal governments, routinely issues advisories in smog-prone cities, usually on the day before a high level of ozone is predicted. Similarly, some provinces and municipalities have developed air-quality indices to provide daily advisories. The intent is to encourage people and industries to take actions to reduce air pollution and to avoid unnecessary exposure by staying inside buildings and by not engaging in outdoor exercise that involves deep breathing.

According to data of the Ontario Ministry of the Environment, in 2002, southern Ontario experienced its worst-ever smog summer, with about one-third of the days between June and early September having air so polluted by ozone and other chemicals that it was considered a health hazard. The smog was caused by emissions from the many vehicles and other sources in that well-populated region, coupled with weather that was hotter and sunnier than normal—conditions that favour the photochemical formation of ozone. It appears that this sort of health-threatening smog is now well established in extensive, highly populated regions of southern Ontario.

References

Environment Canada. 2002. *Smog.*
    www.msc-smc.ec.gc.ca/cd/factsheets/smog/
Ontario Medical Association. 2002. *Smog-wise.*
    www.oma.org/phealth/smogmain.htm

Especially important have been sulphur dioxide, soot, and other emissions associated with the combustion of coal and other fossil fuels. The most severe exposures to pollutants in urban environments typically occur during prolonged temperature inversions, which prevent the dispersion of emissions and result in smogs rich in SO_2 and particulates.

Coal has long been used around the world to heat homes and other buildings. Its associated emissions have been regarded as a problem in cities and towns in Europe since at least 1500. With the beginning of the Industrial Revolution, which initially used coal as its principal energy source, air pollution worsened markedly. The first convincing link between air pollution and a substantial increase in the death rate of an exposed human population was made in relation to Glasgow, Scotland, in 1909, where about 1000 deaths were attributed to noxious smog that developed during an episode of atmospheric inversion.

The most infamous "killer smog" in North America occurred in 1948 in Donora, Pennsylvania. A temperature inversion and fog persisted in the Donora Valley for four days, but emissions from several large factories continued. High concentrations of SO_2 and particulates built up in the local atmosphere. The smog resulted in increased mortality in the local population (20 deaths in a population of only 14 100). An additional 43% of the population became ill, 10% severely so. The most common symptoms were irritation of the eyes and respiratory tract, sometimes accompanied by coughing, headache, and vomiting.

The world's most notorious "killer smog" afflicted London, England, in 1952, when an extensive temperature inversion and fog stabilized over southern England. In London, emissions of pollutants, mostly associated with coal combustion, transformed a natural "white fog" into a noxious "black fog." Visibility was terrible—people lost their way while walking or driving, even falling off wharves into the Thames River, and airplanes became lost while trying to taxi at the airport. The air pollution episode lasted for four days, but was followed by another 14 days with a higher-than-usual death rate. Overall, about 3900 deaths were attributed to this episode of noxious air pollution. Most affected people were elderly or very young or had severe, pre-existing respiratory or heart diseases.

Until about the early 1960s, severe episodes of urban air pollution were rather common in the industrialized cities of North America and western Europe. Most of these smogs were caused by the widespread burning of coal in fireplaces and furnaces in homes, electrical utilities, and factories. The poor-quality urban air affected the health of people and animals and also damaged vegetation. In many cities, only certain species of plants that can tolerate air pollution could grow. Examples of pollution-tolerant trees that are commonly grown in Canada include Norway maple (*Acer platanoides*), silver maple (*Acer saccharinum*), linden (*Tilia europaea*), tree-of-heaven (*Ailanthus altissima*), and ginkgo (*Ginkgo biloba*).

More recently, governments have brought in legislation that has required large reductions in the emissions of air pollutants, particularly in cities. In Canada, for example, the enactment of various federal, provincial, and municipal laws related to air pollutants has substantially improved urban air quality. Air quality has been similarly improved under legislation enacted in the U.S., Britain, and other countries since the 1960s.

Of course, the killer smogs were extreme air pollution events. More typically, the urban atmosphere is contaminated by much smaller concentrations of SO_2, NO_x, O_3, volatile organic compounds, and particulates. Many studies have investigated the effects of chronic exposures to urban air contaminants on human health. The results of some studies suggest that modern urban air quality is still sufficiently degraded to cause chronic damage to human health (especially by increasing the incidence of lung disease, asthma, and eye irritation), although other studies have not found this to be the case. In any event, effective actions have been taken in Canada and other relatively wealthy nations. Visibly threatening, even lethal, episodes of air pollution like those described above no longer occur in those countries, although they could return if control standards were relaxed.

Unfortunately, in the cities of some rapidly developing countries, such as China, India, Indonesia, and Mexico, poorly regulated industrial and urban growth is resulting in drastic declines in air quality. Although not yet well studied, these may be modern tragedies of urban air pollution.

Cases of Ecological Damage

In this section we examine two case studies of ecological damage caused by air pollution. The first example describes natural air pollution at the Smoking Hills, a remote locality in the Northwest Territories. The second case examines the ecological effects of emissions from large smelters at Sudbury, Ontario.

The Smoking Hills

The Smoking Hills are located in the Northwest Territories on the mainland shore of the Beaufort Sea in the western Arctic. At various places along the coast, bituminous shale occurs as seams in the seacliffs. The shale contains pyritic sulphur, which becomes oxidized to sulphate when exposed to atmospheric oxygen through erosion of the cliffs. The oxidation produces heat (i.e., the reaction is exothermic), which under insulating conditions can increase the temperature enough to spontaneously ignite the bituminous materials. These smoulder, releasing SO_2 to the atmosphere. The nearby tundra is fumigated with this toxic gas. The first recorded sighting of the Smoking Hills was in 1826 by John Richardson, an explorer. However, the burns were long known to Inuit in the area and are probably thousands of years old.

Winds at the Smoking Hills often blow the SO_2-laden air masses ("plumes") inland at ground level, so the tundra ecosystem is directly fumigated. The air pollution is most intense at the edge of the seacliff, where the plumes begin to spread inland. Concentrations of SO_2 at the cliff edge are as high as 2 ppm, and then rapidly decrease farther inland in a more or less *exponential* manner

FIGURE 16.1 | Sulphur Dioxide Concentration at the Smoking Hills, NWT

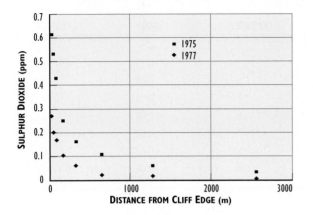

The data are averages of 8- and 14-day sampling periods, respectively. The averages include times when SO₂ concentrations were high, as well as those when the sampling sites were not fumigated because the plumes were blowing out to sea.
Source: Modified from Gizyn (1980)

(Figure 16.1). This *spatial gradient* of air pollution occurs because the gases become progressively diluted in the ambient atmosphere with increasing distance from the points of emission.

The pollution by SO_2 has severely acidified the soil. Acidic conditions in freshwater ponds reach pH 2 or less,

compared with pH 8 or greater outside the fumigation area (see In Detail 19.1 for an explanation of pH). The extreme acidification causes metals to become solubilized from minerals in the soil and aquatic sediment (Table 16.4). High concentrations of dissolved metals are toxic to both terrestrial and aquatic organisms. In addition, sulphate occurs in high concentrations in both soil and water at the Smoking Hills. This is mostly a result of the dry deposition of SO_2 from the atmosphere and its subsequent oxidation to SO_4^{2-} within the ecosystem (see Chapter 19).

The high concentration of SO_2 in the air, and the acidity and soluble metals in the soil and water, render fumigated habitats toxic to most species of plants, animals, and microorganisms. Close to the edge of the seacliff in fumigated areas, where the pollution is most intense, no vegetation occurs at all—there is total ecological degradation. Farther inland, the pollution becomes less severe, and a few pollution-tolerant species of plants can grow. The most notable of these are arctic wormwood (*Artemisia tilesii*), polargrass (*Arctagrostis latifolia*), a lichen (*Cladonia bellidiflora*), and a moss (*Pohlia nutans*). These few pollution-tolerant species have replaced the much greater richness of species of the unpolluted tundra, which includes arctic willow (*Salix arctica*), mountain avens (*Dryas integrifolia*), and more than 70 other species (Freedman *et al.*, 1990).

Pollution-tolerant communities also occur in acidic ponds at the Smoking Hills. Even the most acidic ponds,

Photo 16.1   Natural air pollution at the Smoking Hills, at the edge of the Beaufort Sea in the Northwest Territories, is caused by seams of bituminous shale that have spontaneously ignited. The sulphurous plumes blow inland and fumigate the nearby tundra.

TABLE 16.4	Chemistry of Tundra Ponds at the Smoking Hills, NWT

The data are in ppm and are averages for the indicated sample sizes.

pH RANGE	NUMBER OF PONDS	ALUMINUM	IRON	MANGANESE	NICKEL	SULPHATE
1.8–2.5	4	270	500	61	6.3	8200
2.6–3.5	14	5.5	18	15	0.21	890
3.6–4.5	9	1.1	1.2	3.6	0.04	156
4.6–5.5	1	<0.6	0.5	2.3	0.04	813
5.6–6.5	1	<0.2	0.2	1.8	0.06	713
6.6–7.5	4	<0.8	<0.04	0.7	0.02	360
7.6–8.5	8	<0.7	0.1	<0.5	0.004	106
8.6–9.7	5	<0.2	0.1	0.5	0.01	31

Source: Modified from Havas and Hutchinson (1983)

which have a pH as low as 1.8, support at least six species of algae. These algae are extremely tolerant of acidity and dissolved metals and are not found in non-acidic waterbodies. In contrast to the acidic waterbodies, unpolluted ponds are alkaline, with pHs greater than 8, and they support rich algal communities of more than 90 species. A few acid-tolerant invertebrates also occur in acidic ponds (but only at pHs greater than 2.8), including a crustacean (*Brachionus urceolaris*) and an insect midge (*Chironomus riparius*). The invertebrate fauna of non-acidic ponds is much richer in species and more productive (Havas and Hutchinson, 1983).

Photo 16.2   Soil and surface waters at the Smoking Hills have been severely acidified by the deposition of sulphur dioxide. The acidity causes metals to go into solution, exacerbating the toxic conditions. This pond has been affected by atmospheric SO_2, as well as by acidic, metal-laden drainage water that has passed through roasted shale.

The most important lesson to be learned from the Smoking Hills is that "natural" pollution can cause ecological damage that is as intense as that associated with anthropogenic pollution. Clearly, SO_2 can damage ecosystems regardless of the source of emissions. In addition, the natural pollution at the Smoking Hills has stressed ecosystems for a long time, at least thousands of years, and the ecological effects have likely reached a steady-state condition. The study of the Smoking Hills provides some understanding of the long-term effects of severe air pollution, which include

- a simplification of biodiversity and ecosystems;
- disruption of productivity and nutrient cycling; and
- the development of unusual communities of pollution-tolerant species.

Metal Smelters Near Sudbury

In 1883, while blasting bedrock during construction of the Canadian Pacific Railroad, a worker with some knowledge of prospecting discovered a rich body of metal-bearing ore in the vicinity of Sudbury, Ontario. The principal metals in the ore are nickel and copper. However, valuable quantities of iron, cobalt, gold, silver, and other metals are also produced from the Sudbury mines, as are sulphur and selenium.

One of the world's largest industrial complexes has been developed to mine and process the rich ore bodies near Sudbury. The facilities include underground mines, an open-pit mine, two ore-processing mills with tailings-disposal areas, several smelters, metal refineries, sulphuric-acid plants, and various secondary installations. The

Photo 16.3   A view of a roast bed near Sudbury, around 1925. The roast bed had a bottom layer of wood (in the foreground), upon which heaps of sulphide ore were piled (background) using the track-mounted gantry with its continuous-feed apparatus.

Source: Inco Limited Archives

industrial activities around Sudbury provide the primary economic base for a regional population of more than 155 000 people.

The metals in the Sudbury ore occur as sulphide minerals. Consequently, an important step in processing is high-temperature roasting of the minerals in the presence of oxygen, which converts the sulphide-sulphur into gaseous SO_2. The roasting increases the concentration of valuable metals in the residual material, which can then be smelted and refined into pure metals (see also Figure 13.1, page 214).

The large-scale roasting and smelting have resulted in huge emissions of SO_2 and metal-containing particulates to the atmosphere in the Sudbury area, causing severe pollution and ecological damage. Until 1928, the ore roasting was conducted in huge open pits known as roast beds. These consisted of a layer of locally harvested cordwood covered with heaps of sulphide ore. The wood was ignited, and the resulting heat kindled the metal sulphides, releasing additional heat because the oxidation reaction is exothermic. Eventually, the roast bed was hot enough to support a self-sustaining combustion of the ore, which continued to burn and smoulder for several months. After the roasting was completed, the combustion was quenched with water. When the nickel and copper concentrates had cooled, they were collected and shipped to a refinery for further processing.

As is evident in the accompanying photographs, this crude roasting process resulted in intense, ground-level fumigation of the landscape with toxic SO_2, acidic mist, and metal-containing particulates. The pollution quickly devastated ecosystems near the roast beds. The denuding of the terrestrial ecosystems resulted in massive erosion of soil from slopes, exposing the bedrock, which became pitted and blackened by reaction with the sulphurous fumes.

About 30 roast beds operated in the Sudbury region. These emitted an estimated 270 000 t/y of SO_2, plus huge but undocumented amounts of metallic particulates. These early, extremely toxic, ground-level emissions caused the worst of the ecological damage in the Sudbury area.

In 1928, the government of Ontario prohibited any further use of roast beds. All roasting was then conducted at smelters located at Coniston, Copper Cliff, and Falconbridge, all in the vicinity of Sudbury. Smelters are huge industrial facilities that contain their roasting chambers within buildings. Most of their emissions of waste gases and particulates are vented high into the atmosphere through smokestacks, which greatly reduces the severity of ground-level pollution.

The largest smelter was built at Copper Cliff in 1929. Initially it had a single smokestack. Two others were added

Photo 16.4   Heat from the burning wood ignited the sulphide ore, which then smouldered for several months, giving off dense plumes of SO_2 and metal-laden particulates. After the sulphur was oxidized and driven from the ore into the atmosphere, the fires were quenched and the metal concentrates collected and taken away for further processing. The plumes killed nearby vegetation, caused local soil and surface waters to become toxic because of acidity and metals, and resulted in severe erosion and exposure of naked bedrock.

Source: Inco Limited Archives

Photo 16.5 This is a view of a hillside damaged by emissions of pollutants close to the Copper Cliff smelter near Sudbury. The worst damage was caused by roast beds, but fumigations from the smelter have also been important. Following the devastation of the forest that once grew here, soil eroded and collected in nearby basins. The exposed, naked bedrock became blackened and pitted through reactions with the acidic fumigations.

in 1936. In 1972, the three stacks were replaced with a single, 381-m-tall "superstack" (the world's tallest chimney). At the same time, the Coniston smelter was closed and its production shifted to Copper Cliff. The Falconbridge smelter, with smokestacks of 93 m and 140 m, is owned by another company and continues to operate.

The commissioning of the superstack in 1972 allowed pollutants to be vented high enough into the atmosphere to make ground-level fumigations infrequent. This resulted in a great improvement of air quality in the Sudbury area. Tall smokestacks facilitate the dispersion and mixing of emissions into ambient air. This is known as the "dilution solution to pollution."

Because the superstack is so tall, its emissions are well dispersed into the atmosphere. Little of the vented SO_2 is deposited locally, a fact reflected by the relatively good air quality in the region since 1972. In fact, studies have indicated that only about 1% of the SO_2 emissions are deposited within 40 km of the superstack. This means that 99% of the SO_2 is exported over longer distances, avoiding local damage but contributing to the acidification of precipitation over a large region (see Chapter 19). The plume from the superstack can be detected chemically at distances up to 150 km away.

In addition to the use of tall smokestacks, other technologies have been installed to reduce the emissions of toxic chemicals. As a result, environmental conditions in the Sudbury region have greatly improved. Devices such as electrostatic precipitators are used to recover metal-containing dusts from the smelter flue-gases, while SO_2 emissions have been reduced by installing wet scrubbers, building sulphuric-acid plants, and constructing a facility to separate iron sulphides from the more valuable sulphides of nickel and copper.

Emissions of SO_2 in the Sudbury area peaked during 1960–72, when annual discharges from the three smelters averaged 2.25 million tonnes. At that time, Sudbury was the world's largest source of anthropogenic SO_2 emissions, responsible for about 4% of global releases through human activities. Emissions of SO_2 from the Sudbury smelters have decreased greatly since that time, to about 1.5 million t/y during 1973–77, 0.67 million t/y during 1978–93, 0.27 million t/y during 1994–2000, and 0.25 million t/y during 2001–03. The recent decreased emissions are due mainly to expensive investments in pollution abatement technologies, including equipment for flue-gas desulphurization. Still, the emissions of SO_2 from the Sudbury smelters remain very large.

The post-superstack air quality in the Sudbury region represents a great improvement over the sulphurous past. Toxic fumigations with SO_2, acidic mists, and metal particulates were much more frequent and intense when roast beds were in use, as well as prior to 1972 when the smelters had shorter stacks and little pollution-control technology had been installed. In large degree, the extensive ecological damage in the Sudbury region resulted from the earlier emissions of pollutants. Other disturbances added to that damage, however, including the clear-cutting of forests to provide fuel for roast beds and the starting of wildfires by prospectors and by sparks from steam-powered railroad engines. The modern emissions of SO_2 and other pollutants in the Sudbury region, while still large, are well dispersed and only infrequently cause acute biological damage. In fact, a substantial ecological recovery has occurred since the superstack was commissioned in 1972.

Large areas of land and surface water in the Sudbury region were severely damaged by pollution from the roast-beds and smelters. Before 1972, the smelters were large point sources of emissions, so the severity of the ecological damage decreased rapidly with distance. Over the years, ecologists have documented vegetation damage in the

Sudbury area. In 1970, about 100 km^2 of land around the smelters were characterized as "severely barren," and another 360 km^2 had "impoverished" vegetation, including a lack of conifers in the forest (Watson and Richardson, 1972). White pine (*Pinus strobus*), an economically important tree in the region, is sensitive to air pollution. This species showed diagnostic SO$_2$-injuries over an area of about 6400 km^2.

Pollution was especially damaging around Copper Cliff, the location of the largest smelter. The most degraded terrestrial habitats occur within several kilometres of this facility and support almost no vegetation. Hills and slopes in this zone are denuded of vegetation, their soil is eroded, and the exposed bedrock has been blackened by reaction with acidic fumigations. Only a few plant species that have evolved pollution-tolerant populations grow in this area, including several species of grasses, other herbaceous plants, and stunted, shrub-sized plants of red maple (*Acer rubrum*) (see also Chapter 18).

The intensity of pollution-related stress rapidly lessens at greater distances from the smelters (i.e., a spatial gradient exists), and damage to vegetation is correspondingly less intense. About 3–8 km from the Copper Cliff smelter, remnants of forest survive in places where the local topography provided some protection from fumigations. However, denuded and blackened hilltops are common in this patchily vegetated zone. Trees in the remnant stands are stunted, with many dead branches and other injuries. These trees include relatively pollution-tolerant species such as red maple, white birch (*Betula papyrifera*), red oak (*Quercus rubra*), trembling aspen (*Populus tremuloides*), and large-toothed aspen (*P. grandidentata*). The forest cover beyond 8 km is almost continuous, but the biomass and biodiversity of the stands are impoverished. Beyond about 20–30 km from the smelters, the forests are little affected by pollution, and stands consist of a mixture of conifer and hardwood trees, as is typical of the region (Freedman and Hutchinson, 1980).

Lakes close to the Sudbury smelters have also been severely degraded by atmospheric pollution. The lakes have been acidified by the deposition of SO$_2$ and contain high concentrations of toxic nickel, copper, and other metals. The toxified water bodies contain species-poor communities of pollution-tolerant algae, plants, and zooplankton. They lack fish, mostly because of their acidity.

Improvements in ground-level air quality since the building of the superstack in 1972 have resulted in dramatic ecological recoveries in the Sudbury area. Where eroded soil collected in flat, moist basins, wet meadows have developed. These are dominated by hairgrass (*Deschampsia caespitosa*), the local populations of which are genetically tolerant to toxic nickel and copper in the soil (see Chapter 18). Other plant communities have also benefited greatly from the reduction in air pollution, although their ecological recovery is still impeded by residual soil toxicity associated with acidification and metals.

Lakes have also begun to recover. For example, the pH of a small lake near the closed Coniston smelter increased from 4.1 to 5.8 between 1972 and 1984, while the aqueous concentrations of copper, nickel, and sulphate declined by 60–90% (Hutchinson and Havas, 1985). The reduced toxicity of waterbodies has resulted in increased aquatic productivity, and species previously excluded by toxicity have invaded the lakes.

Since the early 1970s, the ecological recovery of degraded landscapes around Sudbury has been assisted by various management practices. The most important of these has been the liming of soil to reduce toxicity associated with acidity and metals. Also important have been the sowing of seeds of grasses and other plants that are known to be tolerant of the toxic conditions, the addition of fertilizer, and the planting of tree seedlings. Similar efforts in lakes have mostly involved liming to reduce their acidity and metal toxicity, which has allowed a degree of natural recovery of the biota. These efforts of reclamation, along with the natural regeneration that has occurred because of the greatly decreased pollution since the superstack was built, have helped to improve degraded habitats in the Sudbury region.

The case of Sudbury is perhaps the world's best-documented example of ecological damage caused by toxic gases and metals emitted from smelters. There are, however, additional examples of ecological damage around other smelters in Canada, affecting smaller areas. These examples include smelters processing lead and zinc at Trail, British Columbia; gold at Yellowknife, Northwest Territories; nickel at Thompson, Manitoba; copper at Flin Flon, Manitoba; iron at Wawa, Ontario; and copper at Rouyn-Noranda, Quebec.

All of these smelters are large, point sources of emissions of pollutants into the atmosphere. All developed spatial gradients in the intensity of pollution, which decreased exponentially with increasing distance from the source of emissions until the ambient condition is reached. The patterns of ecological damage track these spatial gradients of toxic stress.

Conclusions

Gaseous air pollutants such as sulphur dioxide and nitric oxide are emitted from a variety of sources, which range from large power plants and smelters to individual automobiles and home furnaces. However, some important gaseous pollutants are not emitted to the atmosphere; rather, secondary gases such as ozone are formed by photochemical reactions involving sunlight and emitted oxides of nitrogen and hydrocarbons. If their concentrations are high enough, gaseous air pollutants (often in combination with particulates) can be a risk to human health, and they may also cause damage to ecosystems. Because these risks are now well known, many governments have taken steps to reduce the emissions of the most important air pollutants. This is particularly the case for relatively wealthy countries, such as Canada, the U.S., nations of the European Union, and Japan. Although the emissions of air pollutants in those countries remain large, they are generally stabilizing or even decreasing. However, in rapidly developing economies, such as China and India, hasty and poorly controlled industrialization is resulting in rapidly worsening air pollution.

Key Terms

atmospheric inversion	photochemical air pollutant
smog	oxidizing smog
hypersensitivity	secondary pollutant
hidden injury	primary pollutant

Questions for Review

1. Compare the natural and anthropogenic emissions of sulphur and nitrogen compounds. Why do the sources of emission vary between regions and countries?

2. Why is too much ozone in the lower atmosphere an environmental problem? Why does this differ from the stratosphere, where too little ozone is considered a problem?

3. What are the differences between primary and secondary air pollutants? Give examples of each.

4. Why has air pollution decreased so much in the Sudbury region, and what are the ecological responses to this environmental change?

Questions for Discussion

1. Compare, in broad terms, the patterns of ecological damage caused by "natural" air pollution at the Smoking Hills with that caused by smelters near Sudbury. Why is it useful to study the ecological effects of natural pollution?

2. Existing clean-air technologies could be used to greatly reduce the emissions of air pollutants. Considering the damage that pollutants cause to human health, ecosystems, and other values, why are these technologies not being used more extensively? Consider factors associated with economics, politics, scientific uncertainty about air pollution damage, and the benefits of having cleaner air. Contrast the lack of action with the successes achieved in controlling the emissions of ozone-depleting substances through the Montreal Protocol.

3. Epidemiological (statistical) studies suggest that human health may be affected by ambient levels of air pollutants in urban areas, particularly through increased incidences of respiratory diseases, such as asthma. However, the statistical data are rather weak, and only a relatively small proportion of the urban population appears to be affected. What are some issues that decision makers must consider when deliberating about additional controls on the release of air pollutants in urban areas?

4. Like most other smelters built during the twentieth century, the ones at Sudbury caused obvious damage to ecosystems and human health. Why were those large industrial facilities not shut down or better controlled by the governments of the day? Moreover, new smelters are being built in Canada and in other countries. Are there risks of again causing those kinds of terrible damage?

Exploring Issues

1. You have been asked to assess the potential ecological effects of building a new metal smelter in a region that is now wilderness. The smelter will emit sulphur dioxide to the atmosphere. Based on what you know about pollution damage at the Smoking Hills, around Sudbury, and at other smelters in Canada, what would be the most important considerations to incorporate into the environmental impact assessment? Focus on the potential effects on terrestrial and aquatic ecosystems.

References

Anderson, S.O. and K.M. Sarma. 2005. *Protecting The Ozone Layer: The United Nations History*. London, UK: Earthscan Publications.

Barker, J.R. and D.T. Tingey. 1992. *Air Pollution Effects on Biodiversity*. New York: Van Nostrand Reinhold.

Boubel, R.W., D.L. Fox, D.B. Turner, and A.C. Stern. 1994. *Fundamentals of Air Pollution*. 3rd ed. San Diego, CA: Academic Press.

Brimblecombe, P. 1996. *Air Composition and Chemistry*. 2nd ed. Cambridge, UK: Cambridge University Press.

Environment Canada. 1999. *Ground-Level Ozone: Occurrence and Transport in Eastern North America*. Report to the Canada – United States Air Quality Committee. www.ec.gc.ca/pdb/can_us/can_us_glozone/intro_e.cfm

Environment Canada. 2005. *2002 National Pollutant Release Inventory (NPRI) Data*. www.ec.gc.ca/pdb/npri/npri_dat_rep_e.cfm

Freedman, B. 1995. *Environmental Ecology*. 2nd ed. San Diego, CA: Academic.

Freedman, B. and T.C. Hutchinson. 1980. Long-term effects of smelter pollution at Sudbury, Ontario, on forest community composition. *Can. J. Bot.*, **58**: 2123–2140.

Freedman, B., V. Zobens, and T.C. Hutchinson. 1990. Intense, natural pollution affects arctic tundra vegetation at the Smoking Hills, Canada. *Ecology*, **71**: 492–503.

Furmanczyk, T. 1994. *National Urban Air Quality Trends, 1981–1990*. Ottawa: Environmental Protection Service. Environment Canada, EPS 7/UP/4.

Gizyn, W. 1980. *The Chemistry and Environmental Impact of the Bituminous Shale Fires at the Smoking Hills, NWT*. M.Sc. Thesis, University of Toronto.

Havas, M. and T.C. Hutchinson. 1983. The Smoking Hills: Natural acidification of an aquatic ecosystem. *Nature*, **301**: 23–27.

Hemond, H.F. and E.J. Fechner. 1999. *Chemical Fate and Transport in the Environment*. 2nd ed. San Diego, CA: Academic.

Hester, R.E. and R.M. Harrison. 1998. *Air Pollution and Health*. Cambridge, UK: Royal Society of Chemistry.

Holgate, S.T., J.M. Samet, R.L. Maynard, and H.S. Koren (eds). 1999. *Air Pollution and Health*. San Diego, CA: Academic Press.

Hutchinson, T.C. and M. Havas. 1985. Recovery of previously acidified lakes near Coniston, Canada following reductions in atmospheric sulphur and metal emissions. *Water, Air, & Soil Pollution*, **20**: 20–32.

Maynard, R.L. and P. Brimblecombe (eds.). 2001. *The Urban Atmosphere and Its Effects*. Hackensack, NJ: World Scientific Publishing Company

Parson. E. 2003. *Protecting the Ozone Layer: Science and Strategy*. Oxford, UK: Oxford University Press.

Pepper, I.L., C.P. Gerba, and M.L. Brusseau (eds.). 1996. *Pollution Science*. San Diego, CA: Academic Press.

Roberts, T.M. 1984. Effects of air pollutants in agriculture and forestry. *Atmospheric Environment*, **18**: 629–652.

Seinfeld, J.H. and S.H. Pandis. 1998. *Atmospheric Chemistry and Physics: From Air Pollution to Climate Change*. New York: Wiley-Interscience.

Shriner, D.S. 1990. Responses of vegetation to atmospheric deposition and air pollution. In: *Acidic Deposition: State of Science and Technology. Vol. III. Terrestrial, Materials, Health,*

and Visibility Effects. Washington, DC: Superintendent of Documents, U.S. Government Printing Office.

Stern, A.C. 1976. *Air Pollution*. 3rd ed. San Diego, CA: Academic.

The Ozone Hole. 2005. *The Ozone Hole*. Pocono Pines, PA: The Ozone Hole. www.theozonehole.com/

Townsend, C.R., M. Begon, and J.L. Harper. 2002. *Essentials of Ecology*. 2nd ed. Cambridge, UK: Blackwell Publishers.

U.S. Environmental Protection Agency. 2005. *Air Trends*. www.epa.gov/airtrends/

Wark, K. Jr., C.F. Warner, and W.T. Davis. 1998. *Air Pollution: Its Origin and Control*. 3rd ed. Menlo Park, CA: Addison-Wesley.

Watson, W.Y. and D.H. Richardson. 1972. Appreciating the potential of a devastated land. *Forestry Chronicle*, **48**: 312–315.

Winterhalder, E.K. 1978. A historical perspective of mining and reclamation in Sudbury. *Proceedings, 3rd Annual Meeting, Canadian Land Reclamation Association*. Guelph, ON.

Wise, W. 1968. *Killer Smog*. New York: Ballantyne.

Wise, W. 2001. *Killer Smog: The World's Worst Air Pollution Disaster*. New York: Author's Guild.

World Meteorological Organization. 2002. *Scientific Assessment of Ozone Depletion*. Geneva, Switzerland: United Nations Environment Program. www.al.noaa.gov/WWWHD/pubdocs/Assessment02.html

World Resources Institute. 2005. *Earth Trends. The Environmental Information Portal*. Washington, DC: WRI.

Informative Websites

Air & Waste Management Association. www.awma.org/

The Air and Waste Management Association is a non-profit organization that aims to expand scientific and technological responses to environmental concerns. You will find more information about the organization as well as links to other related sites.

Environment Canada. Criteria Air Contaminant Emission Summaries. www.ec.gc.ca/pdb/ape/cape_home_e.cfm

Environment Canada provides these tables of provincial and national emissions of key air pollutants.

Environmental Literacy Council. Air & Climate. www.enviroliteracy.org/category.php/1.html

This non-governmental organization provides information about air pollution and other environmental problems.

Global Emissions Inventory Activity (GEIA). www.geiacenter.org/

This website contains data on the emissions of a wide range of air pollutants.

Meteorological Service of Canada. 2002. www.msc-smc.ec.gc.ca/

The Meteorological Service monitors atmospheric variables, including those related to air quality.

The Ozone Hole. www.theozonehole.com/

This website is loaded with useful and up-to-date information about the ozone hole.

Urban Atmospheric Pollution.
http://sima.com.mx/sima/df/conteng.html

Visit this site to find definitions and the effects of pollutants such as ozone, sulphur dioxide, hydrocarbons, lead, and carbon monoxide on plant and human life.

U.S. Global Change Research Information Office.
www.gcrio.org/

This key U.S. government website provides information on ozone depletion and other global atmospheric issues.

World Resources Institute. EarthTrends. The Environmental Information Portal.
http://earthtrends.wri.org/index.cfm

This website contains interesting data about health, environmental quality, and effects of environmental stressors.

Atmospheric Gases and Climate Change

17

CHAPTER OBJECTIVES

After completing this chapter, you will be able to

1. Outline the physical basis of Earth's greenhouse effect, and describe how human influences may be causing it to intensify.

2. Explain the term "radiatively active gas" (RAG).

3. Describe how the various RAGs vary in their effectiveness and importance in Earth's greenhouse effect.

4. Identify which RAGs have been increasing in concentration in the atmosphere, and give the reasons for these changes.

5. Explain the probable climatic consequences of an intensification of the greenhouse effect, and describe the resulting ecological effects.

6. Discuss different strategies for reducing the intensity of the greenhouse effect.

CHAPTER OUTLINE

Introduction

In this chapter we examine how Earth's naturally occurring *"greenhouse effect"* keeps the planet's surface relatively warm. We also describe how certain atmospheric constituents influence this phenomenon. These constituents are known as *radiatively active gases* (*RAGs*; see below). It is well documented that the concentrations of some of these RAGs, particularly carbon dioxide, are increasing because of emissions associated with various human activities. Potentially, these increased emissions could intensify Earth's greenhouse effect, which would result in global warming. This would be an extremely important environmental change, with potentially devastating consequences for both natural ecosystems and the human economy.

The Greenhouse Effect

Earth's greenhouse effect is a well-understood physical phenomenon, thought to be critical in maintaining the planet's average surface temperature at about 15°C. Without this influence, Earth's average surface temperature would be about –18°C, or 33° cooler than it actually is. This would be frostier than organisms could tolerate over the long term, mainly because at –18°C, water is in a solid state. Liquid water is crucial to the proper functioning of organisms and ecosystems. At Earth's actual average temperature of 15°C, water is unfrozen for much or all of the year (depending on location). This means that enzymes can function and physiology can proceed efficiently, as can the many important ecological processes that involve liquid water.

To understand the nature of Earth's greenhouse effect, it is necessary to comprehend the planet's **energy budget**. As described in Chapter 4, an energy budget is a physical analysis that deals with

1. all of the energy coming into a system;
2. all of the energy going out; and
3. any difference that might be internally transformed or stored.

Solar electromagnetic radiation is the major input of energy to Earth. On average, this energy arrives at a rate of about 8.4 J/cm^2•min. Much of the incoming solar radiation penetrates Earth's atmosphere and is absorbed by the surface of the planet. However, the surface temperature does not increase excessively because Earth dissipates its absorbed solar energy by emitting long-wave infrared radiation. Earth's surface temperature is determined by the equilibrium rates at which (a) solar energy is absorbed by the surface, and (b) the absorbed energy is re-radiated in a longer-wavelength form (see Figure 4.2).

If Earth's atmosphere were transparent to the long-wave infrared radiated by the surface, then that radiation would travel unobstructed to outer space. However, this is not the case, because so-called **radiatively active gases** (**RAGs**; also known as "greenhouse gases") are present in the atmosphere. RAGs efficiently absorb infrared radiation, becoming heated as a consequence. They then dissipate some of this thermal energy through yet another re-radiation. (This re-radiated energy has a longer wavelength than the electromagnetic energy that was originally absorbed. This is necessary to satisfy the second law of thermodynamics.) The re-radiated energy of the RAGs is emitted in all directions, including back toward Earth's surface. The net effect of the various energy transformations and re-radiations involving atmospheric RAGs is a reduction in Earth's rate of cooling. Thus, the equilibrium temperature of the planet's surface is warmer than it would be if the RAGs were not present in the atmosphere.

The process just described is known as the **greenhouse effect** because its physical mechanism is similar to the warming of a glass-encased space by solar radiation. The encasing glass of a greenhouse is transparent to incoming solar radiation. The solar energy is absorbed by, and therefore heats, internal surfaces of the greenhouse, such as plants,

Photo 17.1 The combustion of fossil fuels for transportation and industrial energy is the leading anthropogenic source of emissions of carbon dioxide to the atmosphere.

soil, and other materials. These warmed surfaces then dissipate the absorbed energy by re-radiating longer-wave infrared radiation. However, much of the infrared energy is absorbed by the greenhouse's glass and humid atmosphere, which are somewhat opaque to these wavelengths of electromagnetic radiation. The absorption of some re-radiated infrared slows the rate of cooling of the greenhouse, causing it to heat up rapidly on sunny days. (In addition, a greenhouse is an enclosed space, so it traps heat because its warmed interior air cannot be dissipated by convection higher into the atmosphere, with cooler air drawn in below.)

Radiatively Active Gases

Water vapour (H_2O) is the most important of the radiatively active constituents of Earth's atmosphere, followed by carbon dioxide (CO_2). Lesser roles are played by trace atmospheric concentrations of methane (CH_4), nitrous oxide (N_2O), ozone (O_3), carbon tetrachloride (CCl_4), and chlorofluorocarbons (CFCs). These latter compounds are, however, much stronger absorbers of infrared wavelengths than is CO_2 (i.e., on a per-molecule basis, they are more efficient RAGs). A molecule of CH_4 is about 21 times more effective than one of CO_2 at absorbing infrared radiation, while N_2O is 310 times more effective; O_3, 17 times; CCl_4, 1400 times; and CFCs, 3800–8100 times (these numbers are known as the "greenhouse warming potential"; CO_2 has a value of 1.0).

There is no evidence that the concentration of water vapour in the atmosphere has increased recently. However, concentrations of all the other RAGs have increased markedly during the past several centuries because of emissions associated with human activities (CDIAC, 2005). Prior to 1750, the atmospheric concentration of CO_2 was about 280 ppm, while in 2003 it was about 376 ppm (this change is discussed in more detail in the next section). During the same period, CH_4 increased from 0.7 ppm to 1.8 ppm, N_2O from 0.27 ppm to 0.32 ppm, CCl_4 from essentially zero to 0.10 ppb, tropospheric O_3 from 0.025 ppm to 0.034 ppm, and CFCs from zero to 1.2 ppb. These concentration increases have been especially rapid since the middle of the twentieth century, coinciding with enormous increases in the human population, industrialization, and deforestation.

Because the various RAGs are known to help control Earth's greenhouse effect, it is reasonable to hypothesize that their increasing concentrations may intensify that process. A stronger greenhouse effect may lead to global warming. Such an environmental change could be con-sidered an anthropogenic enhancement of Earth's naturally occurring greenhouse effect. Overall, the increased concentration of CO_2 has been estimated to account for about 53% of this possible enhancement of the greenhouse effect, while CH_4 is responsible for 17%; CFCs, for 13%; O_3, for 12%; and N_2O, for 5% (CDIAC, 2005).

Carbon Dioxide in the Atmosphere

Concentrations of CO_2 in the atmosphere have been increasing steadily for at least the past century. The data record supporting this change is excellent and, in fact, demonstrates one of the most convincing examples of long-term changes in environmental chemistry. Atmospheric CO_2 has been monitored continuously since 1958 at an observatory located on Mauna Loa, a mountain on the island of Hawaii (Figure 17.1). These data clearly show steadily increasing concentrations of CO_2 in the atmosphere during the past four decades.

A seasonal cycle of CO_2 concentration is illustrated in Figure 17.2, using data from a site in the Canadian Arctic. The annual periodicity is caused by high rates of CO_2 uptake by vegetation of the Northern Hemisphere during

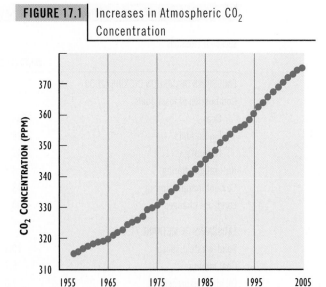

FIGURE 17.1 | Increases in Atmospheric CO_2 Concentration

These data are from measurements made on Mauna Loa, Hawaii. Each datum represents an annual average.

Source: Data from Keeling and Whorf (2005)

FIGURE 17.2 Seasonal Changes in Atmospheric CO_2 Concentration

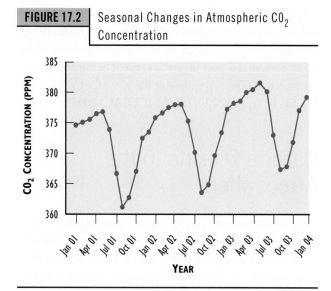

These data are based on measurements made at Alert, Ellesmere Island, Nunavut. A similar pattern is seen at Mauna Loa.

Source: Data from Keeling and Whorf (2005)

the growing season. This seasonal CO_2 fixation occurs at high enough rates to depress the concentration of this gas in the global atmosphere. The obvious long-term pattern, however, is one of a gradual net increase of CO_2 concentration over the years, as is clearly shown in Figure 17.1.

The increased concentrations of atmospheric CO_2 are due to emissions associated with various human activities. The two most important causes of anthropogenic CO_2 emissions, discussed in more detail in the following sections, are

- the combustion of fossil fuels—a process that results in the carbon content of the fuel being oxidized to CO_2, which is emitted into the atmosphere; and

- deforestation—an ecological change in which mature forests storing large amounts of organic carbon in their biomass are converted into ecosystems that contain much less; the difference in carbon storage is balanced by a CO_2 release to the atmosphere.

CO_2 Emissions from Burning Fossil Fuels

Fossil fuels are the most important source of energy in industrialized countries, followed by hydroelectricity, nuclear power, and relatively minor sources such as wood, solar, and wind energies (Chapter 13). The rates of utilization of coal, petroleum, natural gas, and oil sand have increased enormously during the past century, mostly to

TABLE 17.1	Emissions of Important Greenhouse Gases		
SOURCE OF EMISSIONS	EMISSIONS (10^6 tonne/year)		
	UNITED STATES	CANADA	GLOBAL
EMISSIONS OF CARBON DIOXIDE (2000)			
Combustion of fossil fuels			
Coal	2085	108.3	8140
Liquid fuels	2228	170.3	10 485
Natural gas	1247	146.4	4687
Natural gas flaring	4.8	5.5	117
Cement manufacturing	43.7	6.3	829
Land-use changes	−404	97.3	7637
EMISSIONS OF METHANE (1994)			
Solid-waste disposal	10.4	0.82	43
Coal mining	5.7	0.39	37
Oil and gas production	7.6	1.70	44
Wet rice agriculture	0.63	–	101
Livestock	8.6	0.96	113
EMISSIONS OF CHLOROFLUOROCARBONS			
Various sources	0.090	0.008	0.40

Source: CDIAC (2005)

satisfy surging energy demands for industry, transportation, and space heating.

Between 1860 and 1869, during the middle part of the Industrial Revolution, the combustion of fossil fuels, mainly coal, resulted in the global emission of about 421 million t of CO_2 per year (CDIAC, 2005). By the year 2000, global emissions from fossil-fuel combustion had increased by a factor of 58 to 24.3 billion t/y (Figure 17.3). About 97% of the current industrial emission of CO_2 is due to the combustion of fossil fuels, of which 44% is from liquid hydrocarbons, 34% from coal, and 19% from natural gas. The remaining 3% is associated with cement manufacturing. See Table 17.1.

The current global industrial emissions are equivalent to about 3.9 tCO_2/person•year (in 2000; Table 17.2). Of course, per capita use of fossil fuels differs greatly among countries, depending on their degree of industrialization, types of energy sources, climate, and other factors. The per capita emissions of CO_2 are greatest in wealthy, fuel-intensive, industrialized countries (Table 17.2 and Appendix C, Table 13). Several petroleum-producing countries have particularly large per capita emissions of CO_2 because huge quantities of natural gas are flared at their wellheads and refineries. For example, Qatar has emissions of 56 tCO_2/person•year.

Not surprisingly, people living in relatively poor, less developed countries are responsible for much smaller emissions of CO_2 from fossil-fuel combustion. For example,

TABLE 17.2	Per Capita Emissions of Carbon Dioxide by Selected Countries

Data are for industrial sources of emission (mostly fossil fuels), in units of tonnes of CO_2 per person•year in 2001. See Appendix C, Table 13 for additional country data.

COUNTRY	EMISSIONS (t/y PER CAPITA)
GLOBAL AVERAGE	3.9
United States	19.8
Canada	*16.5*
Japan	9.3
Mexico	3.7
Brazil	1.8
Haiti	0.2
Tanzania	0.1

Source: Data from World Resources Institute (2005)

Burundi, Cambodia, Chad, Nepal, and Uganda emit only 0.2 tCO_2/person•year from this source.

Future emissions of CO_2 from fossil-fuel combustion are predicted to be much larger than those occurring today, mainly because of the anticipated industrialization of poorer countries as they develop economically. One prediction suggests that global emissions during the mid-twenty-first century will be in the range of 8–15 billion t/y of CO_2-C, exceeding current levels by a factor of about two.

CO_2 Emissions from Clearing Mature Forest

Mature forest stores large quantities of organic carbon in the living and dead biomass of its vegetation, on the forest floor, and in the soil. All other kinds of ecosystems, including relatively young forests that are regenerating from disturbance, store much less organic carbon. This observation suggests that whenever an area of mature forest is disturbed by harvesting its trees, or is cleared to provide new land for agricultural use, less organic carbon will be stored on the land. The depletion of stored carbon may be a relatively short-term phenomenon, as occurs when a harvested stand is allowed to regenerate back to another mature forest. However, where a forest is converted into an agricultural ecosystem, there is a long-term decrease in the amount of carbon stored on the land. In either case, the difference in the average quantity of organic carbon stored in the ecosystem is balanced by an emission of CO_2 into the atmosphere. The CO_2 release occurs by decomposition of the biomass of the mature forest or by fire.

FIGURE 17.3	Trends in Global CO_2 Emissions by the Burning of Fossil Fuels, Since 1750

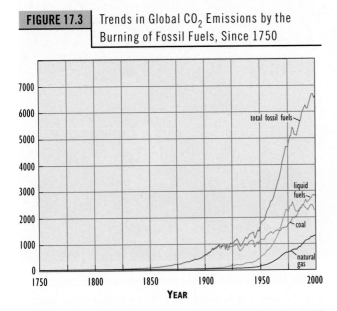

Source: Data from Marland et al. (2005)

To a lesser degree, a carbon loss also occurs when natural grassland is converted to cultivated agriculture.

It is well known that humans have caused enormous reductions in the area of mature forest in most regions of the world (Chapters 12 and 14). These changes began slowly, with the domestication of fire and its widespread use in improving the habitat of hunted animals. Deforestation proceeded more rapidly when it was discovered that fertile agricultural land could be developed by removing the natural forest cover. (The harvested trees were also valuable commodities.) Deforestation has proceeded especially quickly during the past several centuries because of population growth and industrialization.

Prior to any substantial clearing of Earth's natural forests, the global terrestrial vegetation stored an estimated 900 billion t of organic carbon (Figure 17.4). About 90% of that carbon was stored in forest, of which 50% was in tropical forest. Now, only about 560 billion t of carbon are stored in terrestrial vegetation, a 38% decrease overall. Moreover, the quantities of global vegetation biomass are diminishing further as additional areas of forest are con-

verted into ecosystems, especially agricultural ones, which store much less carbon.

During the 150-year period from 1850 to 2000, changes in land-use (mostly conversions of forest into agricultural land) resulted in the emission of about 528 billion t of CO_2. This quantity is about half the emissions due to fossil-fuel combustion during the same period (about 1040 billion t of CO_2). More recently, in 2000, combustions of fossil fuels emitted about 24.3 billion t of CO_2 into the atmosphere each year, while deforestation accounted for another 7.6 billion t/y.

As noted previously, forest and grassland ecosystems store large amounts of carbon in the biomass of their vegetation and soil. When these "high-carbon" ecosystems are converted into agricultural or urban ones, there is a large emission of organic carbon to the atmosphere (mostly as CO_2 from decomposition and fires). The disturbance of forests by harvesting timber also results in a large emission of CO_2 because mature stands support much more biomass carbon than younger ones (and old-growth forests store the most). However, the carbon-emission scenario

Photo 17.2 The conversion of carbon-dense ecosystems, such as forest, into agricultural and urban ecosystems that store much less carbon is an important source of CO_2 emissions. This site on the island of Sumatra has just had its tree cover felled and the resulting woody debris burned. The land will be planted with a variety of crops. Deforestation is proceeding rapidly in this region of Indonesia, and in most tropical countries.

FIGURE 17.4 | Key Compartments and Fluxes of the Global Carbon Cycle

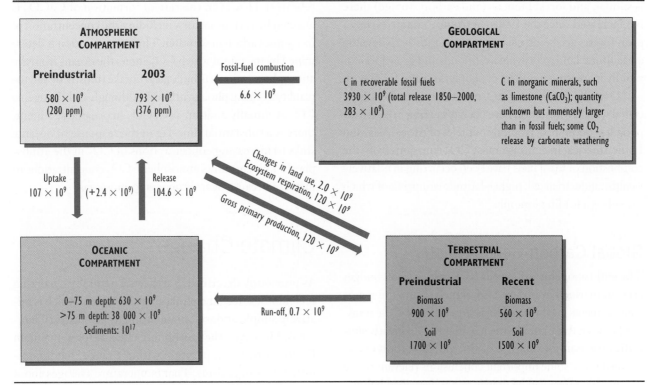

The amounts of carbon stored in the various compartments are in units of tonnes of carbon, while the transfers between compartments are in t/y of carbon.

Sources: Data from Blasing (1985), Solomon *et al.* (1985), and CDIAC (2005).

is complicated by what is done with the harvested timber. For example, if the tree biomass is burned as a fuel, the release of CO_2 to the atmosphere occurs rapidly. On the other hand, if the harvested wood is used to manufacture lumber, which can have a long lifespan in buildings, furniture, and violins, the release of CO_2 to the atmosphere occurs slowly. It must also be remembered that much of the initial release of CO_2 is eventually offset by the regeneration of the harvested forest (unless this is prevented, which is the case of deforestation to develop agricultural or urban land-use).

Table 17.3 shows large differences between regions in their emissions of CO_2 from changes in land-use. In North America, extensive forest clearing began when the continent was colonized by Europeans and continued until the 1920s. Since then, however, large areas of marginally economical agricultural land have been returned to forest. Overall, the net emission of CO_2 by changes in forest area has recently been close to zero—that is, agricultural land is regenerating back to forest about as quickly as forest elsewhere in North America is being converted into

TABLE 17.3 | Net Emissions of CO_2 to the Atmosphere as a Result of Land-Use Changes in Selected Regions

Negative numbers indicate that additional carbon is being stored in ecosystem biomass.

REGION	EMISSION OF CO_2 (10^6 tonne/year)			
	1850	1900	1950	2000
Canada	23	44	133	97
United States	593	907	−334	−404
Europe	202	166	91	−66
Developed Pacific Region	8	80	125	14
Former Soviet Union	215	212	48	74
China	374	236	1065	−47
North Africa & Middle East	15	64	158	85
Tropical Americas	81	209	675	2361
Tropical Asia	314	592	1248	4117
Tropical Africa	21	46	225	1406
GLOBAL	1845	2557	3433	7638

Source: Data from Houghton and Hackler (2002)

agricultural and urban land-uses. The European situation is similar, and forest biomass (and carbon storage) there has increased since the 1920s. In tropical countries, however, forests are being cleared rapidly, mostly to develop agricultural land to provide livelihoods and grow food for rapidly increasing numbers of people, and also for export.

Overall, in modern times, most CO_2 emissions associated with deforestation have been occurring in relatively poor, less developed, tropical countries of Africa, Asia, and Latin America. In contrast, most CO_2 emissions from the combustion of fossil fuels have been occurring in relatively wealthy, industrialized, higher-latitude countries, of which Canada is a leading example.

Global Carbon Geochemistry

The anthropogenic influences on Earth's carbon budget are summarized in Figure 17.4, which shows the major compartments in which carbon is stored as well as the transfers between those compartments. Figure 17.4 greatly simplifies the complex nature of the global carbon cycle. Nevertheless, some important conclusions relevant to the greenhouse effect can be drawn, as are described below.

Anthropogenic emissions have caused a 37% increase to occur in the amount of CO_2 stored in the atmosphere, from about 580×10^9 t of CO_2-C in pre-industrial times to 793×10^9 t in 2003. The atmospheric concentration of CO_2 has increased accordingly, from about 280 ppm to 376 ppm during the same period.

Before humans began to modify the character of Earth's ecosystems, particularly through deforestation, the global emission and fixation of atmospheric CO_2 were probably in balance. In other words, on a global basis, gross primary production (GPP) was approximately equal to ecosystem respiration (ER), and biologically fixed carbon was not changing over time. However, deforestation is now resulting in huge emissions of CO_2, amounting to about 2.0×10^9 t/y of CO_2-C. Overall, modern terrestrial ecosystems are storing about 38% less carbon in their vegetation and 12% less in soil, compared with pre-industrial times.

Ultimately, the oceans are the most important sink for CO_2 emitted through human activities. The oceans have a net absorption of about 2.4×10^9 t/y of CO_2-C from the atmosphere. However, this is less than the anthropogenic emissions of 8.6×10^9 t/y of CO_2-C and, therefore, the amount of CO_2 stored in the atmosphere is increasing. The oceans have an enormous capacity for absorbing atmospheric CO_2, which is ultimately stored as calcium carbonate ($CaCO_3$), a mineral that accumulates in sediment

(mostly as the shells of mollusks, forams, and other invertebrates). However, the rate of formation of $CaCO_3$ is affected by various factors, including the concentration of inorganic carbon in seawater. This concentration is determined by the rate at which CO_2 enters the oceans from the atmosphere, minus its biological uptake (mostly by phytoplankton during photosynthesis). Although anthropogenic CO_2 eventually ends up as $CaCO_3$ in oceanic sediment, there is a substantial time-lag in the response of oceanic sinks to increasing concentrations of CO_2 in the atmosphere. This lag allows atmospheric CO_2 concentrations to increase because of anthropogenic emissions.

Climate Change

As previously described, Earth has a naturally occurring greenhouse effect, the physical mechanism of which is relatively simple and well understood by scientists (Chapter 4). Moreover, the greenhouse effect helps to maintain Earth's surface temperature within a range that is comfortable for organisms. That temperature averages about 15°C, or 33° warmer than it would be under a non-greenhouse atmosphere. It is also well documented that the concentrations of CO_2 and other radiatively active gases are increasing in Earth's atmosphere. It has been hypothesized that this increase will intensify the planet's natural greenhouse effect.

Although this potential intensification of the greenhouse effect remains a hypothesis, it is an extremely important one. If this environmental change does happen, it would cause many secondary climatic and ecological changes, some of which could be catastrophic for both exploited and natural ecosystems.

One of the most important indicators of **climate change** is the temperature of the surface atmosphere. Air temperature is measured routinely in many parts of the world. These data can be used to calculate estimates of the average surface temperature of Earth and to detect changes over time. However, the air-temperature records suffer from several important problems:

- Air temperature is extremely variable over time and space. The unfavourable ratio of signal to noise in such data makes it difficult to detect long-term trends.

- Most of the older data are less accurate than modern records. (Detailed and accurate recordings of surface air temperatures began around 1880.)

- Weather-monitoring stations are commonly located in urbanized areas, and their data are influenced by the so-called urban "heat island." This effect is characterized by typically warmer conditions in urban areas than in surrounding, rural places. Some initially rural weather stations have become surrounded by urban land-uses, resulting in a "contamination" of their air-temperature records.

- Global temperatures can respond to influences other than changes in the greenhouse effect, such as the cooling effects of volcanic eruptions that inject masses of reflective aerosols into the upper atmosphere.

In spite of the difficulties with the data used to estimate Earth's average surface temperature, recent analyses suggest that there has been a definite warming trend since the mid-nineteenth century. The average global surface temperature has increased by more than 0.6°C over the past 150 years (Figure 17.5). This warming reflects the end of a 400-year period of climate cooling, known as the "Little Ice Age," which lasted until the mid-1800s (Figure 17.6). However, there appears to have been a particular intensification of warming during the most recent several decades. Note also that the recent warming trend

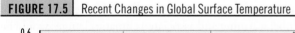

FIGURE 17.5 | Recent Changes in Global Surface Temperature

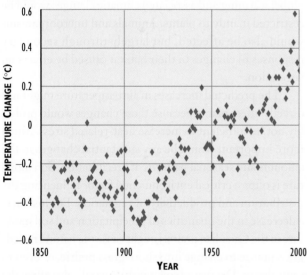

The data are the global annual average temperature anomaly (°C), calculated relative to the average for the period 1961–90. A negative value means that the year was relatively cool, while a positive number means it was warmer.

Source: Data from Jones *et al.* (2001)

FIGURE 17.6 | Patterns of Deviation of Global Average Surface Temperature from Present Conditions

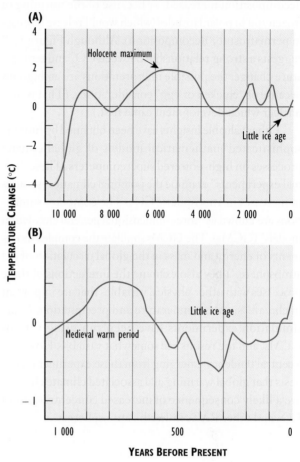

Curve (a) shows the long-term trends since the end of the most recent ice age. Curve (b) shows the trends during the past millennium. Note that a value of "zero" means that no temperature change (deviation) has occurred.

Sources: Modified from Intergovernmental Panel on Climate Change (1990) and Environment Canada (1995)

is not without precedent—even warmer periods have occurred during the past 10 000 years (Figure 17.6).

Moreover, paleoclimatic studies of long-term changes have provided rather convincing evidence of a link between concentrations of atmospheric CO_2 and climatic warming. Especially valuable data come from a core of glacial ice taken in Antarctica, representing a time record of 160 000 y (Figure 17.7). Results of this important study suggest a strong correlation between CO_2 concentration and air temperature, implying a possible causal relationship. It is not clear, however, whether increased concentrations of CO_2 caused warming via an intensified greenhouse effect, or possibly the opposite. An increase in CO_2 emissions from ecosystems could have been a result of climatic warming, perhaps because the rate of biomass decomposition increased, or because of the warming of frozen soil in polar latitudes (which would release biomass in permafrost for decomposition). Although Figure 17.7 suggests a strong relationship between CO_2 and temperature change, the possible interpretations are ambiguous because of "chicken or egg" considerations. (That is, it is unclear which development came first.)

Other valuable insights have been obtained by running sophisticated mathematical models of global climate processes on high-powered supercomputers. These "virtual experiments" examine the potential climatic responses to increases in atmospheric CO_2. The computer simulations are known as "three-dimensional general circulation models" (GCMs). The GCMs simulate the complex movements of energy and mass in the global circulation of the atmosphere. They also examine the interactions of these processes with other physical variables that are important in climate, such as temperature and precipitation. Many simulation experiments have been run using various GCMs, and the results are somewhat variable. However, a central tendency emerging from these experiments suggests that global warming and associated climate changes are a likely consequence of increased concentrations of CO_2 and other RAGs in Earth's atmosphere.

Numerous experiments have simulated the scenario of an eventual doubling of CO_2 concentration from its present concentration of about 376 ppm. These experiments suggest that such a doubling could result in an increase of between 1°C and 4°C in the average temperature of Earth's surface atmosphere. The intensity of warming is predicted to be greatest in high-latitude regions, where the temperature increases might be two to three times greater than in the tropics.

Warming of the lower atmosphere will be one change likely to be caused by an increased intensity of the greenhouse effect. However, other changes in climate would also occur indirectly, in response to an increase in air temperature. Among the most important of the indirect changes would be large-scale shifts in the patterns of atmospheric circulation. Such shifts would likely result in changes in the quantities, spatial distribution, and seasonality of precipitation. Changes in precipitation regimes would influence soil moisture, which would greatly affect the distribution and productivity of vegetation, both natural and managed. These changes in precipitation regime would likely cause much more damage to agricultural and wild ecosystems than would any direct effects of the actual warming of the atmosphere (discussed in the next section).

Ecological Effects

In terrestrial ecosystems, the direct, biological effects of global warming and associated climatic changes would be restricted mainly to plants. Animals and microorganisms would also be affected, but largely through secondary responses to changes in their habitat caused by effects on vegetation.

The predicted increases in air temperature might not directly affect plants because these changes would probably not be sufficient to increase heat-related stress. Much more important would be any substantial changes in the amounts and seasonal patterns of precipitation. Soil moisture is often a critical environmental factor influencing the distribution and productivity of vegetation. For instance, a decrease in the quantities of precipitation and soil moisture in the Canadian prairies might cause the natural mixed-grass prairie to change into short-grass prairie, or even to semi-desert. Decreased soil moisture would also affect the types and productivity of crops that could be grown in many regions, making present agricultural systems more difficult or even impossible unless irrigation was practised.

About 14 000 years ago, the continental glaciers started to melt back, and they were about 80% gone by 8000–10 000

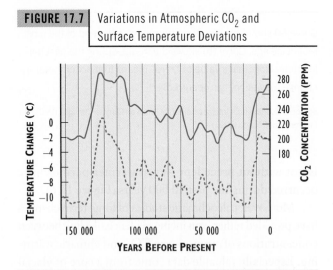

FIGURE 17.7 Variations in Atmospheric CO_2 and Surface Temperature Deviations

These data were obtained by studying a 160 000-year glacial-core record from Vostok, Antarctica. The lower line shows the temperature deviation and the upper line shows the CO_2 concentration.

Source: Modified from Barnola *et al.* (1987, 2003); see also Petit *et al.* (2003)

years ago. During the warming climates that followed, the vegetation in various regions of Canada changed substantially. Paleoecological studies of these vegetation changes involve the examination of fossil pollen grains found in dated sections of cores of lake sediment (these studies are known as *palynology*). This kind of analysis has provided a record of vegetation changes extending to early deglaciation. Research in Canada and elsewhere suggests that plants responded to post-glacial climatic warming in a species-specific manner. This occurred because of the different abilities of species to migrate to and colonize newly available habitats released by glacial meltback. As a result, the species composition of early post-glacial plant communities was different from that occurring today under similar climatic regimes. We can expect the responses of natural vegetation to future climate changes to also be species-specific. This will result in the development of plant communities that are different from those that occur now.

If climatic change results in substantial modifications in the character of plant communities, there will also be adjustments in the species of animals, microbes, and other organisms that can be supported on the landscape. Challenges to indigenous biodiversity will be an important consequence of climate change around the world.

Climate change in tropical countries, which support much larger numbers of species than Canada does, will also have great ecological consequences. For example, most of northern and central South America is now characterized by a warm, humid climate. However, this region is thought to have been considerably drier during the past glacial period, which ended 10 000–14 000 years ago. During that time, much of the tropical region was covered by open-canopied savannah vegetation, while rainforest occurred only in isolated regions of relatively greater rainfall, known as *refugia*. On the larger landscape, the isolated refugia of tropical forest apparently occurred as "islands" within a more extensive matrix of savannah, which is an inhospitable habitat for moist-forest species. The restructuring of tropical ecosystems during the Pleistocene Ice Age, driven by climate change, must have had enormous effects on the multitudes of rare species of the rainforest. Many of those species probably became extinct as a result of the habitat change. If an anthropogenic intensification of the greenhouse effect were to cause substantial changes in the character of tropical habitats over large areas, similar ecological calamities would again occur.

It is important to acknowledge that scientists do not fully understand the likely dynamics of climatic change. Therefore, they are not able to make reliable predictions

Photo 17.3   This is a small "island" of trees in the midst of tundra near Tuktoyaktuk in the Northwest Territories. These short individuals of white spruce (*Picea glauca*) are remnants of a more widespread population that established during a period of warmer climate more than about six centuries ago. If an anthropogenic enhancement of Earth's greenhouse effect results in a warming climate, as has been predicted, then these isolated tree-islands may be focal points from which trees could colonize the tundra.

about changes in precipitation, air temperature, evapotranspiration, and other climatic factors that may occur in particular regions of Canada or elsewhere. It can, however, be reasonably suggested that any large changes in climate, and especially in precipitation, would result in fundamental alterations of the structure and productivity of natural and agricultural vegetation. These ecological changes would have important consequences for the flows of resources that are required by humans, as well as for the habitats of other species.

As was just noted, changes in climate would influence the ability of landscapes to support agriculture. In Canada, this would be especially true of the great expanses of agricultural land in the Prairie Provinces. Much of this land is already ecologically marginal from a rainfall perspective and is vulnerable to years of severe drought. Wheat, for example, is an economically important crop that is grown extensively in areas that were originally short-grass prairie. In North America, an estimated 40% of this 400-million-hectare, semi-arid region has already been desertified as a result of ecological changes associated with agricultural use. Sporadic crop-threatening droughts occur widely. Irrigating the land can alleviate the critical limitations of sparse precipitation in this region. However, insufficient water is available for this purpose, and secondary problems, such as salinization, can be caused by this practice. Therefore, any further losses of soil moisture in this important agricultural region of North America would be extremely damaging to agricultural production as well as to food security.

The extent and severity of forest fires would also likely change in response to decreases in the amounts and distributions of precipitation and evapotranspiration, and to changes in their secondary effects, such as soil moisture. In a typical year, about 1–2 million ha of forest burns in wildfires in Canada. This is highly variable—in some years more than 10 million ha may burn. Modelling experiments have suggested that an increased intensity of the greenhouse effect would cause a drier climate to occur over much of the boreal region of Canada. This could result in about a 50% increase in the annual burned area (Flannigan and Van Wagner, 1991).

In marine ecosystems, increases in seawater temperature would adversely affect some biota. Prolonged increases in water temperature can cause corals to lose their symbiotic algae (known as zooxanthellae), sometimes resulting in the death of the coral. This syndrome of damage, known as coral bleaching, can be induced by unusually high or low water temperatures, changes in salinity, and other environmental stresses. Coral reefs are the world's most biodiverse marine ecosystems, and they are already threatened by many environmental stressors associated with human activities, including coastal pollution, mining of the coral, and overly intensive fisheries.

Another predicted consequence of global warming is the accelerated melting and retreat of glaciers. There is widespread evidence that this change is already occurring rapidly. In Canada, most glaciers in Alberta, British Columbia, Nunavut, and the Yukon are in rapid retreat.

This will have consequences for the flow of rivers that are substantially dependent on glacial meltwater, including several large ones that provide water for many communities in Alberta and Saskatchewan, including Calgary and Edmonton. Rapid glacial retreat is also well documented in the Alps of Europe and on Mount Kilimanjaro in Kenya, the top of which may be ice-free by 2050. It is also affecting the world's most massive glaciers, in Greenland and Antarctica.

An additional predicted effect of global warming is an increase in sea level. This change would be mostly caused by a thermal expansion of seawater, because as water warms, its volume increases. There would also be an influence on sea level from the meltback of massive glaciers, particularly those in Antarctica and Greenland. Even an increase in global sea level of a metre or so would have massive implications for low-lying populated regions (such as the Netherlands in Europe and the Maldives and other archipelagos in the Indian and Pacific Oceans), which would become much more vulnerable to the devastating effects of storm surges. There would also be risks for shallow-water marine ecosystems, such as coral reefs.

It is also predicted that global warming might increase the frequency, and perhaps also the severity, of events of severe weather and climate. This means that hurricanes, tornadoes, and even El Niño events could become more frequent. All of these extremes of weather and climate have well known, devastating effects on economic and ecological systems.

Most of the climate-modelling studies have suggested that the intensity of warming will be much greater at high latitudes. This means that changes in countries like Canada, where the climate ranges from temperate to polar, would be greater than in subtropical and tropical regions. Therefore, relatively wealthy, well-developed countries like Canada and the U.S. may be exposed to most of the damage associated with greenhouse-related climate changes. Less developed, equatorial countries may be less directly affected by these changes. These predictions are, however, highly uncertain.

Effects of CO$_2$ on Plants

Increased concentrations of atmospheric CO$_2$ can directly stimulate the productivity of some species of plants, especially if they are growing under conditions in which moisture and nutrients are relatively abundant. Under such conditions, plant productivity can be constrained by the

Global Focus 17.1

The Kyoto Protocol

Scientists are agreed that the Earth has a naturally occurring greenhouse effect that helps to keep the planet habitable. There is also agreement that this key function is due to the presence of so-called radiatively active gases (RAGs) in the atmosphere. It is also a well-established fact that the concentrations of RAGs are increasing rapidly, particularly carbon dioxide. Although there is still some controversy as to whether the increased RAGs will intensify the greenhouse effect, scientists are rapidly moving toward a consensus that this outcome is likely to occur. Because global warming could have catastrophic consequences for the human economy and the natural world, actions are being proposed, and in some cases taken, by various levels of government.

On the international front, the key initiatives related to scientific research and planning are being led by the United Nations Environment Programme (UNEP) and the World Meteorological Organization (WMO), which, in 1988, established the Intergovernmental Panel on Climate Change (IPCC). The IPCC conducts comprehensive reviews of the science of global warming, with a focus on likely scenarios of climatic, ecological, and economic consequences. The IPCC also does research on ways to slow or prevent the increases in atmospheric RAGs and on how economic and ecological systems might adapt to anticipated climate change. At the international level, the IPCC is the most credible source of information about climate change.

Because of its concerns about the potentially disastrous consequences of global warming, in 1990 the IPCC and other groups of climate scientists recommended that the United Nations (UN) mobilize global leadership to negotiate an international agreement to reduce emissions of greenhouse gases. The UN then established the Intergovernmental Negotiating Committee for a Framework Convention on Climate Change (INC/FCCC), which was given a mandate to draft the terms of a UN Framework Convention on Climate Change (UNFCCC). After a series of difficult international negotiations, the UNFCCC was drafted and then adopted in 1992 at the UN Conference on Environment and Development (UNCED) held in Rio de Janeiro, Brazil.

The objective of the UNFCCC is to stabilize atmospheric RAGs at concentrations that would prevent a dangerous intensification of the planetary greenhouse effect. Nations that are signatory to the UNFCCC, known as "parties to the convention," have agreed to undertake certain actions: compiling information on emissions of RAGs, developing policies to decrease emissions, preparing strategies to adapt to anticipated effects of climate change, and providing financial and scientific support to developing countries. Moreover, the 140 countries that signed on to the UNFCCC in Rio agreed to discuss its implementation at a global forum, which was held in Berlin, Germany, in 1995. At that meeting, it was agreed that it was necessary to reduce global emissions of RAGs and that a further series of international negotiations was needed to reach consensus on an implementation strategy. These negotiations were completed at another meeting, held in Kyoto, Japan, in late 1997. The outcome of that key meeting was the Kyoto Protocol.

According to the terms of the Kyoto Protocol, the world's nations are divided into three groups:

- **Annex I consists of developed and rapidly developing countries,** including the United States, Canada, countries of the European Union, Japan, Russia, and Australia. It also includes rapidly developing countries that are major emitters of RAGs, such as China, India, and Indonesia; however, these are excluded from the emission-reduction obligations of the wealthier Annex I countries.
- **Annex II consists of the same developed countries as in Annex I** (consisting of 38 developed countries) but not the ones that are rapidly developing (also known as economies in transition). The Protocol specifies that the Annex II countries have special obligations to reduce their emissions (overall by 5.2% compared with 1990 levels), and they must also help developing countries by providing financial and technological resources to reduce emissions and adapt to adverse effects of climate change.
- **Annex III consists of the world's least-developed countries,** which have ratified the Kyoto Protocol but otherwise have no immediate obligations to reduce their emissions of RAGs.

In addition, many organizations have "observer" status, including the UN and about 50 intergovernmental and 650 non-governmental organizations (NGOs), including the Organization of the Petroleum Exporting Countries (OPEC), the Umbrella Group (Australia, Canada, Japan, U.S.A.), the G-77 (a group of 132 developing countries), and other NGOs representing the environment, business, industry, labour, indigenous cultures, research and academic interests, and others.

Global Focus 17.1 (continued)

For the Kyoto Protocol to become legally binding, it had to be ratified by at least 55 parties to the UNFCCC Convention (ratification means that a national government formally agrees to participate), including enough Annex I countries to account for at least 55% of the total CO_2 emissions of all industrialized countries (in 1990). Canada, the European Union, and Japan all ratified in 2002, and when Russia did so in 2004, the 55% emissions criterion was reached, making the Kyoto Protocol a legal treaty. Unfortunately, as of January 2006, the U.S. and Australia had not ratified the Kyoto Protocol and showed no signs of doing so.

Key aspects of the Kyoto Protocol are the binding targets it sets for the reduction of RAG emissions by developed countries that have ratified the agreement. It is important to understand, however, that the Kyoto Protocol is only a first step toward stabilizing and reducing global emissions of RAGs—once it is implemented, the intent is to then negotiate additional protocols that will include reductions by rapidly developing countries such as China and India, and well as improved criteria for developed countries.

The commitments of Canada are typical of those of developed countries of Annex II. When Canada ratified in December 2002, it committed to reduce its national emissions of CO_2 by 6% below the levels in 1990, and to achieve this by 2008–12. To accomplish such a large reduction is, however, a formidable challenge. In fact, in 2005, Canadian emissions of CO_2 had increased by more than 20% since 1990 because of rapid economic and population growth during the period. In fact, Canada has not yet developed an effective strategy for meeting its legal obligations under the Kyoto Protocol, largely because of the intense political and economic controversies that are engaged by the actions that would be necessary (see also Canadian Focus 17.1).

Many other developed countries, however, will have little difficulty in meeting their obligations, which are similar to those of Canada (i.e., a 6% reduction below 1990 levels by 2008–12). For instance, since 1990, most countries of western Europe have extensively replaced coal-burning industrial utilities with ones that use natural gas, which results in a large reduction of CO_2 emissions. Also, most countries of the former Soviet Union, including Russia, have suffered a large downsizing of their industrial sectors since 1990, making it easy for them to meet their Kyoto targets. These economic restructurings, which had no direct linkage to the Kyoto Protocol, did not occur in Canada, the U.S., or Australia. The only ways for these latter countries to reduce their emissions of CO_2 and other RAGs is to rapidly change the amounts and ways in which energy is used in their economies by aggressively enacting conservation measures while also moving away from a heavy reliance on fossil fuels. It will take an extremely high level of political fortitude if they are to achieve such changes, and without such determination, countries like Canada are likely to fail to meet their Kyoto targets.

Additional Reading

United Nations Framework Convention on Climate Change. http://unfccc.int

---

rate at which CO_2 can be acquired from the atmosphere during photosynthesis.

Numerous laboratory experiments have demonstrated that agricultural plants can be more productive when fertilized by CO_2. Some commercial greenhouses increase the productivity of crops such as cucumbers, tomatoes, and some ornamental plants by fertilizing the air with CO_2 at concentrations of 600–2000 ppm.

However, the productivity of most crops grown under field conditions is usually constrained by an inadequate supply of nutrients other than CO_2. The limiting nutrients are most commonly nitrogen, phosphorus, or potassium, and often the availability of water is also a constraint. Under these kinds of field conditions, the responses of plants to CO_2 fertilization are relatively small and short-term, or non-existent.

Increased concentrations of CO_2 can also affect many plants by decreasing their rate of water loss by transpiration. Most water loss by plants occurs through tiny pores, known as stomata, on their leaf surfaces. The size of the stomatal opening is controlled by specialized guard cells. Activity of the guard cells is influenced by CO_2, and stomata tend to close partially or entirely when atmospheric concentrations of CO_2 are high. The availability of moisture is an important factor influencing plant productivity in many agricultural and forest ecosystems. Consequently, decreased water losses because of lessened transpiration could be viewed as a beneficial effect.

It appears that some benefits might be realized from CO_2 fertilization and decreased transpiration, particularly in intensively managed agricultural systems. It is important to recognize, however, that these gains are

Global Focus 17.2

Voluntary Actions

Under the terms of the Kyoto Protocol, Canada is obligated to reduce its CO_2 emissions to 6% below the 1990 levels, and to do this by 2008–12. Other developed countries that are parties to the Protocol have similar obligations. In Canada, this resulted in the establishment of an agency known as Voluntary Challenge and Registry Inc. (VCR), funded mostly by Natural Resources Canada. In 2005, the VCR function was transferred to the Canadian Standards Association, a non-governmental organization. The program, now known as GHG Registries, encourages government agencies, private companies, and other organizations to design and implement plans to reduce their emissions of CO_2 and other RAGs, and to report their activities to the program so Canada's progress in meeting its Kyoto obligations can be monitored. In 2005, 292 participants were registered with GHG Registries, of which 150 had submitted relatively detailed, "gold-level" plans for reducing emissions. Other countries, including the United States, have established similar voluntary programs.

The voluntary-action model is useful, and it represents progress toward reducing emissions of greenhouse gases. However, it also suffers from several important deficiencies:

1. Because participation is voluntary, only actions considered economically feasible are seriously undertaken. If more substantial actions are needed to achieve larger reductions in emissions, the voluntary approach will likely not be sufficient. In fact, regulation (including CO_2-emission taxes) will probably be required to encourage reluctant industries and organizations to make the substantial changes that will be required to deal effectively with the risks of global warming.
2. Again, because of the voluntary nature of the model, partners can always choose to not participate. Some companies or industries that emit large amounts of greenhouse gases may not want to co-operate, and there is no specific penalty for doing this.
3. The agencies registering their action plans and progress reports (including GHG Registries in Canada) accept the information provided by their participants with only a cursory scientific and organizational audit of the submitted information. As such, there is a risk of inaccurate reporting.
4. Most participating organizations, especially smaller companies, have little expertise in the science

needed to prepare comprehensive action plans and accurate progress reports. This is especially true of some ecological options for reducing the net emissions of RAGs, such as afforestation.

Nevertheless, it is important to acknowledge that important voluntary initiatives are being undertaken to reduce emissions of RAGs in Canada and other countries. Many participants in the GHG Registries program are implementing more energy-efficient procedures or are switching to alternative energy sources that emit fewer or no RAGs. In 2004, 16 Canadian organizations were listed as "Champions in Action" because of their demonstrated commitment to reducing their emissions. Three examples are presented here:

- In its 2004 progress report, Suncor Energy described a decreased intensity of emissions of RAGs of 4.7% in 2003 compared with the previous year. (This is a measure of emissions per unit of commercial production by the company; because actual production increased by 4% that year, the net emissions of RAGs decreased by only about 1%.) Overall, Suncor reported that its voluntary actions had achieved a cumulative reduction of CO_2 emissions equivalent to 26 million t during 1990 to 2003.
- In its 2003 report, Noranda-Falconbridge noted that improvements in efficiency of its industrial processes had resulted in an 18% reduction of emissions of RAGs between 1989 and 2002, and that a 42% decrease was anticipated by 2010. This had been achieved despite a large increase in metal production (by 17% in 2002 compared with 1989) and was due to an improvement in efficiency. (RAG emissions per unit of metal production decreased by 31% between 1889 and 2002, and are expected to decrease to 46% in 2010.)
- In its 2003 report, the Government of Canada reported that, between 1990 and 2001, it had achieved a 24% reduction of RAG emissions from its diverse operations, and it anticipated a cumulative reduction of 31% by 2010. These reductions were achieved mostly by improved efficiencies of energy use and by switching to cleaner fuels.

Of course, many individual Canadians are also taking actions to reduce their emissions of RAGs. They are doing so by riding a bicycle, driving a smaller car, insulating their home against heat loss, and "reducing, recycling, and reusing" as much as possible.

Nevertheless, many environmental organizations and scientists believe that these positive actions will be grossly insufficient because of their intrinsically limited nature. As such, they will not add up to an effective reduction of emissions of greenhouse gases in Canada, or globally. For example, it is being predicted that Canadian emissions of CO_2, the key greenhouse gas in the Kyoto Protocol, are likely to be at least 20% higher in 2010 than they were in 1990.

Reference and Additional Information

Canadian Standards Association. GHG Registries. www.ghgregistries.ca/

---

likely to be relatively minor. Moreover, the possible benefits would likely be overwhelmed by the negative consequences of climate change that might be caused by an intensification of Earth's greenhouse effect. The distribution and composition of natural and managed ecosystems could be greatly affected by changes in precipitation and other climatic factors. Anthropogenic climate change might cause enormous damage to economic resources in agriculture, forestry, and fisheries, and also to natural biodiversity.

Reducing Atmospheric Carbon Dioxide

Because of the potential consequences of anthropogenic climate change, governments are considering actions that would reduce the concentrations of CO_2 and other RAGs in the atmosphere, or at least slow their rate of increase. This goal could be achieved in two ways: by reducing the emissions of RAGs, and by increasing the rates at which they are removed from the atmosphere. The latter tactic is especially relevant to CO_2, the most important of the anthropogenic greenhouse gases.

Ultimately, large decreases in the emissions of RAGs, particularly CO_2, must be the major tactic of any strategy designed to deal with an intensification of Earth's greenhouse effect. Emissions of CO_2 are, however, associated with many economically important activities, making it extremely difficult to rapidly reduce them. As was previously described, the major CO_2-emitting activities include the use of fossil fuels in industry, transportation, and space heating; the manufacturing of cement; and ecological conversions, particularly of forest to agriculture. Politicians, economists, and environmental scientists all worry about the shorter-term economic effects of actions necessary to rapidly reduce emissions of CO_2 to the atmosphere.

Planting trees is another option that would contribute to a net reduction of CO_2 concentration in the atmosphere. As trees and other plants grow, they fix atmospheric CO_2 into the organic carbon of their accumulating biomass. Depending on the species and growing conditions, that biomass can eventually reach several tonnes of dry weight (per large tree), about half of which is carbon.

Studies have shown that substantial "**carbon credits**" can be gained by planting large numbers of trees in urban or rural environments. The carbon credits are especially large if the tree-planting involves the **afforestation** of agricultural areas. (Afforestation converts land into a forest, while reforestation ensures that another forest regrows on a clear-cut site.) Agroecosystems typically store small quantities of carbon in biomass, while forests store much more per unit area. The carbon-storage function would be optimized if mature or old-growth forests were established as "carbon reserves," and if these ecosystems were maintained in their high-carbon condition for as long as possible. (Harvesting of the mature forests would detract from the carbon-storage function.) Moreover, afforestation of extensive areas would achieve many additional, non-carbon environmental benefits, such as the enhancement of biodiversity.

Although tree-planting and afforestation are attractive options toward reducing CO_2 in the atmosphere, these tactics cannot offset more than a portion of the CO_2 emitted by fossil-fuel combustion and deforestation. An enormous area of land would have to be afforested to achieve full offsets. For example, to fully offset the CO_2 emissions from one 200-MW, coal-fired generating station (which would emit about 0.34 million t/y of CO_2-C) the carbon-fixing services of about 500 000 ha of natural forest of the kind typical of eastern Canada would be required. If the

Canadian Focus 17.1

Politics and the Kyoto Protocol

The Kyoto Protocol is an international agreement intended to be the first co-operative step toward reducing emissions of greenhouse gases to the atmosphere (see Global Focus 17.1). The Protocol requires large reductions from developed countries because they are responsible for disproportionate emissions (on a per capita basis) and can also afford to make the economic and other structural adjustments that may be needed. Under the terms of the Kyoto Protocol, Canada is required to reduce its CO_2 emissions to 6% below their 1990 level by 2008–12.

The U.S. is obligated to a similar reduction—to 7% below its 1990 emissions by 2008–12. In 2001, however, President George W. Bush announced that his administration would not ratify the Kyoto Protocol, whose terms had been negotiated by the previous government of Bill Clinton. Bush's rationale was the belief that ratifying the agreement would be "economically irresponsible" because its obligations could not be met without sacrificing some economic growth. In an attempt to defuse the international and domestic controversies that ensued, Bush claimed his administration would pursue its own, made-in-the-U.S.A. plan for reducing emissions of greenhouse gases. Although a comprehensive plan has not yet been announced by the U.S. government, related pronouncements and actions have reinforced concerns about its intentions. For example, in a speech given in Toronto in 2001, Vice-President Dick Cheney stated: "Conservation may be a sign of personal virtue, but it is not a sufficient basis for a sound, comprehensive energy policy." At the time, Cheney was leading a U.S. task force on energy policy, which recommended that anticipated growth in energy demand should be met by greatly expanding domestic and reliable foreign supplies of fossil fuels, while also considering a greater role for nuclear power. That policy, and the apparent dismissal of a key role for conservation measures, suggests that the present U.S. administration is unlikely to make much progress in reducing domestic emissions of greenhouse gases.

But what about Canada? Ever since the Kyoto Protocol was negotiated in 1997, there has been intense debate about economic risks inherent in its implementation in Canada. Although the federal government has jurisdiction over the negotiation and ratification of international agreements, several provinces believe their economies would be threatened by Kyoto-related measures. The anti-ratification charge has been led by Premier Ralph Klein of Alberta, whose economy is strongly dependent on the mining and use of fossil fuels and their export to the United States. In 2002, Klein characterized the Kyoto Protocol as "the goofiest, most devastating thing ever contemplated by a Canadian government."

Also in 2002, Alberta Environment Minister Lorne Taylor released a study that estimated ratification of the Protocol could cost the Canadian economy $23–$40 billion per year. Dire predictions like these are disputed by many economists and environmental activists, who believe that adopting an emissions-reduction strategy consistent with the Protocol would stimulate the development of renewable energy sources and conservation, while enhancing the high-tech and construction industries and thereby creating many jobs. They also remind us of other important benefits to be realized from decreased costs of health care and less damage caused to agricultural land, forests, and natural ecosystems by extreme weather and other predicted aspects of climate change.

In September 2002, at the United Nations World Summit on Sustainable Development in Johannesburg, South Africa, Prime Minister Jean Chrétien thrilled the international community of climate-change activists and scientists by announcing that Canada would ratify the Kyoto Protocol, and this was done in December of that year. Because all of Canada's federal political parties, except for the Alliance (now the Conservative Party of Canada), had publicly announced their support for ratification, passage through Parliament was assured. Soon after, the Government of Canada announced initiatives aimed at reducing annual CO_2 emissions by 24 million t (24 Mt, megatonnes) by 2010, equivalent to a 4% decrease from the 1990 levels. That plan was predicted to cost $425 million, and it has since been followed by additional proposals to further decrease emissions to the necessary level of about 33 Mt/y of CO_2.

The most recent plan (at the time of writing), announced in April 2005, anticipated federal spending of $10 billion to 2012 and reductions of about 270 Mt during that seven-year period. The plan has the following major elements:

■ The **Climate Fund** is intended to achieve a reduction of 75–115 Mt by establishing a market-based mechanism for purchasing "carbon credits" in Canada and internationally. Such credits could, for example, be based on farming practices that increase carbon storage in soil, on afforestation initiatives, or they might involve purchases from other countries that have met their Kyoto targets (such as Russia, whose emissions have decreased since 1990 because of post-Soviet economic downsizing, along with greater prominence of natural gas in its economy).

Canadian Focus 17.1 (continued)

- The **Partnership Fund** (55–85 Mt) is intended to assist provincial and territorial governments in investing in technological and infrastructural changes to decrease emissions, such as phasing out coal-fired power plants, increasing hydroelectric capacity, and developing technologies to capture CO_2 for long-term storage.
- The **Large Final Emitters** initiative (45 Mt) has a focus on about 700 major sources, such as power plants, oil-and-gas facilities, the mining industry, and factories. Reductions from this sector will involve improvements in process efficiency, fuel-switching, and purchasing carbon credits from domestic and international vendors. There will also be a sector-funded Greenhouse Gas Technology Investment Fund to facilitate a longer-term transition to a lower-carbon economy.
- **GHG Reduction Programs** (40 Mt) will help Canadians reduce their personal emissions through incentives for improved energy efficiency in homes, commercial and institutional buildings, and vehicles.
- **Carbon Sinks** (30 Mt) include actions to increase the amounts of organic carbon stored in forests and agricultural soil, which serve as offsets against emissions of RAGs from other activities.
- **Renewable Energy** (15 Mt) particularly involves incentives to increase the capacity to produce energy using wind (to 4000 MW), sunlight, small-hydro, and biomass.
- **Consumer Action** (5 Mt) involves fostering greener purchasing by Canadians, including the One-Tonne Challenge, which is intended to enhance awareness and actions for reducing personal and family emissions of RAGs.
- **The Automotive Industry** (5.3 Mt) will be a focus of actions to decrease emissions of RAGs from cars and trucks by increased fuel efficiency (including lighter vehicles), hybrid cars, and alternative fuels.
- **Greening Government** (1 Mt) involves actions to reduce emissions by the federal government by about one-third, mostly by enhancing energy efficiency and using alternative energy sources.

In addition to these federal initiatives, other levels of government in Canada have been working on their own action plans to reduce emissions of greenhouse gases, as have companies, institutions, and many individual Canadians (see Global Focus 17.2). However, the overall planning to meet the Kyoto target is fraught with uncertainty, largely because so many of the key initiatives are based on the hope that voluntary actions will be successful, and if not, then large sums of money will be made available to purchase carbon credits from international vendors. Both of these possible outcomes are extremely controversial in political, economic, and environmental arenas. Essentially, it is because of this controversy that the Canadian approach to meeting Kyoto targets has been relatively "soft" in terms of the potential implementation of such measures as carbon taxes and legislated reductions of emissions from particular economic sectors. Moreover, the Conservative Party of Canada has announced that, if it were to be elected into government, it would not implement policies or measures necessary to meet national commitments under the protocol.

Clearly, meeting the requirements of the Kyoto Protocol requires significant changes in energy policy and in other key economic activities. There will have to be a large increase in the use of renewable energy sources that have no or fewer emissions of RAGs (e.g., hydroelectricity, biomass, wind, and solar). There may have to be a reduction in total energy use, achieved through gains in efficiency realized from new technologies and improved policies, such as more reliance on public transit and less use of private vehicles carrying a single passenger. And energy consumption may have to be taxed more heavily to discourage its reckless use. These are politically contentious actions, but from the environmental perspective, these and other Kyoto-friendly initiatives are worthwhile and would represent important progress toward sustainable development.

In any event, in late-2005 (when this text was written), Canada's emissions of RAGs were actually much larger than those of 1990 (at least 20% higher). Although Canadian governments, businesses, and individuals have stated their support for meeting our legal obligations under the Kyoto Protocol, it seems likely that we will badly miss our target. If that happens, it will also be an internationally embarrassing event.

References and Additional Information

David Suzuki Foundation. The Bottom Line on Kyoto. Economic Benefits of Canadian Action. www.davidsuzuki.org/climate_change/Kyoto/Economics/

Canadian Broadcasting Corporation. Kyoto. www.cbc.ca/news/background/kyoto/index.html

Government of Alberta. Climate Change. www3.gov.ab.ca/env/climate.html

Government of Canada. Taking Action on Climate Change. www.climatechange.gc.ca/english/

forest productivity were increased by intensive management on a fertile site, as little as one-tenth of that area might be required, but that would still be a huge area (Freedman *et al.*, 1992). Only a limited amount of land is available, in Canada or elsewhere, for afforestation to provide carbon offsets. The use of larger areas would withdraw too much land from economically productive uses, especially agriculture.

In any event, dealing effectively with an anthropogenic enhancement of the greenhouse effect will require a comprehensive, integrated strategy. Reduced emissions of RAGs must be the major component of that strategy. Carbon offsets such as tree-planting will be a useful element, but will not be sufficient alone.

The most important means of reducing CO_2 emissions would potentially involve the following:

- conservation of energy through more efficient use, which would result in a decreased demand for fossil fuels

- increased use of non-carbon energy technologies (such as solar, wind, tidal, hydro, and nuclear) to displace some uses of fossil fuels

- prevention of further conversions of mature forest into agricultural and other land-uses to avoid the CO_2 emissions that are associated with deforestation

- afforestation, which would increase carbon stored in ecosystems

Implementation of an integrated strategy involving these actions would be politically and economically difficult. Industrialized nations rely heavily on fossil fuels. Changes in this reliance will have huge implications for economic systems, industrial capitalization, resource use, and citizens' expectations of lifestyle. Similarly, deforestation in tropical countries is a primary means by which poor people gain access to opportunities and livelihoods, and harvested timber helps to earn the foreign exchange that is necessary to fund development activities.

The societal changes that would be necessary to effectively deal with an intensified greenhouse effect are revolutionary in their nature and magnitude. Designing the required economic and energy systems will be a tremendous challenge, and implementing them will require enlightened and forceful leadership. Unfortunately, there are no easy solutions to an environmental problem as potentially damaging as an anthropogenic enhancement of the greenhouse effect. Moreover, it is crucial that effective actions be implemented as soon as possible, even before it is definitely known that many of the damages are occurring.

Conclusions

Earth's natural greenhouse effect is caused by the activity of radiatively active gases in the atmosphere, and it helps make the planet habitable. The concentrations of key RAGs are increasing rapidly, particularly carbon dioxide, and this is predicted to intensify the greenhouse effect. This would result in global warming and many other climatic effects, such as changes in precipitation regimes and in the frequency of severe weather events. These climatic changes would have severe consequences for agroecosystems and the human economy in general, and also for natural ecosystems (notwithstanding that, in some places, there might be improvements of agriculture and new opportunities for species and some kinds of ecological communities). At the international level, the Kyoto Protocol is the first action being taken to reduce the emissions of RAGs that threaten to cause global warming. Canada and many other countries (but not the U.S.) have ratified this international treaty and are taking steps to reduce their emissions of greenhouse gases. However, these actions are highly controversial and are not in themselves sufficient to achieve their intended goal of preventing or slowing global warming—future actions will have to be more decisive.

Key Terms

energy budget

radiatively active gases (RAGs)

greenhouse effect

climate change

carbon credits

afforestation

Questions for Review

1. Describe Earth's natural greenhouse effect and the factors that cause it.

2. How are human influences making Earth's greenhouse effect more intense?

3. What is a radiatively active gas (RAG)? What are the most important RAGs in Earth's atmosphere, and how are human actions affecting their concentrations?

4. What are the likely climatic and ecological consequences of an intensification of Earth's greenhouse effect?

Questions for Discussion

1. How might the Canadian economy and the lifestyles of typical Canadians be affected if serious actions are taken to deal with the consequences of an intensified greenhouse effect?

2. The David Suzuki Foundation is an environmental charity that advocates strong actions by Canada to reduce its emissions of greenhouse gases. In a news release in 2002, a spokesperson for the foundation stated, "Industry groups and provinces like Alberta are asking Prime Minister Chrétien to drop plans to ratify Kyoto because they argue it will cost too much. But they are exaggerating the costs and missing the most expensive price tag of all—the cost of not signing Kyoto. Health problems caused by air pollution, insect infestations in…forests, and dry conditions in the prairies will cost us billions of dollars if nothing is done to curb our greenhouse gas emissions." What do you think about these assertions concerning the potential costs and benefits of reducing Canada's emissions of greenhouse gases?

3. The platform of the Conservative Party of Canada includes the following plank (in June, 2005): "The Conservative Party will fight for a clean environment. We will propose workable solutions to make Canada a world leader in clean air, clean water and clean land." Yet, representatives of the Conservatives maintain that, if they were to form the Government of Canada, they would not implement the provisions of the Kyoto Protocol. Do you consider these positions to be inconsistent? Justify your answer.

4. Mostly because of the potential economic effects, the Kyoto Protocol has been highly controversial in Canada and other countries. But even if the provisions of the treaty are fully implemented, there would only be a slowing of the rate of increase of greenhouse gas concentrations in the atmosphere. This is because the rate of emission of CO_2 and other RAGs would still be larger than can be absorbed by the planetary sinks. What do you think about these circumstances? Should the reductions of emissions of RAGs be even larger than required by the Kyoto Protocol? Even if scientists advise that it is necessary to deal with global warming, how would you convince politicians, industrial interests, and other concerned parties that it must be done?

Exploring Issues

1. Your provincial government has struck a committee of politicians and citizens to recommend actions to reduce the net emissions of greenhouse gases. As the principal science advisor to the committee, you have been asked to develop a list of practical options that should be undertaken. What actions would you recommend for implementation immediately, and which more gradually (e.g., progressively during the next 10 years)? Justify each of your recommendations.

2. For one day, make a list of your own activities that result in emissions of carbon dioxide or methane to the atmosphere. These should include direct emissions (e.g., by breathing or driving a vehicle) and indirect ones (as when trees must be harvested to provide you with paper, or organic garbage is disposed into a landfill). Estimate the percentage reduction in emissions that you think you could make without suffering an unacceptable degree of change in your lifestyle.

References

Barnola, J.M., D. Raynaud, Y.K. Korotkevich, and C. Lorius. 1987. Vostok ice core provides 160,000-year record of atmospheric CO_2. *Nature*, **329**: 408–414.

Blasing, T.J. 1985. Background: Carbon Cycle, Climate, and Vegetation Responses. In: *Characterization of Information Requirements for Studies of CO_2 Effects: Water Resources, Agriculture, Fisheries, Forests, and Human Health*. Washington, DC: U.S. Department of Energy. DOE/ER-0236. pp. 9–22.

Bolin, B., B.R. Doos, J. Jager, and R.A. Warrick. 1986. *The Greenhouse Effect, Climatic Change, and Ecosystems*. Chichester, UK: Wiley & Sons. SCOPE Rep. 29.

Brasseur, G.P., J.J. Orlando, and G.S. Tyndall. 1999. *Atmospheric Chemistry and Global Change*. Oxford: Oxford University Press.

Brasseur, G.P., R.G. Prinn, and A.A.P. Pszenny (eds.). 2003. *Atmospheric Chemistry in a Changing World*. Berlin: Springer.

Bryant, E.A. 1997. *Climate Process and Change*. Cambridge: Cambridge University Press.

Carbon Dioxide Information Analysis Centre (CDIAC). 2005. *Trends. A Compendium of Data on Global Change*. Oak Ridge, TN: CDIAC. http://cdiac.esd.ornl.gov/trends/trends.htm

Charlson, R.J. and T.M.L. Wigley. 1994. Sulphate aerosol and climatic change. *Sci. Amer.*, **270** (2): 48–57.

Dale, V.H., R.A. Houghton, and C.A.S. Hall. 1991. Estimating the effects of land-use change on global atmospheric CO_2 concentrations. *Can. J. For. Res.*, **21**: 87–90.

Detwiler, R.P. and C.A.S. Hall. 1988. Tropical forests and the global carbon cycle. *Science*, **239**: 42–47.

Environment Canada. 1995. *The State of Canada's Climate: Monitoring Variability and Change*. Ottawa: Environment Canada. SOE Rep. No. 95-1.

Flanigan, M.D. and C.E. Van Wagner. 1991. Climate change and wildfire in Canada. *Can. J. For. Res.*, **21**: 66–72.

Flavin, C. 1996. Facing up to the risks of climate change. In: *State of the World 1996*. Washington, DC: Worldwatch Institute. pp. 21–39.

Freedman, B. 1995. *Environmental Ecology*. 2nd ed. San Diego, CA: Academic.

Freedman, B. and T. Keith. 1996. Planting trees for carbon credits: A discussion of context, issues, feasibility, and environmental benefits, with particular attention to Canada. *Environ. Rev.*, **4**: 100–111.

Freedman, B., F. Meth, and C. Hickman. 1992. Temperate forest as a carbon-storage reservoir for carbon dioxide emitted by coal-fired generating stations: A case study for New Brunswick, Canada. *For. Ecol. & Manage.*, **15**: 103–127.

Gates, D.M. 1985. *Energy and Ecology*. New York: Sinauer.

Hardy, J.T. 2003. *Climate Change: Causes, Effects, and Solutions*. Hoboken, NJ: Wiley.

Houghton, J. 2004. *Global Warming: The Complete Briefing*. Cambridge, UK: Cambridge University Press.

Houghton, J.T., L.G. Meira Filho, B. Callander, and N. Harris. (eds.). 1996. *Climate Change 1995: The Science of Climate Change*. Cambridge: Cambridge University Press.

Houghton, R.A. 1991. The role of forests in affecting the greenhouse gas composition of the atmosphere. In: *Global Climate Change and Life on Earth*. (R.C. Wyman, ed.). New York: Routledge, Chapman, and Hall. pp. 43–56.

Houghton, R.A. and J.L. Hackler. 2002. *Carbon Flux to the Atmosphere from Land-Use Changes*. Oak Ridge, TN: Carbon Dioxide Information Analysis Center. http://cdiac.esd.ornl.gov/trends/landuse/houghton/houghton.html

Houghton, R.A., G.J. Jenkins, and J.J. Ephraums (eds.); Intergovernmental Panel on Climate Change. 1990. *Climate Change: The IPCC Scientific Assessment*. Cambridge: Cambridge University Press.

Houghton, R.A., J.E. Hobbie, J.M. Melillo, B. Moore, B.J. Peterson, G.R. Shaver, and G.M. Woodwell. 1983. Changes in the carbon content of terrestrial biota and soils between 1860 and 1980: A net release of CO_2 to the atmosphere. *Ecol. Monogr.*, **53**: 235–262.

Jones, P.D., T.J. Osborn, K.R. Briffa, and D.E. Parker. 2001. *Global Monthly and Annual Temperature Anomalies (degrees C), 1856–2000*. Oak Ridge, TN: Carbon Dioxide Information Analysis Centre. http://cdiac.esd.ornl.gov/ftp/trends/temp/jonescru/global.dat

Keeling, C.D. and T.P. Whorf. 2005. *Atmospheric CO_2 records from sites in the SIO air sampling network*. Oak Ridge, TN: Carbon Dioxide Information Analysis Centre. http://cdiac.esd.ornl.gov/trends/co2/contents.htm

Lovejoy, T. and L. Hannah (eds.). 2005. *Climate Change and Biodiversity*. New Haven, CT: Yale University Press.

Lutkemeier, S., P. Kabat, M. Claussen, P.A. Dirmeyer, J.H.C. Gash, L.B. de Guenni, M. Meybeck, R.A. Pielke, C.J. Vorosmarty, and R.W.A. Hutjes (eds.). 2004. *Vegetation, Water, Humans and Climate: A New Perspective on an Interactive System*. Berlin: Springer.

Marland, G., T.A. Boden, and R. J. Andres. 2005. *Global, Regional, and National Fossil Fuel CO_2 Emissions*. Oak Ridge, TN: Carbon Dioxide Information Analysis Centre. http://cdiac.esd.ornl.gov/trends/emis/em_cont.htm

Mooney, H.A., B.G. Drake, R.J. Luxmoore, W.C. Oechel, and L.F. Pitelka. 1991. Predicting ecosystem responses to elevated CO_2 concentrations. *BioScience*, **41**: 96–104.

Peters, R.L., and Darling, J.D.S. 1985. The greenhouse effect and nature reserves. *Bioscience*, **35**: 707–717.

Petit, J.R., D. Raynaud, C. Lorius, J. Jouzel, G. Delaygue, N.I. Barkov, and V.M. Kotlyakov. 2000. *Historical isotopic temperature record from the Vostok ice core*. Oak Ridge, TN: Carbon Dioxide Information Analysis Centre. http://cdiac.esd.ornl.gov/trends/temp/vostok/jouz_tem.htm

Rodhe, H. 1990. A comparison of the contributions of various gases to the greenhouse effect. *Science*, **248**: 1217–1219.

Schneider, S.H. 2003. *Climate Change Policy: A Survey*. Washington, DC: Island Press.

Solomon, A.M., J.R. Trabolka, D.E. Reichle, and L.D. Voorhees. 1985. The global cycle of carbon. In: *Atmospheric Carbon Dioxide and the Global Carbon Cycle*. Washington, DC: U.S. Department of Energy. DOE/ER-0239. pp. 1–13.

Watson, R.T. (ed.). 2002. *Climate Change 2001: Synthesis Report: Third Assessment Report of the Intergovernmental Panel on Climate Change*. Cambridge, UK: Cambridge University Press.

Wigley, T.M.L. and S.C.B. Raper. 1992. Implications for climate and sea level of revised IPCC emissions scenarios. *Nature*, **357**: 293–300.

World Resources Institute. 2005. *Earth Trends. The Environmental Information Portal*. Washington, DC: WRI.

Wyman, R.L. (ed.). 1991. *Global Climate Change and Life on Earth*. New York: Routledge, Chapman, and Hall.

Informative Websites

Climate. www.enviroliteracy.org/subcategory.php/8.html

Will the Earth's climate warm catastrophically? This page attempts to address this question and also discusses the ozone layer, El Niño, and the Kyoto Agreement.

Environment Canada. The Green Lane.

www.ec.gc.ca/envhome.html

This comprehensive site from Environment Canada features pages on climate change, nature, and clean air and water, as well as links to publications, news releases, and related sites.

Environmental Protection Agency. Global Warming.
http://yosemite.epa.gov/oar/globalwarming.nsf/content/index.html

The Environmental Protection Agency discusses emissions and potential impacts and actions related to global warming.

Government of Canada. Taking Action on Climate Change. www.climatechange.gc.ca/english/

This website of the federal government provides links to a wide range of sources of information about Canadian policies and actions to meet its obligations under the Kyoto Protocol.

Intergovernmental Panel on Climate Change.
www.ipcc.ch/

Recognizing the problem of potential global climate change, the World Meteorological Organization (WMO) and the United Nations Environment Programme (UNEP) established the Intergovernmental Panel on Climate Change (IPCC) in 1988. You can read their publications, activities, press releases, and meetings and schedules at this site.

Meteorological Service of Canada.
www.msc-smc.ec.gc.ca/

The Meteorological Service of Canada is our national source for meteorological information. The Service monitors water quantities and provides information and conducts research on climate, atmospheric science, air quality, ice, and other environmental issues.

U.S. Global Change Research Information Office.
www.gcrio.org/

This informative website indexes many links dedicated to climate change.

World Resources Institute. EarthTrends. The Environmental Information Portal.
http://earthtrends.wri.org/

This website contains interesting data about health, environmental quality, and effects of environmental stressors.

Toxic Elements

18

CHAPTER OBJECTIVES

After completing this chapter, you will be able to

1. Describe the ubiquitous distribution of elements in the environment and discuss this distribution in terms of the difference between pollution and contamination.

2. Outline cases of natural pollution by toxic elements and discuss how they provide useful insight into the effects of these stressors.

3. Describe cases of anthropogenic pollution by metals and outline the resulting ecological damage.

CHAPTER OUTLINE

Introduction

All of the naturally occurring chemical elements are ubiquitous (found everywhere) in at least trace concentrations in soil, water, air, and organisms. As long as the detection limits of the available analytical chemistry are low enough, this universal contamination can always be demonstrated.

Organisms require some trace elements as essential micronutrients, including copper, iron, molybdenum, zinc, and in some cases aluminum, nickel, and selenium. Under certain conditions, however, these same elements can accumulate to high concentrations in organisms (this is known as **bioconcentration** and **food-web magnification**) and cause ecological damage (see In Detail 18.1). The trace elements most often associated with environmental toxicity are the heavy metals cadmium, chromium, cobalt, copper, iron, lead, mercury, nickel, silver, tin, and zinc, and lighter elements such as aluminum, arsenic, and selenium.

Some cases of elemental pollution are natural in origin. This usually happens when metal-rich minerals are exposed at the Earth's surface and cause local ecological changes. However, human activities have caused many additional examples of pollution by toxic elements, particularly in the vicinity of large industrial sources such as smelters. In addition, emissions of mercury and lead from power plants and automobiles have caused widespread contamination of remote environments, although it is not yet certain that this is causing ecological damage.

There are also cases of people being poisoned by exposure to toxic elements in their environment. Some historians believe that the decline of the Roman Empire may have been hastened by neurotoxicity caused by chronic lead poisoning. The Romans had significant exposure to lead because they stored acidic beverages (such as wine) in pottery with lead-containing pigments and glazes. As well, their water piping was made of lead (the word "plumbing" is based on the Latin word for lead—*plumbum*). In nineteenth-century Britain, people who made felt top hats developed neurological damage because of their occupational exposure to mercury compounds, used to give a shiny finish to the hats—hence Lewis Carroll's character in *Alice in Wonderland*, the "Mad Hatter," and the common expression, "mad as a hatter."

More recently, thousands of people suffered mercury poisoning during the 1960s after they ate seed grain treated with mercuric fungicides. In one disastrous case, more than 6500 people were poisoned (about 500 died) in Iraq when they ate food prepared from mercury-treated grain. The grain had been donated by a foreign aid program and was intended only for planting. Although the bags of grain were labelled to show the poisonous nature of the seed, many of the victims were illiterate or did not understand the implications of the message or ignored it. About the same time, similar poisonings were caused when people ate mercury-treated seed grain in Iran, Pakistan, and Guatemala. To avoid these problems today, fungicide-treated seed grain is usually coloured red, which warns people not to use it as food.

Mercury also caused thousands of cases of poisoning at Minamata, Japan. A factory had discharged elemental mercury into Minamata Bay. Elemental mercury is not very poisonous, but microbes in the sediment metabolized the metal into methylmercury, which is extremely toxic and bioaccumulating. The methylmercury entered the aquatic food web and caused extensive poisoning of fish-eating birds, domestic cats, and humans (see Global Focus 18.1).

In this chapter, we examine natural and anthropogenic pollution of the environment with toxic elements, and the resulting ecological consequences.

Concentration and Availability

All of the naturally occurring elements are present in all samples of water, soil and rocks, air, and organisms in at least trace concentrations. The term "background concentration" describes the concentration that is not significantly influenced by either anthropogenic emissions or unusual natural exposures. Background concentrations in soil and rock are usually much higher than in water, and most are also higher than in the tissues of organisms (Table 18.1).

However, elements dissolved in water often occur in chemical forms (such as ions) that are relatively easily absorbed by organisms. For this reason, even trace aqueous concentrations may be toxic. In contrast, the much higher concentrations that commonly occur in soil and rocks are mostly insoluble and, therefore, are not particularly bioavailable. Scientists determine the **"total" concentration** of metals in a component of the environment (such as soil, sediment, or rock) by digesting samples in a hot mixture of strong acids. In contrast, the **"available" concentration** is determined from an aqueous (water) extract of the sample. Available concentrations are more relevant to potential toxicity than are total concentrations. In general, available concentrations of toxic elements in

In Detail 18.1

Bioaccumulation and Food-Web Magnification

Certain metals, or their organocompounds such as methylmercury, tend to occur in much higher concentrations in organisms than in the ambient, non-living environment. This phenomenon is known as **bioaccumulation** (also called **bioconcentration**). Similar tendencies are shown by chlorinated hydrocarbons, such as DDT, PCBs, and dioxins (see Chapter 21). Bioaccumulation occurs because certain chemicals have a strong affinity for organisms and therefore concentrate within them in strong preference to the non-living environment. Many of these chemicals dissolve in biological fluids and tissues, such as lipids (fats), in preference to the water or soil in the ambient environment.

Another phenomenon, known as **food-web magnification** (or **food-web concentration** or **biomagnification**), is the tendency for top predators to have the highest concentrations of these chemicals. Organisms are very efficient at assimilating methylmercury and organochlorines from their food. Therefore, these chemicals are absorbed from food and become stored within the organism, rather than being eliminated or excreted. This means that predators at the top of the food web develop the highest concentrations (residues) of these chemicals. Usually, bioaccumulation and food-web magnification progress with age, so the oldest individuals in any population are the most contaminated.

Food-Web Magnification

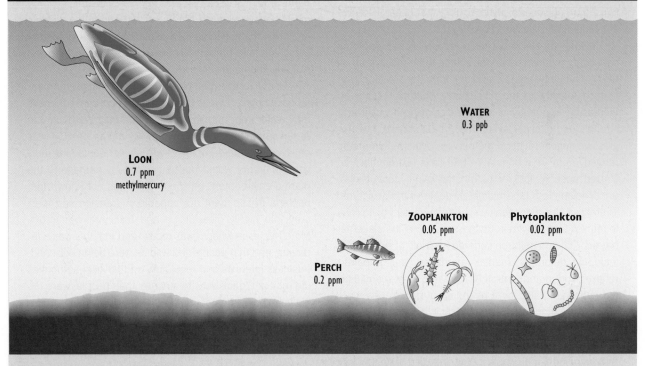

Food-web magnification leads to progressively higher concentrations of methylmercury and chlorinated hydrocarbons in organisms occupying higher positions in the food web. The common loon (*Gavia immer*) is a top predator in many lakes. In some regions of Canada, the bodies of these birds can harbour concentrations of methylmercury so high as to impair their reproduction. The source of the environmental mercury is not yet known for certain, but it may be associated with anthropogenic emissions, such as those from power plants, incinerators, and smelters.

Global Focus 18.1

Mercury in Minamata Bay

Minamata is a town in Japan where industrial emissions from a factory owned by Chisso Corporation caused a famous example of toxic pollution. The factory produced acetaldehyde, which was used to make plastics and other synthetic chemicals. The industrial process used inorganic mercury, and between 1932 and 1968, about 25 t of the metal were dumped into Minamata Bay with wastewater discharges. In the marine environment, the mercury was metabolized into methylmercury by bacteria living in anaerobic sediment. Methylmercury is a highly bioavailable compound that entered the food web and became biomagnified to high concentrations in fish (which contained up to 20 ppm Hg), which in turn were eaten by predatory birds, causing toxicity and reproductive failure. Fish and shellfish were also harvested and eaten by many people living around the bay, which has a long-standing, traditional fishing economy. This caused an episode of severe toxicity that became known as "Minamata Disease."

It took several years for the complex of symptoms caused by methylmercury poisoning to be recognized as being ultimately due to emissions from the acetaldehyde factory. Initially, in the mid-1950s, doctors noticed an increasing frequency of people displaying a novel and strange neurological syndrome, characterized by progressive degeneration of the nervous system. Symptoms ranged from numbness in the limb extremities, to slurred speech, loss of peripheral vision, convulsions, unconsciousness, and ultimately death of many victims. There was also a congenital syndrome caused by toxicity to fetuses by methylmercury passed across the placental barrier. Afflicted children suffered a variety of symptoms, including deformity, mental retardation, and impaired reflexes and motor control. At the same time, many fish-fed cats were killed by a neurological disease, as were many fish-eating birds.

It soon became apparent that the disease was being caused by eating fish harvested from Minamata Bay. Although industrial waste being dumped into the bay was an early suspect, little was done to either reduce the discharges or to prevent people from eating seafood caught in the polluted area. Then, in 1959, scientists from Kumamoto University concluded that an organo-mercurial compound was the cause of the toxic disease. Soon after, it was realized that its origin was inorganic mercury of industrial origin that was being naturally methylated in the bay. The company that caused the pollution challenged these conclusions, although it began to pay compensation to some severely afflicted people (but only if a release was signed that absolved the company of responsibility and eliminated the possibility of future lawsuits; moreover, many affected people were denied any compensation). Despite intense controversy, the company continued to release mercury to the aquatic environment until 1968, when a change in technology eliminated mercury from the manufacturing process.

Ultimately, about 2200 people were "officially" diagnosed as having Minamata Disease as a result of exposure to methylmercury in seafood harvested from the bay. Of these, about 100 died of acute toxicity. In addition, at least 12 000 other people may have suffered milder forms of the disease but were not officially diagnosed with mercury poisoning. In 1973, a Japanese court found the chemical company to have behaved in a highly negligent manner and to be liable for the damages. Many people suffering from mercury-caused disease were awarded compensation, although the payment amounts were disputed as being insufficient and many people received nothing. The bottom line, however, is that many people died of avoidable methylmercury poisoning, and numerous survivors suffered awful physical and mental disabilities.

Useful lessons can be learned from this environmental catastrophe. One is that unanticipated consequences may result from human activities that may be thought to be environmentally safe. In the Minamata case, it was believed that the dumping of wastewater containing inorganic mercury would not cause serious damage to the marine environment. At the time, it was not known that bacteria in sediment are capable of transforming mercury into highly bioavailable and toxic methylmercury. Moreover, even when it was recognized that this was happening, and that people and wildlife were being poisoned, business interests and regulatory and political authorities did not act decisively to ensure that people were no longer exposed to the toxic threat—this laxity greatly compounded the problem. In any event, the tragic case of Minamata Bay has provided society with important understanding about the consequences of discharging mercury into the aquatic environment. However, the broader lesson about unintended consequences of poorly considered economic activities is not yet firmly enshrined in our planning and regulatory systems.

Reference

Harada, M. 2001. *Minamata disease and the mercury pollution of the globe*. Environmental Information Network for Asia and the Pacific.
www.einap.org/envdis/Minamata.html#name

| TABLE 18.1 | Background Concentrations of Elements in Selected Components of the Environment |

ELEMENT	ROCKS (ppm) GRANITE	BASALT	LIMESTONE	SOIL (ppm)	WATER (ppb) OCEANIC	FRESH	TERRESTRIAL PLANTS (ppm)	MAMMAL MUSCLE (ppm)	MARINE FISH (ppm)
Aluminum	77 000	87 600	9 000	71 000	2.0	300	90–530	0.7–28	20
Arsenic	1.5	1.5	1	6	3.7	0.5	0.2–7	0.007–0.09	0.2–10
Cadmium	0.1	0.13	0.03	0.35	0.1	0.1	0.1–2.4	0.1–3.2	0.1–3
Chromium	4	90	11	70	0.3	1.0	0.03–10	<0.002–0.84	0.03–2
Cobalt	1	35	0.1	8	0.02	0.2	0.005–1	0.005–1	0.006–0.05
Copper	13	90	5.5	30	0.3	3.0	5–15	10	0.7–15
Fluoride	1 400	510	220	200	1 300	100	0.02–24	0.05	1 400
Iron	27 000	56 000	17 000	40 000	2.0	500	70–700	180	9–98
Lead	24	3	5.7	35	0.03	3.0	1–13	0.2–3.3	0.001–15
Manganese	400	1 500	620	1 000	0.2	8.0	20–700	0.2–2.3	0.3–4.6
Mercury	0.1	0.01	0.18	0.06	0.3	0.1	0.005–0.02	0.02–0.7	0.4
Molybdenum	2	1	0.16	1.2	10.0	0.5	0.06–3	0.02–0.07	1
Nickel	0.5	150	7	50	0.6	0.5	1–5	1.2	0.1–4
Selenium	0.05	0.05	0.03	0.4	0.2	0.2	0.03	0.4–1.9	0.2
Silver	0.04	0.1	0.12	0.05	0.04	0.3	0.01–0.8	0.009–0.28	0.04–0.1
Tin	3.5	1	0.5	4	0.004	0.01	0.2–2	0.01–2	0
Uranium	4.4	0.43	2.2	2	3.2	0.4	0.005–0.04	0.001–0.003	0.04–0.08
Vanadium	72	250	45	90	2.5	0.5	0.001–0.5	0.002–0.02	0.3
Zinc	52	100	20	90	5.0	1.5	20–400	240	9–80

Source: Data from Bowen (1979)

soil are much smaller than the total concentrations (generally less than 1% of the total value).

Most elements are found in only trace concentrations in the environment (see Table 18.1). In contrast, a few elements typically occur in much higher concentrations, particularly aluminium and iron. These are prominent constituents of rocks and soil, with aluminum concentration averaging about 8% and iron 3–4%. However, almost all of the aluminum and iron in soil and rocks occurs as insoluble minerals that are not readily available for uptake by organisms.

For example, virtually all soil aluminum occurs as insoluble silicate and clay minerals. Although aluminum in these forms comprises about 8% of the soil mass, it is not available for uptake by plants and is, therefore, nontoxic. However, much smaller concentrations of aluminum, typically only a few parts per million (ppm), are found in soil as ions, either bound to organic matter and clay surfaces or freely dissolved in soil water. The ionic forms of aluminum are readily available for biological uptake and may cause toxicity to some species.

Much higher concentrations of soluble, available aluminum occur in strongly acidic environments, especially

when the pH is less than about 5.5. (In fact, most metals are much more soluble under acidic conditions.) Aluminum solubility is also greater in strongly alkaline environments, with pHs higher than about 8. Moreover, different ionic species of aluminum occur at different pHs: Al^{3+} is dominant in strongly acidic environments with a pH of less than 5.0; $AlOH^{2+}$ and $Al(OH)_2^+$ are important under less acidic conditions of pH 4.5–5.5; $Al(OH)_3$, from pH 5.2–9; and $Al(OH)_4^-$, in alkaline environments with a pH greater than about 8.5. Aluminum toxicity is a common problem for organisms living in highly acidic or alkaline environments. This is because of the combined influences of greater solubility and the presence of relatively toxic ions under those conditions.

Toxicity

The toxicity of elements and other chemicals is related to two factors: the exposure (dose) and the vulnerability of an organism to the specific poison. The dose received by an organism is influenced by the available concentration of the poison in the environment and the period of exposure.

Therefore, a long-term exposure to a small available concentration may cause toxicity, particularly in cases in which the element can bioaccumulate and magnify in the food web until a threshold of tolerance is exceeded.

Organisms vary greatly in their **tolerance** of exposures to toxic elements (as well as to other poisons). Consequently, an intense exposure to a potentially toxic chemical may result in some species being poisoned, while tolerant ones may not be damaged and may even benefit from the demise of sensitive species in their community. In addition, genetically based variation for tolerance usually exists within species. This can lead to the evolution of populations (known as *ecotypes*) that are relatively tolerant of toxic exposures (we examine this topic in more detail in the next section).

The most common mechanism of poisoning by toxic elements is damage to an enzyme system. (Organisms have a huge diversity of enzymes, which are proteins that catalyze specific biochemical reactions and are critical to healthy metabolism.) The poisoning is caused because metal ions bind to specific enzymes, changing their shape, which results in loss of their unique catalytic function. Toxic elements may also poison by binding to DNA or RNA, and so disrupting transcription and translation, the processes by which genetic information is used to synthesize specific proteins (including enzymes). Toxic metals can also disrupt DNA replication and hence cell division (see In Detail 6.1).

Typical symptoms of acute poisoning caused by toxic elements in plants include abnormal patterns of growth and development, decreased productivity, impaired reproduction, disease, and ultimately death. Symptoms of chronic toxicity are more difficult to detect and may include "hidden injuries" such as a decrease in productivity. Animals can show a variety of symptoms associated with enzyme disruption, often including neurotoxicity and impaired functioning of the kidneys and other organs.

Natural Pollution

Localized natural pollution sometimes occurs when metal-rich minerals are present at the surface and affect the chemistry of local soil, surface water, and vegetation. These conditions can often be identified by the presence of particular plant species or by a distinctive, stunted, growth form of the vegetation. In combination with chemical analyses, these biological indicators can be used to explore for metal-rich mineralizations, in a technique known as biogeochemical prospecting.

In some cases, natural pollution by metals can be very intense. For example, soil containing up to 3% lead and zinc was found at a site on Baffin Island. In another case, peat that was filtering a metal-rich groundwater spring in New Brunswick accumulated as much as 10% copper. High concentrations of metals in soil are also reflected in the chemistry of plants, particularly in certain genetically adapted, **hyperaccumulator** species that often occur in metal-rich habitats. For example, nickel concentrations as high as 10% have been measured in plants in the genus *Alyssum* growing in Russia, and up to 25% in the blue-coloured latex of *Sebertia acuminata* from New Caledonia in the South Pacific. These hyperaccumulator plants grow on naturally metal-polluted sites.

Serpentine Soil and Vegetation

Some well-studied cases of natural pollution involve soil influenced by *serpentine* minerals, which are rich in nickel, chromium, and cobalt and are associated with asbestos deposits. Soil containing serpentine minerals is toxic to non-adapted plants because of the high concentrations of these metals, in combination with an imbalance of the nutrients calcium and magnesium. Serpentine soil typically contains several thousand ppm of nickel, but can have as much as 25 000 ppm (2.5%) of this metal.

Natural vegetation on serpentine sites is often distinctively stunted. Extensive serpentine "barrens" occur on plateaus in eastern Quebec and western Newfoundland. Those habitats support tundra-like ecosystems in a landscape otherwise covered by boreal coniferous forest.

In some places, serpentine areas support plant species that occur only in that kind of habitat, a narrow distribution that ecologists refer to as **endemic**. In other cases, widespread plant species have evolved locally adapted populations that can cope with the toxic and nutritional stresses of serpentine soil—these are known as **ecotypes**. On non-serpentine sites, the specifically adapted endemics and ecotypes are quickly eliminated by competition with plants that are better adapted to less stressful habitats.

Serpentine sites in northern California support relatively ancient vegetation. These habitats contain 215 endemic species or sub-species of plants. Some of the endemics occur only on particular serpentine sites in California and nowhere else in the world. In contrast, the serpentine barrens in eastern Canada are relatively young, being released from glaciation only about 8000 or fewer years ago. Consequently, not enough time has passed to allow many serpentine endemics or ecotypes to evolve.

Photo 18.1   An extensive area of serpentine-rich rock occurs in Gros Morne National Park in western Newfoundland. Soil rich in serpentine has high concentrations of toxic nickel and cobalt and is poor in nutrients. These conditions are stressful to plants, and can result in the development of an atypically stunted vegetation of limited species diversity, as in this scene. The typical vegetation on non-serpentine soil in this region is a conifer-dominated forest.

These specifically adapted plants are more common in places that have supported vegetation for longer periods of time.

Seleniferous Soil and Vegetation

Semiarid regions in various parts of the world often have areas with soil that contains high concentrations of selenium. These seleniferous habitats may support plants that hyperaccumulate selenium, such as species in the genus *Astragalus* (locoweeds). About 25 North American species of *Astragalus* are hyperaccumulators of selenium. These plants may contain up to 1.5% of selenium in their tissues, storing it in unique amino-acid-like biochemicals, such as selenomethionine. The *Astragalus* species also emit dimethyl selenide and dimethyl diselenide to the atmosphere, giving them a distinctive, unpleasant odour. Livestock that feed on these plants are poisoned by a toxic syndrome known as "alkali disease" or "blind staggers."

Mercury in Aquatic Environments

Even in remote oceanic habitats, mercury often accumulates in high concentrations (as methylmercury, CH_3Hg) in fish, birds, and sea mammals. In marine waters off eastern and western Canada, for example, some large fish may have mercury concentrations in their flesh that exceed what is considered acceptable for human consumption (i.e., more than 0.5 ppm mercury on a fresh-weight basis; Table 18.2). Analysis of old specimens of fish and seabirds in museums has revealed levels of mercury contamination similar to those in modern samples, suggesting that the phenomenon is natural. This contamination of marine animals represents a substantial increase from ambient seawater, which has a trace concentration of mercury of less than 0.1 ppb.

The bioconcentration and food-web magnification of mercury occur because of the progressive accumulation of this metal up the trophic web. Algae initially absorb

TABLE 18.2 Mercury Contamination of Fish Captured Offshore of North America

The data show the average mercury concentration in muscle tissue of species of marine fish. The data are in ppm, measured on a fresh-weight basis. Some data refer to specific size ranges of fish.

SPECIES	MERCURY CONCENTRATION
Swordfish (*Xiphias gladius*) >45 kilogram	1.08
Bluefin tuna (*Thunnus thynnus*) >14 kg	0.89
Yellowfin tuna (*T. albacares*) >32 kg	0.62
Skipjack tuna (*Euthynnus pelamis*) >4 kg	0.21
Atlantic dogfish (*Squalus acanthius*)	0.41
Pacific dogfish (*S. acanthius*)	0.70
Pacific halibut (*Hippoglossus stenolepis*) >45 kg	0.42
Atlantic halibut (*H. hippoglossus*) > 45 kg	0.80

Source: Data from Armstrong (1979)

mercury from the water (as methylmercury), while zooplankton accumulate even larger residues as they graze on the algae. Zooplankton-eating fish accumulate larger quantities still, but the highest residues occur in long-lived top predators, such as large fish and marine mammals (see In Detail 18.1).

Within particular species of marine fish, larger (or older) fish generally have higher mercury concentrations than smaller (or younger) ones. A study of swordfish caught off eastern Canada found that animals heavier than 45 kg had an average mercury concentration of 1.1 ppm, but those weighing 23–45 kg averaged 0.86 ppm, and animals smaller than 23 kg had 0.55 ppm (Armstrong, 1979). It appears that mercury residues become more intense as the animals age and grow larger.

High concentrations of mercury also occur in fish-eating marine mammals and birds, which are top predators in their ecosystem. Studies of adult harp seals (*Phoca groenlandica*) in eastern Canada found an average mercury concentration of 0.34 ppm in muscle and 5.1 ppm in the liver (Armstrong, 1979). High mercury residues also occur in North Atlantic seabirds, with an average of 7 ppm found in feathers of northern skua (*Catharacta skua*), 5 ppm in puffin (*Fratercula arctica*), and 1–2 ppm in fulmar (*Fulmarus glacialis*), kittiwake (*Rissa tridactyla*), razorbill (*Alca torda*), and common murre (*Uria aalge*) (Thompson *et al.*, 1991).

Mercury contamination of fish has also been observed in many remote lakes. For example, about three-quarters of 1700 lakes monitored in Ontario have fish with mer-

cury exceeding 0.5 ppm fresh weight (f.w.) in their flesh. In a remote lake in northern Manitoba, the average mercury concentration in muscle of 53 northern pike (*Esox lucius*) was 2 ppm f.w., and one animal had 5 ppm (McKay, 1985). In general, freshwater fish that are top predators have the highest residues of mercury, and larger or older individuals are the most contaminated.

Federal, provincial, and territorial governments in Canada issue advisories about eating fish taken from particular lakes and rivers where mercury residues in fish are known to be a problem; the advisories may also have information about other contaminants, such as PCBs and dioxins. In Ontario, for example, about three-quarters of more than 1700 monitored waterbodies have some fish with mercury residues in flesh exceeding 0.5 ppm f.w. (Ontario Ministry of the Environment, 2005). The advisories tell people how many fish of particular species and sizes they can eat. The general threshold for concern is 0.61 ppm, but it is as low as 0.26 ppm for pregnant women and children, and no fish with more than 1.84 ppm should be consumed. About 32% of the advisories given for sportfish taken from Ontario lakes result in some level of consumption restriction. In Sweden, about half of the lakes have some fish with mercury exceeding the health advisory limit (i.e., 0.5 ppm), and hundreds of lakes have been "black listed" because their fish are considered unfit for human consumption.

The causes of mercury contamination of lakes are not known for certain. It seems likely that the phenomenon is largely natural in regions that are remote from sources of emission. However, anthropogenic mercury is probably contributing to the problem closer to large emissions sources, such as coal-fired generating stations, municipal incinerators, and smelters. For example, Harp Lake in Ontario is located relatively close to municipal and industrial sources of mercury emissions. Studies found that atmospheric deposition accounted for 57% of the total mercury input to that lake, suggesting a significant anthropogenic influence (Mierle, 1990).

The above discussion of mercury in lakes refers to the many situations in which there are no direct anthropogenic sources of the metal. However, cases of pollution caused directly by industrial emissions are well known. For example, discharges from chlor-alkali and acetaldehyde factories and some older pulp mills have caused local mercury pollution, resulting in high residues of methylmercury in fish and other animals. (The case of Minamata Bay, Japan, involved an acetaldehyde plant; a less severe case in Canada, affecting parts of the English and Wabigoon Rivers in northwestern Ontario, involved a pulp mill.)

Significant bioaccumulation of mercury also occurs when hydroelectric reservoirs are developed. This happens because flooding leaches naturally occurring soil mercury into the reservoir, where it is metabolized into methylmercury by bacteria in oxygen-poor sediment and is then bioaccumulated by fish. Bioaccumulation of mercury occurs especially rapidly in acidic lakes because such conditions favour the production of methylmercury in the sediment, compared with less-available dimethylmercury in non-acidic waterbodies (see Chapter 20).

Anthropogenic Sources

In this section we examine examples of damage caused by emissions of toxic elements from agricultural practices, metal mining, and ore processing; by the use of lead shot in hunting; and by emissions of lead from automobiles.

Pollution from Metal Mining and Processing

During the mining and processing of metals, the various industrial processes can result in significant pollution of air, water, and land (refer to Figure 13.1).

Mining Residues

Areas near mine sites are sometimes degraded by the dumping of metal-rich overburden and excavation waste. Because these materials may be toxic, vegetation development can be restricted to early successional communities, such as sparse grasslands. In some cases, soil toxicity is so severe that few plants manage to establish even after hundreds of years. This can be seen on mine wastes from 2000-year-old Roman lead workings in England and Wales.

Ecologists studying British sites polluted by mine wastes have found that these areas often support populations of plants that are genetically tolerant of the metals. These locally adapted ecotypes can establish themselves and grow in metal-polluted environments, whereas non-tolerant plants of the same species are quickly eliminated by the toxic stress. Conversely, metal-tolerant ecotypes are poor competitors in non-polluted environments and are therefore rare in habitats that are not affected by metal toxicity.

Research into metal-tolerant ecotypes has provided important insights into the process of evolution (see Chapter 6). Metal-tolerant individuals are present in pop-

Photo 18.2   Tailings are fine waste that remains after ore is ground and processed to remove the metal-rich minerals. Tailings may contain high concentrations of toxic metals and can generate large amounts of acidity when exposed to the atmosphere. These conditions make it difficult to establish vegetation after disposal sites are filled. This is a view of a reclaimed area of tailings near Sudbury. Most of the vegetation was sown onto the site, but some native shrubs and trees are also becoming established. The pond in the background is used by breeding and migratory birds, as is the terrestrial habitat.

ulations growing on non-polluted sites, but they are rare. However, the frequency of metal-tolerant genotypes can increase quickly after metal pollution occurs. In places with sharp boundaries between polluted and non-polluted soils, a tolerant plant population can maintain itself over a distance of only a few metres. This is possible because the intense toxic stress of polluted soil strongly favours the survival and reproduction of tolerant individuals. Such a population-level change in genetically based characters, occurring in response to an agent of natural selection (in this case, metal pollution), is a demonstration of evolution (more specifically, microevolution).

Metal-tolerant plant ecotypes have been studied near Sudbury, Ontario, where severe pollution by nickel and copper has been caused by emissions from smelters and roast beds (see Chapter 16). Plant communities of polluted sites are dominated by metal-tolerant ecotypes of several grass species, particularly *Agrostis gigantea* and *Deschampsia caespitosa*. Meadows of these grasses developed rapidly after the extremely tall "superstack" was commissioned in 1972. By dispersing emissions widely, the superstack greatly reduced ground-level SO$_2$ pollution. However, soil in the

TABLE 18.3	Tolerance of the Grass *Deschampsia caespitosa* to Metals

Populations of the grass *Deschampsia caespitosa* were collected from metal-polluted places near Sudbury and from reference sites where metals are not a problem. The index of metal tolerance is based on the root growth that occurs when plants are grown in solutions containing metals, compared with a no-metal control. The smaller the index number, the greater the metal tolerance. In all comparisons presented here, the two populations had statistically significant differences in tolerance to the metal tested, with a probability level of <0.001, except for aluminum, ($p<0.05$). (See note.)

METAL	METAL-POLLUTED SUDBURY SITE	NONPOLLUTED REFERENCE SITE
Nickel	0.96	1.97
Copper	1.06	2.01
Aluminum	1.06	1.21
Lead	1.37	1.90
Zinc	1.55	1.98

Source: Index of metal tolerance modified from Cox and Hutchinson (1979)

Note: A probability value of <0.001 means that there is less than a 0.1% (or 1/1000) likelihood that the difference between the two populations is due to chance alone; $p <0.05$ means there is less than a 5% chance of this.

Sudbury area remained acidic and polluted with nickel, copper, and other metals. The local ecotypes of these grasses can tolerate toxic stress from acidity and metals, but are intolerant of SO_2, which is why the grasslands did not develop until after the superstack began to operate.

The metal tolerance of the grass *D. caespitosa* from the Sudbury area has been well studied. Plants were grown in solutions containing the metals of interest, and the growth was compared with that in control solutions (Table 18.3). The data show that the Sudbury population is markedly more tolerant of nickel and copper, which occur in their native soil environment at concentrations of about 400 ppm, compared with only 20 ppm at non-polluted sites. The Sudbury population of the grass is also more tolerant of aluminum. This is a response to the greater solubility and toxicity of aluminum in acidic soil near the smelters (which has a pH of 3.5–3.9, compared with pH 6.8–7.2 at reference sites).

Metal-Containing Tailings

During the milling process, ore is ground to a fine powder. The powder is separated into a metal-rich fraction, which is roasted and then smelted, plus large quantities of waste "tailings" (refer to Figure 13.1). Although the tailings are a waste, they still contain high concentrations of metals. Consequently, it can be difficult to re-vegetate tailings-disposal areas once they become filled. Sulphide minerals, if present, may also cause toxicity because they generate acidity when oxidized by bacteria. Chemical analyses of tailings from several Canadian mines are shown in Table 18.4. The tailings contain high concentrations of various metals, depending on the ore being processed. The acidic tailings are especially toxic, because most metals are much more soluble and bioavailable under acidic conditions.

Canadian regulators require that tailings-disposal areas be covered with vegetation once they are full of waste or after their associated mine closes. This is done because

TABLE 18.4	Chemical Analyses of Some Metal-Contaminated Tailings

Samples were taken from various sites in the Yukon and northern Ontario. Metal data are in ppm, sulphur in %.

SITE	pH	ARSENIC	CADMIUM	COPPER	NICKEL	LEAD	ZINC	SULPHUR
Gold mine A	1.9	5 200	18	140	13	952	2 400	1.1
Gold mine B	3.2	400	15	613	14	130	9 600	44.4
Gold mine C	6.0	1 350	102	172	15	3 600	6 200	5.7
Gold mine D	6.9	50 000	114	330	20	2 300	18 000	13.5
Gold mine E	7.1	7	3	33	21	1 130	1 060	4.0
Tungsten mine	7.0	–	<1	1 420	22	12	288	6.5
Copper mine	9.0	15	1	1 710	21	9	178	0.1
Nickel mine	3.2	–	<1	392	290	18	291	0.9

Source: Data modified from Kuja (1980)

tailings dumps are aesthetically undesirable and can be sources of wind-borne dust. These environmental problems can be substantially avoided if abandoned tailings dumps are covered with a stable cover of vegetation. In addition, if their associated dams and berms are not structurally sound and become breached by high water flows during severely rainy weather, tailings-disposal areas can be a source of massive water pollution.

To be successfully vegetated, most tailings have to be treated. If the tailings are acidic, a liming treatment is needed to raise the pH to a neutral level and reduce the availability of metals. This may be followed by fertilization to alleviate nutrient deficiency, by the addition of organic matter to improve soil structure and water-holding capacity, and by the sowing of perennial plants. Sometimes, novel techniques are used—for example, the use of acid- or metal-tolerant plant ecotypes in the planting mixture. If the tailings are extremely toxic or acid-generating, they may have to be covered with a locally available overburden, such as glacial till, which is then vegetated. Canadian Focus 18.1 describes the reclamation of tailings-disposal areas in the vicinity of Sudbury.

Smelters

Smelters are large industrial facilities in which ore is roasted. This process oxidizes sulphide minerals and produces large quantities of waste SO_2 and metallic particulates. In some cases, installed pollution-control technologies recover much of the SO_2 and particulates before the flue-gases are vented to the atmosphere. In other cases, however, these wastes are emitted into the environment, where intense pollution and ecological damage may be caused. As recently as several decades ago this was a common practice, and it still is for some older smelters. Newer smelters operate much more cleanly.

Canadian Focus 18.1

Tailings Reclamation at Copper Cliff

The large smelter at Copper Cliff, near Sudbury, Ontario, is serviced by a large mill that produces about 54 000 t of tailings per day (Peters, 1984). The tailings are mixed with water and piped as a slurry to be disposed in low areas surrounded by earthen dikes. In 2005, the tailings dumps covered about 3025 ha, of which 1425 ha had been re-vegetated. Once a tailings dump is full, it is stabilized with a cover of vegetation, which prevents fine dust from blowing into the atmosphere and improves aesthetics and environmental quality. The re-vegetated tailings dumps have a central pond, which is surrounded by gradually sloping grasslands.

The tailings are a finely ground substrate, composed mainly of minerals that are not particularly toxic. However, the tailings contain pyrites that oxidize when exposed to atmospheric oxygen. This generates acidity that can result in a pH lower than 3.7 in the tailings. Under these extremely acidic conditions, metals become available for plant uptake, greatly increasing the toxicity of the tailings. Plant-available metals have been analyzed by extracting samples of tailings using a weak solution of acetic acid. Such analyses have found very high levels of available metals, with concentrations of nickel up to 87 ppm; copper, 81 ppm; and iron, 440 ppm.

The reclamation practices attempt to establish a stable grassland, which can then be naturally invaded by native shrubs, trees, and other plants. The methods used include the following:

1. application of about 900 kg/ha of limestone ($CaCO_3$), which raises the pH of the tailings to 4.5–5.5 and reduces metal availability

2. several fertilization treatments during the initial stages of grassland establishment, particularly with nitrogen-containing fertilizer

3. application of a mulch to improve organic matter in the tailings substrate

4. sowing with a mixture of pasture grasses and legumes

The seed mixture includes annual rye (*Secale cereale*), which is a short-lived "nurse crop" that provides a less stressful microclimate for the tender seedlings of perennial grasses and legumes, thereby enhancing their establishment.

As vegetation develops on the reclaimed tailings-disposal areas, animals begin to invade the habitat. Birds that breed regularly in the grassy habitat and its central pond include mallard and black ducks (*Anas platyrhynchos* and *A. rubripes*), American kestrel (*Falco sparverius*), killdeer (*Charadrius vociferus*), and savannah sparrow (*Passerculus sandwichensis*). A larger number of bird species, about 90, have been observed to use the reclaimed tailings dump and its pond during migration.

Smelters are **point sources** of toxic stress to surrounding ecosystems. Emissions from smelters result in well-defined spatial gradients of both pollution and its resulting ecological damage, which diminishes with increasing distance from the facilities. Studies of damage near smelters indicate the following generalizations:

- Close to the point source, the pollution by atmospheric SO_2 and metals in soil is particularly severe.

- The intensity of pollution decreases rapidly with increasing distance from the smelter.

- Damage to vegetation varies with the intensity of toxic stress. The damages include decreases in ecosystem biomass, productivity, and species diversity, with only a few low-growing species occurring in the most polluted habitats.

- Ecological functions such as nutrient cycling and decomposition are disrupted by toxic metals, gases, and acidity.

The pattern of metal pollution around a point source can be illustrated by the Copper Cliff smelter near Sudbury. Figure 18.1 shows that metal concentrations in the environment decline rapidly with increasing distance from the smelter. These data specifically refer to the forest floor, but similar observations would be seen in soil, vegetation, lakewater, and other components of the ecosystem.

As we saw in Chapter 16, SO_2 has also been an important pollutant in the Sudbury area. Consequently, it is difficult to determine the specific role of toxic metals in causing ecological damage near the smelters. One way of investigating the influence of metals is to grow plants in polluted soil in a greenhouse, where SO_2 is not present. Such *bioassay* experiments have demonstrated that soil collected near the Sudbury smelters is toxic, mainly because of its high concentrations of metals. To a substantial degree, the toxicity persists even after the soil acidity is neutralized by adding lime.

Not all smelters emit both SO_2 and metals. The ecological damage that results from those that emit only metallic particulates have consequently been caused by metal pollution. One well-studied smelter, at Gusum, Sweden, has been operating since 1661 (Tyler, 1984). Zinc is an important pollutant emitted at Gusum, reaching concentrations as high as 2% (20 000 ppm) in surface organic matter close to the point source, compared with less than 200 ppm farther than 6 km away. Levels of copper pollution are similar, reaching 1.7% within 0.3 km, compared with 20 ppm beyond

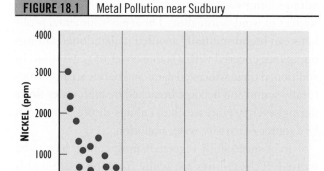

FIGURE 18.1   Metal Pollution near Sudbury

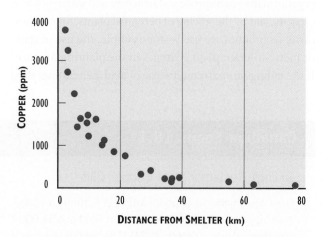

DISTANCE FROM SMELTER (km)

Decades of emissions of metals from the Copper Cliff smelter have caused an accumulation of nickel and copper in various components of the environment. The most intense pollution occurs close to the point source. These data are for metals in the forest floor, that is, the organic-rich layer that overlies the mineral soil. The forest floor effectively binds metals in organic complexes and accumulates much higher residues than the underlying soil. The samples were collected along a transect running south from the smelter.

Source: Freedman and Hutchinson (1980)

6 km. The zinc and copper pollution has caused local ecological damage. Pine and birch trees have died or declined close to the source, and understorey plants, mosses, lichens, and soil-dwelling invertebrates have been damaged. Rates of decomposition and nutrient cycling are also impaired in the most polluted sites. Some species, however, are quite tolerant of the metal pollution at Gusum. These include the grass *Deschampsia flexuosa* and the moss *Pohlia nutans*, which do relatively well in sites that are toxic to other plants.

Use of Inorganic Pesticides

Until the 1970s, inorganic chemicals were widely used as pesticides in agriculture (see also Chapter 22). This was especially true in fruit orchards, where pesticides based on lead arsenate, calcium arsenate, copper sulphate, and related compounds were used to control fungal diseases and arthropod pests. These compounds are now largely displaced by synthetic organic pesticides. Until the mid-1970s, annual spray rates in southern Ontario orchards were as high as 8.7 kg/ha of lead, while arsenic treatments reached 2.7 kg/ha, zinc 7.5 kg/ha, and copper 3.0 kg/ha (Frank *et al.*, 1976). The spray rates depended on the crop being grown, the pest being managed, and the pesticide used, but in some cases, all of these toxic elements were applied in the same orchards.

Residues of these chemicals tended to accumulate in the soil of pesticide-treated orchards. Studies of apple orchards in Ontario found residues as high as 890 ppm of lead and 126 ppm of arsenic in surface soil, compared with background levels of <25 ppm lead and <10 ppm arsenic (Figure 18.2). These accumulations were caused by up to 70 years of spraying lead arsenate as an insecticide, mostly against the codling moth (*Laspeyresia pomonella*), a pest that causes "wormy" apples.

Agricultural soil can also be contaminated by the use of mercury-containing fungicides, especially those that protect newly germinated seedlings from a fungal infection known as "damping-off." This pathogen attacks seedlings at the soil–air interface and causes the weakened plant to fall over and die. Mercury-containing pesticides are also used to control turfgrass diseases on lawns and golf-course putting greens. Mercury residues ranging from 24 to 120 ppm have been measured in the surface soil of putting greens in Ontario, while concentrations up to 9 ppm were found in golf courses in Nova Scotia.

The sowing of seed coated with mercuric fungicide has caused contamination and poisoning of wild animals that consumed the planted grain or scavenged dead herbivores. Alkyl-mercury compounds such as methylmercury are especially hazardous in this respect because this form of mercury is extremely toxic and readily assimilated by animals from their food. Table 18.5 shows the significant mercury contamination of seed-eating wildlife in regions of Alberta where treated seed was used, compared with areas where these exposures did not occur. Use of these fungicides was common until the early 1970s.

Most developed countries prohibited the use of alkyl-mercury fungicides as seed dressings, beginning in the late

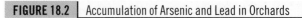

FIGURE 18.2 | Accumulation of Arsenic and Lead in Orchards

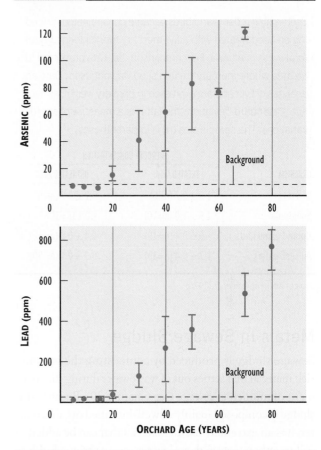

Lead arsenate has been used as an insecticide to combat infestations of apple orchards with codling moth. These data show the progressive accumulation of arsenic and lead in soils of orchards in southern Ontario. The largest residues occurred in the oldest orchards, which had been sprayed for many years. The error bars indicate the range of values about the average.

Source: Modified from Frank *et al.* (1976)

1960s. This ban resulted from the recognition of ecological problems associated with use of these chemicals, especially the poisoning of wild animals. Sweden, for example, prohibited the use of these pesticides in 1966, while approving the use of alkoxyl-alkyl-mercury compounds, which are much less toxic, as replacements. This action rapidly led to decreased mercury contamination of wildlife, such as predatory birds (Figure 18.3). Canada took similar action, although several years later.

As was noted in the introduction to this chapter, humans have also been poisoned by inadvertently eating mercury-treated seed grain.

| TABLE 18.5 | Mercury in Animals Feeding on Treated Seed |

Seed-eating rodents and birds became contaminated by feeding on seed treated with alkyl-mercury fungicide in agricultural areas in Alberta. For comparison, data are presented for an area where mercury-treated seed was not used. Data are analyses of liver and are expressed in ppm dry weight, as average ± standard deviation (the latter is a measure of sample variation). The sample size (n) is in parentheses.

| ORGANISM | MERCURY CONCENTRATION | |
	TREATED AREA	UNTREATED AREA
Rodents	1.3 ± 0.7 (n=6)	0.2 ± 0.2 (n=5)
Songbirds	1.6 ± 1.0 (n=10)	<0.1 (n=3)
Upland game birds	1.9 ± 0.4 (n=19)	0.4 ± 0.2 (n=12)
All seed eaters	1.7 ± 0.4 (n=35)	0.3 ± 0.1 (n=20)

Source: After Fimreite *et al.* (1970)

Metals in Sewage Sludge

Sewage sludge is produced by composting the organic-rich material that settles out of wastewater during the treatment of municipal sewage (see Chapter 20). Because this sludge is composed mainly of well-humified organic matter, it is an extremely useful material that can be added to soil to enhance its tilth and water- and nutrient-holding capacities (these terms are defined in Chapter 14). Sewage sludge also contains important nutrients such as nitrogen and phosphorus and is useful as a slow-release organic fertilizer. Because of these favourable properties, sewage sludge is often applied to agricultural land.

Unfortunately, sewage sludge can contain considerable amounts of metals, particularly if there are significant inputs of industrial waste to the sewerage. Typical concentrations of metals in sludge from several industrialized regions are summarized in Table 18.6. Obviously, metal concentrations vary among sewage sludges from different places, reflecting the kinds of industrial inputs to the wastewater systems. In general, cadmium, copper, nickel, and zinc are the metallic contaminants most likely to cause toxicity to plants when sewage sludge is applied to agricultural land. By eating contaminated produce, humans can also be exposed to metals assimilated by crops from sewage sludge.

The problem of metals in sewage sludge can be largely avoided if industrial and sanitary sewage are treated separately. This is not always done, however. Whatever the case, it is important to monitor the quantities of metals applied to agricultural land with sewage sludge, as well

| FIGURE 18.3 | Mercury Contamination of Swedish Hawks Caused by Alkyl-Mercury Fungicides |

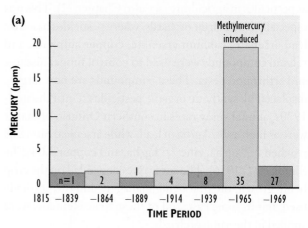

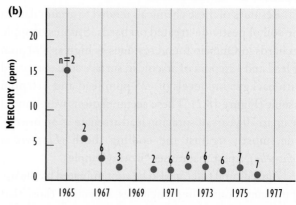

(a) Mercury in feathers of goshawks (*Accipiter gentilis*), during various time periods; **(b)** Mercury in feathers of marsh harriers (*Circus aeruginosus*). Note the large increase in contamination caused by the use of alkyl-mercury fungicides and the rapid decrease that followed the banning of these chemicals in 1966. Sample sizes (n) are indicated.

Source: After Johnels *et al.* (1979)

as any resulting contamination of crops. Because of their beneficial qualities when applied to agricultural or forestry land, sewage sludge is a potentially useful resource. If it is unacceptably contaminated with metals, however, sludge becomes a waste that must be discarded in landfills or the ocean or be incinerated, causing environmental problems instead of providing economic benefits.

Birds and Lead

Millions of birds have suffered lead poisoning in North America each year because they inadvertently ingest spent

TABLE 18.6	Metals in Sewage Sludge	

Data are concentrations in sewage sludge from a variety of locations. Data are in ppm dry weight, with average and/or ranges of values given.

ELEMENT	ONTARIO[1]	NORTH AMERICA AND EUROPE[2]
Arsenic	–	1–18
Cadmium	29 (2–147)	1–1 500
Chromium	4 200 (16–16 000)	20–40 000
Cobalt	–	2–260
Copper	1 100 (162–3 000)	52–11 700
Lead	1 200 (85–4 000)	15–26 000
Manganese	310 (60–500)	60–3 860
Mercury	9 (1–24)	0.1–56
Molybdenum	–	2–1 000
Nickel	390 (7–1 500)	10–53 000
Silver	25 (4–60)	5–150
Vanadium	–	40–700
Zinc	4 500 (610–19 000)	72–49 000

Sources: (1) 10 sewage works, after Van Loon (1974); (2) 300 sewage works, after Page (1974)

shotgun pellets. Most of the spent shot was associated with hunting. In Canada, for example, about 2000 t of lead shot were used by hunters each year in the early 1990s. Although more localized, skeet shooting was also a problem because of the large amount of shot deposited in the vicinity of shooting ranges. It was not unusual for tonnes of lead shot to be spent each year at a single skeet shooting range.

After being ingested by seed-eating birds, lead shot can be retained in the gizzard, the muscular forepouch of their stomach. Hard grit is normally retained in the gizzard and used to grind tough-coated seeds, aiding in their digestion. Unfortunately, shotgun pellets are similar in size and weight to the grit that many species of birds pick up for this purpose. The lead shot becomes abraded in the gizzard, and the bits are swallowed and dissolved by acidic stomach fluid. The lead can then be absorbed into the bloodstream, allowing it to poison the nervous system of the bird, commonly leading to death.

Waterfowl have been especially widely affected, with an estimated 2–3 million individuals, or 2–3% of the North American population, dying each year from lead-shot poisoning in the early 1990s. The retention of just one or two pellets in its gizzard can poison a duck, causing a wasting away of 30–50% of the body weight, neurological toxicity, and ultimately death. Typically, about

10% of the waterfowl in North America had one or more shotgun pellets in their gizzard.

Larger aquatic birds, such as swans, are known to retain lead fishing weights in their gizzard. Lead sinkers or shot have been cited as the cause of 20–50% of the known mortality of trumpeter swans (*Cygnus buccinator*) in parts of their range in western North America. Lead sinkers are also known to poison tundra swans (*C. columbianus*) wintering in the eastern U.S., mute swans (*C. olor*) in Europe, and common loons (*Gavia immer*) in Canada and the United States. In Canada, about 500 t/y of lead fishing sinkers and jigs were lost during the early 1990s.

A related syndrome, caused by ingesting lead shot and bullets, afflicts birds that scavenge dead carcasses. Although the numbers are not well documented, this kind of poisoning is known to kill vultures, eagles, and other scavenging birds. The critically endangered California condor (*Gymnogyps californianus*) has been relatively well studied—about 60% of its known deaths in the wild between 1980 and 1986 were caused by lead toxicity from ingested bullets in carrion.

Because of the widespread poisoning of birds by lead shot, regulators have restricted its use. Lead shot is now banned over most of the United States. In Canada, the use of non-toxic shot has been required in all wetland areas since 1997 and in all other hunting areas since 1999. The use of lead shot for hunting is being replaced mostly by steel and, to a lesser degree, by bismuth shot. The restricted use of lead shot has caused some controversy because many hunters believe that the alternative shot types might cause more crippling deaths. Field tests have, however, shown this effect to be marginal, as long as the inferior ballistic qualities of the alternatives are compensated for by shooting at closer distances or by using a larger size of shot.

Automobile Emissions of Lead

Lead emitted by automobiles has contributed to a general contamination of urban environments. From 1923, but particularly after 1945, tetraethyl lead was added to gasoline as a so-called "anti-knock" compound. The lead increases mechanical efficiency and gasoline economy, while decreasing engine wear. In 1975, about 95% of North American gasoline was leaded at concentrations as high as 770 mg/L. In 1987, only 35% of the gasoline was leaded, the maximum permitted concentration then being 290 mg/L. The decreased use of lead between 1975 and 1987 was largely due to the increased use of catalytic converters to reduce emissions of other automobile pollutants, especially carbon monoxide and hydrocarbons. Automobiles equipped with a catalytic converter can use only unleaded gasoline, because the catalysts, usually platinum, are rendered inactive by lead. The increasing use of unleaded fuels

resulted in a 93% decrease in lead particulates in the air of Canadian cities (comparison of 1977 and 1989).

After 1990, the use of leaded gasoline was banned for most purposes in Canada and the U.S. (except for low-lead

Canadian Focus 18.2

MMT and Trade Law

After the use of tetraethyl lead in gasoline was prohibited in 1990, other compounds were examined for their potential use as "anti-knock" additives to increase engine efficiency in automobiles. One of these is MMT (methylcyclopentadienyl manganese tricarbonyl), an organo-manganese compound.

However, MMT and its breakdown product manganese are toxic chemicals at high doses, as might be experienced during occupational exposures in the chemical industry. The effects of low-level environmental exposures, as would occur from the widespread use of MMT in gasoline, have not been conclusively demonstrated to be significant. However, MMT has been shown to damage the pollution-control systems of automobiles, leading to higher emissions of hydrocarbons that contribute to photochemical smog. Because of its potential effects on health and the environment, the use of MMT as a gasoline additive has been banned in some jurisdictions.

However, Ethyl Corporation of Virginia, the only manufacturer of MMT (it also previously manufactured lead additives for gasoline), has managed to defeat the attempts of governments to prohibit its use. In the first case (in 1995), a U.S. federal judge ruled that the Environmental Protection Agency (EPA) could not ban the manufacturing and use of MMT. This occurred despite the fact that the EPA (the federal agency responsible for regulating environmental pollutants in the U.S.) and many independent experts had serious concerns about the potential health hazards of ambient exposure to MMT and manganese.

Despite the lifting of the U.S. ban on the use of MMT, there is controversy about potential health risks and other environmental damages. Consequently, most gasoline producers in the U.S. have chosen not to use the additive; according to the Environmental Defense Fund, MMT is present in only about 0.02% of gasoline sold in the United States.

Canadian regulators have had similar concerns about MMT. Consequently, its use as a gasoline additive was banned in 1997, but only for a period of one year (this was after MMT use had been legal in Canada for

the previous 20 years). This ban was enacted by Environment Canada in spite of the fact that a study by Health Canada had suggested that no health risks were known to be conclusively associated with the use of MMT in gasoline. However, scientists at Environment Canada believed that the effects of MMT on emissions-control systems of automobiles still contributed to a significant environmental hazard. Moreover, they thought it was prudent to apply the precautionary approach to their evaluation of the potential, low-level health risks of MMT. The **precautionary principle**, an approach to environmental management adopted by Canada and many other countries at the 1992 Earth Summit in Brazil, essentially states that scientific uncertainty is not a sufficient reason to postpone control measures when there is a threat of harm to human health or the environment.

Several agencies were opposed to the ban on MMT by the federal government of Canada. The ban was successfully challenged by the governments of Alberta, Nova Scotia, Quebec, and Saskatchewan, under provisions of the Agreement on Internal Trade (AIT), which regulates trade within Canada. In addition, the Ethyl Corporation threatened to take the federal government to court to challenge the MMT ban, based on fair-trade provisions under the North American Free Trade Agreement (NAFTA). The federal government's own lawyers advised that, under the circumstances, it was likely to lose such a court challenge, and they recommended an out-of-court settlement with Ethyl Corporation. In 1998, the federal government lifted the ban on MMT and paid the Ethyl Corporation a settlement of $19 million to cover its costs and lost profit during the one-year ban.

The case of MMT highlights important points about potentially toxic chemicals in the environment:

1. Toxic effects of low-level exposure to individual compounds and their mixtures can be extremely difficult to demonstrate, if they exist at all.

2. Trade laws negotiated between governments can have a greater influence on environmental regulation than precautionary concerns about potentially important risks to human health and environmental quality.

fuels that may be used in some farm vehicles, marine engines, and large trucks). Consequently, emissions of lead from automobiles in Canada decreased from about 9500 t in 1978 to less than 100 t/y since 1995 (Environment Canada, 1996). However, many other countries, particularly in the less developed world, continue to allow the use of leaded fuels.

Almost all of the lead in gasoline is emitted as particulates through the vehicle tailpipe. The heavier particulates settle out close to the roadway. This results in the buildup of a well-defined gradient of lead pollution, the intensity of which is related to traffic volume. This pattern of roadside lead pollution is illustrated in Table 18.7 (note that this study was made prior to the banning of leaded fuels in Canada). Finer lead particulates are more widely dispersed in the atmosphere and contribute to the general contamination that occurs in cities. Not surprisingly, studies have shown some effects of lead on urban wildlife. For example, pigeons (*Columba livia*) living in cities may contain significant residues of lead and may exhibit symptoms of acute poisoning.

Conclusions

All of the naturally occurring elements are present in at least a trace level of contamination in all components of the environment—air, water, soil, and organisms. Sometimes their concentration is naturally elevated, as occurs when an ore body is present at or near the surface of the ground. Increasingly, however, human activities have been responsible for large emissions of toxic elements to the environment, and in some cases this has resulted in serious damage through pollution of ecosystems and

TABLE 18.7   Lead and Automobiles

Samples of soil, collected near roads of different traffic density in Halifax, Nova Scotia, were analyzed for lead content. Metal data are in ppm dry weight, while average daily traffic (ADT) is in vehicles per day. The background concentration in soil is 14 ppm.

DISTANCE FROM ROAD EDGE (m)	LEAD CONCENTRATION		
	ROAD A 50 000	ROAD B 16 000	ROAD C 3 000
ADT:			
0	3045	1075	465
1	2813	457	118
5	342	136	32
15	223	163	26
30	–	63	26
50	223	95	38
100	–	60	21

Source: Modified from Dale and Freedman (1982)

human toxicity. The worst cases of pollution by toxic elements involve industrial practices that are no longer allowed in Canada or other wealthy countries, such as uncontrolled emissions from metal smelters, the dumping of mercury into aquatic environments, the used of leaded gasoline, and the use of lead shot for hunting. Pollution by toxic elements is still, however, an important environmental issue. Damages to ecosystems and organisms are still being caused by mercury, lead, and other toxic elements that humans are releasing into the ambient environment. This is true of all parts of the world, although pollution by toxic elements in poorer countries is much less controlled than in wealthier ones.

Key Terms

bioconcentration (bioaccumulation)

food-web magnification (food-web concentration biomagnification)

total concentration

available concentration

tolerance

hyperaccumulator

endemic

ecotype

point source

precautionary principle

Questions for Review

1. How can we identify normal levels, contamination, and pollution by metals and other elements given that these substances are ubiquitous in the environment?

2. What are the important sources of metal emissions to the environment?

3. What is the difference between "total" and "available" concentrations of metals?

4. Describe the pattern of general metal pollution around a large point source of emissions, such as a smelter or power plant.

Questions for Discussion

1. Do you think that damages similar to those seen near Sudbury are likely to be caused if a smelter is constructed to process the ore mined at the mineral deposit at Voisey's Bay, Labrador? (Note that the ores in both cases are similar, containing sulphide minerals of nickel and copper.)

2. Important environmental benefits have been gained by banning the use of leaded gasoline in Canada. Why were there long delays in taking similarly vigorous actions against the use of lead shot in hunting and skeet shooting and lead weights in fishing?

3. Pick an element discussed in this chapter and research its benefits, toxicity, effects on the environment, control, and mitigation.

4. Explain the principles of bioaccumulation and biomagnification using the case of methylmercury in aquatic ecosystems. Why do you think these phenomena were unanticipated "surprises" to environmental scientists?

Exploring Issues

1. Assume that Canada and the U.S. are negotiating a treaty to govern their emissions of mercury to the environment. You are a science advisor to the Canadian team. Some members of the team want to press for a "zero emissions" policy, believing that no emissions of mercury to the environment are acceptable. They ask for your advice on this issue. What kinds of information about the toxicity of mercury, to humans and to wild ecosystems, do you need in order to give the team objective advice about the proposed zero-emissions policy? Also, is it physically possible to have zero emissions?

References

Allen, H.E., A.W. Garrison, and G.W. Luther III. 1998. *Metals in Surface Waters.* Chelsea, MI: Ann Arbor Press.

Alloway, B.J. (ed.). 1994. *Heavy Metals in Soils.* 2nd ed. New York, NY: Blackie Academic and Professional.

Armstrong, F.A.J. 1979. Mercury in the aquatic environment. In: *Effects of Mercury in the Canadian Environment.* Associate Committee on Scientific Criteria for Environmental Quality. Ottawa: National Research Council of Canada. NRCC No. 16739. pp. 84–100.

Blakeslee, P.A. 1973. *Monitoring considerations for municipal wastewater effluent and sludge application to the land.* Urbana, IL: U.S. Environmental Protection Agency, U.S. Department of Agriculture, Universities Workshop, July 9–13, 1973.

Bowen, H.J.M. 1979. *Environmental Chemistry of the Elements.* New York: Academic.

Bradshaw, A.D. and M.J. Chadwick. 1981. *The Restoration of Land.* Oxford: Blackwell.

Cox, R.M. and T.C. Hutchinson. 1979. Metal co-tolerances in the grass *Deschampsia caespitosa. Nature*, **279**: 231–233.

Dale, J.M. and B. Freedman. 1982. Lead and zinc contamination of roadside soil and vegetation in Halifax, Nova Scotia. *Proc. N.S. Inst. Sci.*, **32**: 327–336.

Environment Canada. 1996. *Urban Air Quality.* State of the Environment Reporting Organization. Ottawa: Environment Canada. SOE Bull. No. 96-1.

Fimreite, N., R.W. Feif, and J.A. Keith. 1970. Mercury contamination of Canadian prairie seed eaters and their avian predators. *Can. Field-Nat.*, **84**: 269–276.

Foulkes, E.C. (ed.). 1990. *Biological Effects of Heavy Metals.* Boca Raton, FL: CRC Press.

Frank, R., H.E. Braun, K. Ishida, and P. Suda. 1976. Persistent organic and inorganic pesticide residues in orchard soils and vineyards of southern Ontario. *Can. J. Soil Sci.*, **56**: 463–484.

Freedman, B. 1995. *Environmental Ecology.* 2nd ed. San Diego, CA: Academic.

Freedman, B. and T.C. Hutchinson. 1980. Pollutant inputs from the atmosphere and accumulations in soils and vegetation near a nickel-copper smelter at Sudbury, Ontario, Canada. *Can. J. Bot.*, **58**: 108–132.

Gilmour, C.C. and E.A. Henry. 1991. Mercury methylation in aquatic systems affected by acid deposition. *Environ. Pollut.*, **71**: 131–169.

Gunn, J.M. (ed.). 1995. *Restoration and Recovery of an Industrial Region: Progress in Restoring the Smelter-Damaged Landscape near Sudbury, Canada.* New York: Springer.

Johnels, A., G. Tyler, and T. Westermark. 1979. A history of mercury levels in Swedish fauna. *Ambio*, **8**: 160–168.

Kruckeberg, A.R. 1984. *California Serpentine: Flora, Vegetation, Geology, Soils, and Management Problems.* Los Angeles: Univ. of California Press.

Kuja, A.L. 1980. *Revegetation of Mine Tailings using Native Species from Disturbed Sites in Northern Canada.* M.Sc. Thesis, Department of Botany, University of Toronto.

McKay, C. 1985. *Freshwater Fish Contamination in Canadian Waters.* Ottawa: Department of Fisheries and Oceans, Fish Habitat Management Branch, Chemical Hazards Division.

Mierle, G. 1990. Aqueous inputs of mercury to Precambrian Shield lakes in Ontario. *Environ. Contam. & Chem.*, **9**: 843–851.

Ontario Ministry of the Environment. 2005. *The 2005–2006 Guide to Eating Sportfish.* Toronto, ON: Ontario Ministry of the Environment. www.ene.gov.on.ca/envision/guide/index.htm

Page, A.L. 1974. *Fate and Effects of Trace Elements in Sewage Sludge Applied to Agricultural Lands.* Cincinnati, OH: U.S. Environmental Protection Agency, Office of Research and Development. Pub. EPA-670/2-74-005.

Peters, T.H. 1984. Rehabilitation of mine tailings: a case of complete ecosystem reconstruction and revegetation of industrially stressed lands in the Sudbury area, Ontario, Canada. In: *Effects of Pollutants at the Ecosystem Level.* (P.J. Sheehan, D.R. Miller, and P. Bourdeau, eds.), New York: Wiley. pp. 403–421.

Ripley, E.A., R.E. Redmann, and A.A. Crowder. 1996. *Environmental Effects of Mining.* Delray Beach, FL: St. Lucie.

Salomons, W., U. Förstner, and P. Mader (eds.). 1995. *Heavy Metals: Problems and Solutions.* New York: Springer.

Sanderson, G.C. and F.C. Bellrose. 1986. *Lead Poisoning in Waterfowl.* Urbana, IL: Illinois Natural History Society. Spec. Pub. 4.

Sarkar, B. (ed.). 2002. Heavy Metals in the Environment. New York, NY: Marcel Dekker.

Scheuhammer, A.M. and S.L. Norris. 1996. The ecotoxicology of lead shot and lead fishing weights. *Ecotoxicology*, **5**: 279–295.

Spry, D.J. and J.G. Weiner. 1991. Metal bioavailability and toxicity to fish in low-alkalinity lakes: A critical review. *Environ. Pollut.*, **71**: 243–304.

Thompson, D.R., K.C. Hamer, and R.W. Furness. 1991. Mercury accumulation in great skuas (*Catharacta skua*) of known age and sex, and its effect on breeding and survival. *J. Appl. Ecol.*, **28**: 672–684.

Tyler, G. 1984. The impact of heavy metal pollution on forests: A case study of Gusum, Sweden. *Ambio*, **13**: 18–24.

Van Loon, J.C. 1974. *Analysis of Heavy Metals in Sewage Sludge and Liquids Associated with Sludges.* Presented at Canada/Ontario Sludge Handling and Disposal Seminar, Toronto, Sept. 18–19.

Wiemeyer, S.N., J.M. Scott, M.P. Anderson, P.H. Bloom, and C.J. Stafford. 1988. Environmental contaminants in California condors. *J. Wildl. Manage.*, **52**: 238–247.

Wong, M.H.W. and A.D. Bradshaw. 2003. The Restoration and Management of Derelict Land: Modern Approaches. London, UK: World Scientific Publishers.

World Resources Institute. 2005. *Earth Trends. The Environmental Information Portal.* Washington, DC: WRI.

Informative Websites

Air & Waste Management Association. www.awma.org/

The Air and Waste Management Association is a non-profit organization whose goals are to expand scientific and technological responses to environmental concerns. You will find more information about the organization as well as links to other related sites.

Environment Canada. The Green Lane.
www.ec.gc.ca/envhome.html

This comprehensive site from Environment Canada features pages on climate change, nature, clean air and water, as well as links to publications, news releases, and related sites.

U.S. Environmental Protection Agency. Lead in Paint, Dust, and Soil. www.epa.gov/opptintr/lead/

This site is designed to give you access to information on all aspects of Environmental Protection Agency's lead poisoning prevention program.

World Resources Institute. Heavy Metals and Health.
http://pubs.wri.org/pubs_content_text.cfm?ContentID=1380

Graphs, statistics, and tables detail sources of lead exposure in the environment.

19 Acidification

Introduction

Acidification is characterized by increasing concentrations of hydrogen ions (H⁺) in soil or water. It can cause metals and their compounds to ionize, producing ions (such as Al^{3+}) in concentrations high enough to be toxic to plants, animals, and microorganisms. Consequently, increasing acidification is usually interpreted as a degradation of environmental quality. Acidification is caused by many influences, both natural and anthropogenic, but the most widespread problems are associated with a phenomenon commonly known as **acid rain**.

Acid rain has been an important problem in parts of North America since at least the 1950s, but it did not become a high-profile issue until the early 1970s. This rather sudden attention resulted from the discovery that acid rain was a widespread problem in western Europe and the realization that the same conditions were likely to occur in North America. This awareness stimulated much research in Canada and the U.S.—work that demonstrated that acid rain was causing extensive acidification of lakes and streams, and possibly of soil. The acidification of aquatic ecosystems was shown to be resulting in important ecological damage, including the loss of many fish populations. Buildings and other materials are also being damaged because acidity erodes metals, paint, bricks, and some kinds of quarried stone.

Strictly speaking, the phrase "acid rain" refers only to acidic rainfall, which along with snowfall accounts for

In Detail 19.1

Acids and Bases

Acids are defined as substances that donate protons (hydrogen ions, H⁺) in chemical reactions. An aqueous solution is acidic if its concentration of hydrogen ions is more than 1×10^{-7} moles/L. In contrast, bases (alkalis) are substances that donate hydroxyl ions (OH⁻) in chemical reactions. An aqueous solution is basic if it has a concentration of hydroxyl ions of more than 1×10^{-7} moles/L. (A mole is a fundamental unit used to measure the amount of a substance and is equal to 6.02×10^{23} molecules, atoms, or ions. This number is known as Avogadro's constant and is derived from the number of atoms of carbon contained in 12 g (1 mole) of carbon-12.)

Acids and bases react together to form water and a neutral salt. If equal numbers of moles of each are present, the solution has both zero acidity and zero alkalinity, that is, the concentrations of both H⁺ and OH⁻ happen to be exactly 1×10^{-7} moles/L. Such a solution is said to be neutral.

Because extremely wide ranges of H⁺ and OH⁻ concentrations can be encountered in nature and in laboratories, acidity is measured in logarithmic units, referred to as pH (an abbreviation for potential of Hydrogen). pH is defined as $-\log_{10}[H^+]$ (i.e., the negative logarithm to base 10 of the aqueous concentration of hydrogen ion, expressed in units of moles per litre). Acidic solutions have a pH less than 7, while alkaline solutions have a pH greater than 7. Note that a one-unit difference in pH implies a 10-fold difference in the concentration of hydrogen or hydroxyl ions. The scale illustrated here shows the pH of some commonly encountered substances.

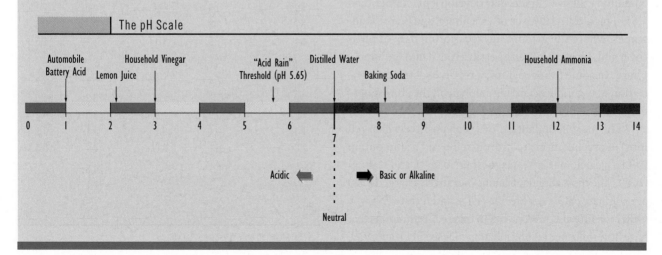

The pH Scale

Automobile Battery Acid · Lemon Juice · Household Vinegar · "Acid Rain" Threshold (pH 5.65) · Distilled Water · Baking Soda · Household Ammonia

0 1 2 3 4 5 6 7 8 9 10 11 12 13 14

Acidic ⇐ | ⇒ Basic or Alkaline

Neutral

wet deposition. However, acidifying chemicals are also deposited from the atmosphere when it is not precipitating, through the **dry deposition** of certain gases and particulates. A suitable phrase to define this complex of processes is the deposition of acidifying substances from the atmosphere, or more simply, **acidifying deposition**.

In this chapter we examine natural and anthropogenic causes of the acidification of ecosystems. We will focus on the chemical qualities of acidic precipitation and dry deposition, their effects on terrestrial and aquatic ecosystems, and how acidification can be avoided or mitigated.

Precipitation Chemistry

Scientists have adopted a functional definition of acidic precipitation as having a pH less than 5.65. This was chosen as the cutoff because at pH 5.65, carbonic acid (H_2CO_3) is in equilibrium with atmospheric CO_2, as follows:

$$CO_2 + H_2O \longleftrightarrow H_2CO_3 \longleftrightarrow$$
$$H^+ + HCO_3^- \longleftrightarrow 2H^+ + CO_3^{2-}$$

This definition assumes that "non-acidic" precipitation is essentially distilled water, in which acidity is determined only by the atmospheric concentration of CO_2 and the amount of carbonic acid that subsequently develops. This is why the threshold below which precipitation is deemed "acidic" is set at the slightly acidic pH of 5.65, rather than at the strict zero-acidity pH of 7.0 (see In Detail 19.1).

It is, however, too simplistic to consider atmospheric moisture as consisting merely of distilled water in a pH equilibrium with gaseous CO_2. Many other chemicals are present in precipitation in trace concentrations. For example, on windy days dust containing calcium and magnesium is blown into the atmosphere, where precipitation containing these elements may develop a pH higher than 5.65. This is especially true of agricultural and prairie landscapes, where the ground surface is often bare of plant cover and soil particles can be easily eroded into the atmosphere. In some other regions, a relatively high concentration of naturally occurring sulphate in the atmosphere may result in precipitation having a pH less than 5.65.

The most abundant cations (i.e., positively charged ions) in precipitation are hydrogen ion (H^+), ammonium (NH_4^+), calcium (Ca^{2+}), magnesium (Mg^{2+}), and sodium (Na^+). The most abundant anions (negatively charged ions) are sulphate (SO_4^{2-}), chloride (Cl^-), and nitrate (NO_3^-). Other ions are also present, but in trace concentrations that have little influence on precipitation pH (see In Detail 19.2).

One of the longest-running North American records of precipitation chemistry is from a research site at Hubbard Brook, New Hampshire, in a region exposed to intense acidifying deposition. During 1967–71, when acid rain was relatively severe, the average pH of precipitation at Hubbard Brook was 4.1, and hydrogen ion accounted for 71% of the total cation equivalents, but this relaxed somewhat to pH 4.3 and 67% by 1991–95 because of decreased industrial emissions, particularly of the acid-forming gas SO_2 (Table 19.1; see In Detail 19.2 for an explanation of equivalents). Sulphate and nitrate are the most important anions in precipitation; in 1967–71 they occurred in a 2.3:1 ratio and accounted for 88% of the anion equivalents, but in 1991–95, the ratio decreased to 1.5:1 because of decreased SO_2 emissions, although these two still contributed 91% of the anion equivalents. These data suggest that most acidity in the precipitation occurs

TABLE 19.1	Chemistry of Precipitation at Hubbard Brook, New Hampshire

These data represent average concentrations (in microequivalents per litre) of various ions in the precipitation during two study periods: 1967–71 and 1991–95. The small difference between the sums of cation and anion equivalents is due to analytical inaccuracies, which is inevitable in even the best chemical data.

CONSTITUENT	1967–71 μeq/L	1967–71 % OF TOTAL EQUIVALENTS	1991–95 μeq/L	1991–95 % OF TOTAL EQUIVALENTS
CATIONS				
H^+	76.6	70.9	50.4	67.4
NH_4^+	13.9	12.9	11.9	15.9
Ca^{2+}	7.2	6.7	3.8	5.0
Na^+	5.2	4.8	5.2	7.0
Mg^{2+}	3.3	3.0	2.0	2.7
Al^{3+}	0.4	0.3	0.4	0.5
K^+	1.5	1.4	1.1	1.5
ANIONS				
SO_4^{2-}	57.4	61.3	39.1	54.2
NO_3^-	25.3	27.0	26.3	36.5
Cl^-	10.9	11.6	6.6	9.2
PO_4^{3-}	0.1	0.1	0.1	0.1
HCO_3^-	<0.1	0.0	<0.1	0.0
Sum of Cations	108.1		74.8	
Sum of Anions	93.7		72.1	
pH	4.12		4.30	

Source: Modified from Buso *et al.* (2003)

In Detail 19.2

Electrochemical Neutrality

The principle of conservation of electrochemical neutrality states that in any electrically neutral solution (i.e., one that does not carry an electrical charge), the total number of positive charges associated with cations must equal that of negative charges of anions. For the purposes of calculating a charge balance, the concentrations of ions must be measured in units known as *equivalents*. These are calculated as the molar concentration multiplied by the number of charges on the ion. (When dealing with precipitation or surface waters, microequivalents, or μeq, are generally the units reported.)

This principle is relevant to the acidification of water. The concentration of H^+ can be determined as the difference in concentrations of the sum of all anion equivalents minus the sum of all cations other than H^+. Therefore, if the total equivalents of anions exceed the total equivalents of cations other than hydrogen ion, then H^+ must go into solution to balance the cation "deficit," as follows:

$$H^+ = (SO_4^{2-} + NO_3^- + Cl^-) - (Na^+ + NH_4^+ + Ca^{2+} + Mg^{2+})$$

The above equation has proven to be quite useful in studies of acidic precipitation. Prior to about 1955, the measurement of pH values was somewhat inaccurate. There were, however, reliable analyses of other important ions in surface waters and precipitation. In such cases, the above equation can be used to calculate pre-1955 pH values, providing important data for historical values of pH in waters sensitive to acidification.

---

as dilute solutions of sulphuric and nitric acids. The precipitation events at Hubbard Brook that are most acidic are associated with storms that have passed over the large metropolitan regions of Boston, New York, and New Jersey. These areas have enormous emissions of SO_2 and NO_x, which are the precursor gases of much of the SO_4^{2-} and NO_3^- in acidic precipitation (as we previously noted in Chapter 16).

Spatial Patterns

Acidic precipitation is a widespread phenomenon in eastern North America (Figure 19.1), Europe, eastern Asia, and elsewhere. In eastern North America prior to the mid-1950s, precipitation with pH below 4.6 affected only relatively local areas, mostly in southern Ontario, New York, Pennsylvania, and New England. Since then, however, this area has expanded considerably. At present, most of southeastern Canada and the eastern U.S. experiences acidic precipitation. It appears that the broad pattern of acidic precipitation in North America existed before the 1950s, but the phenomenon has since become more widespread and its intensity has increased. One of the most important aspects of acidic precipitation is the vast size of the areas it affects.

Precipitation chemistry varies greatly between regions (see Figure 19.1). The variation reflects patterns of emission of SO_2 and NO_x, their degree of oxidation to SO_4^{2-} and NO_3^-, the prevailing direction travelled by contaminated air masses, and the amount of acid-neutralizing dust in the atmosphere. Atmospheric dust is particularly important where vegetation cover is sparse, as in agricultural regions where tiny soil particles are easily eroded into the atmosphere by strong winds blowing over bare fields. Dry, unpaved roads are also important sources of atmospheric dust.

Information on precipitation chemistry at four widely separated Canadian sites is summarized in Table 19.2. Dorset is located in a rural area in the Muskoka region of south-central Ontario. There, the precipitation is highly acidic, with an average pH of 4.1. The precipitation at Dorset has high concentrations of H^+, SO_4^{2-}, and NO_3^-, suggesting its acidity is due mainly to dilute sulphuric and nitric acids. Much of the sulphate and nitrate in precipitation is derived from SO_2 and NO_x emitted by industries and automobiles to the south, which are then transported in the atmosphere before being deposited as acidifying deposition.

The ELA (Experimental Lakes Area) site is in a remote area of northwestern Ontario, located west of Kenora (see Canadian Focus 20.1 on page 383). Like Dorset, the ELA is in a landscape of Precambrian Shield, where bedrock and soil are composed of hard minerals such as granite, gneiss, and quartzite. However, the ELA site is less influenced by air masses affected by anthropogenic emissions, so its pre-

FIGURE 19.1 | Characteristics of Precipitation in Eastern North America

1995–1999 Average pH Distribution

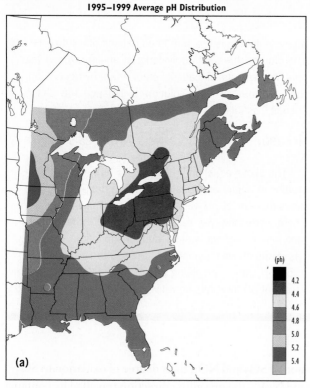

(a)

1995–1999 non-sea-salt SO₄ = Average Wet Deposition (kg/ha/yr)

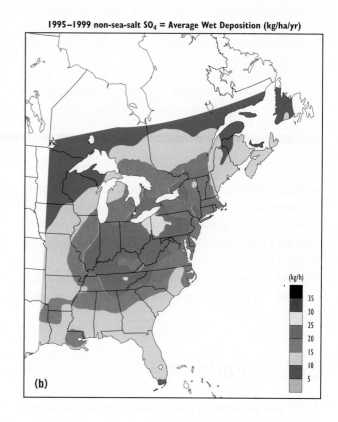

(b)

1995–1999 NO₃ = Average Wet Deposition (kg/ha/yr)

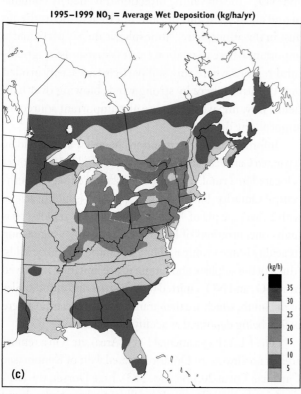

(c)

Points on the curved lines (known as isopleths) have equal annual average values of (a) pH in precipitation; (b) sulphate deposition in precipitation (in kg/ha•y; corrected for sulphate of marine origin); and (c) nitrate deposition (in kg/ha•y). Maps are averages for 1995 to 1999.

Source: Ro and Vet (2002)

TABLE 19.2   Precipitation Chemistry in Various Places in Canada

The data (in µeq/L) are average concentrations in precipitation collected at maritime, continental, and prairie locations. Data are for wet-only precipitation, meaning the collector was open to the atmosphere only during precipitation events.

CONSTITUENT	MARITIME: KEJIMKUJIK, N.S.	POPULATED CONTINENTAL: DORSET, ONT.	REMOTE CONTINENTAL: ELA, ONT.	PRAIRIE: LETHBRIDGE, ALTA.
CATIONS				
H^+	25.1	73.6	18.6	1.0
Ca^{2+}	4.3	10.0	12.0	112.8
Mg^{2+}	2.9	2.4	2.4	25.5
Na^+	26.1	3.9	4.3	9.6
K^+	1.1	1.0	2.0	2.3
NH_4^+	4.2	15.6	18.9	22.2
ANIONS				
SO_4^{2-}	27.5	58.3	27.1	43.5
NO_3^-	9.7	35.5	16.4	20.8
Cl^-	29.5	4.2	5.4	9.9
pH	4.6	4.1	4.7	6.0

Source: Modified from Freedman (1995)

cipitation is less acidic (average pH of 4.7) than at Dorset and has lower concentrations of nitrate and sulphate.

The Kejimkujik site in west-central Nova Scotia is also rather distant from large sources of emissions of SO_2 and NO_x. Kejimkujik often receives air masses that have passed over densely populated areas in the northeastern U.S. and eastern Canada. However, by the time the storm systems reach the Kejimkujik area, much of their acidic material has rained out, so the local precipitation is only moderately acidic (average pH of 4.6). Kejimkujik is also influenced by weather systems that have passed over the Atlantic Ocean. As a result, the precipitation has relatively high concentrations of sodium and chloride. These ions enter the precipitation from atmospheric particulates derived from sea spray. Oceanic saltwater has a pH of about 8 because of the presence of chemicals such as bicarbonate, so marine aerosols have an acid-neutralizing influence on precipitation in coastal regions.

Lethbridge is located in a landscape of mixed-grass prairie in southern Alberta. Precipitation at Lethbridge is non-acidic (average pH of 6.0) because of the acid-neutralizing influence of calcium- and magnesium-rich particulates that are relatively abundant in the atmosphere. These originate with dust blown up from agricultural fields and roads. This dust also accounts for the high concentrations of Ca^{2+} and Mg^{2+} in the precipitation.

Rapid changes in precipitation chemistry can occur at the border between forested landscapes and areas dominated by prairie or agricultural land. A study in southern Ontario examined precipitation at eight places in a mostly forested area with thin soil and Precambrian Shield bedrock, and at three sites just south of the Shield in agricultural terrain with calcium-rich soil (Dillon *et al.*, 1977). The average pH of precipitation among the Shield sites was 4.1–4.2, while at sites south of the Shield it was less acidic, ranging from 4.8 to 5.8. Precipitation was less acidic in the agricultural area because of the local neutralizing influence of dust blown up from fields and roads.

Another important characteristic of acidic precipitation is that, unlike SO_2 and metal particulate pollution, its intensity does not increase closer to large point sources of emissions, such as power plants and smelters. For instance, precipitation is no more acidic close to the superstack at Sudbury than in the larger region, yet the superstack is one of the world's largest point sources of SO_2. Moreover, when that smelter was closed by a strike in 1979, the acidity of local precipitation did not change—it averaged pH 4.49 during the seven-month strike, compared with pH 4.52 during the prior seven months when there were large SO_2 emissions (Scheider *et al.*, 1980).

Fog moisture may also be quite acidic in eastern North America and elsewhere. Fog water collected at high

Photo 19.1 Terrain in the La Cloche highlands of Ontario is extremely sensitive to acidification because of thin soil and hard, quartzitic bedrock (whitish colour in the photo). Lakes in this kind of terrain have very little capability for neutralizing inputs of acidifying substances from the atmosphere, and this is why they acidify so easily.

elevations and at coastal locations is commonly more acidic than pH 4.0, and it can be as acidic as pH 2.5–3.0. At forested sites where fog occurs frequently, large amounts of acidity and other chemicals can be filtered out of the atmosphere by trees. This phenomenon is illustrated in Table 19.3 for a conifer forest on a frequently foggy mountain. The total input of atmospheric moisture to that forest was 264 cm/y, of which rain and snow accounted for 68% and cloudwater deposition the other 32% (fog occurred 40% of the time). However, the concentrations of many chemicals are much higher in cloudwater than in precipitation, so their rates of deposition to the forest are also higher than from precipitation. Fog water accounted for 62% of the H$^+$ deposition and 81% of the inputs of SO$_4^{2-}$ and NO$_3^-$ to the forest.

Transboundary Air Pollution

Acidifying substances and their gaseous precursors are often transported over long distances in the atmosphere, far from their sources of emission. The acidifying chemicals do not respect political boundaries, so emissions occurring in one country can degrade ecosystems and valuable resources in other countries. This transboundary context has helped to focus the attention of governments on the problem of acidifying deposition from the atmosphere.

In western Europe, for example, Scandinavians have justifiably argued that most of the acidifying deposition that has affected parts of their landscape has resulted from emissions of SO$_2$ and NO$_x$ in Germany and England. This international European context was the first well-demonstrated case of so-called **LRTAP**—an acronym for the long-range transport of atmospheric pollutants.

Similar transboundary circumstances occur elsewhere. In eastern North America, for example, there are large populations and industrial centres in the northeastern United States. Emissions of SO$_2$ and NO$_x$ from those areas waft into eastern Canada, worsening damages caused there by local emissions. It has been estimated that U.S. emissions are responsible for 90% of the wet deposition of acidifying nitrogen compounds in eastern Canada, along with 63% of the wet deposition of sulphur compounds, 43% of the dry deposition of nitrogen, and 24% of the dry deposition of sulphur (Shannon and Lecht, 1986). Canada also exports some of its emissions to the U.S., although Canadian emissions account for less than 5% of the total deposition of sulphur and nitrogen compounds in the eastern United States. In total, Canada receives about 4 million tonnes of SO$_2$ per year from the U.S. (Environment Canada, 1999b).

Dry Deposition

Dry deposition occurs during intervals between precipitation events, and it includes

- uptake of the gases SO$_2$ and NO$_x$ by vegetation, soil, and water;
- gravitational settling of larger particles; and
- filtering of finer particulates by vegetation.

TABLE 19.3	Chemistry and Deposition of Cloudwater

Deposition of water and ions were studied in a conifer forest at a high-elevation site on Mount Moosilauke, New Hampshire. Cloudwater deposition occurs when fog is filtered from the atmosphere by trees. Each concentration is stated as a mean value, with standard deviation (a statistical measure of variation) in microequivalents per litre. Precipitation refers to rain and snow; % cloudwater refers to the percentage of the total deposition that was due to cloudwater.

	CONCENTRATION (μeq/L; MEAN ± SD)	DEPOSITION (kilogram/hectare·year)			% CLOUDWATER
		CLOUD	PRECIP.	TOTAL	
H^+	288 ± 193	2.4	1.5	3.9	62
NH_4^+	108 ± 89	16.3	4.2	20.5	80
Na^+	30 ± 29	5.8	1.7	7.5	77
K^+	10 ± 4	3.3	2.1	5.4	61
SO_4^{2-}	342 ± 234	275.8	64.8	340.6	81
NO_3^-	195 ± 175	101.5	23.4	124.9	81
H_2O (cm/y)		84	180	264	32

Source: Modified from Lovett *et al.* (1982)

Forests are particularly effective at absorbing gases and particles from the atmosphere. This happens because trees have a very large and complex surface of foliage and bark, which greatly enhances the rate of dry deposition.

Dry deposition can result in large inputs of substances from the atmosphere, including some that generate acidity when they are chemically transformed within the ecosystem. For instance, atmospheric SO_2 readily dissolves in the surface water of lakes and streams. This gas is also freely absorbed by plants, entering foliage through tiny, abundant pores on their surface known as stomata, and dissolving in the moist film of water that covers the internal cell surfaces. The absorbed SO_2 is oxidized to the anion sulphite (SO_3^{2-}), which is then rapidly oxidized to sulphate (SO_4^{2-}). Because the sulphate is mostly balanced electrochemically by hydrogen ions, acidity is generated by the transformation of SO_2 into SO_4^{2-} (see Figure 19.2 on page 359).

NO_x gas may be similarly dry-deposited and then oxidized to nitrate (NO_3^-), which also generates an equivalent amount of H^+. The gas ammonia (NH_3) and the cation ammonium (NH_4^+) can also be dry-deposited to soil or water, where they can be oxidized by bacteria to nitrate plus equivalent quantities of H^+.

The rates of dry deposition of sulphur and nitrogen compounds are greatest when high concentrations of gaseous NO_x and SO_2 are present in the atmosphere. Such conditions typically occur in urban areas and close to large industrial emissions of those gases. In those places, dry deposition accounts for larger inputs of acidifying substances than does wet deposition. In more remote, less contaminated environments, far from sources of emission, inputs with precipitation are typically larger than dry deposition.

Within 40 km of the largest smelter at Sudbury, about 55% of the atmospheric sulphur deposition occurs as dry deposition (Chan *et al.*, 1984). About 91% of the dry deposition involves SO_2, while the rest is sulphate particulates. However, the superstack at that smelter, being extremely tall (380 m), is effective at dispersing its emissions of SO_2. Consequently, less than 1% of the emitted SO_2 is deposited close to the source (i.e., within 40 km)—almost all of the SO_2 is transported much farther away before it is deposited to the landscape.

Forest Canopies

The first surfaces that precipitation hits in a forest are those of tree foliage and bark. Most incoming rainwater drips through the canopy as so-called "throughfall," while a smaller fraction runs down tree trunks as "stemflow." In addition, some precipitation wets the canopy foliage and then evaporates back to the atmosphere.

Studies of conifer forest in Nova Scotia found that, during the growing season, about 65% of the rainfall reached the ground as throughfall, less than 1% was stemflow, and 34% evaporated back to the atmosphere from wet foliage (Freedman and Prager, 1986). Comparable data for hardwood forest were 75% throughfall, 3% stemflow, and 22% evaporation. The chemistry of throughfall and stemflow is markedly different from that of ambient precipitation. This is partly because the evaporation of water from a wetted canopy is a distillation that concentrates the chemicals in throughfall and stemflow. In addition, certain chemicals are readily leached out of foliage, increasing their concentrations in the throughfall and stemflow. In the Nova Scotia study, the concentration of potassium (K^+) was 10 times higher in throughfall and stemflow than in rainwater, while calcium (Ca^{2+}) and magnesium (Mg^{2+}) were three to four times higher. These changes in ion concentrations affect the acidity because H^+ is removed from solution and exchanged for Ca^{2+}, Mg^{2+}, and K^+ (these are known as *base cations*). The exchange reactions reduced H^+ quantities by 42–66% in throughfall and stemflow, compared with ambient rainfall.

In areas where the atmosphere is heavily contaminated by SO_2, there are large increases in the sulphate concentration in throughfall and stemflow compared with precipitation. This is caused by the washoff and leaching of sulphate that was previously dry deposited to the canopy as particulates and SO_2 gas. Studies at Hubbard Brook found that sulphate deposition was about four times higher in forest than in ambient precipitation (Eaton *et al.*, 1973). Hubbard Brook is located in remote hilly terrain, but in a region of the northeastern U.S. where the atmosphere is contaminated by particulate sulphate and gaseous SO_2. At the Nova Scotian sites, which have a cleaner atmosphere, sulphate deposition was only 45% higher in forest than in precipitation (Freedman and Prager, 1986).

Soil Acidity

Soil acidity is an extremely important factor affecting the growth of vegetation. Soil acidification is a common natural process that has been demonstrated in ecosystems by studies of succession.

One well-known study was made at Glacier Bay in southern Alaska. Glacial meltback there exposes a till substrate with a pH of about 8.0, and containing concentrations as high as 10% of carbonate minerals of calcium and magnesium (Crocker and Major, 1955). This material becomes modified by colonizing vegetation and climatic factors, especially by rainfall, which percolates through the soil and carries away dissolved chemicals. This results in an increased acidity of the soil, reaching about pH 4.8 after 70 years of succession. By that time, a conifer forest is established. The acidification is accompanied by large

declines in the concentrations of Ca, Mg, and carbonates in the soil during succession.

Natural acidification is partly caused by uptake of the nutrients Ca, Mg, and K by vegetation, a process accompanied by the excretion of H^+ and a decrease in the soil's **buffering capacity** (i.e., the ability of the soil to resist further acidification). Another cause of acidification is the leaching of calcium and other cations out of the soil by rainwater.

After precipitation reaches the ground in a terrestrial ecosystem, it percolates downward into the soil. Various chemical changes occur as the water interacts with soil minerals, organic matter, microbes, and plant roots, including the following:

■ Roots and microorganisms selectively absorb, release, and transform chemicals.

■ Ions are exchanged at the surfaces of clay particles, minerals, and organic matter.

■ Insoluble minerals are made soluble by so-called weathering processes, including reactions with acids.

■ Secondary minerals are formed, such as certain kinds of clays and insoluble precipitates of iron and aluminum oxides.

These reactions contribute to important changes in the soil, such as acidification, leaching of calcium and magnesium, and the solubilization of toxic metals, particularly ions of aluminum (such as Al^{3+}; see Chapter 18). All of these processes occur naturally wherever the input of water from precipitation exceeds the amount returned to the atmosphere by evapotranspiration, leaving a surplus to move downward through the soil. These reactions are also strongly influenced by the kind of vegetation growing on the site. For instance, pines, spruces, and oaks tend to cause soil acidification. Acidifying deposition from the atmosphere can potentially increase the rates of some of these processes in soil, thereby increasing the leaching of toxic Al^{3+} and H^+ into surface waters, such as rivers and lakes.

Factors Affecting Soil Acidity

Soil acidity is influenced by numerous chemical transformations and ion exchanges. Some of these are carried out by organisms, while others are non-biological reactions. The most important factors affecting soil acidity are discussed in the following sections.

Carbonic Acid

In many terrestrial ecosystems, such as grassland and forest, the surface litter and upper soil are rich in organic matter and plant roots. Decomposition and respiration result in high concentrations of CO_2 (frequently exceeding 1%) in the atmosphere within the soil. The high CO_2 concentrations result in carbonic acid (H_2CO_3) forming in the soil water, contributing to acidification. This effect is strongest in soil with a pH greater than about 6, and it is unimportant in acidic soil with a pH less than about 5.5.

The Nitrogen Cycle

Soil acidity can be affected by microbial transformations of nitrogen compounds and by the uptake and release of these chemicals by plants (Figure 19.2). Ammonium (NH_4^+) and nitrate (NO_3^-) are especially important in this regard because plants must take up one or both of these essential nutrients, the choice depending largely on soil acidity. In acidic soil (with pH less than about 5.5), almost all inorganic nitrogen occurs as NH_4^+. The NH_4^+ may originate from the *ammonification* of organic-N to form ammonia (NH_3) (a process carried out by many species of microorganisms, as we learned in Chapter 5). Ammonia absorbs one H^+ to form NH_4^+. If the NH_4^+ ion is absorbed by a plant root, an ion of H^+ is excreted into the soil to maintain electrochemical neutrality, so there is no net change in soil acidity. However, if NH_4^+ is added directly to soil (e.g., by atmospheric deposition or by fertilization), then plant uptake of NH_4^+, accompanied by the release of H^+, has an acidifying effect.

In soils with pH greater than 5.5, most inorganic-N occurs as NO_3^-, which is produced by the oxidation of NH_4^+ through the process of *nitrification* (Chapter 5). Nitrification is carried out by the bacteria *Nitrosomonas* and *Nitrobacter*, both of which are intolerant of acidity. The oxidation of NH_4^+ to NO_3^- generates two H^+ ions (Figure 19.2). If the NH_4^+ originated from ammonification of organic-N (which consumes one H^+ for each NH_4^+ produced), the net effect is the release of one H^+ for each NO_3^- ion produced from organic nitrogen. However,

---

FIGURE 19.2 | Acidification Caused by Sulphur and Nitrogen Transformations

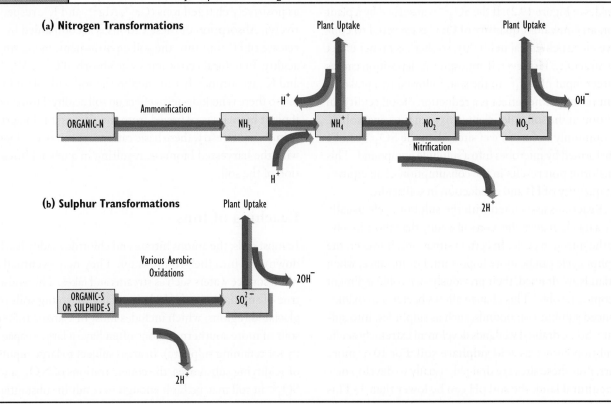

This diagram describes the acidifying effects of some important transformations of nitrogen and sulphur in soil or water.

Source: Modified from Reuss (1985)

if the NO_3^- is absorbed by a plant root, then one OH^- ion is excreted to the soil to maintain electrochemical neutrality, which is equivalent to the consumption of one H^+. In that case, the net effect on soil acidity is zero.

It is well known to farmers and agronomists that the addition of ammonium to soil can have a severely acidifying influence. This happens because the NH_4^+ becomes nitrified into NO_3^-, generating large amounts of acidity. There are two main types of ammonium inputs: the treatment of agricultural fields with fertilizer containing inorganic nitrogen (such as urea or ammonium nitrate), and the deposition of NH_3 gas and NH_4^+ ions from the atmosphere.

The Sulphur Cycle

Much of the sulphur in soil occurs in organically bound forms. Various microbial processes can transform this organic sulphur into more highly oxidized compounds. These include sulphides and elemental sulphur, but in environments well supplied with oxygen, these ultimately become further oxidized to sulphate. Overall, the oxidation of organic sulphur to SO_4^{2-} results in the release of one equivalent of H^+ per equivalent of SO_4^{2-} produced (this is the same as two ions of H^+ per ion of SO_4^{2-} produced; see Figure 19.2). If the SO_4^{2-} is absorbed by a plant root, an equivalent quantity of OH^- is excreted to conserve electrochemical neutrality, so there is no net effect on soil acidity. However, if atmospheric deposition causes a direct input of SO_4^{2-} to the soil, followed by uptake by plant roots, the net effect is a reduction of soil acidity. In addition, if the soil is deficient in oxygen (i.e., anaerobic), as commonly occurs in wet sites, then the SO_4^{2-} can be transformed by microbes into a sulphide compound. This transformation results in the consumption of an equivalent quantity of H^+ and a reduction in soil acidity.

Reactions associated with the sulphur cycle usually have a much smaller effect on soil acidity than those involving the nitrogen cycle. In certain situations, however, the sulphur cycle can be more important. For instance, when wetlands are drained, their previously anaerobic sediment becomes aerobic. This change allows bacteria to oxidize reduced sulphur compounds, such as sulphides, into sulphate. Some drained wetlands develop an extremely acidic condition known as **acid sulphate soil**. For 10 or more years after these sites are drained, usually to develop new agricultural land, the soil pH can be lower than 3. This severely impairs crop growth. To some degree, the acidity generated can be neutralized by adding calcium carbonate (lime) to the soil.

Sometimes, sulphide minerals such as pyrites (iron sulphides) become exposed to atmospheric oxygen. This allows specialized bacteria in the genus *Thiobacillus* to oxidize the sulphides, producing sulphate and oxidized iron ions, according to the following reaction:

$$4 FeS_2 + 15 O_2 + 14 H_2O \longrightarrow$$
$$4 Fe(OH)_3 + 16 H^+ + 8 SO_4^{2-}$$

This phenomenon is known as **acid-mine drainage**. It causes severe acidification of soil and surface waters, sometimes causing a pH less than 2 to develop, along with high concentrations of sulphate and toxic ions of aluminum and iron. Acid-mine drainage is an important problem in areas where disturbances associated with coal and metal mining and processing have resulted in the exposure of mineral sulphides to the atmosphere.

Uptake of Basic Cations by Plants

Terrestrial plants obtain many of their nutrients by absorbing ions from the soil in which they are growing. (A few nutrients, however, are absorbed mainly from the atmosphere, particularly CO_2.) Calcium, magnesium, and potassium are important nutrients that are absorbed from soil as positively charged ions (Ca^{2+}, Mg^{2+}, and K^+, respectively). Absorption of these cations is accompanied by a release of H^+ ions into the soil environment, increasing acidity. In natural ecosystems, the absorbed Ca^{2+}, Mg^{2+}, and K^+ are ultimately returned to the soil with plant litter, so there is no long-term effect on soil acidity. However, if plant biomass is removed from the site, as it is in agriculture and forestry, these basic cations are removed along with the harvested biomass, resulting in a net acidification of the soil.

Leaching of Ions

In most soils, the anions nitrate and chloride readily leach downward into the groundwater. They may eventually reach surface waters such as streams and lakes. This is also true of sulphate, particularly in relatively young soils of glaciated regions, which includes most of Canada (older soils of more southern regions often have a larger capacity for retaining sulphate). In areas subject to large inputs of acidifying substances, the concentrations of NO_3^- and SO_4^{2-} in soil may be high enough to result in substantial rates of leaching of those ions. As these anions leach out of the soil, they are accompanied by cations such as Ca^{2+}, Mg^{2+}, H^+, and Al^{3+}. This results in acidification, nutrient loss, and toxicity (associated with the aluminum ions) in both terrestrial and aquatic ecosystems. For instance, one monitored watershed in south-central Ontario was found to have lost 30% of its soil calcium between 1983 and 1999 (Watmough and Dillon, 2004).

Soil Buffering Systems

Compared with precipitation and surface waters, soil is relatively strongly buffered (i.e., resistant to changes in pH). However, different buffering systems are important at different ranges of soil pH:

- Carbonate minerals of calcium and magnesium provide most of the buffering capacity within the pH range of >8 to 6.2.
- Silicates are important from pH 6.2 to 5.0.
- Cation-exchange capacity buffers from pH 6.2 to 4.2.
- Aluminum transformations buffer from pH 5.0 to 3.0.
- Iron transformations are important from pH 3.8 to 2.4.
- Humic substances buffer from pH 5 to 3.

Many soils in the so-called "circumneutral" pH range of 6–8 are relatively sensitive to acidification, especially if only small amounts of calcium and magnesium carbonates are present. When these kinds of soil are exposed to high inputs of acidifying substances, they can rapidly acidify to pH 3.5–4.5.

Atmospheric Deposition and Soil

The potential effects of atmospheric deposition on soil acidity have been studied in experiments in which simulated acidic "rainwater" is added to soil contained in plastic cylinders, known as lysimeters. These experiments have shown that extremely acidic solutions can cause several changes in soil chemistry:

- an increase in acidity
- increased leaching of calcium, magnesium, and potassium, resulting in the depletion of these nutrients and greater vulnerability of the soil to acidification
- increased solubilization of toxic metal ions—especially of aluminum, but also of iron, manganese, and others

- overwhelming of the ability of soil to absorb sulphate—after which this ion leaches freely, at a rate similar to its input. Because SO_4^{2-} is an anion, its leaching is accompanied by base cations and toxic Al^{3+} and H^+. These may eventually contribute to the acidification and toxicity of surface waters that receive water that has percolated through the soil.

One experiment involved the treatment of sandy soil collected from jack pine (*Pinus banksiana*) stands in northern Ontario with simulated rainwater, adjusted with dilute sulphuric acid to a pH of 5.7, 4, 3, or 2 (Table 19.4). Even treatment with the extremely acidic pH of 2 had little effect on soil acidity, with the pH of the percolating solutions being higher than 6.5 in all treatments. However, the leaching rates of Ca, Mg, total bases (Ca + Mg + K + Na), and sulphate were much higher in the extremely acidic, pH 2 treatment. Overall, this experiment found that the soil was resistant to the effects of acid loading. Eventually, however, the resistance can be overcome by treatment with highly acidic solutions, or perhaps by a long-term exposure to more moderate acidities. It must be borne in mind that experiments such as these are short-term investigations, whereas soil acidification in nature is a slow, long-term process.

TABLE 19.4 | Experimental Leaching of Soil by Acidic Solutions

The data are concentrations, in milliequivalents per litre, of chemicals in water that drained from the bottom of lysimeters containing sandy soil collected from two jack pine (*Pinus banksiana*) stands in northern Ontario. The experiment ran for three years, with simulated rainfall being added at a rate of 100 cm/y as weekly 1–2 hour events. The data are averages of three replicates per treatment.

	pH OF LEACHING SOLUTION	CONCENTRATION IN PERCOLATE (meq/L)			
		Ca	Mg	ALL BASES	SO₄
Soil A	5.7	0.74	0.05	0.99	0.23
	4	0.67	0.05	0.99	0.22
	3	0.75	0.07	1.10	0.15
	2	0.87	0.20	1.35	0.53
Soil B	5.7	0.42	0.17	0.73	0.15
	4	0.45	0.18	0.77	0.15
	3	0.40	0.17	0.70	0.28
	2	3.72	1.47	5.50	5.43

Source: Modified from Morrison (1983)

Researchers monitoring soil chemistry at particular places in the field can determine whether acidification has occurred, although such studies do not necessarily identify the causes of the change. For instance, the conversion of agricultural land into conifer forest usually results in acidification of the soil. In southern Ontario, for example, the afforestation of abandoned farmland with pine or spruce caused the soil to acidify from an initial pH of 5.7 to pH 4.7 after 46 years of forest development (Brand *et al.*, 1986). It is less understood whether already forested sites will become more acidic because of atmospheric inputs of acidifying substances. A study in southern Ontario resampled forest soils after a 16-year interval, in a region where the average pH of precipitation is about 4.1. The study found no further acidification of soil over that period (Linzon and Temple, 1980).

Studies conducted elsewhere in Canada, and in the U.S. and Europe, have also come to rather ambiguous conclusions about the effects of atmospheric deposition on soil acidification. Except where the atmosphere is severely polluted by SO_2, such as near a smelter, there is no convincing evidence that atmospheric deposition has acidified soil on a wide scale. It appears that soil acidification is a potential, long-term risk associated with this type of pollution.

Terrestrial Vegetation

Numerous studies have demonstrated that plants can be injured by treatment with artificial solutions of "acid rain." In almost all of these studies, however, the pH that caused injuries was considerably more acidic than is normally found in ambient precipitation.

For example, experiments in Norway exposed stands of young conifer trees to simulated acid rain for three years (Tveite, 1980). The "control" treatment used solutions of pH 5.6–6.1, while the "acidified" treatments used pH 4 or 3. On average, saplings of lodgepole pine (*Pinus contorta*) receiving the control treatment grew 15–20% less than plants receiving the more acidic treatments! Growth of Scotch pine (*P. sylvestris*) and birch (*Betula pendula*) was also stimulated by the acidic treatments, while spruce (*Picea abies*) was unaffected. However, the moss-dominated ground vegetation of the stands was severely damaged by the most acidic treatment (pH 3).

Because laboratory experiments can be closely controlled, they are useful for determining the effects of varying pH of acidic rainwater on plants. In general, such

Photo 19.2 During the 1980s, many stands of sugar maple (*Acer saccharum*) in Ontario and Quebec suffered severe thinning of their canopy. In some places, many trees died. Some scientists believe that this damage was caused by acid rain, or by other types of air pollution, such as ozone. Alternative hypotheses to explain the damage include climate change, severe winter weather, nutrient imbalances, and a past history of insect infestation. The controversy over the causes of the phenomenon has not been fully resolved, but fortunately, much of the damage disappeared by the mid-1990s. This photo was taken in a severely declining stand near Vineland in southern Ontario.

Source: R. Vinebrooke

experiments do not reduce growth until the solution pH becomes more acidic than about 3.0 (for comparison, the average acidity of precipitation is about pH 4 in regions where the problem is considered "severe"). Moreover, the productivity of some tolerant species can be stimulated by rainwater even more acidic than pH 3. For example, white pine seedlings (*Pinus strobus*) grew more when exposed to mist ranging from pH 2.3 to 4.0 than at pH 5.6 (Wood and Bormann, 1976). In another laboratory experiment, seedlings of 11 tree species were treated with solutions of various pH. Acute injuries to foliage were caused only after a week of treatment at pH 2.6, which is an unnaturally acidic treatment (Percy, 1986).

In general, it appears that trees and other vascular plants have little risk of suffering acute injury from exposure to ambient acidic precipitation. However, stresses associated with acidic precipitation could possibly decrease plant growth, even in the absence of acute injuries. These "hidden injuries" (see Chapter 16) might be caused by subtle disruptions of plant metabolism, or indirectly by effects of changes in soil chemistry. Because acidic precipitation affects extensive regions, even small decreases in plant productivity could result in important economic and ecological damages. Hidden injuries, if they do occur, are most relevant to forest and other kinds of natural vegetation. Agricultural land becomes acidified mostly through management practices such as cropping and the use of nitrogen fertilizer. Moreover, agricultural soil is routinely treated with liming agents to reduce its acidity (liming is discussed at the end of this chapter).

A number of studies in eastern North America and Europe have examined the possible effects of acidic precipitation on forest productivity. Although species of trees in some regions have shown recent decreases in productivity, it has not been conclusively demonstrated that these changes were caused by acidic precipitation or other kinds of atmospheric pollution. Forest productivity decreases naturally as a stand matures, mainly because canopy closure intensifies competition. Forest productivity is also influenced by factors such as climate change and management practices. So far, field research has not clearly separated any influences of acidic precipitation on forest productivity from effects related to succession, climate change, insect defoliation, or other factors. Some forest growth-modelling studies have, however, suggested that productivity could decrease by 10% in eastern Canada if critical deposition rates of sulphate and nitrate are exceeded (Federal/Provincial/Territorial Ministers of Energy and Environment, 1999).

Clearly, the effects of acidifying depositions on soil and vegetation are somewhat ambiguous. However, as the following sections will show, the effects on surface-water ecosystems can be severe.

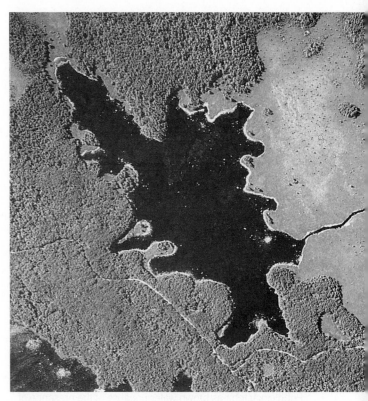

Photo 19.3   About a third of the watershed of Pebbleloggitch Lake, Nova Scotia, is an acidic, organic-rich bog (the fine, light texture in the photo). The rest is covered by mature conifer-dominated forest. The boggy area leaches dissolved organic acids to the lake, giving it a dark-brown colour and making it naturally acidic, with a pH of about 4.5.
Source: J. Kerekes

Surface Waters

Surface waters include streams, rivers, lakes, and ponds (Chapter 14). The chemistry of surface waters is influenced by many factors, including the types of soil and vegetation in the watershed, climatic influences, and rates of deposition of chemicals from the atmosphere.

In regions where the winters are cold and a snowpack accumulates, the spring meltwater that flows into streams, rivers, and lake surfaces tends to be relatively acidic. This so-called **acid shock** phenomenon is caused partly because snowmelt cannot percolate into the frozen, saturated soil. Therefore, the acidity of melted snow cannot be neutralized by interaction with minerals in the soil. In addition, the initial meltwater of the snowpack is considerably more acidic than the later meltwaters. The relatively acidic conditions associated with snowmelt in the spring are responsible for much of the toxicity of acidic surface waters.

The water chemistry of two remote lakes in a region of Nova Scotia subject to acidic precipitation is described in Table 19.5. These lakes receive a sparse input of nutrients, and consequently, they are highly unproductive (*oligotrophic*) and their waters are dilute solutions in comparison with most fresh waters (i.e., their water has low concentrations of dissolved ions). Nevertheless, these lakewaters have higher concentrations of dissolved substances than does the precipitation that falls on them—their sum of cations plus anions averages 440 µeq/L, compared with 135 µeq/L in precipitation. The lakewaters contain relatively high concentrations (compared with precipitation) of calcium, magnesium, sodium, potassium, iron, aluminum, sulphate, chloride, organic carbon, and organic anions (i.e., negative charges associated with dissolved

organic matter). The higher concentrations of these substances occur mainly because they leach from terrestrial soil and eventually migrate into the lakewater. In contrast, concentrations of ammonium and nitrate in the lakewaters are lower than in precipitation, suggesting that atmospheric inputs of these nutrients are "consumed" by biological uptake within the watershed.

Beaverskin Lake is a slightly acidic, oligotrophic lake with very transparent water. Beaverskin Lake (pH 5.3) is less acidic than the local precipitation (pH 4.6) it receives. In comparison, Pebbleloggitch Lake is greatly influenced by a bog that covers about one-third of its watershed. Dissolved organic compounds (known as fulvic acids) leach from the bog into the lake, giving the lakewater a dark-brown colour and an acidity (pH 4.5) similar to that of precipitation. Although these two lakes are located only 1 km apart, they differ markedly in acidity because of the bog's influence on organic acids in tea-coloured Pebbleloggitch Lake. In general, bog-influenced lakes and streams are naturally acidic and usually have an acidity of pH 4–5.

Acidification of Surface Waters

A widespread acidification of weakly buffered surface waters in eastern Canada has been attributed to the deposition of

---

TABLE 19.5 | Chemistry of Two Nova Scotian Lakes

This table summarizes data for the average concentration of chemicals in precipitation, and in the water of two remote lakes in Nova Scotia. Beaverskin Lake has clear water, while Pebbleloggitch has brown water because of the presence of a large bog in its watershed. Both are headwater lakes, which means they do not receive drainage from lakes higher in altitude. Data are in µeq/L.

CONSTITUENT	PRECIPITATION	BEAVERSKIN LAKE	PEBBLELOGGITCH LAKE
CATIONS			
Ca	4.3	20.0	18.0
Mg	2.9	32.0	30.0
Na	26.1	126.0	126.0
K	1.1	8.0	6.0
Fe	<0.1	1.0	4.0
Al	<0.1	2.2	23.4
NH₄	4.2	1.0	2.4
H	29.9	5.0	33.0
ANIONS			
SO₄	27.5	48.7	57.9
Cl	29.5	124.0	111.0
NO₃	9.7	1.0	0.9
Organic anions	<0.1	32.0	66.0
Total cations	68.5	195.2	242.8
Total anions	66.7	205.7	235.8
Total carbon (mg/L)	0.0	4.5	13.8
Colour (Hazen units)	0	6	87
pH	4.6	5.3	4.5

Sources: Kerekes and Freedman (1988) and Freedman and Clair (1987)

FIGURE 19.3 | Sensitivity to Acidification Across Canada

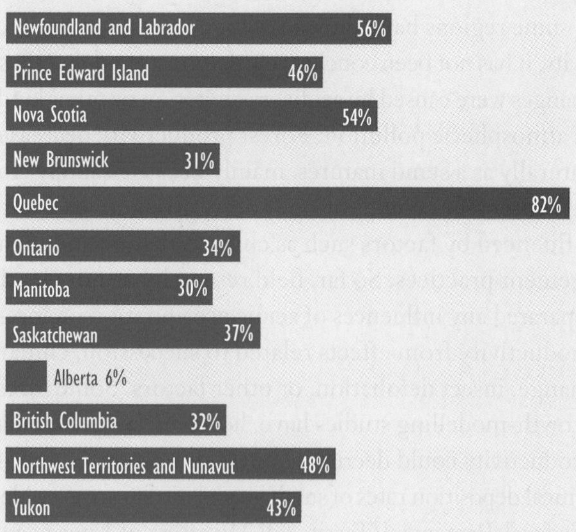

Newfoundland and Labrador	56%
Prince Edward Island	46%
Nova Scotia	54%
New Brunswick	31%
Quebec	82%
Ontario	34%
Manitoba	30%
Saskatchewan	37%
Alberta 6%	
British Columbia	32%
Northwest Territories and Nunavut	48%
Yukon	43%

Data are the percentages of the total terrain with a high sensitivity to aquatic acidification.

Source: Modified from Environment Canada (1988)

acidifying substances from the atmosphere. The eastern U.S. and Scandinavia have also been affected in this way.

A national survey of surface waters was conducted by the Environmental Protection Agency in the U.S. (Baker *et al.*, 1991). From a sample of 28 300 lakes around the U.S., 1180 were identified as acidic. Most of these are in the eastern states. Atmospheric deposition was thought to have acidified 75% of the acidic lakes, while 3% were affected by acid-mine drainage and 22% by natural acidity draining from bogs. Of 64 300 streams sampled, 4670 were acidic, of which 47% were acidified by atmospheric deposition, 26% by acid-mine drainage, and 27% by bogs. Florida has the highest frequency of acidic lakes, mostly because of organic acids draining from natural wetlands. The influence of atmospheric deposition is most important in the northeastern U.S., particularly in the Adirondack Mountains in New York State, where 10% of the lakes have a pH ≤5.0, and 20% a pH ≤5.5.

Although such a comprehensive survey of the status of individual lakes and streams has not been carried out in Canada, acidified surface waters are known to be common, particularly in the eastern part of the country. It has been estimated, for example, that there are more than 14 000 acidic lakes in Ontario, Quebec, and the Atlantic Provinces (Environment Canada, 1996). The sensitivity of Canadian surface waters to acidification has been extensively surveyed (Figure 19.3). Sensitivity can be described by the concentration of alkalinity in water, which is related to the amounts of calcium and magnesium in the soil and rocks of the watershed (the more calcium and magnesium present, the less sensitive the water is to acidification; see also the following section). Surface waters on 46% of Canada's land area (equivalent to about 4.0 million km^2) are considered highly sensitive to acidifying deposition, while another 21% (1.8 million km^2) are moderately sensitive. Overall, surface waters are most sensitive in eastern Canada.

The chemical and biological changes that occur as surface waters become acidified have been examined in important studies in which sulphuric acid was added to lakes, causing them to acidify (Schindler, 1990). These **whole-lake experiments** were conducted in the Experimental Lakes Area (ELA) of northwestern Ontario. The most intensively studied lake, called Lake 223, is a 27-ha, oligotrophic waterbody. Lake 223 was studied for two years before it was experimentally acidified, and then for a number of years afterward. The pH of Lake 223 was initially 6.5, and its alkalinity was 80 μeq/L. Beginning in 1976, sulphuric acid was added to progressively acidify Lake 223. This gradually reduced its pH from 6.5 in 1976 to 5.0–5.1

between 1981 and 1983. The acidity of Lake 223 was then allowed to decrease to pH 5.5–5.8 during 1984–88.

As expected, the concentrations of sulphate and hydrogen ions increased, because these were being added to the lake. Sulphate averaged 35 μmol/L in 1975, compared with 115 μmol/L in 1979. Increased concentrations of manganese (a 980% increase by 1980), zinc (550% increase), aluminum (155%), and sodium (26%) occurred because these chemicals dissolved out of sediment under the acidified conditions. Acidification also caused the water of Lake 223 to become more transparent, which allowed increased light penetration and deeper heating of the lakewater during the summer. Many biological changes also occurred; these are described later in this chapter.

Vulnerability to Acidification

Surface waters that are vulnerable to acidification have a low alkalinity, or **acid-neutralizing capacity**. As H$^+$ is added to lakewater, it is absorbed by acid-neutralizing reactions until the buffering threshold is exceeded. This is followed by a rapid decrease in pH, until a different buffering system comes into play (Figure 19.4). Bicarbonate (HCO$_3^-$) alkalinity is the critical buffering system within the circumneutral pH range of 6–8. When this is depleted, a waterbody acidifies rapidly. Bicarbonate reacts with H$^+$ to form H$_2$O + CO$_2$. This reaction neutralizes added H$^+$, so the pH does not change until the supply of alkalinity is exhausted.

The concentration of bicarbonate in natural waters is influenced by geochemical factors. Particularly important is the presence of mineral carbonates such as limestone (CaCO$_3$) or dolomite (Ca,MgCO$_3$) in the soil or bedrock of the watershed or in the aquatic sediment. As these minerals dissolve, they provide bicarbonate alkalinity to surface waters, giving the water an acid-neutralizing capacity. In general, carbonate-rich watersheds can generate enough alkalinity to neutralize any acidifying inputs from the atmosphere. Surface waters in these types of watersheds are not sensitive to acidification, even if they are located where the atmosphere and precipitation are rather polluted. (There might be exceptions in cases of extremely high rates of dry deposition of SO$_2$.)

The situation is different, however, in watersheds in which the bedrock, soil, and sediment are derived from hard, poorly soluble rocks such as granite, gneiss, and quartzite, which contain very small amounts of carbonate minerals. Watersheds of this type have little capacity for generating alkalinity, and they are readily acidified by wet

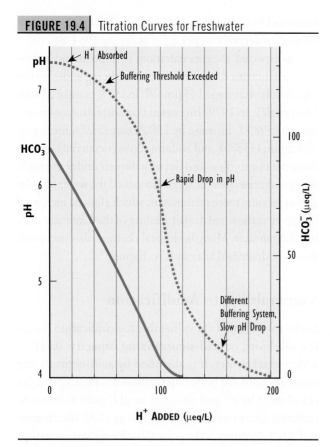

FIGURE 19.4 | Titration Curves for Freshwater

This diagram shows titration curves for a typical freshwater lake. The initial concentration of alkalinity (HCO_3^-; lower curve) was 100 μeq/L. These curves are similar to what is observed when dilute acid is slowly added to clear lakewater with a low concentration of alkalinity. Once the alkalinity is exhausted, the water acidifies rapidly.

Source: Modified from Henriksen (1980)

and dry depositions from the atmosphere. As was previously described, vulnerable watersheds are especially common in eastern Canada, where thin soils derived from carbonate-poor glacial till overlie hard bedrock of granite, gneiss, and quartzite, especially on the Precambrian Shield.

Headwater lakes and streams are at particular risk of acidification. Headwater systems receive no drainage from waterbodies at higher elevation, and their watersheds are usually small. Consequently, there is relatively little opportunity for rainwater to interact with soil and bedrock, and much of the acidity in precipitation is not neutralized before the water reaches headwater lakes and streams.

At high elevation in many mountainous regions, where crustal granite is exposed by erosion, the terrain is often vulnerable to acidification. This is the case in the Rocky Mountains of western North America and the Appalachians

of the eastern United States. Again, the vulnerability occurs because granite contributes little alkalinity to surface waters.

Within vulnerable regions, however, even small pockets of calcareous (i.e., calcium-rich) soil in the watershed can yield enough alkalinity to allow waterbodies to resist acidification. For example, 15 lakes were surveyed in an area of Precambrian Shield in southern Ontario where precipitation is quite acidic (Dillon *et al.*, 1977). Fourteen of the lakes had little alkalinity (range of 95–175 μeq/L), were slightly acidic (pH 5.8–6.7), and were considered vulnerable to further acidification. One lake, however, had some calcium-rich till in its watershed. That lake had a high alkalinity (1200 μeq/L) and a high pH (7.1), and it is unlikely to acidify through atmospheric influences.

Freshwater Organisms

Many changes occur in the biota of aquatic ecosystems as they become acidified. In general, freshwater organisms are considerably more sensitive to the acidification of their habitat than are terrestrial plants.

Freshwater Algae

Many species of microscopic, single-celled algae (*phytoplankton*) live in lakes. The water chemistry greatly influences the particular species that are present. Because species of diatoms (family Bacilliarophyceae) and golden-brown algae (Chrysophyceae) are particularly sensitive to differences in water chemistry, they are useful indicators of environmental conditions. For example, a study of 72 lakes in the Sudbury area found that certain diatom species indicated particular aspects of water chemistry (Dixit *et al.*, 1991), as follows:

1. indicators of acidic water: *Eunotia pectinatus, Fragilaria acidobiontica, Pinnularia subcapitata, Tabellaria quadriseptata*

2. indicators of acidic water with high concentrations of metals (Cu, Ni): *Eunotia exigua, E. tenella, Frustulina rhomboides saxonica, Pinnularia hilseana*

3. indicators of non-acidic water: *Achnanthes lewisiana, Cyclotella meneghiniana, Fragilaria construens, F. crotonensis*

The silica-rich cell walls of diatoms differ in shape for each species, and they persist in lake sediment long after death of the cell. As well, the water-chemistry requirements of many diatom species are known. Consequently, the presence and abundance of diatom cell-wall fossils in dated layers of lake-sediment cores can be used to infer historical communities and water chemistry. This technique has been used to demonstrate that some currently acidic lakes in eastern Canada were not acidic as recently as several decades ago.

During the acidification of Lake 223 in the Experimental Lakes Area, the phytoplankton community changed markedly. Initially, it was dominated by species of golden-brown algae; this changed to dominance by green algae (family Chlorophyceae; Findlay and Kasian, 1986). Although species composition changed substantially, there was little change in the overall diversity of species. A small increase in algal biomass occurred after acidification, apparently caused by increased clarity of the water, which allowed more productivity to occur. The acidification of Lake 223 reached pH 5.0–5.1 during 1981–83, but was allowed to return to pH 5.5–5.6 during 1984–86. When this happened, algal species typical of the pre-acidification community quickly reappeared.

The phytoplankton community of lakes and ponds is much more sensitive to the fertility of the water than to changes in its acidity, being especially sensitive to the supply of phosphorus (see Chapter 20). The primary productivity of almost all freshwaters increases greatly if they are fertilized with phosphorus. This ecological change, known as *eutrophication*, also occurs in acidic waterbodies. This is illustrated by studies of two adjacent lakes in Nova Scotia, Little Springfield Lake and Drain Lake. After construction activity in their watersheds exposed pyrite-containing minerals to the atmosphere, both lakes became very acidic. The acidity was generated through a process similar to acid-mine drainage (Kerekes *et al.*, 1984). Little Springfield Lake had an average pH of 3.7 and supported little algal productivity; it was oligotrophic. However, Drain Lake (pH 4.0) received inputs of phosphorus-rich sewage, and it became eutrophic and highly productive in spite of its extreme acidity.

Periphytes are microscopic algae that live on the surface of sediment, rocks, woody debris, and aquatic plants. The periphyton community can include hundreds of species, even in acidic lakes. Periphytes are especially abundant in lakes with clear water, where their late-summer biomass may develop cloudy or felt-like mats. During the experimental acidification of Lake 223 (in the ELA), a benthic mat of the filamentous green alga *Mougeotia* developed in shallow water after the pH decreased below 5.6. Mats of filamentous algae have been observed in many other acid-

Photo 19.4 This lake near a smelter at Sudbury, Ontario, was acidified to a pH less than 4, mostly by the dry deposition of SO_2 gas from the atmosphere. Since 1972, SO_2 pollution in the vicinity has been greatly abated, allowing the lake to become less acidic over time. Today, the lake again provides habitat for some species that are intolerant of severe acidity.

ified lakes. The reasons for the growth of algal mats are not known, but they may be related to a decrease in herbivorous aquatic invertebrates, resulting in reduced grazing.

Aquatic Plants

Aquatic plants (macrophytes) can be quite abundant in shallow lakes and ponds. Acidification of some lakes has resulted in an increased abundance of aquatic mosses, especially species of *Sphagnum*. In some cases, this has been accompanied by declines of other plants, such as reed (*Phragmites communis*), water lobelia (*Lobelia dortmanna*), and quillwort (*Isoetes* spp.). Moreover, the invasion of lakes by *Sphagnum* may accelerate the process of acidification, because these mosses are extremely efficient at absorbing Ca^{2+}, Mg^{2+}, and other cations from water, which they exchange for H^+. In addition, mats of *Sphagnum* interfere with chemical reactions at the sediment/water interface, hindering the neutralization of acidity that might otherwise occur there.

Communities of aquatic plants differ greatly between clear-water acidic lakes and those with brown, organically stained water. For example, Pebbleloggitch Lake (refer to Table 19.5) has dark-brown, acidic (pH 4.5) water, which prevents the penetration of light into deeper habitats. Consequently, macrophytes can grow only within a shallow fringe of water around the edge of the lake, and only

15% of the bottom is vegetated (Stewart and Freedman, 1989). The most abundant aquatic plants, including the yellow-flowered spatter-dock (*Nuphar variegatum*), have floating leaves. In comparison, nearby Beaverskin Lake has extremely clear water and is somewhat less acidic (pH 5.3). Because of the clarity of its water, virtually the entire bottom receives enough light to support aquatic plants, even to a depth of 6.5 m. Many of the macrophytes, including mats of *Sphagnum* moss, are species that maintain all of their foliage underwater.

Even in acidic lakes, the productivity of macrophytes is stimulated by nutrient additions. Drain Lake (mentioned above), an extremely acidic (pH 4.0) but eutrophic lake, has a lush productivity of aquatic plants. As with phytoplankton, the fertility of lakewaters affects the productivity of aquatic plants much more than acidity does.

Zooplankton

Zooplankton are tiny animals, mostly crustaceans, that live in the water column of lakes and ponds. Most zooplankters filter-feed on phytoplankton cells, but some are predators of other species of zooplankton. Some species are tolerant of acidity and may occur in water as acidic as pH 4 or less. The effects of acidification on zooplankton are complex because several factors are involved:

- the toxicity of H^+ and associated metals, such as Al^{3+}
- changes in the quantities of algae available as food
- changes in predation, especially if zooplankton-eating fish are eliminated from an acidified habitat

A survey of 47 lakes in Ontario found that species of zooplankton could be good indicators of water chemistry (Sprules, 1975). This is similar to the use of phytoplankton species as indicators. Some zooplankton species are indicators of acidic lakes, occurring at pH <5: *Polyphemus pediculus, Daphnia catawba*, and *D. pulicaria*. Others live only in lakes with pH >5: *Tropocyclops prasinus mexicanus, Epischura lacustris, Diaptomus oregonensis, Leptodora kindtii, Daphnia galeata mendotae, D. retrocurva, D. ambigua*, and *D. longiremis*. Some species are apparently indifferent to acidity, occurring over a wide range of pH. For example, *Diaptomus minutus* was the most frequently observed species in the survey, occurring over the pH range 3.8–7.0. Lakes with a pH >5 had 9 to 16 species of zooplankton, with three or four being dominant. More acidic lakes (pH below 5) had

one to seven species, with only one or two dominants.

The experimental acidification of Lake 223 resulted in an increased abundance of zooplankton, an effect attributed to the previously described increase in phytoplankton biomass (Malley *et al.*, 1982). Throughout the acidification of Lake 223, *Diaptomus minutus* and *Cyclops bicuspidatus* remained the most abundant zooplankters. Some other species, however, were intolerant of acidification. This included the opossum shrimp (*Mysis relicta*), a predator that disappeared after the pH decreased below 5.6.

Benthic Invertebrates

Benthic invertebrates live in the sediment of lakes, streams, and other waterbodies. The number of species of these small animals tends to be lower in acidic waters. However, they can still be abundant, especially in acidified waterbodies from which predatory fish have disappeared. The most common benthic invertebrates in acidic lakes are species of insects and crustaceans (although other species of these same groups are intolerant of acidity). Mollusks do not occur in strongly acidic conditions because it is difficult for them to maintain their shells of calcium carbonate. A study of mollusks in more than 1000 lakes in Norway found that no species of clams could tolerate a pH below 6.0, and no snails could tolerate a pH below 5.2 (Okland and Okland, 1986).

Because sediments are relatively strongly buffered, they are much less vulnerable to acidification than the overlying water. For instance, acidity of the sediment did not change much during the experimental acidification of Lake 223 (Kelly *et al.*, 1984). In 1981, when the pH of water just above the sediment was about 5.3, at 0.5 cm into the sediment the pH was 6.0. At a depth of 2.0 cm the pH was 6.7, unchanged from the pre-acidification condition. Because the habitat of benthic invertebrates is well buffered, some species are not catastrophically affected by acidification of the overlying lake. During the acidification of Lake 223, the population of chironomid midges increased and peaked at a water pH of about 5.6 (Mills, 1984). However, the initially abundant population of mayfly larvae disappeared at about pH 5. In addition, the crayfish *Orconectes virilis* became extirpated because of reproductive failure after the pH decreased below 5.6.

Fish

Fish populations are the best-known victims of aquatic acidification. Losses of trout, salmon, and other economically important fish have occurred in acidified surface waters in Canada, the U.S., and Eurasia.

Studies in south-central Ontario have documented losses of fish populations from acidified lakes in the Killarney region (Beamish and Harvey, 1972; Harvey and Lee, 1982). That area is subject to severely acidic precipitation (pH 4.0–4.5), as well as to dry deposition of acidifying SO_2 because of its relative proximity to the smelters at Sudbury. A survey during the early 1970s found that 33 of 150 lakes in the Killarney area had a pH below 4.5.

Local extirpations of several species of fish were actually observed by ecologists working on Lumsden and George Lakes in the Killarney area. There was also evidence for the losses of other fish populations, thanks to eyewitness accounts of historical sport fisheries in currently fishless lakes. The Killarney area has had 17 known extirpations of lake trout (*Salvelinus namaycush*), an important sportfish that cannot breed successfully at a pH below 5.5. There are also extirpations of smallmouth bass (*Micropterus dolomieu*) from 12 lakes in the region, of largemouth bass (*M. salmoides*) and walleye (*Stizostedion vitreum*)

from four lakes, and yellow perch (*Perca flavescens*) and rock bass (*Ambloplites rupestris*) from two others.

The pH of Lumsden Lake was 6.8 in 1961, but only 4.4 in 1971. This change caused reproductive failure and extirpation of lake trout, lake herring (*Coregonus artedii*), and white sucker (*Catostomus commersoni*). When George Lake reached pH 4.8–5.3, lake trout, walleye, burbot (*Lota lota*), and smallmouth bass disappeared. As acidification progressed further, there were losses of northern pike (*Esox lucius*), rock bass, pumpkinseed sunfish (*Lepomis gibbosus*), brown bullhead (*Ictalurus nebulosus*), and white sucker. All of these extirpations resulted from persistent failures of the fish to reproduce in the acidified lakes.

Losses of sportfish populations have also occurred in Nova Scotia, where Atlantic salmon (*Salmo salar*) has been lost from seven highly acidic (pH below 4.7) rivers, but not from rivers with higher pH (Figure 19.5). Lacroix and Townsend (1987) penned juvenile salmon in four acidic streams in Nova Scotia. No fish survived in streams with pH below 4.7, but all survived at higher pH.

Elsewhere, early surveys (from the 1930s) of lakes in the Adirondack Mountains of New York State found brook

FIGURE 19.5 | Catch of Atlantic Salmon in Nova Scotian Rivers

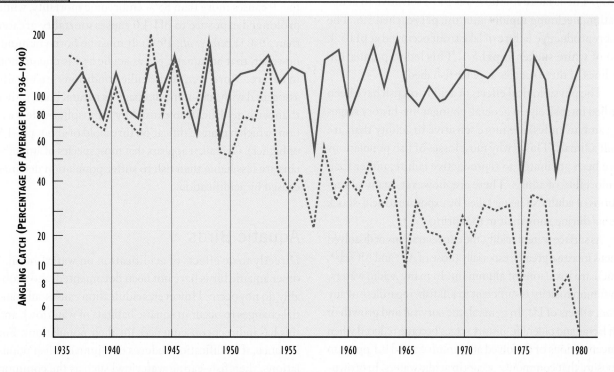

These sport-fishing data are standardized to facilitate comparison among rivers. The top line shows data for rivers with pH greater than 5.0. The bottom line is for rivers with pH 5.0 or less.

Source: Modified from Watt *et al.* (1983)

trout (*Salvelinus fontinalis*) in 82% of the lakes. However, in the 1970s, this species was absent in 43% of 215 lakes in the same region (Schofield, 1982).

An extensive survey of 700 Norwegian lakes in the 1970s found that brown trout (*Salmo trutta*) was absent from 40% of the waterbodies and sparse in another 40% (Wright and Snekvik, 1978). Almost all of those lakes had supported trout populations before the 1950s. Losses of fish populations have been most extensive in southern Norway, where acidifying deposition is most intense.

In eastern North America, the fish species that are most tolerant of acidification are yellow perch, rock bass, central mudminnow (*Umbra limni*), largemouth bass, bluegill (*Lepomis macrochirus*), black bullhead (*Ictalurus melas*), brown bullhead, golden shiner (*Notemigonus crysoleucas*), and American eel (*Anguilla rostrata*). These species are known to occur in some waterbodies with pH more acidic than 4.6. Other species of fish are relatively sensitive to acidification of their habitat; in general, they need a water pH greater than 6 to survive.

Prior to its experimental acidification, Lake 223 supported five species of fish: lake trout, white sucker, fathead minnow (*Pimephales promelas*), pearl dace (*Semotilus margarita*), and slimy sculpin (*Cottus cognatus*) (Mills *et al.*, 1987). The fathead minnow was most sensitive to acidification, declining rapidly after the pH reached 5.6. The first reproductive failure of lake trout occurred at pH 5.4, and of white sucker at pH 5.1. This led to population declines of these species as older fish died.

The physiological effects of acidity on fish have been studied intensively. In general, younger life-history stages (fry and juveniles) are more sensitive to acidity than are adult animals. This is why most losses of fish populations have been attributed to reproductive failure, rather than to mortality of adults. There are, however, many observations of adult fish being killed by exposure to acid-shock events during snowmelt in the spring.

As surface waters acidify, the concentrations of dissolved metals increase greatly, especially those of Al^{3+} and $AlOH^{2+}$, which are toxic ions of aluminum. In many acidic waters, aluminum toxicity is sufficient to kill fish, regardless of any direct effects of H^+. In general, the survival and growth of fish larvae and older life-history stages become reduced when concentrations of dissolved aluminum exceed 0.1 ppm, an exposure that commonly occurs in acidic waters. In brown-coloured water, however, almost all soluble aluminum and other metals occur as organo-metallic complexes. Metals in this state are less bioavailable and much less toxic than the free-ionic forms that occur in clear water with a similar pH.

Amphibians

Amphibians depend on aquatic habitat during at least part of their life cycle. Most Canadian species lay their eggs in water, where their larvae live until metamorphosis occurs, after which the adults utilize nearby terrestrial habitat. Research suggests that some species of amphibians are vulnerable to acidification of their aquatic habitat, while others appear to be indifferent to this environmental change.

A study of amphibian breeding sites in Nova Scotia, covering a range of pH from 3.9 to 9.0, found that the distributions of some species were not obviously influenced by acidity (Dale *et al.*, 1985). The bullfrog (*Rana catesbeiana*) occurred from pH 4.0 to 9.0; spring peeper (*Hyla crucifer*) and yellow-spotted salamander (*Ambystoma maculatum*), from pH 3.9 to 7.8; green frog (*R. clamitans*), from pH 3.9 to 7.3; and wood frog (*R. sylvatica*), from pH 4.3 to 7.8. Yellow-spotted salamander and green, bull, wood, and pickerel (*R. palustris*) frogs all had eggs, developing larvae, and adults present in some habitats at pH 4, suggesting that reproduction was occurring at that extreme acidity. Studies in other regions, however, have shown that some species of amphibians are intolerant of acidity.

Laboratory experiments with 14 species of amphibians have shown that exposing developing eggs to pH 3.7 to 3.9 causes more than 85% embryonic mortality, while prolonged exposure to pH 4.0 causes mortality greater than 50% (Freda *et al.*, 1991). It must be borne in mind, however, that an aquatic pH as acidic as 4 is uncommon in nature. Moreover, such acidic conditions are usually associated with acid-mine drainage or natural bogs, rather than with acidification caused by atmospheric deposition (which has an acidification threshold of about pH 4.5 or higher). Overall, it appears that most species of amphibians are less liable than fish to suffer population declines caused by acidification.

Aquatic Birds

Directly toxic effects of acidification on waterfowl and other aquatic birds have not been documented, and probably do not occur. However, acidification causes substantial changes to occur in aquatic habitats of waterfowl, and this has indirect consequences for their populations. For instance, if acidification reduces or eliminates fish populations, then fish-eating waterfowl such as the common loon (*Gavia immer*) and common merganser (*Mergus merganser*) will suffer, as will piscivorous (fish-eating) raptors such as osprey (*Pandion haliaetus*). However, the extirpation of predatory fish could result in an increased abundance of aquatic insects and zooplankton, which would improve the food resource for other species of waterfowl such as mallard (*Anas platyrhynchos*), black duck (*A. rubripes*), ring-necked duck (*Aythya collaris*), and common golden-eye (*Bucephala clangula*).

The breeding success of common loons was studied on 84 lakes in central Ontario (Alvo *et al.*, 1988). Only 9% of breeding attempts were successful on low-alkalinity lakes (below 40 μeq/L), which are either acidic or vulnerable to acidification because the water has little acid-neutralizing capacity. In contrast, 57% of breeding attempts were successful on lakes with alkalinity of 40–200 μeq/L, and 59% on lakes exceeding 200 μeq/L. These observations likely reflect the size of the fish populations in these lakes.

A study of 79 small lakes and ponds in New Brunswick found that the biomass of aquatic invertebrates in the littoral (shallow, near-shore) zone was greater in acidic waterbodies with pH 4.5–4.9 than in those with a pH greater than 5.5 (Parker *et al.*, 1992). Five species of ducks that feed on invertebrates had an average of 3.5 broods/ha on waterbodies with pH below 5.5, compared with only 0.65 broods/ha at higher pHs. The higher biomass of invertebrates in the more acidic waterbodies was likely due to decreased predation because of a reduced fish community.

Drain Lake in Nova Scotia was previously described as a highly acidic (pH 4.0) but eutrophic lake. Drain Lake is fishless and has large populations of aquatic invertebrates and plants. This habitat allows black ducks and ring-necked ducks to be more productive than is typical for lakes in the region (Kerekes *et al.*, 1984).

Reclamation

Even before acidification became a high-profile issue, wildlife managers in some regions were "improving" habitat for sportfish in brown-coloured lakes by treating the acidic water with powdered limestone (calcium carbonate, $CaCO_3$) or lime (calcium hydroxide, $Ca(OH)_2$). These treatments, known as **liming**, serve to reduce acidity, clarify water, and improve aquatic productivity, particularly of fish. Not surprisingly, much research has also been done on the usefulness of liming treatments in reclaiming surface waters that have been degraded by atmospheric depositions of acidifying substances. Liming of acidified lakes is an exercise in restoration ecology (see In Detail 9.3).

Effects of liming on lake water pH are illustrated in Figure 19.6 for three limed lakes and one reference (i.e., non-limed but acidic) lake in south-central Ontario (Dillon

et al., 1979; Yan *et al.*, 1979). Initially, the treated lakes had a water pH of 4–5, but this was increased by liming to pH 7–8. Middle and Hannah Lakes had a fairly stable pH after treatment, but Lohi quickly drifted back toward an acidic condition. This reflects the sizes of the watersheds of the lakes—Lohi drains a relatively large area and flushes quickly, so its neutralization results are relatively short-lived. Note that fertilizing the lakes with phosphate, which stimulates the productivity of phytoplankton and macrophytes, also has an acid-neutralizing effect, although this is much smaller than that associated with liming.

Initially, the limed lakes in the Ontario study exhibited a drastic decline in the biomass and productivity of phytoplankton and zooplankton. However, the biomass of phytoplankton rather quickly returned to the pre-liming condition, with lingering changes in species composition. Zooplankton recovered more slowly, and even after three years, had not returned to their pre-liming abundance. In addition, fish kept in experimental cages in the limed lakes suffered high rates of mortality. This was likely related to metal toxicity since the experimental lakes were affected by particulate fallout from the Sudbury smelters. The aqueous concentrations of Cu, Ni, Zn, and Al all decreased after the lakes were limed because these metals have a lower solubility in less acidic water. However, the metal concentrations still remained rather high, and continued to exert toxic stress on fish and other biota.

In some regions of Scandinavia, liming is used routinely to treat large numbers of acidified lakes and rivers. This is being done to mitigate the biological damage caused by acidification. Sweden, for example, has the world's largest liming programs (Swedish EPA, 2005). By the late 1970s, about 17 000 lakes in Sweden had been acidified by atmospheric deposition (out of a total of 90 000 lakes), as had many streams and rivers. Of the acidified waterbodies, more than 7000 have been treated with liming agents; about 200 000 t of powdered limestone are used each year for this purpose. Typically, the liming treatment must be repeated on a three-year rotation. In Norway, about 3000 waterbodies have been limed (State of the Environment Norway, 2005). Liming has been conducted much less extensively in North America, largely because the programs are expensive and environmental priorities are different here from those in Scandinavia.

Research on liming has demonstrated that acidified surface waters can be neutralized. It must be understood, however, that liming treats the symptoms of damage in acidified ecosystems, but not the causes of the acidification. Moreover, liming itself represents an environmental stress

FIGURE 19.6  Effects of Lake Liming

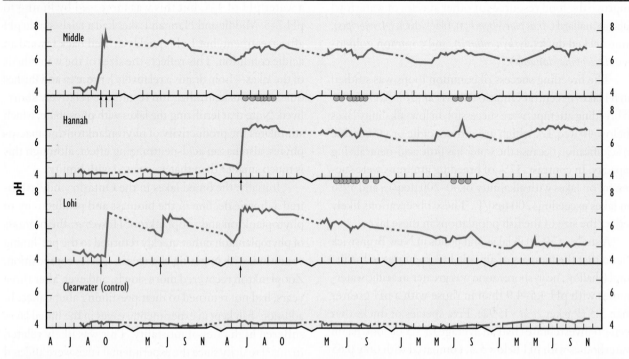

Middle, Hannah, Lohi, and Clearwater Lakes are located in the Sudbury region of Ontario. These lakes were acidified by a combination of dry and wet atmospheric depositions. The times of treatment with neutralizing agents ($CaCO_3$ or $Ca(OH)_2$) are indicated by arrows, and the times of addition of phosphate, by solid dots.

Source: Modified from Dillon *et al.* (1979)

that transforms a waterbody from one polluted condition to another that is still polluted, but less toxic. Liming causes severe damage to acid-adapted ecosystems, resulting in changes in species composition until new communities develop. In general, the most important benefit of liming is that less acidic waters can support fish populations, whereas acidic waters cannot. It is important to recognize, however, that liming is not a long-term solution to the acidification of freshwaters. In part, this is because acidic waterbodies must be periodically retreated as the liming materials are consumed or flushed out of the system.

To some degree, acidified waterbodies may also be managed by fertilization, a treatment that greatly stimulates productivity, as was previously noted for Drain Lake. Acidic lakes that are fertilized can sustain a large biomass of phytoplankton, macrophytes, and invertebrates. This can allow some species of waterfowl to breed in large numbers, even if fish cannot be sustained because of the acidic conditions. However, it is not always appropriate to create large numbers of highly productive lakes. For example, where recreational swimming is an important activity,

large quantities of algae and macrophytes are considered a nuisance. Nevertheless, fertilization is an effective and relatively inexpensive management tool that can enhance ecological conditions in acidified waterbodies.

Reducing Emissions

Ultimately, the extensive damage caused by acidifying atmospheric deposition can be resolved only by reducing the emissions of acid-forming gases. Although this fact is intuitively clear, the issue of emissions reduction remains highly controversial, for reasons such as the following:

- Scientists do not know exactly how much the emissions of SO_2 and/or NO_x must be reduced in order to avoid the damage caused by acidifying deposition.

- Various emission-reduction strategies are possible, and they vary in their economic consequences. For example, would it be more effective to target large point sources of emissions, such as smelters and power plants, while paying less attention to smaller, yet numerous, sources such as automobiles and oil-burning home furnaces? Or should large and small sources both be aggressively curtailed?

- To be effective, emissions reductions must be coordinated among neighbouring countries. For example, what will happen if the government of one country (perhaps one with large emissions of SO_2 and NO_x) does not regard acidifying deposition as a high-priority problem, but neighbouring countries do?

Not surprisingly, industries and regions that are responsible for large emissions of acid-forming gases have

tended to resist the imposition of substantial legislated reductions of their releases. In general, they argue that the scientific justification for these reductions is not yet convincing, while the economic costs of controls are known to be large and disruptive.

In addition, how low should the rates of atmospheric deposition of sulphur and nitrogen compounds be, in order to avoid further acidification of sensitive surface waters or to allow their recovery? The critical rates of deposition of acidifying compounds are influenced, in part, by the vulnerability of the receiving ecosystems—areas with shallow, nutrient-poor soil can sustain much lower inputs of acidifying substances than those with soil rich in calcium.

Although there are many uncertainties about the specific causes and magnitude of the damage caused by the atmospheric deposition of acidifying substances, it is obvi-

FIGURE 19.7 | Critical Loads for Sulphate

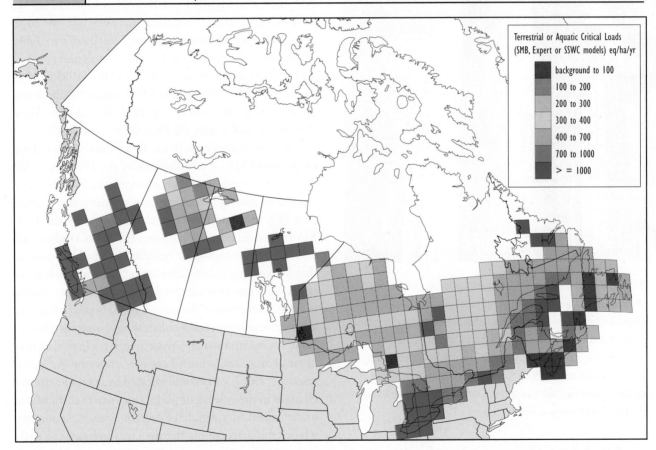

The critical load is the maximum amount of deposition that an ecosystem can sustain without experiencing damage. The critical load is substantially dependent on the acid-neutralizing capacity of the soils, rocks, and surface waters in a region, as well as the sensitivity of species to acidity. This figure shows how the critical loads for sulphate deposition vary in eastern Canada. Data are in kg/ha•y.

Source: Modified from Environment Canada (1998b)

Photo 19.5 The built environment can also be damaged by acidifying depositions from the atmosphere. For example, structures made of limestone, marble, or sandstone become eroded and chemically destabilized by the dry deposition of SO_2 and NO_x gases and by acidic precipitation. Acidifying air pollutants are seriously damaging many famous artifacts of cultural heritage, such as this ancient citadel known as the Acropolis in Athens, Greece.

ous that what goes up (i.e., emissions of acid-precursor gases) must eventually come down (i.e., as acidifying deposition). This commonsense notion is supported by a great deal of scientific evidence. This knowledge, combined with public awareness and concern about acidification in many countries, has spurred politicians to begin to take effec-

tive action. This is resulting in reductions in emissions of SO_2 and NO_x, particularly in relatively wealthy countries in North America and western Europe.

In 1992, the governments of Canada and the U.S. signed a binational air-quality treaty aimed at reducing acidifying deposition in both countries. This agreement, known as the Canada–U.S. Air Quality Agreement, calls for large expenditures by industries and governments to substantially reduce the emissions of air pollutants, especially SO_2. These cutbacks are on top of reductions of emissions that both countries had already achieved during the 1980s. The negotiated emissions target for SO_2 in the year 2000 was 14.4 million tonnes (Mt) per year for the U.S., and 3.2 Mt/y for Canada (including 2.3 Mt/y in eastern Canada). Canada has met its emissions target, but the U.S. exceeded its goal for 2000 and continues to do so. In the U.S., emissions of SO_2 decreased from 23.1 Mt in 1980 to 16.9 Mt in 1995 and 14.6 Mt in 2002, while emissions of NO_x increased slightly from 20.7 Mt in 1980 to 21.8 Mt in 1995 and then decreased to 20.5 Mt in 2002 (Environmental Protection Agency, 2005; refer to Table 16.2). For comparison, the Canadian emissions of SO_2 decreased from 4.7 Mt in 1980 to 2.5 Mt in 1995 and 2.4 Mt in 2002, while emissions of NO_x remained about the same during the overall period at 2.5–2.6 Mt/y (Environment Canada, 2005b; refer to Table 16.2).

A major component of the U.S. initiatives to reduce emissions of SO_2, established under the 1990 Clean Air Act Amendments, is the creation of a marketplace for "emissions trading." In essence, any company that is emitting SO_2 at a rate less than that allowed by the U.S. Environmental Protection Agency (EPA) has a right to sell (or trade) those non-used "credits" to another business that is exceeding its emissions target. This was an important initiative in environmental protection because it helps to set a "market value" for emissions of certain pollutants, and also for investments to reduce those damaging releases. From the environmental perspective, it is a logical instrument because the atmosphere is a "common-property resource" that is owned and affected by everyone, so any changes in the release of pollutants (whether increases or decreases) have a global effect. In essence, a company whose emissions are smaller than its allowance can realize a profit by selling its credits, while another business that has exceeded its target encumbers costs—which can be paid either by purchasing emissions credits or by taking action to reduce its own releases (such as installing SO_2-removal technology, switching to a low-sulphur fuel, or, in extreme cases, shutting down particularly dirty facilities). The flexibility associated with these various options is considered by some economists and politicians to have been an important benefit of the 1990 amendments to the U.S. Clean Air Act (Joskow *et al.*, 2000). Nevertheless, the establishment of a marketplace for releases of pollutants, and the commodification of those emissions, does liberate many companies from the expensive investments that would be required to achieve actual reductions of their emissions of pollutants. This fact has engendered significant controversy, as has the parallel establishment of a global marketplace for tradable emissions of greenhouse gases under the Kyoto Protocol.

But are the cuts in emissions large enough to achieve their intended effects of preventing and repairing acidification of ecosystems? According to the most recent science assessment carried out by Environment Canada, the reductions of SO_2 emissions have resulted in smaller rates of acidifying deposition in eastern Canada (this observation is based on a comparison of data for 1990–94 and 1996–2000; Environment Canada, 2005a). Nevertheless, an estimated 21–75% of eastern Canada (0.5–1.8 million km^2) still receives amounts of acidifying deposition that exceed the critical loads (the smaller numbers correspond to a best-case scenario, and the larger to a worst-case one). Environment Canada also suggests that, to protect ecosystems from further damage caused by acidifying deposition, a further 75% reduction of SO_2 emissions will be required by Canada and the U.S. beyond those agreed to under the existing Air Quality Agreement.

Furthermore, not much action has been taken to reduce the emissions of NO_x, and this appears to be working against the environmental benefits associated with increased control of SO_2. It is crucial that future regulatory actions include reduced emissions of both SO_2 and NO_x and that we continue to monitor and conduct research on acid rain and its environmental damage.

The 1992 air-pollution treaty between Canada and the U.S. is a constructive accomplishment. However, it appears that the reductions of SO_2 emissions are not sufficient in themselves to prevent many of the damages associated with acidifying deposition. So far, there has been little reduction in the acidity of precipitation, so extremely large areas of terrain continue to be affected by this phenomenon. Some lakes, however, appear to be benefiting from the reduced sulphate deposition: in a sample of 202 lakes monitored in eastern Canada since the early 1980s, the acidity of 33% of the lakes has decreased. However, 56% have not changed, and 11% have become more acidic (Environment Canada, 1998b). Overall, about 80% of recently sampled lakes in Nova Scotia had a pH <6, as did 40% of those in Ontario and 25% in New Brunswick (note that pH 6 is considered a critical threshold of tolerance for sensitive fish and other aquatic animals; Environment Canada, 2005). Many of these lakes are naturally acidic because of organic substances leaching from bogs; this is particularly the case of Nova Scotia, where brown-waters comprise about 40% of the acidic lakes. Across eastern Canada, however, an estimated 0.5-0.6 million lakes are thought to be vulnerable to acidification under an acid-deposition regime similar to that current in 2004.

It should also be recognized that pollution control is extremely expensive. For example, it would cost an estimated $600 million annually to further reduce the SO_2 emissions by 50% below the current targets for eastern Canada and the eastern United States. Because of this cost, the policies favouring reduced emissions of SO_2 and NO_x may not be able to survive the frequent challenges mounted by politicians, economists, and business people who do not believe that such actions are necessary.

So far, actions to reduce the emissions of SO_2 and NO_x have been vigorous only in the relatively wealthy regions of North America and western Europe. In other countries, the political focus is mostly on industrial and economic growth. Air pollution and other environmental damages "subsidize" that economic growth and are often paid little heed. As soon as possible, much more political and scientific attention must be devoted to the problems of acidifying deposition and other kinds of pollution in eastern Europe, the former Soviet Union, China, India, Southeast Asia, Mexico, and other rapidly developing countries. In these countries, emissions of SO_2, NO_x, and other important airborne pollutants are galloping out of control.

Conclusions

Acidification is a natural process that occurs as ecosystems interact with climatic and biological influences, for example in bogs and coniferous forest. Acidification is also caused by anthropogenic influences, particularly emissions of SO_2 and NO_x, which oxidize to form acids while in the atmosphere or after they are dry-deposited to ecosystems. Aquatic and terrestrial ecosystems that are vulnerable to acidification have small acid-neutralizing capacities; this is largely a result of small stocks of calcium and magnesium carbonates in their soil and rocks. Low-alkalinity freshwaters are particularly at risk of acidification by atmospheric deposition; higher-alkalinity waters and terrestrial ecosystems are much less vulnerable. When waterbodies acidify to a pH less than about 6, they lose their populations of some fish species as well as other acid-sensitive biota. Acidifying atmospheric influences also causes damage to the built environment by eroding materials made of limestone, marble, and certain metals such as copper. Although some of the ecological damage caused by acidification to lakes and other surface waters can be mitigated by liming (i.e., by adding powdered limestone), this treatment has to be repeated, typically on about a three-year

rotation. The best way to avoid the environmental problems associated with atmospheric deposition is to reduce the emissions of the key acid-precursor gases (i.e., SO_2 and NO_x). To a substantial degree this is being done in many wealthy countries, including Canada. However, rapidly developing countries, such as China and India, are not paying much attention to this environmental problem, and it is rapidly becoming worse as they aggressively increase their supply of commercial energy by burning sulphurous fossil fuels, particularly coal.

Key Terms

acidification	buffering capacity
acid rain	acid sulphate soil
wet deposition	acid-mine drainage
dry deposition	acid shock
acidifying deposition	whole-lake experiment
LRTAP (long-range transport of atmospheric pollutants)	acid-neutralizing capacity
	liming
	critical load

Questions for Review

1. What is the principle of conservation of electrochemical neutrality? How is it relevant to water chemistry? Refer specifically to the acidification of precipitation and surface waters.

2. What environmental influences can cause soil to become acidic? How can this problem be managed?

3. How does habitat acidification affect aquatic biota, including phytoplankton, macrophytes, zooplankton, benthic invertebrates, fish, and birds?

4. Define the term "critical load" and discuss the factors that influence its value for particular kinds of terrain and surface waters.

Questions for Discussion

1. Compare the chemistry of rainwater and lakewater in a region vulnerable to acidification. What are the reasons for the differences?

2. How do both wet and dry depositions of acidifying substances contribute to acidification? Why do the rates and relative importance of these processes vary between urban and rural areas?

3. Are surface waters in your area acidic or likely to become so? Explain your answer in terms of the factors that influence vulnerability to acidification.

4. Explain why relatively wealthy countries have been taking action to reduce their emissions of acid-precursor gases like SO_2 and NO_x, but rapidly developing countries such as China and India have not. What are the likely consequences of these policies?

Exploring Issues

1. Two broad options for dealing with acidifying deposition are emissions reductions to prevent the problem and liming of water and soil to treat the symptoms. Some people have called emissions reductions the "billion dollar solution," and liming the "million dollar solution" because of the potentially greater capital costs associated with technologies for reducing SO_2 and NO_x emissions. Which of these options (or both) do you think is most appropriate for dealing with acidification as an environmental problem? Why?

2. Canada and the U.S. have negotiated a treaty concerning the transboundary movements of air pollutants, with a focus on acidifying deposition from the atmosphere. Major aspects of the treaty are reductions in the emissions of SO_2 and NO_x to the atmosphere. You are a scientist working for Environment Canada and have been given the responsibility of monitoring whether the negotiated emissions reductions have been successful in improving conditions in the province where you live (i.e., whether acidification is becoming less of a problem). How would you design a program of environmental monitoring and research to answer this important question? What ecological and human health questions would you examine?

References

Alvo, R., D.J.J. Hussell, and M. Berrill. 1988. The breeding success of common loons (*Gavia immer*) in relation to alkalinity and other lake characteristics in Ontario. *Can. J. Zool.*, **66**: 746–752.

Baker, J.P. (principal author). 1990. Biological effects of changes in surface water acid-base chemistry. In: *Acidic Deposition: State of Science and Technology. Vol. II. Aquatic Processes and*

Effects. Washington: U.S. Government Printing Office, Superintendent of Documents. pp. 13-1 to 13-381.

Baker, L.A. (principal author). 1990. Current status of surface water acid-base chemistry. In: *Acidic Deposition: State of Science and Technology. Vol. II. Aquatic Processes and Effects* Washington: U.S. Government Printing Office, Superintendent of Documents. pp. 9-1 to 9-367.

Baker, L.A., A.T. Herlihy, P.R., Kaufmann, and J.M. Eilers. 1991. Acidic lakes and streams in the United States: the role of acidic deposition. *Science*, **252**: 1151–1154.

Beamish, R.J. and H.H. Harvey. 1972. Acidification of the La Cloche Mountain Lakes, Ontario, and resulting fish mortalities. *J. Fish. Res. Board Can.*, **29**: 1131–1143.

Brand, D.G., P. Kehoe, and M. Connors. 1986. Coniferous afforestation leads to soil acidification in central Ontario. *Can. J. For. Res.*, **16**: 1289–1391.

Brodin, Y.W. and J.C.I. Kuylenstierna. 1992. Acidification and critical loads in Nordic countries: a background. *Ambio*, **21**: 332–338.

Buso, D.C., G.E. Likens, and J.S. Eaton. 2000. *Chemistry of Precipitation, Streamwater, and Lakewater in the Hubbard Brook Ecosystem Study: A Record of Sampling Protocols and Analytic Procedures.* General Technical Report NE-275. Newtown Square, PA: U.S. Department of Agriculture, Northeast Forest Experiment Station. www.fs.fed.us/ne/newtown_square/publications/technical_reports/pdfs/2000/gtrne275.pdf

Chan, W.S., R.J. Vet, C.U. Ro, A.J.S. Tang, and M.A. Lusis. 1984. Long-term precipitation quality and wet deposition fields in the Sudbury basin. *Atmos. Environ.*, **18**: 1175–1188.

Crocker, R.L. and J. Major. 1955. Soil development in relation to vegetation and surface age at Glacier Bay, Alaska. *J. Ecol.*, **43**: 427–448.

Dale, J.M., B. Freedman, and J. Kerekes. 1985. Acidity and associated water chemistry of amphibian habitats in Nova Scotia. *Can. J. Zool.*, **63**: 97–105.

Dillon, P.J., D.S. Jefferies, W. Snyder, R. Reid, N.D. Yan, D. Evans, J. Moss, and W.A. Scheider. 1977. *Acid Rain in South-Central Ontario: Present Conditions and Future Consequences.* Rexdale, ON: Ontario Ministry of the Environment.

Dillon, P.J., N.D. Yan, W.A. Schieder, and N. Conroy. 1979. Acidic lakes in Ontario, Canada: Characterization, extent, and responses to base and nutrient additions. *Arch. Hydrobiol.*, Suppl. **13**: 317–336.

Dixit, S.S., A.S. Dixit, and J.P. Smol. 1991. Multivariate environmental inferences based on diatom assemblages from Sudbury (Canada) lakes. *Freshwater Biol.*, **26**: 251–266.

Environment Canada. 1988. *Acid Rain: A National Sensitivity Assessment.* Ottawa: Environment Canada, Inland Waters Directorate.

Environment Canada. 1996. *The State of Canada's Environment, 1996.* Ottawa: Government of Canada.

Environment Canada. 1998. *1997 Canadian Acid Rain Assessment. Volume 1. Summary of Results.* Ottawa: Environment Canada.

Environment Canada. 2005a. *2004 Canadian Acid Deposition Science Assessment.* Downsview, ON: Meteorological Service of Canada. www.msc-smc.ec.gc.ca/saib/acid/assessment2004/summary/summary_e.pdf

Environment Canada. 2005b. *2002 National Pollutant Release Inventory (NPRI) Data.* www.ec.gc.ca/pdb/npri/npri_dat_rep_e.cfm

Findlay, D.L. and S.E.M. Kasian. 1986. Phytoplankton community responses to acidification of Lake 223, Experimental Lakes Area, northwestern Ontario. *Water, Air, Soil Pollut.*, **30**: 719–726.

Freda, J., W.J. Sadinski, and W.A. Dunson. 1991. Long term monitoring of amphibians populations with respect to the effects of acidic deposition. *Water, Air, Soil Pollut.*, **55**: 445–462.

Freedman, B. 1995. *Environmental Ecology.* 2nd ed. San Diego, CA: Academic.

Freedman, B. and T.A. Clair. 1987. Ion mass balances and seasonal fluxes from four acidic brownwater streams in Nova Scotia. *Can. J. Fish. Aquat. Sci.*, **44**: 538–548.

Gerhardsson, L., A. Oskarsson, and S. Skerfving. 1994. Acid precipitation—effects on trace elements and human health. *Science of the Total Environment*, **153**: 237–245.

Godbold, D.L. and A. Huttermann (eds.). 1994. *Effects of Acid Rain on Forest Processes.* Hoboken, NJ: Wiley-Liss.

Gunn, J.M. (ed.). 1995. *Restoration and Recovery of an Industrial Region: Progress in Restoring the Smelter-Damaged Landscape Near Sudbury, Canada.* New York: Springer.

Harvey, H.H. and C. Lee. 1982. Historical fisheries changes related to surface water pH changes in Canada. *Acid Rain/Fish., Proc. Int. Symp.*, pp. 45–55.

Henriksen, A. 1980. Acidification of freshwaters—a large scale titration. In: *Ecological Impacts of Acid Precipitation*, (D. Drablos and A. Tollan, eds.). Oslo: SNSF Project. pp. 68–74.

Jeffries, D.S., T.G. Brydges, P.J. Dillon, and W. Keller. 2003. Monitoring the results of Canada/U.S.A. acid rain control programs; some lake responses. *Environmental Monitoring and Assessment*, **88**: 3–19.

Joskow, P.L., A.D. Ellerman, J.-P. Montero, R. Schmatensee, and E.M. Bailey. 2000. *Markets for Clean Air: The U.S. Acid Rain Program.* Cambridge, UK: Cambridge University Press.

Kelly, C.A., J.W.M. Rudd, A. Furutani, and D.W. Schindler. 1984. Effects of lake acidification on rates of organic matter decomposition in sediments. *Limnol. Oceanogr.*, **29**: 687–694.

Kerekes, J. and B. Freedman. 1988. Physical, chemical, and biological characteristics of three watersheds in Kejimkujik National Park, Nova Scotia. *Arch. Environ. Contam. Toxicol.*, **18**: 183–200.

Kerekes, J., B. Freedman, G. Howell, and P. Clifford. 1984. Comparison of the characteristics of an acidic eutrophic and an acidic oligotrophic lake near Halifax, Nova Scotia. *Water Poll. Res. J. Canada*, **19**: 1–10.

Lacroix, G.L. and D.R. Townsend. 1987. Responses of juvenile Atlantic salmon (*Salmo salar*) to episodic increases in acidity of Nova Scotia rivers. *Can. J. Fish. Aquat. Sci.*, **44**: 1475–1484.

Likens, G.E., F.H. Bormann, R.S. Pierce, J.S. Eaton, and R.E. Munn. 1984. Long-term trends in precipitation chemistry at Hubbard Brook, New Hampshire. *Atmos. Environ.*, **18**: 2641–2647.

Lovett, G.M., W.A. Reiners, and R.K. Olson. 1982. Cloud droplet deposition in subalpine balsam fir forests: hydrological and chemical budgets. *Science*, **218**: 1303–1304.

Malley, D.F., D.L. Findlay, and P.S.S. Chang. 1982. Ecological effects of acid precipitation on zooplankton. In: *Acid Precipitation Effects on Ecological Systems* (F.M. D'Itri, ed.), Ann Arbor, MI: Ann Arbor Science. pp. 297–327.

Mills, K.H. 1984. Fish population responses to experimental acidification of a small Ontario lake. In: *Early Biotic Responses to Advancing Lake Acidification* (G.R. Hendry, ed.), Toronto: Butterworth. pp. 117–131.

Mills, K.H., S.M. Chalanchuk, L.C. Mohr, and I.J. Davies. 1987. Responses of fish populations in Lake 223 to 8 years of experimental acidification. *Can. J. Fish. Aquat. Sci.*, **44**, Suppl. 1, 114–125.

Morrison, I.K. 1983. Composition of percolate from reconstructed profiles of jack pine forest soils as influenced by acid input. In: *Effects of Accumulations of Air Pollutants in Forest Ecosystems*. (B. Ulrich and J. Pankrath, eds.). Berlin: Reidel. pp. 195–206.

Natural Resources Canada. 1998. *Effects of Acidic Deposition on Canada's Forests*. Ottawa: Natural Resources Canada.

NAPAP. 1991. *Integrated Assessment Report*. National Acid Precipitation Assessment Program (NAPAP), National Oceanic and Atmospheric Administration: Silver Spring: MD.

NAPAP. 1993. *1992 Report to Congress*. National Acid Precipitation Assessment Program (NAPAP), National Oceanic and Atmospheric Administration: Silver Spring: MD.

NAPAP. 1998. *Biennial Report to Congress: An Integrated Assessment*. National Acid Precipitation Assessment Program (NAPAP), National Oceanic and Atmospheric Administration: Silver Spring: MD.

Parker, G.R., M.J. Petrie, and D.T. Sears. 1992. Waterfowl distribution relative to wetland acidity. *J. Wildl. Manage.*, **56**: 268–274.

Percy, K.E. 1986. The effects of simulated acid rain on germinative capacity, growth, and morphology of forest tree seedlings. *New Phytol.*, **104**: 473–484.

Reuss, J.R. and D.W. Johnson. 1985. Effect of soil processes on the acidification of water by acid precipitation. *J. Environ. Qual.*, **14**: 26–31.

Ro, C.U. and R.J. Vet. 2005. *Analyzed 2000 Data Fields from the National Atmospheric Chemistry Database and Analysis Facility*. Toronto, ON: Air Quality Research Branch, Meteorological Service of Canada, Environment Canada.

Rose, J. (ed.). 1994. *Acid Rain: Current Situation and Remedies*. Yverdon, Switzerland: Gordon & Breach Science Pub.

Schindler, D.W. 1988. Effects of acid rain on freshwater ecosystems. *Science*, **239**: 149–157.

Schindler, D.W. 1990. Experimental perturbations of whole lakes as tests of hypotheses concerning ecosystem structure and function. *Oikos*, **57**: 25–41.

Schindler, D.W., K.H. Mills, D.F. Malley, D.L. Findlay, J.A. Shearer, I.J. Davies, M.A. Turner, G.A. Linsey, and D.A. Cruikshank. 1985. Long-term ecosystem stress: the effects of years of experimental acidification on a small lake. *Science*, **228**: 1395–1401.

Schofield, C.L. 1982. Historical fisheries changes in the United States related to decreases in surface water pH. In: *Proc. Int. Symp. Acid. Rain/Fish*. Bethesda, MD: American Fisheries Society. pp. 57–67.

Shannon, J.D. and B.M. Lecht. 1986. Estimation of source-receptor matrices for deposition of NO_X-N. *Water, Air, Soil Pollut.*, **30**: 815–824.

Sprules, W.G. 1975. Midsummer crustacean zooplankton communities in acid-stressed lakes. *J. Fish. Res. Board Can.*, **32**: 389–395.

State of the Environment Norway. 2005. *Acid Rain*. www.environment.no/templates/themepage____2149.aspx

Stewart, C.C. and B. Freedman. 1989. Comparison of the macrophyte communities of a clearwater and a brown-water oligotrophic lake in Kejimkujik National Park, Nova Scotia. *Water, Air, Soil Pollut.*, **46**: 335–341.

Swedish EPA. 2005. *Acid Rain*. www.internat.naturvardsverket.se/index.php3?main=/documents/pollutants/kalka/acidrain/acidrain.htm

Tveite, B. 1980. Effects of acid precipitation on soil and forest. 9. Tree growth in field experiments. In: *Ecological Impact of Acid Precipitation* (D. Drablos and A. Tollan, eds.). Oslo: SNSF Project. pp. 206–207.

U.S. Environmental Protection Agency. 2005. *Air Trends*. www.epa.gov/airtrends/

Watmough, S.A. and P.J. Dillon. 2004. Major element fluxes from a coniferous watershed in central Ontario, 1982–1999. *Biogeochemistry*, **67**: 369–398.

Watt, W.D., C.D. Scott, and W.J. White. 1983. Evidence of acidification of some Nova Scotia rivers and its impact on Atlantic salmon. *Can. J. Fish. Aquat. Sci.*, **40**: 462–473.

Wood, T. and F.H. Bormann. 1976. *Short-term effects of a simulated acid rain upon the growth and nutrient relations of Pinus strobus*. Upper Darby, PA: Northeastern Forest Experiment Station. U.S.D.A. For. Serv., Gen. Tech. Rep. NE-23. pp. 815–824.

World Resources Institute. 2005. *Earth Trends. The Environmental Information Portal*. Washington, DC: WRI.

Wright, R.F. and E. Snekvik. 1978. Acid precipitation: Chemistry and fish populations in 700 lakes in southernmost Norway. *Verh.-Int. Ver. Theor. Angew. Limnol.*, **20**: 765–775.

Yan, N.D., R.E. Girard, and C.J. Lafrance. 1979. *Survival of Rainbow Trout*, Salmo gairdneri, *in Submerged Enclosures in Lakes Treated with Neutralizing Agents near Sudbury, Ontario*. Rexdale, ON: Ontario Ministry of the Environment.

Informative Websites

Environment Canada. www.ec.gc.ca/acidrain/index.html

This website hosts a state-of-the-environment report concerning emissions and effects of acid rain.

Environment Canada. Criteria Air Contaminants Emission Summaries.

www.ec.gc.ca/pdb/ape/cape_home_e.cfm

Environment Canada compiled this emission inventory, which contains estimates of emissions for more than 60 industrial and non-industrial activities.

The Swedish NGO Secretariat on Acid Rain.
www.acidrain.org/

This website gives a European NGO perspective on the causes and consequences of acidifying deposition.

U.S. Environmental Protection Agency. Acid Rain.
www.epa.gov/air/acidrain.html

This website of the EPA gives the U.S. government's interpretation of the causes and consequences of acid rain, and the ways of avoiding this environmental problem.

U.S. Environmental Protection Agency. U.S.–Canada Air Quality Agreement. www.epa.gov/airmarkets/usca/

This website hosts the text of the Air Quality Agreement between Canada and the U.S. as well as reports on progress made in attainment.

20 Additional Problems of Surface Waters

CHAPTER OBJECTIVES

After completing this chapter, you will be able to

1. Compare and contrast the causes of eutrophication of fresh and marine waters.
2. Explain the evidence that phosphorus is usually the limiting nutrient for eutrophication of freshwaters.
3. Describe the objectives and technologies used in primary, secondary, and tertiary sewage treatment.
4. Explain the role of eutrophication in the damage caused to the ecosystem of Lake Erie.
5. Explain the differences between hydroelectric developments involving reservoirs and run-of-the-river facilities.
6. Describe the environmental damage caused by dams and reservoirs.

CHAPTER OUTLINE

Introduction

Aquatic ecosystems are affected by a wide range of environmental stressors, some natural and some associated with human activities. These stressors affect all levels of the aquatic food web, as well as ecological processes such as productivity and nutrient cycling. The effects of pollution and disturbance on ecosystems are a huge subject area because so many kinds of environmental stressors are affecting diverse aquatic species and ecosystems. Consequently, aspects of the subject are dealt with in various chapters of this book. In previous chapters, we examined the use of aquatic resources (Chapter 12) and the effects of pollution by metals and acidification (Chapters 16, 17, and 18). Here, we look at the effects of hydroelectric developments and eutrophication caused by nutrient enrichment of freshwater ecosystems. The effects on aquatic ecosystems of oil spills, pesticides, forestry, agricultural activities, and urbanization are examined in Chapters 21, 22, 23, 24, and 25.

Eutrophication

Eutrophic waters contain large concentrations of nutrients, and as a result they are highly productive. In contrast, **oligotrophic** waters are much less productive because of a restricted availability of nutrients. **Mesotrophic** waters are intermediate between these two conditions.

Some waterbodies occur in inherently fertile watersheds and are *naturally eutrophic*. So-called **cultural eutrophication**, however, is caused by anthropogenic nutrient inputs, usually through the dumping of sewage or the runoff of fertilizer from agricultural land. Both inland and marine waters can become eutrophic through increases in their nutrient supply, although the problem is more common in freshwaters.

The most conspicuous symptom of eutrophication is a large increase in primary productivity, especially of phytoplankton, which can develop dense populations known as an **algal bloom**. Shallow waterbodies may also experience a vigorous growth of aquatic plants (macrophytes). Since the increased productivity of algae and macrophytes can allow higher trophic levels to be more productive, aquatic invertebrates, fish, and waterfowl may also be abundant in eutrophic waterbodies.

Extremely eutrophic (**hypertrophic**) waters may, however, become severely degraded. Hypertrophic waterbodies develop noxious blooms of cyanobacteria (i.e., blue-green

bacteria) and algae during the summer, which may cause an off-flavour in water used for drinking, and may synthesize and release toxic organic compounds into the water. In addition, the decomposition of the algal biomass requires a large amount of oxygen, severely depleting its concentration in water. The resulting anoxic conditions are extremely stressful to many aquatic animals. Such conditions also facilitate the production and release of hydrogen sulphide (H_2S) and other noxious gases.

Cultural eutrophication, which can degrade both water quality and ecological conditions, is an important environmental problem in many areas. Severe eutrophication can impair the use of a waterbody as a source of drinking water, to support a fishery, or for recreation. Eutrophication can also degrade the ecological values of natural waters.

Causes of Eutrophication

Most lakes in Canada are geologically "young" because they occur on landscapes released from glacial ice only about 8000–12 000 years ago (depending on the area). Many

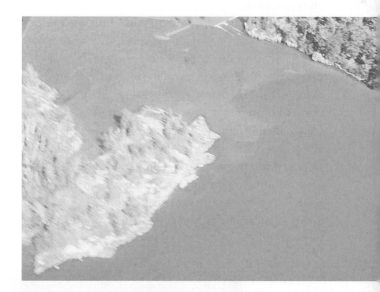

Photo 20.1   Lake-of-the-Woods is a large lake in northwestern Ontario and southeastern Manitoba. Its watershed is largely wild and forested, but Lake-of-the-Woods supports many cottages and a great deal of tourism. There are also nutrient inputs from rivers draining agricultural areas in the U.S. to the south and pulp mills in Ontario to the east. Shallow waters and bays of Lake-of-the-Woods are subject to eutrophication caused by nutrient enrichment. This aerial photograph shows a bloom of algae, indicated by the whitish colour of the water.

Source: P. Dillon

lakes are relatively deep, having had little time to accumulate much sediment in their basins. They also tend to have low rates of nutrient input. Over many centuries, however, lakes of this sort gradually increase in productivity as they accumulate nutrients. They also become shallower due to sedimentation, which results in increased rates of nutrient cycling. The slowly increasing productivity of many lakes over time is a natural expression of eutrophication.

Surface waters may also be naturally eutrophic if they occur in a watershed with fertile soil. This is the case of many lakes and ponds in the prairie region of Canada, particularly shallow waterbodies that recycle their nutrients relatively quickly.

Anthropogenic (cultural) eutrophication involves more rapid increases in the productivity of surface waters. This is most often caused by nutrient loading associated with sewage dumping or by agricultural runoff contaminated by fertilizer. Wherever humans live in large populations or engage in intensive agriculture, there are large inputs of nutrients into lakes, rivers, and other surface waters. In coastal areas, estuaries and shallow, near-shore areas may also be affected by anthropogenic nutrient inputs and eutrophication.

A theory called the **Principle of Limiting Factors** states that certain ecological processes are controlled by whichever environmental factor is present in the least supply relative to demand. According to this theory, the primary production of waterbodies is limited by whichever nutrient is present in least supply relative to its demand (assuming that light, temperature, and oxygen supply are all adequate). Research has shown that, in almost all freshwaters, primary production is limited by the availability of phosphorus, occurring as the phosphate ion (PO_4^{3-}). In contrast, marine waters are usually limited by the availability of inorganic nitrogen, particularly in the form of nitrate (NO_3^-).

Phosphorus as the Limiting Nutrient in Freshwater

During the 1960s and early 1970s, there was much controversy about eutrophication, including which nutrients were the limiting factors to primary production in lakes and other surface waters. Many scientists believed that phosphorus was most important in this regard. Others, however, suggested that dissolved nitrogen, in the form of nitrate or ammonium, was the critical limiting factor in many freshwaters. Plants and algae have relatively large demands for all of those nutrients, which typically occur in low concentrations in water.

It was also suggested that dissolved inorganic carbon (as bicarbonate, HCO_3^-) could be limiting primary productivity. Inorganic carbon is needed in large quantities by autotrophs. In aquatic systems, HCO_3^- is replenished mainly by the diffusion of atmospheric CO_2 into the surface water, which is a rather slow process.

Eventually, several lines of scientific evidence resolved the controversy about limiting nutrients. Studies have convincingly demonstrated that phosphorus is the key nutrient that limits primary production in most freshwaters. Consequently, controlling the rate of phosphorus supply is now known to be critical in the management of eutrophication.

The essential nature of the role of phosphorus is suggested in Table 20.1, which shows its typical concentration in freshwater (an index of "supply") and its concentration in plants (an index of "demand"). Because the ratio of demand to supply for phosphorus is considerably larger than for other important nutrients, it is a likely candidate for the primary limiting factor for the productivity of algae and plants in freshwaters. The data also suggest that the second most important nutrient is inorganic nitrogen, in the form of nitrate or ammonium. In the Great

| TABLE 20.1 | Demand and Supply of Essential Nutrients in Water |

These are indexed by the typical concentrations in freshwater plants and in freshwater.

NUTRIENT	CONCENTRATION IN PLANTS (%)	CONCENTRATION IN WATER (%)	RATIO OF CONCENTRATIONS PLANTS:WATER (APPROX.)
Carbon	45	0.012	3 750
Silicon	1.3	0.00065	2 000
Nitrogen	0.7	0.000023	30 000
Potassium	0.3	0.00023	1 300
Phosphorus	0.08	0.000001	80 000

Source: Modified from Vallentyne (1974)

Lakes, for example, phosphorus concentration in water is typically 30–40 times lower than that of nitrogen (Environment Canada, 1996).

Other information is also consistent with phosphorus being the controlling nutrient for eutrophication in freshwater. Perhaps the most convincing data come from a famous series of experiments conducted in an area of northwestern Ontario known as the Experimental Lakes Area (ELA; see Canadian Focus 20.1). Most of the research applicable to eutrophication has involved the addition of nutrients at various rates and in different combinations to selected lakes, followed by careful monitoring of the ecological responses. In terms of identifying phosphorus as the key nutrient causing eutrophication, the most important **whole-lake experiments** were the following (Schindler, 1978, 1990; Levine and Schindler, 1989):

- For two years, Lake 304 was fertilized with phosphorus, nitrogen, and carbon. It responded by becoming eutrophic. After the fertilization with phosphorus was stopped, Lake 304 returned to its original oligotrophic condition, even though nitrogen and carbon additions were continued.

- The two basins of Lake 226, an hourglass-shaped lake whose two sections are connected by a con-

stricted channel, were isolated with a vinyl curtain. One basin was fertilized with C + N + P in a weight ratio of 10:5:1, while the other received only C + N at 10:5. Only the basin receiving P developed algal blooms. After five years, the nutrient additions were stopped, and the original oligotrophic condition returned within just one year. A similarly rapid recovery was observed in another experiment, involving Lake 303, after fertilization with P was stopped.

- Lake 302N was fertilized with P + N + C. However, these nutrients were injected directly into deep water during the summer, at a time when lakes in the ELA develop a thermal stratification (see In Detail 20.1). Because the nutrients were injected into deep water, primary production in the surface water was not affected and eutrophication did not occur.

Research at ELA also demonstrated that when phosphorus, but not nitrogen and carbon, was deliberately added to lakes, the supply of N and C already in the lake was still capable of supporting P-induced eutrophication. Eutrophication induced a greater rate of fixation of atmospheric dinitrogen (N_2) by blue-green bacteria and an

In Detail 20.1

Lake Stratification

During most of the year, lakes have a rather uniform distribution of temperature throughout their depth. This allows their bottom and surface waters to mix easily under the influence of strong winds. During the summer, however, lakes often develop a persistent *stratified* condition. This is characterized by a surface layer of relatively warm water, several metres thick in most lakes (but thicker in some large lakes), lying above deeper, cooler water. Because the density of warm water is less than that of cool water, the two layers remain physically discrete and do not mix.

The relatively warm, upper water of a stratified lake is known as the *epilimnion*, while the cooler, deeper water is known as the *hypolimnion*. These layers are separated by a zone of rapid change in temperature, known as the *thermocline*. During the autumn, as the epilimnion cools, the stratification diminishes and the two layers become mixed by strong winds.

During stratification, oxygen and other dissolved substances can enter the hypolimnion, but mainly by diffusion across the thermocline. Because this is a slow process, hypolimnetic oxygen can be easily depleted in stratified lakes whose deeper water receives large inputs of organic material. The organic input may be associated with sewage, agricultural runoff, or algal biomass sinking from the epilimnion. The development of anoxic (no oxygen) conditions represents an important degradation of water quality because fish and most other animals cannot live in such an environment. Foul gases such as hydrogen sulphide (H_2S) are also generated.

Sometimes, density gradients associated with dissolved salts may also cause lakes to stratify. In these cases, a surface layer of freshwater sits on top of more saline, deeper water, with the layers separated by a steep chemical and density gradient known as a *halocline*. Lakes that stratify because of temperature gradients during the summer are common throughout Canada, while salt-stratified lakes are rare.

Canadian Focus 20.1

The Experimental Lakes Area

Some of the most famous Canadian research in ecology and environmental science has been conducted in the Experimental Lakes Area (ELA). Research at the ELA, funded mainly by the federal Department of Fisheries and Oceans (DFO), began during the late 1960s. The first two decades of work are closely identified with David Schindler, but hundreds of other Canadian and international scientists from government, universities, and the private sector have been involved in research in the area. Several of the leading scientists working at the ELA, notably Schindler, have won international awards for their outstanding contributions to ecology and environmental science.

The ELA is located in a remote region of northwestern Ontario near the town of Kenora. The area contains a large number of lakes and wetlands. The watersheds are largely forested, with thin soils that overlie hard, Precambrian bedrock within the extensive geological for-

Photo 20.2 This is an aerial view of Lake 226 in the Experimental Lakes Area of northwestern Ontario. This lake was divided into two separate basins with a heavy vinyl curtain. The upper basin in the photograph was fertilized with phosphorus, nitrogen, and carbon, while the lower basin received nitrogen and carbon. Only the basin receiving phosphorus became eutrophic and developed blooms of phytoplankton—a response seen as a whitish hue in the photo.

Source: D. Schindler

mation known as the Canadian Shield. The ELA is not a protected area, so commercial forestry is actively pursued, as are mining exploration and ecotourism. However, there is an understanding among the various interests in the ELA that some of the lakes and their watersheds are being used for scientific research and should not be disturbed.

One of the most important experimental procedures used at the ELA has been the controlled perturbation of entire lakes or wetlands. This is done to investigate the ecological effects of stressors associated with human influences, such as eutrophication, acidification, metal pollution, and flooding of wetlands. Such projects are known as "whole-lake" experiments (and some as "whole-wetland" experiments). The experimental design includes an initial study of the lake or wetland for several years to determine the baseline conditions. The system is then perturbed in some way—for example, by causing it to become eutrophic through the addition of nutrients. The experimental lakes are carefully monitored for a wide range of ecological responses, such as changes in the abundance and productivity of species and communities, changes in nutrient cycling, and changes in chemical and physical factors.

The experimental lakes are paired with reference (non-perturbed) lakes, which are monitored to provide information on natural changes unrelated to the manipulation. Because the reference lakes are monitored for a long time, they also provide extremely useful information relevant to the detection of changes in the ambient environment, such as climate warming.

Unfortunately, research at the Experimental Lakes Area has been periodically threatened by cutbacks in funding, and the future of this world-class facility and its programs is uncertain. Throughout the history of the ELA, the Department of Fisheries and Oceans provided most of the funding to maintain the research infrastructure. Most of the experiments were also funded by DFO and conducted by its personnel or by university scientists working with them. However, during the early 1990s, DFO focused its activities on marine issues, particularly in relation to commercial fish stocks. For several years it looked as if the DFO cutbacks at ELA might result in the facility closing down and its research programs terminating. Fortunately, DFO has decided to continue its funding for ELA, preventing the severe blow to research on freshwater ecosystems in Canada that would have occurred if the facility had closed.

increased rate of diffusion of atmospheric CO_2 into the lakewater. These processes were sufficient to sustain eutrophication.

Eutrophication also causes pronounced changes in the species composition, relative abundance, and biomass of phytoplankton, the most important primary producers in the ELA lakes. Changes in the phytoplankton resulted in effects on organisms at higher levels of the trophic web, such as zooplankton and fish. For example, the productivity of whitefish (*Coregonus clupeaformis*) in hourglass-shaped Lake 226 was greater in the experimentally eutrophied basin than in the oligotrophic basin. The increased fish productivity occurred in response to the greater abundance of their prey of zooplankton and aquatic insects, itself a trophic response to the increased productivity of algae.

Sources and Control of Phosphorus Loading to Surface Waters

In North America, eutrophication was most severe as an environmental problem during the 1960s and 1970s. At that time, the average discharge of phosphorus to inland waters was about 2 kg/person•year. About 84% of the phosphorus loading was associated with the dumping of municipal sewage, and the rest was due to agricultural sewage (from livestock) and fertilizers. In addition, the nitrogen discharge at the time was about 12.5 kg/person•year, of which 36% was from municipal and 64% from agricultural sources.

Because scientists have convincingly demonstrated that phosphorus is the primary limiting nutrient for eutrophication in freshwater, control strategies have focused on reducing the input of that nutrient to surface waters.

Phosphorus in Detergent

One of the first targets was domestic detergents. During the 1960s and early 1970s, detergents contained large concentrations of phosphate compounds, particularly sodium tripolyphosphate, which typically accounted for 50–65% of the weight of the product (12–16% if expressed as P). The phosphates were added as so-called "builders" in the detergent formulation. Builders reduce the activity of calcium, magnesium, and other cations in the wash water, thereby allowing the actual cleaning agents in the detergent (the surfactants) to work more efficiently. During the 1960s and early 1970s, as much as 3 million kg of high-phosphate detergents were used in North America each year, and virtually all of this was eventually flushed into surface waters through the sewage system. Detergent use accounted for as much as one-half of the phosphorus content of wastewater discharges in North America during the early 1970s.

Fortunately, the domestic use of detergent is a highly discrete activity, and good substitute "builders" are available to replace phosphates. Consequently, it was relatively easy to achieve a rapid decrease in phosphorus loading by regulating the use of high-phosphate detergent. In 1970, detergents sold in Canada could contain as much as 16% phosphorus; this was decreased to 2.2% by 1973. Some areas of North America have gone further, virtually banning the sale and use of detergents containing any phosphorus.

Sewage Treatment

In most places, the principal objective of sewage treatment is to reduce inputs of pathogenic microorganisms and oxygen-consuming organic matter to receiving waters. However, in places where surface waters are vulnerable to eutrophication, sewage waste may also be treated to reduce the quantity of phosphorus in the effluent.

All sizeable towns and cities in Canada have facilities to collect the sewage effluent from homes, businesses, institutions, and factories (see also Chapter 25). This infrastructure consists of complex webs of underground sewage pipes and other collection devices. Some municipalities have separate systems for the collection of domestic and industrial wastes, because the latter often contain toxic chemicals that should be treated separately. Some municipalities may also have a separate system of pipes to handle the large volumes of storm flows, which result from runoff of rain and snow meltwater. Eventually, these large quantities of wastewater must be discharged into the ambient environment, usually into a nearby lake, river, or ocean. Wherever possible, it is highly desirable, and environmentally responsible, to treat the wastewater to reduce its concentrations of pollutants, rather than discharge them into aquatic ecosystems.

Regrettably, many municipalities in Canada continue to dump their raw, untreated sewage into a nearby aquatic environment (Chapter 25). This practice is especially common for cities and towns located beside an ocean because well-flushed marine ecosystems have a huge capacity for diluting and biodegrading organic pollutants in sewage. Cities that dump raw sewage into the ocean include Halifax, Saint John, and St. John's on the Atlantic coast, and Victoria on the Pacific coast. Consequently, places like Halifax Harbour have become severely degraded by the aesthetic,

Photo 20.3 Even extremely acidic lakes can become eutrophic if they are fertilized. Drain Lake near Halifax became extremely acidic (pH 4.0) after pyritic minerals in its watershed were exposed to the atmosphere by construction activity. However, the lake also received inputs of sewage, which caused it to become quite eutrophic, allowing it to support a lush productivity of aquatic plants, algae, zooplankton, insects, and waterfowl. The lake was too acidic, however, to support fish.

hygiene-related, and ecological damage associated with environments receiving large amounts of raw, untreated sewage. Although the worst damage is restricted to the vicinity of the sewage outfalls, it is still an important problem that should be responsibly addressed by constructing sewage-treatment facilities.

Compared with many oceanic environments, inland waters such as lakes and rivers have a much smaller capacity for diluting and biodegrading sewage waste. Consequently, most Canadian municipalities located beside an inland waterbody treat their sewage before discharging the effluent. **Sewage treatment** can, however, vary greatly in degree and in the technology used, as is described below (Freedman, 1995; Sierra Legal Defence Fund, 2004).

Primary sewage treatment is relatively simple. It usually involves the screening of raw sewage to remove larger materials, and then allowing the remainder to settle, thereby reducing the amount of suspended organic matter. The resulting effluent is then discharged into the environment, although it may first be treated with a disinfectant (usually a chlorine compound) to kill pathogens, particularly bacteria. Primary treatment typically removes 40–60% of the suspended solids of raw sewage and 5–15% of the phosphorus, while reducing the **biological oxygen demand** (BOD) by 25–40%. (BOD is the capacity of organic material in wastewater to consume oxygen during decomposition.) More advanced primary systems can reduce the suspended solids by 90% and the BOD by 50%. In addition, fecal coliforms are reduced by 45–55%.

Secondary sewage treatment may be applied to the effluent of primary treatment, mostly to further reduce the BOD. Secondary treatment usually involves the use of a biological technology in which aerobic decomposition of organic waste is accomplished by enhancing the activity of the microbial community in an engineered environment. Two such biotechnologies in common use are activated sludge, generated through vigorous aeration of sewage water to enhance decomposition of the organic content, and trickling filters, in which sewage waste passes slowly through a complex physical substrate that supports a large population of microorganisms. These biotechnologies, along with primary treatment, produce large quantities of a humus-like product known as sludge, which can be composted and then spread on agricultural land as an organic-rich conditioner. Sludge may also be incinerated or dumped in a landfill (see Chapter 18). Primary and secondary treatments together remove about 30–50% of the phosphorus from sewage, and reduce the BOD and suspended solids by 85–90% and coliforms by 90–99%.

Tertiary sewage treatment includes processes designed to remove most of the remaining dissolved nutrients from the sewage effluent. Phosphorus removal may be achieved by adding aluminum, iron, calcium, or other chemicals that develop insoluble precipitates with phosphate, which then settle out of the water. These processes can remove 90% or more of the phosphate in the wastewater. Tertiary processes may also be used to remove ammonium and nitrate.

Artificial wetlands are sometimes constructed and used to provide advanced treatment of sewage wastes. The wetlands are engineered to develop a highly productive ecosystem, in which vigorous microbial activity decomposes organic waste while algae and macrophytes decrease nutrient concentrations in the water. Most sewage-treatment wetlands are constructed outdoors, but some are developed inside greenhouses, allowing the system to work during the winter. The efficiency of these systems depends on climate, the rate of flow-through of the sewage waste, and the nature of the engineered wetland. Typically, artificial wetlands are capable of removing up to 30% of the phosphorus from raw sewage, while reducing BOD by as much as 90%.

Tertiary treatment to reduce phosphorus concentration in municipal sewage effluents requires expensive investments in technology and operating costs. Consequently, this practice is pursued only under certain conditions. In Canada, tertiary treatment is used by many communities located beside inland rivers and around the Great Lakes, especially Lakes Erie, Ontario, and St. Clair, all of which have been substantially affected by eutrophication and other types of water pollution (see also Table 25.8). Moreover, because the Great Lakes are affected by effluents originating from sources in both Canada and the U.S., bilateral agreements have been negotiated concerning the loading of phosphorus and other pollutants. To meet the target loadings under these agreements, it is necessary to use tertiary systems to achieve a high degree of phosphorus removal from sewage effluents produced by municipalities in both countries.

Elsewhere in Canada, less attention is generally paid to the removal of phosphorus from municipal sewage effluents. Although municipalities may treat their sewage, only primary or secondary systems are generally used, mostly to reduce the quantities of pathogenic microorganisms and to lower the BOD in the effluents (see Chapter 25).

In addition, agricultural livestock produce enormous amounts of fecal materials. However, their sewage effluent is rarely treated before it is disposed into the environment. Treatment facilities for agricultural sewage are considered too expensive and are not often required by regulators. This happens even though some intensive rearing facilities, such as agroindustrial feedlots and factory farms, may produce huge quantities of relatively concentrated manure, equivalent to the effluent of a small city.

Case Studies of Eutrophication

Canada has an abundance of lakes and other surface waters, many of which receive substantial loadings of nutrients through sewage dumping and the runoff of agricultural fertilizer. Consequently, a great deal of research has examined the causes and consequences of eutrophication as an environmental problem in Canada. The following sections discuss two case studies of eutrophication.

Eutrophication of an Arctic Lake

Meretta and Char Lakes are two small lakes located on Cornwallis Island in northern Canada. Because of the severe climate in the High Arctic, tundra lakes are relatively simple ecosystems. Moreover, nutrient inputs to these waterbodies are naturally small and cycling is slow, so tundra lakes are naturally oligotrophic. Char Lake is a typical, oligotrophic, polar lake, with extremely clear, nutrient-poor water, a low rate of primary production, and low productivity of zooplankton and fish.

Meretta Lake, in contrast, receives sewage from a small community. Because of the nutrient input, it has become moderately eutrophic—a development studied by scientists during the early 1970s (Schindler *et al.*, 1974).

The sewage dumping resulted in phosphorus loading about 13 times larger in Meretta than in Char Lake, while the nitrogen loading was 19 times higher. Consequently, during the growing season, Meretta Lake developed a phytoplankton biomass averaging 12 times greater than in Char Lake, and as much as 40 times greater during the summer algal bloom. During the winter, these lakes are covered with ice, which restricts the rate at which atmospheric oxygen can enter the water. During this time, the decomposition of organic material, mostly sewage waste but also algal biomass, exerts a great demand for oxygen in the bottom water of Meretta Lake, resulting in anoxic conditions. The oxygen depletion causes severe stress to aquatic animals and impairs the reproduction of arctic char (*Salvelinus alpinus*), a type of trout.

This case demonstrates that even polar lakes, which are relatively simple ecosystems because of their severe climatic regime, can exhibit a strong eutrophication response to fertilization with limiting nutrients.

Lake Erie: Eutrophication and Other Stressors

The Great Lakes of North America is one of the world's outstanding freshwater systems. Lake Superior sits at the top of this chain of lakes, with Lakes Michigan, Huron, Erie, and Ontario located below. The lakes and their watersheds drain to the Atlantic Ocean through the St. Lawrence River, itself one of the world's great rivers (there is also some flow to the Mississippi River, through a canal near Chicago). The aggregate surface area of the Great Lakes is about 245 000 km^2, and the system drains a watershed of 539 000 km^2 (Table 20.2).

All of the Great Lakes except Lake Michigan form part of the border between Canada and the United States. Consequently, issues concerning the resources and water quality of the Great Lakes are binational in character. Waters within Canadian jurisdiction are affected by actions in the U.S. and vice versa; especially important are the dumping of sewage and industrial wastes, the conversion of natural forests and wetlands into agricultural and residential land-uses, commercial and sport fishing, and other potentially damaging activities. Recognizing this, the governments of Canada and

TABLE 20.2	Size and Watershed Characteristics of the Great Lakes of North America				
	SUPERIOR	**MICHIGAN**	**HURON**	**ERIE**	**ONTARIO**
Lake surface area (kilometre^2)	82 100	57 800	59 600	25 700	18 960
Average depth (metres)	147	85	59	19	86
Water retention time (years)	191	99	22	2.6	6
Watershed area (km^2)	127 700	118 000	134 100	78 000	64 030
Land use in watershed (%)					
forest	95	50	66	17	56
agriculture	1	23	22	59	32
urban	<1	4	2	9	4
wetland, other	4	23	10	15	8
Population in watershed ($\times 10^3$)	607	10 057	2 694	11 875	8 151
Population density (persons/km^2)	4.8	85.2	20.1	152.2	127.3
Phosphorus loading (10^3 tonne P/y)					
1976–1978	4	6	5	10	17
1988–1990	2	4	3	7	18
target loading	3.4	5.6	4.3	11	7
Phosphorus concentration in open water (microgram/litre)					
1983–1985	3	6	4	23	14
1988–1989	3	5	4	10	6
guideline	5	7	5	10–15	10

Sources: Data from Gregor and Johnson (1980), Neilson *et al.* (1994), Environment Canada (1996), and Environmental Protection Agency (2003)

the U.S. have entered into a number of co-operative agreements regarding the management of resources, the emission of pollutants, and research and monitoring of the condition of their shared Great Lakes ecosystem. Much of the integrated, binational activity is coordinated by the *International Joint Commission*, an administrative body with equal representation from both countries. The Great Lakes Water Quality Agreement, first signed in 1972 and then modified in 1978, 1983, and 1989, commits Canada and the U.S. to maintain and restore the chemical, physical, and ecological integrity of the shared Great Lakes and their watershed.

One of the Great Lakes, Lake Erie, has a relatively small volume and is located in a drainage basin that has rather fertile soil. Consequently, Lake Erie has always been the most productive of the Great Lakes. However, the natural productivity of Lake Erie has been greatly increased as a result of nutrient inputs associated with urban sewage and agricultural drainage. This has created eutrophic conditions in shallower regions of the lake. The western basin of Lake Erie is particularly vulnerable to eutrophication because it is relatively shallow and warm and receives large inputs of sewage and agricultural runoff.

In addition to experiencing nutrient loading, Lake Erie has been affected by other important stressors. These include contamination by potentially toxic chemicals, commercial and recreational fisheries, conversion of most of the natural ecosystems in its watershed into agricultural and urban land uses, and introductions of alien species of plants and animals. This complex of environmental stressors has greatly degraded Lake Erie's water quality and ecosystem. The damage was particularly acute during the late 1960s and early 1970s, when pollution was relatively uncontrolled. Although some of the earlier problems have been alleviated, Lake Erie is still in a degraded condition. In the following sections we examine the most important of the ecological changes in Lake Erie, as a case study of the ecological effects of eutrophication occurring in combination with other stressors (Freedman, 1995).

Oxygen Depletion: Lake Erie develops a stratified condition during the summer, which makes it difficult for oxygen to penetrate to deepwater habitat (see In Detail 20.1). If the deeper water is subject to large demands for oxygen to decompose organic materials, deoxygenation can result. During most summers from the 1950s to 1970s, this condition occurred very widely in Lake Erie, especially in the shallow, western end of the lake. Sewage dumping and algal biomass sinking from the surface water resulted in an intense demand for oxygen, causing extensive deoxygenation of bottom water.

Deoxygenation is extremely harmful to aquatic animals, most of which require free access to oxygen in order to live. The episodes of anoxia in Lake Erie caused great changes in the community of invertebrates living in the sediment (benthos) of the lake. The benthic community was dominated by larvae of species of mayflies (aquatic insects in the order Ephemeroptera). The most common species were *Hexagenia rigida* and *H. limbata*, which lived in surface mud in an abundance of about 400/m^2. However, following a series of severe oxygen depletions during the 1950s, the density of these insects decreased to about 40/m^2, and by 1961 the mayflies had virtually disappeared, occurring in an abundance of less than 1/m^2.

The collapse of abundance of benthic mayflies was widely reported by the popular media, which sensationalized the phenomenon by suggesting that Lake Erie was "dead." This was by no means the case, because the mayflies had been replaced by a benthic fauna that is relatively tolerant of deoxygenation. These included aquatic worms known as tubificids (*Limnodrilus* spp.), insect larvae of the midge family (order Diptera, family Chironomidae), and small species of mollusks (snails in the order Gastropoda and clams in the family Sphaeriidae). The worm-dominated benthos is, however, considered to indicate a substantial degradation of ecological conditions compared with the mayfly-dominated community of well-oxygenated sediment.

Algal Blooms: Because Lake Erie has a greater supply of nutrients, it supports a much larger biomass of phytoplankton than the other Great Lakes. When its eutrophication was most severe, Lake Erie's western basin supported about twice as much algal biomass as Lake Ontario (per unit of surface area), and 11 times more than oligotrophic Lake Superior.

The communities of phytoplankton vary greatly among the sub-basins of Lake Erie and also between its nearshore and offshore waters. The eastern and central basins are relatively deep and unproductive, while the shallower western basin is more productive. In all three basins, however, shallow, nearshore habitat is more productive than offshore water. The algal bloom that occurs during spring in eutrophic water is typically dominated by diatoms of the genus *Melosira*, while the bloom in late summer is dominated by the blue-green bacteria *Anabaena*, *Microcystis*, and *Aphanizomenon*, the diatom *Fragilaria*, and the green alga *Pediastrum*.

In addition, the colonial green alga *Cladophora glomerata* can occur as filamentous mats attached to rocks in shallow habitats along shores. This alga grows in locally fertile habitats in Lake Erie and some of the other Great Lakes. It was especially abundant during the 1960s and 1970s, when storms often caused mats of its biomass to detach from rocky substrates, eventually washing ashore as a malodorous mass or sinking to deeper water to contribute to the development of anoxic conditions.

Studies have shown that the western basin of Lake Erie has always been relatively productive, sustaining a lush growth of aquatic plants and algae and large populations of fish. However, the huge nutrient inputs associated with sewage dumping and agricultural runoff increased the intensity of eutrophication throughout Lake Erie. Fortunately, these problems have been alleviated substantially since the 1970s. This is because inputs of phosphorus to the lake have decreased, mainly through a ban on high-phosphate detergent and the construction of tertiary sewage-treatment plants to service cities and towns.

Changes in Zooplankton: The zooplankton of Lake Erie used to be dominated by relatively large species, such as *Limnocalanus macrurus* and species of *Daphnia*. By the 1960s, however, these had been replaced—mainly by smaller, previously rare species, particularly *Diaptomus siciloides*, which is considered to be an indicator of eutrophic conditions. The greatest changes occurred in the shallow, western basin of the lake, where the midsummer zooplankton density increased from less than about 7000/m^3 prior to 1940 to as much as 110 000/m^3 in 1959. However, even at that time, zooplankton species typical of oligotrophic conditions survived in the deeper, eastern basin.

Changes in the zooplankton community were caused partly by the lake's increasing primary productivity, because single-celled phytoplankton are the food-base of these small crustaceans. In addition, at about the same time that Lake Erie was becoming more eutrophic, its commercial fishery was over-exploiting relatively large species of fish, which are typically piscivorous (i.e., they eat fish). After the demise of the larger piscivorous species, the fish community became dominated by smaller species that feed on zooplankton (known as planktivorous fish). These fish selectively predate on larger species of zooplankton. Therefore, smaller species of zooplankton are favoured and their abundance increases.

Changes in the Fishery: Lake Erie has always supported a large fishery, which typically exceeds the combined landings of all the other Great Lakes. Remarkably, the total catch by the commercial fishery on Lake Erie has been quite stable over the years. This has occurred despite enormous changes in the species of fish present, fishing technology, the intensity of eutrophication, pollution by toxic chemicals, habitat damage caused by damming rivers and streams required for spawning, and sedimentation of shallow habitat by soil eroded from deforested parts of the watershed.

Although the yield of fish from Lake Erie has not declined, the nature of the fish community has changed greatly during the past several centuries. These changes illustrate a severe degradation of the fishery resource and of the natural ecosystem. When the commercial fishery on Lake Erie began in the nineteenth century, the prime targets of exploitation were the largest, most valuable species, especially lake whitefish (*Coregonus clupeaformis*), lake trout (*Salvelinus namaycush*), and lake herring (*Leucichthys artedi*). This is a common pattern whenever a previously unexploited fishery or forest resource is initially harvested— take the best and leave the rest (see Chapter 14).

Unfortunately, populations of the initially most desirable species were rapidly depleted. This happened because the fishing pressure was excessive and could not be sustained by the resource. Also, severe habitat degradation occurred in the lake, caused mainly by erosion and siltation associated with extensive deforestation of the watershed. As the most desirable species disappeared, the fishing industry switched to "second-choice" species, such as blue pike (*Stizostedion vitreum glaucum*), walleye (*S. v. vitreum*), sauger (*S. canadense*), and yellow perch (*Perca flavescens*). Because of over-exploitation and habitat degradation, the species of *Stizostedion* became extirpated or rare by the early 1970s. The fishery then became dominated by relatively small, low-value species such as yellow perch, and by non-indigenous fish such as rainbow smelt (*Osmerus mordax*), freshwater drum (*Aplodinotus grunniens*), and carp (*Cyprinus carpio*). Therefore, although the total yield of fish caught in Lake Erie has remained fairly large and consistent over time, the quality of the economic resource and the integrity of the fish community have been badly degraded by over-fishing and habitat change.

Recent Changes in Environmental Quality: For a number of reasons, ecological conditions have improved markedly in Lake Erie since the late 1970s. This has largely been achieved by the construction of sewage-treatment facilities in cities and towns along the lakeshore in Canada and the U.S. (as well as upstream, especially on the Detroit River and Lake St. Clair). Many of these facilities include technology to reduce phosphorus inputs. More than US$7.5 billion was spent on improving sewage-treatment facilities since 1972, reducing the annual loading of phos-

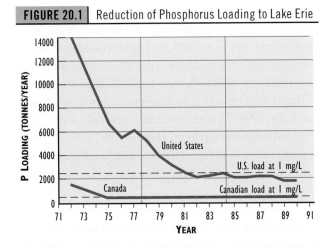

FIGURE 20.1 Reduction of Phosphorus Loading to Lake Erie

These data show the reduction of point-source loadings to Lake Erie, most of which has been achieved by reducing input of sewage and detergent. The dashed lines indicate the Canadian and U.S. target loadings at an effluent concentration of 1 mg/L.
Source: Modified from Dolan (1993)

phorus to Lake Erie from about 27 000 t in 1972, to 6000 t in 1985, and to 3000 t in 1990 (Dolan, 1993; Figure 20.1).

The huge reduction of phosphorus input has alleviated eutrophication in Lake Erie (Makarewicz and Bertram, 1991). The average biomass of phytoplankton, for instance, has decreased from 3.4 g/m^3 in 1970 to 1.2 g/m^3 during 1983–85. The largest biomass of phytoplankton still occurs in the western basin, where it averaged 1.9 g/m^3 during 1983–87, compared with 1.0 g/m^3 in the central basin and 0.6 g/m^3 in the deepest, eastern basin. Blooms of nuisance algae have also decreased in intensity. For example, the blue-green alga *Aphanizomenon flos-aquae* had a standing crop as high as 2.0 g/m^3 in 1970, but only 0.22 g/m^3 during 1983–85. Similarly, diatoms that indicate eutrophic conditions have decreased greatly in abundance, by 85% in the case of *Stephanodiscus binderanus* in the western basin, and by 94% for *Fragilaria capucina*. At the same time, diatoms indicative of mesotrophic or oligotrophic conditions have become more abundant, notably *Asterionella formosa* and *Rhizosolenia eriensis*. Overall, the open water of the previously eutrophic, western basin is now considered to be in a mesotrophic condition, while the eastern basin is now oligotrophic.

The animal communities of Lake Erie have also undergone changes since the 1970s. Species of zooplankton that indicate oligotrophic conditions have become more abundant, while indicators of eutrophication are fewer and are now mostly restricted to the western basin.

Since 1972, the populations of relatively large species of fish have increased greatly, particularly walleye and introduced species of Pacific salmon (*Oncorhynchus* spp.). These are fish-eating species, and their predation has greatly decreased the abundance of smaller, zooplankton-eating fish such as smelt, alewife (*Alosa pseudoharengus*), and shiners (*Notropis* spp.). The decrease of planktivorous fishes has allowed secondary increases to occur in the abundance of larger-bodied zooplankton, such as the waterflea *Daphnia pulicaria*.

The zebra mussel (*Dreissena polymorpha*) is another cause of important ecological change in Lake Erie. This bivalve mollusk, a native of Eurasia, was accidentally introduced to the Great Lakes by the discharge of ballast water from transoceanic ships. The zebra mussel can rapidly attain an extremely dense population (up to 50 000/m^2) on hard, underwater surfaces such as rock, wood, metal, and concrete. The zebra mussel is a filter-feeder, and its huge populations have an enormous capability for removing algal cells from water. Consequently, they may be responsible for some of the recent clarification of Lake Erie and the eutrophic parts of other Great Lakes (Figure 20.2). In addition, the dense populations of zebra mussels have benefited some species of ducks that winter on the Great Lakes, where they feed on benthic mollusks and other invertebrates. However, the invasion of the Great Lakes by zebra mussels has also caused serious damage, including a reduction in the abundance of filter-feeding zooplankton (with secondary effects on planktivorous fish), and the displacement of native mollusks that cannot compete with the dense shoals of this non-native mussel. Industries and water utilities have also suffered damage from the clogging of their water-intake pipes.

Overview of the Lake Erie Case Study: Lake Erie is an important example of the cumulative, detrimental effects of a variety of anthropogenic stressors on the ecological health of a large lake. The stressors that degraded Lake Erie include eutrophication caused by nutrient loading, habitat damage through siltation resulting from deforestation of the watershed, over-exploitation of a potentially renewable natural resource (the fishery), pollution by oxygen-consuming sewage and toxic chemicals, and introductions of alien species. Fortunately, Lake Erie is also beginning to demonstrate that a highly degraded ecosystem can be induced to recover somewhat, assuming that the causes of the damage can be managed effectively. In the case of Lake Erie, the partial recovery was achieved substantially through reduced organic and phosphorus inputs from sewage.

FIGURE 20.2 | Phytoplankton Density in Lake Erie

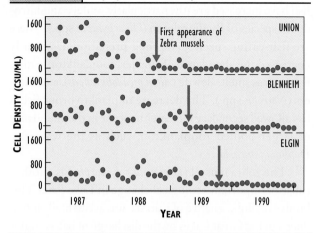

This figure shows how filter-feeding on phytoplankton by zebra mussels has contributed to clarifying the water of Lake Erie (along with the influence of reduced phosphorus loading). The sampling site at Union is at the western end of the lake, while Blenheim and Elgin are progressively east. The zebra mussel invaded Lake Erie from west to east, and there was a lag in the development of its dense shoals along this gradient.

Source: Modified from Edsall and Charlton (1997)

Dams and Impoundments

Dams are structures used to contain flowing water, which backs up behind the barrier to form a lake-like impoundment. Some dams are immense. The world's first very large dam was the 221-m-high Hoover Dam, built in 1935. The world's tallest dam is Rogun in Tajikistan, at 335 m. Dams may be built for various useful purposes: as components of hydroelectric developments, as flood-control structures, and to store water for use in irrigated agriculture or to supply municipal water. There are about 39 000 dams taller than 15 m in the world, of which 48% were constructed primarily as aids to irrigation, 20% to generate hydroelectricity, 15% for water supply, 8% for flood control, and 9% for recreation or other purposes (International Commission on Large Dams, 2003). Canada has 581 dams taller than 15 m and 212 smaller dams; about 67% of these are used for hydroelectricity, 11% for water supply, 9% for flood control, 9% for irrigation, 4% for recreation, and 2% for navigation (the sum exceeds 100% because some dams are multi-purpose).

The construction of dams and impoundments always causes environmental damage, and local people are affected in various ways. For these reasons, these developments are invariably controversial at the local level, and often at national and international levels as well. Such controversy has been sufficient to stop some proposals (often in concert with concerns about economic and energy-supply issues). A high-profile Canadian example of this is the Great Whale development, which was suspended in 1994. This was to be the second phase of a series of hydro megadevelopments proposed by Hydro-Québec in waterways east of James Bay and Hudson Bay. An international example is the Three Gorges Project (see Global Focus 20.1).

Moreover, if today's criteria for acceptable environmental and socio-economic impacts had been applied to earlier proposals, many existing dams and impoundments in the world would not have been constructed. For example, the World Bank progressively upgrades its environmental and socio-economic criteria for funding large dam projects. In 1996, it re-evaluated proposals it had considered during the period 1960 to 1995 (Dorcey *et al.*, 1997) and found that, under the older evaluation criteria, about 10% of the proposals had been considered "unacceptable" for funding. Under the new criteria, however, 26% of these proposals would have been considered unacceptable and another 48% only "potentially acceptable" (the latter could become acceptable if modified to take account of environmental and/or socio-economic concerns).

In this section, we examine the most important environmental effects of dams and impoundments, with an emphasis on those occurring in Canada.

Hydroelectric Developments

Hydroelectricity is produced by using the kinetic energy of flowing water to turn a turbine, which connects to a generator that produces electricity, which is distributed to consumers through a complex network of transmission lines (see Chapter 13). The global use of hydroelectricity is equivalent to 9.3×10^{18} J of energy (in 2001; World Resources Institute, 2005). About 59% of the global use of hydroelectricity occurs in developed countries, and 21% in North America. Canada has invested relatively heavily in the development of hydroelectric resources and accounts for 13% of the global use of this energy source (for comparison, Canada constitutes 0.5% of the global population). Hydroelectricity accounts for about 2.2% of all energy use, but 17% of the use of renewable sources of energy (the others include wind, solar, geothermal, and biomass).

Global Focus 20.1

The Three Gorges Project

China is the most populous country in the world, with 1.32 billion people in 2005. It is also a rapidly developing country—during the 13-year period from 1991 to 2003, the Chinese economy grew by an average of 9.9% per year to a gross domestic product (GDP) of US$1409 billion in 2003 (for comparison, the Canadian GDP was $834 billion in that year and the U.S. GDP was $10 881 billion; WRI, 2005). The impressive economic growth of China has greatly increased its need for massive and reliable sources of commercial energy. To a large degree, this demand has been met through the use of fossil fuels, especially coal and petroleum, much of which must be imported at great expense. Because of the huge drain on fiscal resources associated with importing fossil fuels, as well as the pollution caused by their use, the Government of China has placed a high priority on developing domestic hydroelectric resources, which are a renewable source of energy (see Chapter 13).

The highest-profile hydroelectric development in China, and the largest in the world, is the Three Gorges Project. Construction began in 1993 and is expected to last until 2010, with a total expenditure equivalent to US$22 billion (much of the capital and technology is being provided by foreign companies, including Canadian ones). The project will flood an enormous reservoir in the canyon of the Yangzi River in southeastern China. The main dam will be 0.94 km wide and 182 m high, and the reservoir will extend for 640 km and cover 632 km^2. When completed, the project will have 26 generating units (12 were already operating in mid-2005), which will provide an enormous amount of power (the capacity will be 18 000 MW, almost 10% of the national capacity). The power will mostly be used in southern and central regions of China, where the economy is growing especially quickly.

When completed, the Three Gorges Project is expected to provide the following key benefits to China:

- an enormous amount of electricity, from a renewable source
- some relief from the huge expense of importing fossil fuels
- mitigation of damage associated with periodic disastrous flooding of the Yangzi River, which killed more than one million people in the past century
- improved access for commercial shipping into the interior, which will extend as far as 2400 km inland through a series of locks

- stimulation of additional economic growth because of relatively inexpensive energy and improved transportation
- a proclamation of Chinese greatness and accomplishment.

However, the massive project is also extremely controversial for many reasons, including the following:

- It will dam the flow of a great river—at 6300 km, the Yangzi is the third-longest river in the world (only the Nile and Amazon are longer).
- The reservoir will inundate land settled by people, in some cases for millennia—as many as 1.9 million people must be relocated to higher ground, many of whom will be dispossessed of fertile land and developed property and end up in worsened financial circumstances.
- There are fears about the safety of the dam and its enormous reservoir, partly based on risks of inferior design and construction fostered by corruption in the awarding of some contracts; an engineering failure could be a colossal catastrophe.
- Pollutants are likely to accumulate in the reservoir (at present, they are mostly carried by the river to the ocean), including massive amounts of chemicals released from flooded industrial sites that have not been properly cleaned up.
- The reservoir itself may silt up rather quickly, largely because of accelerated erosion caused by extensive deforestation of the Yangzi watershed.
- About 1300 sites of cultural and historical importance will be destroyed through inundation; only some of their artefacts and structures can be salvaged.

Clearly, the Three Gorges Project is a monumental undertaking of human ingenuity and engineering. It will transform a major part of the surface of the planet and will have gigantic economic and environmental impacts. It is a sobering thought that the extreme benefits, and risks, of such a colossal endeavour are made necessary only by the astonishing increases in the abundance and economic scale of the human enterprise. As enormous as this particular project is, we can expect proposals for others of similar or larger magnitude if the energy and material demands of the burgeoning human economy are to be met.

References and Additional Information

International Rivers Network. *The Three Gorges Campaign.* www.irn.org/programs/threeg/

Embassy of the People's Republic of China in the United States of America. *The Three-Gorges Project.* www.china-embassy.org/eng/zt/sxgc/default.htm

There are three basic ways to harness flows of surface water to generate hydroelectricity:

1. A large **impoundment** is developed when a dam causes riverflow to accumulate and flood an extensive area of land. A large impoundment allows the storage of water from the spring high-flow period so that electricity can be generated according to demand throughout the year. This kind of facility has a large effect on the seasonal variation of below-dam riverflow because it greatly reduces the spring peak flow while increasing the amount of flow during the summer, fall, and winter (Figure 20.3). Large impoundments are the most common type of major hydroelectric facility in Canada.

2. A **run-of-the-river** development directly harnesses the flow of a river to drive turbines, without creating a large impoundment for storage. This kind of facility utilizes riverflow more or less according to its seasonal availability. A run-of-the-river development has little or no capacity to (a) store part of the spring riverflow or to (b) coordinate the timing of its electricity generation with peaks of consumer demand. This kind of hydro development causes much less environmental damage than one involving a large reservoir.

3. A combined system may incorporate elements of the run-of-the-river and the development of a large impoundment. So-called "peaking" systems store water during part of the day and release it during the time of highest demand for electricity, which is generally between 08:00 and 22:00 (Figure 20.4). One variation is the pumped-storage system, in which electricity generated during low-demand parts of the day is used to pump river water into an elevated reservoir; the stored water is later used to generate electricity at the peak-demand time. If the peak-flow system causes large flow variations downriver, important ecological damage may be caused. Other combined systems may have run-of-the-river generators installed on rivers draining into a central reservoir, or installed downriver of a reservoir.

Environmental Effects

Several important environmental benefits are associated with the use of hydroelectricity, the most important of which are

1. the energy source (i.e., flowing water) is renewed through the hydrologic cycle, so hydroelectricity is a renewable source of power;

2. the emissions of greenhouse gases are generally much smaller than those associated with the use of fossil fuels to generate electricity;

3. unlike fossil fuels, there are no substantial direct emissions of SO_2 or NO_x, which are important causes of acid rain;

4. in some regions, impoundments help to control downstream flooding, which might otherwise cause economic damage and risks to people living in floodplains (described later); and

5. substantial recreational or commercial fisheries may develop in reservoirs.

| **FIGURE 20.3** | Effects of Reservoir Development on the Patterns of Seasonal Flow of the Peace River |

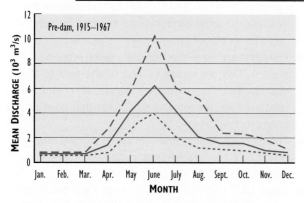

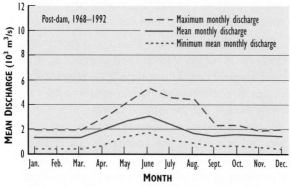

The Bennett Dam and its associated reservoir were built in 1968, so the upper curves (for 1915–67) represent pre-impoundment conditions. The flows were measured at the town of Peace River, Alberta. The most notable changes are (1) an overall reduction in the annual variation of riverflow; (2) a large reduction in peak flow during mid-April to mid-July; and (3) an increase during the low-flow period of September to March.

Source: Modified from Rosenberg *et al.* (1997)

FIGURE 20.4 | Effects of Peaking Discharges on Hourly Mean Discharge to the Nelson River

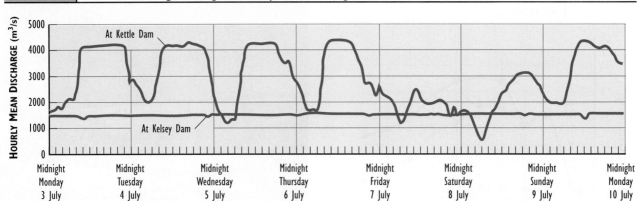

The data are for a one-week period between July 3 and 10, 1984. This figure illustrates the great changes in hydrology that occur downstream because the generation of electricity is timed to meet the peak daily demand. Note the relatively low demand during the weekend. Kelsey Dam is not subject to these peaking discharges and represents the background pattern of low flow in the summer.

Source: Modified from Rosenberg *et al.* (1997)

It must be appreciated, however, that the above statements are rather simplistic, particularly because large quantities of fossil fuels, metals, and other non-renewable resources are used to construct hydroelectric facilities. Moreover, the dams and impoundments cause some important environmental damages, as discussed below (Dorcey *et al.*, 1997; Rosenberg et al., 1997; International Rivers Network, 2005).

Flooding of Wetland and Terrestrial Habitat: Large reservoirs flood extensive areas of terrestrial and wetland habitat. This causes many ecological damages, including the displacement of plants and animals utilizing the original habitats. In some cases, uncommon or rare species may be affected, particularly if unusual habitats such as waterfall spray zones or special wetlands are destroyed. Of course, even while flooding destroys terrestrial and wetland areas, new aquatic habitats are developed, and this provides opportunities for certain fish, waterfowl, and other aquatic species. The productivity of algae, zooplankton, and fish is usually relatively high for several years after the creation of a new reservoir because of the leaching of nutrients from flooded soil.

Food-Web Accumulation of Methylmercury: High concentrations of methylmercury commonly occur in fish and other aquatic animals in reservoirs. This happens because inorganic mercury naturally present in soil becomes methylated by bacteria under the anoxic conditions that develop after flooding. As we learned in Chapter 18, methylmercury is readily bioaccumulated by organisms and further

magnifies up the food web to occur in particularly high concentrations in top predators. It also tends to occur in higher concentrations in older individuals within a population. Mercury concentrations in the flesh of predatory fish in reservoirs are often higher than 1.0 ppm and can exceed 3 ppm. These levels significantly exceed the 0.5 ppm limit for fish intended for human consumption. Fish with high concentrations of methylmercury are also a toxic hazard to natural predators such as osprey (*Pandion haliaetus*), bald eagle (*Haliaeetus leucocephalus*), and river otter (*Lutra canadensis*). In the boreal region of Canada, the concentration of mercury in fish progressively increases after the initial development of a reservoir and persists for 10–30 years or longer (Figure 20.5). In general, this phenomenon is most intense in large, new reservoirs. It is less of a problem in reservoirs developed by raising the water level of a steep-sided lake or river valley with shorter-term storage, or in older impoundments.

Effects of Altered Flows and Obstructions: Many downstream effects result from the construction of dams, other flow-control structures, and diversions of rivers to increase the flow into reservoirs. Changes in the timing and amounts of flow affect the sedimentation regime: decreased flow can result in silt deposition and the infilling of gravel beds used by spawning fish, while scouring associated with increased flow can cause other kinds of habitat damage. Large changes in the flow also affect the productivity of algae and macrophytes, in part by affecting the flux of nutrients in the riverflow. These effects can be particularly acute in riverine marshes, deltas, and estuarine habitat. The

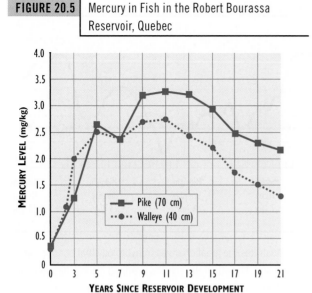

FIGURE 20.5 | Mercury in Fish in the Robert Bourassa Reservoir, Quebec

The data are for mercury in the muscle of fish, expressed in mg/kg (or ppm) on the basis of fresh weight. The data are standardized to fish size; those for pike are for individuals 70 cm long, while those for walleye are for animals 40 cm long. The reservoir was first filled in 1979.

Source: Data from Schetagne *et al.* (2002)

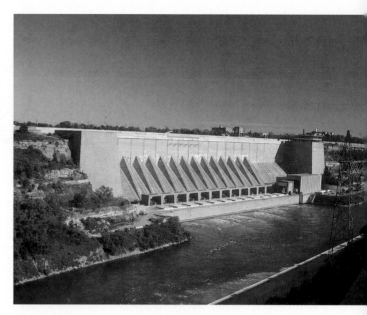

Photo 20.4 This hydroelectric generating station is located on the Niagara River in southern Ontario. It generates electricity mostly at night, using water that has been diverted to a storage reservoir (not visible in the photograph). During the day, however, the riverflow passes over Niagara Falls, a popular tourist destination.

resulting changes in productivity and other habitat characteristics may secondarily affect local populations of aquatic invertebrates, fish, migratory birds, and aquatic mammals. In one rare case in 1984, a torrential flow on the Caniapiscau River in northern Quebec, partly caused by the release of water from an overly full reservoir (due to a week of unusually heavy rain), drowned about 10 000 migrating caribou (*Rangifer tarandus*).

Effects of Obstructions: A high dam can be an insurmountable obstruction to the up-river passage of migratory fish. However, this blockage can sometimes be partially mitigated by installing a fish ladder, by catching migrating fish and transporting them above the dam, or by releasing young fish raised at a hatchery. In addition, juvenile fish migrating to the ocean may be killed or injured during passage through the turbines of a hydroelectric facility. Some of this damage can be avoided by installing screens or deflectors, while also providing an alternative passageway for the migrating fish.

Emissions of Greenhouse Gases: The development of a large reservoir results in conditions suitable for the emission of large amounts of carbon dioxide and methane (both are greenhouse gases) to the atmosphere (see Chapter 17). The

production of methane, which is about 21 times more potent as a greenhouse gas than carbon dioxide, may occur if the flooding results in anaerobic conditions because of the decomposition of large amounts of biomass—the dead trees and litter of drowned forests and the organic matter of inundated wetlands, especially peat bogs. Such oxygen-poor conditions favour the production of methane during decomposition, which out-gasses into the atmosphere. The emission of greenhouse gases is greatest during the first several decades after flooding and then slows to a rate similar to that of natural lakes. Experimental flooding of a wetland at the Experimental Lakes Area in northwestern Ontario resulted in a twenty-fold increase in the rate of methane emission to the atmosphere. Under conditions that are particularly favourable for methane generation, the rate of production of greenhouse-gas warming potential can exceed that of a coal-fired power plant (although this is more characteristic of tropical reservoirs than cooler ones; Rosenberg *et al.*, 1997).

Effects on Biodiversity: Some hydroelectric developments have destroyed the habitat of threatened species or unusual ecosystems. The proliferation of dams on rivers has greatly reduced or extirpated many populations of Atlantic salmon (*Salmo salar*) and Pacific salmon (*Oncorhynchus* spp.). At least 142 stocks of Pacific salmon in western Canada have been lost partly because of hydroelectric dams (in combination with logging, over-fishing, and other stressors), and many others are threatened. Hydroelectric developments threaten the breeding habitat of the harlequin duck (*Histrionicus histrionicus*) in both eastern and western Canada (it is an endangered species in the eastern part of its range). Construction of the Churchill Falls hydro project in Labrador destroyed the habitat of rare species of ferns, mosses, and liverworts in the misty spray zone of the original natural waterfall. Undoubtedly, numerous undocumented losses of rare species and their habitat occurred during the construction of hydroelectric developments in Canada and elsewhere prior to the early 1970s, when biodiversity surveys became a routine component of environmental impact assessments for these projects.

Effects on Local People: The lifestyle of local people can be significantly affected by a hydroelectric development. This is particularly true if a large reservoir is developed in a heavily populated area, which is often the case in less developed countries. For example, in China alone, the Three Gorges Dam is predicted to displace about 1.9 million people when it is completed in 2010; the Danjiangkou Dam (completed in 1974) displaced 383 000 people; the Sanmenxia (1960), 319 000; and the Xinjiang (1961), 306 000. In India, the Dongpinghu Dam (1958) displaced 278 000 people (Goodland, 1994). In such crowded countries, suitable land for relocation of these displaced people is often unavailable. People are also displaced by reservoirs in northern Canada, although typically several hundred or fewer. Almost all are Aboriginal people, who may have to be relocated from traditionally used areas if their villages become flooded. They are also deprived of opportunities to hunt mammals and birds in part of their traditional foraging area, and they may not be able to eat fish from the reservoir or downstream for several decades after its creation (because of health hazards associated with methylmercury). Of course, local economic opportunities exist for some of these people—jobs associated with the construction and maintenance of the hydro facility and its associated infrastructure (such as transmission lines and roads). However, entry into wage employment can be extremely disruptive to traditional subsistence lifestyles, for both individuals and the community. There are also many social and economic disruptions from the influx of people from elsewhere in Canada and from the construction of new roads and towns. For these and other reasons, local people often bitterly resist the development of large hydroelectric facilities (and other large industrial projects) in the areas where they live.

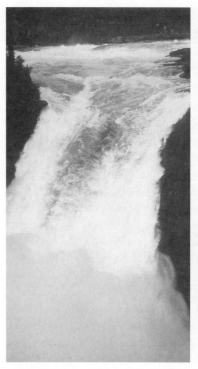

Photo 20.5 Two views of Churchill Falls, Labrador, are shown: (a) the 75-m-tall falls prior to the completion of the 5429-MW generating station in 1974; (b) the greatly reduced flow in 1988 due to the diversion of most riverflow for electricity generation.

Source: A. Luttermann

Case Study: La Grande Complex

The La Grande Complex in Quebec was developed between 1973 and 1996 (Messier, 1998). The development is centred on the La Grande River, but its natural flow has been augmented by diversions of the Caniapiscau River (48% of its flow) and the linked Eastmain and Opinaca Rivers (90% of their flow). The first phase of the development of the La Grande Complex occurred between 1973 and 1985 and resulted in five reservoirs with a total impoundment area of about 11 335 km^2 (including 10 400 km^2 of newly flooded land). Three powerhouses were built, with a total generating capacity of 10 282 MW. The second phase of the development, between 1987 and 1996, added five powerhouses (capacity 4962 MW) and developed three new reservoirs (1618 km^2 including 1134 km^2 of flooded land). During the planning, construction, and operating phases of the development, Hydro-Québec began extensive studies and monitoring of hydrology, climate, ecology, socio-economics, and other issues related to potential environmental impacts.

Canadian Focus 20.2

Hydroelectric Development in Labrador

Hydroelectric power is an economically attractive and renewable source of energy. In the past, areas with a high potential for hydroelectricity were often developed without much consultation with local people, who also may not have received many economic benefits from the project. Local people generally did, however, bear the brunt of the environmental damage, which typically included extensive flooding, changes in the hydrology of rivers used for transportation or for fishing, and sometimes harmful influences on traditional lifestyles and culture.

One example of insensitive hydroelectric development involves the Churchill Falls Project in Labrador, for which construction began in 1967. In 1969, the government of Newfoundland entered into a contract with Hydro-Québec (a Crown Corporation of Quebec) to supply power for 65 years, but at a price that took no account of monetary inflation or the future value of hydroelectricity. In 1971, flooding of the Smallwood Reservoir began, and it eventually covered an immense area of 6700 km². In 1974, a generating station with a capacity of 5429 MW was completed and electricity began to flow to markets in Quebec and the northeastern United States.

It is astonishing by the standards of today, but the Churchill Falls Project was developed with few studies of its potential environmental impacts. For instance, there was little understanding of how the local and regional ecology might be affected by the enormous changes in the hydrology of the Churchill River, one of the great watercourses of eastern Canada. Inevitably, the huge reservoir caused extensive damage through flooding, other habitat changes, and the mobilization of bioavailable methylmercury.

It is also incredible that this immense industrial development occurred without much consultation with the local people, particularly those of the Innu culture, who are the original inhabitants of that region of Labrador. The local Innu had long engaged in subsistence hunting and commercial trapping in the project region, undertaking seasonal migrations to traditional areas where they obtained wild meat as food as well as furs to sell. Most of these people were unaware of the proposed hydroelectric development or its probable consequences for their traditional activities; some of them lost their canoes, cabins, and other possessions to flooding, for which they were not compensated. Many archaeological sites, such as burying grounds, were also lost.

In 1975, planning and construction began for another hydroelectric development, this time to harness the lower Churchill River by building a dam and power plant at Gull Island, about 200 km downriver of Churchill Falls. Although the project was not completed, the development potential remains attractive in terms of industrial and economic considerations. In 1990, and several times since, new proposals were brought forward to develop the hydroelectric potential of the lower Churchill River. Although these plans have generally been supported by development interests in nearby Goose Bay, most of the Innu have been opposed to the proposed new hydro project. Their governing organization, known as Innu Nation, has demanded the following features in any development agreement they would consider signing:

- compensation for damage suffered by Innu during the initial development at Churchill Falls
- a full assessment of the environmental and socio-economic impacts of the proposed new development
- royalties and other compensation, such as specified job and contract opportunities, for Innu persons and companies during the new development
- the settlement of a comprehensive land claim, in view of the assertion of the Innu Nation of aboriginal title for almost all of that region of Labrador

To reinforce their position, the Innu have held public protests in the project area and in Newfoundland. They have also petitioned their case to environmental organizations, power companies, and state governments in the northeastern U.S., where most of the power would be sold. A particularly high-profile demonstration was held to confront a press conference staged by the governments of Quebec and Newfoundland in March of 1998, near the village of Churchill Falls, where they jointly announced a new plan for a hydro development on the Lower Churchill River. This protest by the Innu garnered front-page attention throughout Canada and internationally. The project envisioned at that time would have cost about $10 billion. It would have constructed a new reservoir, dam, and generating facility of 2264 MW at Gull Island, while also increasing the capacity of the existing Upper Churchill Falls station by 1000 MW.

Since then, the governments of Newfoundland and Labrador and Quebec have repeatedly announced their intention to develop a hydro facility on the Lower Churchill River. Consent had not yet, however, been obtained from the Innu people. Nor had a land settlement been achieved, or environmental and socio-economic impact assessments completed. Until all of these needs are satisfied, the proposals for additional hydroelectric development in Labrador will remain extremely contentious, and are unlikely to proceed.

For several years after the new impoundments were flooded, there was a relatively high productivity of phytoplankton and zooplankton. This occurred because of the high concentrations of nutrients, especially phosphorus, that were leached from flooded soil. The resulting large populations of invertebrates and small fish gave rise to relatively high productivity of lake whitefish (*Coregonus clupeaformis*) and northern pike (*Esox lucius*) for several years. However, mercury concentrations up to 3 ppm developed in these and other species of predatory fish. The maximum concentrations in lake whitefish occurred five years after impoundment and subsequently declined, while the concentrations in northern pike peaked after 10 years. The mercury concentrations are expected to return to background levels after 10–25 years for species of fish that feed on invertebrates, and after 20–30 years for fish-eating species.

A large amount of riparian habitat was lost when numerous small streams, ponds, and lakes were flooded. The shores of the reservoirs do not offset this damage because they do not constitute good riparian (riverside) habitat for dependent plants and animals. This is mainly because the annual water-level fluctuations in a reservoir are not the same as those occurring naturally—high water level in the spring and early summer, and low later in the growing season. This prevents the development of true riparian vegetation along the shores of hydroelectric reservoirs.

Changes in the flow regime caused severe erosion of fine-grained sediment and riverbanks in some areas below the dams. In the first few years after they were diverted, the Eastmain and Opinaca Rivers eroded about 120 000 m³/y of fine sediment, but this effect decreased by 90% four years after the diversions. The erosion resulted in higher water turbidity, less light penetration, and higher concentrations of suspended and dissolved organic matter and nutrients. Because of the reduced riverflow, environmental conditions changed drastically in the estuary of the Eastmain River. Initially, this habitat was mostly freshwater and hydrologically dominated by the flow of the river. After the hydroelectric development, however, tidal influences reached as far as 27 km inland, with saltwater intrusions occurring 10–15 km upriver.

The water quality of the La Grande River was less affected, although the flow regime became largely dependent on the managed rate of discharge from the reservoirs. Overall, the flow below the lowest powerhouse (La Grande-1) has approximately doubled. This initially led to erosion of fine sediment and riverbanks (sediment transport increased by a factor of 1.5 in the first year), but

Photo 20.6 Hydroelectric developments in relatively flat terrain can result in the flooding of enormous areas as reservoirs. This view shows a small part of one of the reservoirs behind the LG-1 Dam on the La Grande River. The first phase of this immense hydroelectric development resulted in five reservoirs with a total area exceeding 11 000 km². Source: A. Luttermann

this effect was largely (but not completely) stabilized within five years. The lowest powerhouse is a barrier to any up-river tidal influence and also to migrating fish. Fish productivity has remained similar to the pre-impoundment condition. However, the concentrations of methylmercury in fish have greatly increased. The estuary has retained its largely freshwater condition, and fish populations there have apparently not changed.

The rivers feed into James Bay, a large (88 000 km²), relatively shallow (half of its area is less than 20 m deep) marine ecosystem. Some changes have occurred in the physical oceanography of the river-discharge zones, but the marine ecosystem itself has not notably changed. Shallow-water areas still support lush beds of eelgrass (*Zostera marina*), and large populations of migratory waterfowl and other birds continue to utilize the local estuarine habitat.

Erosion associated with high-water discharges threatened the village of Fort George on the estuary of the La Grande River, forcing the relocation of its inhabitants to a new settlement upstream at Chisasibi (at a cost of about $50 million). The relocation resulted in considerable social and lifestyle disruption for the people, almost all of whom were Cree. The immense impoundments also affected the patterns of land-use by local hunters and trappers, some of whom no longer had access to their traditional areas. Greatly increased winter flows associated with hydro-electricity production have also created unstable ice conditions on the river. Consequently, some former winter travel routes are no longer safe.

Local people and their communities were also greatly affected by the diverse economic effects of the land-claim settlement and seven project-related agreements. (A total of $555 million has been allocated for compensation and remedial work on Cree, Inuit, and Naskapi lands associated with the development of the La Grande Complex.) They were also greatly affected by the entry into wage employment, the construction of a network of roads and other infrastructure, the influx of many non-local people working on the hydro facilities, and by other rapid socio-economic changes. Some of the changes have been viewed favourably but others have not, particularly if they are thought to have degraded the traditional elements of Cree, Inuit, or Naskapi culture.

Impoundments for Flood Control and Irrigation

Some areas are highly vulnerable to flooding in the springtime, especially if the yield of water from the watershed from snowmelt or a severe rain event exceeds the capacity of the river channel, causing spillover onto normally terrestrial habitat. Areas vulnerable to this kind of hydrological influence, known as floodplains, are common in many parts of Canada (see Canadian Focus 20.3). Such flooding may occur regularly or it may happen only in years with unusually high water yield from the watershed. To prevent or reduce the damage caused by flooding, control structures such as dams, reservoirs, and channelled spillways may be constructed.

Some Canadian proposals to develop impoundments for flood control and irrigation have been extremely controversial. Two of the most notable have been the Rafferty-Alameda project in southeastern Saskatchewan and the Oldman Dam in southwestern Alberta.

The Rafferty-Alameda project consists of the Rafferty Dam and Reservoir on the main branch of the Souris River, the Alameda Dam and Reservoir on Moose Mountain Creek, and associated channelizations and

diversions. This project was undertaken to provide the following benefits: water for the irrigation of about 4800 ha of land, regional flood control, storage of municipal water, cooling water for a thermal power plant, and lake-based recreation. However, opponents of the project objected to some of its environmental impacts, which included the displacement of 75 farm families by flooding of the reservoirs, the destruction of habitat of rare prairie plants and animals as well as fish, a degradation of downstream water quality and quantity, and damage to cultural and historical sites. Intense controversy was engendered by this proposal, and a legal challenge forced it to undergo a full-scale environmental impact assessment. This was done, even though construction activities were already at an advanced stage and had to be temporarily halted. The Rafferty Dam was completed in 1992 and the Alameda, in 1994.

It should be noted that the Rafferty-Alameda Project was the subject of a landmark decision in Canadian law, known as the "Rafferty Decision." The project was initially issued a permit by the provincial government, but its opponents initiated legal action based on the need for a full environmental impact assessment (EIA) under the requirements of federal law. In 1989, the Federal Court of Canada ruled that the Department of the Environment (a federal agency) must conduct a comprehensive environmental assessment of the proposed project under the Environmental Assessment and Review Process (EARP). This legal decision gave the federal EARP guidelines the force of law, making it mandatory to do such assessments for any development proposals involving the federal government. This includes any federally funded proposals, even if the development is to be undertaken by another (non-federal) organization, or if there is a risk of an environmental effect on an area of federal responsibility. Much of the political controversy in this case was associated with disagreements between the provincial and federal governments over jurisdictional issues.

The Oldman Dam consists of a dam, a reservoir, and associated structures on the Oldman River. The project was undertaken to provide the following benefits: water for the irrigation of about 68 850 ha of land, regional flood control, storage of municipal water for Lethbridge and Fort McLeod, enhancement of downstream fish populations through flow regulation, and lake-based recreation. However, opponents of the project, including members of the local Peigan Aboriginal nation, objected to some of its likely environmental impacts, which are similar to those

Canadian Focus 20.3

Disastrous Floods

Severe flooding is often a natural catastrophe, killing people or disrupting their lives and causing enormously expensive damage to homes, agriculture, and industry. Flood-control structures, such as dams, reservoirs, and levees can help to prevent flooding in susceptible areas, but they are rarely sufficient to prevent every occurrence. Two famous episodes of catastrophic flooding in Canada occurred in the Saguenay region of Quebec and in southeastern Manitoba.

The Saguenay disaster, in 1996, was caused by an extremely intense July rainstorm that delivered 155 mm of precipitation during a 50-hour period. The resulting severe flooding caused the deaths of 10 people and forced about 16 000 others from their homes. About 1350 houses were destroyed or badly damaged, and 1000 families had to be permanently relocated. There was also a devastating impact on commercial, industrial, and tourism operations. The total economic damage was more than $800 million. Although some of the major rivers feeding into the Saguenay region had flood-control dams and reservoirs in place, these were not adequate to deal with the enormous volume of water generated by the extreme rain event.

A much more extensive event affected the flood plain of the Red River in 1997, as a result of a very high volume of spring runoff from an extremely deep snow-pack that accumulated from several storms. The flooding affected more than 2000 km^2 of relatively flat terrain, and it caused 24 000 people to be evacuated from their homes in southeastern Manitoba and more than 50 000 in North Dakota and Minnesota, including almost all of the population of the city of Grand Forks. The total costs of the damage from this flood exceeded $1 billion. The destruction in Manitoba would have been much worse, but an extensive network of temporary dikes was hurriedly built by local residents, volunteers, and the Canadian army. Along with an existing system of permanent dikes and diversion channels, these protected most of the city of Winnipeg, which otherwise would have been devastated by the flooding (although these dikes exacerbated some of the flooding that occurred south of Winnipeg). Crucial to saving the city was the Red River Floodway, built in 1968 to provide protection from just this kind of severe flooding. (Until the great flood of 1997, many people somewhat derisively referred to this floodway as "Duff's Ditch," after Duff Roblin, the premier who had authorized construction of the project against much political opposition because of its high cost.)

described for the Rafferty-Alameda case. Opponents of the Oldman Dam were successful in a legal action to force the proponents to undertake a full environmental impact assessment (this was the first application of the Rafferty decision of 1989; it was eventually resolved by the Supreme Court of Canada). The EIA was conducted, even though the development was already about 40% completed. Construction of the dam was completed in 1993 (although much controversy remained because some concerns of the environmental review panel were not fully addressed before the permit was granted for completion).

Conclusions

Eutrophication is a natural process in many waterbodies, characterized by increasing productivity resulting from enhanced nutrient supply. In addition, "cultural eutrophication" is a widespread problem caused by anthropogenic influences, most commonly the dumping of inadequately treated sewage of humans or livestock, which deposits large amounts of nutrients into receiving waterbodies. Eutrophication causes severe environmental damage, but it can be controlled by responsibly treating sewage and other nutrient-rich materials before wastewater is released into the environment. Severe environmental damage may also be caused by dams and reservoirs, which may be developed in suitable places for various purposes, such as the generation of hydroelectricity, the control of flooding, or provision of a reliable supply of water for irrigation or municipal needs. The environmental damage may include the flooding of natural habitat, increased mercury concentrations in fish, and the disruption of local people. To a large degree, these damages are an inevitable consequence of any decision to develop a dam and reservoir, and this is the reason why such proposals are always controversial.

Key Terms

eutrophic	primary sewage treatment
oligotrophic	biological oxygen demand (BOD)
mesotrophic	
cultural eutrophication	secondary sewage treatment
algal bloom	tertiary sewage treatment
hypertrophic	artificial wetland
Principle of Limiting Factors	impoundment
whole-lake experiment	run-of-the-river
sewage treatment	

Questions for Review

1. What evidence exists to show that phosphorus is the limiting nutrient for algal productivity in lakes?

2. Lake Erie has been affected by a variety of environmental stressors. Which of these have caused the most damage to the lake?

3. What are the major environmental impacts of hydroelectric developments? Describe each in detail.

4. Why is methylmercury contamination of fish such a common occurrence after the development of a reservoir?

Questions for Discussion

1. How is sewage treated in the community where you live? Describe the environmental benefits of treating your community's sewage, and the damages of not doing so.

2. Compare the major environmental effects of impoundments and run-of-the-river hydroelectric developments.

3. Are there any dams or reservoirs close to where you live? Identify one and prepare a list of the "benefits" and "damages" that it brings to society and the environment.

4. Why do large hydroelectric proposals always engender such intense local controversy?

Exploring Issues

1. A proposal is being made to develop a hydroelectric facility on a large river. There are two development options: (a) a run-of-the-river facility, and (b) a larger dam that would develop an extensive reservoir. Option (b) would generate considerably more electricity. You are an environmental scientist and have been asked to compare the potential environmental impacts of the two proposals. What major topics would you examine in your impact assessment? What do you think the likely results would be (in terms of the relative impacts of the two development options)?

References

Cowx, I.G. (ed.). 2002. *Management and Ecology of Lake and Reservoir Fisheries.* Oxford, UK: Blackwell Publishing.

Dodds, W.K. 2001. *Freshwater Ecology: Concepts and Environmental Applications.* San Diego, CA: Academic Press.

Dolan, D. N. 1993. Point source loadings of phosphorus to Lake Erie: 1986–1990. *J. Great Lakes Res.,* **19**: 212–223.

Dorcey, T., A. Steiner, M. Acreman, and B. Orlando. 1997. *Large Dams: Learning from the Past; Looking at the Future: Workshop Proceedings.* Gland, Switzerland: IUCN.

Environment Canada. 1996. *The State of Canada's Environment, 1996.* Ottawa: Government of Canada.

Environmental Protection Agency. 2003. *The Great Lakes; An Environmental Atlas and Resource Book.* Washington, DC: U.S. Environmental Protection Agency. www.epa.gov/glnpo/atlas/gl-fact1.html

Freedman, B. 1995. *Environmental Ecology.* 2nd ed. San Diego, CA: Academic.

Goodland, R. 1993. *Ethical Priorities in Environmentally Sustainable Energy Systems: The Case of Tropical Hydropower.* World Bank Environment Dept. Working Paper No. 67. Washington, DC: World Bank.

Gregor, D.J. and M.G. Johnson. 1980. Non-point source phosphorus inputs to the Great Lakes. In: *Phosphorus Management Strategies for Lakes.* (R.C. Loehr, C.S. Martin, and W. Rast, eds.). Ann Arbor, MI: Ann Arbor Science. pp. 37–59.

Harper, D. 1992. *Eutrophication of Freshwaters: Principles, Problems, and Restoration.* New York: Chapman & Hall.

Hartman, W.L. 1988. Historical changes in the major fish resources of the Great Lakes. In: *Toxic Contaminants and Ecosystem Health: A Great Lakes Perspective.* (M.S. Evans, ed.). New York: Wiley.

Hebert, P.D.N., C.C. Wilson, M.H. Murdoch, and R. Lazar. 1991. Demography and ecological impact of the invading mollusc *Dreissena polymorpha. Can. J. Zool.,* **69**: 405–409.

Hornig, J.F. 1999. *Social and Environmental Impacts of the James Bay Hydroelectric Project.* Montreal, PQ: McGill-Queen's University Publishing.

International Commission on Large Dams. 2003. *World Register of Dams.* Paris, France: ICOLD.

International Rivers Network. 2005. *Linking Human Rights and Environmental Protection.* Berkeley, CA: International Rivers Network. www.irn.org/

Kalff, J. 2001. *Limnology.* Toronto: Prentice Hall.

Laws, E.A. 2000. *Aquatic Pollution: An Introductory Text.* 3rd ed. New York, NY: John Wiley and Sons.

Levine, S.N. and D.W. Schindler. 1989. Phosphorus, nitrogen, and carbon dynamics of Experimental Lake 303, during recovery from eutrophication. *Can. J. Fish. & Aquat. Sci.,* **46**: 2–10.

Livingston, R.L. 2001. *Eutrophication Processes in Coastal Systems: Origin and Succession of Plankton Blooms and Effects on Secondary Production.* Boca Raton, FL: CRC Press.

Ludyanskiy, M.L., D. McDonald, and D. MacNeil. 1993. Impact of the zebra mussel, a bivalve indicator. *BioScience*, **43**: 533–544.

Mackie, G.L. 1991. Biology of exotic zebra mussel, *Dreissena polymorpha*, in relation to native bivalves and its potential impact in Lake St. Clair. *Hydrobiologia*, **219**: 251–268.

Makarewicz, J.C. and P. Bertram. 1991. Evidence for the restoration of the Lake Erie ecosystem. *BioScience*, **41**: 216–223.

Messier, D. 1998. *The La Grande Rivière Hydroelectric Complex in Northern Quebec.* Montreal, PQ: Hydro-Québec.

Mills, E.L., J.H. Leach, J.T. Carlton, and C.L. Secar. 1993. Exotic species in the Great Lakes: a history of biotic crises and anthropogenic introductions. *J. Great Lakes Res.*, **19**: 1–54.

Neilson, M., S. L'Italien, V. Glumac, D. Williams, and P. Bertram. 1994. Nutrients: Trends and system response. In *State of the Lakes Ecosystem Conference (SOLEC, 1994).* Ottawa: Environment Canada.

Regier, H.A. and W.L. Hartman. 1973. Lake Erie's fish community: 150 years of cultural stresses. *Science*, **180**: 1248–1255.

Rosenberg, D.M., F. Berkes, R.A. Bodaly, R.E. Hecky, C.A. Kelly, and J.W.M. Rudd. 1997. Large-scale impacts of hydroelectric development. Environmental Reviews, **5**: 27–54.

Ryding, S.-O. 1990. *The Control of Eutrophication of Lakes and Reservoirs.* London, UK: Parthenon Publishing Group.

Schetagne, R., J. Therrien, and R. Lalumiere. 2002. Suivi environnemental du complexe La Grande. ... volution des teneurs en mercure dans les poissons. Rapport synthèse 1978–2000. Groupe conseil GENIVARinc. et directio Barrages et Environnement, Hydro-Québec Production. 193 p. et annexe.

Schindler, D.W. 1978. Factors regulating phytoplankton production and standing crop in the world's freshwaters. *Limnol. Oceanogr.*, **23**: 478–486.

Schindler, D.W. 1990. Experimental perturbations of whole lakes as tests of hypotheses concerning ecosystem structure and function. *Oikos*, **57**: 25–41.

Schindler, D.W., J. Kalff, H.E. Welch, G.J. Brunskill, H. Kling, and N. Kritsch. 1974. Eutrophication in the high arctic—Meretta Lake, Cornwallis Island (75°N Lat.). *J. Fish. Res. Bd. Canada*, **31**: 647–662.

Sonzogni, W.C., A. Robertson, and A.M. Beeton. 1983. Great Lakes management: Ecological factors. *Environ. Manage.*, **7**: 531–542.

Vallentyne, J.R. 1974. *The Algal Bowl. Lakes and Man.* Ottawa: Department of the Environment. Special Publication 22.

Wetzel, R.G. 2001. *Limnology: Lake and River Ecosystems.* 3rd ed. San Diego, CA: Academic Press.

World Resources Institute. 2005. *Earth Trends. The Environmental Information Portal.* Washington, DC: WRI.

Informative Websites

Canada Centre for Inland Waters.
www.nwri.ca/cciwdesc-e.html

The Canada Centre for Inland Waters is one of the world's leading centres for water research, generating environmental information and knowledge about the Great Lakes.

Edsall, T. and M. Charlton. *Nearshore Waters of the Great Lakes.* www.on.ec.gc.ca/solec/nearshore-water/paper/intro.html#TOC

This report, co-sponsored by Environment Canada and the Environmental Protection Agency, studies the current conditions of the Great Lakes system and its connecting channels.

Energy Information Administration (EIA). *Annual Energy Outlook 2005 with Projections to 2025.*
www.eia.doe.gov/oiaf/aeo/

This International Energy Outlook presents historical data along with the U.S. EIA's projections of energy consumption and energy prospects through 2025.

Environment Canada. Our Great Lakes.
www.on.ec.gc.ca/greatlakes/

The Our Great Lakes website is an information resource that provides an index of Environment Canada's Great Lakes programs, publications, and databases and is a window to other environmental networks.

Environmental Literacy Council. Hydroelectric Power.
www.enviroliteracy.org/article.php/59.html

You will find links to the Hoover Dam, Grand Coulee Dam, the U.S. Department of Energy, and other related sites, as well as an explanation of why dams have been so controversial.

Experimental Lakes Area.
www.umanitoba.ca/institutes/fisheries/

This is the website for the research done in the Experimental Lakes Area in northwestern Ontario.

Great Lakes Information Network. www.great-lakes.net

The Great Lakes Information Network is a partnership that provides one place online for people to find information relating to the binational Great Lakes region of North America. You can find links, announcements, water levels, and much more information.

International Joint Commission. www.ijc.org/

The International Joint Commission prevents and resolves disputes between the U.S. and Canada under the 1909 Boundary Waters Treaty. Visit this bilingual site for related links, news releases, or publications.

International Rivers Network. www.irn.org/

The International Rivers Network supports local communities working to protect their rivers and watersheds. It does this by working to halt destructive river development projects and encourage equitable and sustainable methods of meeting needs for water, energy, and flood management.

Natural Resources Canada. Hydroelectric Energy.
www.canren.gc.ca/tech_appl/index.asp?CaId=4&PgId=26

This website of Natural Resources Canada contains information about hydroelectric developments, including their environmental effects.

Nonpoint Pollution of Surface Waters with Phosphorus and Nitrogen. www.esa.org/science/Issues/FileEnglish/issue3.pdf

This pdf document of the Ecological Society of America explains the effects of pollution on freshwater by phosphorus and nitrogen.

Nutrient Pollution of Coastal Rivers, Bays, and Seas.
www.esa.org/science/Issues/FileEnglish/issue7.pdf

This pdf document of the Ecological Society of America explains the effects of coastal pollution due to nutrients.

The World Commission on Dams. www.dams.org/

The goals of the Commission are to review the development effectiveness of dams and assess alternatives for water resources and energy development. This site also outlines work programs around the world that the Commission sponsors.

Water Resources Center Archives. Dams and Reservoirs.
www.lib.berkeley.edu/WRCA/dam.html

The University of California, Berkeley's Water Resources Center Archives set up this site, which has links to papers about dams and reservoirs.

Oil Spills 21

CHAPTER OBJECTIVES

After completing this chapter, you will be able to

1. Outline the most common causes of oil spills on land and at sea.
2. Describe how spilled oil becomes dispersed in the environment through evaporation, spreading, and other processes.
3. Explain how hydrocarbons cause toxicity to organisms.
4. Explain how petroleum kills birds and how oiled birds may be rehabilitated.
5. Describe case studies of the ecological effects of oil spills at sea and on land.
6. Discuss the potential consequences of petroleum resource development in the Arctic.

CHAPTER OUTLINE

- Introduction
- Petroleum and Its Refined Products
- Oil Spills
- Toxicity
- Ecological Effects
- Conclusions

Introduction

Petroleum (crude oil) is a non-renewable natural resource (Chapter 13) used mainly as a source of energy. It is also used to manufacture a diverse array of petrochemicals, including synthetic materials such as plastics. Petroleum is mined in huge quantities. Pipelines and ships transport most of this volume, plus its refined products, around the globe. The risks of spillage are always present, and oil spills may cause severe ecological damage.

Petroleum accounts for about 41% of the global production of commercial energy (in 2003; 40% in Canada); (World Resources Institute, 2005). Moreover, the global use of petroleum is increasing rapidly, by about 16% per year between 1993 and 2003. The fastest increases are in regions with a rapidly growing economy, such as China, India, Southeast Asia, and Brazil. Relatively wealthy, developed countries support about 21% of the human population, but they account for 66% of the global use of petroleum—27% in North America, 32% in Europe, and 7% in Japan.

The global reserves of petroleum are about 157 billion t, of which 53% occur in the Middle East, 6% in North America (26% of this 6% is in Canada), and 6% in the former Soviet Union. Almost all mining of petroleum occurs far from the places where it is consumed. The Middle East, for example, is a huge exporter of petroleum and refined products; the amount shipped abroad is about 4.7 times larger than domestic usage in that region (in 2003). In contrast, Europe produces about 93% of the petroleum it consumes, while Asia produces only 44% and the U.S., 37%.

Canada produces about 47% more petroleum than it consumes (Table 21.1). However, about 82% of Canadian production is in sparsely populated areas of Alberta, and 12%

is in similar places in Saskatchewan, while most consumption occurs in densely populated areas throughout the country. Consequently, enormous quantities of petroleum and its refined products are transported over great distances within Canada, mostly by overland pipelines, railroads, and trucks. In addition, western Canada exports large amounts of petroleum and refined products to the central and western U.S. and to Asia; eastern Canada exports to the northeastern U.S. and imports from the Middle East and Latin America. Therefore, even though Canada is self-sufficient in its net production and consumption of petroleum, huge quantities move within, out of, and into the country and its regions.

On the global scale, most petroleum and its refined products are transported by oceanic tankers and overland pipelines. Local distribution systems typically involve smaller tankers, barges, pipelines, railroads, and trucks. There is a risk of accidental spillage from all of these means of transportation. Some of these spills have been spectacular in their volume and resulting environmental damage. In addition, petroleum may be discharged into the environment during the normal operation of tankers, especially if oily bilge water is released to the ocean when cleaning the storage tanks.

Petroleum refineries may also cause pollution of their local environment due to small but frequent spills and the routine discharge of wastewater contaminated with hydrocarbons and trace quantities of metals, sulphides, phenols, and other chemicals. Small-scale dumping of used motor oil and other hydrocarbon wastes is another important, although poorly documented, source of pollution.

In this section we examine the causes of oil spills from these various sources and the ecological damage that can be caused in aquatic and terrestrial environments.

TABLE 21.1	Petroleum Production and Use in Selected Countries in 2004		
Percentage increase since 1994 is given in parentheses. See Appendix C, Table 14 for additional country data of this type.			
COUNTRY	PRODUCTION OF PETROLEUM (10^6 tonne/year)	CONSUMPTION OF PETROLEUM (10^6 t/y)	NET IMPORTS/ EXPORTS (10^6 tonne/year)
Saudi Arabia	506 (16)	80 (35)	426
Russian Fed.	459 (44)	129 (−21)	330
United States	330 (−15)	938 (16)	−608
Canada	*148* (39)	*100* (13)	*48*
World	3868 (19)	3767 (18)	—

Sources: British Petroleum (2005) and World Resources Institute (2005)

Petroleum and Its Refined Products

Petroleum is a naturally occurring mixture of liquid organic compounds, almost all of which are *hydrocarbons* (this term is explained below). Petroleum is a fossil fuel, as are coal, oil shale, oil sand, and natural gas. Fossil fuels are derived from ancient plant biomass that became buried in deep sedimentary formations. Over geologically long periods of time, this biomass was subjected to high pressure, high temperature, and anoxia. Chemical reactions resulted that eventually produced a rich mixture of gaseous, liquid, and solid hydrocarbons. Naturally occurring hydrocarbons can range in complexity from gaseous methane, with a weight of only 16 g/mole, to solid substances found in coal, with molecular weights exceeding 20 000 g/mole. (In chemistry, a "mole" is a standard quantity of a substance, equivalent to the amount contained in 6.02×10^{23} atoms or molecules.)

Hydrocarbons are molecules composed entirely of hydrogen and carbon atoms. Hydrocarbons can be classified into three groups: aliphatic, alicyclic, and aromatic.

- Aliphatic hydrocarbons are compounds in which the carbon atoms are organized in a simple chain. Saturated aliphatics (also called paraffins or alkanes) have a single bond between adjacent carbon atoms; unsaturated molecules have one or more double or triple bonds. These bonds are illustrated by the two-carbon aliphatic hydrocarbons ethane, $H_3C–CH_3$; ethylene, $H_2C = CH_2$; and acetylene, $HC \equiv CH$. Unsaturated aliphatics are relatively unstable and do not occur naturally in petroleum. They are produced during industrial refining, and photochemically in the environment after crude oil is spilled.
- Alicyclic hydrocarbons have some or all of their carbon atoms arranged in a ring structure, which may be saturated or unsaturated.
- Aromatic hydrocarbons contain one or more, five- or six-carbon rings in their molecular structure. The simplest ring, C_6H_6, is known as benzene.

Crude petroleums vary greatly in their specific mixtures of hydrocarbons and other chemicals. They typically consist of about 98% liquid hydrocarbons, less than 1–2% sulphur, and less than 1% nitrogen, plus the metals vanadium and nickel in concentrations up to 0.15%. When petroleum is refined, various hydrocarbon fractions are separated by distillation at different temperatures. This is done to produce such products as natural gas, gasoline, kerosene, heating oil, jet fuel, lubricating oils, waxes, and residual fuel oil (also known as bunker fuel). In addition, a process known as catalytic cracking is used to convert some of the heavier fractions into lighter, more valuable hydrocarbons such as those in gasoline.

Oil Spills

Oil pollution can be caused by any spillage of petroleum or its refined products. The largest spills typically involve a discharge of petroleum or bunker fuel to the ocean from a disabled tanker or drilling platform, to an inland waterway from a barge or ship, or to land or freshwater from a well blowout or broken pipeline. In addition, some enormous oil spills have resulted from acts of warfare.

Terrestrial Oil Spills

Oil spills onto land are relatively common. Between 1989 and 1995, about 3500, mostly relatively small, oil spills per year were reported in Canada (Environment Canada, 1998). About 42% of these occurred in the immediate vicinity of production wells, while 29% were from pipelines and 16% from tanker trucks. During that period, up to 140 000 t of oil were spilled per year in the petroleum-producing areas of Canada, due to accidental spills and well blowouts.

Most large, terrestrial spills involve a ruptured pipeline, either above or below ground. Canada has about 36 000 km of pipeline for transporting petroleum and another 255 000 km of natural gas pipeline (for comparison, there are about 1.4 million km of roads, of which 200 000 are classified as highways; Transport Canada, 2004). Pipeline breaks may be caused by faulty welding, corrosion, or pump malfunctions, as well as by earthquakes and even armed vandals engaged in target practice.

Fortunately, the extensive Canadian network of pipelines incorporates spill sensors and other technologies that allow workers to rapidly shut down damaged sections. Individual accidents can then be kept relatively small and confined. Some other countries use fewer of these technologies and, consequently, may suffer huge petroleum spills from overland pipelines; for example, in northern Russia, some pipelines have become corroded, and insufficient countermeasures are in place to prevent or contain oil spills.

In general, oil spilled on land affects relatively localized areas of terrain because most soils absorb petroleum quickly. However, much larger areas of aquatic habitat can be affected if spilled petroleum reaches a watercourse. Oil spilled onto water, particularly at sea, can affect very extensive areas because wind and currents cause slicks to spread and disperse widely.

Marine Oil Spills

Petroleum spills into the world's oceans amounted to about 1.3 million t/y (in 2001; Table 21.2). This is considerably less than the spillage occurring in the 1970s and early 1980s, which was about 3–6 million t/y (Koons, 1984). In addition to petroleum spillage, there is a substantial natural emission to the oceans of hydrocarbons not derived from petroleum. These chemicals are synthesized and released by marine phytoplankton, at a rate estimated at 26 million t/y. These huge biological releases contribute to the background concentration of hydrocarbons in marine ecosystems, equivalent to about 1 ppb (1 µg/L) in seawater. The biogenic emissions represent natural contamination, and they are well dispersed and do not result in known biological damage.

In addition, there are natural emissions of petroleum to the marine environment oozing from underwater oil seeps. These natural seeps amount to an estimated 0.6 million t/y and can sometimes cause local ecological damage.

Massive spills associated with wrecked supertankers or well platforms at sea attract a great deal of attention, and

deservedly so. It is important to recognize, however, that relatively small but frequent discharges to the environment are associated with urban runoff, oil refineries, "normal" tanker discharges, and other coastal effluents. Because these discharges are frequent, they account for a larger aggregate volume of petroleum than do the rare but spectacular massive spills (see Table 21.2). The chronic coastal discharges are responsible for the local contamination and pollution by hydrocarbons that is typical of coastal cities and harbours everywhere. Overall, based on tanker traffic and the regulatory environment governing the transport and handling of petroleum at sea and on inland waterways, Canada can expect to experience >100 small spills per year (<1 t), >10 medium-sized spills (1–100 t), and >1 major spill (100–10 000 t) (Environment Canada, 1998). A catastrophic spill exceeding 10 000 t is expected about every 15 years.

Discharges of oily washings from tanker storage tanks are an important source of petroleum inputs to the oceans. After a tanker delivers a load of petroleum to a refinery, it fills some of its storage tanks with seawater, which acts as stabilizing ballast while the ship travels to get its next load. As the tanker approaches its destination, the ballast may be discharged into the ocean. This waste water contains hydrocarbon residues equivalent to about 1.5% of the tanker's capacity in the case of bunker fuel, less than 1% for petroleum, and about 0.1% for light refined products such as gasoline. For large oil tankers, this could amount to as much as 800 t of hydrocarbons.

This large, operational source of marine pollution has been decreasing greatly since the 1970s due to widespread adoption of two procedures: the **load-on-top (LOT) method** and the **crude oil washing (COW) method**. LOT separates and contains most of the oily residues before ballast water is discharged to the marine environment (the residual oil is then combined with the next load). If used in calm seas, the LOT technique can recover 99% of the oily residues, although the efficiency may be 90% or less if the tanker has had a turbulent passage. The COW method is a more recent innovation than LOT. It involves washing the petroleum storage tanks with a spray of crude oil before the new cargo is loaded. The spray dissolves the residual sludge, allowing it to combine with the next load. The beauty of the COW method is that it eliminates the need to rinse the empty tanker compartments with seawater, so there are no bilge washings to discharge to the marine environment. Thanks to the widespread use of LOT and COW, operational discharges of petroleum from tankers has been reduced from about 1.1 million t in 1973 to 36 000 t in 2002. Although LOT and COW are now

TABLE 21.2	Estimates of Petroleum Hydrocarbon Inputs to the World's Oceans

Data, in units of 10^3 t/y, are for 2002.

SOURCE	AMOUNT (10^3 t/y)
Natural seeps	600
Operational discharges from tankers and other ships	306
Urban runoff and discharges	140
Accidents involving tankers at sea	100
Atmospheric deposition	54
Other coastal discharges	50
Offshore production losses	37
Losses from marine pipelines	12
Coastal refineries	5
Total discharges	1300

Source: "Best estimate" data from National Academy of Sciences (2003)

widely used, some tankers and other ships continue to illegally discharge oily wastes at sea. This pollution is still an important cause of seabird mortality off the coasts of Canada and other countries.

The most disastrous marine spills of petroleum (several of which are described later in this chapter) include the following supertanker accidents:

- In 1967, the *Torrey Canyon* spilled 117 000 t of petroleum off southern England.
- In 1973, the *Metula* spilled 53 000 t in the Strait of Magellan.
- In 1978, the *Amoco Cadiz* spilled 230 000 t in the English Channel.
- In 1989, the *Exxon Valdez* spilled 36 000 t in southern Alaska.
- In 1993, the *Braer* spilled 84 000 t off the Shetland Islands of Scotland.
- In 1996, the *Sea Empress* spilled 72 000 t off Wales.
- In 1999, the *Erica* spilled 20 000 t into the Bay of Biscay off France and Spain.
- In 2002, the *Prestige* spilled 63 000 t into the Atlantic off France and Spain.
- In 2003, the *Tasman Spirit* spilled 30 000 t off Pakistan.

Canada has had its share of notable tanker spills:

- The *Arrow* ran aground in Chedabucto Bay, Nova Scotia, in 1970, and spilled 11 000 t of bunker-C fuel (a common industrial fuel). About 300 km of shoreline was polluted by the spill and many seabirds were killed (about 2000 dead birds were collected from Chedabucto Bay and another 5000 from Sable Island, 320 km away).
- The *Kurdistan* spilled 7500 t of bunker fuel in Cabot Strait between Newfoundland and Nova Scotia in 1979.
- The *Nestucca* spilled 875 t of bunker fuel in 1988 off Washington State and extensively polluted shorelines on the west side of Vancouver Island, British Columbia. This spill killed many seabirds. About 3600 dead birds of 31 species were collected on the western beaches of Vancouver Island, although the total mortality is estimated at more than 10 000 birds.

Some large accidental spills have occurred from offshore oil drilling platforms. The enormous blowout of the *IXTOC–I* exploration well in the Gulf of Mexico in 1979 resulted in the spillage of about 500 000 t of petroleum,

Photo 21.1 Aquatic birds are among the most evocative and tragic victims of oil spills. This blue-winged teal (*Anas discors*) was killed by a spill of heavy fuel oil on the St. Lawrence River.

representing the largest-ever accidental spill. Other platform spills include a blowout in 1969 off the coast of Santa Barbara in southern California (10 000 t) and the *Ekofisk* accident in 1977 in the North Sea off Norway (30 000 t).

Oil Spills through Warfare

Huge quantities of petroleum and refined products have been spilled during warfare. During the Second World War, for example, German submarines sank 42 tankers off eastern North America, resulting in the spillage of about 417 000 t of oil. Attacks on oil tankers were common during the Iran-Iraq War of 1981–87. In total, there were 314 attacks on oil tankers, 70% of them by Iraqi forces. That war's largest spill occurred in 1983, when Iraq damaged five tankers and three production wells at the Iranian *Nowruz* offshore facility, causing more than 260 000 t of petroleum to spill into the Gulf of Arabia.

The world's largest-ever marine spill occurred during the brief Gulf War of 1991. Iraqi forces deliberately released huge quantities of petroleum (about 0.8 million t, although estimates range as high as 2 million t) into the Gulf of Arabia from a Kuwaiti coastal loading facility. In part, this spill was a tactic of warfare, in an attempt to make it difficult for Allied forces to execute an amphibious landing during the liberation of Kuwait. The spill was mostly, however, an act of economic and ecological terrorism.

The Iraqis also caused an extremely large spillage on land during that war by sabotaging and igniting virtually all of the more than 700 production wells in Kuwait. An estimated 2–6 million t of petroleum per day were emitted from the burning wells. After the Gulf War was over, it took 11 months to control and cap the blowouts. By that time, an estimated 42–126 million t of petroleum had been spilled. About 5–21 million t of the petroleum accumulated as crude-oil lakes in the desert around the blowouts, while most of the rest burned in the atmosphere or evaporated.

More recently, during the aftermath of the U.S.-led invasion of Iraq in 2003, insurgent forces routinely attacked oil-exporting pipelines as acts of resistance and economic terrorism. This caused large petroleum spills to occur, although information about the volumes of pollution is not yet available.

Fate of Spilled Oil

Various natural processes affect petroleum and refined hydrocarbons after they are spilled into the environment (Figure 21.1). Depending on their chemical and physical characteristics, the various hydrocarbon fractions can selectively evaporate, spread, dissolve into water, accumulate as persistent residues, be degraded by microorganisms, or undergo some combination of these processes.

Evaporation of fumes and vapours is important in reducing the amount of spillage remaining in the aquatic or terrestrial environment. Evaporation typically dissipates almost 100% of gasoline spilled at sea, 30–50% of crude oil, and 10% of bunker fuel. In other words, the relatively light, volatile hydrocarbon fractions are selectively evap-

orated, leaving heavier residues behind. Rates of evaporation are increased by warm ambient temperatures and vigorous winds.

Spreading involves the movement of an oil slick over the surface of water or land. Spreading can occur over extremely large areas on water, but it is much more restricted on land because of the high absorptive capacity of soil. Slicks on water are moved about by currents and wind and may eventually wash onto a shore. The degree of spreading on water is influenced by the viscosity of the spilled material and by environmental factors such as wind speed, water turbulence, and the presence of surface ice. One experimental spillage of 1 m^3 of petroleum onto calm seawater created a slick 0.1 mm thick, with a diameter of 100 m, after 100 minutes. A petroleum slick only 0.3 μm thick or less is visible as a sheen on calm water.

Dissolution causes pollution of the water beneath an oil slick. Lighter hydrocarbon fractions are more soluble in water than heavier ones, while aromatics are much more soluble than alkanes (Table 21.3). After a petroleum spill at sea, the hydrocarbon concentration in water several metres beneath the slick may be 4–5 ppm (g/m^3), thousands of times greater than the 1 ppb (mg/m^3) occuring in ambient seawater.

Residual materials remain after the lighter fractions of the spilled petroleum have evaporated or dissolved. At sea, residual materials typically form a gelatinous, water-in-oil emulsion known as "mousse" because of its vague resemblance to the whipped chocolate dessert. Oil spilled offshore usually washes onto shorelines as mousse. Mousse stranded on the shore may weather to form a long-lasting

FIGURE 21.1 | Fate of Spilled Petroleum on Water

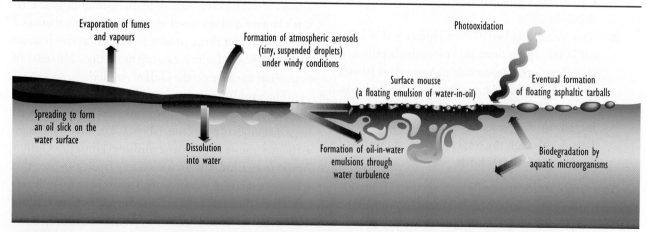

Source: Modified from Clark and MacLeod (1977)

TABLE 21.3	Solubilities of Alkane and Aromatic Hydrocarbons

Solubilities are reported in g/m³ (ppm) in fresh water. Within the aromatics, aqueous solubility decreases with increasing molecular size and with the number of aromatic rings.

HYDROCARBON	SOLUBILITY
ALKANES	
Gases (1–4 carbons)	24–62
Liquids (5–9 carbons)	0.05–39
Kerosenes (10–17 carbons)	$1-2 \times 10^{-4}$
Lubricating oils (23–37 carbons)	$<10^{-7}$
Residual hydrocarbons (>37 carbons)	$<10^{-14}$
AROMATICS	
Benzene (C_6H_6)	1780
Toluene (C_7H_6)	515
Naphthalene ($C_{10}H_8$, two rings)	31

tarry residue on rocks. Alternatively, mousse may eventually combine with particles of sediment on the beach to form sticky, tar-like patties that subsequently become buried or may be washed back to sea during a storm. Mousse that does not wash ashore eventually weathers into dense, semi-solid, floating asphaltic residues known as "tar balls."

Degradation refers to the slow decomposition of spilled materials by organisms and by photo-oxidation by solar ultraviolet radiation. Many species of fungi, bacteria, and other microorganisms can utilize hydrocarbons as an energy source for metabolism. The rate of **biodegradation** varies greatly, however, depending on ambient temperature, the concentration of oxygen, and the availability of key nutrients such as nitrogen and phosphorus. In general, lighter fractions of petroleum are relatively easily decomposed by biological and inorganic oxidations, while heavier fractions resist degradation and can be persistent in the environment.

Toxicity

Acute toxicity caused by petroleum, refined products, or pure hydrocarbons is typically associated with the destruction of cellular membranes—damage that results in tissue death. The toxic effects are influenced by several factors, especially the following:

- the chemical composition of the spilled material, including its component hydrocarbons

- the intensity of exposure (i.e., the amount or concentration of specific hydrocarbons or type of petroleum)

- the frequency of exposure events (i.e., whether the pollution is a single event, chronic [continuous], or frequent [a series of episodes])

- the timing of the exposure (i.e., whether it occurs during a critical time for a species or ecosystem)

- the condition of the spilled material, including thickness of the slick, nature of the emulsion, degree of weathering, and persistence of residues

- any environmental influences on exposure and toxicity, including weather conditions, oxygen status, and the presence of other pollutants

- any toxicity associated with chemical dispersants or detergents used during a cleanup

- the sensitivity of species in the affected ecosystem to toxic effects of hydrocarbons

In addition, severe damage may be caused by methods used during a cleanup, such as the use of dispersants and emulsifiers, hot-water washing, the removal of substrate, burning, and the tilling of oiled soil to improve aeration. Ecological effects are also influenced by any damage caused to "keystone" species, which has disproportionate effects on their community.

Effects on Birds

Seabirds such as cormorants, sea ducks (e.g., eiders, mergansers, scaup, scoters), alcids (e.g., auklets, murres, puffins, and razorbills), and penguins are extremely vulnerable to oil spills. During the non-breeding seasons, a spill can cause enormous mortality to these birds because they may congregate in large, seasonal flocks known as "rafts." Moreover, since alcids and penguins have low reproductive rates, their abundance can take a long time to recover from mass mortality caused by an oil spill. Murres, for example, do not begin to breed until they are five years old, lay only a one-egg clutch, and fledge only about 0.5 young per pair of breeding adults per year.

Seabirds are killed because their feathers become fouled with oil when they dive through or swim in oil-polluted water. The birds lose critical insulation and buoyancy and die from excessive heat loss leading to hypothermia or by drowning. They also ingest highly toxic oil while attempting to clean their feathers by preening. In addition, bird embryos can be killed by even a light oiling of the egg from the feathers of a contaminated parent.

The size of a petroleum spill is not an accurate indicator of its potential for causing damage to bird populations. The ecological context is also critically important: even a small spill in a sensitive habitat can wreak havoc. For example, in 1981, a relatively small discharge of oily bilge water from the tanker *Stylis* off Norway killed about 30 000 seabirds. This happened because the spill affected a critical habitat where seabirds are abundant during the winter. In another case, more than 16 000 oiled Magellanic penguins (*Spheniscus magellanicus*) were discovered on beaches in Argentina in 1991, even though no offshore slick could be found. The oil likely came from the bilge washings of a passing tanker. Similar damage occurs chronically off Newfoundland and Nova Scotia because of illegal discharges of oily bilge water by tankers. In January 1997, about 30 000 murres and other seabirds were killed in this way near Cape St. Mary's in southern Newfoundland.

Ecological Effects

In the following sections we will use case studies of oil spills to investigate ecological damage caused by both oil pollution and cleanup methods. We will examine spills from wrecked supertankers and offshore drilling platforms, chronic emissions near petroleum refineries, and oiling of terrestrial vegetation.

Oil Spills from Wrecked Tankers

The *Torrey Canyon*

The *Torrey Canyon* wreck in 1967 is one of the most famous supertanker accidents. The ship was bound for a refinery in Wales with 117 000 t of crude oil when it ran aground. Its entire cargo was spilled, polluting hundreds of kilometres of coastline. Seabirds were among the most tragic victims of this spill, with at least 30 000 killed. Although almost 8000 oiled birds were captured and cleaned, the rehabilitation methods of the time were not very successful. Only a few of the birds survived long enough to be released, and post-release survival can be poor (see In Detail 21.1).

Immediately after the wreck of the *Torrey Canyon*, an intensive cleanup of oiled beaches began. This effort used large amounts of detergent and dispersant to create oil-in-water emulsions on polluted shorelines. The emulsions were then rinsed back to sea using pressurized water

streams from hoses. Unfortunately, the chemicals used as emulsifiers were extremely toxic to marine organisms. The enthusiastic use of these materials greatly increased the toxic damage already caused by the petroleum to the flora and fauna of beaches and intertidal and subtidal habitats.

However, emulsifiers were not used during the cleanup of rocky beaches. There, the marine algae, although damaged by oily residues, preserved some of their regenerative tissue and regrew relatively quickly. Some species of intertidal invertebrates also proved rather tolerant to oiling. Many limpets (*Patella* spp.), for example, survived and were later able to graze on algae on oiled rocks. In all cases, however, damage to marine species was much more severe wherever detergent or dispersant had been used during the cleanup.

The unanticipated damage caused by toxic emulsifiers was an important lesson from the cleanup of the *Torrey Canyon* disaster. Soon after, less toxic dispersants were developed for use in oil-spill emergencies. Techniques improved too, so these chemicals could be used more judiciously, mainly to clean sites of high value for industrial or recreational purposes and to treat offshore locations where ecological damage would be less.

A post-oiling succession occurred after the *Torrey Canyon* spill, which eventually restored ecosystems natural to the region. Oiled habitat in the rocky intertidal zone was initially colonized by the opportunistic green alga *Enteromorpha*. As invertebrate herbivores recovered, this alga was grazed and replaced by species of seaweeds, which are the typical algae of rocky intertidal habitats. Except for lingering effects on seabird populations, ecological damage caused by the *Torrey Canyon* spill turned out to be relatively short term because the recovery was vigorous.

In habitat cleaned with emulsifiers, however, the recovery was slower. Some areas took up to 10 years to recover communities similar to those present before the spill.

The *Amoco Cadiz*

About a decade after the *Torrey Canyon* accident, another supertanker ran aground in 1978 in the same general area, but closer to France. This was the *Amoco Cadiz*, whose wreck spilled 233 000 t of petroleum and fouled about 360 km of shoreline. A 140-km portion of the fouled coast was heavily oiled. The intensive cleanup of some polluted beaches involved digging up and removing oily sand, sediment, and petroleum residue. Detergent and low-toxicity dispersants were used only to remove fouling residues in

In Detail 21.1

Cleaning Oiled Birds

Birds may become oiled if they swim or dive in water polluted by oil. Because of the great empathy that people have for these tragic victims of pollution, intense efforts are often made to rehabilitate oiled birds by cleaning them of residues and treating their poisoning (Clark, 1984; Holmes, 1984; Harvey-Clark, 1990).

The first significant effort to do this was after the *Torrey Canyon* spill of 1967, when about 8000 oiled birds, mostly murres (*Uria aalge*) and razorbills (*Alca torda*), were cleaned. Unfortunately, the methods available at that time for rehabilitating oiled birds were not very effective, and only 6% of the treated animals survived for more than one month. Similarly, more than 1600 oiled birds were cleaned after the Santa Barbara spill in 1969, mostly western grebes (*Aechmophorus occidentalis*) and loons (*Gavia immer*), but only 15% of these birds survived.

These early rehabilitation treatments were not successful because biologists did not yet understand that more is needed than just removing oily residues from birds—their physiological stress (including poisoning) must also be addressed. Biologists determined several reasons for the deaths of oiled birds:

- Since birds were not captured and treated soon enough after being oiled, they became hypothermic (excessively cooled). Also, the birds were ingesting petroleum residues while trying to clean themselves.

- The methods for removing oily residues from birds involved the use of harsh solvents and emulsifiers that were themselves toxic, caused damage to feather structure, or did not clean the feathers sufficiently.

- Most oiled birds are hypoglycemic to some degree, a condition involving low blood sugar and weight loss and requiring rapid treatment with a glucose solution.

- An important effect of hydrocarbon poisoning in birds, particularly by aromatics, is disruption of the ability to regulate ion concentrations (especially sodium and potassium) in blood plasma. This condition requires the oral administration of an electrolyte solution.

- Aromatic hydrocarbons are toxic to red blood cells, resulting in a hemolytic anemia that needs several weeks of treatment by appropriate nutrition.

Today, much better procedures are available to capture, clean, and rehabilitate oiled birds. These improved techniques have been developed through trial and error while treating accidentally oiled birds, as well as by research on experimentally oiled animals. Because it is now known that oiled birds must be treated as soon as possible, spill-response teams try to capture them quickly. This reduces the stress and toxicity the animals experience before they can be cleaned. In addition, relatively gentle cleaning solutions, known as polysorbates, are used to de-oil birds, and electrolyte solutions and glucose are routinely administered to treat dehydration and hypoglycemia.

The methods of post-cleaning rehabilitation and release have also been improved. Typically, birds are kept for seven to ten days after cleaning. They are released as soon as the waterproofing of their feathers has been restored, their salt-excreting metabolism has recovered, their anemia is corrected, and they have started to regain lost weight.

As a result of these improved methods, up to 75% of oiled birds may be released after timely cleaning and rehabilitation. However, the success rate varies greatly, depending on bird species, the type of oil, and other factors—particularly how much time has passed between the oiling event and the capture and treatment.

Despite the relatively successful cleaning techniques of today, studies have shown that the post-release survival of birds is poor. It appears that less than 1% of treated and released seabirds may survive for even one year (Sharp, 1996). With such poor survival, it is questionable whether any substantial ecological benefit is gained from the cleaning programs. It is expensive to treat oiled birds, and large numbers of volunteers are needed, including specialists such as veterinarians. It is, of course, enormously better to avoid oil spills altogether than to try to deal with the terrible damage caused to wild animals and ecosystems.

---

harbours and to disperse floating masses of mousse in offshore habitat. Many of the ecological damages caused by oil pollution and the cleanup were less severe than in the case of the *Torrey Canyon*. Recovery from the *Amoco Cadiz* spill was also rapid and was substantially complete within several years. However, some effects on benthic invertebrates lasted for a decade, and there was lingering damage to local colonies of alcid seabirds.

The *Exxon Valdez*

The most damaging tanker accident ever to occur in North American waters was the wreck of the *Exxon Valdez* in southern Alaska. About one-quarter of the petroleum produced in the U.S. is mined in northern Alaska. A 1280-km pipeline carries petroleum from oil fields on the North Slope south to the port of Valdez in southern Alaska. The oil is then transported to markets in the western U.S. by a fleet of supertankers. The first part of the oceanic passage runs through a narrow but well-charted shipping channel in Prince William Sound.

Before the *Exxon Valdez* accident on March 23, 1989, tankers had navigated that passage about 16 000 times. However, the *Exxon Valdez*, the newest tanker in the Exxon fleet, was incompetently steered onto a submerged reef, resulting in a spill of 36 000 t of its 176 000-t load of petroleum. About 40% of the spill washed onto shoreline habitat of Prince William Sound, while 25% was carried out of the sound by currents, and 35% evaporated at sea. Less than 10% of the spill was recovered or burned.

The grounding of the *Exxon Valdez* could have been avoided by more sensible operation of the tanker. At the time that the ship went aground, its bridge was under the command of an unqualified mate. Unaccountably, the captain was in his cabin. Only some 10 minutes after assuming control of the ship, the mate, who was not sufficiently familiar with the shipping channel and its aids to navigation, had run the huge supertanker onto an unforgiving reef.

The damage caused by the grounding of the tanker was compounded by a lack of preparedness by industry and government for dealing with an oil-spill emergency at the port of Valdez. Essential equipment for containment and oil recovery was not immediately available, and it took too long to mobilize trained personnel. Consequently, despite favourable sea conditions during the first critical days after the grounding, few effective oil-spill countermeasures were mounted. Not until the second day of the

---

Global Focus 21.1

Cross-Boundary Pollution on the West Coast

In late December, 1988, the oil-carrying barge *Nestucca* broke loose from the tug that was towing it in coastal waters off Washington State. Unfortunately, the hull of the *Nestucca* suffered a 2-m gash when it collided with the tug as its crew tried to re-establish a towline, spilling about 890 t of heavy bunker fuel into the ocean. Initially, it was thought the spill was small, because only a sheen of hydrocarbons could be seen on the surface. As it turned out, however, most of the spilled fuel was suspended below the surface as sticky globs of heavy oil that could not be visually tracked. The oil weathered in the environment into a gelatinous, sticky mousse that became widely dispersed by currents running northward along the coast. The thick mousse eventually fouled beaches in Washington and then, beginning two weeks after the spill, large amounts washed onto more than 150 km of coast on western Vancouver Island. About 10 300 oiled seabirds or their carcasses washed onto beaches, primarily on Vancouver Island, but the total mortality probably exceeded 50 000 because most dead birds would have sunk offshore. Despite an intensive effort mounted by various levels of government and by hundreds of volunteers, almost all of the oiled birds that were captured alive soon died. Damage was also caused to eagles and other wildlife and to fishery habitat used by aboriginal communities and commercial interests.

Because the heavy oil had been spilled in U.S. waters by a U.S. company, but most of the ecological damage occurred in coastal waters or on beaches in Canada, a cross-boundary dimension helped to focus the attention of governments to deal with the calamity and prevent future ones. Several months after the *Nestucca* incident, the much larger *Exxon Valdez* spill in southern Alaska greatly added to the anxiety in both countries about the risks of large oil spills from the fleet of huge tankers that was ferrying northern petroleum to markets in the western United States. Partly because of this binational attention, more stringent regulations were enacted in both Canada and the U.S. to try to prevent these kinds of catastrophes (both the *Nestucca* and *Exxon Valdez* spills were caused by operator negligence, and thus were preventable accidents), and more effective action plans were developed to enhance capabilities for oil-spill countermeasures and cleanups. In addition, Environment Canada sued the U.S. company responsible for the *Nestucca* spill and eventually collected CAN$4.4 million in damages. This money was used to rehabilitate a seabird colony on Langara Island, a critical habitat off Vancouver Island.

spill was it possible to off-load unspilled petroleum from the *Exxon Valdez* to another tanker, and not until the third day were floating booms deployed to contain part of the spill. Unfortunately, a gale developed on the fourth day, making it impossible to contain or recover spilled petroleum, which subsequently became widely dispersed.

The region around Prince William Sound is famous for its spectacular scenery and important populations of wildlife. Some ecological communities and species populations were severely damaged by the oil spill. However, significant controversies have arisen both from the poor understanding of some ecological effects of the oil spill and from the role of science and scientists in sorting out legal and political aspects of the disaster (Holloway, 1996; Weins, 1996). For a long time, some scientists were prohibited from sharing their information because of legal needs for confidentiality. Controversies arose among scientists, environmental advocates, and other interest groups about the scale and intensity of some of the reported ecological impacts.

About 1900 km of shoreline habitat in Prince William Sound and its surrounding area was oiled to some degree. A survey of shorelines found that 140 km were "heavily oiled," meaning that there was at least a 6-m-wide oiled substrate. Another 93 km were "moderately oiled" (3- to 6-m-wide oiled beach), 323 km were "lightly oiled" (3-m wide), and the rest was "very lightly oiled" (<10% cover of oil). Overall, about 20% of the shoreline of the Sound, plus 14% of beaches on the nearby Kenai Peninsula and Kodiak Island, suffered some degree of oiling.

A heroic and extremely expensive effort was undertaken to clean up some of the petroleum residues of the spill, particularly from oiled beaches. About 11 000 people were involved in that cleanup, which cost the Exxon corporation about US$2.5 billion. The U.S. federal government spent an additional US$154 million. Petroleum residues were removed from some heavily oiled beaches with machines and people wielding shovels and bags. Other places were cleaned by rinsing with hot or cold water. On some beaches, people actually wiped oiled rocks with absorbent cloths, a procedure ironically referred to as "rock polishing."

These cleanup efforts helped greatly. They were subsequently aided by natural processes, especially winter storms and microbial degradation of residues. Consequently, the amount of petroleum residues on rocks and beaches declined rapidly in the years following the spill. One survey of 28 oiled sites found an average of 37% surface

Photo 21.2   The top photo shows a heavily oiled beach on Green Island, Prince William Sound, Alaska, soon after the *Exxon Valdez* disaster in 1989. The site was cleaned with warm-water washing in 1989, and then cleaned manually in 1990. In 1990 and 1991, it was fertilized to enhance microbial breakdown of the petroleum residues. The bottom photo shows the greatly improved condition of the same beach in 1992, as a result of both natural and managed cleanups. Although little visible damage occurs on the surface, there are still hydrocarbon residues deeper in the substrate.
Source: Exxon Corporation

oil cover in the first post-spill summer of 1989, but less than 2% in 1990. Another survey in 1991, after two post-spill winters and three summers, found that fewer than 2% of the beaches in Prince William Sound still had visible surface residues of oil, compared with 20% in the first summer after the spill. However, subsurface residues still existed in many places, and still do. The long-term implications of this less visible, lingering contamination are not fully known.

Initially, severe damage was caused to the seaweed-dominated intertidal zone of oiled beaches. These effects were made worse by certain cleanup methods, particularly those involving washing with pressurized hot water. Fortunately, much of this damage proved to be short term. By the end of the summer of 1991, a substantial recovery of intertidal seaweeds and invertebrates had begun, although there were lingering effects on the community structure, and vestiges of oil were still present 15 years later at some sites.

Prince William Sound supports large populations of salmon and herring and important fisheries for these species. In 1988, before the oil spill, the catch had a value of about US$90 million. The fishery was closed in 1989 because of the spill, and Exxon paid compensation of US$302 million to displaced fishers and processors (many of whom were also employed in the cleanup, earning US$105 million in wages and vessel charters).

In 1990, the harvest of pink salmon (*Oncorhynchus gorbuscha*) in the Sound was 44 million fish, larger than the previous record-high catch of 29 million fish. These were two-year-old fish, about one-quarter of which would have passed through the Sound during their migration from rivers to the sea in 1989, the year of the spill. The rest of those juvenile salmon had been released from hatcheries. The 1991 catch of pink salmon was also large, at 37 million fish. There was also a large harvest of herring (*Clupea harengus pallasi*) in 1990, when 7500 t were landed. The largest catch in a decade was made in 1991, when 10 800 t were taken. These data suggest that these fisheries were not obviously degraded by the oil spill.

Sea otters (*Enhydra lutris*) were the hardest-hit marine mammals. More than 3500 individuals were killed by oiling, out of a population of 5000–10 000 in the Sound. A total of 357 oiled sea otters were captured and treated, of which 223 survived and were released or placed in zoos.

Seabirds may be extremely abundant in the region, particularly in the autumn when some species "stage" to prepare for their southern migration. At that time, about 10 million seabirds may inhabit the Sound. Fortunately, the *Exxon Valdez* disaster happened in late winter, but there were still about 600 000 seabirds present. About 36 000 dead birds were found, but many additional corpses sank or drifted out to sea, and the total mortality was 375 000–435 000 seabirds.

About 400 people, 140 boats, and 5 aircraft were hired by Exxon to capture and rehabilitate oiled birds. In total, they managed to treat 1600 birds of 71 species. About one-half of the captured birds died of their oil-caused injuries. The rest were treated and released to the wild, but the lingering effects of hydrocarbon poisoning likely prevented most of them from surviving for long.

Although severe ecological damage was caused by the *Exxon Valdez* spill, the recovery was rapid. Waves and winter storms quickly removed most of the spill residues. Even bird and mammal populations that suffered large mortality recovered their abundance to within the natural range of variation within a decade or less. From a strictly environmental perspective, the ecosystems affected by the disaster showed an impressive amount of resilience. However, people and local communities were also affected by this calamity, and surveys have shown that their bad memories are deeply ingrained.

Oil Spills from Offshore Drill Platforms

The world's largest accidental spill was a blowout (an uncontrolled discharge from a wellhead) in 1979 from the *IXTOC-I*, a Mexican drilling platform being used for petroleum exploration in the Gulf of Mexico. This blowout remained uncontrolled for more than nine months, resulting in a continuous spillage that amounted to an estimated 476 000 t of petroleum. About 50% of the spill is thought to have evaporated into the atmosphere, while 25% sank to the bottom, 12% was degraded photochemically or by microorganisms, 6% was burned or recovered near the spill site, and 7% fouled about 600 km of shoreline in Mexico and Texas.

This enormous blowout caused great economic damage by fouling beaches important to tourism. In addition, the fishing industry was damaged by the oiling of boats and gear, by the prevention of fishing near slicks, and by the tainting of commercial species of fish and invertebrates with foul-tasting hydrocarbons. Many birds, sea mammals, sea turtles, and other wildlife were oiled and died, although these and other ecological damages were not well documented.

Another offshore blowout occurred in 1969 off Santa Barbara in southern California. This spill involved about 10 000 t of petroleum and fouled about 230 km of coastline. Birds were the most obviously tragic victims of this blowout, with about 9000 killed, or half of the population present at the time of the spill. About 60% of the dead birds were grebes and loons, which winter in the area in large numbers. Although attempts were made to capture and clean oiled birds, the efforts were not very successful.

Coastal ecosystems were also severely damaged, especially in rocky intertidal habitat, but recovery was fairly rapid. Within only one year, barnacles began re-colonizing intertidal habitat, even establishing themselves on rocks still covered with asphaltic residue. Beaches used for recreation were cleaned by the removal of petroleum and oily sand, by blasting with water or steam, or by spraying with solvent to wash the oily residues back to sea. As with the *Torrey Canyon* cleanup, these methods greatly exacerbated the ecological damage. Organisms were removed along with petroleum residue, and some of the cleaning agents were highly toxic.

Oil Spills in the Arctic Ocean

About 59% of Canada's potential oil reserves and 40% of the potential gas reserves occur in its Arctic regions (Environment Canada, 1996). There are also large potential reserves in Alaska. For this reason, exploratory drilling is widespread, and there are production wells in the western Arctic (near Norman Wells in the boreal zone). The exploration, production, and transport of hydrocarbons from the Arctic carries the risk of accidental spillage in terrestrial or marine environments. The consequences of a petroleum spill in the Arctic Ocean are potentially catastrophic. Such a spill could result from a tanker accident in ice-choked arctic waters or from operations at an offshore oil well.

Climatic conditions in the Arctic are severe—a factor that greatly increases the likelihood of spills from offshore oil wells through equipment failure or human error. Furthermore, the cold, icy conditions of the long, arctic winter would make it difficult to quickly drill an offshore relief well, a necessary step in controlling a blowout. Containing or cleaning up a spill in arctic seas would also be extremely difficult.

In fact, some scientists have suggested that an offshore blowout of an exploration or production well in the Arctic Ocean could remain uncontrolled for several years. Such an event would result in an enormous, uncontainable spill of petroleum. Because of entrapment under sea ice and the cold, nutrient-poor conditions, spilled oil would not evaporate or dissolve into seawater very effectively, and microbial biodegradation would be extremely slow. Consequently, the amount of spilled oil would not decrease much over time, and most of the initial toxicity

would persist. (Note that the spill from the *Exxon Valdez* occurred in boreal waters of southern Alaska, which are subject to much less severe temperature and ice conditions than occur in the Arctic Ocean.)

Most of the arctic marine wildlife, particularly migratory seabirds and marine mammals, is extremely vulnerable to the effects of an oil spill. When they return to their northern breeding habitat in the early summer, marine birds and mammals often aggregate in dense populations in patches of ice-free water, known as leads and polynyas, within the greater expanse of sea ice. Unfortunately, these open-water habitats are places where spilled petroleum would accumulate. Enormous mortality of migrating sea ducks, murres, seals, whales, polar bears and other species would result as they became oiled by sticky residues. Because of the persistence of petroleum residues in the cold Arctic Ocean, this threat would persist for years, and long-term, debilitating damage to populations of these animals would result. Potential damage to fish, zooplankton, and other components of the marine ecosystem are little known, but might be less intensive than the effects on marine birds and mammals.

A number of exploration wells have been drilled on the continental shelf of the Arctic Ocean off northern Canada and Alaska (and also in boreal and temperate waters off Newfoundland and Nova Scotia, where production wells now operate). Fortunately, there have not been any large spills of petroleum from the offshore drilling activities in the Arctic Ocean of North America (although there have been several blowouts involving natural gas). However, in spite of the adoption of the most modern spill-prevention technologies, a severe spill may be inevitable during offshore exploration and production activity in the Arctic. Such an accident would cause enormous ecological damage, from which recovery would be extremely slow.

Effects of Chronic Oil Pollution

Environments around tanker terminals and coastal petroleum refineries are chronically exposed to small but frequent oil spills, discharges of contaminated waste water, and airborne contaminants from industrial sources. Similarly, coastal ecosystems near cities and towns, both marine and freshwater, are chronically affected by oil and fuel that are dumped into sewers, which often discharge these wastes directly into the aquatic environment. Chronic exposures such as these are much less intense than the severe pollution associated with wrecked tankers, but ecological damage still results.

Photo 21.3   A one-year-old petroleum spill near Norman Wells, Northwest Territories. The dominant shoreline plant is the sedge *Carex aquatilis*. The foliage of this plant was killed by oiling, but its rhizomes in the sediment survived. The plants grew new foliage that penetrated the floating residue without suffering much damage.

Chronic exposure to hydrocarbons and other pollutants has been blamed for unusually high frequencies of cancers and other diseases in fish and shellfish. Although the exact causes of many of these wildlife diseases have not been determined, many scientists believe they are somehow caused by chronic pollution. One study, for example, found an unusually large incidence of gonadal tumours in fish (up to 100% among older male fish) sampled from a polluted river near Detroit, Michigan. However, epidemics of wildlife diseases are not always observed in chronically polluted environments.

Ecological damage at the community level has been observed near the effluent discharge from some coastal petroleum refineries. Extensive studies in Britain, for example, have shown a deterioration of salt-marsh vegetation near oil refineries. Exposed bare mud was found where well-vegetated, grassy salt marshes had occurred previously. In places where industry made serious efforts to

reduce the emission of pollutants, new vegetation was able to re-colonize the mud and re-develop a salt marsh.

Terrestrial Oil Spills

Although oil spills cause severe damage to terrestrial vegetation, usually only relatively local areas are affected (except in the case of extremely large spills). This is because soil, particularly if organic-rich, has a great absorptive capacity for petroleum. In addition, much of the oil spilled on land tends to accumulate in low spots and does not spread widely. This is particularly true in much of northern Canada, where deep infiltration of petroleum into the soil may be prevented by impenetrable bedrock or permafrost. The relatively localized impacts of many terrestrial spills of petroleum are very different from the effects in aquatic environments, in which spilled oil spreads widely and can affect an enormous area.

Research has also shown that a wide range of natural, soil-dwelling microorganisms are able to utilize petroleum residues as a metabolic substrate. These oil-degrading bacteria, fungi, and other microbes are widespread in soils and waters. After soil becomes polluted by an oil spill, these microorganisms proliferate rapidly, responding to the presence of hydrocarbons that they can use as a source of metabolic energy.

Petroleum is a carbon-rich substrate, but it is highly deficient in other nutrients such as nitrogen and phosphorus. Consequently, the vigour of microbial responses to oiling, and the rate of decomposition of petroleum residues, can be increased greatly by fertilizing oiled soil. Microbial decomposition of residues can also be increased by occasionally tilling the soil to increase the availability of oxygen. In general, fertilization is a relatively inexpensive but effective way of speeding up the rate of degradation of petroleum residues, while avoiding the severe damage associated with a physical cleanup. In agricultural areas in temperate regions of Canada, fertilization plus tillage can be used effectively to biodegrade petroleum residues in soil.

Of course, any spilled oil that reaches groundwater or surface waters causes severe damage there. Petroleum spills into high-energy streams and rivers become extensively dispersed, and some of the residues eventually flow into lakes or the ocean. Oil that finds its way into ponds and lakes can be quite persistent. It accumulates around the margins of those waterbodies, damaging vegetation and wildlife habitat. Studies have shown, however, that after spilled petroleum has weathered for a year or more, the toxicity of the residues has decreased to a point at which aquatic plants may grow through surface slicks without suffering much damage. The phytoplankton and zooplankton communities of ponds and lakes are also somewhat resistant to the effects of weathered oil; although there is initial damage, recovery can occur after several years have passed. However, any waterfowl that attempt to feed on oiled lakes or ponds quickly become fouled with residues, and this is usually fatal.

Terrestrial Spills in the Arctic

Much exploration for petroleum has occurred in the Arctic, mostly since the late 1960s. Discoveries in Alaska were large enough to allow the construction of a pipeline to carry petroleum from the North Slope to the southern port of Valdez, for shipment to the lower American states by tankers (such as the *Exxon Valdez*). There have also been major discoveries of petroleum in the Canadian Arctic, but these are not yet large enough to make their commercial development feasible.

Future exploration in northwestern Canada may discover reserves of petroleum large enough to justify the construction of a southward pipeline, most likely along the valley of the Mackenzie River. In fact, a pipeline along this route was considered in the early 1970s, to carry both Alaskan petroleum and the smaller quantity of oil that had been discovered in and near the Mackenzie River delta in Canada.

During *environmental impact assessments* of petroleum exploration and pipeline construction in the Arctic, researchers studied the potential effects of accidental oil spills on tundra and boreal forest ecosystems. Some of the Canadian research involved experimental spills of petroleum onto plots of vegetation. The initial damage was documented and the subsequent recovery monitored over time. These studies found that crude oil behaved as a herbicide to terrestrial vegetation, killing foliage and woody tissue. In many species of plants, however, the perennating (regenerating) tissues were not all killed, allowing regrowth after the oiling.

These general observations are illustrated by a study conducted in the western Arctic (Table 21.4). The experimental oiling caused a rapid defoliation of plants. This damage is reflected by the small values of foliar cover after the oiling, in contrast to the non-oiled, reference vegetation, whose cover did not change much. Black spruce (*Picea mariana*) trees are dominant in the boreal forest sites. Although the spruce trees did not die immediately after oiling, they became more vulnerable to physiological stress associated with the hard arctic winter. As a result, the oiled trees eventually died, but they took several years to do so.

After the initial damage, many plant species of the forest and tundra began to recover. Black spruce was a notable exception, as no seedlings of this tree were observed during the five-year period of the study. Lichens and mosses also recovered slowly from the oiling.

Of course, the environmental consequences of northern oil development are much broader than the ecological effects of petroleum spills on land or in water. The construction of infrastructure such as roads and pipelines in remote and inhospitable terrain would have a variety of environmental consequences. In addition, the influx of large sums of money and wage employment into small northern towns would have huge socio-economic impacts, some of them positive, but others disruptive. As with all industrial activities, any potential damage to the eco-

TABLE 21.4	Effects of Experimental Spills of Crude Oil on Arctic Vegetation

The plant communities studied in the western Canadian Arctic were (1) mature black spruce (*Picea mariana*) boreal forest, (2) 40-year-old spruce forest, (3) cotton-grass (*Eriophorum vaginatum*) wet-meadow tundra, and (4) dwarf-shrub tundra. The oiled vegetation was treated with petroleum at 9 L/m^2, while the reference vegetation was not oiled. The forest study area is near Norman Wells, and the tundra is near Tuktoyaktuk, both in the Northwest Territories.

COMMUNITY TYPE	TREATMENT	COVER (%) OF PLANT FOLIAGE			
				POST-SPILL	
		PRE-SPILL	1 y	2 y	5 y
Mature boreal forest	Reference	195	215	255	240
	Oiled	350	18	10	20
40-year-old forest	Reference	355	360	260	235
	Oiled	420	20	20	95
Cotton-grass tundra	Reference	339	284	268	–
	Oiled	358	26	34	–
Dwarf-shrub tundra	Reference	339	338	292	–
	Oiled	322	55	82	–

Sources: Modified from Freedman and Hutchinson (1976) and Hutchinson and Freedman (1978)

logical and socio-economic environments must be identified and, as far as possible, minimized. The residual damage must then be balanced against the economic and social benefits accruing from the development of fossil-fuel resources.

Conclusions

Petroleum is a vital natural resource that must be transported over great distances from places where it is mined to where it is consumed. Refined products, such as gasoline and kerosene, are also transported widely. There are always risks of accidental spills, and even deliberate ones (e.g., as acts of war or terrorism). When they occur, extreme damage may be caused to the environment. There have been some spectacularly large petroleum spills, particu-

larly as a result of shipping accidents involving large tankers, as well as incidents during war and terrorism in the Middle East. These large spills have had devastating effects on wild animals and local ecosystems, although post-event recovery has often allowed much of the initial damage to be repaired. In some cases, the natural recovery was aided by massive cleanup efforts and wildlife rehabilitation. It is important to recognize, however, that most large oil spills are accidents, and so they can be prevented. This can be done if tankers, pipelines, and other equipment used to transport petroleum is designed and maintained to a high standard of reliability, if effective spill-containment measures are in place, and if personnel work diligently to prevent these disasters. It is always best to avoid oil spills and other kinds of environmental emergencies than to engage in very expensive post-spill actions to clean them up and speed an ecological recovery.

Key Terms

petroleum (crude oil)

hydrocarbons

load-on-top (LOT) method

crude oil washing (COW) method

biodegradation

Questions for Review

1. What are the causes of petroleum spills to the oceans?

2. Why were the ecological effects of the *Amoco Cadiz* oil spill generally fewer and shorter-lasting than those of the *Torrey Canyon*?

3. Explain why fertilization can be an effective way of treating the residues of oil spills.

4. Why does oil spilled on water typically affect a much larger area than a comparable volume spilled on land?

Questions for Discussion

1. Considering the poor survival of aquatic birds after they have been "rehabilitated" and returned to the ocean, do you think that it is worthwhile to try to treat these victims of oils spills?

2. In view of the ecological risks, do you think that oil exploration and extraction should be allowed in the Canadian Arctic?

3. Why is it not possible to prevent all spills of petroleum?

4. Examine the data in Appendix C, Table 14 and use them to inform a written discussion of the reasons for the international trade in petroleum. Consider both the global context and that of North America (i.e., Canada, the U.S., and Mexico).

Exploring Issues

1. A proposal has been made to build a large oil refinery on the coast (choose whichever one you live closest to). The crude oil will be brought to the refinery by tanker ships, and the refined products will be distributed by ship, train, and truck. You are a scientist working as an environmental consultant and have been asked to recommend spill-prevention and countermeasure tactics to protect the marine and terrestrial environment around the new refinery. Provide a list of practices that would provide this function of spill prevention and countermeasures.

References

Alexander, V. and K. Van Cleve. 1983. The Alaska pipeline: a success story. *Ann. Rev. Ecol. System.*, **14**: 443–463.

Baker, B., B. Campbell, R. Gist, L. Lowry, S. Nickerson, C. Schwartz, and L. Stratton. 1989. *Exxon Valdez* oil spill: the first eight weeks. *Alaska Fish & Game*, **21 (4)**: 2–37.

Baker, J.M. (ed.) 1976. *Marine Ecology and Oil Pollution*. New York: Wiley.

Berger, A.E. 1993. *Effects of the Nestucca oil spill on seabirds along the coast of Vancouver Island in 1989*. Vancouver: Canadian Wildlife Service. Tech. Rep. Ser. No. 179.

Boesch, D.F. and N.N. Robelais (eds.). 1987. *Long-term Environmental Effects of Offshore Oil and Gas Development*. London: Elsevier Science Publishers.

Bourne, W.R.P. 1976. Seabirds and pollution. In: R. Johnston, ed. *Marine Pollution*. London: Academic. pp. 403–502.

Brebbia, C.A. (ed.). 2001. *Oil Spill Modelling and Processes*. Billerica, MA: Computational Mechanics, Inc.

British Petroleum. 2005. *Statistical Review of World Energy, 2004*. http://www.bp.com.

Cairns, J.L. and A.L. Buikema (eds.). 1984. *Restoration of Habitats Impacted by Oil Spills*. Boston: Butterworth.

Clark, R.B. 1984. Impact of oil pollution on seabirds. *Environ. Pollut., Ser. A*, **33**: 1–22.

Clark, R.C. and W.D. MacLeod. 1977. Inputs, transport mechanisms, and observed concentrations of petroleum in the marine environment. In: D.C. Malins, ed. *Effects of Petroleum on Arctic and Subarctic Marine Environments and Organisms, Vol. 1*. New York: Academic. pp. 91–224.

Cormack, D. 1983. *Response to Oil and Chemical Marine Pollution*. London: Applied Science.

Davidson, A. 1990. *In the Wake of the Exxon Valdez*. Toronto: Douglas & McIntyre.

Earle, S. 1992. Assessing the damage one year later (after the Gulf oil spill). *National Geographic*, **179 (2)**: 122–134.

Engelhardt, F.R. (ed.) 1985. *Petroleum Effects in the Arctic Environment*. New York: Elsevier Press.

Environment Canada. 1996. *The State of Canada's Environment, 1996*. Ottawa: Government of Canada.

Environment Canada. 1998. *Summary of Spill Events in Canada, 1984–1995*. Ottawa: Environmental Emergencies Program, Environment Canada.

Foster, M.S. and R.W. Holmes. 1977. The Santa Barbara oil spill: an ecological disaster In: J. Cairns, K.L. Dickson, and E.E. Herricks, eds. *Recovery and Restoration of Damaged Ecosystems*. Charlottesville, VA: University Press of Virginia. pp. 166–190.

Freedman, B. 1995. *Environmental Ecology*. 2nd ed. San Diego, CA: Academic.

Freedman, B. and T.C. Hutchinson. 1976. Physical and biological effects of experimental crude oil spills on low arctic tundra in the vicinity of Tuktoyaktuk, NWT, Canada. *Can. J. Bot.*, **54**: 2219–2230.

GESAMP. 1991. *Carcinogens: Their Significance as Marine Pollutants*. London: International Marine Organization. Joint Group of Experts on the Scientific Aspects of Marine Pollution (GESAMP), Report 46.

GESAMP. 1993. *Impact of Oil and Related Chemicals and Wastes in the Marine Environment*. London: International Marine Organization. Joint Group of Experts on the Scientific Aspects of Marine Pollution (GESAMP), Report 50.

Harvey-Clark, C. 1990. Veterinary treatment of oiled seabirds. *Bull. B.C. Veterinary Medical Assoc.*, **28 (4)**: 24–33.

Holloway, M. 1996. Sounding out science. *Sci. Amer.*, **275 (4)**: 106–112.

Holloway, M. and J. Horgan. 1991. Soiled shores. *Sci. Amer.*, **265 (4)**: 103–116.

Holmes, W.N. 1984. Petroleum pollutants in the marine environment and their possible effects on seabirds. *Rev. Environ. Toxicol.*, **1**: 251–317.

Hutchinson, T.C. and B. Freedman. 1978. Effects of experimental crude oil spills on subarctic boreal forest vegetation near Norman Wells, NWT, Canada. *Can. J. Bot.*, **56**: 2424–2433.

Jenssen, B.M. 1994. Effects of oil pollution, chemically treated oil, and cleaning on the thermal balance of birds. *Environ. Pollut.*, **86**: 207–215.

Keeble, J. 1999. *Out of the Channel: The Exxon Valdez Oil Spill in Prince William Sound*. Seattle, WA: Eastern Washington University Press.

Koons, C.B. 1984. Input of petroleum to the marine environment. *Marine Tech. Soc. J.*, **18**: 97–112.

Koons, C.B. and H.O. Jahns. 1992. The fate of oil from the *Exxon Valdez*—a perspective. *Marine Tech. Soc. J.*, **26**: 61–69.

Malins, D.C. (ed.). 1977. *Effects of Petroleum on Arctic and Subarctic Marine Environments and Organisms*, 2 vol. New York: Academic.

Milne, A.R. and R.H. Herlinveaux. 1977. *Crude Oil in Cold Water*. Sidney, BC: Department of Fisheries and Department of the Environment.

National Academy of Sciences (U.S.). 2003. *Oil in the Sea: Impacts, Fates, and Effects*. Washington, DC: National Academy of Sciences.

National Research Council (NRC). 1985. *Oil in the Sea: Inputs, Fates, and Effects*. Washington: National Academy Press.

National Research Council (NRC). 1989. *Using Oil Spill Dispersants in the Sea*. Washington: National Academy Press.

Neff, J.M. and J.W. Anderson. 1981. *Response of Marine Mammals to Petroleum and Specific Petroleum Hydrocarbons*. London: Applied Science.

NOAA. 1982. *Ecological Study of the Amoco Cadiz Oil Spill*. U.S. Department of Commerce. Washington: National Oceanic and Atmospheric Administration (NOAA).

Paine, R.T., J.L. Ruesink, A. Sun, E.L. Soulanille, M.L. Wonham, C.D.G. Harley, D.R. Brumbaugh, and D.L. Secord. 1996. Trouble on oiled waters: lessons from the *Exxon Valdez* oil spill. *Annu. Rev. Ecol. System.*, **27**: 197–235.

Piatt, J.F., H.R. Carter, and D.N. Nettleship. 1991. Effects of oil pollution on marine bird populations. In: J. White, ed. *The Effects of Oil on Wildlife: Research, Rehabilitation, and General Concerns*. Hanover, NH: Sheridan. pp. 126–141.

Pimlott, D., D. Brown, and K. Sam. 1976. *Oil Under the Ice*. Ottawa: Canadian Arctic Resources Committee.

Sharp, B.E. 1996. Post-release survival of oiled, cleaned seabirds in North America. *Ibis*, **138**: 222–228.

Southward, A.J. and E.C. Southward. 1978. Recolonization of rocky shores in Cornwall after use of toxic dispersants to clean up the *Torrey Canyon* spill. *J. Fish. Res. Bd. Canada*, **35**: 682–706.

Sprague, J.B., J.H. Vandermeulen, and P.G. Wells. 1982. *Oil and Dispersants in Canadian Seas—Research Appraisal and Recommendations*. Environment Canada, Environmental Protection Service, Economic and Technical Review Report EPS.3-EC-82-2.

Steinhart, C.E. and J.S. Steinhart. 1972. *Blowout: A Case Study of the Santa Barbara Oil Spill*. Belmont, CA: Duxbury.

Transport Canada. 2004. *Transportation in Canada 2003. Annual Report*. Ottawa: Transport Canada.

Warner, F. 1991. The environmental consequences of the Gulf War. *Environment*, **33 (5)**: 7–26.

Weins, J.A. 1996. Oil, seabirds, and science: the effects of the *Exxon Valdez* oil spill. *BioScience*, **46**: 587–597.

Wells, P.G., J.N. Butler, and J.S. Hughes. 1995. *Exxon Valdez Oil Spill: Fate and Effects in Alaskan Waters*. Philadelphia: American Society for Testing and Materials.

World Resources Institute (WRI). 2001. *World Resources 2000–2001*. New York: Oxford University Press.

World Resources Institute. 2005. *Earth Trends. The Environmental Information Portal*. http://earthtrends.wri.org

Informative Websites

Alaska Regional Response Team. http://akrrt.org/

This website describes the action plan of the state of Alaska for dealing with oil spills.

America Petroleum Institute (API). http://api-ec.api.org

The API is an industry association. Its website contains much useful information about petroleum and the prevention of spills.

Environmental Technology Centre. http://etcentre.org

This Environment Canada website includes databases covering oil spills, chemical synonyms, brochures, analytical chemistry, and hydrocarbon and oil properties.

International Tanker Owners Pollution Federation Limited (ITOPF). http://www.itopf.com/

This is a website of a federation of industrial interests; it is rich with information about marine transportation and spillage of petroleum.

Oil Program. www.epa.gov/oilspill/

This website has information about the U.S. Environmental Protection Agency's program for preventing, preparing for, and responding to oil spills.

World Resources Institute. EarthTrends. The Environmental Information Portal.
http://earthtrends.wri.org

This rich website has information on reserves and stocks of petroleum and other fossil fuels.

Pesticides

22

CHAPTER OBJECTIVES

After completing this chapter, you will be able to

1. Explain the notions of "pest" and "weed," and give three reasons why it may be useful to decrease pest abundance under certain circumstances.
2. Differentiate pesticides by their target pests.
3. Classify pesticides by their major chemical groups, including inorganics, natural organics, organochlorines, organophosphates, carbamates, and biologicals.
4. Outline the environmental risks and benefits of pesticide use in sanitation, agriculture, forestry, and horticulture.
5. Explain why there is a global contamination of organisms with DDT and related organochlorines.
6. Describe the ecological damage caused by DDT and other organochlorine insecticides.
7. Outline the ecological damage caused by carbofuran, and discuss why it took so long for the use of this insecticide to be banned in North America.
8. Describe the economic benefits and ecological risks of pesticide use in forestry.
9. Outline the concept of integrated pest management, and discuss whether it is applicable to all pest-management problems.

CHAPTER OUTLINE

- Introduction
- The Nature of Pesticides
- Pesticide Use
- Environmental Effects
- Integrated Pest Management
- Conclusions

Introduction

Humans are constantly engaged in struggles against potentially debilitating competitors and diseases. **Pesticides** are substances used to gain an advantage in many of those ecological interactions. Pesticides are commonly used to protect crop plants, livestock, domestic animals, and humans from damage and diseases caused by microorganisms, fungi, insects, rodents, and other "*pests,*" and to defend crops from competition with unwanted but abundant plants (i.e., "*weeds*").

It is important to understand that the words "pest" and "weed" are highly contextual in their use. In most situations, for example, white-tailed deer are highly valued for their wild beauty, and they provide economic and subsistence benefits through hunting. However, this same species may be considered a pest when it feeds in gardens, agricultural fields, or forestry plantations. The same is true, to a greater or lesser degree, of many other species that are considered pests or weeds.

Humans have been using pesticides for a long time (Hayes, 1991). There are records of unspecified chemicals being used by Egyptians to drive fleas from their homes about 3500 years ago. Arsenic has been used as an insecticide in China for at least 2900 years. In his epic poem the *Odyssey*, the Greek poet Homer (writing about 2800 years ago) referred to the burning of sulphur (which generates toxic SO_2 gas) to purge homes and buildings of fleas and other vermin.

Pesticide use has, however, become much more common in modern times, and an enormously wider variety of substances is being used. About 300 insecticides, 290 herbicides, 165 fungicides, and many other pesticidal chemicals are available in more than 3000 different formulations. Strictly speaking, a commercial pesticide product is a formulation of several chemicals; the "active ingredient" actually attacks the pest, while various "inert ingredients" enhance the effectiveness of the pesticide (see In Detail 22.1). Even more "commercial products" are available because many of them involve similar formulations manufactured by different companies. In all cases, the successful use of a pesticide requires the choice of an appropriate substance and its proper application.

Almost all pesticides are chemicals. Some are natural biochemicals that are extracted from plants grown for that purpose, while other pesticides are inorganic chemicals based on toxic metals or compounds of arsenic. Most modern pesticides, however, are organic chemicals that have been synthesized by chemists. The costs of developing a new pesticide and testing it for its efficacy (effectiveness against pests), toxicological properties, and environmental effects are quite large, equivalent to tens of millions of dollars per chemical. However, if an effective pesticide against an important pest is discovered, the profits are potentially huge, and therefore industry willingly pays the high development costs.

Humans have acquired important benefits from many uses of pesticides, including

- increased yields of crops, because of protection from diseases, competition, defoliation, and parasites;
- prevention of much spoilage and destruction of stored food; and
- prevention of certain diseases, thereby conserving health and saving the lives of millions of people and domestic animals.

It has been estimated that pests destroy 37% of the potential yield of plant crops in North America (Pimentel *et al.*, 1992). It has also been reckoned that for every dollar spent on pesticides in North American agriculture, there is a four-dollar gain in benefits through increased crop yield and prevention of damage to stored products. (These data include only "conventional" economic costs and benefits—the value of environmental damage caused by pesticide use was not considered. See Chapter 12 for an explanation of ecological economics.)

This is not to say, however, that more pesticide use would achieve even better results. In fact, it has been argued that pesticide use in North America could be decreased by one-half without greatly affecting crop yields. Cutting pesticide use in half would achieve important environmental benefits through reduced ecological damage (Pimentel *et al.*, 1991). In fact, the European Union (EU) has taken some rather forceful steps to reduce pesticide use within its jurisdiction (Pesticide News, 2003). In 2003, the permits for 320 pesticides were revoked, and it is estimated that as many as another 180 could be lost by 2008; in total, 64% of the pesticides registered for use in 1993 would no longer be legal in 2008. In large part, the withdrawals involve pesticides of relatively minor commercial use, for which the owners do not want to invest the large amounts of money needed to assure the EU regulators that their products are safe to people and the environment. Similar actions are also occurring in North America, but they are less advanced than in the European Union.

Because of the substantial benefits derived from pesticides, their use has increased enormously during the past

In Detail 22.1

Pesticides, Formulations, and Inert Ingredients

A commercial pesticide product is a mixture of chemicals that can be used to kill or otherwise control pests. The so-called "active ingredient" is the chemical that actually attacks the pest, while "inert ingredients" are other materials added to the formulation to enhance its effectiveness. The inert ingredients may do this by making the pesticide easier to apply (e.g., by making the active ingredient soluble in water), by helping it to spread or stick to leaf surfaces, or by stabilizing the formulation to increase its shelf life.

Many inert ingredients are, however, chemically and biologically active, so they are not really passive—it is more realistic to refer to them as "other ingredients." In general, the total percentage of other ingredients in a pesticide is specified on the product label, but their exact identity and concentrations are not given because they are considered proprietary information of commercial value. Sometimes, however, the manufacturer will release a list of other ingredients, and even information about their concentration. Some inert ingredients carry risks of causing toxicity through normal use of the pesticide; those of particular concern include chlorobenzene, dioctyl phthalate, formaldehyde, hexane, hydroquinone, isophorone, nonylphenol, phenol, and rhodamine.

One inert ingredient that has engendered controversy about its potential toxicity to exposed humans is nonylphenol (NP), which is used as an emulsifier in various pesticide formulations. NP is a degradation product of nonylphenol ethoxylates (NPEs), a class of organic compounds within a broader group known as alkylphenol ethoxylates (APEs). NPEs have been used for decades as detergents, emulsifiers, and wetting and dispersing agents. They are used in diverse manufacturing processes for paints, paper, pesticides, petrochemicals, resins, steel, and textiles and are components of many cleaning products, degreasers, and detergents. NPEs occur in many consumer products, including cleaners, cosmetics, paints, and pesticides.

NPEs and their main degradation product (i.e., NP) are not natural chemicals—they are manufactured, and their environmental residues are entirely anthropogenic. NP and NPEs mostly enter the environment with industrial and municipal wastewater effluents. NPEs degrade via complex microbial reactions, and some metabolites are bioactive through toxicity and estrogenic (i.e., hormonal) effects, including NP, nonylphenol diethoxylate, nonylphenol ethoxylate, nonylphenoxyacetic acid, and nonylphenoxyethoxyacetic acid. These may have a moderate persistence in the environment, especially in anaerobic habitats and in groundwater, and they have a widespread but low level of contamination and bioaccumulation. Species vary widely in their vulnerability to toxicity from NP and NPEs, but many studies have reported toxic and estrogenic effects on aquatic organisms. Some toxicologists believe that humans are also significantly exposed to risks from these chemicals, through consumer products, food, and other pathways. In a recent risk assessment, Environment Canada concluded that "nonylphenol and its ethoxylates are entering the environment in a quantity or concentration…that have or may have an immediate or long-term harmful effect on the environment or its biological diversity," and so they should be regulated as "toxic" chemicals under the *Canadian Environmental Protection Act*. Although these chemicals are not "considered a priority for investigation of options to reduce human exposure through control of sources," it was recommended that further studies of their bioactivity and environmental risks be undertaken.

Although the major releases of NP and related chemicals are via industrial and municipal effluents, they are also present as "other ingredients" in pesticides. This has led to controversy about damage caused to people and wild organisms exposed to NPEs and NP through pesticide use. The case of NPEs and their metabolites reinforces the fact that product formulations should be known and comprehensively evaluated when considering the risks of pesticide use to human and environmental safety.

References

Environment Canada. 2001. *Assessment Report; Nonylphenol and Its Ethoxylates*. Ottawa, ON: Environment Canada.
www.ec.gc.ca/substances/ese/eng/psap/final/npe.cfm

EPA. 2005. *"Inert or "Other" Ingredients in Pesticide Products*. Washington, DC: U.S. Environmental Protection Agency.
www.epa.gov/oppfod01/cb/ppdc/inert.htm

half-century. For example, pesticide use increased ten-fold in North America between 1945 and 1989 (Pimentel *et al.*, 1992), although it has levelled off during the past decade or so. Pesticide use is now a firmly integrated component of the technological systems used in modern agriculture, forestry, horticulture, and public health management in most parts of the world.

Unfortunately, the considerable benefits of pesticides are partially offset by damage their use causes to ecosystems and sometimes to human health. Each year, about one million people are poisoned by pesticides, with 20 000 fatalities (Pimentel *et al.*, 1992). Although developing countries account for only about 20% of global pesticide use, they sustain about half of the poisonings. This is because relatively toxic insecticides are used in many developing countries, by a work force whose widespread illiteracy hinders the comprehension of instructions for proper use, and whose safety is compromised both by poor enforcement of regulations and by inadequate use of protective equipment and clothing. The most tragic case of pesticide-related poisoning occurred in 1984 at Bhopal, India. About 2800 people were killed and 20 000 seriously poisoned when a factory accidentally released 40 t of methyl isocyanate vapour to the atmosphere. Methyl isocyanate is a precursor chemical of carbamate insecticides (Rozencranz, 1988).

In addition, many pesticide applications cause ecological damage by killing **non-target organisms** (i.e., organisms that are not considered pests). This damage is particularly important when **broad-spectrum pesticides** are used, which are toxic to organisms other than the specific pest. Pesticides used as *broadcast sprays* are applied over a large area, such as an agricultural field, a lawn, or a stand of forest. If a broad-spectrum pesticide is broadcast-sprayed, many non-target organisms are exposed and may be unintentionally damaged or killed. For example, in a typical agricultural field or forestry plantation, only a few plant species are abundant enough to compete significantly with crops and reduce their productivity. These are the "weeds" that are the targets of a broadcast herbicide application. However, many other plant species are also affected. Many of the non-target plants provide habitat or food for animals and help prevent erosion and nutrient loss. These ecological benefits are degraded by the **non-target damage**. Similarly, broadcast insecticide spraying causes non-target mortality to numerous arthropods (including beneficial insects) in addition to the pest species, and birds, mammals, and other creatures may also be poisoned. The non-target mortality may include predators and competi-

tors of the pest species. This may cause secondary damage by releasing the pest from some of its ecological controls. The great challenge of pest control is to develop more effective, pest-specific pesticides and to invent non-pesticidal methods.

Pesticide use is expanding rapidly in extent and intensity. It now occurs in all countries, although to greatly varying degrees. Although much is known about the environmental damage caused by pesticide use, not all of the potential effects are understood. In this chapter we examine the nature of pesticides, their most important uses, and the characteristics of commonly used chemicals. We then examine cases of ecological damage caused by the routine use of pesticides to deal with pest-management problems.

The Nature of Pesticides

Classification by Target

Pesticides are defined by their usefulness in killing or otherwise decreasing the abundance of species that are deemed to be "pests." Pesticides are, however, an extremely diverse group of chemicals. To better understand the usefulness and toxicity of pesticides, and the damage they cause, it is necessary to categorize them in various ways. One classification is based on their intended targets:

- **Fungicides** are used to protect crop plants and animals from fungi that cause diseases and other damage.

- **Herbicides** are used to kill weeds—that is, unwanted plants that interfere with some human purpose. Most herbicide use in agriculture and forestry is intended to release crop plants from competition, while horticultural use is mostly for aesthetics.

- **Insecticides** are used to kill insects that are pests in agriculture, horticulture, or forestry, or that spread deadly diseases, such as the mosquito vectors of malaria, yellow fever, and encephalitis.

- *Acaricides* are used to kill mites that are pests in agriculture, and ticks that are vectors of certain ailments such as Lyme disease and typhus.

- *Molluscicides* are used to kill snails and slugs in agriculture and gardens, and aquatic snails that can be vectors of diseases such as schistosomiasis.

- *Nematicides* are used against nematodes, which can cause important damage to the roots of agricultural plants.

- *Rodenticides* are used to control populations of small mammals, such as mice, rats, gophers, and other rodents that are pests in agriculture or around the home.

- *Avicides* are used to kill birds, which are sometimes considered pests in agriculture.

- *Piscicides* are used to kill fish, which may be pests in aquaculture.

- *Algicides* are used to kill unwanted growths of algae, for example, in swimming pools.

- *Bactericides, disinfectants, and antibiotics* are used to control infections and diseases caused by bacteria. (Note that antibiotics are not actually classified as "pesticides" under the Pest Control Products Act.)

Chemical Classification

Because almost all pesticides are chemicals, they can be categorized according to similarities in chemical structure. The most important groups of pesticides are described below (see Table 22.1 for a summary). (A few "non-chemical" pesticide formulations are based on microbes; these are discussed later under "Biological Pesticides.")

Inorganic Pesticides

Inorganic pesticides are compounds that contain arsenic, copper, lead, or mercury. They are highly persistent in terrestrial environments, being only slowly dispersed by leaching and erosion by wind and water. Recently, inorganic pesticides have been widely replaced by synthetic organics, and they are now being used much less than in the past. Prominent examples of inorganic pesticides include *Bordeaux mixture*, a mixture of copper-based compounds that is used as a fungicide to protect fruit and vegetable

---

TABLE 22.1 | Some Important Pesticides

See Freedman (1995) for chemical formulae of these pesticides.

CLASS	MAJOR USE	IMPORTANT EXAMPLES
1. INORGANIC PESTICIDES		
a) Bordeaux mixture	fungicide	tetracupric + pentacupric sulphate (copper sulphates)
b) arsenicals	herbicides and insecticides	arsenic trioxide, sodium arsenite, calcium arsenate, Paris green, lead arsenate
2. ORGANIC PESTICIDES		
a) natural organics	mostly insecticides	nicotine, nicotine sulphate, pyrethroids, red squill, rotenone, strychnine
b) organo-mercurials	fungicides	phenyl mercuric acetate, methyl mercury, methoxyethyl mercuric chloride
c) phenols	fungicides	trichlorophenol, pentachlorophenol
d) chlorinated hydrocarbons		
DDT and relatives	insecticides	DDT, DDD, or TDE, methoxychlor
lindane	insecticide	lindane
cyclodienes	insecticides	chlordane, heptachlor, aldrin, dieldrin
chlorophenoxy acids	herbicides	2,4-D, 2,4,5-T, MCPA, silvex
e) organophosphates	insecticides	diazinon parathion, methyl parathion, fenitrothion, malathion, monocrotophos, phosphamidon
f) carbamates	mostly insecticides	carbaryl, aminocarb, carbofuran, aldicarb, methiocarb
g) triazines	herbicides	simazine, atrazine, hexazinone, cynazine, metribuzin
h) amides	herbicides	alachlor, metolachlor
i) thiocarbamates	herbicides	butylate
j) dinitroaniline	herbicide	trifluralin
k) organophosphorus compound	herbicide	glyphosate
l) acetaldehyde polymer	molluscicide	metaldehyde
m) pyrethroids (synthetic)	insecticides	cypermethrin, deltamethrin, permethrin, tetramethrin

crops; and *arsenicals* such as arsenic trioxide, sodium arsenite, and calcium arsenate, which are used as herbicides and soil sterilants. Paris green, lead arsenate, and calcium arsenate are used as insecticides.

Organic Pesticides

Most organic pesticides are artificially synthesized chemicals, but some are natural toxins produced by certain species of plants and extracted and used as pesticides. Important examples include the following.

Natural organic pesticides are extracted from plants. Nicotine and related alkaloids, for example, are extracted from tobacco (*Nicotiana tabacum*) and used as insecticides, usually applied as nicotine sulphate. Pyrethrum is a complex of chemicals extracted from flowers of daisy-like plants (*Chrysanthemum cinerariaefolium* and *C. coccinium*) and used as an insecticide. Rotenone is extracted from several tropical shrubs (*Derris elliptica* and *Lonchocarpus utilis*) and used as an insecticide, rodenticide, or piscicide. Red squill, extracted from the sea onion (*Scilla maritima*), is another rodenticide. Strychnine is a rodenticide extracted from the tropical plant *Strychnos nux-vomica*.

Synthetic organometallic pesticides are used mainly as fungicides. They include organomercurials such as methylmercury and phenylmercuric acetate.

Phenols include trichlorophenols, tetrachlorophenol, and pentachlorophenol, all of which are fungicides that are used to preserve wood and other organic materials.

Chlorinated hydrocarbons (organochlorines) are a diverse group of synthetic pesticides. Residues of most organochlorines are quite persistent, having a half-life of about 10 years in soil. Persistent chemicals can remain in the environment for many years because they are not easily degraded by microorganisms or by physical agents such as sunlight or heat. The persistence of organochlorines, coupled with their strongly lipophilic nature (i.e., they are virtually insoluble in water, but highly soluble in fats and lipids), means that they become *bioconcentrated* and food-web magnified, with the highest concentrations occurring in top predators (bioconcentration and food-web magnification are explained in In Detail 18.1 in Chapter 18 and Figure 22.1 on page 437).

Organochlorines include the following:

- *DDT and its insecticidal relatives*, such as DDD and methoxychlor, were once widely used as insecticides. Because of bans in North America

and Europe in the early 1970s, use of these chemicals is now mainly confined to tropical countries. A persistent metabolite of DDT and DDD, the non-insecticidal chemical DDE, accumulates in organisms (see In Detail 22.2).

- *Lindane* is the active constituent of hexachlorocyclohexane, an insecticide.

- *Cyclodienes* are highly chlorinated cyclic hydrocarbons, such as chlordane, heptachlor, aldrin, and dieldrin, all of which are used as insecticides.

- *Chlorophenoxy acids* have growth-regulating influences on plants and are used as herbicides against broad-leafed angiosperm weeds. The most important compound is 2,4-D, but others include 2,4,5-T, MCPA, and silvex.

- *Other organochlorines*, such as polychlorinated biphenyls (PCBs), dioxins, and furans, are also produced by human activities and released into the environment. These chlorinated hydrocarbons are not pesticides but are mentioned here because their ecotoxicological properties are similar to those of pesticidal organochlorines: they are persistent in the environment, and their lipophilic nature means that they bioconcentrate and food-web magnify.

Organophosphorus pesticides are used mostly as insecticides, acaricides, and nematicides. These chemicals are not very persistent in the environment, but most are extremely toxic to arthropods and also to non-target fish, birds, and mammals. Parathion, fenitrothion, malathion, and phosphamidon are prominent examples of organophosphate insecticides. Glyphosate, a phosphonoalkyl compound, is an important herbicide (this chemical is not very toxic to animals).

Carbamate pesticides have a moderate persistence in the environment but are highly toxic to arthropods, and in some cases to vertebrates. Aminocarb, carbaryl, and carbofuran are important carbamate insecticides.

Triazine pesticides are used mostly as herbicides and sometimes as soil sterilants. Prominent examples are atrazine, simazine, and hexazinone.

Synthetic pyrethroids are analogues of natural pyrethrum and are used mostly as insecticides and acaricides in agriculture. The pyrethroids are highly toxic to invertebrates and fish, but they are of variable toxicity to mammals and of low toxicity to birds. Important examples are cyper-

In Detail 22.2

DDT Residues

DDT and DDD, once widely used as insecticides, are found as residues in organisms throughout the biosphere, particularly in fatty tissues. However, DDT and DDD are metabolized by animals into DDE, a non-insecticidal organochlorine. Like DDT and DDD, DDE is a persistent and bioaccumulating chemical. Most accounts of DDT residues actually report "total DDT"; that is, DDT + DDD + DDE. In most cases, DDE accounts for almost all of the total DDT residue.

---

methrin, deltamethrin, permethrin, synthetic pyrethrum and pyrethrins, and tetramethrin.

Biological Pesticides

Biological pesticides are formulations of microbes that are pathogenic to specific pests and, consequently, have a relatively narrow spectrum of activity in ecosystems. The best examples are insecticides based on the bacterium *Bacillus thuringiensis* (*B.t.*), types of which are used against moths, flies, and beetles. Insecticides based on nuclear polyhedrosis virus (NPV) and insect hormones have also been developed.

GMOs and Pesticides

Genetically modified organisms (GMOs; see In Detail 6.3) have been biologically "engineered" by inserting portions of DNA from another species into their genome. This high-tech procedure has been used to develop new varieties of commercial crops that are more resistant to certain pesticides or pests, which can make it easier to cultivate them. For example, GMO varieties of soybean and canola have been developed to be resistant to the herbicide glyphosate. This means that glyphosate can be used on these crops, providing reduced costs of energy and machinery to control weeds. In addition, there are now GMO varieties of maize (corn) that contain DNA of the insecticidal bacterium *Bacillus thuringiensis*, which provides resistance to some insect pests and allows farmers to use less insecticide. These and other GMO crops are now widely cultivated in North America, although they are banned in many countries, including most of Europe and Brazil. The use of these GMO crops is controversial because there is relatively little knowledge about the biological and ecological risks of their use, including the potential escape of their GMO factors to wild plants.

Pesticide Use

The global use of pesticides is about 3 million t/y, a total that includes insecticides, herbicides, fungicides, preservatives, and disinfectants (Briggs, 1992; Pimentel *et al.*, 1992). During the early 1990s, trade in these chemicals had a value of about US$20 billion/y (Pimentel *et al.*, 1992).

About 61% (by weight) of all pesticides used in the U.S. in 1997 were herbicides; insecticides accounted for 11%; fungicides for 7%; and "other chemicals" for 21% (mostly used as soil fumigants) (Gianessi and Marselli, 2001). Data for Canada are not available but would be similar to those for the U.S. (Canada accounts for about one-ninth of the North American market for pesticides). Total expenditures for pesticides in the U.S. were about US$10 billion in 1997. The following is a top-15 list of pesticides used in the U.S., in terms of amounts used per year:

1. atrazine; herbicide; 33.9×10^6 kg active ingredient per year
2. metolachlor; herbicide; 30.6
3. metam sodium; soil fumigant; 27.3
4. 2,4-D; herbicide; 18.5
5. 1,3-D; soil fumigant; 15.8
6. glyphosate; herbicide; 15.8
7. methyl bromide; soil fumigant; 14.9
8. acetochlor; herbicide; 14.8
9. pendimethalin; herbicide; 12.4
10. trifluralin; herbicide; 10.1
11. cynazine; herbicide; 9.2
12. alachlor; herbicide; 6.9
13. chloropicrin; soil fumigant; 6.3
14. chlorpyrifos; insecticide; 6.2
15. copper compounds; fungicide; 6.2

In addition, about 35×10^6 kg of sulphur was used as a fungicide, 47×10^6 kg of oil as an insecticide, and 22×10^6 kg of sulphuric acid as a fumigant. Strictly speaking, these chemicals are not considered pesticides, even though they may be used against certain pests.

The most important uses of pesticides are in agriculture and forestry, around the home, and in human health and sanitation programs. We examine these uses in the following sections.

Pesticide Use for Human Health

Various species of insects and ticks are **vectors** that transmit pathogens between organisms of the same species, or from alternate hosts to people or to domestic and wild animals. Often, alternate hosts are not affected by the pathogens, but the final host can be seriously afflicted.

The most important vectored human diseases are the following:

- malaria, caused by the protozoan *Plasmodium* and spread among humans by mosquitoes, most commonly species of *Anopheles*

- yellow fever, encephalitis, and West Nile virus caused by viruses and spread by mosquitoes

- sleeping sickness, caused by the protozoan *Trypanosoma* and spread by the tsetse fly *Glossina*

- plague or black death, caused by the bacterium *Pasteurella pestis* and transmitted by the rat flea *Xenopsylla cheops*

- typhoid fever, caused by the bacterium *Rickettsia prowazeki* and transmitted by the body louse *Pediculus humanus*

- schistosomiasis, or bilharziasis, caused by the blood fluke *Schistosoma*, with freshwater snails as the alternate host

To varying degrees, the incidence of these debilitating maladies can be controlled by using pesticides against the invertebrate vectors or the alternate hosts. The abundance of mosquitoes, for example, can be reduced by spraying insecticide in their aquatic breeding habitat or by applying a persistent insecticide to the interior walls of buildings, on which these insects commonly rest. Similarly, people infested with body lice may receive a surface dusting with an insecticide—this was an early use of DDT. Plague can be controlled by using rodenticides along with sanitation programs to reduce rat populations. Over the past half-century, pesticides have decreased the abundance

of vectors and alternate hosts and have spared hundreds of millions of humans from the deadly or debilitating effects of certain diseases, particularly in tropical countries. (This has been an important factor in reducing death rates and allowing rapid population growth, particularly in less developed countries.)

In fact, the first important use of the insecticide DDT was in Naples, Italy, during the Second World War, to prevent a potentially deadly plague of typhus that could have decimated Allied troops and the civilian population. Because of the enormous success of this use of DDT and its contribution to the victorious war effort, the British Prime Minister at the time, Winston Churchill, referred to the insecticide as "that miraculous DDT powder."

Malaria has long been an important disease in tropical countries. During the 1950s, about 5% of the world's population was infected with malaria. The use of insecticides to reduce the abundance of mosquitoes has achieved huge reductions in the incidence of malaria in some countries. For instance, during 1933–35, India recorded about 100 million cases of malaria per year and 750 000 deaths. However, the incidence of malaria was reduced to 150 000 cases and 1500 deaths in 1966, mostly because of spraying with DDT and draining mosquito-breeding wetlands (McEwen and Stephenson, 1979). Similarly, 2.9 million cases of malaria occurred in Sri Lanka in 1934, and 2.8 million in 1946. DDT use reduced this incidence to only 17 cases in 1963 (Hayes, 1991). However, malaria has recently been resurging in some tropical countries, partly because mosquitoes have developed a genetically based tolerance of previously effective insecticides. Many people are again being exposed to the malarial parasite, although the disease itself can today be controlled by drugs that prevent *Plasmodium* from multiplying in the blood. (However, there are signs that the *Plasmodium* is becoming resistant to these drugs.)

Pesticides and Agriculture

Modern agriculture is a highly technological activity. Machines, energy, fertilizer, pesticides, and high-yield crop varieties are used in intensive management systems to grow crops (see Chapters 14 and 24). The roles of pesticides are to control the abundance of

- weeds that compete with crop plants;

- arthropods, nematodes, and rodents that feed on the crops or the produce; and

■ microbial diseases that can kill the crop or diminish its yield.

Undeniably, these uses of pesticides are important factors in modern agriculture. Even with pesticide use, the damages caused by pests and diseases around the world are equivalent to about 24% of the potential crop of wheat, 46% of rice, 35% of corn (maize), 55% of sugar cane, 37% of grapes, and 28% of vegetables (McEwen and Stephenson, 1979). In North America alone, pests destroy about 37% of the potential production of food and fibre crops (Pimentel *et al.*, 1992).

Of course, management practices in agriculture have intensified greatly, particularly during the twentieth century. This change has resulted in substantial increases in crop productivity. The gains in agricultural yield have been largely achieved by the combined influences of

■ increased use of fossil-fuelled mechanization;

■ application of fertilizer;

■ cultivation of improved crop varieties grown in monocultural systems; and

■ use of pesticides.

The revolutionary changes in agrotechnology are sometimes referred to as the *"green revolution."* Although agricultural yields have increased greatly, it must be recognized that the gains are highly subsidized by

■ intense use (and depletion) of non-renewable resources such as fossil fuels and metals;

■ depletion of potentially renewable resources such as soil fertility and tilth, and groundwater and surface water required for irrigation;

■ loss of soil mass through erosion;

■ ecological damage associated with conversions of natural ecosystems into agricultural systems; and

■ ecotoxicological damage caused by the use of pesticides (see also Chapters 14 and 24).

In the U.S., for example, the yield of corn was typically about 1.4 t/ha•y in 1933, but this increased to 4.2 t/ha•y in 1963 and 5.1–7.1 t/ha•y during 1978–84. In Mexico, wheat yields increased from 0.75 t/ha•y in 1945 to 2.6 t/ha•y in 1964. The typical yield of rice in Japan increased from a pre-war level of 1.8 t/ha•y to 4.0 t/ha•y in 1963, while in the U.S., rice yields have reached 4.9–5.5 t/ha•y (Hayes, 1991). Similar gains in agricultural yield have been realized in Canada (see Figure 14.1).

Of course, it remains to be seen whether the intensified agricultural systems will be sustainable over the long term. Several factors threaten sustainability: intensive agriculture's reliance on non-renewable energy and material resources, the potential vulnerability of genetically narrow crop varieties to pests and diseases, and the ecological damage that is caused.

Almost all intensively managed agricultural systems depend to some degree on pest control. High-yield crop varieties are often vulnerable to infestation by insect pests, to diseases, and to competition from weeds. Pesticides are routinely prescribed to manage those problems. Moreover, monocultural systems result in reduced populations of natural predators and parasites, an ecological change that can exacerbate existing pest problems and allow new ones to develop. Some ecologists have described intensively managed agricultural systems as a **pesticide "treadmill,"** because they rely on pesticides, often in increasing quantities, to deal with unanticipated pest problems that emerge as "surprises."

The use of pesticides in Canadian agriculture has increased greatly in recent decades. Herbicides were applied to 25.9 million ha of farmland in 2001, representing a three-fold increase over 1971 (see Table 14.11, Chapter 14). Insecticides and fungicides were applied to 4.8 million ha in 2001, a five-fold increase over 1971. Overall, pesticide use in North American agriculture increased by about ten-fold between 1945 and 1989 (Pimentel *et al.*, 1992). Interestingly, during that same period, crop losses (to insects only) actually increased somewhat, from about 7% in 1941–51 to 13% during 1951–74 (Hayes, 1991). These trends, which seem to contradict each other, may be due to a combination of factors, such as the development of increased tolerance by some pests to previously effective pesticides, the emergence of new pests through accidental introductions, changes in predator–prey relationships caused by pesticide use, and the introduction of new crop varieties that happen to be vulnerable to pests.

Agricultural damages caused by arthropod pests vary greatly. Sometimes there is direct competition with humans for a food resource, as when insects defoliate crops in fields or attack stored grain and other foods. Such depredations can sometimes obliterate agricultural yield, as can happen during acute infestations by locusts such as the spur-throated grasshopper (*Melanoplus* spp.) in North America and the desert locust (*Schistocerca gregaria*) of Eurasia. More commonly, however, insects reduce crop yield only somewhat. The corn borer (*Ostrinia nubilalis*), for instance, caused an average 9% loss of corn yield of in North America between 1963 and 1973 (McEwen and Stephenson, 1979).

In some cases, however, even minor consumption of crop biomass by insects can make the produce unsaleable. This is the situation with damage caused to apples by codling moth (*Carpocapsa pomonella*). "Wormy" apples containing larvae of this insect are not very saleable to consumers, but as many as 90% of the apples in unsprayed orchards may be infested (McEwen and Stephenson, 1979). Even minor discolorations of fruit, such as those caused by apple scab and russeting of oranges (which do not significantly affect crop productivity or nutritional quality), are treated as unacceptable by many consumers, greatly reducing the economic value of the crop. Therefore, seemingly unimportant crop damage can be a critical economic consideration for farmers and food industries. Frequently, pesticides are used to combat economic problems, even if their use to deal with such damage is unnecessary from the ecological perspective. As with some potentially life-saving drugs, pesticides are over-prescribed for some uses in modern society.

Much pesticide use in agriculture is targeted against weeds. "Weed" plants interfere with the productivity of crop plants by competing for limited resources of light, water, and nutrients. (Of course, "weediness" is partly a matter of context—in other situations, such as in a flower garden, some weed species may have positive attributes.) It is well known that weeds, if abundant, can cause large decreases in the productivity of agricultural crops, often by 50–90%. This is the reason why farmers have always taken measures to reduce weed populations, initially by hand-pulling them and later by mechanical cultivation (ploughing) to disrupt their growth. More recently, however, chemical herbicides have been widely used to prevent infestations of agricultural weeds. In the U.S., for example, herbicides are typically used on 85% of the planted area for most crops (Gianessi and Sankula, 2003). The crops receiving the most herbicide are canola (on 99% of the cultivated area), dry beans (99%), carrots (98%), maize (98%), rice (98%) sugarbeet (98%), peanuts (97%), green beans (96%), soybeans (96%), tomatoes (96%), blueberry (95%), citrus (95%), cotton (95%), and potatoes (93%). Herbicide use in wheat fields is relatively low (55% of the area), presumably because mechanical cultivation associated with sowing is comparatively effective in reducing weed populations for this crop.

According to Gianessi and Sankula (2003), if herbicide use were discontinued for the 40 crops they studied, then weed management would have to rely on increased mechanical cultivation and manual weeding. This would have an estimated annual cost of US$14 billion, or about double the direct costs of herbicide use (US$6.6 billion per year). If herbicide use were discontinued and replaced by alternative practices, they estimate that 35 of the 40 crops studied would suffer a decline in productivity, by an average of 21% (range of 5–67%). Overall, the 21% productivity loss would have a value of about US$21 billion per year (including $13 billion in lost productivity and $8 billion in increased costs of management). Note that the "direct costs" of herbicide use cited above (i.e., $6.6 billion per year) do not include the value of environmental damage that might be caused, for instance, by toxicity to non-target plants, wildlife, or agricultural workers. It must be remembered, however, that non-herbicidal methods of weed control also cause environmental damage; this is particularly true of mechanical cultivation, which increases soil erosion. No-till management systems, which greatly reduce rates of erosion, must rely on the use of herbicide to control weeds.

Of course, the weeds must be vulnerable to the toxicity of the herbicide being used against them, while the crop plant must be tolerant. A number of herbicides are toxic to broad-leaved weeds (i.e., to dicotyledonous plants) but not to corn, wheat, barley, or other crops in the grass family (these are monocotyledonous plants). Consequently, herbicides are widely used in grain agriculture in North America. For instance, about 98% of the maize and rice acreage is treated.

Some important diseases of agricultural plants can also be managed with pesticides. Sometimes, insecticides are sprayed to control arthropod vectors of microbial diseases. More commonly, fungicides are used to control pathogenic fungi such as late blight (*Phytophthora infestans*) of potato, apple scab (*Venturia inequalis*), powdery mildew (*Sphaerotheca pannosa*) of peach, and seedrot and damping-off of many crop species by pythium (*Pythium* spp.). Fungicides are also used to help prevent the spoilage of stored crops by fungi such as *Aspergillus flavus*, which can grow in stored legumes, grains, and nuts, producing deadly aflatoxins that make those foods poisonous to humans and livestock.

Pesticides in Forestry

Pesticide use in agriculture is much greater than in forestry. Nevertheless, pesticide use in forestry is important, because extensive areas of natural and semi-natural ecosystems, supporting mainly indigenous elements of biodiversity, are sprayed. In contrast, pesticide use in agriculture involves more intensely disturbed agroecosystems dominated by non-native species.

The use of pesticides in forestry raises a great deal of controversy, sometimes moreso than when the same chemicals are used in agriculture. The controversy partly concerns damage that may be caused to the many native species of wildlife that are exposed to forestry sprays. In addition, spraying in forestry is mostly undertaken by government agencies and large companies, while pesticide use in agriculture commonly involves individual farmers working a family farm. Most people have greater empathy for individuals than for big government or big business, and this can influence their opinions about pesticide use.

Pesticides are used in forestry mainly to control epidemics of defoliating insects and to manage weeds in reforested areas and plantations. If uncontrolled, these pests can decrease tree productivity. The largest insecticide spraying campaigns in North American forestry have been undertaken against spruce budworm (*Choristoneura fumiferana*), particularly in New Brunswick, where a cumulative area of about 49 million ha was sprayed between 1952 and 1992 (we examine this as a case study later in this chapter). Other important spray programs include those against gypsy moth (*Lymantria dispar*), an introduced pest that defoliates many tree species and causes extensive damage in the eastern U.S. and southeastern Canada; hemlock looper (*Lambdina fiscellaria*); bark beetles (especially species of *Ambrosia* and *Ips*); and some other insect pests. Between 1980 and 1995, insect damage to commercial forest was equivalent to about one-half of the amount of timber harvested by industry (Environment Canada, 1996).

Herbicide use in forestry started to become common during the 1950s. Herbicides are used mainly to reduce competition from weeds, in order to increase the growth of conifer seedlings (a case study is presented later).

Pesticide Use around the Home and in Horticulture

Pesticides are also commonly used in and around homes. For instance, insecticides are routinely used to kill household insects such as cockroaches and flies, and baits containing rodenticide are used to poison rats and mice. As well, large amounts of pesticides are used in horticulture.

Herbicides are especially widely applied, mostly to achieve the monocultural, grassy-lawn aesthetic that many homeowners seek. To this end, herbicides are used to kill broad-leaved plants such as dandelion and plantain. The "weed" in common "weed-and-feed" lawn preparations refers to the herbicidal action of 2,4-D, dicamba, or mecoprop.

Some of the most intensive pesticide use occurs in the management of golf courses, particularly on the putting greens, where the quality of the lawn must be extremely consistent. Fungicides are used in especially large amounts, mostly to prevent turf-grass diseases. On a per-unit-area basis, the use of pesticides on golf-course putting greens is more intensive than most applications in agriculture.

Environmental Effects

Pesticide applications are intended to manage the impacts of a pest, or a community of pests, by reducing its abundance and ecological influence below an economically or aesthetically acceptable threshold. This objective can sometimes be achieved selectively, and so avoid non-target damage. For example, rodenticides can be used judiciously to kill rats and mice around homes, while minimizing toxic exposures to non-target mammals such as cats, dogs, and children (although never eliminating the risk).

More typically, however, pesticide use involves less-selective, broadcast applications, usually by spraying. Crop-dusting aircraft or tractor-drawn sprayers are often used, resulting in the exposure of many non-target species to the spray. The non-target organisms may live on the sprayed site, or they may live off-site and suffer exposure through aerial or aquatic **drift** of the pesticide. Non-target exposures include both direct contact with the sprayed pesticide and indirect exposure through the food web.

The ecotoxicological risks inherent in non-target exposures to pesticides (and other chemicals) are influenced by a complex of variables, as we previously examined in Chapter 15. Several points should be considered when interpreting exposures of non-target organisms, including people, to pesticides and other chemicals:

- All chemicals are potentially toxic.
- Not all exposures to potentially toxic chemicals result in poisoning (because organisms are to some degree tolerant to exposures to pesticides and other chemicals).
- Not only some pesticides, but also some naturally occurring chemicals, are extremely toxic to many organisms, including humans.
- Humans are subject to both involuntary and—as with cigarette smoke and prescription and recreational drugs—voluntary exposures to certain toxic chemicals.

Pesticides vary enormously in their toxicity. Herbicides, for example, are extremely toxic to at least some types of plants, but are not necessarily poisonous to animals, which differ in important physiological respects from plants. In contrast, many insecticides and rodenticides are toxic to a wide range of animals and can cause non-target poisoning of diverse species, including humans.

The acute toxicity of a chemical to animals is defined by its LD_{50}, or the dose required to kill one-half of a test population that is exposed through food, water, or air (see also Chapter 15). The oral LD_{50} for rats is a commonly used indicator of acute toxicity to mammals. Rats are widely used in toxicological research and are similar to humans in many aspects of their physiology. Table 22.2 compares the acute toxicities of a wide range of pesticides and some other chemicals, using rat oral LD_{50} (see also Table 15.3, Chapter 15). Note that some of the most poisonous chemicals listed are natural biochemicals (e.g., saxitoxin, a neurotoxin produced by marine algae, and the cause of paralytic shellfish poisoning in humans and other mammals). Others are chemicals to which some people expose themselves in their pursuit of pleasure (e.g., nicotine, the addicting alkaloid in tobacco).

By poisoning organisms, pesticides may cause changes to habitat. This can exert indirect ecotoxicological stresses on some species. For example, herbicides kill plants and thereby change the habitat of animals, perhaps depriving herbivores of their preferred foods. Similarly, broad-spectrum insecticides kill large numbers of arthropods, which reduces the availability of food for birds and other animals. These and other indirect effects of pesticide use can result in significant ecological damage and are additive to the direct, toxic effects of these chemicals.

In the remainder of this chapter, we will examine several case studies of particular uses of pesticides. These are useful in illustrating the broader principles and patterns of the ecological damage caused by these chemicals.

Environmental Effects of DDT and Related Organochlorines

The first case study involves DDT and related organochlorine insecticides, such as DDD, dieldrin, and aldrin. These chemicals were once widely used in Canada and most other industrialized countries. Although these chemicals were banned here in the early 1970s, they continue to be important insecticides in some less developed nations.

DDT and its relatives are persistent in the environment. Consequently, there are still substantial residues in

| TABLE 22.2 | Acute Toxicity of Various Chemicals to Rats |

The oral LD_{50}, stated here in milligrams of chemical per kilogram of body weight, is the amount required to kill 50% of a trial population, exposed through their food in a controlled laboratory test.

CHEMICAL	RAT ORAL LD_{50} (mg/kg)
TCDD (dioxin isomer)	0.01
tetrodotoxin (globefish toxin)	0.01
saxitoxin (paralytic shellfish neurotoxin)	0.3
aldicarb (insecticide)	0.8
TEPP (insecticide)	6.8
carbofuran (insecticide)	10
parathion (insecticide)	13
methylparathion (insecticide)	14
phosphamidon (insecticide)	24
strychnine (rodenticide)	30
deltamethrin (insecticide)	31
aminocarb (insecticide)	39
nicotine (alkaloid in tobacco)	50
methiocarb (molluscicide)	65
lindane (insecticide)	88
diazinon (insecticide)	108
paraquat (herbicide)	150
caffeine (alkaloid in coffee and tea)	200
DDT (insecticide)	200
fenitrothion (insecticide)	250
2,4-D (herbicide)	370
2,4,5-T (herbicide)	500
carbaryl (insecticide)	500
triclopyr (herbicide)	650
mirex (insecticide)	740
DDE (DDT, DDD metabolite)	880
tetramethrin (insecticide)	1 000
hexazinone (herbicide)	1 690
acetylsalicylic acid (Aspirin)	1 700
atrazine (herbicide)	1 750
malathion (insecticide)	2 000
sodium hypochlorite (household bleach)	2 000
sodium bicarbonate (baking soda)	3 500
sodium chloride (table salt)	3 750
permethrin (insecticide)	3 800
DDD (insecticide)	4 000
glyphosate (herbicide)	5 600
picloram (herbicide)	8 200
captan (fungicide)	9 000
ethanol (drinking alcohol)	13 700
fosamine (herbicide)	24 000
sucrose (table sugar)	30 000

Source: Modified from Freedman (1995)

the ecosystems of Canada and other developed countries, even though these chemicals have not been used there for several decades. In part, this also results from the continued use of these chemicals in some tropical countries as small amounts of residue from that use are transported to high-latitude countries by global cycling processes. In addition, organochlorines are more persistent in cooler environments than warmer ones. As a result, these and some non-insecticidal organochlorines (such as PCBs and dioxins; see In Detail 22.3) are still important contaminants in Canada.

DDT was first synthesized in 1874, although its insecticidal properties were not discovered until 1939. It was first used successfully during the Second World War, especially in programs to control body lice, mosquitoes, and other disease vectors. DDT was quickly recognized as an extremely effective insecticide, and immediately after the war, it became widely used in agriculture, forestry, and spray programs against malaria. The use of DDT peaked in 1970, when 175 million kg were manufactured globally.

At about that time, however, developed countries began to ban most applications of DDT because its use was causing severe ecological damage, including the contamination of humans and their agricultural food web. Some researchers thought that this contamination could be resulting in human illnesses, such as increases in cancer and liver disease. However, DDT use has continued in some other countries, especially in the tropics, mostly in programs against mosquito vectors of disease.

Even in those tropical countries, the use of DDT and other organochlorine insecticides has been diminishing. This is partly because many pests have developed a genetically based *tolerance* of these chemicals (also sometimes known as *resistance*), which decreases the effectiveness of the pesticides. The development of tolerance is an evolutionary process. Exposure to a toxic substance selects for tolerant individuals within genetically variable populations (see also Chapters 6 and 15). Although tolerant individuals are normally rare in unsprayed populations, they can rapidly become dominant in sprayed habitat. The insecticide does not kill them, so they survive to reproduce, passing on the genes for tolerance to their offspring. Reviews of pesticide tolerance found more than 450 species of insects and mites with populations tolerant to at least one insecticide, along with more than 100 examples of fungicide-resistant plant pathogens, 55 herbicide-tolerant weeds, and five rodents resistant to anticoagulants (NRC, 1986; Winston, 1997). Tolerance is

especially common among flies (order Diptera), with 156 tolerant species.

Two physical and chemical properties of organochlorines have an important influence on their ability to cause ecological damage. First, chlorinated hydrocarbons are highly persistent in the environment because they are not easily degraded by microorganisms or by physical agents such as sunlight or heat. For example, DDT has a typical half-life in soil of about 3–10 years. DDE is the primary breakdown product of DDT, and it has a similar **persistence**.

In addition, DDT and related organochlorines are extremely insoluble in water and so cannot be "diluted" into this abundant solvent. On the other hand, these chemicals are highly soluble in fats, or lipids, which occur mostly in organisms. Therefore, DDT and related

TABLE 22.3	Typical Residues of DDT in the Environment in the 1960s and Early 1970s
COMPONENT	**CONCENTRATION (ppm)**
Non-living Environment	
Atmosphere	$1 \times 10^{-5} - 2 \times 10^{-10}$
Atmospheric dust	0.3
Rainwater	5×10^{-4}
Fresh surfacewater	1×10^{-5}
Seawater	1×10^{-6}
Natural soil	0.01
Agricultural soil	2.0
Terrestrial Organisms	
Plants	0.05
Terrestrial insects	1.0
Soil-dwelling invertebrates	4.0
Small mammals	0.5
Predatory mammals	1.0
Insectivorous birds	2.0
Aquatic Organisms	
Aquatic plants	0.01
Zooplankton	0.05
Benthic invertebrates	0.1
Freshwater fish	2.0
Marine fish	0.5
Fish-eating birds	10
Humans	
Vegetable foods	0.02
Meat foods	0.2
Humans (in fat)	6.0

Sources: Data from Edwards (1975) and Freedman (1995)

In Detail 22.3

Chemical Structure of Organochlorines

Organochlorines are a diverse group of compounds that are made up of atoms of carbon, hydrogen, and chlorine. Their biochemical activity (including toxicity) and potential usefulness depend entirely on their chemical structure. Certain organochlorines are used as insecticides (e.g., DDT, DDD, dieldrin), herbicides (e.g., 2,4,-D, 2,4,5-T), or insulating fluids (PCBs). Others have no particular use, but are nevertheless environmental contaminants. For example, DDT and DDD are metabolized in organisms to DDE, which can accumulate to a high concentration. The extremely toxic dioxin TCDD is synthesized as a contaminant during the manufacturing of certain organochlorines (e.g., trichlorophenol) and through reactions occurring when organic wastes are incinerated.

The following diagrams show the specific chemical structures of environmentally important organochlorines. In the diagrams, the ring-like structures are derived from benzene, which has the formula C_6H_6. Organochlorines are formed by the substitution of one or more of the H atoms by chlorine atoms. Note the following:

- There is great similarity among DDT, DDD, and DDE, which differ by only a single chlorine atom.
- Similarly, 2,4-D and 2,4,5-T differ by only one chlorine atom.
- PCBs are a complex mixture of molecules with a basic biphenyl structure, but varying in the amount of substitution of chlorine for hydrogen atoms; in the diagram, "X" can be either H or Cl.
- TCDD, strictly speaking, is not an organochlorine because it contains two oxygen atoms.

DDT or 2,2-bis-(p-chlorophenyl)-1,1,1-trichloroethane (an insecticide)

DDD or 2,2-bis-(p-chlorophenyl)-1,1-dichloroethane (an insecticide)

DDE or 2,2-bis-(p-chlorophenyl)-1,1-dichloroethylene (a non-insecticidal metabolite)

2,4-D or 2,4-dichlorophenoxyacetic acid (a herbicide)

2,4,5-T or 2,4,5-trichlorophenoxyacetic acid (a herbicide)

PCBs or polychlorinated biphenyls (electrical insulating fluid)

X = H or Cl

TCDD or 2,3,7,8-tetrachlorodibenzo-p-dioxin (a trace contaminant)

FIGURE 22.1 | Residues of PCBs in the Food Web of Lake Ontario

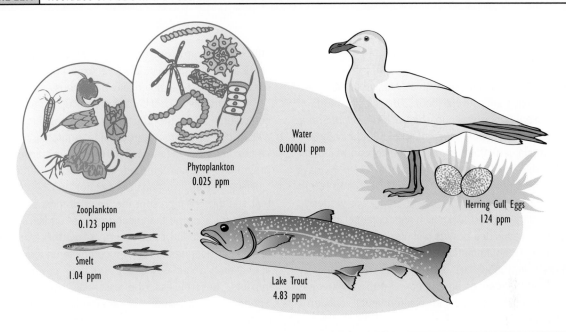

Water
0.00001 ppm

Phytoplankton
0.025 ppm

Zooplankton
0.123 ppm

Smelt
1.04 ppm

Lake Trout
4.83 ppm

Herring Gull Eggs
124 ppm

Organochlorine insecticides, such as DDT, DDD, and dieldrin, show the same pattern of bioaccumulation and biomagnification as PCBs, but their residue levels are different.

Source: Modified from Environmental Protection Agency (2003)

organochlorines have a strong affinity for organisms, and they accumulate in living things in strong preference to the non-living environment; this is called **bioconcentration**. Moreover, organisms are efficient at assimilating any organochlorines present in their food. As a result, predators at the top of the food web develop the highest concentrations of organochlorine residues, particularly in their fatty tissues (this is known as **food-web magnification**, **food-web concentration,** or **biomagnification**). Both bioconcentration and food-web magnification tend to be progressive with age; that is, the oldest individuals in a population are the most contaminated (see In Detail 18.1).

The bioconcentration and food-web magnification properties of DDT are illustrated in Figure 22.1 and Table 22.3. Note that concentrations of DDT are minute in air, water, and non-agricultural soil, compared with the much higher residues in organisms. Note also that concentrations in plants are lower than in herbivores and that residues are highest at the top of the food web, for instance, in predatory birds and humans.

Another characteristic of DDT and other organochlorines is their ubiquity—their residues are present in organisms throughout the biosphere. This extraordinarily widespread contamination with organochlorines occurs because these chemicals enter a global cycle, becoming widely dispersed in the bodies of migrating organisms and after entering the atmosphere by evaporation and in wind-eroded dust. Residues of DDT are found even in organisms in Antarctica, a place far remote from areas where DDT was ever used. In one study, the concentration of "total DDT" (see In Detail 22.2) in the fat of skuas (a marine bird; *Catharacta maccormicki*) was 5 ppm (1 µg/g = 1 ppm). Smaller residues (<0.44 ppm) were found in birds feeding lower in the food web, such as fulmar (*Fulmarus glacialoides*) and macaroni penguin (*Eudyptes chrysolophus*) (Norheim *et al.*, 1982).

Although organochlorine residues are ubiquitous in the biosphere, much higher concentrations occur in animals that live close to areas where these chemicals have been used, such as North America. Marine mammals feed at or near the top of their food web and are long-lived, and for these reasons, they can have extremely high residues of organochlorines. For example, harbour porpoises (*Phocoena phocoena*) in Atlantic Canada have had DDT residues as high as 520 ppm in their fat (Edwards, 1975).

Silent Spring

Rachael Carson, an American biologist, wrote many scientific articles and several books, the most famous of which, *Silent Spring*, was published in 1962. *Silent Spring* was aimed at a popular audience, and it is a lively and controversial indictment of pesticide use as it was practised during the 1950s and early 1960s. The book pays particular attention to the use of DDT and other organochlorine insecticides. *Silent Spring* was written to warn society about the known and potential dangers that these pesticides pose to wildlife, as well as to people through contamination of their food. *Silent Spring* achieved that objective and, in fact, was a literary bombshell that caused an eruption of public awareness about pesticide issues and environmental concerns more generally.

Rachael Carson wrote about the effects of DDT and its organochlorine relatives on both wildlife and people. Although these insecticides are clearly useful in killing pests, Carson described how they were also causing extensive non-target mortality to non-pest arthropods, as well as to birds, mammals, and other wildlife. She also warned that humans were being widely contaminated by organochlorines, with significant residues being found, for example, in the milk of nursing mothers. She noted, "For the first time in the history of the world, every human being is now subjected to dangerous chemicals, from the moment of conception until death." Although little was known about the subject at the time, Carson warned that the chronic, low-level exposure of people to organochlorines was potentially dangerous.

A best-seller, *Silent Spring* stirred up an enormous controversy about the effects of anthropogenic chemicals in the environment. Pesticide-manufacturing companies mounted their own information and advertising programs. They attempted to discredit Carson by labelling her an irresponsible agitator and by claiming that she did not represent the views of most scientists. In fact, some of the technical details of Carson's analysis were later found to be incorrect, but this is not surprising considering the highly incomplete understanding at the time about pesticides and their environmental impacts. Nevertheless, the essential thesis of *Silent Spring* was that organochlorine insecticides can widely contaminate organisms and the environment, that they are persistent, and that they cause widespread damage. In large part, these assertions have proven to be correct.

Unfortunately, Rachael Carson died an early death from cancer in 1964, just as the importance of *Silent Spring* and its message was becoming widely recognized. Today, Carson is well known as one of the most influential environmentalists in history, a pioneer who deserves much of the credit for the birth of the environmental movement during the mid-1960s. Like all environmentalists, Rachael Carson promoted an ethic of human responsibility for taking care of the biosphere and its species.

Large residues of organochlorines also occur in some top-predator birds, especially raptors (e.g., falcons, hawks, eagles, and owls). In North America, prior to the ban of DDT, residues averaged 12 ppm (with a maximum of 356 ppm) in a sample of 69 bald eagles (*Haliaeetus leucocephalus*), up to 460 ppm among 11 western grebes (*Aechmophorus occidentalis*), and up to 131 ppm among 13 herring gulls (*Larus argentatus*) (Edwards, 1975).

Intense exposures to DDT and other organochlorines caused important ecological damage, including bird poisonings. During the 1950s and 1960s, bird kills resulted when DDT was sprayed in urban areas to kill beetle vectors of Dutch elm disease. This disease is caused by a fungal pathogen (*Ceratocystis ulmi*) that was introduced to North America from Europe. The fungus is transported between trees by elm bark-beetles, which can be controlled to some degree by using insecticide. Spraying for this purpose was intensive, typically involving an application of 0.7–1.4 kg DDT per tree. As a result, birds feeding on invertebrates in sprayed sites were exposed to lethal doses of DDT. One study in New Hampshire found 117 dead birds of various species in a 6-ha spray area. It was estimated that 70% of the breeding robins (*Turdus migratorius*) had been killed (Wurster *et al.*, 1965). So much avian mortality occurred in sprayed neighbourhoods that bird song was markedly reduced—hence the title of Rachael Carson's 1962 book *Silent Spring*, often considered a harbinger of the environmental movement in North America (In Detail 22.4).

In addition to the acute poisoning caused by chlorinated hydrocarbons in sprayed areas, more insidious damage was also caused to birds and other wildlife over large regions. Many species experienced long-term chronic toxicity, often occurring well away from sprayed areas. It took years of population monitoring and ecotoxicological research before organochlorines were identified as the cause of this widespread damage. In fact, we can characterize the chronic poisoning of birds and other wildlife as an unanticipated ecological "surprise," occurring because scientists (and society) had no experience with the long-term effects of persistent, biomagnifying organochlorines.

Species of raptorial birds were among the prominent victims of organochlorine insecticides. These birds are vulnerable because they feed at the top of their food web, and therefore accumulate high concentrations of organochlorines. Breeding populations of various raptors suffered large declines. Severely affected species in North America included the peregrine falcon (*Falco peregrinus*), osprey (*Pandion haliaetus*), bald eagle (*Haliaeetus leucocephalus*), and golden eagle (*Aquila chrysaetos*) (see Canadian Focus 22.1).

In all cases, these species were exposed to a "cocktail" of organochlorines. This mixture included the insecticides DDT, DDD (both are metabolized to DDE), aldrin, dieldrin, and heptachlor, as well as PCBs, a group of non-insecticides with many industrial uses. Researchers have investigated the relative importance of these different organochlorines in causing the population declines of raptors. It appears that DDT was the more important toxin to birds in North America, while cyclodienes (particularly dieldrin) were more important in Britain (Moriarty, 1999; Cooper, 1991).

Damage caused to predatory birds was mainly associated with chronic effects on reproduction, rather than toxicity caused to adults. Reproductive damage included the production of thin eggshells that could break under an

Canadian Focus 22.1

Organochlorines and the Peregrine Falcon

The most famous avian decline caused by organochlorines involved the peregrine falcon. Its decreasing populations were first noticed in the early 1950s in North America and western Europe (Peakall, 1990; Freedman, 1995). By 1970, the population of peregrines breeding in eastern North America (known as the *anatum* sub-species, or, *Falco peregrinus anatum*) had stopped reproducing and was critically endangered. At the same time, the population of the *tundrius* sub-species of the Arctic was declining rapidly. Only the *pealei* sub-species that breeds on Pacific islands off British Columbia and Alaska had normal reproductive success and a stable population.

Pealei falcons do not migrate. Moreover, they live in a region where pesticides are not used, and they feed mainly on non-migratory seabirds. In contrast, *anatum* peregrines breed in a region where organochlorine pesticides were widely used, and they fed on contaminated prey. The arctic *tundrius* peregrines breed in a remote wilderness where pesticides are not used, but they winter in Central and South America where their food is contaminated by organochlorines, as is their prey of migratory waterfowl and shorebirds in the Arctic. Studies by wildlife toxicologists demonstrated that populations of peregrine falcons with high residues of organochlorines were laying thin-shelled eggs and suffering other kinds

of reproductive impairment. This damage was causing their populations to collapse.

By 1975, the *anatum* peregrines had become extirpated in eastern North America, while the arctic *tundrius* sub-species had declined to only about 450 pairs from historical levels of 5000–8000 pairs.

Fortunately, many countries (including Canada, the U.S., and most other industrialized nations) banned further use of DDT and most other organochlorines in the early 1970s. Residues in the food of peregrines and other raptors have decreased, allowing their populations to stabilize or recover. By 1985, arctic peregrines were stable or increasing in abundance, and small breeding populations had re-established in more southern regions.

The recovery of peregrines has been enhanced by a program (funded in Canada by the Canadian Wildlife Service) in which these falcons were bred in captivity to provide young birds for release into the former range of the eastern *anatum* sub-species. Several thousand peregrines were released in Canada and the U.S., and many of these birds survived and bred. Some of the peregrines were released in cities, where tall buildings provide cliff-like nesting habitat and abundant pigeons (rock dove, *Columba livia*) and other urban birds as suitable prey. Thanks to declining residues of organochlorine pesticides and PCBs in North America, resulting from legislated bans on the use of these chemicals, the peregrine falcon is on its way back.

incubating parent, high mortality of embryos and nestlings, and abnormal adult behaviour. The numbers of chicks declined, resulting in rapid depletions of populations.

Since the ban on most uses of DDT and other organochlorines in North America, their residues in wildlife have been declining. Some of the best data illustrating this decrease have been obtained by analyzing eggs of herring gulls (*Larus argentatus*) breeding on islands in the Great Lakes (Table 22.4). Although eggs from various places differ in their organochlorine residues (depending on local sources of contamination), they all exhibited large decreases in DDE and PCB concentrations from 1971 to 1989. Well-documented decreases in residues of organochlorines have also occurred in eggs of double-crested cormorants (*Phalacrocorax auritus*) in other regions of Canada.

Modern Insecticides and Birds

The Case of Carbofuran

The most important replacements for DDT and related organochlorine insecticides have been organophosphate and carbamate chemicals. These poison insects and other arthropods by inhibiting a specific enzyme, acetylcholine esterase (AChE), which is critical in the transmission of nerve impulses. Vertebrates such as amphibians, fish, birds, and mammals are also highly sensitive to poisoning of their AChE enzyme system. In all of these animals, acute poisoning by organophosphate and carbamate insecticides can cause tremors, convulsions, and ultimately death. More than 30 insecticides registered in Canada are extremely poisonous to birds in this manner (Mineau, 1999).

Carbofuran, a carbamate insecticide, can be used for many purposes in agriculture. Available as a liquid suspension, carbofuran is diluted in water and broadcast-sprayed against pests such as grasshoppers and leaf beetles. It is also available in a granular formulation, in which the insecticide coats grit particles and is sown along with seeds to protect tender seedlings from insect damage. In Canada, the granular formulation has been commonly used in the sowing of canola and maize.

Unfortunately, wildlife is exposed to toxic doses of carbofuran when it is used in either of these formulations. For example, if not all of the carbofuran granules are buried within the planting furrows, they can remain exposed on the ground surface (Mineau, 1993). In one method of seeding, commonly used when planting corn in Ontario, 15–31% of the carbofuran granules remained exposed on the surface, equivalent to 515–1065 exposed granules per metre of furrow. Methods used to plant canola in western

| TABLE 22.4 | Changes in the Residues of DDE and PCBs in Bird Eggs in Canada |

Eggs of herring gull and double-crested cormorant have shown decreasing residues since DDT, PCBs, and other persistent organochlorines were banned in North America in the early 1970s. Residues are measured in ppm.

(A) HERRING GULL EGGS

YEAR	BIG SISTER ISLAND, ON		MUGGS ISLAND, ON	
	DDE	PCBs	DDE	PCBs
1971–1974	58	151	23	139
1975–1978	29	105	16	123
1979–1982	14	65	11	66
1983–1986	9	30	5	40
1987–1989	5	28	4	21

(B) DOUBLE-CRESTED CORMORANT EGGS

YEAR	STRAIT OF GEORGIA, BC		ST. LAWRENCE, QC	
	DDE	PCBs	DDE	PCBs
1971–1974	4	8	6	8
1975–1978	–	–	2	8
1979–1982	1	4	2	7
1983–1986	0.5	2	2	6
1987–1989	0.5	2	1	4

Sources: Modified from Bishop and Weseloh (1990) and Environment Canada (1993)

Canada often left about 5% of the applied granules on the surface. These granules can be ingested by seed-eating birds, which require hard particles in that size range as "grit" for grinding hard seeds in their muscular gizzard. The carbofuran is extremely toxic—consumption of a mere one to five granules is enough to kill a small bird. Raptors and mammals may then be secondarily poisoned when they scavenge the birds' dead bodies.

In addition, if carbofuran-treated fields become flooded, as often happens during the spring and autumn, the surface water may contain large residues of the insecticide. This is particularly the case if the soil and water are acidic, because this condition greatly reduces the breakdown rate of carbofuran into less toxic chemicals.

Of all the pesticides used recently in North American agriculture, carbofuran has probably caused the most non-target mortality of birds and other wild animals. Even though there is no systematic program for reporting bird kills caused by pesticide use in Canada or the U.S., an astonishingly large number of toxic incidents have been documented for carbofuran (Mineau, 1993). A few of these incidents are described below.

Granular carbofuran:

- More than 2000 Lapland longspurs (*Calcarius lapponicus*), a seed-eating finch, were killed in a freshly planted canola field in Saskatchewan in May 1984.

- As many as 1200 birds, mostly savannah sparrows (*Passerculus sandwichensis*), were killed in turnip and radish fields in British Columbia in September 1986.

Flooded fields polluted by carbofuran:

- More than 1000 green-winged teal (*Anas carolinensis*) were killed within hours of landing in a flooded turnip field in British Columbia in the autumn of 1975.

- About 50 mallards (*Anas platyrhynchos*) and pintails (*A. acuta*) were poisoned in flooded fields in British Columbia in December 1973.

- A total of 2450 dead widgeon (*Mareca americana*) were found one day after the spraying of an alfalfa field in California in March 1974.

These examples represent only a small fraction of the known bird kills caused by the routine use of carbofuran in North American agriculture. There are also, of course, larger numbers of unreported incidents.

Because carbofuran use in agriculture carries such a well-known risk of poisoning birds and other wildlife, ecologists and environmentalists have lobbied intensely to have its registration for agricultural uses withdrawn, or at least more tightly controlled. In 1993, the U.S. Environmental Protection Agency announced that the sand-based granular formulation of carbofuran was banned, except for some relatively minor uses and one major use (with rice crops) for which there was no suitable alternative. In 1996, Agriculture Canada, the federal agency that regulates pesticide use in Canada, announced a ban on most agricultural uses of carbofuran, which took effect in 1997. This ban prohibited most uses of carbofuran in liquid suspension, as well as use of granular formulations containing 10% carbofuran. In 1999, the ban was expanded to include all uses of carbofuran in Canada.

Diazinon and Monocrotophos

Other modern insecticides are also poisoning Canadian birds. Diazinon, an organophosphate insecticide, has caused numerous cases of mass mortality. For instance, in the late 1980s, there were at least five events in which entire flocks of Canada goose (*Branta canadensis*) were killed when they fed on grass on golf courses in southern Ontario that had been treated to reduce infestations of turf insects (Mineau, 1999). The geese died within minutes, as is typical of acute poisoning by AChE inhibitors. Similar toxic events have occurred in the U.S., including one in which 700 Brant geese (*Branta bernicla*) were killed on a golf course in New York. Diazinon has been banned for use on golf courses in the U.S., but it can still be used in Canada for that purpose and also for horticultural and agricultural use.

In 1996, it was discovered that agricultural use of monocrotophos and other organophosphate insecticides against grasshoppers in Argentina was killing large numbers of Swainson's hawks (*Buteo swainsoni*). This raptor breeds in western Canada and the U.S. and winters on the pampas of South America. Populations of Swainson's hawks had been declining for several years. However, it was not until some birds were fitted with satellite transmitters and followed to Argentina that wildlife toxicologists discovered a probable cause of the decline—poorly regulated use of monocrotophos on the wintering grounds of the birds. Field studies in Argentina in 1996 discovered that more than 20 000 Swainson's hawks had been killed in just one agricultural area (other regions were not surveyed), out of a total breeding population of only 400 000 birds (of which 40 000–100 000 breed in Canada).

Monocrotophos is extremely toxic to birds, although it is not very persistent in the environment. Because of the risk of ecological damage, monocrotophos has been banned in the U.S. and was never registered for use in Canada. In Argentina, however, the insecticide could be legally used. Swainson's hawks were exposed to lethal doses of monocrotophos when they fluttered behind spray tractors to feed on grasshoppers flushed by the machinery, and also when they later fed on insecticide-contaminated prey.

Pest Problems in Forestry

Pesticides are used much more extensively in agriculture than in forestry (about 80% of pesticide sales in Canada are for use in agriculture, 12% for domestic and industrial use, and 2% for forestry purposes; Environment Canada,

1996). However, forestry case studies better illustrate many of the ecological effects of pesticide use because forests (and clear-cuts) support mainly native species and natural or semi-natural ecosystems. In contrast, agricultural ecosystems are typically dominated by non-native species and are intensively managed, making them less amenable to the examination of some ecological effects of pesticides.

Spruce Budworm

The largest insecticide spray programs in North American forestry have been mounted against spruce budworm (*Choristoneura fumiferana*), particularly in New Brunswick. Spruce budworm is a moth whose larvae are an important pest of fir- and spruce-dominated forest. Infestations can affect forests over tens of millions of hectares, and trees

Photo 22.1   This is an area of intensive forest damage caused by spruce budworm on the Cape Breton highlands, Nova Scotia. The living trees fringing the bog are black spruce, which is relatively resistant to this insect. The extensive area of dead trees was dominated by balsam fir, a vulnerable species. This photo was taken about eight years after the collapse of the outbreak.

FIGURE 22.2 | Forest Area in Canada Defoliated by Spruce Budworm in the Twentieth Century

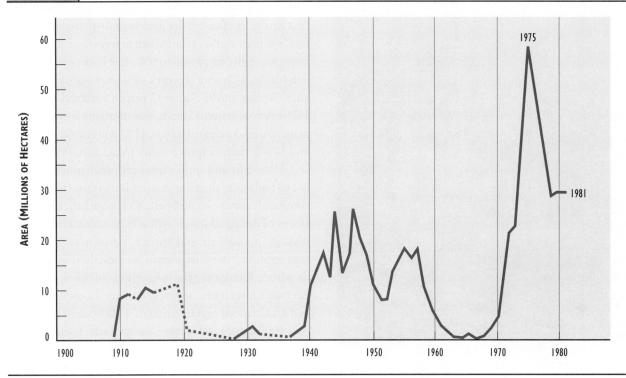

The areas correspond to stands suffering severe or moderate defoliation.

Source: Modified from Kettela (1983)

are killed after a number of years of defoliation. Mature stands dominated by balsam fir (*Abies balsamea*) are particularly vulnerable to damage. Spruces are also a preferred food, especially white spruce (*Picea glauca*). Red spruce (*P. rubens*) and black spruce (*P. mariana*) are less apt to suffer lethal damage.

Spruce budworm is a native insect that is always present in small populations in its fir-spruce habitat. However, it occasionally irrupts to an enormous abundance, and this is when it becomes a pest. Under normal conditions, only about five larvae occur on each conifer tree. This can increase to about 2000 per tree at the beginning of an irruption, and to more than 20 000 per tree during the peak. A local outbreak is typically sustained for 6 to 10 years, and then collapses. Studies in Quebec have shown that outbreaks have occurred at an average interval of about 35 years (Blais, 1985). Outbreaks of spruce budworm are typically synchronous (occurring at the same time) over extensive areas of susceptible forest, although there are great variations in the abundance of budworm among stands in different areas. The exact reasons for the irruptions are not known, but they may involve several years of warm, dry weather in the springtime, which favours larval survival.

Forest Damage

It appears that the extent of the damage caused by spruce budworm may have increased during the three outbreaks of the twentieth century. The outbreak that began in 1910 affected about 10 million ha, one that started in 1940 involved 25 million ha, and one beginning in 1970 affected more than 55 million ha (Figure 22.2). The enlarging areas of budworm infestation may be related to an increase in the extent of vulnerable fir-spruce forest. This may have been due to

- forestry practices such as clear-cutting;
- protection of forests from wildfire;
- regeneration of conifer stands on abandoned farmland, particularly since the 1920s; and
- spraying of infested stands with insecticide—a practice that may help maintain the habitat in a condition suitable for budworm.

Enormous damage has been caused by budworm to economically important forest. During the most recent outbreak (1971–84), tree mortality was equivalent to more than 38 million m³/y (this is cubic metres of saleable tim-

Photo 22.2 This photo shows a ground-level view of a stand damaged by spruce budworm on Cape Breton Island. Although the mature balsam fir trees have been killed, dense regeneration of young fir is occurring in the understorey. After about 40–50 years, another mature forest will have regenerated, ready for harvesting by spruce budworm or by humans.

ber, which can be manufactured into paper or lumber). During the peak of the infestation, substantial tree mortality occurred over about 26.5 million ha in eastern Canada (Ostaff, 1985).

The rapid development of a budworm infestation can be illustrated by the case of Cape Breton Island (Ostaff and MacLean, 1989). No defoliation caused by budworm was observed in 1973, but in 1974, moderate-to-severe defoliation occurred over 165 000 ha. This increased to 486 000 ha in 1975, and to 1.22 million ha in 1976, when virtually all of the vulnerable fir-spruce forest was infested.

Irruptions of budworm can last for 10 or more years, with the damage to trees increasing over time. During the first two years of severe defoliation of fir-dominated forest on Cape Breton, 4% of the balsam fir trees died. The cumulative mortality increased to 9% after four years of heavy defoliation, 37% after six years, 48% after eight years, 75% after 10 years, and 95% after 12 years (Ostaff and MacLean, 1989). Across eastern Canada, tree mortality averaged 85% in mature fir-dominated stands, 42% in immature fir stands, and 36% in mature spruce stands (MacLean, 1990).

Mature fir and spruce trees are much more vulnerable to budworm than are smaller immature trees, which commonly survive an outbreak. Consequently, the understorey of damaged stands typically contains a dense population of small fir and spruce. Known as "advanced regeneration," this is important in re-establishing the next fir-spruce forest after the infestation collapses. On Cape Breton, for instance, severely damaged stands typically had an advanced regeneration of 45 000 small balsam fir plus 3000 spruce per hectare, most of which survived the infestation (MacLean, 1988). After the mature trees die and the canopy opens up, the small conifers grow rapidly and establish another fir-spruce forest, which becomes vulnerable decades later to a budworm irruption.

These observations suggest that, over the long term, the budworm/forest interaction can be viewed as an ecologically stable, cyclic succession. The natural cycle of disturbance and recovery has probably been continuing for thousands of years, although it is possible that human influences have increased its scale since the nineteenth century.

Of course, spruce budworm causes great economic instability in the forest products industry, which is in competition with this insect for the fir-spruce resource. The periodic irruptions of budworm severely damage the forest, making it difficult for humans to plan their own orderly harvesting and management of the resource. Spraying is one way of dealing with this problem, by limiting defoliation and preventing some tree mortality. The objective of spraying is not to eradicate the budworm, but to decrease the damage it causes, and thereby maintain the forest resource and its dependent economy.

Insecticide Spraying

After the Second World War, DDT was used against spruce budworm. In 1953 alone, 804 000 ha of forest were sprayed with this insecticide in Quebec and New Brunswick. By 1968, when further use of DDT for this purpose was banned in Canada, a total of about 15 million ha had been sprayed at least once (Ennis and Caldwell, 1991). In New Brunswick alone, 5.75 million kg of DDT were sprayed onto budworm-infested forest (Armstrong, 1985).

After the use of DDT against budworm was banned in 1968, the insecticides used were fenitrothion and phosphamidon, both organophosphate insecticides, and aminocarb, a carbamate. Of these, fenitrothion was used most widely. By 1985, phosphamidon had been sprayed over 8.1 million ha, aminocarb on 19 million ha, and fenitrothion on 64 million ha (these are cumulative sums of annual sprayed areas—most stands were treated a number of times; Ennis and Caldwell, 1991). New Brunswick had the biggest spray program for "protection" of the forest resource against budworm—up to 1985, a cumulative total of 69 million ha was treated in that province, while 37 million ha were sprayed in Quebec; 10 million ha in Maine; and 1.7 million ha in Newfoundland. The most extensive spraying in New Brunswick was in 1976, when 4.2 million ha were treated. There has been much less spraying since then, declining to less than 1 million ha after 1985, to less than 0.5 million ha after 1990, and to zero after 1993 due to collapse of the budworm outbreak.

During the late 1980s, a biological insecticide based on the bacterium *Bacillus thuringiensis* var. *kurstaki* (abbreviated *B.t.*) began to displace the synthetic organic pesticides in budworm spray programs. *B.t.* is toxic to most lepidopterans (i.e., moths and butterflies) and to some other insects, including blackflies and mosquitoes. Otherwise, this insecticide causes little non-target damage. Initially, budworm control using *B.t.* was variable in effectiveness, and the cost was high compared with fenitrothion. More recently, however, the technology and cost of spraying *B.t.* have improved. This, along with concern about ecological damage caused by fenitrothion, has resulted in *B.t.* becoming the insecticide of choice in spray programs against budworm.

Non-target Damage

The synthetic organic insecticides used against spruce budworm caused a great deal of non-target mortality. Typical spray rates and toxicities for the most important insecticides are summarized in Table 22.5. Among these insecticides, DDT is the least toxic to the budworm itself, but is the most toxic to salmonid fish. Perhaps the most important reason for the 1968 ban on using DDT against budworm was the mortality caused to economically important sportfish, particularly to Atlantic salmon (*Salmo salar*) and brook trout (*Salvelinus fontinalis*).

The insecticides that replaced DDT are more toxic to budworm and can therefore be sprayed at lower rates while achieving the same degree of pest control. Although these insecticides are less toxic to fish than is DDT, they can be very poisonous to other animals. Fenitrothion and aminocarb, for example, are extremely toxic to all arthropods. Spraying forest with these insecticides results in an enormous kill of non-target insects and spiders, including many predators of budworm. One study estimated that a typical fenitrothion spray killed as many as 7.5 million individuals of hundreds of species of arthropods per hectare, although more than 90% of the dead biomass was budworm (Varty, 1975). Overall, a typical spray with fenitrothion

TABLE 22.5   Acute Toxicity of Insecticides Used against Spruce Budworm

Typical application rates for forestry purposes are stated in kilograms per hectare. Acute toxicity to spruce budworm larvae and selected vertebrate species was determined under controlled laboratory conditions. The units for toxicity to budworm are in micrograms per centimetre^2 of body surface; for trout, data are ppm in water; and for pheasant and rat, data are ppm in food. Note: 96-h LC_{50} is the concentration in water that killed 50% of the population of trout after a 96-hour exposure.

INSECTICIDE	TYPICAL APPLICATION RATE (kg/ha)	CONTACT TOXICITY TO BUDWORM (LD_{50}; μg/cm^2)	RAINBOW TROUT 96-h LC_{50} (ppm)	PHEASANT ORAL LD_{50} (ppm)	RAT ORAL LD_{50} (ppm)
DDT	0.3–2.2	1.3	0.009	1334	87–500
Phosphamidon	0.3	0.39	7.8	4.2	15–33
Fenitrothion	0.21	0.31	2.4	56	250–600
Aminocarb	0.07	0.04	13.5	42	30
Mexacarbate	0.07	0.04	12.0	4.6	15–63

Source: Freedman (1995)

caused a short-term decrease in arthropod biomass of 35%, and a decrease in total numbers of 50% (Agriculture Canada, 1993). Studies showed, however, that the non-target damage to arthropods was temporary and that long-term decreases in abundance were not detectable (Varty, 1975; Millikin, 1990). The post-spray recovery was due mainly to re-colonization from non-sprayed forest, along with increases by arthropods that survived the spraying.

Bird populations are unusually abundant in infested forest because spruce budworm is a plentiful and nutritious food for insect-eating animals. In fact, some species of birds are uncommon except in budworm-infested forest. In one study, the breeding population of bay-breasted warbler increased from only 0.25 pairs/ha in non-infested forest to 30 pairs/ha during a budworm outbreak, while Tennessee warbler increased from 0 pairs/ha to 12.5 pairs/ha (Morris et al., 1958).

During an outbreak of spruce budworm, most species of birds rely heavily on its larvae as food for raising nestlings. One study estimated that birds eat about 89 000 budworm larvae and pupae per hectare of infested forest, compared with 6000/ha in stands without an irruption

(Crawford et al., 1983). In spite of the enthusiastic effort, bird predation has no substantial effect on the abundance of budworm during an outbreak—birds consume only 2% or less of the larvae in outbreak stands. In essence, insectivorous birds are satiated by the superabundant budworm resource and are incapable of controlling the huge population of larvae. Predation by birds may, however, be more important in reducing less abundant budworm populations, and perhaps in helping to lengthen the intervals between serious outbreaks.

Because birds are abundant in budworm-infested forest, they are exposed to insecticide spray. Although some of the insecticides used against budworm are extremely toxic to birds, for several reasons it has proved difficult to document actual damage caused to avian populations by spraying. First, it is extremely difficult to find dead or dying birds in forest habitat because they occur in a small density and are quickly scavenged by other animals. Even with all the insecticide spraying in New Brunswick between 1965 and 1987, the Canadian Wildlife Service has records of only 125 dead birds (Busby et al., 1989)—a gross underestimate of the actual mortality from spraying.

TABLE 22.6   Effects of Forest Spraying on Bird Populations

The data show the effects of forest spraying with fenitrothion on breeding birds in the Gaspé region of Quebec. The operational spraying procedure is to treat stands twice, about one week apart. In this study, birds were censused for five days before spraying, then for seven days after the initial spray on May 21, 1976, and again for five days after the second spray on May 30. The sprayed stand ("Spr") was treated with fenitrothion at 0.56 kilograms per hectare, while the unsprayed reference stand ("Ref") was used to monitor population changes unrelated to spraying. Bird density is expressed as numbers/10 hectares. Only prominent species are listed.

SPECIES	PRE-SPRAY		FIRST SPRAY		SECOND SPRAY	
	SPR	REF	SPR	REF	SPR	REF
Total Bird Abundance	46.1	39.1	52.1	57.7	68.8	75.8
Number of Species	23	23	41	35	41	39
Boreal chickadee (*Parus hudsonicus*)	2.5	4.3	1.5	1.5	1.4	1.1
Winter wren (*Troglodytes troglodytes*)	1.0	3.9	2.3	4.6	1.7	3.0
American robin (*Turdus migratorius*)	3.5	3.6	4.8	3.3	5.3	1.8
Ruby-crowned kinglet (*Regulus calendula*)	8.6	4.5	5.9	3.8	4.4	6.4
Tennessee warbler (*Vermivora peregrina*)	0.0	0.0	0.3	1.5	2.3	5.8
Magnolia warbler (*Dendroica magnolia*)	0.0	0.0	0.1	1.5	0.8	3.1
Cape May warbler (*Dendroica tigrina*)	0.0	0.0	2.0	3.1	4.3	4.0
Yellow-rumped warbler (*Dendroica coronata*)	0.5	0.3	7.7	6.3	10.8	8.2
Bay-breasted warbler (*Dendroica castanea*)	0.0	0.0	0.3	0.3	2.5	4.5
Dark-eyed junco (*Junco hyemalis*)	9.6	4.1	4.2	1.8	4.5	0.5
White-throated sparrow (*Zonotrichia albicollis*)	8.9	9.6	9.7	10.5	10.4	8.4
Fox sparrow (*Paserella iliaca*)	2.1	3.8	3.3	4.2	2.5	3.1

Source: Modified from Kingsbury and McLeod (1981)

In addition, it is difficult to detect population-level changes resulting from mortality of breeding birds in forest. A census of forest birds is taken by mapping the locations from which male birds sing; this information is used to determine the boundaries of their territories. The song censuses are conducted in the spring over a period of 4–6 weeks. During this time, bird populations are quite variable because migratory species are returning from their wintering grounds, and they arrive at different times. Moreover, if a territory-holding bird happens to be killed by an insecticide spray, it is usually quickly replaced from a "surplus" of non-breeding individuals that wander extensively, searching for habitat not occupied by another of their species. Because of the temporal variations in bird abundance and the rapid replacement of killed individuals, it is difficult to document mortality or population changes caused by insecticide spraying.

Phosphamidon is extremely poisonous to birds (Table 22.5), and its use in budworm spraying may have caused severe mortality of some species. One study suggested that as many as 376 000 ruby-crowned kinglets were killed in New Brunswick during the 1975 spray season, mostly by phosphamidon (Pearce and Peakall, 1977). Because they forage high in the canopy, ruby-crowned kinglets are relatively vulnerable to insecticide exposure during an aerial spray. The damage caused to birds was the most important reason why phosphamidon was banned for use against budworm after 1975.

Fenitrothion is less poisonous to birds, but it has a small margin of toxicological safety during operational sprays. While a normal application appears to cause little avian mortality, exposure to a double spray, as commonly occurs with overlapping spray swaths, can be lethal. Studies of white-throated sparrows found much greater mortality and behavioural impairment after an experimental double application of fenitrothion, compared with the normal spray rate (Busby *et al.*, 1989).

Table 22.6 shows the effects of a fenitrothion spray on birds in a forest in Quebec. When interpreting these census data, the trends in the sprayed habitat should be compared with those of the non-sprayed (reference) forest. The comparison is necessary because the "pre-spray" census was conducted in mid-May, when many migratory birds (e.g., most warbler species) had not yet returned to their breeding habitat. Consequently, the total avian abundance in the pre-spray census was smaller than occurs later in the breeding season. If the data are considered in this relative sense, they suggest that the fenitrothion spraying had no obvious effects on the abundance or species composition of the avian community. It is likely, however, that birds were poisoned by fenitrothion during the spray and that the damage was not reflected in the population census for the reasons discussed earlier.

It should also be recognized that a budworm outbreak causes severe damage to the mature forest, with substantial effects on the habitat of wildlife. Table 22.7 illustrates the effects of this habitat change on bird populations. Defoliation by budworm caused relatively little damage to Stand A. The decreased populations of some birds in this stand (e.g., solitary vireo, many warbler species) were caused by decreased food availability because the outbreak had collapsed and budworm is a critical resource. In contrast, Stand B was intensely damaged by defoliation. The habitat changes included many dead trees (called "snags") and a lush growth of understorey plants, including a vigorous regeneration of small fir trees. In this stand, the decreased abundance of some birds (e.g., solitary vireo, Tennessee warbler, black-throated green warbler, blackburnian warbler, and bay-breasted warbler) resulted from the changes in vegetation as well as the reduced availability of larvae as food. Note, in addition, that some birds (e.g., least flycatcher, magnolia warbler, and white-throated sparrow) do well in recently disturbed stands—they benefitted from the habitat associated with budworm damage.

Overall, it appears that the demonstrated ecological effects of post-DDT spray programs against spruce budworm have been relatively short in duration and moderate in intensity (with the exception of the effects of phosphamidon on birds). Residues of such chemicals as fenitrothion and aminocarb are not long lived, and no magnification occurs within the food web. Although substantial mortality has been caused to many non-target species, long-term decreases in their populations have not been documented (bearing in mind that such effects are difficult to demonstrate, particularly at larger spatial scales). For example, although many individual birds have undoubtedly been poisoned by insecticide toxicity, measurable damage to their breeding populations has not been demonstrated.

Spray Policies

Spraying insecticide on forest infested by spruce budworm has various economic benefits associated with protection of conifer trees, an important natural resource. As a result, decision makers and regulators have considered spray programs necessary. Many ecologists, however, come to different conclusions about the benefits and costs of spraying, because they value ecological damage more highly than do resource managers and regulators. Ecologists and environmental activists are not, however, the people who make the decisions about undertaking insecticide spray programs to manage populations of budworm or other pests.

After 1986, fenitrothion was the only synthetic insecticide used against budworm. In 1993, a **risk assessment** of this use (Pauli *et al.*, 1993) concluded that many of its ecotoxicological damages were significant:

> *The weight of evidence accumulated with respect to the identified and potential negative impacts caused by the forestry use of fenitrothion on non-target fauna…and their potential ecological implications, supports the conclusion that the large-scale spraying of fenitrothion for forest pest control, as currently practised operationally, is environmentally unacceptable.*

Partly because of the strong conclusions of this risk assessment, the registration of fenitrothion for use in budworm spray programs in Canada was withdrawn in 1995. This action left *B.t.*, a bacterial insecticide that causes little non-target damage, as the major insecticide available for spraying against spruce budworm.

Possible Alternatives to Spraying Insecticides

In addition to the ecotoxicity caused by insecticides, spray programs against budworm have drawbacks from a forest-management perspective. Within limits, treating infested stands with insecticide maintains fir-spruce forests "alive and green" and therefore available as a resource for the economically important forest industry. However, spraying also maintains good habitat for budworm and, consequently, may prolong its population outbreaks. Agencies that spray insecticides can become "locked" into this pest-management strategy and must continue to spray if the forest resource is to be maintained in an economically viable condition. In the absence of an alternative practice, spraying may be perceived to be the best available short-term strategy. Clearly, however, annual spray programs over extensive areas are not desirable.

TABLE 22.7	Abundance of Birds During and After a Spruce Budworm Outbreak

The data are from a study in New Brunswick. Stand A was monitored for eight years during an infestation (1952–59), and then for six post-outbreak years (to 1965). Stand A suffered little damage to its trees. (The average age of balsam fir trees was 120 years in both sampling periods.) Stand B was censused for five infestation years (1955–59) and for five post-outbreak years (to 1964). Stand B suffered intense damage to its trees. (The balsam fir averaged older than 80 years when the infestation began, but <10 years old afterward because so many mature trees had died.) The bird data are in numbers/40 hectares; pr = present. Only prominent species are listed.

	STAND A		STAND B	
SPECIES	DURING OUTBREAK	POST-OUTBREAK	DURING OUTBREAK	POST-OUTBREAK
Total Bird Abundance	192	95	201	84
Yellow-bellied flycatcher *(Empidonax flavifrons)*	4.6	pr	5.1	0.0
Least flycatcher *(Empidonax minimus)*	3.9	2.8	2.1	15.9
Winter wren *(Troglodytes troglodytes)*	5.9	8.2	2.2	3.3
Swainson's thrush *(Catharus ustulatus)*	15.1	11.9	14.0	8.7
Golden-crowned kinglet *(Regulus satrapa)*	8.9	3.0	2.3	0.0
Ruby-crowned kinglet *(Regulus calendula)*	pr	10.1	1.1	2.7
Solitary vireo *(Vireo solitarius)*	8.3	pr	7.7	0.0
Tennessee warbler *(Vermivora peregrina)*	9.9	0.0	25.7	0.0
Magnolia warbler *(Dendroica magnolia)*	22.0	7.9	1.3	14.9
Yellow-rumped warbler *(Dendroica coronata)*	7.1	1.6	5.1	2.1
Black-throated green warbler *(Dendroica virens)*	11.9	4.2	11.8	4.2
Blackburnian warbler *(Dendroica fusca)*	17.1	5.3	19.5	1.5
Bay-breasted warbler *(Dendroica castanea)*	55.8	16.4	78.2	2.0
Dark-eyed junco *(Junco hyemalis)*	5.9	3.5	8.4	4.1
White-throated sparrow *(Zonotrichia albicollis)*	9.3	5.0	11.4	19.5

Source: Modified from Gage and Miller (1978)

One alternative to spraying insecticides may be the use of management practices aimed at reducing the vulnerability of stands to budworm infestation. For example, relatively tolerant species such as black spruce might be planted extensively. Alternatively, the landscape could be structured so that the total area of mature but vulnerable forest is kept small. If the landscape mosaic was dominated by less vulnerable stands that were harvested by industry at about the rate at which the trees matured, a smaller area would be vulnerable to budworm infestation. It must be recognized, however, that such actions would represent a huge intensification of forest management and would cause enormous changes in the ecological character of the landscape. Little is known about the long-term economic viability or ecological consequences of such changes in forest-management strategy.

Further research into alternative methods of budworm control may yield novel methods that are effective. Some promise has been demonstrated by the release of large numbers of tiny *Trichogramma* wasps that are parasites of budworm, by the use of synthetic hormones that disrupt moulting or mating, and by several other innovative biotechnologies. So far, however, none of these methods have proven sufficiently effective for use in operational programs to reduce epidemic populations of budworm.

If regulators decide that the resource damage caused by spruce budworm must be controlled, it is highly desirable to utilize the least damaging, but still effective, options. At present, effective control appears to require insecticide, with the only available one being *B.t.* If *B.t.* proves to be sufficiently effective, the use of synthetic organic insecticides in budworm spray programs, with their attendant ecotoxicological damage, will be history.

Use of Herbicides in Forestry

The most common use of herbicides in forestry is to keep weeds from competing with young conifers. This use allows economically desirable conifers to grow more rapidly so that harvests can be made more frequently (Newton and Knight, 1981; Freedman, 1995). Minor uses of herbicides in forestry are to prepare sites for planting, to increase visibility along roads by reducing the amount of shrubby vegetation, and to reduce the habitat available for animals that impede conifer regeneration, such as rabbits and hares.

The forestry use of herbicides accounts for a small fraction of the total use of these chemicals, less than about 2% in Canada. However, forestry herbicide use affects the habitat of a diversity of native species, whereas this is much

less the case in agricultural and horticultural use. In 2002, about 243 000 ha of forestland were treated with herbicides in Canada (CCRM, 2005).

As in agriculture and horticulture, there are alternatives to the use of herbicides in forestry. These options include crushing competing vegetation with large machines, manual cutting of weeds with brush saws, prescribed burning, and even using sheep to selectively browse weedy plants. These alternatives can provide a useful degree of weed control, but foresters generally regard them as more expensive and less effective than herbicide use.

There are also some disadvantages of herbicide use in forestry. As with any pesticide, the successful use of herbicides for management requires the selection of an appropriate chemical and its proper application. If the right choices are not made, the weeds will not be adequately controlled, and the conifer crop may be injured. In addition, the suppression of "weeds" affects the useful ecological services that they provide, such as helping to control erosion and reducing losses of soluble nutrients by leaching. Using herbicides also reduces employment opportunities available in manual weed-management programs. For these and other reasons, including the fears that many people have about the potential toxicological risks of pesticides in the environment, the use of herbicides (and insecticides) in Canadian forestry has been very controversial.

Weeds in Forestry

Any disturbance of a forest is followed by a vigorous regeneration involving many species of plants that compete for access to space, nutrients, and moisture. This is true whether the disturbance is caused by a natural fire, insect attack, or by clear-cutting. During the first 10 to 15 years of succession, the plant community is typically dominated by many plants other than the conifers desired by the forest industry. This can be illustrated by examining vegetation data for young clear-cuts in Nova Scotia, in which conifers contributed only 4–9% of the vegetation cover (Table 22.8). Other plants that are not economically desirable (at least not from the forestry perspective) are much more abundant in the regeneration. These "weeds" include ferns, monocotyledonous plants such as sedges and grasses, dicotyledonous herbs such as asters and goldenrods, low shrubs such as raspberries and blackberries, and taller shrubs such as birches, maples, and cherries. The dominance of the site by "undesirable" plants inhibits the growth of commercially desired conifers and provides an economic justification for a weed-management treatment.

Photo 22.3 This is a four-year-old clear-cut of a coniferous forest in Nova Scotia. Almost all of the vegetation is considered (by foresters) to be non-commercial "weeds" that compete with desired conifer seedlings for space, water, and nutrients. The objective of a silvicultural herbicide treatment is to reduce the abundance of weeds, allowing the conifers to grow more quickly.

The effects of competing vegetation on conifer productivity are illustrated by a study of a site in New Brunswick that had been treated with herbicides 28 years previously (MacLean and Morgan, 1983). Prior to the herbicide

| TABLE 22.8 | Dominant Vegetation in Disturbed Forest |

The vegetation was examined in four 4–6-year-old clear-cuts of conifer forest in Nova Scotia. The data represent the range of average plant cover among the four sites, expressed as the percentage of the ground that is obscured by foliage. Because of overlap, values can exceed 100%.

	COVER (%)
Mosses and liverworts	1–10
Lichens	1
Ferns and clubmosses	17–44
Conifers	4–9
Monocots (grasses, sedges)	6–29
Dicots – herbs	15–44
– woody shrubs	11–34
– raspberry	12–32
Total plant cover	103–153

Source: Modified from Freedman (1995)

treatment, the vigorously growing vegetation had been dominated by angiosperm shrubs, which formed a dense, 2-m-tall canopy that overtopped the shorter conifers. The herbicide spray had released the conifers from some of the stresses of competition. The study consequently found, 28 years after the herbicide treatment, that the biomass of balsam fir on the sprayed plots was about three times larger than on an adjacent unsprayed plot. From the forestry perspective, this means that the herbicide treatment allowed a conifer-dominated stand to develop more quickly, shortening the time to the next harvest.

Toxicological and Ecological Effects

The silvicultural objective of herbicide spraying is to manage vegetation by changing its character. After a herbicide treatment in forestry, the abundance of competing vegetation is initially decreased, although it then rapidly recovers. In essence, a herbicide treatment returns the postharvest regeneration (usually post–clear-cutting) to an earlier successional stage, while for several years releasing small conifer plants from some effects of competition. The overall changes in vegetation are illustrated using data from a study in Nova Scotia, in which a substantial recovery occurred within only one growing season after a herbicide treatment (Table 22.9). The regeneration involved species whose seeds colonize sprayed sites, as well as many plants that were not killed by the herbicide. This study found that no species of plants were eliminated from herbicided clearcuts, although there were large differences in their relative abundance between sprayed and reference plots. This is because different species vary in susceptibility to herbicides and in their ability to recover from this disturbance.

Animals that utilize regenerating clear-cuts as habitat are also affected by herbicide treatment. This can be caused by two types of influences: direct toxicity of the pesticide and changes in the character of the habitat.

Compared with many insecticides, herbicides used in forestry (such as 2,4,5-T, 2,4-D, glyphosate, hexazinone, triclopyr, and atrazine) are not very toxic to animals (see Table 22.2 for data on acute toxicity). At exposures encountered by animals during typical forestry uses, the direct toxicological risks from these chemicals are small and probably unimportant. This is particularly true of glyphosate, the most commonly used silvicultural herbicide.

Glyphosate is extremely toxic to most plants, acting by blocking the metabolic synthesis of several essential amino acids. All plants and some microorganisms have this metabolic pathway, but other organisms, including all ani-

TABLE 22.9	Recovery of Vegetation after an Herbicide Treatment

Regenerating clear-cuts were treated with the herbicide glyphosate at two sites in Nova Scotia. The reference ("Ref") plots were not sprayed and illustrate the normal recovery of vegetation after clear-cutting. The sprayed ("Spr") plots were sampled for one year before the herbicide treatment, and the post-spray recovery was then monitored for up to six years. The data are percentage plant cover, measured at the end of the summer.

	PRE-SPRAY	POST-SPRAY			
		YEAR 1	YEAR 2	YEAR 3	YEAR 6
Site 1					
Ref	74	102	140	156	174
Spr	97	36	77	118	145
Site 2					
Ref	97	113	139	153	159
Spr	99	43	124	134	132

Source: Modified from Freedman *et al.* (1993)

mals, obtain these amino acids in the food they eat. Consequently, glyphosate is relatively non-toxic to animals (see Tables 15.2 and 22.2).

Since the toxicity of glyphosate to animals is relatively low, it is unlikely that any animals inhabiting a sprayed clear-cut would be poisoned by exposure to this herbicide. The fact remains, however, that glyphosate causes large changes in habitat because it affects the productivity and biomass of plants. Birds and other animals can be affected by a decreased availability of berries and other plant foods. In addition, the reduced foliage biomass on sprayed clear-cuts sustains smaller populations of insects and spiders, which are important foods for most birds. These indirect effects of herbicide spraying affect birds and other wildlife, even if the animals are not directly poisoned by the herbicide.

A study in Nova Scotia found only small changes in the abundance of birds that were breeding on clear-cuts treated with glyphosate (Table 22.10). The data indicate that the avian abundance decreased between the pre-spray and first post-spray years. However, this change also occurred on the reference (i.e., non-sprayed) plot, suggesting it was caused by a factor, such as bad weather, unrelated to the herbicide treatment. In the second year after spraying, the abundance of birds on the sprayed plots was similar to that in the first post-spray year, while the

abundance on the unsprayed plot increased to about the pre-spray value.

The most common species on the clear-cuts were white-throated sparrow and common yellowthroat (Table 22.10). These had a decreased abundance on both the sprayed and reference plots up to the second year after spraying and then recovered by the fourth post-spray year. On the reference plot, song sparrow and Lincoln's sparrow declined in abundance during the course of the study, whereas on the sprayed plots, they were most abundant in the second and fourth years after spraying. The reference plot became colonized by some new species, including black-and-white warbler, red-eyed vireo, ruby-throated hummingbird, and palm warbler. These species did not invade the sprayed plots because the herbicide treatment caused their habitat to revert to a younger successional stage that was less favourable to these birds.

Most studies of the effects of herbicides on deer and moose have examined the availability of their foods. Broad-leaved shrubs are a preferred food (known as *browse*) for most species of deer, but they are also important weeds in forestry and are therefore a target of herbicide treatments. The quantity of browse, although initially reduced by herbicide spraying, is often increased in the longer term through the regeneration of shrubs. For example, studies in Maine found that several years after spraying, the availability of browse was greater on treated clear-cuts, partly because the height of the shrub canopy was lower, giving white-tailed deer easier access to this food (Newton *et al.*, 1989). This is not always the case, however, and some stud-

Photo 22.4 A helicopter releases a silvicultural application of the herbicide glyphosate to a clear-cut in Nova Scotia.

TABLE 22.10	Populations of Breeding Birds on Herbicide-Treated Clear-Cuts

Average data are presented for four sprayed plots and one reference plot from a study in Nova Scotia. Sprayed plots were treated with glyphosate. The data are pairs of breeding birds per kilometre^2, surveyed for one year before the herbicide treatment (year 0), and then for four post-spray years. Only abundant species are listed here.

SPECIES		SPRAYED PLOTS				REFERENCE PLOT			
	YEAR:	0	1	2	4	0	1	2	4
Alder flycatcher		36	7	17	63	20	40	41	102
American robin		14	21	30	31	10	10	20	10
Red-eyed vireo		0	0	0	4	0	10	31	41
Magnolia warbler		5	5	5	102	0	20	20	143
Palm warbler		0	4	18	53	0	10	51	31
Mourning warbler		50	13	12	19	71	41	20	31
Common yellowthroat		151	140	90	136	122	112	122	163
Lincoln's sparrow		23	20	41	44	20	<1	<1	0
White-throated sparrow		203	118	89	155	143	71	93	163
Dark-eyed junco		42	62	61	69	31	41	61	102
Song sparrow		43	28	60	86	41	20	10	10
American goldfinch		52	24	15	13	61	41	20	20
Total bird abundance		623	447	444	805	539	396	528	836

Source: Modified from MacKinnon and Freedman (1993)

ies have shown that herbicide spraying may decrease habitat quality for deer.

Overall, field research suggests that herbicide use in forestry has relatively small effects on birds and other wildlife that utilize clear-cuts as habitat. Other disturbances associated with forestry cause much larger effects on wildlife, particularly clear-cutting and plantation establishment (see Chapter 23).

The hazards to humans from herbicide use in forestry have also been intensely scrutinized. The concerns include occupational risks for people engaged in spraying or working in recently sprayed areas, as well as possible risks for the general population. These issues are highly controversial and are not fully resolved. Much of the concern has focused on phenoxy herbicides such as 2,4,5-T and 2,4-D, partly because 2,4,5-T may contain a trace contamination of TCDD, an extremely toxic type of dioxin. However, the use of other herbicides, such as glyphosate, is also controversial.

It is somewhat reassuring to know that many scientists believe that herbicides can be used safely in forestry (and in agriculture and horticulture), provided the instructions for their use are followed carefully. Many scientists also believe that herbicides do not cause undue risks to sprayers or people living near the treated areas. These are among the reasons why governments have registered these pesticides for uses that are economically beneficial—they allow greater productivity of both agricultural and forest crops. It must be remembered, however, that scientists have not achieved a full consensus on these issues. Partly for this reason, the use of pesticides in forestry and for other purposes continues to be controversial.

Integrated Pest Management

Pesticides are commonly used in agriculture, horticulture, and forestry. It is clear from this fact that most politicians, bureaucrats, and resource managers—and many scientists—have decided that the environmental "costs" associated with the use of pesticides are "acceptable," in view of economic benefits that are achieved. It is debatable, however, whether reliance on pesticide use is desirable over the long term. This is particularly true for those pesticides that are toxic to a broad spectrum of organisms. Most people would prefer that less reliance be placed on such non-specific methods of pest control.

A much preferable approach is known as **integrated pest management (IPM)**, which employs an array of complementary tactics toward achieving pest control, with the aim of fewer environmental and health risks. Elements of an IPM system can include the following:

- use of natural predators, parasites, and other biological agents that can help to control a pest, while causing few non-target damages

- use of crop varieties that are resistant to pests

- management of habitat to make it less suitable for pests

- careful monitoring of pest abundance, so control measures are undertaken only when necessary

- use of pesticides—but only if absolutely required as a component of an integrated strategy of pest management

A successful IPM program can greatly reduce, but is not necessarily able to eliminate, a reliance on pesticides. For example, for many years the cultivation of cotton in the southern U.S. has relied on the intensive application of insecticides against pests such as the boll weevil. Widespread use of an IPM system to control this insect in Texas cottonfields reduced insecticide use from 8.8 million kg in 1964 to 1.05 million kg in 1976 (Bottrell and Smith, 1982). However, some insecticide use against this pest has remained necessary.

Wherever possible, IPM systems utilize control methods that are as specific as possible to the pest and so avoid or greatly reduce non-target damage. Some of the best examples of such specific methods involve **biological control** (i.e., the use of a biological agent). The usefulness of biological control can be illustrated with the following successes controlling introduced agricultural pests (Freedman, 1995).

The cottony-cushion scale (*Icyera purchasi*) is a sap-sucking insect that was accidentally introduced to the U.S., where it became a serious threat to citrus agriculture. Research in its native Australia discovered that the pest was naturally controlled by certain insect predators and parasites. In 1888, two of its predators, a lady beetle and a parasitic fly, were introduced to California. This allowed virtually total control over this potentially disastrous pest. Unfortunately, this biological control was disrupted when DDT and other broad-spectrum insecticides were used to deal with other orchard pests beginning in the late 1940s.

Canadian Focus 22.2

Municipal Bans on Pesticide Use in Horticulture

Some Canadian municipalities have passed or are considering enacting bans on the routine use of pesticides to manage lawns and gardens. This has come as a response to the concerns of many citizens about the exposure of humans and pets to pesticide residues in the urban environment. Because most pesticide use in horticulture is essentially for cosmetic purposes and alternative pest-management practices are generally available, it is believed that no substantial economic damage would be caused by the pesticide bans.

For example, in 2000, the Halifax Regional Municipality enacted a bylaw that prohibits the use of horticultural pesticides within 50 m of any park or playground, daycare centre, senior-citizen residence, public school, university, church, or hospital. In the remaining places where pesticides can still be used, homeowners using the chemicals are required to seek a permit and, if granted, to post a prominent sign with a skull-and-crossbones symbol for one day before and four days after the application. In 2004, 3365 permit applications were received, of which 99% were to use insecticide against chinch bugs (*Blissus leucopterus*) in lawns. About 98% of the applications were made by lawn-care companies on behalf of their clients, and 82% were approved. The Halifax bylaw is controversial and was resisted by lawn-care companies, some gardeners, and other interests. The bylaw has, however, been widely lauded as a step forward in the broader environmental sense. Similar bylaws are being enacted by many other Canadian municipalities.

In 1991, for example, the town of Hudson, Quebec, passed a bylaw regulating horticultural pesticide use. Opponents of that law included lawn-care companies and pesticide manufacturers, and they were successful in having it struck down by the Quebec Court of Appeal. In 2000, however, the Supreme Court of Canada reversed that decision and made it legal for municipalities to regulate pesticide use on lands within their jurisdiction. It is likely that the use of pesticides for cosmetic horticultural purposes will become increasingly restricted in Canada and in many other countries as well.

St. John's wort (*Hypericum perforatum*), a common weed, is toxic to cattle. This plant became a serious pest in North American pastures after it was introduced from Europe. In 1943, two leaf beetles that feed on this plant were released in North America, and this pest is no longer an important problem.

The prickly pear cactus (*Opuntia stricta*) was imported to Australia from North America and grown as an ornamental plant. It escaped and became a serious weed in rangelands. This pest was controlled by the introduction of one of its herbivores, a species of moth whose larvae feed on the cactus.

Ragwort (*Senecio jacobea*) is a Eurasian plant that has been introduced to North America, South America, and Australia. It has become an important weed in rangeland because it crowds out native plants and is toxic to cattle. Several of the Eurasian herbivores of ragwort are now being used to control its abundance, including the cinnabar moth, ragwort flea beetle, and ragwort seed fly.

The screw-worm fly (*Callitroga hominivorax*) causes serious damage to cattle when its larvae feed on open wounds. This pest has been controlled in some areas through the release of large numbers of male flies that were reared in laboratories and sterilized by irradiation. Because female screw-worm flies mate only once, copulation with a sterile male results in unsuccessful reproduction. If this happens to enough females, the abundance of the pest decreases to an acceptable level.

Unfortunately, biological control may not be suitable for all pest problems. In fact, biological control has not succeeded in controlling most of the pests for which it has been attempted. For example, the list of failures includes forest pests such as spruce budworm and gypsy moth. Researchers have investigated the potential for controlling budworm using pest-specific biological methods, such as bacteria, viruses, and other agents of budworm-specific diseases; wasps that parasitize and kill budworm larvae; and the use of sex and developmental hormones to disrupt the mating and growth of the pest. Some of these biological control methods have shown promise. However, they do not yet achieve a consistent kill of budworm and are relatively expensive. For these reasons, they are not considered ready for routine use against this important pest.

One viable alternative to the broadcast spraying of synthetic insecticides to control budworm has been found—an insecticide derived from the bacterium *B.t.* (discussed earlier). Research into other biological controls continues, and some methods may prove successful. These would allow managers to develop an effective, integrated pest-management system that does not rely on broadcast spraying of insecticides, even relatively specific ones such as *B.t.*

At the present time, however, it appears that society will continue to rely heavily on pesticide use in intensively managed systems in agriculture and forestry. This will happen even though the intensive systems cause ecological damage (partly because this damage is not properly accounted for as an economic "cost").

It is important that additional research is supported in order to develop viable methods of biological control and other elements of IPM systems. This is necessary if the present reliance on the pesticide treadmill is to be replaced with less damaging methods of pest management. Such a change would deliver substantial benefits to society, because the agricultural and forestry systems that we require for sustenance could be managed on a more ecologically sustainable basis. In part, this will require that more attention is directed to the ecological damage caused by the intensive use of pesticides.

Because of this damage, it is highly desirable that effective, non-pesticidal alternatives to pest control are discovered as quickly as possible. Until this happens, pesticide use should be reduced to the lowest levels that continue to effectively control the pests. Some researchers have recently argued that pesticide use in North America is much greater than necessary and that it could be decreased without causing a significant adverse effect on crop yields. In fact, the European community has already passed legislation requiring that agricultural pesticide use be reduced by half, and many pesticides have been banned. More serious consideration should also be given to such actions in Canada.

Conclusions

Pesticides are a wide range of substances that are used to gain an advantage over species that cause diseases or are pests in agriculture, forestry, or horticulture. However, the use of many pesticides carries risks of causing important damage to human health or the environment. Pesticides have become an integrated component of most of the intensive systems by which foods and other crops are grown, and there are not yet good replacements for all of their uses. For this reason, the use of pesticides will continue into the foreseeable future. Nevertheless, it is important that more research be done to find effective ways of reducing the dependence on pesticides, especially on integrated pest-management systems and on means of biological control of particular pests. In the meantime, it is important that pesticide use be reduced to the lowest degree possible and that the most damaging chemicals be withdrawn from legal use.

Key Terms

pesticide	drift
non-target organism	persistence
broad-spectrum pesticide	bioconcentration
non-target damage	food-web magnification
fungicide	(food-web concentration,
herbicide	biomagnification)
insecticide	risk assessment
vector	integrated pest management
pesticide treadmill	(IPM)
	biological control

Questions for Review

1. Classify pesticides according to their intended targets and also by their major chemical groups.

2. What are "pests"? Why do people consider it necessary to manage their abundance in agriculture, horticulture, forestry, and public health?

3. What characteristics of organochlorines have caused them to become global contaminants? Why do they pose special toxicological risks for top predators?

4. If spruce budworm is a native insect, why is the damage it causes to conifer forest considered to be a problem?

Questions for Discussion

1. Identify and compare the benefits and environmental risks associated with pesticide use in agriculture, horticulture, and forestry.

2. Are there effective alternatives to the continued use of pesticides? Consider the roles of integrated pest management, biological controls, and other options.

3. For many common uses of pesticides, there are already alternative ways of managing the targeted pest. For example, weeds in a lawn can often be controlled by digging them out, rather than by using a herbicide. Pest rodents could be trapped instead of killed with a rodenticide. What do you think should be the key considerations when deciding whether to use pesticides or alternative means of control in such cases?

4. Some people believe that the use of pesticides should be allowed only in extreme cases, for example to save human lives or to prevent a food catastrophe. Most pesticide use, however, is much more routine than this. What do you think about this issue? Should it be made more difficult for people to use pesticides? Or should farmers and other potential users have freedom to make their own choices about pesticide use?

Exploring Issues

1. A large corporation is seeking permission from the government to market a new insecticide in Canada. You are a wildlife biologist and have been asked to recommend studies to identify whether unacceptable damages would be caused to animals, plants, or ecosystems by the new insecticide. How would you design such a study? What specific questions would you want to answer?

2. You are an environmental scientist and have been asked to provide expert advice about a proposed new municipal bylaw regulating the cosmetic use of pesticides in horticulture. The bylaw itself would be similar to the one used in Halifax, as described in Canadian Focus 22.2. From the environmental perspective, what would you consider to be the benefits and problems with the proposed bylaw?

References

Agriculture Canada. 1993. *Registration Status of Fenitrothion Insecticide*. Ottawa: Agriculture Canada, Food Production and Inspection Branch. Discussion Report 093-01.

Armstrong, J.A. 1985. Spruce budworm control program in eastern Canada. In: *Advances in Spruce Budworms Research*. Ottawa: Canadian Forestry Service. pp. 384–385.

Bishop, C. and D.V. Weseloh. 1990. *Contaminants in Herring Gull Eggs from the Great Lakes*. Ottawa: Environment Canada, State of the Environment Reporting. SOE Fact Sheet 90-2.

Blais, J.R. 1985. The ecology of the eastern spruce budworm: a review and discussion. In: *Recent Advances in Spruce Budworms Research*. Ottawa: Canadian Forestry Service. pp. 49–59.

Bottrell, D.G. and R.F. Smith. 1982. Integrated pest management. *Environ. Sci. Technol.*, **16**: 282A–288A.

Briggs, S.A. 1992. *Basic Guide to Pesticides: Their Characteristics and Hazards*. Washington: Taylor & Francis.

Busby, D.G., L.M. White, P.A. Pearce, and P. Mineau. 1989. Fenitrothion effects on forest songbirds: a critical new look. In: *Environmental Effects of Fenitrothion Use in Forestry*. Dartmouth, NS: Environment Canada, Conservation and Protection. pp. 43–108.

Canadian Council of Forest Ministers. 1995. *Compendium of Canadian Forestry Statistics, 1994*. Ottawa: Canadian Council of Forest Ministers.

Canadian Council of Forest Ministers (CCRM). 2005. *Compendium of Canadian Forestry Statistics*. Ottawa, ON: CCRM. nfdp.ccfm.org/compendium/index_e.php

Carson, R. 1962. *Silent Spring*. Boston: Houghton-Mifflin.

Cooper, K. 1991. Effects of pesticides on wildlife. In: W.C. Hayes and E.R. Laws, eds. *Handbook of Pesticide Toxicology. Vol. 1, General Principles*. San Diego, CA: Academic. pp. 463–496.

Crawford, H.S., R.W. Titterington, and D.T. Jennings. 1983. Bird predation and spruce budworm populations. *J. Forestry*, **81**: 433–435.

Edwards, C.A. 1975. *Persistent Pesticides in the Environment*. Cleveland: CRC Press.

Ennis, T. and E.T.N. Caldwell. 1991. Spruce budworm, chemical and biological control. In: L.P.S. van der Geest and H.H. Evenhuis, eds. *Tortricid Pests, Their Biology, Natural Enemies, and Control*. Amsterdam: Elsevier. pp. 621–641.

Environment Canada. 1993. *Toxic Contaminants in the Environment: Persistent Organochlorines*. Ottawa: Environment Canada. State of the Environment Reporting.

Environment Canada. 1996. *The State of Canada's Environment, 1996*. Ottawa: Government of Canada.

Environmental Protection Agency. 2003. *The Great Lakes; An Environmental Atlas and Resource Book*. Washington, DC: U.S. Environmental Protection Agency. www.epa.gov/glnpo/atlas/gl-fact1.html.

Freedman, B. 1995. *Environmental Ecology*. 2nd ed. San Diego, CA: Academic.

Freedman, B., R. Morash, and D. MacKinnon. 1993. Short-term changes in vegetation after the silvicultural spraying of glyphosate herbicide onto regenerating clear-cuts in Nova Scotia, Canada. *Can. J. For. Res.*, **23**: 2300–2311.

Gage, S.H. and C.A. Miller. 1978. *A Long-Term Bird Census in Spruce Budworm-Prone Balsam Fir Habitats in Northwestern New Brunswick*. Fredericton, NB: Maritimes Forest Research Centre. Inf. Rep. M-X-84.

Gianessi, L.P. and M.B. Marselli. 2000. *Pesticide Use in U.S. Crop Production*. Washington, DC: National Centre for Food and Agricultural Policy.

Gianessi, L.P. and S. Sankula. 2003. *The Value of Herbicides in U.S. Crop Production*. Washington, DC: National Centre for Food and Agricultural Policy.

Grossbard, E. and D. Atkinson (eds.). 1985. *The Herbicide Glyphosate*. London: Butterworths.

Hayes, W.J. 1991. Introduction. In: W.C. Hayes and E.R. Laws, eds. *Handbook of Pesticide Toxicology. Vol. 1, General Principles*. San Diego, CA: Academic. pp. 1–37.

Kamrin, M.A. (ed.). 1997. *Pesticide Profiles: Toxicity, Environmental Impact, and Fate*. Boca Raton, FL: Lewis Publishers.

Kettela, E. 1983. *A Cartographic History of Spruce Budworm Defoliation from 1967 to 1981 in Eastern North America*. Fredericton, NB: Canadian Forestry Service. Maritimes Forest Research Centre. Inf. Rep. DPC-X-14.

Kingsbury, P.D. and B.B. McLeod. 1981. *Fenitrothion and Forest Avifauna Studies on the Effects of High Dosage Applications*. Sault Ste. Marie, ON: Canadian Forestry Service. Forest Pest Management Institute. Rep. FPM-X-43.

Krieger, R. 2001. *Handbook of Pesticide Toxicology*. 2nd ed. San Diego, CA: Academic Press.

MacKay, D., W.Y. Shiu, and K.-C. Ma. 1997. *Illustrated Handbook of Physical-Chemical Properties and Environmental Fate for Organic Chemicals: Pesticide Chemicals*. Boca Raton, FL: Lewis Publishers.

Mackinnon, D. and B. Freedman. 1993. Effects of silvicultural use of the herbicide glyphosate on breeding birds of regenerating clear-cuts in Nova Scotia, Canada. *J. Appl. Ecol.*, **30**: 395–406.

MacLean, D.A. 1988. Effects of spruce budworm outbreaks on vegetation, structure, and succession of balsam fir forests on Cape Breton Island, Canada. In: M.J.A. Werger, P.J.M. van der Aart, H.J. During, and J.J.A. Verhoeven, eds. *Plant Form and Vegetation Structure*. The Hague, The Netherlands: SPB Academic. pp. 253–261.

MacLean, D.A. 1990. Impact of forest pests and fire on stand growth and timber yield: implications for forest management planning. *Can. J. For. Res*, **20**: 391–404.

MacLean, D.A. and M.G. Morgan. 1983. Long-term growth and yield response of young fir to manual and chemical release from shrub competition. *For. Chron.*, **59**: 177–183.

McEwen, F.L. and G.R. Stephenson. 1979. *The Use and Significance of Pesticides in the Environment*. New York: Wiley.

Millikin, R.L. 1990. Effects of fenitrothion on the arthropod food of tree-foraging forest songbirds. *Can. J. Zool.*, **68**: 2235–2242.

Milne, G.W.A. 1994. *CRC Handbook of Pesticides*. Boca Raton, FL: CRC Press.

Mineau, P. 1993. *The Hazard of Carbofuran to Birds and Other Vertebrate Wildlife*. Ottawa: Environment Canada, Canadian Wildlife Service, Wildlife Toxicology Section. Tech. Rep. No. 177.

Mineau, P. 1999. *Pesticides and Wild Birds*. Ottawa, ON: Canadian Wildlife Service. www.hww.ca/hww2.asp?id=230

Moriarty, F. 1999. *Ecotoxicology: The Study of Pollutants in Ecosystems*. 3rd ed. London: Academic.

Morris, R.F., W.F. Cheshire, C.A. Miller, and D.G. Mott. 1958. The numerical response of avian and mammalian predators during a gradation of the spruce budworm. *Ecology*, **39**: 487–494.

National Research Council (NRC). 1986. *Pesticide Resistance*. NRC. Washington: National Academy Press.

National Research Council. Committee on Pest and Pathogen Control through Management of Biological Control Agents and Enhanced Cycles and Natural Processes. 1996. *Ecologically Based Pest Management: New Solutions for a New Century*. Washington, DC: National Academy Press.

Newton, M. and F.B. Knight. 1981. *Handbook of Weed and Insect Control Chemicals for Forest Resource Managers*. Beaverton, OR: Timber.

Newton, M., E.C. Cole, R.A. Lautenschlager, D.E. White, and M.L. McCormack. 1989. Browse availability after conifer release in Maine's spruce-fir forests. *J. Wildl. Manage.*, **53**: 643–649.

Norheim, G., L. Somme, and G. Holt. 1982. Mercury and persistent chlorinated hydrocarbons in Antarctic birds. *Environ. Pollut., (Ser. A)*, **28**: 233–240.

Ostaff, D.P. 1985. Quantifying effects of spruce budworm damage in eastern Canada. In: *Recent Advances in Spruce Budworms Research*. Ottawa: Canadian Forestry Service. pp. 247–248.

Ostaff, D.P. and D.A. MacLean. 1989. Spruce budworm populations, defoliation, and changes in stand condition during an uncontrolled spruce budworm outbreak on Cape Breton Island, Nova Scotia. *Can. J. For. Res.*, **19**: 1077–1086.

Pauli, B.D., S.B. Holmes, R.J. Sebastien, and G.P. Rawn. 1993. *Fenitrothion Risk Assessment*. Ottawa: Canadian Wildlife Service. Tech. Rep. Ser. No. 165.

Peakall, D.B. 1990. Prospects for the peregrine falcon, *Falco peregrinus*, in the nineties. *Can. Field-Nat.*, **104**: 168–173.

Pearce, P.A. and D.B. Peakall. 1977. The impact of fenitrothion on bird populations in New Brunswick. NRCC **16073**: 299–305. Ottawa: National Research Council of Canada.

Pesticide News. 2003. *European Union Pesticide Clear Out*. www.pan-uk.org/pestnews/pn57/pn57p8.htm

Pimentel, D. (ed.). 1997. *Techniques for Reducing Pesticide Use: Economic and Environmental Benefits*. New York, NY: John Wiley & Sons.

Pimentel, D. and H. Lehman (eds.). 1992. *The Pesticide Question: Environment, Economics, and Ethics*. New York: Chapman & Hall.

Pimentel, D., H. Acquay, M. Biltonen, P. Rice, M. Silva, J. Nelson, V. Lipner, S. Giordano, A. Horowitz, and M. D'Amare. 1992. Environmental and economic costs of pesticide use. *Bioscience*, **42**: 750–760.

Pimentel, D., L. McLaughlin, A. Zepp, B. Lakitan, T. Kraus, P. Kleinman, F. Vancini, W.J. Roach, E. Graap, W.S. Keeton, and S. Selig. 1991. Environmental and economic effects of reducing pesticide use. *Bioscience*, **41**: 402–409.

Rozencranz, A. 1988. Bhopal, transnational corporations, and hazardous technologies. *Ambio*, **17**: 336–341.

Sassman, J., R. Pienta, M. Jacobs, and J. Cioffi. 1984. *Pesticide Background Statements. Vol. 1, Herbicides*. Washington: USDA Forest Service.

Stenersen, J. 2004. *Chemical Pesticides: Mode of Action and Toxicology*. Boca Raton, FL: CRC Press.

Varty, I.W. 1975. Side effects of pest control projects on terrestrial arthropods other than the target species. In: M.L. Prebble, ed. *Aerial Control of Forest Insects in Canada*. Ottawa: Department of the Environment. pp. 266–275.

Winston, M.L. 1997. *Nature Wars: People vs. Pests*. Cambridge, MA: Harvard University Press.

World Resources Institute. 2005. *Earth Trends. The Environmental Information Portal*. Washington, DC: WRI.

Wurster, D.H., C.F. Wurster, and W.N. Strickland. 1965. Bird mortality following DDT spray for Dutch elm disease. *Ecology*, **46**: 488–499.

Informative Websites

Biological Control: A Guide to Natural Enemies in North America. www.nysaes.cornell.edu/ent/biocontrol/

From Cornell University comes this guide that provides photographs and descriptions of biological control agents of insect, disease, and weed pests in North America.

CropLife America. www.croplifeamerica.org/

CropLife America is the not-for-profit trade organization representing the major manufacturers, formulators, and distributors of pest-control products.

Environment Canada. The Green Lane. www.ec.gc.ca/envhome.html

This comprehensive site from Environment Canada features pages on climate change, nature, and clean air and water, as well as links to publications, news releases, and related sites.

Health Canada. www.hc-sc.gc.ca/

Health Canada is the agency of the federal government with the responsibility of registering pesticides for use in Canada.

Hinterland Who's Who. Pesticides and Wild Birds. www.hww.ca/hww2.asp?id=230

Environment Canada hosts this site, which explains what pesticides are and their effects on birds.

Iowa State Entomology Index: Integrated Pest Management. www.ent.iastate.edu/List/integrated_pest_management.html

Visit this site to find links to dozens of pest management–related sites.

National Pesticide Information Centre.
http://npic.orst.edu/

The NPIC is a collaboration of Oregon State University and the U.S. Environmental Protection Service, and is intended to provide easily accessible information about pesticides and their risks to health and the environment.

U.S. Environmental Protection Agency. Pesticides.
www.epa.gov/pesticides/

The EPA has an excellent website with information about pesticides and their environmental effects.

World Wildlife Fund—Canada. www.wwf.ca

The World Wildlife Fund is one of Canada's leading environmental organizations. The website explains the WWF's perspective on environmental problems associated with pesticides and suggests ways of reducing their use.

CBC **Canadian Case 4**

Oily Birds

Massive oil spills in the ocean, usually caused by a wrecked tanker ship or drilling platform, always engender extremely high-profile controversy and public concern and often require very costly clean-up efforts. Because these industrial accidents cause enormous damage to public and political goodwill, while also having massive environmental and economic costs, the marine shipping industry has invested huge sums of money to construct tankers and coastal facilities (such as petroleum refineries) that are relatively safe to operate. Coastal nations have also enacted strict laws to regulate the marine shipping industry so that it can safely transport economically critical petroleum and its refined products to different places around the world.

It is therefore astonishing to learn that deliberate pollution of the marine environment is still a common occurrence. This kind of intentional pollution usually involves the dumping of crude oil or refined products (such as heavy fuel oil) from tankers or other large ships that routinely clean their ballast and oil-storage tanks at sea, even though this procedure is illegal. By law, the shipping operators are required to perform these functions at ports equipped with facilities to receive and clean the oily wastes. However, by illegally dumping while at sea, the operators can save the money associated with the fees charged for anti-pollution services. They also save the valuable time required to dispose of oily wastes in port — this time is worth considerable money to the shipping companies that are paid to deliver and off-load their cargoes as quickly as possible.

For these reasons, marine ships may dump their oily wastes at sea while in transit between ports. Unfortunately, this unlawful practice may cause terrible ecological damage, particularly if large numbers of seabirds become fouled by contact with the spilled oil. This is, for example, a remarkably common occurrence off the southern coast of Newfoundland. A study released in 2004 suggested that as many as 400 000 seabirds, mostly murres, may be killed annually as a result of foul-

ing by oil deliberately spilled by marine shipping. This is a huge kill of seabirds, and along with the excessive hunting of some species, it is causing their populations to rapidly decline.

It is sobering to know that this kind of wanton and deliberate pollution is happening in spite of the existence of strong laws intended to prevent the dumping of petroleum at sea and regardless of public revulsion about the ecological damage that it causes. In coastal waters under Canadian jurisdiction, the enforcement problem appears to be related to several factors:

- A weak and inconsistent effort by government agencies to detect ships that are violating our marine-protection laws.
- Conflict between federal agencies that have overlapping jurisdictional interests.
- Courts that are unwilling to assign large financial penalties to convicted offenders.

Considering the terrible ecological damage that is caused by the illegal dumping of oil in Canadian coastal waters, one might think that these seemingly minor administrative problems could be overcome so as to allow for effective enforcement of our anti-pollution laws. Unfortunately, this is not yet happening. Canadian politicians and their governmental administrators have not yet responded to the clearly expressed demands of Canadians to stop marine oil pollution. It appears that this important environmental problem can only be resolved by effective public advocacy to embarrass the responsible bureaucrats and politicians and to compel them to enforce the laws that Canada has in place to protect the environmental quality and biota of our coastal waters.

The issue of illegal dumping of oil into coastal waters by marine shipping is explored in the accompanying CBC video resource.

Questions

1. There is abundant evidence that commercial shipping interests continue to pollute the marine environment with petroleum and other noxious substances? Why are they not more environmentally responsible?

Canadian Case 4

2. The accompanying CBC video resource, *Oily Birds*, suggests that Canada has a carefully thought-out set of laws to prevent the dumping of petroleum into coastal waters and to severely prosecute convicted offenders. Why do you think this system is not working well to prevent the pollution?

Video Resource

"Oily Birds," CBC The National, November 24, 2003.

Selected References

Environment Canada. 2005. Birds Oiled at Sea.
http://www.atl.ec.gc.ca/boas/index_e.html
International Tanker Owners Pollution Federation Ltd. 2005. Effects of Marine Oil Spills.
http://www.itopf.com/effects.html

Environmental Effects of Forestry

23

CHAPTER OBJECTIVES

After completing this chapter, you will be able to

1. Explain how forest harvesting removes nutrient capital from the site.
2. Outline how forestry can damage aquatic ecosystems, and how many of those effects can be avoided.
3. Describe how clear-cutting affects biodiversity.
4. Describe the special qualities of old-growth forest, and how they are affected by timber harvesting.
5. Discuss the ecological consequences of the conversion of natural forests into intensively managed plantations.
6. Explain the concept of integrated forest management.

CHAPTER OUTLINE

Introduction

Forestry includes both the harvesting of trees and the management of post-harvest succession to foster the regeneration of another forest. Forest science guides these activities by providing an understanding of the environmental factors that affect timber productivity and regeneration. The broad goal of commercial forestry is to provide sustainable harvests of tree biomass that can be used to manufacture lumber, paper, and other industrial products.

Forestry is an extremely important economic activity in many parts of the world. This is particularly true in Canada, where an enormous industrial enterprise depends on a continuous supply of tree biomass for the production of products that have a great economic value ($71 billion in 2004; see Chapter 14 for forestry-related economics).

Of course, to achieve the great economic benefits of commercial forestry, trees must be harvested from extensive areas of mature forest. In Canada, **clear-cutting** is by far the most common method of forest harvesting. In clear-cutting, all of the economically useful trees are harvested at the same time. In recent years, clear-cutting has accounted for about 91% of the annual harvest in Canada (refer to Table 14.13).

It is important to understand, however, that clear-cutting is not the same as **deforestation**. Deforestation involves the permanent conversion of a forest into some other kind of ecosystem, such as an agricultural or urbanized land-use. In Canada and most other industrialized countries, clear-cutting is generally followed by the regeneration of another forest. In fact, it is common practice in Canada to manage the post-harvest succession to speed up the rate of regeneration. This means that the next harvest can be made after a relatively short time, allowing more profit to be made. (This period of time is known as a harvest *rotation*.) In this sense, commercial forestry as it is usually practised does not result in a net deforestation—if appropriately managed, the forest resource is not depleted. Even though about 1 million ha of forest are harvested each year in Canada, the rate of net deforestation is essentially zero (refer to Table 14.12).

Harvesting can be viewed as a type of disturbance of the forest ecosystem, followed by regeneration. Other forestry-related disturbances are associated with silvicultural activities, such as preparing the site for planting, thinning dense stands, and applying herbicide or insecticide to deal with pest problems. **Silviculture** is practised over an extensive area in Canada. For instance, about 634 million tree seedlings were planted on 428 400 ha of

clear-cuts in 2002, equivalent to 44% of the area harvested. (The other 56% regenerated naturally, without planting.) Some of the planted areas are managed quite intensively to develop **plantations**. These are highly productive tree farms, which can be viewed as agroforestry systems in which trees are cultivated. Because plantations are tree-dominated ecosystems, they are considered to be forest, although they lack many of the ecological and aesthetic values of a natural forest.

Even though the normal practice of forestry in Canada and other developed countries does not result in deforestation, important ecological changes still result, some of them damaging to the environment. These changes can have important consequences for the renewability of the timber resource, for other economic resources such as hunted animals and recreational opportunities, and for ecological values such as indigenous biodiversity.

In this chapter we examine some of the ecological damage associated with the harvesting and management of forests, with a focus on effects on site capability, hunted animals, and biodiversity. Some additional effects of forestry are discussed in other chapters. (We examined effects of pesticide spraying in Chapter 22 and implications of disturbance for carbon storage and CO_2 emissions in Chapter 17, and we will look at effects of tropical deforestation on global biodiversity in Chapter 26.)

Forest Harvesting and Site Capability

In Chapter 14, we defined *site capability* as the potential of land to sustain the productivity of agricultural crops. Site capability is also relevant to forestry, being an indicator of the ability of land to sustain the productivity of trees. Site capability is a complex attribute, involving the amounts of nutrients and organic matter in soil, the availability of moisture, and other factors influencing plant growth. These factors are influenced by soil type, climate, drainage, rates of nutrient cycling and decomposition, and the kinds of plant and microbial communities present.

The ability of soil to supply plants with nutrients is a critical aspect of site capability in forestry. In large part, this ecological function depends on the **nutrient capital** of the site, or the amounts of nutrients present in the soil, in living vegetation, and in dead organic matter. When trees are harvested from an area, the large amount of nutrients in their biomass is also removed. This can deplete the nutrient capital of the site.

Forests may be harvested using a variety of methods, which vary in the amount of biomass and nutrients removed from the site. **Selection harvesting** is a relatively "soft," non-intensive system because it involves the harvest of only some of the trees from a stand, leaving others behind, with the forest remaining substantially intact. The most intensive kinds of harvests are *clear-cuts*, in which all economically useful trees are removed from an area. The smallest clear-cuts, typically involving a hectare or less of forest, are known as *group-selection harvests*. More typically, clear-cuts entail the harvesting of trees from larger areas, on the order of 20–100 ha. The largest clear-cuts can extend over hundreds, and even thousands, of hectares. Such extensive operations, however, are unusual, being generally associated with the salvaging of trees damaged by wildfire, windstorm, or insect infestation.

There are also some less intensive methods of clear-cutting. A *shelterwood harvest* is a staged clear-cut, in which some larger trees of the economically most desirable species are left standing during the initial cut. These provide a seed source and a partially shaded environment that encourages natural regeneration. Once regeneration is well underway, the large "leave" trees are harvested. *Strip-cuts* are another staged harvest, in which long, narrow clear-cuts are made at intervals, with uncut forest left in between to provide a source of seed to regenerate desirable tree species in the cut strips. Once the regeneration is established, another strip-cut is made, again leaving intact forest on one of the sides. This system of progressive strip-cutting continues until all the forest in the management block (i.e., in the specific area being managed this way) has been harvested. Typically, areas are harvested in three to four strips. To regenerate trees on the final strips, foresters may rely on so-called *advanced regeneration*—that is, on small individuals of tree species that existed in the stand prior to harvesting and survived the disturbance of clear-cutting. Alternatively, they may plant the last strip with seedlings.

Clear-cutting systems also vary in how intensively the biomass of individual trees is harvested. The usual *stem-only* harvest involves the removal of tree trunks, leaving the roots, stumps, and logging "slash" (i.e., cut branches and foliage) on the site. The harvested logs can then be processed into lumber, plywood, or pulp for manufacturing paper. A *whole-tree harvest* is more intensive because it takes all of the above-ground biomass of the trees, including branches and foliage. Whole-tree harvests recover considerably more biomass than stem-only harvests. This can be an advantage if the wood will be used as a source of energy (i.e., as fuel).

Photo 23.1 This photo shows a three-year-old shelterwood cut of hardwood forest in Nova Scotia. About 60% of the trees were removed during the harvest, but many of the "best" trees were left to grow into relatively high-quality sawlogs and to shed seeds to promote natural regeneration of the site. This silvicultural treatment produces a complex habitat that supports a mixture of birds and other wildlife typical of both clear-cuts and mature forest.

Nutrient Losses During Harvesting

Although intensive harvests such as whole-tree clear-cuts increase the yield of biomass, they also increase the removal of nutrients. Some scientists have suggested that the nutrient removals associated with successive whole-tree harvests could degrade the capability of sites to sustain tree productivity. The problem would be especially severe if intensive harvests were conducted over short rotations. This might not allow sufficient time for the nutrient capital to recover through natural inputs, such as precipitation, nitrogen fixation, and weathering of minerals in rocks (Figure 23.1).

FIGURE 23.1 | Effects of Harvest Intensity and Length of Rotation on Nutrient Capital

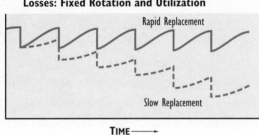

(a) Variation in Rotation Length: Fixed Utilization

Long Rotation: e.g., 100 y

Nutrient Loss in Harvested Materials

Short Rotation: e.g., 50 y

TIME→

(b) Variation in Utilization: Fixed Rotation Length

Stem Harvesting

Whole-Tree Harvesting

TIME→

(c) Variation in Rates of Replacement of Nutrient Losses: Fixed Rotation and Utilization

Rapid Replacement

Slow Replacement

TIME→

MAGNITUDE OF THE SITE NUTRIENT CAPITAL →

Diagram (a) suggests that a relatively long rotation can allow harvested nutrients to be replenished by inputs through rainfall, weathering of minerals, nitrogen fixation, and other means. An adequate post-harvest recovery period means that harvesting is sustainable with respect to nutrient capital. Under the shorter rotation (dashed line), the harvested nutrients are not totally replenished between successive clear-cuts, resulting in a degradation of site nutrient capital. Site capability can also be degraded by an increase in the intensity of the harvest. This is illustrated in diagram (b), in which a whole-tree clear-cut removes twice as much nutrient as a stem-only harvest. Diagram (c) indicates that fertile sites (solid line) are less likely to be degraded by intensive harvests over short rotations, compared with less fertile sites (dashed line).

Source: Modified from Kimmins (2003)

Site impoverishment caused by intensive cropping is a well-known problem in farming, in which severely degraded land may have to be abandoned for some or all agricultural purposes. Usually this problem can be managed, to a greater or lesser degree, by applying fertilizer to

the land. Sometimes, however, the degradation of site capability, especially tilth, is too severe, and this simple mitigation is not successful. Of course, the harvest rotation in agriculture is usually annual, whereas the rotation period in forestry typically ranges from about 20 to 100 years. However, each forest harvest involves the removal of a huge quantity of biomass, and thus of nutrients.

Compare, for example, the amounts of biomass and nutrients removed by clear-cuts of a conifer forest in Nova Scotia (Table 23.1). In this case, a whole-tree clear-cut yielded 30% more biomass than a stem-only harvest. The increased yield may be an advantage of the whole-tree method, particularly if the harvest is to be used for energy production. The increased harvest of biomass is, however, mostly due to the removal of nutrient-rich tissues such as foliage and small branches. Consequently, the whole-tree harvest removed up to twice as many nutrients as did the stem-only clear-cut. In effect, a 30% increase in biomass yield by the whole-tree method was "purchased" at the ecological "expense" of 54–99% increases in the removal of nutrients.

Unfortunately, there are few useful studies that allow foresters to compare the productivity of subsequent harvest rotations on the same site. Such studies would take more than 50–100 years, requiring several generations of foresters! Therefore, it is difficult to evaluate the implications of nutrient removal by clear-cutting. Overall, however, it appears that a degradation of site nutrient capital is a less severe problem in forest harvesting than in agriculture. Consequently, nutrient removals by harvesting should be viewed as a potential long-term problem. Because forestry is an economically important activity, and the maintenance of site capability is critical to the sustainability of the enterprise, scientists should continue to study the effects of harvesting on nutrient capital. In the short term, however, forestry causes more immediate damages to site capability and biodiversity that deserve our attention.

Leaching of Nutrients

The disturbance of forested land can increase the rate at which dissolved nutrients are transported downward into the soil with percolating rainwater (a process known as *leaching*). If the nutrients leach deeper into the soil than tree roots can penetrate, they are effectively lost from the "working" nutrient capital of the site. Eventually, leaching nutrients can find their way into groundwater and surface waters.

The nutrients with the greatest tendency to leach are nitrate and potassium, both of which are highly water soluble. However, calcium, magnesium, and sulphate may

TABLE 23.1	Removals of Biomass and Nutrients by Clear-Cuts of a Conifer Forest in Nova Scotia

This study involved weighing the biomass harvested by a stem-only clear-cut and a whole-tree clear-cut (each 0.5 ha). Nutrient concentrations were determined for subsamples of the biomass and were used to calculate the amounts of nutrients removed. Biomass is stated in tonnes/hectare, and nutrients in kilograms/hectare. "Percentage increase" refers to the whole-tree removals, compared with stem-only removals.

BIOMASS COMPONENT	BIOMASS (t/ha)	N (kg/ha)	P (kg/ha)	K (kg/ha)	Ca (kg/ha)	Mg (kg/ha)
STEM-ONLY CLEAR-CUT						
Tree stems	105.2	98	16	92	181	17
WHOLE-TREE CLEAR-CUT						
Tree stems	117.7	120	18	76	219	20
Branches and foliage	34.8	119	17	57	118	17
Total harvest	152.5	239	35	133	337	37
Percentage increase	30%	99%	93%	74%	54%	81%
Nutrients in the forest floor		900	62	110	290	32
Nutrients in the mineral soil (top 30 cm)		3 860	1 220	13 300	5 460	1 740

Source: Modified from Freedman *et al.* (1981)

also leach in significant amounts. Of course, following a clear-cut, any nutrient losses by leaching are in addition to the nutrients removed with tree biomass. Both of these sources of loss reduce site nutrient capital.

A well-known study of nutrient leaching caused by forest disturbance was done at Hubbard Brook, New Hampshire. This large-scale experiment involved felling all the trees on a 16-ha watershed, but without removing any biomass—the cut trees were left lying on the ground. The entire watershed was then treated with herbicide for three years to suppress any regeneration. This experiment was designed to examine the effects of intense disturbance, by de-vegetation, on the biological control of watershed functions such as nutrient cycling and hydrology. The research was not intended to examine the effects of typical forestry practices. Still, important insights were gained into the effects of disturbance on ecological processes.

Overall, during a ten-year period following the cutting, the de-vegetated watershed lost 50 kg/ha•y of NO_3-N (i.e., nitrogen in the form of nitrate), 45 kg/ha•y of Ca, and 17 kg/ha•y of K in streamflow (Bormann and Likens, 1994; Table 23.2 shows data for the first three years, which were the most dramatic). The ten-year losses from the disturbed watershed were much larger than from an undisturbed reference watershed: 4.3 kg/ha•y of NO_3-N, 13 kg/ha•y of Ca, and 2.2 kg/ha•y of K. In part, the increased losses of nutrients in streamwater were due to a 31% annual increase in the yield of water from the

de-vegetated watershed (this was the average during the first three years after cutting). The increased flow of streamwater was caused by the disruption of transpiration from plant foliage. However, increases in nutrient concentration in the streamwater were more important: during the first three years of the study, NO_3 increased by an average factor of 40; K, by 11; Ca, by 5.2; and Mg, by 3.9. The total losses of N, Ca, and Mg in the streamwater were similar to the amounts of those nutrients in the aboveground biomass of the forest.

Because this experiment in de-vegetation did not involve a typical forest management practice, the measured effects were unrealistically large. However, watershed-level studies of clear-cutting and other typical forestry practices have also found an increase of nutrient leaching, although to a lesser degree than that caused by the de-vegetation at Hubbard Brook. For example, in the first three years after the clear-cutting of a 391-ha watershed in New Brunswick, there was an increased loss of nitrate in streamwater of 7 kg NO_3-N/ha•y (Krause, 1982). A study of nine clear-cut watersheds in New Hampshire found an average nitrate loss of 18 kg NO_3-N/ha•y during the first four years, compared with 3.5 kg/ha•y for five uncut watersheds (Martin *et al.*, 1986). In addition, calcium losses from the clear-cuts averaged 28 kg/ha•y, compared with 13 kg/ha•y for reference watersheds, while potassium losses were 6 kg/ha•y compared with 2 kg/ha•y. However, other studies have found smaller effects of

| TABLE 23.2 | Nutrient Losses in Streamflow after Deforestation |

The watershed is located at Hubbard Brook, New Hampshire. The data represent *net flux*, or the difference between inputs from precipitation and outputs due to streamflow. The data are reported for the first three years following experimental deforestation of a 16-ha watershed. The deforested area and an uncut reference watershed of similar size are compared. Losses of material are stated in kilograms per hectare per three-year period.

	LOSSES OF MATERIAL (kg/ha·3y)	
SUBSTANCE	DEFORESTED WATERSHED	REFERENCE WATERSHED
Nitrate (as NO$_3$-N)	−114.1	+2.3
Calcium	−77.7	−9.0
Silicate (as SiO$_2$-Si)	−30.6	−15.9
Potassium	−30.3	−1.5
Aluminum	−21.1	−3.0
Magnesium	−15.6	−2.6
Sodium	−15.4	−6.1
Sulphate (as SO$_4$-S)	−2.8	−4.1
Ammonium (as NH$_4$-N)	+1.6	+2.2
Total dissolved substances	−307.8	−36.9

Source: Modified from Bormann and Likens (1979)

clear-cutting on nutrient losses with streamflow, especially when only a portion of the watershed was cut.

Nitrate and other highly soluble ions are leached from watersheds after clear-cutting (and after other disturbances, such as wildfire) for several reasons. First, disturbance stimulates the activity of microbes involved in the decomposition of organic matter. This occurs because removal of the forest canopy results in warmer surface soil, and decreased uptake by plants leads to an increased availability of inorganic nutrients and moisture. Second, disturbance often stimulates the microbial processes of ammonification and nitrification (see Chapter 5), leading to increased rates of production of nitrate, which is extremely soluble and readily lost from soil.

Forestry and Erosion

Forestry activities can cause severe losses of soil, or **erosion**, particularly in terrain with steep slopes. In most cases, erosion is triggered by improper practices such as constructing poor logging roads, using streams as trails to haul logs, running log-removal trails down slopes instead of along

them, and harvesting trees from steep slopes that are extremely vulnerable to soil loss. Overall, road building is the most important cause of erosion in forestry lands, particularly where culverts (i.e., channelled stream crossings) are not sufficiently large or numerous, or are poorly installed or maintained.

Severe erosion causes many environmental damages. In extreme cases, the loss of soil may expose bedrock, making forest regeneration very difficult. Soil loss also represents a depletion of site nutrient capital. In addition, erosion causes secondary damages to aquatic habitats. These include silt deposition (*siltation*), which degrades aquatic habitats by covering gravel substrates important to spawning fish. Also, the shallower water increases the risk of flooding.

Erosion is an important, yet largely avoidable, environmental effect of forestry. The irresponsible practices that can cause erosion have been restricted by provincial regulations and occur less frequently now than in the past. Practices that help to reduce erosion include the following:

- planning the routes of forest roads to avoid stream crossings as much as possible
- installing a sufficient number of adequately sized culverts
- avoiding the disturbance of stream channels by heavy equipment
- leaving buffer strips of uncut forest beside watercourses
- using log-removal practices that minimize disturbance of the forest floor (such as cable yarding—a procedure in which a tall spar anchors cables radiating into the clear-cut, allowing logs to be dragged to a central place without the use of a heavy, wheeled skidder)
- allowing vegetation to regenerate quickly, which speeds the re-establishment of biological moderation of erosion
- deciding to selectively harvest, or not to harvest, steep sites that are extremely sensitive to erosion

It has become a common operational practice in Canada to leave strips of uncut forest beside streams, rivers, and lakes. These buffer zones greatly reduce the erosion of streambanks, eliminate temperature increases in the water, maintain riparian (lake- and stream-side) habitat for wildlife, and mitigate some of the aesthetic damage from forest harvesting. While it is widely accepted that riparian buffers provide important benefits, there is no consensus about how wide the uncut strips should be. This is an economically important consideration, because large areas of valuable timber are withdrawn from the potential harvest when buffer strips are left. The requirements in New Brunswick, for example, are for a 30-m buffer on each side of a watercourse, with wider buffers recommended in some circumstances (i.e., 60 m if the bank slope exceeds 24°, and up to 100 m beside surface waters that are commonly used for recreation or as a source of drinking water). In some cases, selective harvesting of trees may be allowed within riparian buffers, as long as this does not compromise the ecological services provided by these *special management zones*. About 9% of the "productive" forest on Crown land in New Brunswick has been set aside as riparian buffers. Similar regulations have been enacted or are being considered by all other provinces.

Forestry and Hydrology

Forests have a strong influence on the hydrology of watersheds. Large amounts of water are evaporated into the atmosphere by forest vegetation, especially by trees (this is known as *transpiration*; *evapotranspiration* also includes the evaporation of water from non-living surfaces). In the absence of transpiration, an equivalent quantity of water would leave the watershed as streamflow or seepage to deep groundwater.

For example, studies of four forested watersheds in Nova Scotia found that evapotranspiration was equivalent to 15–29% of the annual inputs of water from precipitation, with runoff by streams accounting for the other 71–85% (these watersheds had no substantial drainage to deep groundwater; Freedman *et al.*, 1985).

The hydrologic budget of forested watersheds is extremely seasonal, particularly in the temperate and boreal climates typical of forested regions of Canada. This seasonality can be illustrated by the hydrology of the Mersey River watershed in Nova Scotia (Figure 23.2). The annual input of water from precipitation is about 146 cm/y, with 82% arriving as rain and 18% as snow. About 62% of the annual input is dispersed by riverflow and 38% by evapotranspiration. The months from November to January have somewhat higher amounts of precipitation, although this seasonal variation is small in comparison with some other regions of Canada. The seasonal variations of evapotranspiration, runoff, and groundwater storage are much more substantial. Evapotranspiration is highest during the growing season of May to September, resulting in sparse runoff. Runoff is greater during late autumn and early winter, when there is little transpiration. However, much of the pre-

cipitation during this period serves to re-charge groundwater storage, which becomes depleted by the uptake of water by vegetation during the growing season. Runoff is greatest during the spring, when the accumulated snowpack melts quickly, resulting in a spate of riverflow.

Disturbances such as wildfire and timber harvesting can substantially change the hydrology of watersheds. The seasonality and quantities of flow can change, and erosion, flooding, and other damages can occur downstream. In addition, some poorly drained sites may become wetter because reduced transpiration can raise the height of the water table. In general, the increase in streamflow is related to the proportion of the watershed that was disturbed. After an entire watershed is clear-cut, the increase in streamflow can be as much as 40% in the first year. The increase is proportionately less after partial cuts.

Clear-cuts usually regenerate quickly, and in some cases, the vigorous re-growth of shrubs and herbs can restore most of the original foliage area in as few as four to six years. Consequently, the biggest increases in streamflow occur in the first year after cutting, followed by rapid recovery to the pre-harvest condition. In the temperate and boreal climates prevalent in much of Canada, the largest increases in streamflow occur during late spring, summer, and early autumn, these being the seasons in which transpiration is normally most important.

Hydrology can also be affected by a change in the type of forest on the watershed. For example, if an area of hardwood forest is converted into conifer plantations, the annual streamflow may decrease. This happens because the conifers maintain foliage throughout the year, extending the transpiration season into times when angiosperm trees lack foliage.

Weeds, Regeneration, and Reorganization

Clear-cuts and other disturbances caused by forestry usually regenerate rather quickly through the ecological process of succession. Initially, however, most of the regenerating biomass involves plants other than the tree species that foresters consider desirable. As a result, the vigorous re-growth is often regarded as detrimental to silvicultural objectives. Such non-crop plants may be viewed as "weeds," and their abundance may be controlled by a herbicide application (see Chapter 22).

However, a rapid re-vegetation of clear-cuts and other disturbed lands confers some important ecological bene-

FIGURE 23.2 | Seasonal Hydrology of the Mersey River in Nova Scotia

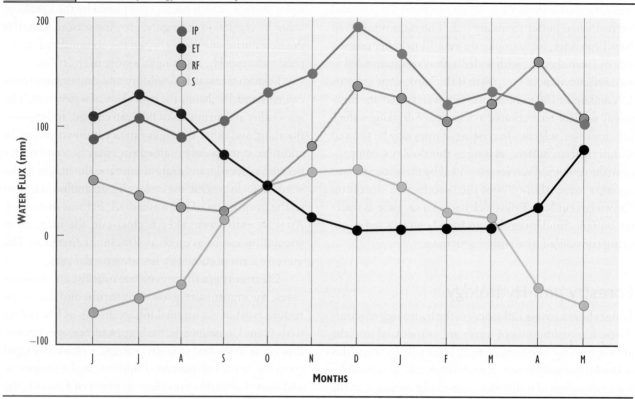

Water inputs from incident precipitation (IP) into the 723-km^2 watershed, and riverflow (RF) from the watershed, are displayed as monthly averages for the period 1968–82. Evapotranspiration (ET) was estimated with a climatic model, and groundwater storage (S) was calculated as IP – RF – ET.

Source: Modified from Freedman *et al.* (1985)

fits. The regenerating plants influence the ecological "reorganization" of disturbed lands. They re-establish a measure of biological control over nutrient cycling, erosion, and hydrology, while also restoring habitat for animals. These values are degraded by disturbance of the site, but are restored during the successional recovery.

For example, during the first few years after clear-cutting, fast-growing vegetation restores a high rate of nutrient uptake from the soil. In performing this uptake, the regenerating vegetation acts as a biological "sponge," tying up some of the soluble nutrients that might otherwise be leached from the site. Eventually, the early successional plants die, and their nutrients become recycled by decomposition. The absorbed nutrients are then made available to trees. In addition, a rapid regeneration of plants on sites disturbed by forestry helps to re-establish biological control over soil losses from erosion. The re-vegetation of clear-cuts also restores habitat for birds, mammals, and other wildlife. Clearly, the re-organization phase of succession is enhanced by the rapid regeneration

of many plant species on recent clear-cuts, including those considered to be economic weeds by foresters.

Forestry and Biodiversity

Clear-cutting and other forestry practices inflict intense disturbances on forests. They cause dramatic changes in the habitat available to support species of plants, animals, and microbes, and their various communities. Some species benefit from habitat changes that occur because of forestry, but others suffer severe damage.

Biodiversity was previously defined (in Chapter 7) as "the richness of biological variation." Biodiversity is often considered within three levels of organization:

1. genetic variation within populations and species

2. numbers of species (*species richness*)

3. the variety and dynamics of ecological communities on larger scales, such as landscapes

In the following sections, we shall examine the effects of forestry on aspects of Canadian biodiversity. The effects of clear-cutting on plants, mammals, birds, and fish will be discussed, largely because these groups have been relatively well studied in the context of forestry. The effects on other elements of indigenous biodiversity, such as insects, spiders, fungi, and microorganisms, are also important, but they have not yet been examined in much detail.

Vegetation

Any severe disturbance results in changes in the dominant species and sizes of plants living on the site. Because they have such a great influence on local environmental conditions, trees are the dominant organisms in forests. When the dominance of tree-sized plants is reduced by clear-cutting, many species of smaller plants take advantage of the relatively uncompetitive conditions that occur after the severe disturbance. These plants dominate the initial stages of post-harvest succession. They are reduced in abundance, however, or even eliminated from the community, once several decades of regeneration have gone by and tree-sized plants have been able to re-establish their dominance.

Many plants of early post-cutting succession can only be successful in open habitats of the sort created by disturbance—they are intolerant of the shade and other stressful conditions beneath a closed forest canopy. These relatively short-lived *ruderal* plants can typically disperse widely. This propagation strategy is necessary because of the ephemeral nature of their habitat (see Chapter 9). Examples of ruderal plants that proliferate in clear-cuts and other recently disturbed forests include asters, goldenrods, grasses, and sedges. A specific example is the fireweed (*Epilobium angustifolium*), a purple-flowered herbaceous plant that is often abundant after wildfire (hence its name) and also after clear-cutting. Some woody plants are also ruderals, being most abundant during the recovery after forest disturbance. Examples are the red raspberry (*Rubus strigosus*), pin cherry (*Prunus pensylvanica*), and elderberry (*Sambucus racemosa*). Because of their requirement for open, recently disrupted habitat, ruderal plants benefit greatly from clear-cutting and other disturbances associated with forestry.

Unlike ruderal plants, some other species are tolerant of the environmental stress occurring beneath a closed forest canopy. Examples of such plants are white trillium (*Trillium grandiflorum*), shield fern (*Dryopteris marginalis*), feather-mosses (such as *Pleurozium schreberi* and *Hylocomium splendens*), and often certain lichens, such as

lungwort (*Lobaria pulmonaria*). These species are not very tolerant of open conditions, and they decrease in abundance after clear-cutting. Once suitable conditions re-develop during the successional recovery, these plants may again increase in abundance.

In general, once a clear-cut has had two to four years to regenerate, the plant community is actually richer in species than the mature forest that was harvested (this is particularly true of vascular plants). The increase in species diversity occurs because recently disturbed habitats are relatively rich in resources such as light, nutrients, and water. Under these open conditions, many species of low-growing plants can be supported on the site, including a diversity of ruderal plants. In comparison, naturally stressful habitats, such as the understorey beneath mature, closed-canopied forests, generally support fewer species of plants.

Data from a study of a hardwood forest in Nova Scotia can be used to illustrate the species-rich nature of the vegetation after clear-cuts (Crowell and Freedman, 1994). That study examined a number of stands of mature forest, as well as clear-cuts of various ages. The number of plant species in ground vegetation (occurring within 2 m above the surface) averaged $11/m^2$ on two 1-year-old clear-cuts, increasing to $14/m^2$ on 6-year-old clear-cuts. Mature forest and clear-cuts older than 30 years had fewer species—typically $3–6/m^2$ in stands with a closed canopy dominated by species of maple trees, but $9–11/m^2$ in birch-dominated stands, which have a more open canopy. This comparison suggests that many species of plants, especially ruderals, can freely utilize open habitats associated with clear-cutting. However, species requiring mature forest habitat may be threatened by this kind of disturbance.

Deer, Moose, Elk, and Caribou

White-tailed deer (*Odocoileus virginianus*) and mule deer (*O. hemionus*) are the most common wild ungulates in southern Canada. These deer feed on woody stems (also known as browse) and low-growing herbaceous plants, and they need brushy habitat for at least part of their yearly range.

During the twentieth century, the abundance of white-tailed and mule deer increased over much of their range. In fact, these deer are now more abundant in parts of their range than they were before the European colonization of Canada, when extensive landscapes were covered with mature and old-growth forests. In Nova Scotia, for example, white-tailed deer were uncommon when Europeans first began to settle the land. In fact, the species was soon extirpated by over-hunting. However, white-tailed deer were re-established in the nineteenth century, by both deliberate introductions and natural immigration from New Brunswick. Today, this species is probably more abundant in Nova Scotia than at any time since deglaciation.

The modern abundance of white-tailed deer in Canada is largely due to a widespread availability of early-successional, shrubby habitat. While-tailed deer have proliferated mainly because human activities have increased the area of this kind of habitat, and in some regions, have decreased the populations of natural predators. The shrubby habitat was created by the abandonment of agricultural land, the harvesting of forests, and wildfire. All three factors result in habitat dominated for several decades by shrub-sized plants, with a rich understorey of forbs (herbaceous, dicotyledonous plants) and graminoids (monocotyledonous species, especially grasses, sedges, and rushes).

The shrubby habitat tends to be distributed over the landscape as a mosaic of stands in various stages of succession within a matrix of mature forest. This spatial arrangement enhances the suitability of the landscape for white-tailed deer if the following conditions are also present:

- extensive production of nutritious and palatable browse in younger stands
- abundance of ecotonal (i.e., edge) habitat
- adequate availability of good "yarding" habitat of mature coniferous forest, which provides critical shelter in regions where winters are severe and snow is deep

If these habitat qualities occur within a mosaic of stands of various ages, the landscape is more favourable to deer than either extensive clear-cuts or unbroken expanses of mature forest.

The central parts of large clear-cuts are not well used by deer, as they like to be close to protective forest cover. A study in eastern Canada found that white-tailed deer fed about seven times more intensively in the centre of clear-cuts less than 80 ha in area than in the middle of larger clear-cuts up to 410 ha in size (Drolet, 1978). In fact, optimal clear-cuts for white-tailed deer are rather small in size, although this varies regionally. For example, clear-cuts smaller than 4 ha in New Brunswick and smaller than 2 ha in southern Ontario have been recommended to improve habitat for white-tailed deer.

To some degree, the amount of useful habitat on larger clear-cuts can be increased if they have an irregular shape. Erratic shapes have a higher ratio of edge to surface area than do circular, square, or rectangular shapes. Consequently, irregular-shaped clear-cuts provide more edge habitat, while also making the central part of the clear-cut more accessible to deer.

White-tailed and mule deer eat a variety of woody plants, forbs, and graminoids, and these foods are often much more abundant on cutover and burned sites than in mature forest. After clear-cutting, the biomass of browse and herbaceous plants typically increases to a maximum after about 8 to 15 years, followed by a decline as the tree canopy matures and shades the understorey vegetation. This successional pattern is illustrated in Table 23.3 for stands of various ages following clear-cutting in Nova Scotia. The quantity of browse peaked at about 8 to 13 years and then declined. The pattern for herbaceous plants was similar, but with the biomass peaking at two to six years after clear-cutting.

Browse is not only more abundant, but also of better nutritional quality in clear-cuts and burns than in mature forest. Recently sprouted, rapidly growing twigs tend to have higher concentrations of protein, nitrogen, and phosphorus, and they are more succulent and more easily digested than the older browse found in mature forest.

Although food for deer is relatively abundant and of good quality on clear-cuts, other characteristics of managed forestry land can restrict the use of these habitats. The central parts of large clear-cuts may be too far from protective forest cover to be well utilized. Clear-cuts may also have physical obstructions to deer movements, such as tangles of logging slash. They may also have excessively deep snow during winter because snowfall is not intercepted by an overhead canopy of conifer trees. This can be important, because deer movement is severely restricted by snow deeper than 50–70 cm.

In areas with severe winters, it is critical that timber harvesting be planned to ensure the availability of suitable "yarding" habitat of mature conifer forest. In these places, the winter microclimate is less severe; some browse is available, and snow depths are not excessive. In some regions, winter-yarding habitat may be more important to deer than the amount and quality of summer habitat. Since particular yards are often used for years by deer from an extensive area, these critical habitats should be protected from any cutting that might detract from their use.

Finally, ongoing disturbances in forest management areas can affect habitat use by deer. These include frequent traffic along logging roads, noise from harvesting operations, and the excessive hunting pressure that can result from easy access along forestry roads.

TABLE 23.3	Shrub and Herb Biomass in Stands of Different Ages

The data are from a region of maple-birch forest in Nova Scotia. Stands aged 20 years and younger had been disturbed by clear-cutting. Biomass is reported in tonnes of dry weight per hectare.

STAND AGE (y)	NUMBER OF STANDS SAMPLED	SHRUB BIOMASS (t/ha)		HERB BIOMASS (t/ha)	
		AVERAGE	RANGE	AVERAGE	RANGE
1	2	0.45	0.4–0.5	1.1	0.93–1.2
2	2	1.9	1.8–2.1	1.6	1.4–1.7
3–6	4	8.2	6.6–12.2	1.7	1.5–2.1
8–13	5	17.6	16.9–18.7	0.57	0.27–1.0
20	1	10.9	–	0.14	–
30–40	3	4.8	0.8–7.9	0.25	0.10–0.47
50–75	5	2.4	1.1–3.9	0.23	0.70–0.45

Source: Modified from Crowell and Freedman (1994)

Moose (*Alces alces*) and elk (or wapiti, *Cervus elaphus*) may also benefit from some kinds of forest-harvesting practices. Moose feed primarily on browse, although they also eat aquatic and terrestrial herbs during the summer. Elk graze primarily on graminoids and forbs during the growing season, but eat browse during the winter when herbs are less available. Because the availability of browse and herbs usually increases after forest harvesting, the habitat of moose and elk can be improved by some kinds of forest management. In general, however, these species are less favoured by forestry than are white-tailed and mule deer.

The woodland caribou (*Rangifer tarandus*; known as reindeer in Eurasia) is another abundant species of deer in Canada, particularly in the north. Woodland caribou require an extensive habitat of mature coniferous forest, particularly during the winter, when so-called "reindeer mosses" (actually species of lichens, genus *Cladina*) make up much of their diet. These lichens grow on the forest floor and are most abundant in relatively open conifer stands that are 40 to 100 years old. However, if the tree density is high enough to allow the canopy to close as the forest matures, these lichens decline and become replaced by feather mosses, which are not palatable to caribou. Disturbance of forests by wildfire and logging can regenerate the supply of reindeer lichens in areas with extensive closed-canopied stands. In general, however, caribou are not favoured by extensive logging of their habitat.

All the species of wild ungulates in Canada are important in hunting, an activity that generates significant economic value while also providing subsistence for many rural people (see Chapter 14). Increasingly, foresters and wildlife biologists are working together to develop inte-grated management plans that accommodate the need to harvest both timber and ungulates from landscapes. These plans can allow the maintenance of relatively large populations of white-tailed deer, mule deer, moose, and elk, even while clear-cutting and other forestry practices take place. We will examine *integrated forest management* in more detail at the end of this chapter.

Smaller Mammals

Hares and rabbits are abundant in most regions of Canada and are economically important as small game, as pests, and in recreational wildlife viewing. These animals feed by browsing and grazing and can benefit from the increase in availability of low-growing shrubs and herbs as a result of forest harvesting, abandonment of agricultural land, and wildfire. In fact, hares and rabbits can be abundant enough to significantly impede tree regeneration by girdling (gnawing the bark around a sapling, killing it) and clipping (chewing the foliage and growing points of a young tree).

Other small mammals include mice, voles, shrews, and moles, which are important as components of terrestrial food webs. These small mammals sometimes impede forest regeneration by consuming tree seeds and by girdling young trees. In other cases, they are considered beneficial because they can eat large quantities of potentially damaging insects.

Most studies report that forest harvesting has relatively minor effects on small mammals. For example, no substantial differences were found in the overall abundance, species richness, or diversity of small mammals

| TABLE 23.4 | Comparison of Small-Mammal Communities among Habitat Types | | | |

Data are from different habitats in a maple-birch forest in Nova Scotia. Abundance is indexed by the numbers of animals caught per 100 days of trapping effort. Species richness is the number of species observed.

SPECIES	UNCUT FOREST	CLEAR-CUTS	STRIP-CUTS	SHELTERWOOD
Short-tailed shrew (*Blarina brevicauda*)	3.9	3.4	2.5	3.4
Masked shrew (*Sorex cinereus*)	2.2	4.9	2.2	2.3
Red-backed vole (*Clethrionomys gapperi*)	7.0	6.0	4.9	4.9
Deer mouse (*Peromyscus maniculatus*)	1.0	0.7	0.4	3.0
Meadow vole (*Microtus pennsylvanicus*)	0.2	2.8	2.6	0.6
Eastern chipmunk (*Tamias striatus*)	0.2	0.2	0.7	0.4
Woodland jumping mouse (*Napaeozapus insignis*)	2.9	0.3	2.9	4.7
Total abundance	17.4	18.3	16.2	19.3
Species richness	7	7	7	7

Source: Modified from Swan *et al.* (1984)

when mature forest, three- to five-year-old clear-cuts, strip-cuts, and shelterwood cuts were compared in Nova Scotia (Table 23.4).

Pine marten (*Martes americana*) and fisher (*M. pennanti*) are small carnivores with extensive natural ranges in North America. Unfortunately, these furbearers have suffered large population declines in many areas, mainly because they have been trapped too intensively. In addition, over much of their range, marten and fisher appear to depend partly on the complex habitat structure of older-growth coniferous forest. Consequently, they are considered to be at risk from forest harvesting and management.

Birds

Many species of birds require mature forest as habitat for breeding or wintering or during migration. However, many other species need the types of habitat that occur during the early stages of forest succession, including those created through such forestry activities as clear-cutting.

Ruffed grouse (*Bonasa umbellus*) are commonly hunted in Canada. Also hunted, but to a lesser degree, are spruce grouse (*Canachites canadensis*) and blue grouse (*Dendragapus obscurus*). Populations of these so-called "upland game birds" are generally favoured by landscape mosaics that include both mature forest and younger, brushy stands.

Ruffed grouse occur in a variety of habitats, but they prefer areas dominated by hardwood forest with some conifers mixed in, especially stands dominated by poplars and birches. These birds feed mainly on the foliage, young twigs, catkins, and buds of woody plants, also eating fleshy

fruits when available. In Nova Scotia, ruffed grouse utilize clear-cuts of maple-birch forest that are five or more years old. Clear-cuts of aspen forest in Minnesota become suitable for ruffed grouse after 4 to 12 years of regeneration, and they are then used as breeding habitat for 10 to 15 years, while older aspen stands are important as wintering habitat (Gullion, 1988). Wildlife biologists recommend that, to provide optimal habitat for ruffed grouse in regions of aspen forest, forestry should be conducted in such a way as to create a mosaic of different-aged stands, each 10 ha or less in area, with adjacent stands differing in age by 10 to 15 years.

Wildlife managers often refer to the great diversity of birds that are not hunted as "non-game" species. These birds can, however, be economically important. For example, they may be useful predators of insects that damage trees or other crops, and they are the objects of bird-watching (or "birding"), an increasingly popular outdoor sport.

Forestry affects individual species of non-game birds, as well as their communities, in terms of density and species diversity. These effects are indirect, being caused by changes in the physical structure and plant-species composition of the available habitat. Important aspects of habitat structure for birds include the quantities of living and dead plant biomass, their distribution in both vertical and horizontal planes, and the nature of *ecotones* that occur where different habitats meet.

An important aspect of horizontal structure is the distribution of patches of distinct habitats, either within a stand or on a landscape. The shapes of the patches affect their ratio of edge to area (and thus the amount of ecotonal habitat). Patch size is also important because small, isolated habitats cannot sustain species of birds that maintain large territories. The species composition of the vegetation affects the food types and other habitat elements occurring in a particular stand. The presence of cavity trees, dead trees (snags), and logs on the forest floor is also critical to many species of birds and other animals (this is discussed in the next section). Finally, the abundance of many bird species often increases in stands in which there is an outbreak of insects, such as spruce budworm (see Chapter 22).

Many birders have a general knowledge of the relationships between bird species and habitats. They use this understanding to predict the species they might see under certain conditions. Ecologists know enough about the specific requirements of some birds to be able to manage their habitat. The best forestry-related example of this practice is the use of prescribed fire to create even-aged stands of jack pine (*Pinus banksiana*) in Michigan. This ensures an appropriate habitat for the Kirtland's warbler (*Dendroica kirtlandii*), a rare and endangered species.

Of course, each bird species has particular habitat needs. If the physical and botanical character of a habitat is changed by a major disturbance such as wildfire or clear-cutting, many species of birds can no longer breed in the affected stand. The same disturbance, however, will create habitat opportunities for early successional birds. These changes are illustrated in Table 23.5, which compares the birds in mature stands and in clear-cuts of hardwood forest. The mature forest supported an avian community with an average population of 663 pairs/km², dominated by ovenbird, least flycatcher, red-eyed vireo, black-throated green warbler, and hermit thrush. The three- to five-year-old clear-cuts supported a slightly less abundant population of 588 pairs/km², dominated by chestnut-sided warbler, common yellowthroat, white-throated sparrow, and dark-eyed junco. Forest and clear-cuts thus supported similar densities of breeding birds, but almost entirely different species. This occurred because the forest and clear-cuts provide very different habitats in terms of physical structure and the species composition and productivity of vegetation. Although clear-cutting deprived mature-forest birds of habitat, it created opportunities for early successional species.

Welsh and Fillman (1980) examined the effects on birds of clear-cutting spruce forest in northern Ontario.

TABLE 23.5 Breeding Birds in Mature Forest and Adjacent Clear-Cuts in Nova Scotia

The three stands of mature forest had a closed canopy dominated by maple and birch, while the three clear-cuts (three to five years old) had a vigorous regeneration of shrubs and herbaceous plants. Less abundant bird species are not included here. Data are in pairs/kilometre².

SPECIES	FOREST			CLEAR-CUTS		
	A	B	C	A	B	C
Ruby-throated hummingbird (*Archilochus colubris*)	0	0	0	25	30	15
Least flycatcher (*Empidonax minimus*)	290	120	0	0	0	0
Hermit thrush (*Catharus guttatus*)	60	40	30	0	0	0
Red-eyed vireo (*Vireo olivaceous*)	80	50	30	0	0	0
Black-and-white warbler (*Mniotilta varia*)	15	50	40	0	0	0
Black-throated green warbler (*Dendroica virens*)	50	30	30	0	0	0
Chestnut-sided warbler (*Dendroica pensylvanica*)	0	0	0	100	40	190
Ovenbird (*Seiurus aurocapillus*)	150	120	200	0	0	0
Common yellowthroat (*Geothlypis trichas*)	0	0	0	25	300	130
American redstart (*Setophaga ruticilla*)	15	80	100	0	0	0
Dark-eyed junco (*Junco hyemalis*)	15	20	15	50	70	30
White-throated sparrow (*Zonotrichia albicollis*)	0	20	0	90	190	100
Song sparrow (*Melospiza melodia*)	0	0	0	90	70	0
Total density (pairs/km²)	815	660	515	435	745	585
Number of species	12	16	9	10	8	7

Source: Modified from Freedman *et al.* (1981)

Photo 23.2   This is a two-year-old clear-cut of hardwood forest in Nova Scotia. Birds typically breeding in this habitat include dark-eyed junco (*Junco hyemalis*), white-throated sparrow (*Zonotrichia albicollis*), song sparrow (*Melospiza melodia*), and common snipe (*Capella gallinago*).

Photo 23.3   This is an eight-year-old clear-cut of hardwood forest in Nova Scotia. Birds breeding in this habitat include chestnut-sided warbler (*Dendroica pensylvanica*), common yellowthroat (*Geothlypis trichas*), and alder flycatcher (*Empidonax alnorum*).

In that study, the largest populations of breeding birds (1020–1970 pairs/km^2) occurred in moderate-aged (11 to 24 years) clear-cuts. This was a higher population level than in uncut spruce forest (561 pairs/km^2). The smallest densities of birds occurred in a three-year-old clear-cut with about 200 pairs/km^2. By five years after the cutting, this had increased to 690 pairs/km^2. In general, the clear-cuts and mature spruce forest supported different species of birds, although there was some overlap.

Cavity Trees, Snags, and Large Woody Debris

Living trees with *cavities*, standing dead trees (*snags*), and logs lying on the forest floor (i.e., *coarse* or *large woody debris*) are critical elements of habitat for many species of animals. This is particularly true of many birds, which use these habitat features for nesting, as substrates for foraging, and as perches for hunting, resting, or singing. In fact, about one-third or more of the birds that breed in temperate and boreal forest depend on these features, particularly on cavities.

For example, all 12 species of woodpeckers that breed in Canada excavate cavities in snags or in living, heart-rotted trees. These cavities are used as nesting sites, for roosting at night, or for both purposes. In addition, most species of woodpeckers forage for their food of invertebrates by drilling and excavating into the bark and wood of dead and living trees. Many other species of birds nest in the abandoned cavities made by woodpeckers or use natural cavities that have formed in rotten parts of trees. Some other birds nest in or beneath woody debris or build platform nests on snags or living trees that have suffered damage to their tops.

Because so many species of birds depend on cavities, maintaining this habitat feature has become an important consideration in forest management. The issue is especially prominent in the older-growth forests of the west coast, where as many as six species of woodpeckers can co-occur in relatively large populations, along with many other cavity-dependent species. If we wish these species to remain in regions where forestry is being practised, part of the management area must be maintained as mature or old-growth forest. If plantations are established, these should be designed to provide habitat for birds that require snags and dead logs. For example, cavity trees can be left standing during the harvest. Cavity- and snag-dependent species are also better accommodated by less intensive harvesting techniques, such as selection cuts.

Freshwater Biota

Forestry practices can degrade freshwater habitats in four major ways:

- by siltation (i.e., the settling of soil eroded from the land and streambanks)
- by increases in water temperature caused by the removal of shading vegetation from stream edges
- by blocking stream channels with logging debris
- by changes in hydrology

Damage may also be caused by chemical and fuel spills and as a result of pesticide spraying (see Chapter 22). All of these assaults on freshwater habitat can affect populations of fish, amphibians, and aquatic invertebrates. These problems can be especially severe in hilly or mountainous terrain because of the many small streams and rivers that occur there, and because the soil on steep slopes is highly vulnerable to erosion.

In most cases, it is possible to avoid or mitigate many of the damages to aquatic ecosystems. As we previously noted, rates of erosion can be greatly reduced if roads and culverts are constructed carefully, logs are hauled correctly, and riparian buffers of uncut forest are left beside watercourses. Leaving buffer strips also avoids an excessive accumulation of logging debris in streams, as does avoiding the felling of trees into aquatic habitats. In addition, riparian buffers are extremely effective at preventing increases in water temperature because they provide shade to streams even if nearby habitat has been clear-cut.

Old-Growth Forest

An old-growth forest is a late-successional (climax) ecosystem. Old-growth forest is characterized by the presence of old trees, a multi-aged population structure (i.e., all age classes are represented, from young to old), and a complex physical structure. The structure includes multiple layers within the canopy, big trees, many large snags, and dead logs lying on the forest floor. In some ecological contexts, the term "old-growth" has also been used to refer to senescent populations of shorter-lived species of trees, such as older stands of poplar, birch, or cherry. This is not, however, the meaning of "old-growth forest" being considered here.

Old-growth forest is a natural ecosystem with unique and special values that are not replicated elsewhere. For this reason, it is considered to have great intrinsic value

Photo 23.4 Snags, or dead standing trees, are a critical habitat element for many species of animals. This photo shows four young kestrels (*Falco sparverius*) that recently fledged from their nest site in a natural cavity in a pine snag left in a clear-cut in Nova Scotia.

Source: I.A. McLaren

and to be an important component of natural heritage. It supports some species of plants and animals that do not occur in other Canadian habitats. (This is, admittedly, a relatively minor attribute of temperate and boreal old-growth forest—tropical, old-growth forest sustains enormously larger numbers of dependent species; see Chapters 7 and 26.) In addition, old-growth forest delivers important ecological services, such as furnishing clean water and air, and it has economic value for outdoor recreation and ecotourism.

Photo 23.5   This photo of a riparian buffer of uncut forest beside a stream in New Brunswick was taken in winter. The shading vegetation prevents the increases in water temperature that would be caused by clear-cutting to the stream edge. It also helps to prevent erosion, and maintains a corridor of intact, mature vegetation for continued use by wildlife.

Source: M. Sullivan

Old-growth forest was once much more extensive in Canada (and elsewhere in the world) than it is today. In eastern Canada, for example, extensive tracts of old-growth forest have been cleared for agriculture or were converted into younger, second-growth forest by timber harvesting. As a result, there is very little of this ecosystem type left in the eastern provinces, where only one to a few percent of the total forest cover is now in an old-growth condition.

Old-growth forest is more abundant in parts of western Canada, particularly on the Pacific coast of British Columbia. There, the wet climatic regime favours the development of this kind of natural ecosystem (since wildfires are uncommon). Even in British Columbia, however, extensive tracts of old-growth forest have been logged or converted to urbanized land-use, especially in the vicinities of Vancouver and Victoria. And because old-growth timber is such a valuable natural resource, much of the remaining old-growth forest is threatened by forestry. It is likely that virtually all of the remaining old-growth forest will be logged during the next several decades and converted into second-growth forest, which will be harvested before it attains an old-growth condition. The only exceptions will be those tracts of old-growth forest that are protected in ecological reserves and parks.

Because old-growth forest is now rare in regions of eastern Canada where it was once widespread, the preservation of the remnants is a high priority for environmentalists and conservationists. This is also the case in western Canada, especially in coastal British Columbia, where there are enormous controversies over the continued logging of the remaining tracts of old-growth rainforest (see Canadian Focus 23.1).

Some of the key characteristics of old-growth forest, including its elements of biodiversity, can be accommodated by so-called *new forestry* harvesting systems that are relatively "soft" in the intensity of disturbance that they cause. The best example of a new forestry system is selection cutting with snag and cavity-tree retention. Because only some of the economically valuable timber is removed during a selection harvest, the physical and ecological integrity of the forest is left substantially intact, conserving many of the old-growth values.

There are, however, limits to what can be achieved through new forestry practices. If a goal of society is to preserve old-growth forest as a special type of natural ecosystem, this is best done by establishing large, landscape-scale protected areas. The size of the protected areas is a critical factor since they must be large enough to sustain the long-term ecological dynamics that permit old-growth forest to develop, particularly the natural disturbance regime. This landscape perspective is important because particular stands of old-growth forest cannot be preserved forever—they will inevitably become degraded by natural disturbance and/or environmental change. Consequently, old-growth forest can be sustained only if large protected areas are designated to preserve the necessary ecological dynamics.

Old-growth forest is an extremely valuable natural resource, perhaps more so than any other type of forest in Canada. This is because it contains large individuals of economically desirable tree species. This kind of timber can be used to manufacture relatively valuable products, such as fine-grained, large-dimension lumber and plywood. Stands of old-growth forest are rarely, however, managed by foresters as a renewable, natural resource. Rather, they are almost invariably "mined" by harvesting, followed by silvicultural management to convert the site into a younger, second-growth forest. The second-growth forest will only be allowed to develop into a middle-aged forest before it is again harvested.

There is a strong economic rationale for this kind of management strategy. In the old-growth condition, a forest does not sustain a positive net production of biomass.

Canadian Focus 23.1

Controversy over the Old-Growth Forest of Clayoquot Sound

Clayoquot Sound is an embayment of the Pacific Ocean, reaching inland in central Vancouver Island to encompass a watershed of about 263 000 ha. Because of the mountainous terrain, a great variety of habitats is found in this region, including extensive forest on the interior mountains and the flatter coastal plain. The climatic regime is mild temperate, and there is an abundance of rainfall.

The high-rainfall regime has an important influence on the kinds of forest that develop in the region. The wet climate means that wildfire is rare, a factor that encourages the natural development of an old-growth rainforest. Coastal, temperate, old-growth rainforest is a rare kind of natural ecosystem because few places on Earth have the environmental conditions necessary for its development.

Before commercial timber harvesting began in the region, most of the forest of Clayoquot Sound was in an old-growth condition. Many of the trees are very large and old—some individuals are more than 3 m in diameter and more than 1000 years old. In addition, old-growth trees have fine-grained wood because of their slow growth rate, making them extremely valuable for manufacturing lumber.

Because of the extensive logging of old-growth forests in Clayoquot Sound (and elsewhere), this ecosystem type is much less extensive today than it used to be. This is particularly true of the coastal plain and lower elevations in the mountains, where the most accessible old-growth forest was found. Today, about 80% of the remaining old-growth forest occurs at higher elevations and on steeper slopes.

Almost all of the stands of old-growth timber that are logged on Vancouver Island and elsewhere in coastal British Columbia return to forest. In large part, the second-growth forest is dominated by the same species of trees that dominate the old-growth forest. The second-growth forest is, however, harvested as soon as its trees are large enough to be used for manufacturing lumber or pulp, and this occurs at a much younger age than is required to re-develop the old-growth condition. Enormous controversy has arisen over the rapid and extensive conversion of old-growth into second-growth forest. Many people believe that old-growth forest has great intrinsic value because it is a distinct natural ecosystem. This forest is also valued for cultural, aesthetic, and ecological reasons.

Environmentalists have targeted the remaining old-growth forest of the Clayoquot Sound area for protection and have focused a great deal of activism to that end. In

Photo 23.6   This landscape in the Clayoquot Sound region of Vancouver Island used to be covered mainly by old-growth rainforest. Because the valley floor contained the largest trees and was relatively accessible, it was harvested first, in this case, about 15 years before the photo was taken. The clear-cuts are regenerating well through a combination of planted seedlings and natural seeding-in, and another mixed-species forest will again develop. This forest will, however, be harvested long before it attains an old-growth condition. The stands at mid-slope were clear-cut about three years before the photo was taken, while the upper slopes have not yet been harvested. Note the erosion associated with the logging road at mid-slope. Erosion is a common result of logging roads built in mountainous terrain.

part, this has occurred because the area is rather accessible and is traversed by many people as they travel to Pacific Rim National Park on the west coast of Vancouver Island. In fact, there is more extensive old-growth forest elsewhere on Vancouver Island and on the British Columbia mainland. However, because of the remote nature of those other forests, protests there would have been less effective in attracting media and public attention than actions in the Clayoquot Sound region.

The most intense protests began in March 1993, soon after the government of British Columbia purchased stock in a logging company that had a licence to harvest timber in the Clayoquot Sound region. Several weeks later, the government issued permits for logging over 74% of the area. This sparked an explosion of public demonstrations, including a large gathering of concerned people at Clayoquot Sound. Some of these people travelled across Canada by train as part of a media event that symbolically began in Newfoundland and ended in coastal British Columbia. In addition to the protests and publicity stunts, there were blockades of logging roads and other kinds of civil disobedience, leading to the arrest of more than 850 people.

In October, Mike Harcourt, then premier of British Columbia, announced the establishment of a Scientific Panel for Sustainable Ecosystem Management in Clayoquot Sound. The panel was made up of 23 members, including experts in ecology, biodiversity, forestry, ecotourism, and other interests relevant to old-growth forest and the regional controversy. The mandate of this highly regarded group was to "make forest practice in Clayoquot not only the best in the province, but the best in the world."

In June 1995, after a series of public meetings and other deliberations, the panel released a report containing 120 recommendations. These were accepted by the government of British Columbia and passed into law in July. The panel recommended that sustainable ecosystem management should be the over-riding objective for the Clayoquot Sound region, and that all activities, including those associated with forestry, should be conducted with that objective in mind.

Many of the recommendations advocated silvicultural systems that would retain the most important ecological characteristics of old-growth rainforest, such as an uneven age structure, snags and cavity trees, coarse woody debris, and healthy aquatic ecosystems. The panel felt that, in large part, those objectives could be met by restricting the proportion of any large watershed that could be converted into younger age classes at any time. This could be accomplished by limiting the cut rate within any watershed to no more than 1% of the area per year. That practice would ensure that sufficient areas of natural old-growth forest, or of managed forest having most of the habitat values of old-growth forest, would be present at any time to satisfy the needs of dependent species.

The panel also recommended that significant areas within the Clayoquot Sound region be protected from any forestry, particularly those areas and sites that have great value because of their natural ecological features, aesthetics, cultural significance, or utility for recreation and ecotourism.

The recommendations of the panel, and their acceptance by government, satisfied most (but not all) people regarding the ecological sustainability of the forest-management plan for the Clayoquot Sound region. The panel's work should not, however, be regarded as a perfect model of sustainability or as a permanent solution to the controversy over forestry in the old-growth forest of Clayoquot Sound or elsewhere in Canada.

Despite these positive actions, the controversy over

logging the old-growth rainforest in Clayoquot Sound has not disappeared. Although logging companies and the provincial government committed themselves to implementing the recommendations of the Scientific Panel, the development of the new, ecosystem-based management plan did not happen in a timely fashion. Public protests again erupted over the continuation of relatively intensive logging practices in places within Clayoquot Sound, such as logging on steep slopes vulnerable to erosion, the continued use of clear-cutting rather than selection-harvesting systems, harvesting at rates (within watersheds) much greater than recommended by the Panel, and failure to monitor the effects of logging at the ecosystem level (Friends of Clayoquot Sound, 2002). New public protests were sparked by the resumption of road building and extensive logging on Catface Mountain.

Several important lessons can be learned from this on-going controversy.

(1) Scientists can recommend actions to make forestry more environmentally sustainable (this is also potentially true of all other economic activities).

(2) The various interested parties may commit to undertake recommended changes, thereby alleviating the economic and political disruptions associated with public controversy.

(3) Economic and political priorities may again shift, however, and thereby delay or prevent the implementation of changes.

(4) Therefore, citizens and environmentalists should always be skeptical about promises made by government and industry to protect environmental quality. Moreover, there is never a guarantee that a different government will not change agreed-upon rules (including legislation) in ways that provide less protection for the environment. It is even possible that the evolving priorities of future generations of Canadians may support such an action.

The best hope of preventing future damage is to ensure that the social contract of Canadian forestry always includes an obligation to (1) conduct industrial activities in a manner that does not degrade the timber resource, (2) maintain non-timber economic values such as hunted species and ecotourism, and (3) sustain the hydrologic and carbon-storage functions of old-growth forest and other elements of natural, ecological heritage. All of these forest values are important and must be maintained, and it is crucial that Canadians understand this. Unless this happens, the controversy will surely continue.

This happens because, at the stand level, the productivity by living trees is approximately balanced by the deaths of other individuals through disease, accident, or old age. If the primary objective of management is to optimize the productivity of tree biomass, it is better to harvest middle-aged stands soon after their net productivity starts to decrease—that is, before they attain the old-growth condition. Of course, this kind of economic thinking does not take account of the special ecological and aesthetic values of old-growth forest, which are degraded by logging.

Because old-growth forest has particular structural characteristics, some species of wildlife can occur only in this kind of habitat. This is especially true of tropical old-growth forest. In Canada, animals that depend substantially on old-growth forest include the marbled murrelet (*Brachyramphus marmoratus*), the northern spotted owl (*Strix occidentalis caurina*), and the American marten (*Martes americana*). In addition, some species of plants are more abundant in old-growth than in younger, mature forests. Examples include the Pacific yew (*Taxus brevifolia*) and the lungwort lichen (*Lobaria pulmonaria*). However, the species that depend on old-growth forest in Canada have not yet been well investigated. Ongoing studies will discover additional examples, especially of insects, lichens, mosses, and other less conspicuous elements of forest biodiversity. All of these indigenous biodiversity values are endangered by the continued logging of old-growth forest in Canada.

Plantation Establishment

Clear-cutting of natural forest in Canada is often followed by the planting of a new crop of trees, usually of a conifer species, which may then be intensively managed to increase the productivity of the stand. This practice results in the development of a plantation or tree-farm, which is an anthropogenic forest of a relatively simple character compared with the natural, mature or old-growth, mixed-species forest that originally occupied the site. This *ecological conversion* has important implications for biodiversity because many indigenous species of the original, natural forest are unable to utilize the habitat available in a plantation.

The most important habitat changes are related to differences in the tree species and physical structure of the plantation compared to the natural forest that is being replaced. A typical plantation is dominated by a population of trees of the same species and of similar size and age (in population ecology this is known as a *cohort*; in agriculture it is referred to as a *monoculture*). This is a greatly simpli-

fied ecosystem compared with many natural forests, which may contain trees of various species, sizes, and ages. Such changes are greatest when hardwood-dominated, mixed hardwood-conifer, or old-growth forests are replaced by conifer plantations. The changes are fewer if natural, even-aged conifer forests are replaced with conifer plantations.

Of course, any changes in vegetation and habitat have secondary effects on the species of animals that can be sustained. Studies of intensively managed conifer plantations in New Brunswick have found that they can sustain an abundant population of breeding birds (Table 23.6). In fact, a 15-year-old spruce plantation supported a larger bird population than did nearby stands of natural forest, while species richness was similar. In this study, many bird species of the natural, conifer-dominated forest began to invade the developing plantations once the trees were older than about 10 years.

Plantations are particularly deficient in cavity trees, snags, and large woody debris. Consequently, they support few of the many species that require these critical habitat features. For example, in New Brunswick, conifer plantations are established by clear-cutting natural forest, then preparing the site for planting using large machines that crush the logging debris and topple any unharvested trees

Photo 23.7   Forestry plantations are deficient in tree cavities, which are needed by many birds as places in which to nest and roost. In this study in New Brunswick, artificial cavities were placed in various kinds of plantations, and also in natural forest, to see whether this critical habitat feature was limiting the use of the habitats by certain species of birds. Birds nested only in the artificial cavities that were erected in plantations, suggesting that this habitat feature was limiting their abundance there.

Photo 23.8 This 28-year-old plantation of white spruce (*Picea glauca*) in New Brunswick is a conifer forest, but it is simple in physical and biological structure. Although this habitat supports some native species of plants and animals, many other species are eliminated by the scarcity of critical habitat elements, such as cavity trees and large woody debris.

and snags. This kind of harvesting and intensive management results in the presence of almost no cavity trees or snags and little coarse debris (Table 23.7).

If conifer plantations provide adequate winter cover and browse, snowshoe hares (*Lepus americanus*) can maintain large populations. In fact, these animals sometimes cause economic damage by feeding on the bark and shoots of small trees. As soon as the trees mature and start to produce sizable cone crops, red squirrels (*Tamiasciurus hudsonicus*) also find conifer plantations to be acceptable habitat.

Sometimes, plantations are established on previously agricultural or industrial lands (this is known as *afforestation*). Depending on the sort of habitat that results, these plantations are likely to enhance the populations of indigenous species by providing opportunities for forest species. This can be an important benefit in some regions of Canada where agriculture is the dominant land-use, for example, in southern Ontario. However, even greater biodiversity benefits would be attained if an attempt were made to restore a more natural forest, rather than a monocultural plantation.

Landscape Considerations

Biodiversity at the landscape level is related to the distribution and richness of ecological communities, including their dynamics over time (see Chapter 7). If a landscape is covered uniformly with only one or a few types of community, it has little biodiversity at this level. In contrast, an area with a complex and dynamic mosaic of communities has much greater landscape-level biodiversity. *Landscape ecology* involves the study of the patterns and dynamics of communities on landscapes (and seascapes).

Landscape-level biodiversity is greatly influenced by catastrophic disturbances that result in some stands or "patches" of late-successional communities being replaced with younger ones. Natural causes of these *stand-replacing disturbances* include wildfire, windstorms, volcanic eruptions, and insect irruptions. Human activities associated with agriculture and forestry can have similar effects.

Sometimes, forest harvesting is designed to mimic the natural patch-disturbance regime. For example, many pine forests are naturally disturbed by periodic wildfires, which may kill most of the mature trees. Soon afterward, a new cohort of tree seedlings establishes, and these grow into another mature forest. To some degree, foresters can emulate this natural cycle of disturbance when they prepare plans to harvest and manage pine forest.

Usually, however, forestry imposes an anthropogenic patch dynamic onto the forest landscape. For instance, this may occur if forestry creates an unnatural mosaic of clear-cuts and plantations of various ages, interspersed in checkerboard fashion within a matrix of any remaining natural forest and non-forest communities. In some cases, a landscape mosaic of this kind may even be recommended by game managers, because (as we have already seen) it can favour certain hunted species, such as deer and ruffed grouse.

However, the patch dynamics created by the harvesting and management of forests have important implica-

TABLE 23.6	Breeding Birds in Natural Forest and Plantations

Natural, mixed-species forest and spruce and pine plantations were surveyed in New Brunswick. The plantations were surveyed at 3, 6, 7, and 15 years of age, and the natural stands were 60 years old. Only abundant species are listed here. Data are given as pairs/10 hectares; stand age is in years.

| SPECIES | PLANTATIONS | | | | FOREST | |
	3 y	6 y	7 y	15 y	60 y	60 y
Yellow-bellied flycatcher (*Empidonax flaviventris*)	0.0	0.0	0.0	6.9	4.1	1.3
Alder flycatcher (*Empidonax alnorum*)	0.0	5.3	4.3	13.4	0.0	0.0
Hermit thrush (*Hylocichla guttata*)	0.0	0.0	0.0	2.0	2.2	2.6
Magnolia warbler (*Dendroica magnolia*)	0.0	1.9	0.0	13.4	9.3	2.6
Yellow-rumped warbler (*Dendroica coronata*)	0.0	0.0	0.0	5.5	2.2	1.3
Black-throated green warbler (*Dendroica virens*)	0.0	0.0	0.0	0.0	2.2	5.5
Blackburnian warbler (*Dendroica fusca*)	0.0	0.0	0.0	0.0	4.5	6.0
Common yellowthroat (*Geothlypis trichas*)	0.9	15.5	9.2	15.3	0.0	0.0
Song sparrow (*Melospiza melodia*)	4.8	4.4	7.9	0.0	0.0	0.0
Lincoln's sparrow (*Melospiza lincolnii*)	4.4	1.2	17.2	6.0	0.0	0.0
White-throated sparrow (*Zonotrichia albicollis*)	0.0	12.6	5.3	8.4	1.5	0.4
Northern junco (*Junco hyemalis*)	3.5	1.0	0.8	2.5	2.2	0.4
Total bird density	15.7	53.9	47.2	102	57.8	50.6
Number of species	16	20	22	38	42	32

Source: Modified from Johnson and Freedman (2002)

tions for many other elements of biodiversity. For example, if the remaining patches of unharvested natural forest are too small or isolated from each other, they will not be able to sustain all of their native species and communities over the long term. These losses would have negative implications for natural values and for the ecological sustainability of the entire forestry system (see Chapter 12).

Forestry creates fragmented landscapes, containing successionally dynamic patches of silvicultural and natural-forest habitats. Many species of native wildlife find the silvicultural habitats to be adequate for their purposes. Such habitats and their dynamics are, however, incapable of supporting other native elements of biodiversity, whose survival may be placed at risk. If these values are to be protected, they must be accommodated within large patches of natural forest that are protected as ecological reserves.

To achieve a balance between the economic needs of forestry and the need to conserve indigenous biodiversity, the size, shape, and spatial arrangement of the patches on managed landscapes, and particularly the ecological reserves, must be considered. For example, if the protected areas are too few, small, isolated, or young to accommodate all of the biodiversity objectives, then it will be necessary to design a landscape that is more ecologically appropriate. Some design options that have been recom-

mended to meet the biodiversity objectives of ecological reserves are described in Chapter 26.

Some of the National Parks of Canada are among the largest protected areas in the world. Yet many of these are too small to maintain viable populations of some species, or to maintain the ecological dynamics required to allow old-growth forest to persist on the landscape. The species that are most at risk need extensive areas of suitable habitat to sustain their populations. Such species include grizzly bear (*Ursus arctos*), wolf (*Canis lupus*), spotted owl, and marbled murrelet. Even the largest national parks in Canada may not be big enough to sustain these species over the centuries.

In such cases, the protected areas and their surrounding land must be managed as "greater reserves"—that is, as an integrated ecosystem. If forestry continues to be an important economic activity in the area surrounding protected reserves, it must be conducted with a view to sustaining those species and natural communities that might be at risk on the greater landscape. In many cases, this will require changes in the forestry management system. Such changes might include maintaining a network of protected areas connected by corridors and incorporating critical habitat elements, such as cavity trees, snags, and coarse woody debris, into managed stands.

TABLE 23.7	Snags and Coarse Woody Debris in Natural Forest and Plantations

Natural mature forest and conifer plantations were surveyed in New Brunswick. Data are for snags (standing dead trees) and woody debris with diameter greater than 5 cm. Basal area is the cross-sectional area of snags or trees and is a forestry measure related to biomass. Volume is also related to biomass.

	SNAGS		COARSE WOODY DEBRIS	
	DENSITY (no./ha)	BASAL AREA (m^2/ha)	DENSITY (10^3/ha)	VOLUME (m^3/ha)
STANDS OF MATURE, NATURAL FOREST				
Hardwood-dominated	138	3.5	0.28	18.7
Mixedwood	188	3.6	0.30	19.9
Mixedwood	200	5.4	0.36	13.0
Mixedwood	270	4.1	0.27	32.7
Conifer-dominated	698	11.4	0.48	41.6
Conifer-dominated	1115	19.5	0.86	45.4
Conifer-dominated	467	12.7	1.03	56.5
STANDS OF PLANTATION FOREST				
21-year-old spruce	13	0.03	0.13	0.6
15-year-old spruce	0	0.00	0.17	8.9
13-year-old spruce	13	0.20	0.56	14.1
8-year-old spruce	50	0.20	2.73	28.0
7-year-old spruce	0	0.00	2.20	23.9
6-year-old larch	0	0.00	2.04	32.1
5-year-old spruce	0	0.00	2.18	23.7
4-year-old spruce	0	0.00	3.25	52.2

Source: Modified from Freedman *et al.* (1996)

Canadian Focus 23.2

The Greater Fundy Ecosystem

The Greater Fundy Ecosystem (GFE) consists of Fundy National Park plus its surrounding area in southern New Brunswick. Although the National Park is a relatively large protected area (comprising 206 km^2), it is too small to fully sustain some important ecological values, such as viable populations of species that have large territories (e.g., black bear and pileated woodpecker) or certain types of natural ecosystems, particularly old-growth forest.

For these reasons, some ecologists believe that the ecological reserve function of Fundy National Park is threatened by forestry and other economic activities occurring in its surrounding landscape, particularly the development of forest plantations adjacent to the park boundary. In effect, the natural ecosystems of the park are becoming insularized within a matrix of plantations and other intensively managed habitats. (In the sense meant here, insularization is a process in which a reserve becomes surrounded by different, hostile habitat, much like an island in an ocean.) Forestry is not the only important ecological stressor within the GFE. Local stressors include tourism, agriculture, and residential development, while regional ones include climate change and acid rain. However, these stressors are considered less important within the GFE than the extensive conversion of natural forest into plantations.

Most of the natural forest in the GFE is dominated by mixed-species stands of spruce and balsam fir, with lesser amounts of birch, maple, and other tree species. Most of the conifer-dominated stands have been damaged by recent infestations of spruce budworm. From the forestry perspective, the damaged stands represent a degraded natural resource. Often, the residual economic value of the timber is extracted from budworm-damaged stands by clear-cutting, and the site is then converted into a single-species plantation of conifers. These trees will be harvested for pulpwood on an approximate 40-year rotation or for sawlogs on a 60-year rotation.

A team of scientists and resource managers from government, universities, and industry came together as the Greater Fundy Ecosystem Research Group to address ecological changes and issues within the GFE. The GFE Research Group is also a partner in the Fundy Model Forest, one of 10 model forests in a national network funded by the Canadian Forest Service. The broad goal of the model-forest program is to demonstrate sustainable forestry in Canada. In most cases, this is pursued through work on sustainable timber harvests, on management options that increase forest productivity, and on the integrated management of timber, hunted wildlife, and water resources. These, plus indigenous biodiversity, natural ecosystems, and protected areas, are all important priorities in the Fundy Model Forest.

The larger, conceptual mission of the GFE Research Group was to design an "ecologically sustainable landscape" in the Greater Fundy Ecosystem. This must sustain two clusters of values:

■ long-term harvests of economically important commodities—especially timber, but also hunted animals and agricultural crops—and opportunities for ecotourism
■ acceptable levels of other ecological values, such as sustainable populations of native species and viable areas of natural ecosystems

This agenda acknowledges that the National Park cannot be managed in isolation from environmental influences originating in its surrounding area. This is an example of ecosystem-based management because an attempt is being made to manage the entire GFE as a single, integrated ecosystem.

Most of the work of the GFE Research Group has been directed at acquiring a better understanding of the ecological consequences of forest conversion and

reserve insularization, particularly for biodiversity at the levels of species, community, and landscape. The program of ecological research began in 1992 but was able to build on a considerable body of earlier work. The research results have been incorporated into recommended changes to forestry practices, aimed toward the use of ecologically more appropriate systems of harvesting and management in the region. These recommendations have been subject to broad, consensus-building consultations and have been offered for integration into forestry management plans.

The recommendations incorporate two approaches:

■ a landscape-level approach directed toward the management of community types, age-class distributions, and connectedness of patches
■ a finer-grained strategy that addresses the needs of particular threatened species and communities

The recommendations focus on the following:

■ the use of management practices that are compatible with the natural disturbance regime and the geological factors, soils, and other "enduring features" that are important on the landscape
■ the maintenance of water quality and habitats of aquatic species—a goal to be achieved mainly through the protection of riparian buffers
■ the conservation of cavity trees, snags, and large woody debris as critical habitat features
■ the completion of a network of protected areas to represent all natural community types in the model forest

The recommendations of the GFE Research Group were endorsed as "desirable" by the partnership of the Fundy Model Forest during a workshop. Work is now progressing toward incorporating the recommendations into forestry management plans. The next phase of work will be to determine whether key aspects of the forestry management plans are actually achieving their goals of sustaining indigenous biodiversity and ecosystem functions.

Integrated Forest Management

Increasingly, in many parts of Canada, foresters are working with other interested parties to develop **integrated forest management** plans that accommodate the need to harvest timber from forested landscapes while also sustaining other values. Usually, these plans focus on finding ways to conduct forestry while continuing to support populations of hunted species such as deer and elk and fished species such as trout and salmon. In some cases, significant efforts are also made to accommodate other uses and values, such as non-consumptive recreation and ecotourism

Global Focus 23.1

Is Canada "The Brazil of the North"?

Forestry practices are highly controversial in Canada. Sometimes, to gain an edge in the public sphere, individuals or organizations may use relatively extreme rhetoric when making arguments for or against an environmental position. In the 1990s, for example, opponents of intensive forestry practices were claiming that Canada should be viewed as "the Brazil of the North" because of the kinds of forestry being practised here. The point was being especially made in reference to the clear-cutting of old-growth coastal rainforest in British Columbia. But is it reasonable to assign a "Brazil of the North" label to Canada?

Obviously, Canada and Brazil are different places in terms of people, culture, economy, and natural ecosystems. Nevertheless, there are key similarities with respect to forests and forestry between the two countries, as well as major differences. For example, although both countries are still heavily forested, each has lost a major part of the original forest to agricultural development and urbanization. In Brazil, the worst losses are of Atlantic tropical and subtropical forest, as well as forest in Amazonia; in Canada, it is mostly temperate forest in southern regions of the eastern provinces. Both countries have a large forest industry, although Canada's is much more export-oriented. Both countries have designated many protected areas (such as national parks), but neither has designated enough such areas, and appropriate stewardship is deficient in both (e.g., not preventing damage caused by illegal logging or poaching of wildlife, controlling the damage caused by transportation corridors and tourism facilities, or protecting indigenous cultures).

A key ecological difference is in the biodiversity supported by Canada and Brazil. Canada has many indigenous species, but only a few of them are endemic (i.e., species with a local distribution and that occur nowhere else). This is mostly because Canada is a relatively young country, in the ecological sense, having only been released from continental glaciation about 10 000 years ago. In marked contrast, the natural ecosystems of Brazil are much older, and most have developed under subtropical and tropical climatic regimes. The humid forests of such regions support much higher levels of biodiversity, including many endemic species, compared with the natural ecosystems of Canada, which range from polar to temperate. In this vital respect, deforestation in Brazil causes more grievous damage to

biodiversity than it does in Canada because many more species and ecosystem types are affected, and the risks of extinction are greater. This context does not trivialize the importance of avoiding actions that cause native species or natural ecosystems of Canada to become at risk, but it is a valid comparison.

There are many other comparisons that could be made when trying to understand whether we are the "Brazil of the North" or they are the "Canada of the South" (see selected data, below). Ultimately, however, subjective rhetoric is not particularly helpful when trying to help people develop informed opinions about important environmental issues.

Comparison of Forests and Forestry		
	CANADA	**BRAZIL**
Human population (2004)	32×10^6	179×10^6
Total land area	997.1×10^6 ha	854.7×10^6 ha
Forest area (in 2000)	244.6×10^6 ha	543.9×10^6 ha
Deforestation, 1990–2000	0.0%	−4.0%
Original forest as % of land area	66.0%	91.0%
Forest in 1996 as % of land area	64.0%	66.0%
Protected areas as % of land area	6.3%	18.0%
Forest harvest (1999–2001)	182.6×10^6 m^3/y	234.5×10^6 m^3/y
Average trade in forest products (1999–2001)		
Imports	US$4.1 billion	US$0.9 billion
Exports	US$25.7 billion	US$2.8 billion
Number of vascular plant species	3270	56215
Number of fish species	128	471
Number of amphibian species	44	695
Number of reptile species	39	651
Number of bird species	472	1712
Number of mammal species	211	578

Source: Data from World Resources Institute (2005)

(e.g., birding and hiking). Canadian Focus 23.2 describes an example of various interest groups working to develop an integrated management plan for a region in New Brunswick known as the "Greater Fundy Ecosystem."

By co-operating in the design of integrated management plans, the forest industry is attempting to come to grips with some of the important controversies that are arising from their woodland operations. Society expects that the vast forests of Canada will continue to deliver a wide range of ecological goods and services. These include the substantial economic benefits from timber harvesting, while also satisfying the needs of sport hunters, fishers, hikers, and other outdoor recreationists. Even while they are used in these ways, forest landscapes are also expected to provide such ecologically important services as clean air and water and carbon storage, and to sustain native biodiversity.

The forest industry is making some progress in the directions society expects of it, but much more has to be done. This is particularly true of the need to set aside additional areas that are protected from commercial forestry. If they are large enough, the protected areas can allow ecological processes to continue in a manner unfettered by major human influences so that natural ecosystems can develop and native species can sustain their populations. In addition, management systems will have to change to accommodate more of the habitat needs of Canadian biodiversity on harvested sites.

If the Canadian forest industry is to legitimately claim that it is conducting its operations in an ecologically sustainable manner, it must achieve several broad objectives. First, it is critical that the rate of harvesting forest biomass does not exceed the rate of forest productivity. At the same time, it is necessary that other economic values be sustained, such as viable populations of hunted animals and opportunities for outdoor recreation. Finally, it is critical that no indigenous elements of Canadian biodiversity are rendered endangered by forestry. Although the forest industry has been making headway toward improving its environmental practices in Canada, not all of the requirements of ecologically sustainable forestry are being satisfied. Therefore, considerably more progress is required in this direction.

Conclusions

Forestry is a key economic sector in Canada, each year affecting millions of hectares of landscape. Timber harvesting and management of the subsequent regeneration cause many environmental changes, including decreases of carbon storage, alterations of hydrology, erosion, and effects on the habitat of wildlife. Because timber harvesting and silvicultural practices are severe disturbances of forested sites, some environmental damage is inevitable. To a large degree, however, many of the damages could be mitigated by adopting different forestry practices than are currently used. These include less use of the predominant clear-cutting system, replacing it with softer practices such as selection harvesting. Greater attention to the protection of aquatic habitat is also necessary, for example by retaining buffer strips of uncut forest along all watercourses. Some damage to the critical habitat of wildlife on cutovers can also be mitigated, for instance, by retaining cavity trees and by greater reliance on natural regeneration rather than plantations. It is also necessary to protect larger areas of natural forest from intensive resource harvesting. This requires the design and implementation of a connected network of protected areas sufficient to conserve those species and ecological communities that are incompatible with use of the landscape for forestry purposes.

Key Terms

forestry

clear-cutting

deforestation

silviculture

plantation

nutrient capital

selection harvesting

erosion

biodiversity

integrated forest
    management

Questions for Review

1. How do forestry practices threaten the nutrient capital and site quality of harvested stands?

2. How does timber harvesting affect the hydrology of streams and rivers?

3. What elements should an integrated management plan include for a typical forested watershed in your region? Consider the needs to ensure a constant supply of timber, deer, sportfish, clean water, and habitat for non-game species.

4. What are the characteristics of a typical old-growth forest in the region where you live? Do you think that the special values of that old-growth forest can be accommodated by forestry, or can old-growth forest be preserved only by creating large protected areas where trees are not harvested? What are the economic implications of setting aside such large tracts of potentially valuable timber? What are the ecological implications?

Questions for Discussion

1. Consider a typical forest in the region where you live. What are the dominant species of trees, other plants, and animals that live in that forest? What are some important interactions among those species? Consider, for example, the habitat needs of certain animals, including the foods they eat.

2. Are forest products important in your life and in the functioning of your community? Compile a list that shows how trees are used for energy, lumber, paper, and other products. Also consider non-timber uses of forests, such as hunted animals, recreation, and provision of clean air and water.

3. How might forest resources make a larger contribution to the Canadian economy, or to that of your region? Would it be possible, for example, to harvest more wood without degrading the timber resource? Could more people be employed in woodland operations if harvesting and management activities were less mechanized? Consider also the prospects for reducing exports of raw materials such as logs, through increased local processing into manufactured products.

4. Why is it essential that a large and connected system of protected areas be a key part of any landscape-scale plan for ecologically sustainable forestry?

Exploring Issues

1. A proposal is being made to build a lumber mill in an area that is currently wilderness. About 40% of the forest in the area is in an old-growth condition (i.e., older than 200 years). You are an ecologist, working as part of a team of scientists to assess the potential environmental impacts of the forest management plan to supply timber to the proposed sawmill. Your responsibility is to consider the sustainability of the supply of timber and other forest resources, as well as effects on rare species and natural ecosystems. What would you examine to ensure that the forest management is ecologically sustainable?

References

Barnes, B.V., S. Spurr, D. Zak, and S. Denton. 1998. *Forest Ecology*. 4th ed. New York, NY: John Wiley & Sons.

Berger, J.J. 1998. *Understanding Forests*. San Francisco, CA: Sierra Club.

Bormann, F.H. and G.E. Likens. 1994. *Pattern and Process in a Forested Ecosystem*. New York: Springer.

Boyce, M.S. and A. Haney (eds.). 1997. *Ecosystem Management: Applications for Sustainable Forest and Wildlife Resources*. New Haven, CT: Yale University Press.

Buskirk, S.W. 1992. Conserving circumboreal forests for martens and fisher. *Conservation Biology*, **6**: 318–320.

Canadian Council for Forest Ministers (CCRM). 2005. *Compendium of Canadian Forestry Statistics*. Ottawa: CCRM. http://nfdp.ccfm.org/compendium/index_e.php

Crowell, M. and B. Freedman. 1994. Vegetation development during a post-clearcutting chronosequence of hardwood forest in Nova Scotia, Canada. *Canadian Journal of Forest Research*, **24**: 260–271.

Drolet, C.A. 1978. Use of forest clear-cuts by white-tailed deer in southern New Brunswick and central Nova Scotia. *Can. Field-Nat.*, **92**: 275–282.

Freedman, B. 1995. *Environmental Ecology*. 2nd ed. San Diego, CA: Academic.

Freedman, B., R. Morash, and A.J. Hanson. 1981. Biomass and nutrient removals by conventional and whole-tree clear-cutting of a red spruce-balsam fir stand in central Nova Scotia. *Canadian J. For. Res.*, **11**: 249–257.

Freedman, B., C. Stewart, and U. Prager. 1985. *Patterns of Water Chemistry of Four Drainage Basins in Central Nova Scotia*. Moncton, NB: Environment Canada, Inland Waters Directorate, Water Quality Branch. Technical Report IWD-AR-WQB-85-93.

Freedman, B., S. Woodley, and J. Loo. 1994. Forestry practices and biodiversity, with particular reference to the Maritime Provinces of eastern Canada. *Env. Rev.*, **2**: 33–77.

Freedman, B., V. Zelazny, D. Beaudette, T. Fleming, S. Flemming, G. Forbes, G. Johnson, and S. Woodley. 1996. Biodiversity implications of changes in the quantity of dead organic matter in managed forests. *Env. Rev.*, **4**: 238–265.

Gillis, A.M. 1990. The new forestry: an ecosystem approach to land management. *BioScience*, **40**: 558–562.

Godfrey, W.E. 1986. *The Birds of Canada*. 2nd ed. Ottawa: National Museums of Canada.

Gullion, G.W. 1988. Aspen management for ruffed grouse. In: *Integrating Forest Management for Wildlife and Fish*. St. Paul, MN: North Central Forest Experiment Station. U.S.D.A. For. Serv., Gen. Tech. Rep. NC-122. pp. 9–12.

Harris, L.D. 1984. *The Fragmented Forest*. Chicago: University of Chicago Press.

Hunter, M.L. 1999. *Maintaining Biodiversity in Forest Ecosystems*. Cambridge, UK: Cambridge University Press.

Hunter, M.L. 2003. *Wildlife, Forests, and Forestry: Principles of Managing Forests for Biological Diversity*. Englewood Cliffs, NJ: Prentice Hall.

Johnson, G.A.M. and B. Freedman. 2002. Breeding birds in forestry plantations and natural forest in the vicinity of Fundy National Park, New Brunswick. *Canadian Field-Naturalist*, **116:** 475–487.

Kimmins, J.P. 2005. *Forest Ecology.* 3rd ed. New York: Macmillan.

Kimmins, J.P. 1997. *Balancing Act: Environmental Issues in Forestry.* 2nd ed. Vancouver, BC: University of British Columbia Press.

Kimmins, J.P. 2003. *Forest Ecology: A Foundation for Sustainable Management.* 2nd ed. Upper Saddle River, NJ: Prentice Hall College Division.

Krause, H. H. 1982. Nitrate formation and movement before and after clear-cutting of a monitored watershed in central New Brunswick. *Canadian Journal of Forest Research*, 12: 922–930.

Likens, G.E. and F.H. Bormann. 1999. *Biogeochemistry of a Forested Ecosystem.* 2nd ed. New York: Springer.

Martin, C.W., R.S. Pierce, G.E. Likens, and F.H. Bormann. 1986. *Clearcutting Affects Stream Chemistry in the White Mountains of New Hampshire.* Broomall, PA: Northeastern Forest Experiment Stations. USDA For. Serv. Research Paper NE-579.

Maser, C. 1990. *The Redesigned Forest.* Toronto: Stoddart.

Maser, C., R.F. Tarant, J.M. Trappe, and J.F. Franklin. 1988. *From the Forest to the Sea: A Story of Fallen Trees.* Portland, OR: Pacific Northwest Research Station. USDA For. Serv., Gen. Tech. Rep. PNW-GTR-229.

McRae, D.J., L.C. Duchesne, B. Freedman, T.J. Lynham, and S. Woodley. 2001. Differences between wildfire and clearcutting and their implications in forest management. *Environmental Reviews*, **9:** 223–260.

Morgan, K. and B. Freedman. 1986. Breeding bird communities in a hardwood forest succession in Nova Scotia. *Can. Field-Nat.*, **100:** 506–519.

Natural Resources Canada. 2004. *The State of Canada's Forests 2003–2004.* Ottawa, ON: Natural Resources Canada. www.nrcan-rncan.gc.ca/cfs-scf/national/what-quoi/sof/latest_e.html

Swan, D., B. Freedman, and T. Dilworth. 1984. Effects of various hardwood forest management practices on small mammals in central Nova Scotia. *Can. Field-Nat.*, **98:** 362–364.

Swanson, F.J. and J.F. Franklin. 1992. New forestry principles from ecosystem analysis of Pacific Northwest forests. *Ecological Applications*, **2:** 262–274.

Welsh, D. and D.R. Fillman. 1980. The impact of forest cutting on boreal bird populations. *American Birds*, **34:** 84–94.

World Resources Institute. 2005. *Earth Trends. The Environmental Information Portal.* Washington, DC: WRI. http://earthtrends.wri.org/

Informative Websites

Canadian Council of Forest Ministers (CCFM). National Forestry Database Program. http://nfdp.ccfm.org/

The CCFM is an intergovernmental organization representing federal, provincial, and territorial forest ministers. This website is a rich compendium of data about forests and forestry in Canada.

Canadian Forest Service (CFS). www.nrcan.gc.ca/cfs-scf/

The CFS is the federal organization with a national responsibility for dealing with forest-resource and environmental issues. This website contains much useful information and many links.

Canadian Forest Service. The Canadian Model Forest Network. www.modelforest.net/

What's a model forest? The Canadian Forest Service hosts this site that answers the question with publications, forums, and links.

Ecoforestry Institute. http://ecoforestry.ca/

Ecoforestry is a long-term ecologically sustainable and economically sound alternative to current conventional forest management. Visit this site to learn more and find out about upcoming events.

Ecological Society of America (ESA). *Applying Ecological Principles to Management of the U.S. National Forests.* www.esa.org/science/Issues/FileEnglish/issue6.pdf

This publication of the ESA explains how the practice of industrial forestry can be improved by better integration of ecological principles.

Environmental Literacy Council. Forests. www.enviroliteracy.org/subcategory.php/20.html

Forest fires, ecology, and forestry are among the topics covered at this website sponsored by the Environmental Literacy Council.

Food and Agriculture Organization of the United Nations. www.fao.org/forestry/index.jsp

The FAO forestry program addresses how to use trees, forests, and related resources to improve economic, environmental, and social conditions while ensuring that the resource is conserved to meet the needs of future generations.

Forests.org. Forest Conservation Portal. http://forests.org/

This website provides links to a wide array of organizations concerned with forests and their sustainable use.

Friends of Clayoquot Sound. www.focs.ca/

The Friends of Clayoquot Sound is a grassroots environmental organization that is opposed to the logging of old-growth forest, while supporting ecoforestry in second-growth forests, local manufacturing, and reduced consumption. It is especially active in central Vancouver Island.

U.S. Department of Agriculture (USDA) Forest Service. www.fs.fed.us/

The USDA Forest Service is a federal agency that manages public lands in national forests and grasslands. You can find databases, publications, and links to related departments at this comprehensive site.

24 Agriculture and the Environment

Introduction

Agriculture can be defined as the art, or science, of cultivating the soil, producing crops, and raising livestock. Even relatively simple agricultural practices can greatly increase the production of food, compared with the hunting and gathering of wild animals and plants. Prior to the development of agriculture, which first appeared around 10 500 years ago, perhaps 5–10 million people were able to subsist through a hunter-gatherer lifestyle. Today, the world supports an enormous population of humans (more than 6.4 billion in 2005), and almost all of them depend for survival on the agricultural production of food (fishing and hunting also provide some food). Clearly, the development of agricultural practices and technologies, and their enormous improvements over time, are among the most crucial of the "revolutions" in the socio-cultural evolution of *Homo sapiens*.

Agriculture was probably first practised in the Fertile Crescent, a region of southwestern Asia that includes parts of what are now Iran, Iraq, Israel, Jordan, Syria, and Turkey. Similar developments may have occurred simultaneously in China, although the archaeological evidence is less clear. Other cultures discovered the benefits of agriculture somewhat later, in part through the domestication of local species of plants and animals (e.g., in parts of Central America, western South America, and New Guinea). In most instances, however, domesticated species were imported from elsewhere, as in Australia, Europe, and North America. In any event, beginning with the cultivation and then domestication of a few useful species of plants and animals, agricultural technology has advanced to the point where it is able to support an enormous population of humans and our mutualist species (see also Chapter 10).

Modern agriculture involves a number of distinct management practices. In the case of crop plants, these include selective breeding, tillage, fertilizer application, pesticide use, irrigation, and harvesting. Each practice is used to increase the yield of biomass that can be harvested for food or other uses. The practices are typically used in various combinations (i.e., as a management system), which are undertaken as an integrated strategy of ecosystem and species management to achieve a large crop production. These management practices may also, however, cause important environmental damages.

We previously examined agricultural production and economics in Chapter 14. In this chapter we investigate many of the environmental damages associated with agriculture, with particular attention to effects in Canada. We will explore the intensive cultivation of crop plants and livestock separately, and also examine the softer management practices used in organic agriculture.

Cultivation of Crop Plants

Almost all of the important agricultural crops have been domesticated. **Domestication** refers to the substantial modification of crops through the selective breeding of cultivated races ("cultivars"), which are now genetically, anatomically, and physiologically different from their wild, "progenitor" species. Crop plants have been selectively bred to increase their yield and response to management practices and to enhance their palatability. In some cases, thousands of years of domestication have resulted in crop plants that bear so little resemblance to their wild progenitors that they are now incapable of maintaining themselves in the absence of human management. For example, several millennia of selective breeding of maize (corn) have resulted in its cob becoming tightly wrapped within leafy bracts. No longer capable of scattering from the cob, its seeds cannot germinate and develop new plants unless assisted by humans.

A few crop plants have not yet been domesticated. For example, the lowbush blueberry (*Vaccinium angustifolium*) has been cultivated intensively for only the past several decades. In this case, the habitat of wild plants (in the genetic sense) is being intensively managed to increase their abundance and fruit production as a perennial crop. Because little selective breeding has been conducted, the lowbush blueberry is not considered a domesticated plant. Nonetheless, despite this and a few other exceptions, almost all of the world's important agricultural plants have been greatly modified through selective breeding and domestication.

Most crop plants are grown as food while others are used as sources of fibre, fuel, and medicines. Important domesticated food plants include the following:

- **Small grains:** barley (*Hordeum vulgare*), canola (rape, *Brassica napus*), maize (corn, *Zea mays*), millet (*Panicum miliaceum*), oats (*Avena sativa*), rice (*Oryza sativa*), sorghum (*Sorghum vulgare*), wheat (*Triticum aestivum*, *T. durum*, and *T. compactum*)
- **Legumes (pulses):** broad bean (*Vicia faba*), common garden bean (*Phaseolus vulgaris*), garden pea (*Pisum sativum*), lentil (*Lens culinaris*), peanut (*Arachis hypogaea*), soybean (*Glycine max*)

- **Sweet fruits:** apple (*Malus domestica*), banana (*Musa sapientum*), grape (*Vitis vinifera*), grapefruit (*Citrus maxima*), mango (*Mangifera indica*), orange (*Citrus sinensis*), peach (*Prunus persica*), pear (*Pyrus communis*), plum (*Prunus domestica*), raspberry (*Rubus idaeus*), strawberry (*Fragaria virginiana* and *F. chiloensis*), sweet cherry (*Prunus avium*), watermelon (*Citrullus lanatus*)

- **Vegetable fruits:** cucumber (*Cucumis sativus*), pumpkin (squash, *Cucurbita pepo*), red pepper (*Capsicum annuum*), tomato (*Lycopersicon esculentum*)

- **Root and tuber crops:** beet (*Beta vulgaris*), carrot (*Daucus carota*), garlic (*Allium sativum*), onion (*Allium cepa*), parsnip (*Pastinaca sativa*), potato (*Solanum tuberosum*), radish (*Raphanus sativus*), sweet potato (*Ipomoea batatas*), turnip (*Brassica rapa*)

- **Vegetable crops:** asparagus (*Asparagus officinalis*); broccoli, cabbage, cauliflower (all varieties of *Brassica oleracea*); celery (*Apium graveolens*); lettuce (*Lactuca sativa*); spinach (*Spinacia oleracea*)

- **Edible oil crops:** canola, oil palm (*Elaeis guineensis*), olive (*Olea europaea*), peanut, soybean

- **Sugar crops:** sugar beet (*Beta vulgaris*), sugar cane (*Saccharum officinarum*)

- **Herbs and spices:** chili pepper (*Capsicum annuum*), mint (*Mentha* spp.), pepper (*Piper nigrum*)

- **Beverages:** cocoa (*Theobroma cacao*), coffee (*Coffea arabica*), cola (*Cola acuminata*), hops (*Humulus lupulus*), tea (*Camellia sinensis*)

- **Recreational drugs:** cannabis (marijuana, *Cannabis sativa*), coca (*Erythroxylum coca*), opium poppy (*Papaver somniferum*), tobacco (*Nicotiana tabacum*)

Other domesticated plants are cultivated as sources of fibre, which is used to manufacture thread, woven textiles, cordage (such as rope), and paper. Important fibre plants include cotton (*Gossypium hirsutum*), flax (*Linum usitatissimum*), and hemp (*Cannabis sativa*). Some species of trees, such as pines (*Pinus* species), poplars (*Populus* spp.), Douglas-fir (*Pseudotsuga menziesii*), and spruces (*Picea* spp.), are grown in plantations (called **agroforestry**) as sources of fibre. A few plants are grown for energy production, such as maize, sugar cane, and other carbohydrate-rich crops that are fermented to manufacture industrial ethanol that is used to power motor vehicles (usually as a mixture with gasoline known as gasohol). Other crops are grown as sources of natural rubber (e.g., para rubber, *Hevea brasiliensis*), for medicinal purposes (e.g., digitalis, *Digitalis purpurea*), as chewing gum (e.g., chicle, *Achras zapota*), as natural dyes (e.g., indigo, *Indigofera tinctoria*), or for other relatively minor uses.

Humans use many parts of plants. Those parts used for food include seeds (e.g., wheat, beans, and other grains and pulses), flowers (broccoli), fruits (tomato, melons), leaves (lettuce, cabbage), stems (asparagus, celery), and roots, tubers, and other underground tissues (radish, potato, onion). In many cases, the edible parts are tissues that evolved to store energy for the plant, such as swollen leaves and stems, and tubers. In other cases, the edible parts are energy-rich tissues involved in sexual reproduction, such as seeds and fruits. An important part of the domestication process is the selective breeding of crop species to exaggerate their desirable traits. As previously noted, this usually results in the development of cultivars that are extremely different from their wild ancestors.

Production of Crop Plants

The above lists suggest a rather rich diversity of crop species. We must remember, however, that the inventory of cultivated plants is only a tiny fraction of the number of species that are potentially useful as foods or for other

Photo 24.1 Agricultural plants are usually intensively managed to develop a monoculture, which is an ecosystem comprised almost entirely of a single crop species. This cornfield is in southern Ontario.

purposes (there are about 250 000 species of vascular plants; see Table 7.2). Many other species are probably useful but have not been either examined for their potential cultivation or domesticated. Overall, humans eat several thousand species of plants, of which only about 200 species have been domesticated. Of these, only 12 species account for about 80% of the global food production (Diamond, 1999): the cereals wheat, maize, rice, barley, and sorghum; the pulse soybean; the root or tuber crops potato, manioc, and sweet potato; the sugar sources sugar cane and sugar beet; and the soft fruit banana. Of these top 12 crops, the cereals account for about 50% of the calories consumed by humans.

As we examined in Chapter 14, the cultivation of agricultural crops is an extremely important economic activity in Canada. The national production of cereal crops averaged 43 million tonnes during 2001–03 (a 16% decrease from a decade earlier), while that of root and tuber crops was 5.3 million tonnes (29% increase), and meat 3.5 million tonnes (54% increase) (Statistics Canada, 2005a, b, c). The most important plant crops grown in Canada are listed in Table 24.1. Note the general increase in crop productivity (yield) during the 20-year period, due to an intensification of management practices. Note also the large increases in the production of certain crops, in particular canola, pulses, and soybean. The production of certain grains, such as wheat, barley, and maize, also substantially increased, largely in response to increased opportunities to export these agricultural commodities.

Photo 24.2   Orchards of apples, peaches, and pears are forest-like in structure, but they contain only one species of tree (the crop) and are intensively managed to increase production and control pests and diseases. This orchard is on the Niagara Peninsula of southern Ontario.

Management Systems

Various kinds of management practices and systems, varying greatly in their intensity, can be applied to the cultivation of any crop plant (or to livestock). The most intensive management systems may involve soil tillage, planting and harvesting a **monoculture** (only one species), and application of fertilizer and pesticides. Intensive agricultural systems are typically used on relatively large farms and rely

TABLE 24.1	Production of Leading Plant Crops in Canada in 2004 and 1984					
CROP	AREA HARVESTED (10⁶ ha)		PRODUCTION (10⁶ t)		YIELD (t/ha)	
	2004	1984	2004	1984	2004	1984
Wheat	10.37	13.16	23.6	21.2	2.30	1.61
Canola	5.18	3.07	6.67	3.41	1.40	1.11
Barley	4.77	4.91	12.3	10.3	2.80	2.26
Oats	2.02	1.82	3.69	2.58	2.30	1.93
Pulses	2.35	0.17	2.99	0.22	1.90	1.17
Maize	1.23	1.15	9.59	6.78	7.80	5.90
Soybean	1.25	0.41	2.27	0.92	2.20	2.26
Rye	0.28	0.36	0.33	0.65	2.20	1.80
Potatoes	0.18	0.12	5.36	2.78	29.60	23.80
Sugar beet	0.014	0.027	0.68	0.93	56.20	34.30

Source: Data from Statistics Canada (2005a, b)

on specialized, fossil-fuelled machinery to carry out the various management practices (known as **mechanization**). Intensive systems may also be used on smaller farms, allowing greater production on limited areas of land.

The use of intensive management systems is now common in relatively developed countries, such as Canada. It also occurs in commercial, plantation-style agriculture in less developed countries, where commodities are produced mostly for an export market. In contrast, subsistence farming, commonly practised by poor people in less developed countries, involves little or no use of fertilizer or pesticides and no mechanization. Organic agricultural systems used in developed countries also typically eschew the use of synthetic fertilizers and pesticides.

Key practices for growing crop plants in intensively managed agricultural systems include the following:

- selective breeding of crop varieties for higher yield, greater response to management practices, adaptation to local climatic or soil conditions, and disease or herbicide resistance

- tilling the soil to make it easier for seeds to establish and to reduce the intensity of competition by weeds

- planting of crop plants at optimal spacing, often as a monoculture, to increase their productivity and ease of harvesting

- applying fertilizer using inorganic nutrients or organic matter (including animal dung) to enhance the nutrient supply

- irrigating to enhance the availability of water

- controlling weeds by mechanical means (such as tillage) or by herbicide spraying

- controlling invertebrate pests using pesticides (most commonly insecticides and nematicides), by introducing specific diseases or predators of the pests, or by managing the habitat to make it less suitable for the pest

- controlling fungal pathogens using fungicides or by managing the habitat to make it less suitable for the fungus

- intensive harvesting of the crop biomass

- developing crop-rotation and mixed-cropping systems that maintain site quality and help prevent the buildup of pests and pathogens

- using mechanized systems for tilling the soil, planting seed, applying fertilizer and pesticides, and harvesting the crop

- cultivating some crops, such as tomatoes and cucumbers, in greenhouses

- developing so-called "organic" systems that maintain high crop yields while reducing or eliminating the use of inorganic fertilizer and synthetic pesticides

As we noted previously, intensive management systems vary greatly among crop species and among regions, and it is far beyond the scope of this chapter to describe such systems in detail. Nevertheless, we can get an idea of what intensive management systems can involve by examining several case studies dealing with the intensive cultivation of crops in Canadian agriculture (see Canadian Focus 24.1, 24.2, and 24.3). Practices used in organic agriculture are examined later in this chapter.

Management of Livestock

Livestock are raised primarily as sources of food. The most important domesticated mammalian livestock in Canada are the cow (*Bos taurus*), horse (*Equus caballus*), pig (*Sus scrofa*), sheep (*Ovis aries*), and goat (*Capra hircus*). The most important birds are chicken (*Gallus gallus*), duck (*Anas platyrhynchos*), and turkey (*Meleagris gallopavo*). The most important cultivated fish are Atlantic salmon (*Salmo salar*) and rainbow trout (*Oncorhyncus mykiss*) (the cultivation of fish is known as **aquaculture**). Ranching of non-domesticated animals, such as bison (*Bison bison*) and elk (*Cervus elaphus*), is also gaining in popularity.

Livestock in developed countries like Canada are mostly grown under intensive management systems. In large part this involves rearing animals on so-called "factory farms," although beef cattle may spend much of their lives foraging on rangeland, as do sheep. Key practices for growing livestock under intensive management include the following:

- selective breeding of livestock varieties for higher yield and greater response to management practices

- developing "tame" or converted (seeded) pastures to supply fresh fodder and hayfields for direct hay feeding, silage production, or use as bedding

- feeding livestock with concentrated feeds manufactured from fish, offal, pulses, and other products, together with mineral supplements

- using antibiotics and other medicines to prevent or treat diseases

Canadian Focus 24.1

Growing Wheat on the Prairies

Wheat is the most important crop grown in Canada, ranking first in both area under cultivation (10 million ha in 2004) and harvest (24 million tonnes). Most wheat is grown on large, mechanized farms in the Prairie Provinces. The management system used depends on the climatic zone and soil type. The practices described here are recommended for spring-planted wheat in the dark-brown soil zone of Saskatchewan (Saskatchewan Agriculture and Food, 1999).

Tillage: No tillage is recommended; the wheat is direct-seeded (i.e., without ploughing) using tractor-drawn machinery.

Choosing the Variety: Different varieties are used in the various climatic regions of the Prairie Provinces (about eight varieties are commonly grown). They are bred to be adapted to local growing conditions, responsive to management practices, and resistant to diseases and pests.

Planting: Wheat is seeded directly through the stubble of the previous crop (over-wintering stubble helps prevent erosion, conserves soil moisture, and adds organic matter). The recommended planting rate is 0.11 m^3 of seed per hectare.

Fertilizing: Nitrogen is added at about 50 kg N/ha and phosphorus at 25 kg P/ha.

Weed Control: One or more herbicide treatments are required, including a pre-planting treatment with glyphosate.

Pathogens: Various fungal pathogens may affect wheat, including stem rust (*Puccinia graminis tritici*), loose smut (*Ustilago tritici*), and powdery mildew (*Erysiphe graminis*). These may be controlled by planting resistant varieties, by cultural practices that make the habitat less suitable for the pathogen, and by using fungicide. Wheat is also susceptible to bacterial pathogens such as leaf blight (*Pseudomonas syringae*). These are managed by

Photo 24.3 Farming in Canada mostly involves intensively managed, highly mechanized operations. This photo shows a combine harvesting a wheat crop in south-central Alberta.

Source: M. Willison

the use of disease-free seed and by growing wheat in rotation with other crops.

Insect Control: Various insects are pests of wheat, including irruptions of grasshoppers (*Melanoplus* spp.) and the orange wheat-blossom midge (*Sitodiplosis mosellana*). One or more insecticide treatments may be required. Some insect pests can be controlled by cultural practices, including residue management and growing wheat in rotation with other crops.

Harvesting: Wheat is harvested by specialized combine harvesters.

Other Considerations: This management system should be a component of a crop rotation: year 1, canola; year 2, spring wheat; year 3, lentils; year 4, durum wheat; year 5, summer fallow. There is no tillage except at the beginning of year 1 (canola); all other crops are direct-seeded. The practice of direct-seeding helps to reduce erosion.

■ using growth hormones to increase production in certain animals (particularly cows)

■ killing natural predators of free-ranging livestock, such as bear, cougar, coyote, and wolf

■ confining livestock in dense feedlots or factory farms, with feeding to satiation and other intensive husbandry practices

■ developing organic systems that maintain high yields of livestock, while reducing or eliminating such intensive practices as close confinement and the routine use of medicines and growth hormones

Again, it is beyond the scope of this chapter to describe intensive management systems for livestock in detail. We

Canadian Focus 24.2

Growing Potatoes in the Maritimes

One of the most intensive agricultural management systems in Canada involves potato cultivation in the Maritime Provinces, particularly in Prince Edward Island and New Brunswick. The management practices described below are typically used on relatively large, mechanized farms (Atlantic Potato Committee, 1993; Hanson, 1996).

Tillage: The primary tillage is done before planting to break up the soil and facilitate drainage and aeration. This may be done in late autumn or early spring. Tilling in the spring avoids some erosion from sloped fields ploughed in the autumn and left without a cover of crop residue or winter rye. However, spring tilling requires the fields to be dry enough to support heavy machinery, and usually results in a later seeding and less growing time for the crop. A lighter, secondary tillage prepares the seedbed and is followed by periodic between-row tillage to reduce weeds as the crop grows.

Choosing the Variety: Specific varieties are grown, depending on site conditions and whether the crop is to be used as table potatoes, manufactured into frozen fries or potato chips, or used as "seed" (see below). About 20–25 varieties are cultivated in the Maritimes (of which 6–8 comprise about 80% of the crop). However, this is only a fraction of the potato's varietal diversity—hundreds of local cultivars are grown in the Andean highlands, where this crop was first domesticated.

Preparing the "Seed": Potatoes are grown from "seed," which are 35–65-g slices of a tuber containing several "eyes" (buds from which shoots can sprout). The "seed" is surface-sterilized and dusted with a fungicide to prevent soft rot and other diseases. This is a vegetative, or clonal, means of propagation that results in plants being genetically identical.

Planting: Once the soil temperature exceeds 7°C, a monoculture of seed potatoes is planted 15–40 cm apart and 8–13 cm deep, in rows about 90 cm apart, equivalent to a density of 28–74/m². A wider spacing is used for food crops and a closer one for new seed potatoes. A tractor-drawn planter is used.

Fertilizing: Potatoes are a "soil-depleting" crop, so fields must be treated with fertilizer, typically at a rate of 800–1000 kg/ha•y with a 15-15-15 NPK fertilizer (i.e., the fertilizer contains 15% each of nitrogen, phosphorus, and potassium, so each is added at 125–150 kg/ha). Fertilizer is applied when the seed is planted and often during the growing season as well.

Liming: The optimum soil pH is 5.5–6.0, largely to prevent fungal disease. This pH range is maintained by the addition of agricultural lime or crushed limestone.

Weed Control: Weeds are controlled by between-row tillage, done several times during the growing season. Herbicide may also be used, typically at one spray per year.

Fungal Pathogens: Late blight (*Phytopthora infestans*) is a disease that can destroy potato crops, and it is controlled by growing resistant varieties, destroying waste tubers, and spraying fungicide. Other fungal diseases include early blight (*Alternaria solani*), verticillium wilt (*Verticillium* spp.), and pathogens that cause stored tubers to rot. These are controlled with fungicide and by cultivation practices that develop conditions less favourable to the pathogens. Typically, 5–15 fungicide treatments are required per year, depending on the severity of the problem.

Other Pathogens: Bacterial and viral diseases are controlled by growing disease-free seedstock and using cultivation practices that are less favourable to the pathogens.

Pest Control: Colorado potato beetle (*Leptinotarsa decemlineata*) is the most important pest, but other beetles, aphids, and additional insects may also cause damage. Typically two to five sprays of a synthetic insecticide are needed per year. The root-lesion nematode (*Pratylenchus neglectus*) and other nematodes are controlled through crop rotation or by fumigation with a nematicide.

Top-Killing: This aid to harvesting involves one to two late-season sprays with a non-systemic herbicide to kill the potato vines and induce the tubers to form a firmer skin, which gives protection during harvesting and storage. Although the vines will die back naturally, top-killing with herbicide allows for controlled timing of the harvest.

Harvesting: Specialized tractor-drawn machinery is used to harvest, typically four rows at a time, at a speed of 1.6–2.4 km/hr.

Other Considerations: Continuous cultivation of potatoes results in a depletion of tilth, loss of organic matter, compaction by heavy machinery, erosion from slopes, and a buildup of pathogens and pests. Consequently, potatoes are best grown in a three-year rotation with a cereal or forage crop. Measures to enhance soil organic matter are recommended, such as adding livestock manure, leaving crop residues, and incorporating a green-manure crop into the rotation. It should be noted that potatoes can be grown without pesticides, although this is considered impractical in industrial agriculture.

can, however, examine case studies to get an idea of what such systems may involve (see Canadian Focus 24.3).

Environmental Impacts of Agricultural Practices

All of the agricultural practices noted above and their associated management systems cause environmental damages of various kinds. We briefly examine the most important of these in the following sections.

Declining Fertility

Soil fertility refers to the ability of the ecosystem to supply the nutrients required to sustain crop productivity. Soil fertility is influenced by the amount of nutrients present and by factors affecting their availability to plants, such as drainage, tilth, and the quantity and type of organic matter in the soil. We previously examined these factors in Chapter 14 under the topic of **agricultural site capability**. Site quality can be degraded by agricultural practices, which can result in the erosion of topsoil, the loss of organic matter and nutrients, and the buildup of weed populations. These degradations result in decreased crop yields, which may increase the use of intensive man-

agement practices (such as fertilizer and herbicide application) to try to compensate for the damage. Allowing site quality to degrade is a non-sustainable use of agricultural land.

Nutrient Loss: As plants grow, they take up nutrients from the soil (Table 24.2 illustrates typical data for crop plants). When a crop is harvested, the nutrients contained in the biomass are removed from the site (in Chapter 23 we examined this problem in a forestry context). The ability of the soil to supply nutrients can diminish if the removal exceeds the rate at which the nutrient "capital" is regenerated by atmospheric deposition, nitrogen fixation, and the weathering of soil minerals. In fact, nutrient depletion is a common problem with intensively managed agricultural systems; it is most often treated by applying inorganic fertilizer to the land. However, careful attention to conservation of the soil's organic matter and nutrient capital can greatly alleviate the problem of nutrient depletion and may even eliminate the need to add inorganic fertilizer (we examine this later in the context of organic agriculture). Nevertheless, fertilizer application has increased greatly in Canada: in 1971, fertilizer was added to about 3.6 million ha in the prairie region, but this increased to 24 million ha in 2000 (see Chapter 14 for additional data). Fertilizer application rates are, however, considerably lower in Canada than in some other

Canadian Focus 24.3

Raising Livestock on Factory Farms

Enormous numbers of animals are raised each year in Canada to provide meat, milk, eggs, and other products. In 2003, about 526 million chickens were slaughtered in Canada, as were 19.7 million turkeys. The most important larger animals are cows (14.7 million alive, including 1.1 million milk cows), pigs (14.8 million), and sheep (1.0 million) (Agriculture and Agrifood Canada, 2005).

To increase productivity, most poultry, cows, and pigs are reared on "factory farms" under conditions of close confinement and feeding to satiation, along with other intensive management practices. (Many cows spend much of their lives feeding on rangeland or pasture, only being kept under close confinement during a feedlot "finishing" phase of rapid growth before slaughter.) Because of the obvious potential for treating animals cruelly under such conditions, livestock rearing on

factory farms has become highly controversial. Animal-rights groups have protested against the conditions imposed on livestock during rearing, transportation, and slaughter. In addition, many people choose to not purchase foods known to come from factory farms or to adopt a vegetarian lifestyle (many do not wish to participate in what they consider an inhumane economic activity). Partly because of these protests, organizations such as Agriculture Canada, the Canadian Federation of Humane Societies, and food-industry associations have developed guidelines for acceptable treatment of livestock. The following is a selected list of recommended practices for rearing livestock; all are routinely used on industrial farms and are considered "acceptable" by federal regulators (Agriculture Canada, 1984, 1989, 1990, 1991). It is important to understand, however, that many farmers raise their livestock under considerably more humane conditions.

Canadian Focus 24.3 (continued)

Poultry

- The distal third of the beak and the tips of the toes may be amputated to prevent injuries from fighting under close confinement.
- Non-saleable chicks may be euthanized by high-speed maceration, lethal CO_2 or CO exposure, electrocution, or decapitation.
- Day-old chicks may be transported from a hatchery to a rearing facility in boxes containing no more than 100 chicks, and providing each with a floor space of at least 21 cm^2 (this is about four times the surface area of a $1 coin). The transportation time should not exceed 48 hours.
- For the production of eggs by chickens living in open pens, mature birds (up to 1.8 kg) should be provided with at least 0.2 m^2 per bird (about three times the area of a letter-sized piece of paper). For the production of meat in open pens, mature birds (heavier than 3.6 kg) require 0.186 m^2 each. This is considered sufficient to allow the chickens to stand, turn around, and stretch their wings. (Note that smaller chickens may be provided with less space.)
- For chickens reared in cages, mature birds (up to 2.2 kg) should have at least 0.045 m^2 per bird (about 0.75 times the area of a letter-sized paper). No more than seven adult birds should be in one cage.
- The concentration of ammonia in the air during rearing should not exceed 25 ppm. (At this level, humans would experience considerable discomfort.)

Cows

- A mature dairy cow (>800 kg) confined in a tie-stall (in which the animal is tethered by the head) should be provided with a space at least 1.4 m wide and 1.8 m long (2.5 m^2). A mature cow (>700 kg) confined in a free stall (non-tethered) should have a space at least 1.2 m wide and 2.25 m long (2.7 m^2). These dimensions are considered sufficient to allow the cow to groom, get up and lie down normally, and stretch its limbs. (Smaller animals may be provided with less space.)
- Mature beef cattle confined in a feedlot, with paved ground and a shed for cover, should be provided with a space of at least 4.5 m^2 per animal.
- If there is no shed, the space should be at least 8 m^2. A somewhat larger area is needed if the ground is not paved.

Photo 24.4 Most beef cows in Canada spend much of their lives grazing on wild forage. Later on, they may be rounded up and kept for some time in a feedlot, where they grow rapidly prior to slaughter. These cows are grazing on a "tame" pasture of non-native grasses and forbs in Prince Edward Island.

Pigs

- Mature pigs (>110 kg) confined in a slat-floored stall (this allows drainage of feces and urine) should be provided with a space of at least 0.81 m^2 per animal. In a non-slatted stall, there should be at least 1.03 m^2 per animal. These dimensions are considered sufficient to allow the pig to get up and lie down comfortably. (Smaller animals may be provided with less space.)
- Breeding sows (up to 275 kg) kept in individual stalls should be provided with a space at least 70 cm wide and 210 cm long (1.5 m^2).

There are also recommended practices for transporting livestock from rearing facilities to slaughterhouses, which is usually by truck or train. Guidelines for the humane killing of animals also exist; this is usually done by electrocution, shooting, or bleeding, and sometimes by lethal injection. All of these practices are controversial because many people regard them as inhumane. Moreover, facilities for rearing, transporting, and slaughtering animals are inspected irregularly, and sometimes infrequently. This means that, in many respects, compliance with the guidelines is voluntary.

| TABLE 24.2 | Annual Uptake of Key Nutrients by Selected Crop Plants | | |

All data are in kg/ha.

CROP	NITROGEN	PHOSPHORUS	POTASSIUM
Maize (corn)	200	40	200
Soybean	375	30	134
Wheat	210	25	150
Oats	170	25	140
Barley	170	25	140
Alfalfa	500	40	450
Orchard grass	335	50	350
Bluegrass	225	25	165
Potato	211	40	321
Hardwood forest	95	9	30

Sources: Data from Hausenbuiller (1985) and Atlantic Potato Committee (1993)

countries: in 2000, an average of about 54 kg of fertilizer were applied per hectare of agricultural land in Canada, compared with 301 kg/ha in Japan, 228 kg/ha in Germany, 286 kg/ha in Britain, 212 kg/ha in France, and 103 kg/ha in the U.S. (World Resources Institute, 2005). In countries with the highest rates of fertilizer application, agricultural land is relatively valuable and property taxes are high; this creates an economic incentive to use more intensive management practices to increase the rate of productivity.

Often, the rate of fertilizer application is intended to satiate the needs of the crop so its productivity is not limited by nutrient availability. This may result in an excess of nutrients in the soil, causing several environmental problems: pollution of groundwater with nitrate; eutrophication of surface water; acidification caused by the nitrification of ammonium to nitrate, followed by the leaching of nitrate; the emission of nitrous oxide to the atmosphere; and the need to use herbicide to control the weeds that flourish under artificially rich conditions.

Fertilizers are manufactured from non-renewable resources, using large amounts of energy. In Canada, the principal sources of agricultural fertilizer are urea and ammonium nitrate, manufactured by combining nitrogen gas with hydrogen obtained from methane (or natural gas); phosphate fertilizer processed from mined rock phosphate; and potassium manufactured from mined potash. Fertilizer manufacturing has huge costs, including the depletion of non-renewable resources of energy and materials.

Organic Matter: Soil organic matter is a crucial factor affecting fertility and site capability. Organic matter has a strong influence on water- and nutrient-holding capacity, soil aeration, drainage, and tilth (see also Chapter 14). Typical agricultural soil has an organic concentration of 1–10% (it can exceed 90% in the peaty soil of drained wetlands, but this soil is relatively uncommon in agriculture). This is considerably less than occurs in the soil of natural prairie or forest. These ecosystems have a surface layer of litter and humus, and within the mineral soil itself, the concentration of organic matter is at least 15–30% higher than in agricultural soil (Acton and Gregorich, 1995). Therefore, when an area of prairie or forest is converted to agriculture use, there is a significant decrease in the amount of organic matter on the surface and within the mineral soil (Figure 24.1). The lack of organic matter is widely regarded as an important problem affecting the sustainability of agricultural production. Several practices are recommended for increasing the concentration of organic matter in agricultural soil:

- adding crop residues
- adding livestock manure
- adding other organic-rich materials, such as composted municipal waste or sewage sludge
- using no-tillage or low-tillage systems, because ploughing encourages the decomposition of soil organic matter (no-tillage involves sowing seeds by drilling them directly into the ground without prior cultivation)

The use of no-tillage in combination with fertilizer application appears to be especially effective at increasing the amount of organic matter in prairie soil (Figure 24.1).

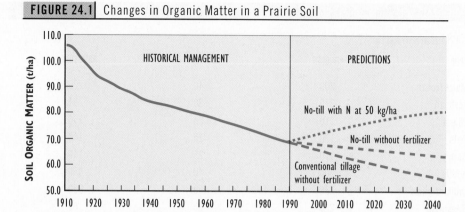

FIGURE 24.1 Changes in Organic Matter in a Prairie Soil

The data are for the surface 30 cm of soil and reflect historical management practices of annual tillage and fertilizer application. The data since 1990 show the potential effects on soil organic matter of (a) conventional tillage without fertilizer, (b) no-tillage without fertilizer, and (c) no-tillage with nitrogen fertilizer application at 50 kg/h•y.

Source: Modified from Acton and Gregorich (1995)

The regular addition of manure is also extremely useful. A 50-year study in Ontario found that annual additions of manure increased the organic matter content in the soil from an initial 85 t/ha to 100 t/ha, compared with 56 t/ha where no manure was applied (this is within the plough depth of the soil, about the surface 30 cm; Environment Canada, 1996).

Soil Erosion: Soil is eroded by wind and by the surface runoff of rain and melted snow. Although erosion is a natural process, its rate can be greatly increased by agricultural practices, and this may become a serious environmental problem. Erosion represents the loss of soil capital, which can impoverish site capability for continued agricultural use. Severe erosion can result in deep gullying of fields, a damage which is almost impossible to rehabilitate. Erosion also causes important ecological damage in aquatic ecosystems by increasing sedimentation and turbidity (both are destructive of fish habitat). Wind-eroded soil can also be a local nuisance to people (e.g., as a source of dirt inside homes and by soiling laundry hung out to dry), and in severe cases, it can literally bury machinery and buildings (as occurred on the prairies during the "dust-bowl" years of the 1930s).

Agricultural practices that increase the rate of soil erosion include the following:

- cultivating land on moderate to steep slopes
- ploughing furrows up and down slopes rather than contouring along them

- leaving fields without a cover (such as stubble or a cover-crop) during the winter

Averaged across Canada, about 20% of the cultivated land is at severe or high risk of water erosion. However, this varies greatly among the provinces, with British Columbia having 75% of its cultivated land in this risk category; New Brunswick, 80%; and Prince Edward Island, 81% (Table 24.3). Although land in the southern Prairie Provinces is at relatively low risk from water erosion, it is more prone to wind erosion (because there are few trees, and fields are often left bare in the winter). On average, 36% of the cultivated land in the prairies (i.e., in areas formerly occupied by native grassland) is at severe or high risk of wind erosion, and 29% is at moderate risk.

Fortunately, the implementation of soil-conservation practices (such as those listed below) can substantially reduce the risks of erosion by wind or water:

- leaving crop residues and/or stubble in the field
- using longer crop rotations
- incorporating a forage crop into the rotation
- growing winter cover-crops
- planting perennial shelter-belts (such as trees)
- strip-cropping
- contour cultivating
- not cultivating beside streams (i.e., leaving a riparian buffer)

TABLE 24.3	Risk of Erosion by Water on Cultivated Land				

Data are % of cultivated land.

PROVINCE	NEGLIGIBLE	LOW	MODERATE	HIGH	SEVERE
British Columbia	5	8	13	3	72
Alberta	39	16	17	10	18
Saskatchewan	51	26	19	3	1
Manitoba	35	41	6	4	14
Ontario	12	11	24	25	27
Quebec	18	21	14	4	43
New Brunswick	0	4	16	13	67
Nova Scotia	3	6	4	3	84
Prince Edward Island	1	7	11	37	44
CANADA	40	23	17	7	13

Source: Modified from Acton and Gregorich (1995)

- using no-till or low-till planting
- maintaining perennial pastures (instead of converting erosion-prone land into cultivated crops)

The use of soil-conservation practices is increasing in Canada, which is helping to reduce the intensity of erosion as an environmental problem. For example, in 1991, 42% of Canadian farmers had incorporated a forage crop into their rotation, while 15% maintained a windbreak, 13% left a grassed riparian strip, 10% practised contour ploughing, 10% used a winter cover-crop, 9% practised strip-cropping, and 22% used other erosion-control practices (often, some of these practices are used in combination; Environment Canada, 1996). The use of conservation-tillage systems is also increasing: in 1991, no-tillage and mulch-tillage accounted for 8% and 24%, respectively, of the seeded area in Canada, while conventional tillage accounted for 70% (note, however, that conservation tillage requires more herbicide use; Figure 24.2). In addition, between 1989 and 1994, about 522 000 ha of cropland were converted into erosion-resistant permanent pasture in the western provinces (i.e., Manitoba to British Columbia). Overall, between 1981 and 1991, the risk of wind erosion decreased by about 7% in the Prairie Provinces, and the risk of water erosion decreased by about 17% in British Columbia, 11% in the Prairie Provinces, and 16% in Ontario and Quebec (it increased by 0.5% in the Maritime Provinces due to an increase in row-cropping, mostly of potatoes).

Compaction: The frequent passage of heavy machinery or the yarding of livestock in dense populations can compact the air spaces in soil, a condition known as **compaction**.

Soil compaction is a serious problem that may result in waterlogging, oxygen-poor conditions, impaired nutrient cycling, poor root growth, and decreased crop productivity. Soil compaction can be largely avoided by reducing

FIGURE 24.2	Costs of Tillage Systems

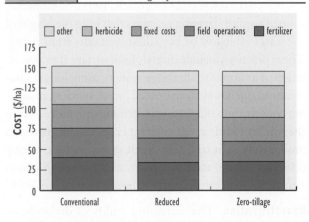

The data are for prairie wheat, obtained by a survey of 250 fields in Alberta during 1988–92. Conventional tillage results in crop residues being incorporated into the soil. Reduced tillage leaves crop residues on the surface, helping to reduce erosion. Zero-tillage involves no cultivation; the crop seed is drilled into the ground. Note that the three systems have rather similar overall costs; $152, $146, and $145, respectively. The no-tillage system incurs higher herbicide cost because tillage helps to reduce the abundance of weeds. The greater use of herbicide is, however, offset by lower operating and fertilizer costs. There is also, of course, a substantial environmental benefit of less erosion.

Source: Modified from Acton and Gregorich (1995)

the passage of heavy machinery over fields, using large tires to spread the load, and reducing the density of livestock kept in penned outdoor stockades.

Salinization: The buildup of soluble salts in the soil surface, or **salinization,** is an important agricultural problem in drier regions. The most important salts are usually sulphates and chlorides of sodium, calcium, and magnesium, which in severe cases are visible as a whitish crust on the surface. Salinization occurs when there are high concentrations of soluble salts in the soil and high rates of evaporation that exceed the water input from precipitation (this brings the salts to the surface where they are deposited). Irrigation practices can be an important cause of salinization, particularly if insufficient water is added to allow dissolved salts to drain to below the rooting depth of the crop. Saline soil is toxic to most crop plants, largely because of interference with the uptake of water, along with ion imbalance and toxicity. In Canada, this problem is mostly restricted to low-rainfall parts of the Prairie Provinces and to a small region of southeastern British Columbia. About 2% of the cultivated area in the prairies has more than 15% of its area affected by salinization, while 36% has 1–15% of the land affected, and the remaining 62% has less than 1% affected (Acton and Gregorich, 1995). Salinization control requires farming practices that keep the height of the water table low or keep dissolved salts from rising. These practices include diversions of surface flow, installation of a subsurface drainage system, using longer crop rotations (including deep-rooted forage species), practising conservation tillage, and increasing organic matter in the soil. In addition, salt-tolerant crops can be grown on moderately salinized soil. Such crops include barley (*Hordeum vulgare*) and forage plants such as alfalfa (*Medicago sativa*) and slender wheatgrass (*Agropyron trachycaulum*).

Desertification: The increasing aridity of drylands, or **desertification,** is an environmental change that can make agriculture difficult or impossible. Desertification may be affecting as much as 30% of the land surface of the planet, directly affecting 250 million people and putting another billion at risk in about 100 countries (FAO, 2005). Desertification is a complex problem, caused by both natural climate change and anthropogenic influences. Particularly important are unsustainable land-use practices in drylands, such as overgrazing, intensive cultivation, deforestation (often to obtain fuelwood), and improper irrigation. These practices can cause the loss of topsoil and vegetation cover and a degradation of agricultural capability; these effects are greatly intensified by prolonged drought.

Desertification is largely a problem of regions that are already marginal in terms of the availability of precipitation and soil moisture to support agriculture. The best-known cases of desertification occur in less developed countries, such as dryland regions in northern and central Africa, south and central Asia, and Latin America. It is also, however, an important problem in the interior of North America and Australia. In Canada, a region of about 300 000 km² in southern Alberta and Saskatchewan is at particular risk of desertification. This region experienced widespread loss of topsoil by wind erosion during the extended drought of the 1930s and is still vulnerable to this kind of degradation. The best agricultural land use in this semiarid region is livestock grazing on unbroken perennial range; the development of "tame" pastures and the cultivation of annual crops are more likely to cause land degradation by desertification.

Pollution Caused by Agricultural Practices

Various agricultural practices can result in pollution of the environment (or, in less severe cases, contamination) by toxic chemicals, sewage pathogens, and other substances (see Chapter 15).

Pollution of Water

Groundwater and surface waters can become polluted by runoff containing agricultural fertilizer, livestock sewage, and pesticides. Inputs of nutrients and organic matter from fertilizers and sewage can cause severe ecological damage to surface waters through eutrophication and oxygen depletion. These changes, coupled with the presence of pathogenic and parasitic microbes and invertebrates, can result in surface waters becoming unsuitable for use as drinking water for people, and perhaps even for livestock or for use in irrigation (see Canadian Focus 14.1).

The most intense problems involve the disposal of the enormous amounts of manure produced by large numbers of livestock kept in feedlots and factory farms. These animals produce about 12 million t/y of manure in Canada, considerably more than the amount of human feces produced (about 2.2 million t/y). Moreover, human fecal waste is mostly treated in sewage-treatment plants (see Chapter 25) rather than dumped into surface waters or onto agricultural land, as is commonly done with livestock manure.

Canadian Focus 24.4

Hemp—An Environmentally "Friendly" Crop

Hemp (*Cannabis sativa*), an annual plant indigenous to central Asia, has been domesticated and used as a multi-purpose crop for about 10 000 years. It has been selectively bred and cultivated for many uses, including fibre, oilseed, and energy. In addition, varieties with a high concentration of the psychoactive alkaloid tetrahydrocannabinol (THC) have been used as non-addictive, recreational drugs (as marijuana and a refined product known as hashish). Varieties used as drugs have a tissue THC concentration of 5–25%, while so-called "fibre" hemp has less than 0.3%.

Fibres extracted from hemp stems can be manufactured into a wide range of useful products: clothing, sails, paper, rope, thread, and building materials. Oil from the seeds can be used to make cosmetics, soap, paint base, varnish, liquid fuel, and edible products (such as margarine). The residue of fibre extraction can be used to manufacture a diverse array of industrial chemicals, and oil-pressing residue is a high-protein additive to livestock feed.

Because of its usefulness, hemp has been cultivated in much of the world. It was one of the first crops brought to North America during the European colonization. In the U.S., for example, hemp was grown by George Washington as a plantation crop, the Declaration of Independence was written on hemp paper, and hemp cloth was sewn into the first American flag. Hemp was also widely grown in southern Canada, where six large processing mills were operating in 1925. In 1937, however, the cultivation and possession of hemp were made illegal in the U.S., and similar legislation was enacted in Canada in 1938. This happened because many citizens and legislators were worried about the abuse of marijuana as a recreational drug that would "corrupt" youth. Apart from the concentration of THC, marijuana plants are virtually identical to fibre hemp plants, so it was felt that the only sure way to ban the drug was to outlaw all varieties. As it turned out, the health hazards associated with smoking marijuana are much less than were popularly feared in the late 1930s and 1940s; nevertheless, the cultivation and possession of marijuana are still banned in the U.S. and Canada. Many countries in Africa, Asia, and Europe never did ban the cultivation of hemp and continue to grow this extremely useful crop.

In recent years, however, attention in North America has again focused on hemp as a potentially valuable crop. Following more than a decade of lobbying by agricultural interests, permission was given in 1998 for the licensed industrial cultivation of low-THC hemp in Canada. Although its cultivation remains illegal in the U.S., hemp is grown commercially on large tracts of sovereign Navajo land in the southwestern states. The increasing cultivation of hemp is part of a worldwide trend: the global value of hemp products was about $5 million in 1993, but increased to $200 million in 1997 and $790 million in 2004.

The re-emergence of hemp as a major agricultural crop could result in some environmental benefits, as a result of both the displacement of more damaging crops and reduced use of natural resources. The environmental benefits of hemp arise from several features of its management.

- It can be cultivated with little fertilizer, insecticide, or herbicide application. (However, hemp does best on better-quality sites and may benefit from fertilizer application.)
- Once the seedlings are established, it is tolerant of drought and can be grown in semiarid regions.
- It is a high-quality, high-yield fibre crop, and so could displace much of the cultivation of cotton, which requires intensive fertilizer and pesticide applications and often irrigation.
- It can be grown in rotation with other crops, such as maize and alfalfa, contributing to agricultural sustainability.
- Its biomass yield is so high, typically 7–15 t/ha•y of dry stalk, that it can be grown as a renewable and CO_2-neutral biomass fuel to displace some use of wood and fossil fuels.
- Its deep root system helps to bind the soil and prevent erosion.
- Useful, diverse, high-quality products can be made from all parts of the plant.
- Hemp paper can be manufactured using fewer processing chemicals than are needed for wood pulp, and it can be recycled more times because of its longer fibres. Moreover, the displacement of tree-based paper helps to conserve forest.
- Ongoing research is finding new industrial uses for hemp, such as the manufacturing of high-tensile composite materials (similar to fibreglass) and cellulose-based polymers.

▶

Canadian Focus 24.4 (continued)

Although the widespread cultivation of hemp might benefit the environment, it is important to recognize that it is not a panacea. As with all crops, large areas of natural habitat could be displaced in order to cultivate hemp. Moreover, the environmental benefits of hemp cultivation can be realized only through integration with larger societal actions to achieve less waste of energy and material resources, including much more recycling and reusing of disused materials, and moderation of the consumerist culture of wealthy countries, such as Canada.

Sources: Twomey (1996) and British Columbia Ministry of Agriculture and Food (1999)

The most important agricultural pollutant of groundwater is nitrate, which originates with manure applications to farmland and intensive fertilizer use. This problem occurs because the nitrate ion (NO_3^-) leaches readily with water percolating through the soil to groundwater (nitrate is highly soluble in water and is not retained by ion-exchange reactions in the soil). Nitrate pollution of aquifers is a hazard for people using groundwater as a source of drinking water. Although nitrate itself is not very toxic, it is converted by microorganisms in the human gut to nitrite, which when absorbed into the blood strongly binds with hemoglobin (forming a compound known as methemoglobin). This reduces the capacity of the blood to carry oxygen. Children are especially vulnerable to this effect; the "blue-baby syndrome" refers to oxygen-starved infants poisoned by high concentrations of nitrate in their drinking water or food.

Nitrate pollution of groundwater is a widespread problem—a study of 900 rural wells in southern Ontario found that 15% had nitrate concentrations exceeding the safe limit (10 ppm of NO_3-N; Health Canada guideline). A similar study in the Okanagan Valley of British Columbia found 33% of wells with nitrate contamination (Acton and Gregorich, 1995). In fact, nitrate concentrations exceeding hundreds of ppm (as NO_3-N) have been found in groundwater in agricultural regions of Canada as a result of the application of manure and/or fertilizer. This important and extensive problem can only be resolved through more prudent fertilizer application practices in agriculture and by prohibiting the disposal of untreated manure onto agricultural land. Manure should undergo sewage treatment just like human sewage does (see Chapters 20 and 25).

The dumping of raw livestock manure can also pollute groundwater and surface waters with fecal coliforms and other intestinal pathogens and parasites. These are health hazards to anyone using the polluted waterbody or aquifer as a source of drinking water or even for swimming. Health Canada has set a safe limit of 50 coliforms/L for drinking water, but this limit is commonly exceeded in well waters in areas where untreated livestock manure is spread onto agricultural land. A study in southern Ontario found that 32% of 900 rural wells had coliform counts exceeding the safe limit; another in Ile d'Orléans in Quebec found that 83% of 35 sampled wells exceeded the limit (Acton and Gregorich, 1995).

Groundwater and surface waters can also be contaminated by pesticides used in agriculture. Pesticide use has increased enormously in Canadian agriculture since 1971 (Figure 24.3). Moreover, some commonly used pesticides are highly leachable in soil; important examples include atrazine, dinoseb, metolachlor, metribuzin, and simazine. Once a pesticide reaches groundwater, it can persist for a long time. Atrazine, for example, typically persists for at least five years. A study of 900 wells in southern Ontario found that 12% had detectable concentrations of pesticides (mainly atrazine), although only 0.2% had residues exceeding the limit considered safe (i.e., 5 µg/L of atrazine). Another study in the Annapolis Valley of Nova Scotia found pesticides in 41% of domestic wells (again, most frequently atrazine; none exceeded the safe limit) (Acton and Gregorich, 1995).

Contamination of Agricultural Soil

An important cause of contamination of agricultural soil by potentially toxic substances is the addition of sewage sludge that contains metals and other industrial chemicals (see Chapter 18). Sewage sludge is an excellent source of organic matter that can enhance agricultural soil. However, if it contains industrial waste, it may have high concentrations of metals and other materials and should not be added to agricultural soil because of the risk of contaminating humans and natural food webs.

Potentially, agricultural soil can also be contaminated by persistent pesticides. This is not generally considered a critical problem in Canada (although some environmental

FIGURE 24.3 | Changes in Pesticide Use in Agriculture in the Prairie Ecozone

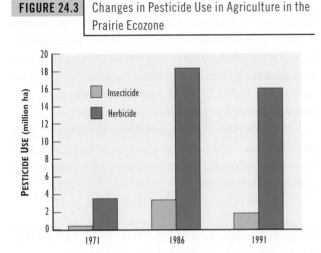

Source: Modified from Acton and Gregorich (1995)

scientists believe that we do not know enough about the longer-term effects of pesticide contamination on soil organisms and nutrient cycling). This lack of concern is largely due to several reasons: most modern pesticides tend to break down quickly, or they are tightly bound within the soil and so are not highly bioavailable, or they are soluble in water and so leach downward to where non-target damage is unlikely. Nevertheless, some agricultural soils retain significant residues of highly persistent organochlorine insecticides (such as DDT and dieldrin; Chapter 22) or inorganic pesticides containing lead and arsenic (Chapter 18). More recently, important damage has been caused to wildlife (including wild birds and mammals) by seasonal residues of carbofuran, diazinon, and some other insecticides (see Chapter 22).

Conversion of Natural Ecosystems into Agroecosystems

Extremely large areas of natural habitat have been converted into ecosystems used for the production of food (**agroecosystems**). This ecological change has resulted in huge losses of natural ecosystems and, in some regions, has had grievous consequences for indigenous biodiversity (see Chapter 26).

Agricultural conversion is the leading cause of deforestation in the world today, particularly in subtropical and tropical countries. In southern Canada (especially in southern Quebec and Ontario), almost all of the initially forested land with good capability for agriculture has been converted into crop production (or into urbanized land-use). The

deforestation has imperilled the Carolinian forest ecosystem and its many endangered species in southwestern Ontario (see Chapters 8 and 26). Similarly, the tall-grass prairie of southeastern Manitoba and southwestern Ontario (the Windsor area) has become critically endangered through agricultural conversion, as have the semidesert and desert of extreme southern Saskatchewan, Alberta, and British Columbia. Although not yet critically endangered, the mixed-grass and short-grass prairies of western Canada are also threatened by agricultural conversion. In fact, most of the rare and endangered plants and animals of the original, natural ecosystems of southern Canada are at risk as a result of the loss of their natural habitat to agriculture.

The damage to biodiversity occurs because agricultural ecosystems provide poor habitat for native species. This is mainly because agroecosystems are simple in physical structure (especially compared with natural forest) and strongly dominated by non-native plants and animals. For example, natural hardwood forest in southern Quebec and Ontario may sustain a diverse assemblage of several hundred species of native vascular plants, bryophytes, and lichens, as well as more than 80 species of birds and other vertebrate animals and perhaps thousands of invertebrate species. If that natural forest were converted to, for example, cultivated pasture for livestock, it would become dominated by only a few forage plants that are not native to Canada. These alien plants would include barnyard grass (*Dactylis glomerata*), meadow grass (*Alopecurus pratensis*), ryegrass (*Lolium perenne* and *L. multiflorum*), timothy (*Phleum pratense*), alfalfa (*Medicago sativa*), red clover (*Trifolium pratense*), and white clover (*Trifolium repens*). The pasture would also support other plants, including species considered "weeds," but almost all would also be alien species. Although highly productive in an agricultural context, such meadows are extremely degraded from the ecological perspective. The same is true, more or less, of other agroecosystems in Canada—they provide poor habitat for native species (the only notable exception is unbroken pasture in the Prairie Provinces; i.e., grazing land that has never been ploughed and sown with alien forage plants).

The conversion of natural ecosystems into agroecosystems is an ongoing problem in all countries. Governmental conservation agencies and private organizations such as the Nature Conservancy of Canada are attempting to purchase the best surviving tracts of natural habitat to protect them from being destroyed. However, limited funds are available for this purpose in Canada, and the losses of natural habitat are still proceeding rapidly (see Chapter 26).

Emissions of Greenhouse Gases

Deforestation and other conversions of natural habitat to agricultural use also result in enormous emissions of carbon dioxide into the atmosphere (see Chapter 17). Natural ecosystems store a large amount of carbon in their plant biomass and soil. Because agroecosystems store much less organic carbon, a net consequence of agricultural conversion is a large emission of CO_2 to the atmosphere. Since 1850, such conversions have resulted in almost as much CO_2 emission as has occurred through the combustion of fossil fuels. Prior to 1750, the atmospheric concentration of CO_2 was about 280 ppm, while in 2003 it was 376 ppm. This change in atmospheric chemistry is an important environmental problem because the increasing concentration of CO_2 may be helping to intensify Earth's greenhouse effect. In fact, increased CO_2 is thought to be responsible for about 60% of the anthropogenic enhancement of the greenhouse effect.

In addition, fertilizer application to agricultural land results in a high concentration of nitrate in the soil. This encourages the process of denitrification, which results in the emission of gaseous nitrous oxide (N_2O) to the atmosphere (see Chapter 5). N_2O is also a greenhouse gas, having about 310 times the warming potential of CO_2. The atmospheric concentration of N_2O has increased from about 0.27 ppm in 1750 to 0.32 in 2003; this gas is responsible for about 5% of the anthropogenic enhancement of Earth's greenhouse effect.

Organic Agriculture

In **organic agriculture**, crops are grown using relatively natural methods of maintaining soil fertility, and pest-control methods that do not involve synthetic pesticides. Compared with conventional agricultural systems, less environmental damage is associated with organic agriculture, and it tends to result in more stable crop yields, which may even be higher than in some kinds of conventional agriculture (Table 24.4). Moreover, operating costs may be lower in organic agriculture because expensive fertilizer and pesticides are not used. Overall, compared with more intensive agricultural systems, organic practices better sustain soil quality, energy and material resources, and also ecological integrity.

Organic Agriculture and Soil Fertility

A major focus of organic agriculture is the maintenance of soil fertility by enhancing natural pathways of nutrient cycling as well as soil tilth (see Chapter 14). In natural ecosystems, microorganisms continuously recycle inorganic nutrients (such as nitrate, ammonium, phosphate, and potassium) from dead organic matter, most of which is plant litter. The microorganisms metabolize the complex organic forms of nutrients, converting them to simple inorganic forms. The fixation of atmospheric nitrogen gas (N_2) by microorganisms is also an important source of nitrogen input in organic agriculture (this involves legume-bacterial symbioses as well as free-living bacteria; see Chapter 5). Overall, the release of inorganic nutrients is typically slow enough that they can be effectively taken up by crop plants, so relatively little is lost to groundwater or surface water.

In conventional agriculture, most inorganic nutrients are added directly in the form of synthetic fertilizer. In contrast, organic methods of maintaining fertility focus on the management and enhancement of soil organic matter, from which natural decomposition makes inorganic

| TABLE 24.4 | Comparison of Conventional and Organic Agriculture in Southern Ontario |

Gross margin is the revenue from the sale of a crop minus the direct costs of its production. The data are five-year averages during 1986–90, involving the study of 234 ha of land managed by conventional practices and 228 ha of organic agriculture.

CROP	YIELD (t/ha)		GROSS MARGIN ($/ha)	
	Conventional	Organic	Conventional	Organic
Maize	5.5	6.4	85	485
Winter wheat	2.9	3.3	175	453

Source: Modified from Henning (1994)

nutrients available to crops. Organic matter is also critical to enhancing tilth, a soil property that helps to bind nutrients and release them slowly for efficient uptake, hold water so that it can be used more effectively by growing plants, and give the soil an aggregated structure with good aeration and easy penetration by roots. Tilth becomes degraded in conventional agricultural systems because tillage increases the rate of decomposition of organic matter, there are relatively small inputs of new organic matter from crop debris, and heavy machines compact the soil.

Organic farmers enhance the organic content and fertility of cultivated soil in three major ways.

- They add livestock dung and urine (often these are first composted) to the soil—these materials contain organic matter and nutrients. However, as mentioned earlier, this practice can pollute groundwater and surface water with nutrients and intestinal pathogens and cause local air pollution with ammonia and odours.

- They add green manure—living plant biomass that is incorporated into the soil by ploughing. The most fertile green manure is legume biomass, such as alfalfa and clover, because these fix atmospheric nitrogen gas, making them a good organic source of nitrogenous fertilizer. Organic farmers also often grow legumes in a crop rotation to maintain levels of soil nitrogen.

- They add **compost**, or partially decomposed and humified organic material, to the soil. Composting is a partly aerobic process by which microorganisms and soil animals fragment and decompose organic material, eventually forming complex, high-molecular-weight humic substances. These are resistant to further decay and are extremely useful as a soil conditioner and organic fertilizer.

It is important to understand that growing plants take up the same inorganic forms of nutrients (such as nitrate, ammonium, and phosphate) from soil regardless of whether these are supplied by organic practices or with manufactured fertilizer. The important difference is in the role of ecological processes versus manufacturing—organic methods rely heavily on renewable sources of energy and materials, rather than non-renewable resources. Overall, the longer-term effects on soil fertility and tilth using organic practices are much less damaging than those associated with conventional, intensive agriculture.

Organic Agriculture and Pest Management

All agroecosystems have problems with pests. In conventional agriculture, pests are usually managed using pesticides (often within the context of integrated pest management; see Chapter 22). Although pesticides can reduce the effects of pests on productivity, their use may also cause environmental damage. Instead of synthetic, manufactured pesticides, organic farmers rely on other methods of pest management, such as the following.

- using crop varieties that are resistant to pests and diseases

- using biological pest management by introducing or enhancing populations of natural predators, parasites, or diseases

- changing habitat conditions to make them less suitable for pests, for example by growing crops in mixed culture rather than in monoculture, by rotating crops or using a fallow period to avoid a buildup of pest populations, and by using mechanical methods of weed control such as hand pulling and shallow inter-row ploughing

- undertaking careful monitoring of pest abundance so that specific control tactics are used only when necessary

- using pesticides that are based on natural products, for example an insecticide based on the bacterium *Bacillus thuringiensis* (*Bt*) that may be considered acceptable in organic agriculture, or one based on pyrethrum, which is extracted from a daisy-like plant, but not synthetic analogues of these, such as genetically engineered *Bt* or synthesized pyrethroids.

Organic farmers, as well as the consumers of their produce, must be relatively tolerant of some of the damage and lower yields that pests may cause. For example, most consumers of organic produce are satisfied with apples that have some blemishes caused by the scab fungus (*Venturia inaequalis*); this aesthetic problem does not affect the nutritional quality or safety of the apples. In conventional agriculture, this cosmetic damage is managed by applying fungicide, so as to provide consumers with apples having an aesthetic quality (i.e., blemish-free) they have been conditioned to expect.

Use of Antibiotics, Growth-Regulating Compounds, and Transgenic Crops

Intensive livestock rearing may involve keeping animals together under crowded conditions in poorly ventilated environments, often continuously exposed to their own manure and urine. Animals kept in such unsanitary conditions are vulnerable to infection, which may retard their growth or kill them. In conventional agriculture, this problem is managed partly through the use of antibiotics, which may be given to sick animals or added continuously to the feed of the entire herd as a prophylactic treatment. Ultimately, humans are exposed to small residues of antibiotics when they eat the products of these animals. Although this low-level exposure has not been conclusively demonstrated to pose an unacceptable health risk to people, this issue is nevertheless controversial. Another potential problem lies in the development of antibiotic-resistant pathogens, resulting in antibiotics becoming less effective for medical purposes.

Organic farmers might use antibiotics to treat an infection in a particular sick animal, but they do not continuously add them to livestock feed. In addition, many raise their animals under more open and sanitary conditions than those used in conventional agriculture. Animals that are relatively free of the stresses of crowding and constant exposure to manure are more resistant to diseases and have less need for antibiotic treatment.

In addition, some industrial systems for raising livestock use synthetic hormones, such as bovine growth hormone, that increase the growth rate of animals or the production of milk. Inevitably, these hormones persist as trace contaminants in animal products that are consumed by humans. Although no risk to humans has been conclusively demonstrated from these exposures, there is controversy about the potential effects. Organic farmers do not use synthetic growth hormones to enhance the productivity of their livestock.

Another recent innovation in agriculture is the use of so-called "transgenic" crops, which have been genetically modified through the introduction of genetic material (DNA or RNA) from another species (see In Detail 6.3). The intention of this bioengineering is to confer some advantage to the crop plant that cannot be developed through selective breeding, which relies only on the intrinsic genetic information (genome) naturally present in the species. Varieties of several important crop plants grown in Canada are transgenic and have been patented by the private companies that developed and market them. For example, a transgenic variety of canola is resistant to glyphosate, allowing that herbicide to be used as part of the management system of the crop. Transgenic varieties of maize and potato produce the insecticide naturally synthesized by *Bt* and so are resistant to some insect pests. Transgenic crops are increasingly being grown in conventional agriculture in Canada and elsewhere, but they are not generally used in organic agriculture.

Organic versus Conventional Agriculture

Many people believe that organically grown food is safer or more nutritious than food grown by conventional agriculture. This belief is mainly influenced by the knowledge that non-organic foods often have traces of contamination with pesticides, antibiotics, and growth hormones and the belief that this contamination poses a health risk. This topic is highly controversial, but it is important to understand that scientific research has not conclusively demonstrated that organically grown foods are generally safer or more nutritious than conventional agricultural produce.

From the purely environmental perspective, the most important benefits of organic agriculture are reduced use of non-renewable sources of energy and materials, better health of the agroecosystem, and enhanced sustainability of food production. Clearly, the environmental damages and resource depletion associated with organic agriculture are less than those of conventional systems. However, because organic agriculture is not yet widely practised, the produce is often relatively expensive to buy. Nevertheless, society and the environment receive a considerable net benefit from the use of organic agricultural systems.

It appears that organic agricultural systems will not become more widely adopted until a number of socioeconomic conditions change. First, more consumers must be willing to pay the higher costs of organically grown food and to accept a lower aesthetic quality in certain foodstuffs. Second, vested agricultural interests in business, government, and universities must become more sympathetic to the goals and softer environmental impact of organic agriculture. These institutions must support more research to advance organic agriculture and promote its use. Finally, the practitioners of conventional agricultural systems must deal more directly with the environmental damages associated with their activities, especially the use of manufactured pesticides and fertilizers. If this were done, it would probably eliminate or even reverse the existing price differential between food produced by organic and by conventional agricultural systems.

Conclusions

Agriculture is a huge and necessary economic enterprise because it provides food for billions of people. A variety of crops are grown in various parts of the world, many of them domesticated, but only a few key crops account for most of the food production—barley, maize, manioc, potato, rice, sorghum, soybean, sweet potato, and wheat. Much environmental damage is associated with agriculture, including pollution, degraded fertility of the land, and the destruction of natural habitats through conversion. In addition, livestock may not be treated well in the industrial agro-food system, often being subjected to unnecessarily inhumane conditions while being cultivated, transported, or slaughtered. Much of the damage associated with agriculture can be avoided by using more organic means of production and processing. This is the major environmental advantage of organic foods, along with the perception of health benefits by many consumers. Although organic foods are usually somewhat more expensive to purchase than conventionally produced foods, the price differential is more than offset by the environmental benefits associated with improved stewardship of agricultural land, the conservation of non-renewable resources, and decreased pollution.

Key Terms

domestication

agroforestry

monoculture

mechanization

aquaculture

agricultural site capability

compaction

salinization

desertification

agroecosystem

organic agriculture

compost

Questions for Review

1. What are the processes by which plants and animals become domesticated? How do these processes work?

2. Make a list of the most important food crops, both plant and animal, that are grown in Canada. For comparison, make a list for any selected country not in North America.

3. Make a list of the most important environmental effects of agriculture. Which of them do you think could be avoided relatively easily, and which not?

4. How is the production of agricultural crops important to you? How does agriculture contribute to the size and functioning of the Canadian economy?

Questions for Discussion

1. Can humans be viewed as a domesticated species? Explain your answer.

2. Agricultural activities cause serious and widespread environmental damage in terms of pollution and losses of natural habitats. Why do these damages seem to attract less attention than those associated with forestry, fossil-fuel and metal mining, and other industrial activities? Are agriculture-related environmental damages being treated seriously enough?

3. Consider the practices used in raising livestock on factory farms and in transporting and processing them in industrial slaughterhouses. Do you think that these animals are being treated in an ethically acceptable manner?

4. Canadian agriculture is highly mechanized and depends on the use of large amounts of fossil fuels and non-renewable materials such as steel and plastics. How do these circumstances pose risks for the longer-term sustainability of agriculture in Canada?

Exploring Issues

1. Select a crop plant or animal that is cultivated in the province where you live. Contact your provincial agricultural department to find out what practices are recommended for growing the crop and what its production costs and economic value are. (This information may be available from the department's website.)

2. Make a list of key agricultural practices (such as tillage, planting, fertilizer application, and pest control), and compare how they are done in conventional and organic agriculture. Based on your comparison, do you think organic agriculture causes fewer environmental damages than conventional practices?

3. A committee of the House of Parliament is examining organic agriculture in Canada. The committee has asked you to compare the environmental effects of conventional and organic agricultural practices. What information about crop production and ecological impact would you assemble for the committee?

References

Acton, D.F. and L.J. Gregorich (eds.). 1995. *The Health of Our Soils: Toward Sustainable Agriculture in Canada.* Ottawa, ON: Agriculture and Agri-Food Canada. http://res2.agr.gc.ca/publications/hs/index_e.htm

Agriculture Canada. 1984. *Recommended Code of Practice for the Care and Handling of Pigs*. Ottawa, ON: Agriculture Canada.

Agriculture Canada. 1989. *Recommended Code of Practice for the Care and Handling of Poultry from Hatchery to Processing Plant*. Ottawa, ON: Agriculture Canada.

Agriculture Canada. 1990. *Recommended Code of Practice for the Care and Handling of Dairy Cattle*. Ottawa, ON: Agriculture Canada.

Agriculture Canada. 1991. *Recommended Code of Practice for the Care and Handling of Farm Animals: Beef Cattle*. Ottawa, ON: Agriculture Canada.

Atlantic Potato Committee. 1993. *Atlantic Canada Potato Guide*. Fredericton, NB: Atlantic Provinces Agricultural Services Co-ordinating Committee.

British Columbia Ministry of Agriculture and Food. 1999. *Industrial Hemp*. www.agf.gov.bc.ca/croplive/plant/horticult/hemp/hempinfo.pdf

Carroll, C.R., J.H. Vandermeer, and P. Rossett. 1990. *Agroecology*. New York: McGraw Hill.

Clay, J. 2003. *World Agriculture and the Environment. A Commodity-by-Commodity to Impacts and Practices*. Washington, DC: Island Press.

Clements, D. and A. Shrestra. 2004. *New Dimensions in Agroecology*. New York: Food Products Press.

Conford, P. (ed.). 1992. *A Future for the Land. Organic Practice from a Global Perspective*. Bideford, UK: Green Books.

Diamond, J. 1999. *Guns, Germs, and Steel. The Fates of Human Societies*. New York: W.W. Norton.

Environment Canada. 1996. *The State of Canada's Environment, 1996*. Ottawa, ON: Government of Canada.

Food and Agricultural Organization (FAO). 2005. *Desertification*. www.fao.org/desertification/default.asp?lang=en

Gliessman, S.R. 1997. *Agroecology: Ecological Processes in Sustainable Agriculture*. Boca Raton, FL: CRC Press.

Hanson, D.J. 1996. *Maritimes Region Survey of Integrated Pest Management (IPM) in Three Crops: Apples, Blueberries and Potatoes*. Dartmouth, NS: Environment Canada, Pollution Reduction Division.

Hausenbuiller, R.L. 1985. *Soil Science: Principle and Practices*. 3rd ed. Dubuque, IA: Wm. C. Brown.

Henning, J. 1994. Economics of organic farming in Canada. pp. 143–159 *In*: N.H. Lampkin, and S. Padel (eds.). *The Economics of Organic Farming. An International Perspective*. New York: CAB International Publishers.

Loomis, R.S. and D.J. Connor. 1992. *Crop Ecology: Productivity and Management in Agricultural Systems*. Cambridge, UK: Cambridge University Press.

Magdoff, F. and R.R. Weil. 2004. *Soil Organic Matter in Sustainable Agriculture*. Boca Raton, FL: CRC Press.

Saskatchewan Agriculture and Food. 1999. *Crop Planning Guide 1999—Dark Brown Soil Zone*. www.agr.gov.sk.ca/crops/barley/agronomic_information/cpgdkbrown99

Soule, J.D. and J.K. Piper. 1992. *Farming in Nature's Image: An Ecological Approach to Agriculture*. New York: Island Press.

Statistics Canada. 2005a. *CANSIM. Table 001-0010. Estimated areas, yield, production and average farm price of principal field crops, in metric units, annual*. http://estat.statcan.ca.ezproxy.library.dal.ca/cgi-win/cnsmcgi.exe?LANG=E&USECII=1&ESTATTheme=920

Statistics Canada. 2005b. *CANSIM. Table 001-0014. Area, production and farm value of potatoes, annual*. http://estat.statcan.ca.ezproxy.library.dal.ca/cgi-win/cnsmcgi.exe?LANG=E&USECII=1&ESTATTheme=920

Statistics Canada. 2005c. *CANSIM. Table 003-0037. Meat production, supply and disappearance in Canada, annual*. http://estat.statcan.ca.ezproxy.library.dal.ca/cgi-win/cnsmcgi.exe?LANG=E&USECII=1&ESTATTheme=920

Twomey, S. 1996. The re-emergence of fibre hemp in Canada. *Global Biodiversity* **5**(4): 9–11.

United Nations Food and Agriculture Organization (FAO). 2005. *FAOSTAT: FAO Statistical Databases*. http://faostat.fao.org

World Resources Institute. 2005. *Earth Trends. The Environmental Information Portal*. Washington, DC: WRI. www.wri.org/

Informative Websites

Agriculture and Agri-Food Canada.
www.agr.gc.ca/index_e.phtml

You can find anything you ever wanted to know about agriculture and food in Canada at this site.

Agriculture and Agri-Food Canada. ManureNet.
http://res2.agr.gc.ca/initiatives/manurenet

Unbelievably, there is a Canadian site dedicated to manure management. It's bilingual, too.

Canada-Ontario Agriculture Green Plan.
http://res2.agr.gc.ca/initiatives/manurenet/env_prog/gp/

You can download the pdf version of the Canada–Ontario Agriculture Green Plan, as well as read about the many programs supported by this initiative.

FAOSTAT. FAO Statistical Databases.
http://faostat.fao.org/

The Food and Agriculture Organization (FAO) of the United Nations is an international organization that focuses on agricultural development and production. This website provides access to a wide range of useful information about agriculture, forestry, and fisheries.

Food and Agriculture Organization of the United Nations. www.fao.org/

If you're curious about the United Nations' opinion about the state of food in the world, see its website to learn more.

GRACE Factory Farm Project. http://factoryfarm.org/

GRACE (Global Resource Action Center for the Environment) is dedicated to eliminating factory farming in favour of a sustainable

food production system that is healthful and humane, economically viable, and environmentally sound.

HowToCompost.org. www.howtocompost.org/

This website is designed to be a hub for all composting information.

Permaculture.

http://metalab.unc.edu/london/permaculture.html

This page consists of links to many articles, search engines, and mailing lists related to agriculture.

Union of Concerned Scientists. Food and Environment.

www.ucsusa.org/food_and_environment/sustainable_food

The Union of Concerned Scientists felt they should prepare a site that discussed sustainable agriculture and provided updates on relevant issues.

VOT (Vegan Organic Trust). www.veganorganic.net/

VOT's mission is to move toward a world where social justice prevails, where animals have a legitimate place, and the fear of hunger and malnutrition are absent.

World Resources Institute. EarthTrends. The Environmental Information Portal.

http://earthtrends.wri.org/

The WRI is a leading environmental organization that provides excellent information about resource issues.

Worldwatch Institute. www.worldwatch.org/

This international organization provides useful information on a wide range of topics, including the environmental impacts of agriculture, sustainability of agriculture, and food security.

Canadian Case 5

Organic Foods

So-called "organic foods" are produced from plant crops grown without the use of synthetic fertilizer or persistent pesticides. The cultivation of transgenic (or genetically modified; GM) crops is also prohibited, as is the irradiation of foods to keep them from spoiling. Organic meats are prepared from livestock reared on organic feed and without using growth hormones or prophylactic antibiotics. (Veterinarians may prescribe antibiotics for treatment of a known bacterial infection or disease, but there must be sufficient time for the medicine to clear from the animal before it is used to supply any foodstuff.) The label of "organic" can be attached to foods eaten directly by people, such as apples and eggs, or it can be used to label such prepared foods as breakfast cereal, bread, pasta, butter, or cheese. Several non-governmental organizations provide third-party inspections for the certification of food growers and manufacturers as reliable producers of organic foods. Some governments have enacted legislation specifying the criteria for certification, although in Canada only voluntary guidelines are in place.

During the past several years, the production and sale of organic foods has been a rapidly developing sector of the marketplace in North America and Western Europe. Total sales are increasing by 10% to 20% annually and they exceed $15 billion in North America and about $1 billion in Canada, equivalent to about 2% of total food sales (Organic Trade Association, 2004). Major food-retailing chains and smaller outlets both have greatly expanded the varieties and amounts of organic choices that they offer to Canadian consumers. This rapid change in food retailing is occurring because many people are choosing to purchase organic foods in preference to non-organic ones. The shift in consumer demand is being driven by the increasingly widespread belief of many consumers that organic foods are healthier for themselves and their families.

As was discussed in more detail in Chapter 24, the practice of organic agriculture results in substantially fewer environmental damages, and it is often kinder to livestock. There may also be nutritional benefits of organic foods, associated with avoidance of the potential health hazards of pesticide and antibiotic residues, and perhaps also improved nutrient content and flavour. This is a controversial area, however, and some scientists do not believe that there are significant nutritional advantages of organic foods. Nevertheless, the softer environmental effects of the production systems are themselves a good reason why consumers should choose to purchase organic foods.

Unfortunately, a disadvantage of organic foods is that they tend to cost more at the retail level. In part, this is due to the higher costs of production and certification, but as is discussed in the CBC video, *An Organic Food Primer*, there may also be a significant degree of profiteering in the marketplace, occurring because the supply of organic foods is relatively small compared with the consumer demand.

Questions

1. Are you a consumer of organic foods? If so, why? If not, why not?

2. Why do the production systems of organic foods result in fewer environmental damages than those of non-organic production systems?

Video Resource

"An Organic Food Primer." CBC Marketplace, 2002.

Selected References

Canadian Organic Growers. **The National Information Network for Organic Farmers, Gardeners, and Consumers.** www.cog.ca/

Organic Trade Association. 2004. **Manufacturer Survey Overview.** www.ota.com/pics/documents/2004 SurveyOverview.pdf

Urban Ecology

25

Introduction

The Development of Urban Areas

Urban areas are cities, towns, and other places where people live in dense populations. Most urban people are engaged in economic activities that function efficiently in dense populations, such as commerce, manufacturing, education, and services. In contrast, resource-based economic activities, such as cultivating food and harvesting minerals, fossil fuels, timber, or wildlife, occur primarily in rural areas. Modern cities import energy, food, and material resources from the local countryside as well as from countries around the world in an increasingly global commerce. The resource-related connections between cities and rural areas exist at all spatial scales (i.e., local, regional, and global) and are an integral but often insufficiently appreciated aspect of urban ecology.

The development of dense habitations (initially villages) during human socio-technological evolution began about 10 000 years ago, when the advancement of agricultural practices allowed the production of local surpluses of food (i.e., that exceeded the subsistence needs of the farmers). The excess food encouraged the development of artisanal skills and other specialized activities that were most efficiently performed in a central place such as a village or town. New societal activities included organized religion and political systems and the means of administering these over wide areas through hierarchical religious, political, and military structures.

The first villages were probably supported by both settled agriculture and local hunting-and-gathering activities. By about 9000 years ago, small farming villages were relatively widespread in some regions, particularly in the Fertile Crescent (see Chapter 24). By 8500 years ago, that region boasted sizeable walled towns. Similar developments also occurred in China and probably elsewhere in southern Asia.

From these humble beginnings, urbanization of the human population has proceeded, especially rapidly during the past century. Only about 2.5% of the human population lived in towns and cities in 1800 and 5–10% in 1900. Today, about half of the human population lives in urban places, and this is predicted to rise to two-thirds by 2025 (or about 5 billion people). About 90% of this increase in urban populations will occur in poorer, less developed countries (see also Chapter 10). Globally, the urban population is now growing about four times as quickly as the rural population, largely because of the migration of huge numbers of people from the countryside to built-up areas. In Canada, about 20% of the population lived in towns and cities in 1871; 38% in 1900; 63% in 1950; and 80% in 2005 (of which 45% live in cities larger than 750 000 people; see Chapter 11).

In 1750, few cities supported more than 50 000 people (e.g., London was the only one in England and there were none in North America). In 1830, New York and Philadelphia were the only North American cities with a population greater than 100 000. By 1910, however, 52 cities in North America supported more than 100 000 people (New York was the largest, with more than one million). In 1950, New York and Tokyo were the only two "**megacities**" in the world (i.e., having a population greater than 10 million). By 2003 there were 20 megacities, of which 17 were in the developing world, and in 2015, there may be 22 megacities (UN DESA, 2005). The world's largest megacities are listed in Table 10.8 (Chapter 10).

No effective discussion of urban population policies has occurred in any country. Consequently, no population policies exist for urban areas in Canada or elsewhere. How

Photo 25.1   Urban environments are highly artificial. This shopping atrium has semi-natural light, numerous potted plants (all tropical species), an atmosphere that is temperature-controlled for comfort, and an overall ambience contrived to stimulate efficient consumerism.

large should cities be, in order to provide people with safe and clean places to live, while also supplying the goods and services that urban areas can deliver most effectively? If the largest cities are considered over-populated, how can continued population growth be discouraged? Can people be encouraged to move to smaller centres? These and other questions related to urban population policies are extremely controversial, but all will eventually have to be addressed.

Urban Ecosystems

Any urbanized area can be viewed as an ecosystem, because it has

1. a need for enormous *inputs* of energy and materials to sustain its human population and diverse economic activities and to maintain its structure and grow;

2. a complex *metabolism*, including well-developed webs of transfer, processing, and storage of material, energy, and information among interacting organisms and economic sectors; and

3. immense *outputs* of heat and waste materials, which are disposed of in surrounding ecosystems, causing pollution and other environmental problems.

Of course, the habitats of cities and towns are very strongly influenced by human activities; collectively they comprise an "urban-industrial techno-ecosystem" (Chapter 8). The structure of this highly anthropogenic ecosystem is dominated by the dwellings, businesses, factories, roads, and other infrastructure of human society, while also supporting remnants of relatively natural habitats in parks and other less developed spaces. Humans are the dominant species in the urban ecosystem. Although many other species are supported, many of them are not native to the region. Important ecological functions also occur within the urban ecosystem, such as biological productivity and water and nutrient cycling, but these processes are greatly influenced by humans.

All urban areas are intrinsically dependent on surrounding ecosystems to provide them with needed resources and to assimilate the wastes generated. The **ecological footprint** of an urban population is the area of ecoscape (i.e., landscape and seascape) required to supply the necessary food, materials, energy, waste disposal, and other crucial goods and services (see Table 25.1).

An average Canadian has an estimated ecological footprint of about 8.6 ha (Ventoulis et al., 2004). This is the third-most intensive national footprint in the world, after the U.S. (9.6 ha) and the United Arab Emirates (9.0 ha). Some additional comparisons among developed countries: France, 5.7 ha; United Kingdom, 4.7 ha; Germany, 4.3 ha; and Japan, 3.9 ha. Of course, people living in less developed countries have much smaller ecological footprints: Bangladesh, 0.5 ha; Haiti, 0.6 ha; Ethiopia, 0.7 ha; Vietnam, 0.8 ha; and Peru, 1.3 ha. The major influences on the differences in these ecological footprints are related to the intensity of energy and material use and waste production within the national economies.

Based on the Canadian national footprint of 8.6 ha, the footprints of Canada's five largest cities (population data from Table 11.8) are the following:

1. Toronto   41.8 million ha
2. Montreal   30.1
3. Vancouver   17.8
4. Ottawa–Hull   9.5
5. Calgary   8.3

These footprints are about 76 times larger than the actual areas of these cities. Without such enormous regions to draw upon for resources, these and all other Canadian urban areas would be unable to survive.

The Organization of Cities

Urban Planning

Urban ecosystems have extremely complex structures and functions (although no more so than natural ecosystems). To some degree, their development has occurred in an orderly fashion, with certain areas being designated for particular kinds of structures and activities. **Urban planning** is the active process of designing and organizing the structure and function of cities. As such, urban planning contributes to the information needed by legislators and other decision makers to develop sensible and efficient sitings of

- buildings, including homes, industrial facilities, institutions (such as hospitals and schools), and commercial properties;
- infrastructure for transportation, utilities, and waste management, such as roads, railways,

TABLE 25.1	The Ecological Footprint of an Average Canadian

The ecological footprint is the land area in hectares required to supply the goods and services required by an average Canadian (2004 data). The columns represent the following land units:

- ENERGY is the area of natural habitat (especially forest) required to offset the fossil-fuel CO_2 emitted to provide the average goods and services used per person.
- DEGRADED LAND is the area of built-up environment used.
- GARDEN is the area used for vegetable and fruit production.
- CROP refers to cultivated land used mainly for grain production.
- PASTURE is the area used for the production of animal products.
- FOREST is the area required to provide forest products.

	ENERGY	DEGRADED LAND	GARDEN	CROP	PASTURE	FOREST	TOTAL
Food	0.66		0.04	1.20	0.66	0.04	2.60
Housing	0.82	0.16	<0.01			0.80	1.78
Transportation	1.58	0.20					1.78
Consumer Goods	1.04	0.02		0.12	0.26	0.34	1.78
Services	0.58	0.02					0.60
TOTAL	4.68	0.40	0.04	1.32	0.92	1.18	8.54

Sources: Modified from Wackernagel and Rees (1996) and Ventoulis *et al.* (2004)

public-transit routes, electrical transmission and pipeline corridors, sewers and sewage-treatment facilities, and solid-waste disposal areas; and

- green spaces, including parks, playing fields, and boulevards.

Well-planned urban areas have relatively pleasant neighbourhoods where people live and work. In contrast, poorly planned cities can be chaotic, dirty, and unpleasant. In general, urban planning is relatively effective in wealthy, developed countries such as Canada, but much less so in poorer, developing countries where the population is growing and urbanization is proceeding most rapidly.

The dominant planning paradigm since the Second World War has involved the segregation of major land-uses and economic activities into different areas. This kind of urban planning has greatly influenced the design of modern cities, including all those in Canada. It has resulted in many urban people living in discrete suburbs, shopping in large malls, working in factory or office complexes and industrial parks, and commuting long distances among these distinct land-use types. However, this type of planning has contributed to some important urban problems, including the following:

- the rapid growth of huge, multi-city, urbanized regions (sometimes known as conurbations)
- the inefficient segregation of residences from places of work and commerce
- long commuting times for workers
- congested transportation systems
- the decay of neighbourhood life
- environmental problems such as air and water pollution, wasteful use of energy and materials, paving of valuable farmland (many urban areas are located on excellent agricultural land), and losses of natural habitat.

Some of these problems are examined in more detail later in this chapter.

The paradigm of widely segregated land-use is now being challenged by the concept of a more integrated, "neighbourhood" design of urban areas. This involves the development of relatively compact, self-sufficient communities containing a mixture of residential and commercial land-uses. In some respects, this harkens back to more traditional elements of community design, in which housing, employment, local commerce, and recreation were within easy walking distance of each other. The

TABLE 25.2	Land-Use in Some Canadian Cities			

The data show the percentage distribution of land-use in selected cities in 1995.

LAND-USE	VANCOUVER	CALGARY	TORONTO	OTTAWA
Residential	63%	35%	39%	44%
Commercial	6	16	29	7
Agricultural	–	14	2	–
Transportation	7	–	2	13
Institutional	5	12	28[1]	10
Industrial		12	6	– 7
Parks	8	16	–	18

(1) Includes industrial and parks

Source: National Round Table on the Environment and the Economy (1998)

re-emergence of this concept in urban planning has been substantially influenced by the ideas of Jane Jacobs, a geographer who taught at the University of Toronto.

Urban Land-Use

Urbanized areas cover about 20 000 km² of Canada, only 0.2% of the total land. Canada is, nevertheless, a highly urbanized country because 80% of its population (about 22 million people) lives in cities and towns.

Although patterns of land-use vary among cities in Canada, the dominant uses are for residential, commercial, industrial, and transportation purposes (Table 25.2). As such, urban areas are mostly occupied by single-family homes, duplexes, and apartment buildings; commercial, industrial, and institutional buildings; parking lots and paved roads; and other built structures. Non-paved areas are mostly grassy lawns. All of these urban "habitats" are highly anthropogenic in character—they are, after all, places where large numbers of people live, work, and play. Some urban green spaces also contain habitat for certain elements of native biodiversity, as we examine later.

Urban Transportation

All urban areas have complex systems for moving people and goods. The physical infrastructure for transportation includes roads, parking lots, railroads, subways, airports, and water routes, plus the many kinds of vehicles that operate on these corridors. From the turn of the twentieth century to the 1950s, public transit systems were the most commonly used means of personal transportation in Canadian cities. However, use of public transit has substantially declined since then because of the enormous growth in the use of automobiles (Figure 25.1).

Most urban transportation in Canada involves the use of motorized vehicles (Table 25.3). On average, about 93% of passenger-kilometres are travelled by private vehicle (car or light truck); 4% by bus; 3% by rapid transit and rail; and less than 1% by other means (such as bicycles). About 75% of trips are made by car or truck; 14% by public transit; 10% by walking; and 1% by bicycle. In general, larger cities have a better developed infrastructure for public transit. For example, in Metropolitan Toronto, 65% of total trips are by automobile or small truck; 30% by public transit; 4% on foot; and 1% by bicycle (Global Urban Observatory, 1999).

These general patterns are also shown by the costs of transportation in Canada (Table 25.4). In 2004, the average household expenditure on all forms of transportation was about $9208, or about 17% of total household spending. About 83% of transportation spending was associated with owning and operating cars or light trucks. Only about 0.6% was spent on bicycles, even though these are the most energy-efficient means of transportation in urban areas (see In Detail 25.1 on page 517).

Photo 25.2   A large amount of space is allocated to cars and other vehicles in Canadian cities, particularly in the form of roads and parking areas. If intelligent lifeforms on a voyage of discovery were to hover in their spacecraft over a Canadian city, they might initially conclude that the dominant form of life is the automobile.

Urban Sprawl

Canadian cities are growing rapidly for two reasons: (1) most immigrants prefer to live in urban areas and (2) there is ongoing migration of people from rural districts. Both of these groups are seeking economic opportunities, as well as the cultural and lifestyle benefits of living in large centres. Because of the population growth, urbanized areas are spreading into adjacent rural habitats. This phenomenon is known as "urban sprawl."

Initially, all cities and towns in Canada were developed on land previously occupied by natural ecosystems. While this still happens today, much of the sprawl involves the conversion of agroecosystems into urbanized areas. When agricultural land is lost, there is a net depletion of the ability of the landscape to provide food. This is an important problem in parts of southern Canada, where much of the highest-capability land in the country is being converted into residential and commercial habitats. This is particularly true in southern Ontario (especially in the Toronto region and the Niagara Peninsula), in the Vancouver area, and around Montreal.

Urban sprawl is also a great threat to natural habitats, particularly in areas sustaining rare kinds of ecosystems. For example, the area around Victoria, British Columbia is the only place in Canada where dry forest dominated by Garry oak occurs. This forest is habitat to many rare species and is one of the most endangered natural ecosystems in Canada. The continued expansion of residential areas is the greatest cause of endangerment of this coastal oak forest. Conservation agencies in government and the private sector, including the Nature Conservancy of Canada, are attempting to acquire and protect the surviving patches of this rare forest type.

Urban sprawl can also be a threat to the ability of landscapes to provide key environmental "services," such as clean water. One such case involves an area known as the Oak Ridges Moraine, which has become a rallying point for habitat protection against further urbanization in the Greater Toronto Area. The Moraine is a 160-km-long, 1950 km² ridge located north of the city,

and it is composed of hilly terrain underlain by glacial deposits of sand and gravel. Because of its relatively poor fertility, much of the Moraine has remained forested or is used for pasture or other relatively low-intensity agricultural purposes. Groundwater originating in the Moraine is a source of wellwater recharge for about 250 000 people and is the wellspring of 65 rivers and streams and many wetlands. With the rapid growth of the greater Toronto region, however, the Moraine has been subject to increasing pressure for residential and commercial development. Extensive clearing of its forested and pasture areas would degrade the ability of the Moraine to provide clean groundwater for use by people and to support streams and wetlands. Loss of the existing forest would also destroy habitat for many native species that are rare in the region.

In response to intense lobbying from groups seeking to limit new development on the Moraine, the Government of Ontario formed an advisory panel to provide advice about the regulation of land-use in the area. The panel provided many recommendations, including the need to protect about 92% of the Moraine from intensive development, and these were key in the preparation of provincial legislation known as *The Oak Ridges Moraine Conservation Act, 2001*. The Act was used to prepare a comprehensive land-use plan, including provisions for core natural areas and linkages among them, comprising about 62% of the Moraine. In May 2002, the premier of Ontario announced the formation of a non-profit Oak Ridges Moraine Foundation and provided $15 million to fund public education, monitor the Moraine, develop trails, and secure natural habitats. The federal government also announced that land it owns on the Moraine, about 30 km², would be kept as greenspace free of intensive development. These are positive actions, although there is still residual pressure from some landowners to allow more residential and commercial development in the area. Fortunately, the land-use plan cannot be amended for its first 10 years, and this interval may allow increased support to develop for conservation of greenspace in the Oak Ridges Moraine.

Although owning a car or truck is widely viewed as a desirable aspect of the Canadian lifestyle, the reliance on personal motor vehicles seriously affects environmental quality in cities and towns. Compared with other means of urban transportation, personal motor vehicles emit more air pollution, require more physical infrastructure (such as roads and parking space), use more material and energy resources, and are more costly to own and operate. Significant safety hazards are also associated with the use of personal motor vehicles—3032 Canadians died in vehicular accidents in 2001, equivalent to about 1.4% of all deaths in that year (see Table 15.4).

FIGURE 25.1 | Changes in Urban Transportation in Canada

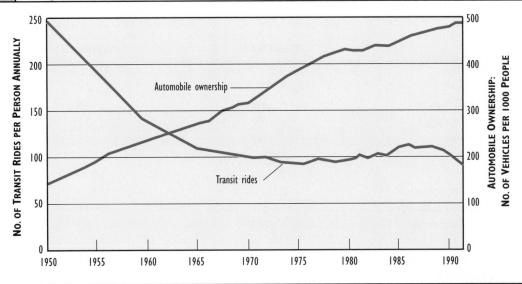

The data show the trends in the use of urban transit systems and in automobile ownership since 1950.

Source: Modified from Environment Canada (1996b)

Urban Pollution

Urban pollution includes elevated concentrations of chemicals and particulates, increased noise and heat, and impaired aesthetics. We briefly examine each of these topics in the following sections.

Chemical Pollution of Soil, Water, and Air

Urban environments commonly have higher concentrations of various chemicals than typically occur in rural places. As well, a wider range of chemicals is present, including numerous synthetic ones. Often, chemical pollution of the urban environment is sufficient to damage the health of people, animals, and vegetation.

Soil in urban areas may become polluted by a wide range of substances, including petroleum products, halogenated hydrocarbons (such as PCBs), and metals. This is illustrated by the following examples.

Hydrocarbon spills: Liquid hydrocarbons, such as gasoline, fuel oil, paints, and solvents (e.g., for dry-cleaning), are stored in many places, including underground tanks at gasoline stations and fuel-oil tanks in homes and commercial, industrial,

TABLE 25.3 | Means of Transportation in Some Canadian Cities

Data are for 1995 and are the annual number of passenger-kilometres travelled by vehicle (x10^9), with percentage of total in parentheses.

CITY	AUTOS & LIGHT TRUCKS	BUS	RAPID TRANSIT	PASSENGER RAIL	OTHER
Toronto	60 (89.5%)	2.46 (3.7%)	2.15 (3.2%)	1.93 (2.9%)	0.46 (0.7%)
Montreal	48 (90.5)	1.93 (3.6)	1.95 (3.7)	0.56 (1.1)	0.56 (1.1)
Vancouver	22 (88.0)	1.85 (7.4)	0.72 (2.9)	0.05 (0.2)	0.41 (1.6)
Ottawa–Hull	16 (94.1)	0.65 (3.8)	0.0	0.0	0.35 (2.1)
Edmonton	17 (94.4)	0.51 (2.9)	0.0	0.0	0.49 (2.7)
Calgary	16 (94.1)	0.49 (2.9)	0.0	0.0	0.51 (3.0)
URBAN CANADA	258 (93.3)	9.91 (3.6)	4.81 (1.7)	2.56 (0.9)	1.40 (0.5)

Source: Modified from National Round Table on the Environment and the Economy (1998)

TABLE 25.4	Costs of Transportation in Canada	

Data are for 2004 and are the average annual household expenditures on transportation in Canada.

ITEM	PER HOUSEHOLD ($)	PERCENTAGE
Vehicle purchase	4039	43.9
New car or truck	2892	31.4
Used car or truck (net)	608	6.6
Bicycle or motorcycle	297	3.2
Boat, aircraft	243	2.6
Fuel	2088	22.7
Insurance	456	5.0
Other operating expenses	1285	13.9
Repairs and maintenance	668	7.2
Parts and accessories	618	6.7
Other costs	225	2.6
Vehicle rental or lease	71	0.8
Parking and tolls	108	1.3
Lessons and licence fees	46	0.5
Commercial transportation	1106	12.0
Urban transit	203	2.2
Taxi	54	0.6
Air	586	6.4
Rail	19	0.2
Bus	74	0.8
Ferry	27	0.3
Other	144	1.6
Total transportation costs	**9208**	

Sources: Modified from Transport Canada (2004); number of households is from 2001 census (Statistics Canada, 2005)

and institutional buildings. Smaller amounts of fuels are contained in all cars, trucks, and other vehicles. Spills of some kinds of liquid fuels can be extremely hazardous because of the risk of a fire or explosion. In addition, if liquid hydrocarbons are spilled onto soil, they quickly penetrate and cause local pollution. Much more extensive pollution occurs if spilled hydrocarbons reach groundwater, where they may spread widely as a plume of tainted water. This can ruin the usefulness of an aquifer as drinking water: as little as 1 ppm of hydrocarbons can result in discernible tainting, and even smaller concentrations of certain chemicals are considered a health risk. It is difficult or impossible to contain a hydrocarbon spill once it reaches groundwater or to rehabilitate a polluted aquifer. It is much easier to avoid hydrocarbon spills than to deal with the environmental damage they cause.

Metals: Urban soil can become polluted by metals in many ways, for example by industrial waste in or near metal-recycling yards and plating facilities. People who live near

metal-recycling factories may be exposed to significant pollution through atmospheric dustfall. For example, severe soil pollution was found in a downtown Toronto residential neighbourhood near a car-battery recycling factory. Lead concentrations in surface soil near the factory commonly exceeded several thousand ppm (one soil sample had more than 5% lead), and some residents had elevated levels of lead in their blood and hair. This astonishing land-use conflict occurred because of earlier, inappropriate land-use planning (i.e., when less attention was placed on environmental concerns). However, the battery-recycling factory still remains in the residential neighbourhood, although it operates much more cleanly than in the past.

Lead pollution of urban soil has also been caused by residues of old paints, which often had very high concentrations of lead-containing pigments (commonly exceeding 0.5% by volume and reaching 38% in the dried residue), especially in white and red colours. (Lead has

In Detail 25.1

The Bicycle: A Green Machine

Invented in the late nineteenth century, the bicycle rapidly became recognized as an efficient, safe, and fun way to get around. Even today, with all of the advances in the development of technologies for powered transportation, the bicycle is still the most efficient means of transporting people on land. This fact is illustrated by comparing the energy typically required to transport a passenger using various technologies (Holcomb, 1987):

Automobile (1 occupant)	1163 cal/km
Automobile (2 occupants)	581
Transit bus	575
Transit rail	553
Walking	63
Bicycling	22

Unlike motorized forms of transportation, bicycle use does not emit air pollutants such as NO_x, SO_2, hydrocarbons, or particulates. Moreover, bicycle manufacturing requires far less material and energy resources, and less physical infrastructure is needed to support these vehicles in terms of space appropriated for roads and parking. Therefore, bicycles represent an environmentally soft (or "green") alternative to motorized vehicles for personal transportation.

There are an estimated 800 million bicycles in the world, about twice the number of automobiles. Canadians own about 13 million bicycles, or 0.42 per person. However, in spite of this number, only about 1% of all trips are made using a bicycle (i.e., many bicycles are not well used in Canada). Great environmental benefits would result if more Canadians used bicycles instead of motor vehicles as a means of personal transportation. These benefits include less air pollution, smaller costs of transportation infrastructure in cities, and less use of energy and material resources. Personal benefits include the convenience of bicycle travel and improved health from frequent exercise.

However, bicycle riding can be dangerous, mostly because of the risk of collisions with motor vehicles. About 2% of vehicle-related deaths in North America involve bicyclists (although motor vehicles account for the other 98%, the per-trip and per-kilometre risk of death associated with bicycle use is more than twice as great; Insurance Institute for Highway Safety, 1999). In the U.S. in 1998, there were 758 bicycle-related fatalities (compared with about 31 700 motor-vehicle deaths); Canadian data are about 10% of that. However, bicycle fatalities have decreased by 24% since 1975, mainly because many cyclists now wear a helmet (about 98% of fatalities involved people without a helmet). Safer bicycle use requires separate lanes along busy roadways, improved awareness by automobile and truck drivers of the need to share the road with bicycle riders (and vice versa), and increased use of safety equipment by bicycle users (particularly true of helmets, and lights and reflective devices at night).

The use of bicycles in Canadian cities can be encouraged in the following ways: by developing a network of cycleways (separate paths for bicycles), bike lanes, and paved shoulders on major roads; by providing secure parking facilities at workplaces and public-transit stations (the latter is known as "bike and ride"); by having a fleet of bicycles for free use or inexpensive rental from a network of pick-up and drop-off centres (this system, used in Copenhagen and several other European cities, is being tried on a smaller scale in a few places in North America); and by educating people about the advantages of bicycle transport and safety issues.

Other ways to increase bicycle use would be much more difficult and time-consuming to implement. For example, urban-planning options could encourage people to live closer to their workplaces, giving them shorter commutes. In addition, legislation could ensure that people using motorized transport pay the full costs of their choice of transportation by withdrawing subsidies for the construction of roads, bridges, parking lots, and other infrastructure and by applying realistic taxes (such as user fees) to offset the costs of associated air pollution and resource depletion.

---

now mostly been replaced in household paints by titanium and other less toxic metals). Soil close to busy highways is also affected by lead from leaded gasoline (this problem has substantially dissipated since the 1990 ban on leaded gasoline in Canada; see Figure 25.2 and Chapter 18).

Eutrophication: Lakes and rivers in urban areas often have an enriched nutrient supply, resulting in increased productivity and eutrophication. The nutrient inputs originate from fertilizer use in horticulture, leaching from septic fields, and sometimes sewage dumping. Urban waterbodies are also commonly polluted with coliform bacteria and other intestinal pathogens and parasites originating from sewage and surface runoff contaminated by pet and bird feces. Lakes and rivers may also be affected by spilled fuel, metals, garbage dumping, and sedimentation with soil eroded during construction activities. Any of these influences on urban lakes may render them less suitable or even unfit as a source of drinking water or for recreational

purposes. Eutrophication and sedimentation also cause significant ecological damage in many urban waterbodies.

Urban air pollution can also be severe, causing life-threatening health problems for many people, particularly the old or very young and those with respiratory diseases. Severe pollution by sulphur dioxide and particulates was once relatively common in North American and western

FIGURE 25.2 | Air Quality Trends in Urban Canada

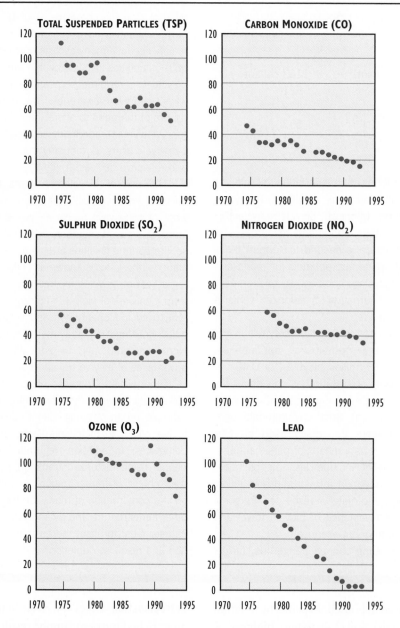

These data are from sampling stations located in urban areas throughout Canada. The data for each year are the percentage change from a standard level for each pollutant.

Source: Modified from Environment Canada (1999)

European cities, largely because coal was burned as an industrial and residential fuel. This problem has, however, been greatly alleviated since the early 1960s because of clean-air regulations in developed countries (see Chapter 16). However, this kind of reducing smog is still severe and even worsening in many rapidly developing countries, where a lower priority is given to enforcing clean-air laws.

In spite of great improvements since the 1960s, cities in Canada and other developed countries continue to be affected by significant levels of air pollution (see Chapter 16). The following are particularly important.

Suspended particulates: Largely originating with emissions from vehicles, furnaces, and other combustion sources, suspended particulates are most commonly fine aerosols of ammonium sulphate and ammonium nitrate along with sooty organic materials. At high concentrations they form a particulate haze that interferes with visibility and is a health hazard to people with respiratory problems. In general, air pollution by suspended particulates has decreased markedly in Canadian cities during the past several decades, mainly because of better emission controls on power plants, other industrial sources, and vehicles, and because many people have switched to natural gas as a heating fuel.

Oxidants: Cities with a sunny climate and a large number of motor vehicles often develop a photochemical (oxidizing) smog during the day, characterized by high concentrations of ozone, peroxy acetyl nitrate (PAN), and NO_x (Chapter 16). The ozone component is responsible for most of the environmental damage as it is toxic to many plants, irritates people's eyes and respiratory tracts, and physically degrades many kinds of materials and pigments. Canada's worst photochemical smog occurs in southern Ontario and Quebec, extending from Windsor to Quebec City, and to a lesser degree in the greater Vancouver area and around Saint John, NB. Canada's air quality objective for ozone (82 ppb) is exceeded on about 25% of summer days in the Quebec–Windsor corridor, where maximum hourly concentrations can exceed 160 ppb (Environment Canada, 1996b). Niagara Falls, Sarnia, Windsor, and Guelph are among the smoggiest cities in Canada, exceeding ozone guidelines for more than 50 days per year (Figure 25.3). The photochemical smog in this region occurs because of local emissions of NO_x and volatile organics (these are precursors in the photochemical production of ozone; see Chapter 16), as well as those blowing in from urban areas in the nearby United States. In contrast, local emissions are the major cause of ozone smog in the Vancouver area. Air pollution by oxidants has been decreasing in Canadian cities during the past several decades, although significant problems still occur during most summers.

FIGURE 25.3 | Ground-Level Ozone in Canadian Cities

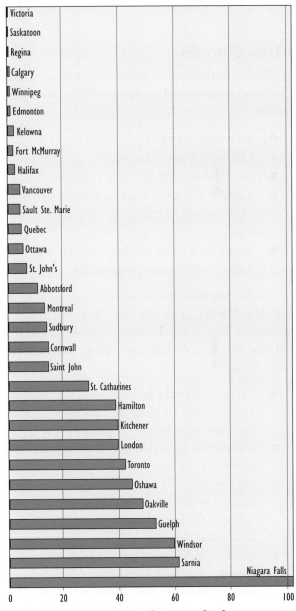

The data show the number of hours per year in which the Canadian guideline for ground-level ozone (82 ppb) was exceeded at urban air-quality monitoring stations during the period 1985–94.

Source: Modified from Environment Canada (1996b)

SO₂ and NOₓ gases: Although so-called "reducing smog" is much less of a problem than before, urban atmospheres still have higher concentrations of SO_2 and NO_x than rural areas. The dry deposition of these gases damages marble, limestone, sandstone, and other acid-sensitive building materials and statues, and it contributes to the acidification of aquatic habitats (Chapter 19). In addition, these gases may be directly toxic to sensitive urban plants and lichens.

Urban Climate

The climate of urban regions is significantly different from that of nearby rural areas. Compared with rural areas, cities typically

- are warmer by 3–6°C;
- have 5–10% more cloud cover;
- receive about 20% less solar radiation;
- have 20–30% lower wind speeds (although wind-tunnelling can increase airspeeds near large buildings);
- have 5–15% lower relative humidity; and
- receive 5–15% more precipitation.

The best known of the climatic differences, called the "heat island" effect, refers to the 3–6°C difference in temperature. Cities are consistently warmer than nearby rural areas because of the following influences on the urban energy budget:

- the emission of large amounts of heat (thermal energy) from buildings and machines (including motor vehicles)
- interference by buildings with the dispersion of warmed air by wind
- the absorption of solar radiation by dark urban surfaces (especially roads and parking lots paved with asphalt), followed by the re-radiation of long-wave infrared energy
- a relative lack of plant foliage in urban areas (the atmosphere is cooled through the evaporation of water from foliage, also known as transpiration)

Thermal Pollution

Thermal pollution occurs when an increase in environmental temperature is sufficient to result in ecological change. Thermal pollution is due to the direct discharge of heat into the environment, often from a point source into an aquatic ecosystem. As the water becomes warmer,

the respiration rate of poikilothermic (cold-blooded) organisms increases, approximately doubling for every 10°C increase in temperature. At the same time, the amount of dissolved oxygen in the water decreases (because the solubility of gases is less in warm water). In combination, the increased metabolism and decreased availability of oxygen cause physiological stress to aquatic organisms. The degree of warming of their environment determines the severity of this stress. Associated ecological problems include changes in the communities of fish, invertebrates, aquatic plants, and algae. Extreme thermal pollution can result in anoxic water, accelerated eutrophication, and fish kills. The ecological effects of thermal pollution can reduce the potential for recreational, industrial, and/or drinking water uses of a waterbody.

Thermal pollution is usually associated with point-source discharges of warmed water from fossil-fuelled or nuclear power plants or other large industrial facilities. These places often use a local waterbody as a source of cooling water. The warmed water is then returned to the environment to dissipate its increased heat content. For example, power plants are typically 30–40% efficient in converting the energy content of their fuel into electricity; the other 60–70% of that energy must be dissipated. The power plants employ heat exchangers to warm the cooling water, which is then released into the environment. Some receiving waterbodies may, however, be too small to absorb all the heat received without becoming excessively warmed (e.g., by more than about 5°C) and suffering ecological damage. In such cases, some of the heat may be dissipated into the atmosphere using special facilities, such as a constructed, shallow cooling pond, in which surface evaporation cools the water before its release into the natural environment; a "wet" cooling tower, in which the water is cooled by spraying it into the air; or a "dry" cooling tower, which uses a system of heat exchangers to transfer heat into the atmosphere (both of these towers are uncommon because of their high costs of construction and operation). Alternatively, some of the "waste" heat may be used to warm nearby buildings, or in commercial greenhouses to grow vegetable crops in winter (e.g., near Bruce Nuclear Generating Station in Ontario), or in an aquaculture facility to grow fish (more commonly done in western Europe than in North America).

Noise Pollution

Urban areas are typically much noisier than rural ones. Most of the noise comes from the operation of various kinds of machines that are abundant in urban places: air conditioners, lawnmowers, automobiles, heavy trucks, and air compressors. Loud music may also be important. **Noise pollution** begins when the level of ambient sound becomes distracting to the normal activities of people (e.g., by making it difficult to understand a conversation or to have a restful sleep).

Noise intensity (also called sound pressure or loudness) is measured in units known as decibels (dB). An increase of 10 dB is approximately equivalent to a doubling of the loudness. When the distance from a point source is doubled, the noise level decreases by about 6 dB. However, when the distance from a linear source of noise (such as a busy highway) is doubled, the sound level decreases by only about 3 dB.

At high intensities, noise pollution can cause a progressive and permanent hearing impairment, initially involving a decreased ability to perceive higher-pitched sound. Under prolonged exposure, the hearing loss may progress through much of the auditory range. Hearing loss is caused by both the duration and intensity of exposure. For example, an occupational exposure to 115 dB may be permitted for no longer than 15 minutes, while exposure to 100 dB may be allowed for two hours and 90 dB for up to eight hours. Noise becomes painful at about 140 dB, although prolonged exposure to levels above 80–90 dB can result in long-term hearing loss. The noise levels typically associated with exposure to various noise sources are shown in Table 25.5.

People may be exposed to excessive noise levels in various ways. Non-voluntary exposures occur in the ambient environment, such as near a road with heavy truck traffic. Occupational exposures can occur in noisy factories or hangars where jet engines are serviced. Voluntary exposures to excessive noise levels are also common, mostly when people attend thunderous rock concerts or use headphones to listen to loud music. It is well known that permanent hearing loss is common among rock musicians as well as people who regularly listen to loud music at concerts, clubs, or using headphones. Frequent target-shooting with firearms can also result in long-term hearing loss unless effective ear protection is used.

Various levels of government in Canada have set criteria for permissible exposures to noise. For example, Health Canada sets standards and guidelines for occupational exposures, while provincial and municipal governments deal with particular sources (such as the amount of noise a vehicle can make) as well as noise levels in the ambient environment. Various actions can reduce the noise intensity in occupational and urban environments. Vehicles

TABLE 25.5	Sound Pressure Levels Associated with Various Sources of Noise
SOURCE OF NOISE	**SOUND PRESSURE (dB)**
Barely perceptible	3
Whisper	20
Secluded forest	30
Bedroom	40
Public library	50
Normal conversation	60
Business office	70
Automobile traffic	70
Heavy truck traffic	80
Air compressor	80
Snowmobile	85
Jackhammer	88
Chainsaw	90
Industrial jointer-planer	100
Pile driver	100
Pneumatic drill	110
Rock concert	120
Jet aircraft (at 100 m)	130
Jet engine (at 25 m)	140

Source: Modified from Timerson (1999)

and other machines are required to have noise-absorbing devices (mufflers) that must perform according to regulated standards. Machines in the work environment may also be muffled, and workers may be advised or required to wear hearing protection. However, significant levels of noise pollution are a pervasive characteristic of cities and of many occupational and recreational environments.

Aesthetic Pollution

Aesthetic pollution is substantially a matter of cultural values. It commonly involves visual images that are displeasing to many (but not necessarily all) people. As such, the criteria for aesthetic pollution cannot be precisely defined. For example, many people might find the following objectionable: a neighbourhood of dirty, run-down buildings; an area cluttered with garbage; a street with a viewscape blocked with gaudy billboards, neon advertising, and other promotions; overhead utility wires; spaghetti-like networks of roads, overpasses, and underpasses crowded with grid-locked vehicles; and paved open spaces without trees, shrubs, or flowering plants. There is, however, no broad consensus about what constitutes aesthetic pollution—some people might find that these scenes have aesthetic merit and may even seek them out.

Aesthetic pollution is not generally considered as important a problem as chemical, noise, or thermal pollution. Nevertheless, urban planners, neighbourhood activists, and other concerned people try to reduce the aesthetic pollution of cities and towns to some degree. For example, many urban areas have bylaws that require property owners to keep their properties clean and in good repair. Some places require that utility cables be buried, or they ban some kinds of advertising. (For example, in order to conserve pastoral viewscapes, unrestricted highway billboards are not allowed on Prince Edward Island.) Reducing aesthetic pollution in urban areas makes them nicer places in which to live and work.

Waste Management

Any discarded materials can be viewed as **waste**. Solid wastes are extremely variable in composition and include discarded food, leaves and lawn clippings, newspapers and other papers, glass and plastic bottles, cans, disposable diapers, construction debris, industrial chemicals, old cars, and disused furniture. Liquid wastes include sewage and discarded industrial and household materials. Gaseous wastes include products of combustion or industrial reactions. **Hazardous wastes** are flammable, corrosive, explosive, toxic (also called **toxic waste**), or otherwise dangerous, and they should either be treated before disposal or discarded in ways that prevent environmental damage (e.g., into a specially designed, secure landfill).

Humans have always produced wastes of many kinds. However, the amount and complexity of discarded materials have increased enormously as a result of industrial and technological development coupled with the growth of population and consumerism. Activities in urban areas produce huge amounts of waste. **Waste management** is the handling of discarded materials, using various methods.

Dumping is the long-term disposal of disused material. The disposal of solid wastes by **dumping** usually occurs into a sanitary landfill (see below). Liquid wastes are most commonly discarded into a nearby lake or river, with or without treatment to reduce the amount of organic matter, toxins such as metals and dissolved hydrocarbons, and pathogens. Gaseous wastes are usually dumped into the atmosphere, although the amount of damaging gases (such as SO_2) and fine particulates may be reduced by pollution-control technologies.

Incineration is the combustion of solid wastes to reduce the amount of organic material. Small-scale **incineration** may involve open burning. However, incineration in urban areas and industrial plants is conducted in large, specially engineered facilities designed to burn efficiently, while controlling the emissions of pollutants to the atmosphere. The residual material, consisting of ash, metals, glass, and other non-combustibles, is usually disposed of in a secure landfill. Overall, incinerators reduce the volume of waste by 70–90% (depending on the organic content); the rest is ash. If the heat produced is used to generate electricity or industrial steam, the incinerator is known as a "waste-to-energy" facility.

Recycling involves the processing of discarded materials into useful products. For example, aluminum pop cans can be collected and re-manufactured into new containers, window frames, or other products. **Recycling** is an extremely attractive waste-management option for three major reasons: (1) it reduces the total amount of waste, (2) it produces valuable commodities from discarded materials, and (3) it helps to conserve non-renewable resources (such as metals and fossil fuels) and some renewable ones (such as trees used to manufacture paper). Easily recyclable materials include glass, all metals, many plastics, and almost all kinds of paper. In fact, these discarded materials should be regarded as "resources" rather than "wastes."

Composting is a type of recycling in which discarded organic materials are allowed to partially decay under warm, moist, oxygen-rich conditions. Backyard **composting** is done in simple bins or piles. To enhance the availability of oxygen, advanced commercial composting systems turn the material occasionally or force air through matter contained in a vessel. All food wastes, lawn clippings, leaves, paper, sawdust, sewage sludge, and other organic discards can be composted. The material produced, known as compost, is rich in humified organic matter and is extremely useful in enhancing the tilth and fertility of garden and agricultural soil (see Chapters 14 and 24).

Reuse involves finding another use for discarded materials, usually with relatively little modification. **Reuse** is an attractive waste-management option for the same reasons noted for recycling. It is even more effective at conserving resources than recycling, because no effort is put into re-manufacturing (other than repairs, if necessary). Reuse is a common practice with discarded furniture, appliances, books, tools, clothes, and other consumer products. Increasingly, institutions and industries are finding ways to reuse paper, cardboard boxes, other containers, wooden pallets, and other disused materials. Often, reusing networks are organized among industries, universities, hospitals, and other institutions, because "waste" materials produced by one partner may be a "resource" for another.

Waste reduction and prevention are not, strictly speaking, waste-management methods. Rather, they are intended to reduce the amounts of waste that must be handled by the above methods. **Waste reduction** and **waste prevention** include the consumer choice to buy products that are not excessively packaged or are sold in reusable, returnable containers. Consumers can also choose to buy less—to have fewer shoes and items of clothing, to own fewer (or no) automobiles, and to adopt other elements of a less consumerist lifestyle. Industries also have many options to reduce or prevent waste production. For example, wood-processing industries once routinely incinerated or land-filled waste tree bark and sawdust, but today they routinely use them to manufacture pulp or as a source of energy. In fact, some Canadian pulp mills now satisfy most of their needs for raw fibre by using sawdust and trimmings from nearby sawmills.

The various ways of managing waste materials vary greatly in their environmental impacts. In general, environmental problems associated with the generation and disposal of wastes are lessened by adopting any of the following "**R**'s" into our individual and corporate lifestyles: refuse (or waste prevention), reduce, reuse, and recycle.

Municipal Solid Waste

Municipal solid waste (MSW) is generated by households, businesses, and institutions such as schools and hospitals. The components of MSW are extremely diverse, but do not include sewage sludge (discussed in the following section) or wastes generated by heavy industry.

Until fairly recently, all MSW was disposed in "open dumps," a practice that may still occur in smaller communities in Canada and in poorer parts of the world. Usually, open dumps are situated in a relatively out-of-the-way natural basin, such as a lake, wetland, or other low area, which is gradually in-filled with waste. Many environmental damages are associated with open dumps, including the pollution of groundwater and surface water by toxic leachate, foul smells, smoke from open burns used to decrease the volume of garbage, large populations of pest animals, and terrible aesthetics. In the 1920s, engineers began to design **sanitary landfills**, where MSW is

Photo 25.3   Solid-waste management is an important function carried out by municipal governments. This image shows a pile of discarded material placed at the curbside for collection. Much of this material could have been recycled, but instead it will be land-filled.

dumped, compacted by heavy machines (such as bulldozers), and covered with about 10 cm of clean dirt at the end of each day. This reduces odours and populations of rodents, gulls, insects, and other pests.

Sanitary landfills became common in developed countries during the 1940s, and advanced variations are now used by Canadian municipalities (although not by all smaller towns and villages). Modern sanitary landfills include the following elements in their construction:

- one or several impervious linings of clay, plastic, or concrete that prevent the downward leaching of water that could contain high concentrations of ammonium, metals, and other toxic chemicals

- a cutoff wall of concrete or other impervious material around the edge of the landfill to prevent the sideways migration of polluted water

- a system of pipes and gravel drains to collect leachate for treatment before the water is released into the environment

- a system of piping to collect methane, an important greenhouse gas produced by anaerobic decomposition of organic matter in the landfill, which can be burned to produce useful electricity or heat

Global Focus 25.1

Garbage—A Canadian Export to Michigan

For more than 25 years, municipal and provincial government agencies have been trying to find a sensible way for the Greater Toronto Area (GTA) to dispose of the enormous amounts of solid waste it generates. The urgency was made worse in the late 1980s, when most of the local sanitary landfills were becoming full and had to close. In fact, the last local disposal site in the GTA, the Keele Valley landfill, closed in 2002. The GTA is not the only region in Ontario with this sort of problem—other municipalities are also faced with a garbage-disposal crisis.

Various planning and public-consultation processes have occurred since the late 1970s, which resulted in suggestions for new landfill sites and/or incinerators to deal with solid wastes from the GTA. However, all of the proposals were rejected by politicians as too controversial, mostly because of intense opposition from people living in the vicinity of the proposed facilities. One longer-distance proposal involved shipping municipal waste of the GTA and other municipalities to Kirkland Lake for disposal in an abandoned open-pit mine (the Adams Mine), but this was also rejected.

Eventually, with a garbage crisis looming, a decision was made to deal with much of Ontario's non-hazardous solid waste by shipping it to Michigan for disposal into privately owned sanitary landfills. This is not regarded as a long-term solution to the disposal of the waste, but rather it is a coping tactic to deal with the problem until a more sensible plan is enacted for disposal within Ontario. In any event, in 2004, about 3.25 million t of Ontario waste were being shipped to Michigan. This was equivalent to 1900 tractor-trailer loads per week and represented about 34% of the Ontario waste that is disposed of into landfills. (The province generates about 12 million t of waste annually, of which 2.4 million t is diverted from landfills by recycling and other means.) About 38% of the Ontario waste that is sent to Michigan is from the Greater Toronto Area, the rest being from private industrial companies and other municipalities, including Durham, Peel, and York. The cost to the GTA alone was about $150 million in 2004.

Not surprisingly, many people in Michigan are not happy about receiving so much solid waste as an import from Canada. Although a lot of money is being made by the private interests that own and run the sanitary landfills in Michigan, and they and their employees are paying taxes to various levels of government, there is intense controversy about being seen as an international dumping ground. It was even an issue in the 2004 U.S. presidential campaign—in a speech in Detroit, the Democratic candidate, John Kerry, said, "It's time to end Canadian trash dumping in Michigan." An initial step toward greater regulation occurred in May 2005, when the state of Michigan passed a legislative package that restricts the import of solid wastes (from Canada as well as neighbouring states). The state government now has emergency powers to close its border to such waste if it identifies substantial health, safety, or environmental threats. In addition, the importing of disused tires and beverage containers was prohibited (the import of hazardous and toxic wastes was already banned), and there are new regulations for certifying commercial operators in the industry and for larger fines for violations. As time passes, it is likely that state or federal legislators will further restrict the import of solid wastes to Michigan and may eventually ban the commercial trade altogether.

When that happens, municipalities in Ontario will have to deal with their own solid wastes through more local solutions for disposal. In most respects, local disposal of solid wastes (having first recovered as much of the recyclable and reusable components as possible) into advanced sanitary landfills is the sensible and responsible way to deal with this kind of problem.

References

City of Toronto. 2005. City of Toronto: Solid Waste Management—Facts About Toronto's Trash. www.city.toronto.on.ca/garbage/facts.htm

CNW Group. 2005. Ontario Facing a Waste Disposal Crisis. www.newswire.ca/en/releases/archive/May2005/17/c0053.html

In spite of these advanced design elements, residual problems of groundwater and surface water contamination and methane emissions to the atmosphere may still occur.

Another way of disposing of MSW is to burn it (see Incineration, above). During the nineteenth century, some cities burned much of their organic garbage using crude facilities known as cremators or cone-shaped "teepee" burners. However, these caused intense local air pollution and were replaced by the land-filling of MSW. Beginning in the 1930s, some cities built more efficient burning facilities called incinerators, but these were also dirty and most were shut down by the late 1960s. However, beginning in the 1970s, newer, cleaner incinerators were built, known as "waste-to-energy" or "resource recovery" facilities. These incinerators burn organic MSW efficiently and have technology installed to reduce the emissions of particulates and other air pollutants. However, the ash produced by incinerators is considered a toxic waste that must be disposed of in a secure landfill.

All municipalities in Canada need facilities for handling their solid wastes. However, public attitudes play a crucial role in the waste management decisions. Any new proposal to develop a sanitary landfill, incinerator, recycling plant, or any other MSW-related facility is sure to be opposed by people living near the proposed site. This phenomenon is referred to as "NIMBY," an acronym for not in my backyard. If local opposition becomes highly vocal and widespread, municipal bureaucrats and politicians often do not approve the proposal. This creates an extremely important problem for people attempting to deal with waste-management issues. It also strongly motivates engineers to design landfills and incinerators to operate as cleanly as possible, and to act to reduce and recycle discarded materials much more efficiently than in the past.

About 31 million tonnes of MSW was generated in Canada in 2002 (all solid non-hazardous waste; Statistics Canada, 2004). Of this total, about 75% was land-filled, 21% was recycled or composted, and 4% was incinerated (Table 25.6). However, these figures vary widely across Canada, depending on the size and density of the urban population (programs to recycle and reuse are more economic in larger centres) and on the priority placed by municipal and provincial/territorial governments on advanced (but relatively expensive) options for the management of solid wastes. Increasingly, however, governments are requiring or encouraging options that decrease the amount of solid waste that must be handled by landfilling or incineration.

About 3900 landfills operated in Canada in 1996, most of which served small communities (Gies, 1997). About 38% of those landfills, mainly the largest, had some or all of the advanced engineering features listed above. The other 62% are mostly smaller facilities, and most will be phased out in the near future in favour of better engineered landfills. As well, 67 municipal incinerators operated in 1996, of which 16% recovered energy as electricity. About 1400 municipalities offered curbside recycling programs, while 259 operated facilities for composting organic waste, and 178 had materials-recovery facilities (which sort, process, and market recyclable materials separated from MSW). Of course, many individual Canadians are also reducing the amount of solid waste they generate; for example, there were more than 1.2 million backyard composters in Canada in 1996.

Almost all Canadian municipalities are taking significant steps to reduce the amount of discarded material that must be land-filled or incinerated. Most are developing sophisticated systems for diverting material away from the waste stream and are achieving growing success. For example, the following cities have achieved significant diversions of residential MSW from landfills, mostly by instituting various kinds of recycling programs: Greater Summerside, PEI, 66% diversion of MSW; Guelph, ON, 58%; Edmonton, AB, 58%; Vancouver, BC, 53%; Halifax, NS, 42%; Ottawa, ON, 32%; and Toronto, ON, 32% (2003 data, obtained directly from a sample of municipal governments).

The diversity of diversion methods can be illustrated by the case of Edmonton, a city of about one million people. Edmontonians disposed of about 313 000 tonnes of residential MSW in 2003 (City of Edmonton, 2005). Of this total, 131 000 t was land-filled, 142 000 t was

---

TABLE 25.6 | Municipal Waste Management in Canada

Data are for 2002. Disposal includes land-filled plus incinerated waste. Diverted includes recycled and reused waste.

JURISDICTION	SOLID WASTE (10^6 t/y)	DISPOSAL (%)	DIVERTED (%)
Alberta	3.52	81	17
British Columbia	3.88	71	29
Manitoba	1.14	80	20
New Brunswick	0.54	77	23
Newfoundland & Labrador	0.42	91	9
NWT, Nunavut, Yukon	0.09	90	10
Nova Scotia	0.52	75	25
Ontario	12.20	80	20
PEI	0.08	75	25
Quebec	8.28	79	21
Saskatchewan	0.95	84	16
TOTAL	31.61	79	21

Source: Modified from Statistics Canada (2004)

composted, and 40 000 t was recycled. The overall diversion rate was 58%. Key elements of the diversion stream were the following (data in thousands of tonnes):

- Blue-box collection of recyclables (individual households)   29.8
- Blue-box collection of recyclables (multifamily)   3.9
- Recycling depots   6.4
- Other beverage-container recycling   23.7
- Christmas tree chipping   0.2

Municipal Wastewater Treatment

Issues associated with municipal wastewater include its amount and composition, ways of treating the material, and ecological effects of its disposal. First, we should distinguish among major kinds of wastewater.

Sewage is wastewater containing the fecal matter of humans and other animals plus food waste from kitchens and commercial food processing. In urban areas, sewage is collected using a complex system of underground pipes (called sanitary sewers) and taken to a central place for treatment and/or disposal.

Industrial wastewater may contain many kinds of liquids, including toxic and hazardous wastes. As we noted previously, toxic waste is poisonous, while hazardous waste may be explosive, flammable, or dangerous for other reasons. Many urban areas have separate systems for collecting and treating toxic and hazardous industrial wastewater.

Stormwater is surface runoff of rainfall and snowmelt. In municipal areas, it is typically collected using surface drains that feed into a combined sewage-stormflow system, or using a more advanced drainage system that keeps these wastewaters separate. Stormwater is not as grossly polluted as sewage or industrial wastewater, but it does contain significant amounts of fecal material (from wild birds and pets), metals, waste motor oil, road salt, and other substances.

Sewage Treatment

In most places, the principal objective of sewage treatment is to reduce the amounts of pathogenic microorganisms and oxygen-consuming organic matter entering the receiving waters. In places where surface waters are vulnerable to eutrophication, sewage may also be treated to reduce

Photo 25.4 This sewage-treatment complex serves a population of about 918 000 in the city of Calgary. Because the discharge goes into the Bow River (a relatively small waterbody) the treatment must be of a high standard to prevent ecological degradation of the river. In fact, this is perhaps the most advanced system in Canada, with tertiary treatment, ultraviolet disinfection, and use of the composted sewage sludge as a soil conditioner.

Source: Courtesy of the City of Calgary/Bonnybrook Wastewater Treatment Plant

the amounts of nutrients, especially phosphorus and nitrogen (see also Chapter 20).

All towns and cities in Canada have networks of underground pipes to collect the sewage effluent from homes, businesses, institutions, and factories. (Low-density residential areas may have septic systems installed at individual homes.) Some municipalities have separate systems for sewage and stormwater. Eventually, all wastewater is discharged to the environment, usually into a nearby lake, river, or ocean. To avoid environmental damage, the wastewater should be treated to reduce its pollutant load before being discharged into an aquatic ecosystem.

However, some towns and cities in Canada still dump raw sewage. Most of these municipalities are located beside an ocean and rely on the local marine ecosystem to dilute and biodegrade organic pollutants and pathogens in the sewage. Because inland waters such as lakes and rivers have a much smaller capacity for diluting and biodegrading sewage wastes, most Canadian municipalities located beside these waters treat their sewage. (See Chapter 20 for a description of the various kinds of sewage-treatment systems.)

TABLE 25.7 | Municipal Wastewater Treatment in Canada

The data show the percentage of people served by primary, secondary, and tertiary wastewater treatment systems in 1999, and the populations (in millions) of municipalities.

| | WASTEWATER TREATMENT SYSTEM | | | | NUMBER OF PEOPLE |
REGION	NONE	PRIMARY	SECONDARY	TERTIARY	(millions)
Atlantic	45.2	17.1	37.4	0.3	1.3
Quebec	2.8	43.4	49.2	4.7	5.7
Ontario	0.1	5.7	22.9	71.3	8.9
Prairies	0.3	0.5	40.2	59.0	3.8
BC	1.4	35.3	55.3	8.0	3.0

Source: Modified from Environment Canada (2001)

About 74% of Canadians were serviced by municipal wastewater treatment systems in 1999 (the rest used septic tanks, other private treatment systems, or lived in municipalities that dump non-treated sewage; Statistics Canada, 2003). Of the municipal populations, about 40% were serviced by tertiary treatment, 38% by secondary treatment, and 19% by primary treatment (these terms are explained in Chapter 20). The remaining 3% had their sewage dumped untreated into the environment. Relatively advanced, tertiary systems are used mostly in Ontario and the Prairies (Table 25.7), mainly because these regions discharge their treated wastewater into rivers and lakes, so a higher level of water treatment is needed to prevent environmental damage. The lowest standard of wastewater treatment is in parts of Atlantic Canada, Quebec, and British Columbia, where cities dump untreated sewage into coastal waters or large rivers.

More detailed case information about sewage treatment in Canada is given in Table 25.8. Because of concerns about environmental quality in local receiving waters, particularly regarding fecal pathogens and ecological degradation, some cities (e.g., Calgary, Edmonton, and Toronto) have invested in higher-level systems of water treatment. As a result, local water quality has substantially improved. In contrast, coastal cities, such as Halifax and Victoria, continue to discharge poorly treated sewage to the nearshore ocean, relying on "free environmental services" to dilute and biodegrade their effluents.

Environmental damages associated with the discharge of untreated or poorly treated sewage include the following:

- the contamination of receiving waters with human fecal pathogens, such as coliform bacteria and viruses, which renders the area unfit for swimming or other recreational purposes or for use as drinking water

- ecological damage caused by the deoxygenation of water and sediment through the decomposition of organic wastes, resulting in the deaths of many organisms and the development of foul odours

- stimulation of algal blooms through fertilization with nutrients from sewage effluent

- contamination of the environment with persistent, potentially toxic chemicals, such as metals and organochlorines

- aesthetic damage associated with the presence of sewage waste

These environmental damages, which can be severe, are largely avoided if municipalities invest in sewage treatment facilities. Because of this widely recognized fact, all Canadian cities and towns, including coastal ones, will probably develop facilities to treat their wastewater during the next several decades.

Urban Biodiversity

Urban areas are highly impoverished in the quantity and quality of habitat available to support species of plants, animals, and microorganisms. Nevertheless, many wild organisms do occur there. Even parking lots, sidewalks, and industrial areas, which from an ecological perspective are extremely degraded habitats, manage to support some elements of biodiversity. However, most species occurring in habitats of this type are not indigenous to the region.

Still, some urban places are relatively natural in character and are maintained in this condition as natural-area

| TABLE 25.8 | Selected Cases of Municipal Wastewater Treatment in Canada |

(A) CITIES WITH RELATIVELY ADVANCED TREATMENT

CALGARY, ALBERTA
- Population served: 918 000
- Volume of sewage: 164 billion L/y
- Receiving waterbody: Bow River
- Treatment: 100% tertiary with ultraviolet disinfection; the sewage sludge is composted and used as a soil conditioner.
- Problems: this is the most advanced treatment system of any city in Canada; its discharges consistently meet the tough provincial standards. There are no overflows of the treatment system because of separate collection systems for sanitary sewers and stormwater. Nevertheless, because of the relatively small size of the Bow River, there is some ecological degradation around the outfalls.
- Source control: large emissions sources are closely monitored and are prosecuted if discharges exceed the regulated allowances.
- Improvements: further investments and upgrades will increase the efficiency of tertiary treatment and disinfection, and will expand the system to deal with a rapidly growing population.

TORONTO, ONTARIO
- Population served: 2.5 million
- Volume of sewage: 455 billion L/y
- Receiving waterbodies: Lake Ontario (443 billion L/y) and Don River (12 billion L/y)
- Treatment: four treatment plants; sewage receives secondary treatment with phosphorus removal; chlorine disinfection; 55% of sludge is incinerated, 8% applied to agricultural land, 30% land-filled, and 7% processed into fertilizer pellets.
- Problems: large stormflows may overwhelm the system, resulting in the discharge of raw or incompletely treated sewage (about 2% of the total sewerage volume per year); the Don River is ecologically degraded by inputs of wastewater and other pollutants, while local habitats of Lake Ontario are more moderately affected.
- Source control: large emissions sources are monitored and prosecuted if discharges exceed permitted amounts.
- Improvements: new investments and regulations will increase the separation of sanitary and storm sewage and control sources to reduce inputs of toxic substances; strong efforts are being made to apply more of the sludge to agricultural land and to end incineration; plans are being made to replace chlorination by UV-disinfection.

(B) CITIES WITH POOR TREATMENT

HALIFAX-DARTMOUTH, NOVA SCOTIA
- Population served: 354 000
- Volume of sewage: 68.2 billion L/y
- Receiving waterbodies: Halifax Harbour and nearby coastal areas
- Treatment: essentially none for the major outfalls; some smaller municipal areas have secondary or tertiary treatment; about 66 billion L of raw sewage is dumped annually.
- Problems: the vicinities of 40 discharge outfalls are ecologically degraded by inputs of raw sewage.
- Source control: there is little control of discharges into the sewage system and little monitoring.
- Improvements: the construction of an advanced primary treatment system is underway; planning is underway for a source-control program to divert toxic substances from the system.

VICTORIA, BRITISH COLUMBIA
- Population served: 326 000
- Volume of sewage: 38 billion L/y
- Receiving waterbodies: Strait of Juan de Fuca, some into Strait of Georgia
- Treatment: essentially none for the two largest outfalls, which only screen out particles larger than 6 mm before discharge; one area has primary treatment and several others have secondary treatment; sludge is mostly land-filled; about 34 billion L of raw sewage is disposed annually.
- Problems: the vicinities of the three discharge outfalls are ecologically degraded by inputs of raw sewage.
- Source control: a source-control program was implemented in 1995, but with little monitoring and little effect on effluent quality.
- Improvements: in 1992, residents voted against the construction of a sewage-treatment system; there has been no substantial progess since then.

Source: Modified from Sierra Legal Defence Fund (2004); This document is a "sewage report card" for 20 Canadian cities.

parks. Some prominent Canadian examples of natural-area parks include Stanley Park in Vancouver, a series of parks along the Bow River in Calgary and the North Saskatchewan River in Edmonton, Assiniboine Park in Winnipeg, High Park and Hanlan's Point in Toronto, Bois de Liesse in Montreal, Point Pleasant Park in Halifax, and Signal Hill in St. John's. These green spaces are remnants of natural habitat that have survived the urbanization process relatively intact. As such, they contain ecological communities dominated by mostly native species.

More typically, however, urban habitats are dominated by alien species, which were introduced in various ways. Most non-native plants were introduced (1) as seeds contained in soil carried by ships as ballast, which was dumped in ports when cargo was picked up (this was particularly important before the twentieth century); (2) as seeds contaminating the seedstock of crop plants (now less of a problem because weed seeds are "cleaned" from commercial seedstock); or (3) as plants deliberately introduced for use in agriculture, forestry, or horticulture. Some alien plants have found good habitat in urban areas, where they thrive and aggressively out-compete native species. Such **invasive** non-native plants are an extremely important ecological problem and can be regarded as a kind of biological "pollution" (see also Chapters 1 and 26).

Non-native animals are also common in urban areas. Some, such as the house mouse (*Mus musculus*) and Norway rat (*Rattus norvegicus*), were introduced accidentally when these rodents escaped from infested ships and cargoes. Others were deliberately introduced. For example, the rock dove (pigeon; *Columba livea*), starling (*Sturnus vulgaris*), and house sparrow (*Passer domesticus*) were introduced by a nineteenth-century society of gentlemen who were dedicated to bringing all of the birds mentioned in the plays of William Shakespeare to North America. Of the various species that these misguided naturalists attempted to introduce, only these three have established widespread breeding populations (although a small number of skylarks [*Alauda arvensis*] also persist in Vancouver).

Huge numbers of alien species now have wild, self-maintaining populations in urban areas in Canada. Some of these plants and animals and the ecological "problems" associated with them include the following:

- The dandelion (*Taraxacum officinale*), a perennial, herbaceous plant originally native to alpine habitat in Europe, now occurs in temperate regions throughout the world, probably having been introduced in ships' ballast. The dandelion is widely viewed as a weed in lawns and pastures.

Photo 25.5 Stanley Park in Vancouver is a green space with a mixture of natural and cultural values. This lake, known as Lost Lagoon, supports a mixture of non-native waterfowl (such as mute swans), as well as many native ducks and other birds that spend the winter and subsist largely on human handouts.

- Japanese knotweed (*Polygonum cuspidatum*) is a perennial, herbaceous plant that grows up to 2 m tall and is native to Japan. It has attractive foliage and was widely introduced for horticultural use. It can be highly invasive in disturbed areas.

- The sticky touch-me-not (*Impatiens glandulifera*) is an annual wildflower native to the Himalayas. It was introduced through horticulture and can be invasive in gardens and wetlands.

- Goutweed (*Aegopodium variegatum*) is a perennial, herbaceous plant native to Eurasia that was widely introduced through horticulture and is invasive in gardens and other disturbed habitats.

- Purple loosestrife (*Lythrum salicaria*) is a perennial, herbaceous plant of Eurasia that was introduced through ships' ballast and horticulture, and is a serious invader of wetlands.

- St. John's wort (*Hypericum perforatum*) is a perennial, herbaceous plant of Europe that was introduced probably through ships' ballast and is now a serious weed of pastures (causing a photosensitivity disease in cattle).

- Norway maple (*Acer platanoides*) is a native tree in Europe that was introduced for horticultural use. It invades natural hardwood forest.

Photo 25.6 Streets with large numbers of mature trees are relatively pleasant, compared with places in which the urban forest is sparse or missing. This residential street in Halifax is mostly forested with alien species of trees, such as Norway maple (*Acer platanoides*) and linden (*Tilia cordata*).

- The oriental cockroach (*Blatta orientalis*) is an insect native to eastern Asia. Probably introduced accidentally from ships, it is now a serious pest in homes and other places where food is stored.
- The garden snail (*Cepaea hortensis*) is a terrestrial mollusk native to Europe. It was probably accidentally introduced with ships' ballast and is a garden pest in some regions.
- The house mouse and Norway rat are rodents native to Eurasia that were accidentally introduced from ships, and they are now serious pests in homes and other places where food is stored.
- The starling, rock dove, and house sparrow are songbirds native to Eurasia that were deliberately introduced by European settlers anxious to have familiar species from their homeland in the Americas. They displace native birds from nesting sites and are invasive pests.

These and other free-living, alien species are the most abundant plants and animals in Canadian urban areas. Of course, the domestic dog (*Canis familiaris*), domestic cat (*Felis catus*), and other pets are also common, non-native species in our cities and towns. (Although Aboriginal peoples have lived in the Americas for at least 12 000 years, the human species might also be considered non-indigenous to these continents.)

The characteristics of various kinds of urban ecosystems have been studied in Canada. Many urban habitats are highly disturbed and are actively managed to keep them in an early stage of succession. Urban lawns, for example, are mown frequently to prevent their vegetation from developing beyond a stage dominated by low-growing, herbaceous plants. Moreover, because most lawn-growers want a monoculture of only one or two species of grasses, they may apply herbicide to kill unwanted dicotyledonous plants, such as clovers, dandelion, and other "weeds." The most commonly grown grass in lawns in temperate-zone countries is the Kentucky blue grass (*Poa pratensis*), which, despite its common name, is actually a Eurasian species. Also cultivated in some regions are ryegrass (*Lolium perenne*), red fescue (*Festuca rubra*), and bent grasses (*Agrostis* spp.); these are also alien species. Other elements of the intensive management of urban lawns include fertilization, insecticide application, and irrigation. Some ecologists recommend less intensive systems of lawn management, including greater tolerance of such non-grass plants as red clover (*Trifolium pratense*), black medic (*Medicago lupulina*), and other legumes, which fix atmospheric nitrogen and so reduce the need for fertilizer application. Even such species as dandelion and buttercup (*Ranunculus acris*) can be tolerated in lawns and viewed as attractive "wildflowers" rather than as "weeds."

The **urban forest** is another prominent habitat in cities and towns, although it does not always support native species. Neighbourhoods with abundant trees can be studied using the same methods used to examine natural forest. One study looked at the urban forest in residential, institutional, and parkland areas of Halifax (Table 25.9). Older residential neighbourhoods had a tree biomass similar to that of natural forest in the region, although the stem density was considerably less (most trees in the mature urban forest are relatively large). Younger residential neighbourhoods had a smaller tree biomass but a higher density, suggesting a pattern of succession in the urban forest. Even an institutional neighbourhood, consisting mostly of several hospitals and a university, had a substantial tree population.

The majority of trees in the urban forest of Halifax are alien species (this is also true of most cities in Canada; Table 25.10). In the oldest residential area sampled, about 72% of the trees were non-native, the most common being Norway maple (*Acer platanoides*), linden (*Tilia europaea*), European ash (*Fraxinus excelsior*), Scotch elm (*Ulmus glabra*), and rowan (*Sorbus aucuparia*). An eight-year-old residential neighbourhood had a much larger percent-

TABLE 25.9 | Characteristics of the Urban Forest in Halifax

Tree density, biomass, and carbon storage are shown for stands of urban forest in different kinds of neighbourhoods. The data for rural natural forest are the range for four mature hardwood stands.

NEIGHBOURHOOD	DENSITY (no. /ha)	BIOMASS (t/ha)	CARBON (t/ha)
70-year-old residential	145	131	65.5
50-year-old residential	158	19	9.5
<8-year-old residential	241	17	8.5
Institutional	50	21	10.6
Natural-area park A	1318	177	88.4
Natural-area park B	1578	110	54.8
Natural forest	1710–2560	112–233	56–117

Source: Freedman *et al.* (1996)

age of native trees (about 92%), which had survived the clearing of the original natural forest when the suburb was developed. However, most of the local homeowners are choosing non-native species for their horticultural plantings, so their prominence will increase rapidly as the neighbourhood ages.

The displacement of native plant species by alien ones can result in important ecological damage, especially if the foreign ones become invasive. Some ecologists believe that horticulturists should place much greater emphasis on the use of native plants, rather than risk the serious problems associated with biological "pollution" by alien species.

The urban forest provides many useful ecological services. For example, large amounts of carbon are stored in urban trees, helping to offset some emissions of CO_2 from the combustion of fossil fuels. Urban parks and well-

In Detail 25.2

Urban Naturalization

Urban naturalization is a "new" kind of horticultural practice that favours the use of native plants to achieve pleasing aesthetics in gardening. It is a more natural alternative to conventional horticultural practices, in which there is a very strong preference for the cultivation of alien plants. Naturalization avoids many of the ecological problems associated with growing alien plants, which can become invasive and damage natural habitats and may be vectors of deadly diseases of native species (see Chapter 26).

But what is meant by terms such as "native" and "natural?" In the sense intended here, and in the context of the Americas, a native (indigenous) species is one that was present in an ecoregion before about 1500 (i.e., in pre-Columbian times). If a species was introduced afterward, either deliberately or accidentally, and then developed self-maintaining populations, it would be considered "naturalized" but not indigenous (they may also be viewed as "invasive aliens" that

cause ecological damage). "Natural communities" are considered to be self-organizing, co-evolved assemblages of native species that occur in habitats appropriate for their survival.

Because many native plants are beautiful and can grow well in habitats provided by horticultural gardens, they can be easily cultivated. In fact, they may do very well because they are pre-adapted to local climate, soil, and other aspects of the habitat. They may be grown in contrived but pleasing arrangements of flowering plants, shrubs, and trees, as is commonly done in horticulture, or they may be managed to create a facsimile of a natural community. If naturalization is used to replace conventional horticultural habitats, such as lawns and gardens dominated by alien species, it will result in areas being better suited to support native birds and other animals. This kind of gardening can create beautiful spaces, but they have a softer ecological footprint. Although naturalized gardens are still uncommon, they are attracting increasing attention from people seeking to express a more natural view of their world.

| TABLE 25.10 | Prominent Street Trees in Selected Canadian Cities |

The data show the frequency of the seven most abundant species growing in urban forests of four cities. Frequency is given as the percentage of the total number of trees, and Origin is (N) native to North America or (I) introduced.

CITY	PROMINENT TREE SPECIES	FREQUENCY	ORIGIN
VANCOUVER, BC	Japanese cherry (*Prunus serrulata*)	11	I
	sour cherry (*Prunus cerasus*)	9	I
	Norway maple (*Acer platanoides*)	6	I
	red maple (*Acer rubrum*)	4	N
	linden (*Tilia cordata*)	4	I
	weeping birch (*Betula pendula*)	3	I
	hornbeam (*Carpinus betulus*)	2	I
WINNIPEG, MB	white elm (*Ulmus americana*)	25	N
	poplar (*Populus spp.*)	15	N
	Manitoba maple (*Acer negundo*)	10	N
	green ash (*Fraxinus pennsylvanica*)	10	N
	bur oak (*Quercus macrocarpa*)	10	N
	basswood (*Tilia americana*)	10	N
	black ash (*Fraxinus nigra*)	5	N
LONDON, ON	silver maple (*Acer saccharinum*)	20	N
	Norway maple (*Acer platanoides*)	15	I
	honey-locust (*Gleditsia triacanthos*)	8	N
	sugar maple (*Acer saccharum*)	5	N
	green ash (*Fraxinus pennsylvanica*)	5	N
	linden (*Tilia cordata*)	5	I
	red oak (*Quercus rubra*)	2	N
HALIFAX, NS	Norway maple (*Acer platanoides*)	30	I
	linden (*Tilia cordata*)	20	I
	white elm (*Ulmus americana*)	15	N
	Scotch elm (*Ulmus glabra*)	5	I
	European ash (*Fraxinus excelsior*)	5	I
	red oak (*Quercus rubra*)	5	N
	horse chestnut (*Aesculus hippocastanum*)	5	I

Source: Data compiled from municipal governments

treed residential areas can store as much carbon in tree biomass as a natural forest can (Table 25.9). In addition, well-placed trees can reduce wind speeds near buildings, which decreases the air-infiltration rate and thereby conserves heat during cold weather. Trees also shade homes and buildings, greatly reducing the energy needed for air conditioning during warm weather. Transpiration from tree foliage also helps to cool the ambient urban atmosphere, as does the shading of streets, lawns, and other areas. Urban trees also absorb some air pollutants (such as SO_2 and particulates), help to reduce noise levels, and greatly improve outdoor aesthetics. A well-developed urban forest also provides habitat for lower-growing plants and animals in built-up areas.

Another study in Halifax also examined the non-tree vegetation (Turner *et al.*, 2005). In an older residential neighbourhood, an average of 87% of the low-growing species were aliens as were 84% of the shrubs and trees. Even in a more recent suburban development, which still had remnants of native habitat, 77% of the low vegetation and 69% of the woody plants were aliens. These observations are not particularly surprising, in light of the results of surveys of commercial horticultural businesses in the study area, which offered few or no native species for sale.

Avian communities in Canadian cities and towns have also been studied, for birds are considered good indicators of ecological integrity (see Chapter 27). A study of birds in different Toronto neighbourhoods found that even commercial and industrial habitats sustained some species. However, about 97% of the birds in those habitats were alien species, such as rock dove, starling, and house sparrow (Table 25.11). These introduced species also dominated the bird fauna of residential neighbourhoods, accounting for 64–94% of the birds present. However, the residential areas had a significant amount of habitat with abundant trees, shrubs, and other plants, allowing some native birds to live in small numbers, including American robin (*Turdus migratorius*), blue jay (*Cyanocitta cristata*), and cardinal (*Cardinalis cardinalis*). Of all the Toronto habitats surveyed, only a natural-area park had a relatively low fraction of non-native birds (25%). The mostly forested habitat of that park sustained 26 species of birds, most of which were not seen in the other, highly anthropogenic urban habitats. Not surprisingly, this study found that the more natural the vegetation in the urban habitat, the larger the number of native birds that was supported. Even relatively small areas of natural habitat in urban areas could sustain breeding by native birds.

Waterfowl are also abundant in urban areas with aquatic habitat, such as beside an ocean or near a lake or river. For

Photo 25.7   Urban biodiversity can be pleasant, but it is often managed in a highly contrived manner and is dominated by alien plants and animals. Almost none of the species visible in this horticultural urban park in Halifax are native to Canada.

example, many cities have wild breeding populations of "giant" Canada goose (*Branta canadensis maxima*), descended from birds released in these places since the 1950s. These birds find that grassy lawns near water provide suitable feed-

TABLE 25.11	Density of Birds in Various Urban Habitats in Toronto						

The data are the average numbers of birds observed per km^2 during censuses in May and June. Only the most abundant species are included. The asterisk (*) indicates a non-native species.

SPECIES	DOWNTOWN COMMERCIAL	DOWNTOWN INDUSTRIAL	MATURE RESIDENTIAL A	MATURE RESIDENTIAL B	YOUNGER RESIDENTIAL	GRASSY PARK	NATURAL PARK
Rock dove*	106	188	247	131	3	94	0
Chimney swift	0	13	14	3	2	8	19
Flicker	0	0	0	0	2	9	19
Blue jay	0	0	6	19	18	0	7
Common crow	0	0	0	13	3	5	38
American robin	0	0	28	87	174	73	25
Starling*	72	196	426	116	285	427	89
House sparrow*	87	167	517	353	487	121	65
Common grackle	4	7	18	25	120	24	81
Cardinal	0	0	0	12	5	0	15
TOTAL BIRDS	277	566	1256	778	1223	788	609
No. of species	5	5	7	11	15	10	26
% Non-native	96	97	94	77	64	80	25

Source: Modified from Savard (1978)

ing habitat, and their population in some cities has increased to thousands of birds. However, many of these geese have lost the habit of migrating, and some people consider their abundance and year-round presence to be a nuisance. Several cities (e.g., Toronto) are attempting to alleviate their goose "over-population" by capturing animals and shipping them to willing host cities elsewhere. Some cities are culling the geese by killing part of the population.

During the spring and fall migrations, some Canadian cities with aquatic habitat support large numbers of native waterfowl and other bird species. Some waterfowl remain during the winter if open water is present. Urban bird watchers from Victoria to St. John's often spend time viewing the numerous native species of ducks, geese, swans, gulls, shorebirds, and other migrating and wintering birds in the local aquatic habitats. Each autumn, for example, the Toronto waterfront provides habitat for thousands of oldsquaw ducks (*Clangula hyemalis*) migrating from their arctic breeding grounds. St. John's is the only city in the world where ivory gulls (*Pagophila eburnea*) can be seen regularly (small numbers of these rare gulls winter along coastal Newfoundland).

Some native mammals also occur in urban habitats. Grey (black) squirrels (*Sciurus carolinensis*) and raccoons (*Procyon lotor*) may even inhabit downtown residential neighbourhoods as long as there is some open forest available. Urban areas with more extensive shrubby and forested habitat may sustain white-tailed deer (*Odocoileus virgini-*

anus), red fox (*Vulpes vulpes*), striped skunk (*Mephites mephites*), and coyote (*Canis latrans*). The key to sustaining populations of native animals in urban areas is to maintain as much relatively natural habitat as possible, dominated by native plants. If this is done, even inner-city backyards can provide habitat for some Canadian native animals. This function is greatly enhanced by the deliberate naturalization of urban habitats by using native plants in horticulture (see In Detail 25.2 on page 531).

Conclusions

Urban ecosystems sustain humans, associated non-native organisms, and some native species and remnants of natural habitats. However, urban ecosystems are ecological "islands" that draw upon the surrounding region to continuously supply immense quantities of natural resources and to assimilate their wastes. The great challenge for urban ecologists is to develop a better understanding of the structure and function of the urban-industrial techno-ecosystem, including the exchanges of materials and energy and the factors affecting biodiversity values. This knowledge can help to identify ecologically pathological relationships, which can then be mitigated to reduce the urban-industrial ecological footprint. If this is done, then modern cities can become more ecologically sustainable than is now the case.

Key Terms

megacity	dumping
ecological footprint	incineration
urban planning	recycling
thermal pollution	composting
noise pollution	reuse
aesthetic pollution	waste reduction
waste	waste prevention
hazardous waste	R's
toxic waste	sanitary landfill
waste management	invasive
	urban forest

Questions for Review

1. What changes were important in the development of urban places during the socio-cultural evolution of our species?

2. What is an ecological footprint? What are its key components?

3. Characterize the urban ecosystem of your community in terms of its structural (e.g., species composition, habitats) and functional (e.g., resource use, waste generation) attributes.

4. What are the major characteristics of urban and rural biodiversity in Canada?

Questions for Discussion

1. Make a list of factors important in the ecological footprint of your community. How might these be changed in order to decrease the size of the footprint?

2. Why do so few people use a bicycle as their routine means of transportation in spite of its mechanical efficiency and low cost?

3. How does your daily lifestyle contribute to the pollution of your community environment?

4. Define the terms dumping (disposal), incineration, recycling, composting, reuse, and waste production and prevention. What role does each of these play in waste management in your community?

5. What are the major practices used to treat urban sewage? Why have some Canadian cities chosen to treat their sewage in an environmentally responsible way, while others have not?

6. Characterize the principal elements of urban biodiversity in your community. How can habitats be naturalized in order to support more indigenous species?

7. Use the footprint calculator provided by Redefining Progress (an environmental organization) to calculate your ecological footprint. Try doing a "virtual experiment" by varying aspects of your lifestyle in the calculator to see what effect it has on your personal footprint. For example, see what happens if you ride a bike, use public transit, or fly in an airplane. Go to: www.rprogress.org/newprojects/ecolFoot.shtml

Exploring Issues

1. Your municipal government is seeking ways to make the community function in a less damaging, more sustainable manner and has hired you to provide advice. What studies would you undertake to determine ways in which urban functions (such as transportation, sewage treatment, and management of solid materials and wastes), land-use patterns, and biodiversity can be improved to contribute to the goal of sustainability? What do you think your recommendations would be?

References

Berkowitz, A.R., C.H. Nilon, and K.S. Hollweg. 2002. *Understanding Urban Ecosystems.* Berlin: Springer Verlag.

Breuste, J., H. Feldmann, and O. Ohlmann (eds.). 1998. *Urban Ecology.* Berlin: Springer Verlag Telos.

City of Edmonton. 2005. *2003 Waste Management Branch Annual Report.* www.edmonton.ca/Environment/Waste Management/PDF/2003%20Annual%20Review.pdf

Environment Canada. 1996a. *The State of Canada's Environment, 1996.* Ottawa, ON: Environment Canada.

Environment Canada. 1996b. *Urban Air Quality.* Ottawa, ON: Environment Canada.

Environment Canada. 1999. *Air Quality Trends in Canadian Cities, 1979–1992.* Ottawa, ON: State of the Environment Reporting, Environment Canada. www.ec.gc.ca/pdb/uaqt/aqfact_e.html

Environment Canada. 2001. *Municipal Population Served by Wastewater Treatment.* Ottawa, ON: State of the Environment Reporting, Environment Canada.

Fincher, R. and J.M. Jacobs (eds.). 1998. *Cities of Difference.* New York: Guilford Press.

Freedman, B. and J. Riley. 1980. Population trends of various species of birds wintering in southern Ontario. *Ontario Field Biologist,* **34**: 49–79.

Freedman, B., S. Love, and B. O'Neil. 1996. Tree species, biomass, and carbon storage in stands of urban forest of varying character in Halifax, Nova Scotia, Canada. *Canadian Field-Naturalist,* **110**: 675–682.

Gies, G. 1997. The state of garbage in Canada. *BioCycle,* March: 78–81.

Gill, D. and P. Bonnett. 1973. *Nature in the Urban Landscape: A Study of City Ecosystems.* Baltimore, MD: York Press.

Holcomb, M.C. 1987. *Transportation Energy Data Book,* 9th ed. Oak Ridge National Laboratory, Oak Ridge, TN.

Insurance Institute for Highway Safety. 1999. *Safety Facts.* www.highwaysafety.org/safety_facts/safety.htm

Jacobs, J. 1961. *The Death and Life of Great American Cities.* New York: Random House.

Jacobs, J. 1969. *The Economy of Cities.* New York: Random House.

Kraas, F. 2005. *Megacities Documentation.* Cologne, Germany: Megacity Taskforce of the International Geographical Union. www.megacities.uni-koeln.de/index.htmly

Kreith, F. (ed.). 1994. *Handbook of Solid Waste Management.* New York: McGraw-Hill.

Kryter, K.D. 1985. *The Effects of Noise.* 2nd ed. Orlando, FL: Academic Press.

Landsberg, H.E. 1981. *The Urban Climate.* New York: Academic Press.

Langford, T.E.L. 1990. *Ecological Effects of Thermal Discharges.* Amsterdam: Elsevier Science.

Lowe, M.D. 1989. *The Bicycle: Vehicle for a Small Planet.* Washington, DC: Worldwatch Institute.

Luccarelli, M. 1995. *Lewis Mumford and the Ecological Region: The Politics of Planning.* New York: Guilford Press.

Nathanson, J.A. 1997. *Basic Environmental Technology: Water Supply, Waste Management, and Pollution Control.* 2nd ed. Upper Saddle River, NJ: Prentice Hall.

National Audubon Society. 1999. *The 100th Christmas Bird Count.* www.birdsource.com/cbc/index.html

National Round Table on the Environment and the Economy (NRTEE). 1998. *Greenhouse Gas Emissions from Urban Transportation: Backgrounder.* Ottawa: NRTEE.

Platt, R.H., R.A. Rowntree, and P.C. Muick. 1994. *The Ecological City: Preserving and Restoring Urban Biodiversity.* Amherst, MA: University of Massachusetts Press.

Ponting, C. 1991. *A Green History of the World.* London, UK: Sinclair-Stevenson.

Redefining Progress. 2005. *Ecological Footprint Analysis.* Washington, DC: Redefining Progess. www.rprogress.org/newprojects/ecolFoot.shtml

Rees, W.E. 1992. Ecological footprints and appropriated carrying capacity: What urban economics leaves out. *Environment and Urbanization,* **4**: 121–130.

Rees, W.E. 1997. Is "sustainable city" an oxymoron? *Local Environment,* **2**: 303–310.

Savard, J.-P. 1978. *Birds in Metropolitan Toronto: Distribution, Relationships with Habitat Features, and Nesting Sites.* Unpublished M.Sc. Thesis, University of Toronto.

Sierra Legal Defense Fund. 2004. *The National Sewage Report Card, Number, 3.* www.sierralegal.org/reports/sewage_report_card_III.pdf

Statistics Canada. 2003. *Human Activity and the Environment. Annual Statistics 2003.* estat.statcan.ca/content/english/articles/other/0000316-201-XIE.pdf

Statistics Canada. 2004. *Waste Management Industry. Business and Government Sectors 2002.* www.statcan.ca/english/freepub/16F0023XIE/16F0023XIE2002001.pdf

Statistics Canada. 2005. *Household size, by provinces and territories (2001 census).* Ottawa, ON: Statistics Canada. www40.statcan.ca/l01/cst01/famil53a.htm?sdi=households%20number

Timerson, B.J. 1999. *A Guide to Noise Control in Minnesota.* Minnesota Pollution Control Agency. www.pca.state.mn.us/programs/pubs/noise.pdf

Transport Canada. 1997. *Transportation in Canada, 1997.* Ottawa: Transport Canada.

Transport Canada. 2004. *Transportation in Canada, 2004.* Ottawa, ON: Transport Canada. www.tc.gc.ca/pol/en/Report/anre2004/add2004-e.pdf

Turner, K., L. Lefler, and B. Freedman. 2004. Plant communities of selected urbanized areas of Halifax, Nova Scotia, Canada. *Landscape and Urban Planning,* 191–206.

United Nations Department of Economic and Social Affairs (UN DESA). 2005. *World Urbanization Prospects. The 2003 Revision.* New York: United Nations Department of Economic and Social Affairs, Population Division. www.un.org/esa/population/publications/wup2003/WUP2003Report.pdf

United Nations Global Urban Observatory. 1999. *Global Urban Indicators Database.* www.urbanobservatory.org/indicators/database/

Venetoulis, J., D. Chazan, and C. Gaudet. 2004. *Ecological Footprint of Nations.* Washington, DC: Redefining Progess. www.rprogress.org/newpubs/2004/footprintnations2004.pdf

Wackernagel, M. and W.E. Rees. 1996. *Our Ecological Footprint: Reducing Human Impact on the Earth.* Gabriola Island, BC: New Society.

World Resources Institute. 1998. *World Resources, 1998–99. A Guide to the Global Environment: Environmental Change and Human Health.* New York: Oxford University Press.

World Resources Institute. 2005. *Earth Trends. The Environmental Information Portal.* Washington, DC: WRI. www.wri.org/

Informative Websites

Ecocity. www.ecocity.com/

This website contains numerous links of interest to urban ecology.

Environment Canada. The Green Lane.
www.ec.gc.ca/envhome.html

This comprehensive site from Environment Canada features pages on climate change, nature, clean air and water, as well as links to publications, news releases, and related sites.

Environmental Literacy Council. Urban Air.
www.enviroliteracy.org/subcategory.php/40.html

Problems with air pollution have existed since the 1300s. This page contains links to further reading.

Environmental Literacy Council. Waste Management.
www.enviroliteracy.org/subcategory.php/41.html

Waste is a natural part of the human life cycle. Learn about its history, related legislation, and recycling from this page.

Evergreen. www.evergreen.ca/

Evergreen is an environmental organization dedicated to increasing the amount of vegetated greenspace in Canadian communities.

The Internet Consumer Recycling Guide.
www.obviously.com/recycle/

This recycling guide provides a starting point for consumers in the USA and Canada searching the net for recycling information. The goal is to help make recycling so easy and automatic that it blends into the flow of everyday life.

Redefining Progress. www.rprogress.org/index.shtml

Redefining Progress works with a broad array of partners to shift the economy and public policy toward sustainability. This site has a calculator for a personal ecological footprint.

Urban Ecology. www.urbanecology.org/

This is the website of an environmental organization dedicated to making cities into more sustainable ecosystems.

World Resources Institute. EarthTrends. The Environmental Information Portal. earthtrends.wri.org/

The WRI is a leading environmental organization that provides excellent information about resource issues.

The Biodiversity Crisis 26

CHAPTER OBJECTIVES

After completing this chapter, you will be able to

1. Outline how humans are causing the modern crisis of extinction and endangerment.
2. Give examples of species that have been made extinct through human activities, including cases from Canada.
3. Explain how a system of protected areas is critical to the preservation of biodiversity.
4. Outline the roles of governments, non-governmental organizations, scientists, and citizens in conserving species and other elements of biodiversity.

CHAPTER OUTLINE

- Introduction
- Extinction as a Natural Process
- Extinctions and Endangerment Caused by Humans
- Tropical Deforestation
- Species Declines
- Back from the Brink
- Canadian Species and Ecosystems at Risk
- The Importance of Protected Areas
- International Conservation Activities
- Conclusions

Introduction

Earlier, we defined biodiversity as the total richness of biological variation and discussed reasons why it is important (see Chapter 7). In this chapter, we examine the many threats to biodiversity that are associated with human activities. We emphasize permanent damage caused to biodiversity, particularly that associated with losses of species and distinctive, natural ecosystems.

Extinction refers to the loss of some *taxon* over all of its range on Earth. (The word taxon refers to any taxonomically defined group of organisms, such as sub-species, species, genus, family, order, etc.) **Extirpation** refers to a more local disappearance, with the taxon still surviving elsewhere. Extinction represents an irretrievable loss of a unique portion of the biological richness of Earth, whereas it may be possible to re-establish an extirpated taxon from a surviving population elsewhere.

Extinctions have always occurred as a result of natural influences. These include random catastrophes as well as the long-term effects of environmental change—for example, climate or biological interactions such as disease or predation (see Chapter 7). In modern times, however, and probably for the past 10 000 years or so, almost all extinctions have been caused by anthropogenic influences, particularly over-harvesting and destruction of habitat. In fact, an enormous increase in the rate of extinctions has been one of the most important consequences of humans becoming the dominant species on Earth. Species are now disappearing so quickly that we refer to the phenomenon as an extinction crisis, or as a biodiversity crisis.

All species are unique, a fact that gives them great intrinsic value—this is a central tenet of the *biocentric world view* (see Chapter 1). Therefore, from an ethical perspective, irretrievable losses of biodiversity are a shameful consequence of the way humans are using their power to exploit and manage other species and ecosystems. This is also a foolish way for humans to administer their global empowerment, because unique species are disappearing before they have been investigated for any potential usefulness in medicine or agriculture, and before we understand their importance as components of ecosystems. Human actions that result in extinctions can only be regarded as ecologically dangerous behaviour.

In this chapter, we examine the modern biodiversity crisis—the reasons why it is happening, ways of repairing some of the damage already done, and how to prevent further losses.

Extinction as a Natural Process

Life has existed on Earth for approximately 3.5 billion years. Almost all of the species that have lived during that period of time are now extinct, having disappeared "naturally" for some reason or other. (Of course, the rest of those species are *extant*, or still living today.) In many cases, the extinct species could not adapt to changes that occurred in their environment, such as shifts in climate or increases in the intensity of disease, predation, or competition with other species. Many other species, however, disappeared during brief episodes of **mass extinction**, which may have been caused by unpredictable catastrophes such as a meteorite hitting the Earth.

The geological record clearly shows that numerous species and broader groups of organisms (such as genera, families, and phyla) have appeared and disappeared over time (see Chapter 6). For example, many phyla of invertebrate animals evolved during an evolutionary proliferation around the beginning of the Cambrian era some 570 million years ago. Subsequently, most of those phyla and their numerous species became extinct. About 15 to 20 extinct phyla from that period were discovered in a renowned fossil deposit known as the Burgess Shale, in Yoho National Park in southeastern British Columbia. Each of those extinct phyla represented a novel, fantastic, evolutionary "experiment" in invertebrate form and function. We only know about these ancient extinct creatures because their fragile body structures became fossilized under extraordinary geological circumstances (Gould, 1989).

The fossil record is filled with many other definitive examples of ancient extinctions. However, the rates of extinction, and of the subsequent evolutionary radiation of new species, have not been uniform over time. The geological record clearly shows that relatively low and uniform rates of extinction persisted for extremely long periods of time. However, those tranquil eras were punctuated by about nine catastrophic events of mass extinction.

The most intense episode of mass extinction occurred at the end of the Permian era, about 245 million years ago. This natural catastrophe resulted in the loss of 54% of the existing families of marine organisms, including 84% of the genera and 96% of the species (Erwin, 1990). Another mass extinction occurred at the end of the Cretaceous period, about 65 million years ago. This famous extinction event involved the last of the dinosaurs and pterosaurs (flying reptiles), along with many other taxa, totalling perhaps three-quarters of the species living at the time. Many scientists believe that this crisis of paleobiodiversity was caused by a meteorite hitting Earth. Such a catastrophe would have caused a deadly tsunami, while also ejecting enormous quantities of dust into the atmosphere, resulting in a cooling of the climate that most plant and animal species were unable to tolerate.

During the past several centuries, Earth's existing heritage of biodiversity has been buffeted by another mass extinction. This is an ongoing catastrophe, which will certainly intensify into the foreseeable future. This ecological calamity is not a natural phenomenon. Rather, it is being caused by the influences and activities of modern humans.

Extinctions and Endangerment Caused by Humans

Numerous human activities are causing species to become **endangered** or extinct. (Species are considered endangered if, because of a small population or loss of habitat, they are at high risk of becoming extirpated or extinct.) The most important cause is the destruction of natural ecosystems and their conversion into habitats that are unsuitable for the original species, a problem that is especially acute in tropical countries. Excessive harvesting of some species is also significant, as is damage caused by introduced predators, diseases, and competitors. Any of these stressors can cause populations to become small and fragmented, resulting in much greater risks of extirpation or extinction (Figure 26.1).

Because of these anthropogenic influences, the past several centuries have witnessed huge increases in the global rate of extinction and in the number of species threatened with this catastrophe. Our knowledge of recently extinct and endangered species is relatively complete for large and conspicuous species such as vertebrate animals, particularly those of temperate and higher-latitude countries, where most biologists live. In fact, there have been more than 700 known extinctions of vertebrate animals during the past four centuries, including about 100 species of mammals and 167 species of birds. All of these extinctions were caused by human influences. Enormously larger numbers of species are at grave risk of suffering extinction.

Unfortunately, we know much less about extinctions among other groups of organisms. This is particularly true of the enormous diversity of relatively small, poorly known

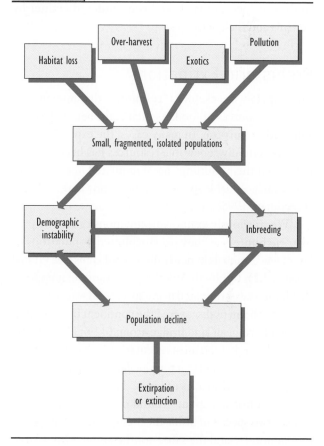

FIGURE 26.1 | The Extinction Vortex

Extinction can be caused by various influences and activities of humans, such as habitat loss, excessive harvesting, and introductions of exotic diseases, predators, and competitors. As a result of these stressors, large, continuously distributed populations may fragment into small isolated units that are vulnerable to deleterious effects of inbreeding, population instability, and random catastrophes. These can cause endangered populations to decline further and may ultimately result in extirpation or extinction. Conservation biologists refer to this accelerating, downward spiral of endangerment as the "extinction vortex."

species that live in tropical ecosystems, especially in old-growth rainforest. Undoubtedly, huge numbers of tropical species, particularly plants and invertebrates, have become extinct during the past several centuries as their natural forest habitat was converted into agricultural and other land-uses. We can refer to these losses as "hidden extinctions" because so few of the extinct species had been discovered and named by taxonomists. Moreover, these hidden extinctions continue to occur rapidly, in fact at an accelerating rate, because their poorly explored tropical habitats are being destroyed so quickly.

In the following sections we will examine selected case studies of species that have been rendered extinct by humans and their activities.

Prehistoric Extinctions

Many species are useful as "resources" that humans can harvest as sources of food, medicine, timber, fuel, or for some other purpose. In many cases, the exploitation of these potentially renewable resources has been so insatiable that their "mining" has culminated in extinction. These once-valuable species now occur nowhere on Earth (Freedman, 1995).

We previously examined extinctions caused by prehistoric hunters as they over-exploited populations of large, naive animals in newly discovered lands (see Global Focus 12.2). In North America, for example, it appears that hunters exterminated many species of large mammals soon after humans discovered the continent by migrating across a Beringean land bridge around 11 or 12 millennia ago, at the end of the most recent ice age. Known extinctions occuring around that time include 77 species of mammals and several species of birds. The losses include 10 species of horse, a giant ground sloth, four species of camels, two species of bison, the mastodon, several species of mammoths, and the sabre-toothed tiger. Other large animals became extinct when South America was colonized somewhat later.

Colonizations by humans also caused prehistoric mass extinctions in other places. Australia and New Guinea were discovered about 50 000 years ago. Soon after, many species of marsupials, large flightless birds, and tortoises became extinct. New Zealand was colonized less than 1000 years ago. Within two centuries, 30 species of large birds were extinct, among them a goose, a swan, and 26 species of large flightless birds known as moas. The extinctions on New Zealand proceeded as a wave that spread from northern North Island, the initial point of colonization, to South Island. Many of the moas were driven by hunters and their dogs to convenient butchering sites, where the great piles of bones were later used by European farmers as a source of phosphate fertilizer.

In a similar fashion, the human colonization of Madagascar, about 1500 years ago, resulted in the extinction of 14 species of lemurs, 6–12 species of giant, flightless elephant birds, and various other large, edible animals. Other well-known cases of prehistoric mass extinctions occurred on Hawaii, New Caledonia, Fiji, the West Indies, and numerous other islands.

Many of the **endemic** (local) species that existed only on small islands were particularly vulnerable to extinction. One reason for this is that island species occur in small, isolated populations. Moreover, it is thought that many birds of remote islands had not experienced intense predation during their recent history and, consequently, had evolved to be flightless, relatively large, and unafraid of predators. Such species were extremely vulnerable to hunting by humans once their islands were discovered. In addition, most island species did not co-occur with closely competing organisms. Consequently, they were easily displaced when more capable species were introduced. Finally, human colonization of remote islands, particularly by Europeans, resulted in extensive destruction of natural habitats as they were cleared for agricultural, urban, and tourism developments. The islands also became ecologically degraded by introduced plants, animals, and diseases.

For these reasons, the biotas of remote islands have suffered particularly high rates of extinction. For example, at one time, each of the approximately 800 islands of the southern Pacific Ocean may have supported several endemic species of flightless rails (a family of marsh birds known as Rallidae), plus other unique birds and reptiles. As these islands were discovered and colonized by prehistoric Polynesians, perhaps thousands of these endemic species became extinct through over-hunting and habitat damage. For instance, a study of bird bones recovered at an archaeological site on the island of Ua Huka found that 14 of the 16 original birds no longer occur there, including 10 endemic species that had been rendered extinct. The extinctions worsened when Europeans secondarily colonized these and other oceanic islands, because of the great habitat losses that occurred during "development." In fact, of the 167 taxa of birds (including 95 species) around the world that are known to have become extinct since 1600, all but nine lived on islands.

The problem of extinction-prone island biotas can be further illustrated by the case of the Hawaiian Islands, an ancient, remote archipelago of volcanic outcroppings in the Pacific Ocean. When these islands were first discovered by Polynesian seafarers, there were at least 86 species of birds, including 68 that occurred nowhere else. Of those 68 endemics, 24 are now extinct and 29 are endangered. Similarly, the native flora at the time consisted of as many as 2000 species of flowering (angiosperm) plants, of which 94–98% were endemic. During the past several hundred years, more than 100 of the indigenous plants have become extinct, and more than 500 have become threatened or endangered. The extinctions and endangerment of Hawaiian species have largely been caused by the extensive conversion of natural habitats into agricultural and urbanized land-uses, coupled with introductions of invasive species, including alien predators, competitors, virulent disease organisms, and destructive herbivores such as goats.

Species Made Extinct or Endangered by Over-Harvesting

Unsustainable harvesting has caused some of the most famous cases of extinction and endangerment, in some instances involving species that were initially extremely abundant. We will illustrate this phenomenon by referring to the dodo, the great auk, the passenger pigeon, and a few other notable cases. These are typical examples of the devastating effects that insatiable killing can have on vulnerable populations of wild creatures.

The dodo (*Raphus cucullatus*) was a turkey-sized, flightless bird that disappeared in 1681, making it the first well-documented extinction. The loss of this species is immortalized in everyday language by the phrase "dead as a dodo," which is used as a metaphor for an irrevocable loss. We also sometimes use the word "dodo" to describe an old-fashioned or stupid person. This etymology derives from the hapless dodo's apparent inability to adapt to threats posed by the human colonists of Mauritius, the only place where this bird lived. Mauritius is a small island in the Indian Ocean, discovered by Portuguese sailors in 1507. In 1598 it was colonized by the Dutch, who hunted the dodo for meat, gathered its eggs, and cleared its habitat for agriculture. They also released cats, pigs, and monkeys that preyed on dodos and destroyed their ground-level nests. These stressors caused the dodo to decline rapidly and become extinct.

The great auk (*Pinguinus impennis*), a flightless seabird, was the first well-documented anthropogenic extinction of a species whose range included North America. Early mariners knew the great auk as the original "pennegoin," although it belonged to a different family of birds (Alcidae) from the superficially similar penguins (Spheniscidae) of the Southern Hemisphere. The great auk lived throughout the north Atlantic region, breeding on a few islands off eastern Newfoundland, in the Gulf of St. Lawrence, around Iceland, and north of Scotland.

This large seabird was initially abundant in its breeding colonies. Because it was flightless, it could be killed quite easily. Consequently, the great auk had long been exploited by Aboriginal people inhabiting what is now known as Newfoundland, and also by Icelanders and European fishers, as a source of fresh meat, eggs, and oil. Unfortunately, the great auk developed into a valuable economic commodity when its feathers became sought after for stuffing mattresses in the mid-1700s. This resulted in a relentless slaughter that quickly caused the great auk to become extinct.

One of the largest breeding colonies of great auks was on Funk Island off Newfoundland. In 1785, an observer described the harvest of great auks and other seabirds on Funk Island (Nettleship and Evans, 1985):

> *It has been customary of late years, for several crews of men to live all summer on that island, for the sole purpose of killing birds for the sake of their feathers, the destruction of which they have made is incredible. If a stop is not soon put to that practice, the whole breed will be diminished to almost nothing, particularly the penguins.*

The great auk was, in fact, extirpated from Funk Island in the early 1800s. The last two individuals of this species ever seen alive were killed in 1844 by several Icelanders who were searching for specimens to sell to a bird "collector." Because of their extreme rarity at the time, great auks and their eggs were precious to collectors—they were, unfortunately, too valuable to let live.

The passenger pigeon (*Ectopistes migratorius*) possibly numbered 3 to 5 billion individuals three centuries ago, when it may have been the world's most populous landbird. The passenger pigeon bred in southeastern Canada and the northeastern U.S. in mature forests of oak, beech, hickory, and chestnut. These trees produce large seeds known as "mast," upon which this bird fed. In the autumn, passenger pigeons migrated to the southeastern United States. They flew in enormous flocks, described as being so dense as to obscure the sun, and taking hours to pass. The birds roosted communally during winter nights, often in such large numbers that they would kill trees through the excessive deposition of guano (bird feces), while breaking stout limbs under their weight.

The naturalist John Lawson described an impressive passage of these pigeons in the Carolinas (Feduccia, 1985):

> *I saw such prodigious flocks of these pigeons…in 1701–2…that they had broke down the limbs of a great many trees all over these woods, whereupon they chanced to sit and roost…These pigeons, about sun-rise…would fly by us in such vast flocks, that they would be near a quarter of an hour, before they were all passed by; and as soon as that flock was gone, another would come; and so successively one after another, for the rest of the morning.*

The seemingly unlimited abundance of passenger pigeons, and their habit of migrating and breeding in large and dense groups, made them an easy target for market hunters who sold the carcasses in cities and towns. During the early 1800s there was a well-organized hunt of passenger pigeons to supply urban markets with cheap meat. During seasons when the hunt was on, "wagon loads of them...poured into the market...and pigeons became the order of the day at dinner, breakfast, and supper, until the very name became sickening" (A. Wilson in 1829; quoted in Feduccia, 1985).

The sizes of the harvests were staggering. For example, about one billion pigeons were taken in 1869 in breeding colonies in Michigan alone. The intensity of the commercial exploitation far exceeded sustainability, and this, along with destruction of much of the breeding habitat, caused the passenger pigeon to decline rapidly in abundance. The last known attempt at nesting was in 1894, and the last known individual died a lonely death in the Cincinnati Zoo in 1914.

The Carolina parakeet (*Conuropsis carolinensis*) used to breed widely in the southeastern United States. This parakeet was a fairly common, brightly plumaged, fruit- and seed-eating bird that foraged and roosted in groups, especially in mature hardwood forest. Carolina parakeets were not hunted as a valuable commodity. Rather, they were exterminated because they were regarded as an agricultural pest, owing to damage they caused while feeding in orchards and grain fields. Unfortunately, Carolina parakeets were an easy mark for eradication because they nested and fed communally. Also, they tended to assemble around wounded colleagues, allowing an entire flock to be wiped out easily by a hunter. The last record of a flock of these parakeets was in 1904, and the last known individual died in a zoo in 1914.

Steller's sea cow (*Hydrodamalis stelleri*) was a sea mammal related to the manatees. It lived in subarctic waters around the Aleutian Islands in the Bering Sea and was hunted by Aboriginal people of the region. Soon after this shy and inoffensive species was "discovered" by Russian explorers in 1741, it became hunted as a source of food and hides. Steller's sea cow was rendered extinct after only 26 years of exploitation.

The Caribbean monk seal (*Monachus tropicalis*) lived in the Caribbean Sea and Gulf of Mexico. This species was encountered, and eaten, on Christopher Columbus's second voyage to the Americas in 1494. Populations of the Caribbean monk seal were depleted by an eighteenth-century commercial hunt for its meat and blubber. The last survivors were exterminated by the subsistence hunting of local fishers.

The Eskimo curlew (*Numenius borealis*) is a large sandpiper that was still abundant as recently as 1.5 centuries ago. The Eskimo curlew was exploited by market hunters during its migrations through the prairies and coasts of Canada and the U.S., and also on its wintering grounds on the pampas (grasslands) and coasts of South America. The uncontrolled hunting caused this bird to become rare by the end of the nineteenth century. The last observed nesting attempt was in 1866, and the last specimen "collected" (by shooting) was in Labrador in 1922. For some decades the Eskimo curlew was thought to be extinct, but recently, very small numbers of this perilously endangered bird have been seen by a few naturalists.

The right whale (*Balaena glacialis*) once ranged over all temperate waters of the Northern Hemisphere. Because of its slow speed, surface swimming behaviour, and rich oil content, plus the fact that it floated when dead, early whalers considered this the "right" whale to hunt. Due to commercial over-hunting of right whales for their blubber, which was rendered into oil to fuel the lamps of Europe, the populations of this species collapsed over its entire range. The right whale has been extirpated from the eastern Atlantic Ocean off Europe and is critically endangered in the western Pacific off Korea and Japan.

Only a few hundred right whales survive in the northwest Atlantic Ocean. Most of these animals spend much of the summer and autumn in the mouth of the Bay of Fundy and off southwestern Nova Scotia. They migrate south to winter along the southeastern U.S. and eastern Caribbean. Although not hunted for decades, the population of right whales has been slow to recover, largely because of mortality caused by collisions with ships and entanglement in fishing gear.

Species Made Extinct or Endangered by Habitat Destruction

Many species have been rendered endangered or extinct because their natural habitats were converted to agricultural or other land-uses or were damaged by alien invasive species. We will first examine several examples of this phenomenon, and then discuss the modern destruction of tropical forest—the human activity that is causing the most extinctions today.

The American ivory-billed woodpecker (*Campephilus principalis principalis*) lived in the southeastern U.S., where it bred in extensive areas of mature, bottomland, hardwood forest and cypress swamp. Most of this habitat was heavily logged or converted to agriculture by the early 1900s, driving the population of ivory-billed woodpeckers into a rapid decline. There had been no sightings of this species in North America since the early 1960s, but astonishingly, in 2005, one individual was photographed in a remote forest tract in Arkansas, prompting hope that the species might yet be recovered. A closely related sub-species, the critically endangered Cuban ivory-billed woodpecker (*Campephilus principalis bairdii*), may still occur in very small numbers in mountain forests in Cuba.

The black-footed ferret (*Mustela nigripes*) was first "discovered" in the prairies of North America in 1851. Because of habitat loss, this predator has become extirpated in Canada and endangered in the United States. Extensive areas of its habitat of natural short-grass and mixed-grass prairie were converted into agricultural use. Also, its principal food, the prairie dog (*Cynomys ludovicianus*), has declined in abundance. The prairie dog has been relentlessly poisoned as a perceived pest of rangeland. With little habitat or food, the black-footed ferret is unable to survive over most of its former range.

The Furbish's lousewort (*Pedicularis furbishiae*) is an herbaceous plant that grows only along a 230-km stretch of the Saint John River valley in New Brunswick and Maine. This species had been considered extinct. In 1976, however, it was "re-discovered" by a botanist doing field studies of the potential environmental impacts of a proposed hydroelectric reservoir on the upper Saint John River in Maine. That industrial development would have obliterated the only known habitat of the lousewort. For that, and other environmental and economic reasons, the dam was not constructed.

Tropical Deforestation

Tropical forest is Earth's most biodiverse ecosystem—its richness of species is phenomenal. Moreover, this poorly explored biome is thought to contain millions of as-yet-unnamed species, particularly of insects (Chapter 7). Because so many tropical-forest species have local distributions, the clearing of this ecosystem causes a disproportionate number of extinctions (i.e., in comparison with extinctions due to the destruction of other kinds of natural ecosystems).

Photo 26.1 The greatest modern threats to biodiversity are associated with deforestation in tropical countries. This area in West Kalimantan in Indonesian Borneo was, until recently, covered in old-growth tropical rainforest. The forest was initially logged to recover its largest trees, which were used to manufacture timber and plywood for export. A secondary harvest was then made of smaller trees for local use, after which the area was converted to agricultural land-use through a practice known as slash-and-burn. At the time the photo was taken, people had just moved into the area and were engaging in subsistence agriculture. Few native species can survive in this ecologically degraded habitat.

It is well known that the rate of deforestation in most tropical countries has increased alarmingly during the past century, particularly in the past several decades. This is in marked contrast to the situation in most higher-latitude countries, where forest cover has been relatively stable (see Chapter 14). In North America, for example, there was little net change in forest cover between 1990 and 2000 (Table 26.1). In contrast, most countries of Central and South America had substantial losses of forest cover during that period, as did most tropical countries of Africa and Asia. Overall, the developing world lost 32 million ha of forest between 1990 and 2000, and most of that was tropical forest (World Resources Institute, 2005). Globally, the rate of clearing of tropical rainforest during the 1980s and 1990s was equivalent to about 1% of that biome per year—a rate that, if maintained, would imply a half-life for that biome of only about 70 years.

Most tropical deforestation is caused by the conversion of forest into subsistence agriculture by poor people. This agricultural conversion is greatly increased whenever

Canadian Focus 26.1

Alien Invaders

During the past five centuries, and at an accelerating pace, Canada has become host to an enormous number of alien species of plants, animals, and microorganisms. Many of these non-natives were introduced intentionally, while others were introduced accidentally. Some have caused severe ecological damage by invading natural ecosystems and displacing indigenous species or by becoming serious predators or pathogens of native biota. Others are causing great economic damage as pests in agriculture, forestry, horticulture, or in the home. Canada is not unique in this circumstance—all countries are suffering grave ecological and economic damage from invasive aliens. In fact, this syndrome is one of the greatest environmental problems facing the planet.

There is a litany of examples of invasive aliens in Canada. The following cases include some of the most important invaders, in terms of the ecological damage they cause.

Invaders of Natural Habitats

■ Garlic mustard (*Alliaria petiolata*) is a native of Eurasia that was accidentally introduced to North America, possibly as a contaminant of crop seed or by hitchhiking in soil carried as ship ballast that was dumped at a port. This herbaceous plant is invasive of moist, bottomland forests of southern Ontario and Quebec, where it crowds out native understorey plants, some of which are rare in Canada.

■ Gorse (*Ulex europaea*) is a European shrub that was introduced as an attractive horticultural species. It has become invasive in coastal British Columbia, where it displaces many at-risk plants of dry forests of Garry oak (*Quercus garryana*) and Douglas-fir (*Pseudotsuga menziesii*).

■ Purple loosestrife (*Lythrum salicaria*) is an herbaceous plant of Eurasia that was introduced as an ornamental plant or with ship ballast. It can dominate marshy wetlands and degrade the habitat for native plants and animals.

■ Leafy spurge (*Euphorbia esula*) was accidentally introduced as a contaminant of crop seed. It aggressively invades prairie habitats and displaces rare native species.

■ The brown spruce longhorn beetle (*Tetropium fuscum*) is a Eurasian insect that arrived in Halifax one or more decades ago, probably carried in wood used to secure ship cargoes. It is attacking and killing native spruce trees in the Halifax area, especially red spruce (*Picea rubens*), and it may be a threat to the entire boreal forest. An attempt is being made to eradicate this beetle by cutting and burning any spruce trees in which it is present.

■ Chestnut blight (*Endothia parasitica*) and Dutch elm disease (*Ceratocystis ulmi*) are Asian fungal pathogens that were brought to North America with horticultural stock of non-native trees. These diseases have wiped out native chestnut and elms wherever they have encountered them, causing terrible damage to natural forests. A similar recent case involving alien fungi introduced through horticulture involves the butternut canker (*Sirococcus clavigignenti*), which is now killing native butternut trees (*Juglans cinerea*).

■ The common carp (*Cyprinus carpio*) is a Eurasian fish introduced as a source of food and sport. It damages shallow-water habitats by uprooting aquatic plants and sediment while feeding and nesting.

■ The zebra mussel (*Dreissenia polymorpha*) arrived to the Great Lakes in ballast water of ships sailing from Europe. It causes enormous damage by displacing native mollusks and by fouling water pipes and other structures.

■ The green crab (*Carcinus maenas*) arrived in ballast water in the mid-nineteenth century and is now firmly established on the East Coast. It feeds broadly and has caused declines in abundance of a wide range of native invertebrates.

■ The green fleece (*Codium fragile*) is a marine alga from Eurasia that has recently (since about 1990) established on both the Atlantic and Pacific coasts. It aggressively displaces native seaweeds, particularly in the Atlantic.

Invaders of Anthropogenic Ecosystems

■ The starling (*Sturnus vulgaris*), English sparrow (*Passer domesticus*), and rock dove (*Columba livea*) are Eurasian birds that were introduced to North America by "homesick" European immigrants. They are now extremely abundant and displace native birds from breeding sites, compete with them for food, and foul urban areas with their excrement.

■ The common rat (*Rattus norvegicus*), house mouse (*Mus musculus*), and Oriental cockroach (*Blatta orientalis*) are non-native animals that are pests in many homes.

Canadian Focus 26.1 (continued)

- The dandelion (*Taraxacum officinale*), crabgrass (*Digitaria sanguinalis*), and common plantain (*Plantago major*) are among the many alien plants that have been introduced to North America, mostly by accident, and are now considered pests of horticulture.
- Bull thistle (*Cirsium vulgare*), groundsel (*Senecio jacobea*), and St. John's wort (*Hypericum perforatum*) are among the many invasive aliens that degrade pastures by crowding out more nutritious plants or by being distasteful or poisonous to livestock.
- Couch grass (*Agropyron repens*), field thistle (*Cirsium arvense*), and lamb's quarter (*Chenopodium album*) are among the many non-native plants that are important weeds of cultivated agriculture because they compete intensely with crop plants.

TABLE 26.1 Changes in Forest Area in Selected Countries of the Americas

Area is stated in units of 10^6 hectares, and deforestation rate as percentage change from original extent and from 1990 to 2000.

COUNTRY	NATURAL FOREST AREA (2000) (10^6 ha)	FOREST AS % OF ORIGINAL	FOREST CHANGE IN 2000 AS % OF 1990
NORTH AMERICA			
Canada	244.6	91.2	−0.0
United States	209.8	60.2	+1.3
CENTRAL AMERICA AND CARIBBEAN			
Honduras	5.3	51.6	−10.6
Nicaragua	3.2	44.3	−27.3
Panama	2.8	62.0	−16.2
Guatemala	2.7	46.2	−19.8
Mexico	54.9	63.4	−10.6
Cuba	1.9	28.8	+1.1
Belize	1.3	95.7	−21.2
Costa Rica	1.8	34.9	−13.1
SOUTH AMERICA			
Paraguay	23.3	44.5	−5.3
Ecuador	10.4	66.4	−11.9
Venezuela	48.6	83.6	−5.4
Bolivia	53.0	77.2	−8.1
Brazil	538.9	66.4	−4.3
Columbia	49.5	53.5	−3.6
Peru	64.6	86.6	−4.7
Guyana	16.9	97.4	0.0
Suriname	14.1	95.6	0.0
Argentina	33.7	59.5	−10.1
Chile	13.5	40.6	−7.5
WORLD	3863	53.4	−3.6

Source: Data from World Resources Institute (2005)

access to the forest interior is improved. When roads are constructed for timber extraction or mineral exploration, deforestation often follows rapidly. The complex social causes of deforestation include population growth, inequality of land ownership, and the displacement of poor people by mechanization and the global commercialization of agriculture. Because of these factors, enormous numbers of poor people are seeking arable land in most of the less developed countries. These people need land on which they can grow food for subsistence and for some cash income.

The forest conversion often involves a system of *shifting cultivation*, in which the trees are felled, the woody debris burned, and the land used to grow mixed crops for several years. By that time, fertility has declined and weeds have become abundant. The land is then abandoned for a fallow period of several decades. This allows a secondary forest to regenerate, while nearby patches of forest are cleared to provide new land for cultivation.

A more intensive system of subsistence agriculture, known as *slash-and-burn*, results in a more permanent conversion of the land into crop production. Slash-and-burn also involves cutting and burning the forest. After the forest is gone, however, the land is used continuously, without a fallow period during which a secondary forest may re-grow and site fertility regenerate.

Much tropical forest is also being cleared to provide land for industrial agriculture (e.g., to develop oil-palm plantations, sugar-cane fields, and cattle pasture), and also by commercial logging. Tropical deforestation is also caused by flooding during the development of hydroelectric reservoirs, by the harvesting of wood to manufacture charcoal, and by the harvesting of fuelwood, especially near towns and cities. Wood is the predominant cooking fuel in many tropical countries, particularly for poorer, rural people—for most of the world's humans, the energy crisis involves fuelwood, not fossil fuels (see Chapter 14).

Because so many species live in tropical forest, the modern rate of deforestation of this biome is having catastrophic consequences for global biodiversity. This damage will become increasingly important in the future, assuming the present relentless pace of tropical deforestation continues.

Fortunately, a widespread awareness and concern about this important ecological problem has developed. This has recently stimulated a great deal of research on the conservation and protection of tropical forests, and governments have started to set aside substantial areas as ecological reserves, national parks, and other kinds of **protected areas**. Thousands of sites, comprising hundreds of millions of hectares, have now received some sort of "protection" in tropical countries.

The effectiveness of this protected status varies greatly, however. It depends on factors that influence governmental commitments to conserving forest and other indigenous ecosystems and to protecting biodiversity more generally. Political stability and priorities are especially important considerations—these are critical to addressing the social causes of the destruction of tropical ecosystems. Social factors include poverty, population growth, inequalities of the distributions of wealth and land, industrial forest mining to earn foreign exchange, and corruption. More directly, political stability and priorities determine whether enough money is available to support a system of protected areas and to find effective means to control the poaching of animals and timber and to prevent other encroachments.

Poaching (i.e., illegal harvesting) of endangered wildlife is a terrible problem for species that have economic value on the international black market (see Global Focus 26.1). This can be illustrated by the black rhino (*Diceros bicornis*) and the elephant (*Loxodonta africana*) in a game reserve in Zambia, Africa. In the early 1970s, the Luangwa Valley contained about 100 000 elephants and 4000–12 000 black rhinos (Leader-Williams *et al.*, 1990). Unfortunately, these relatively large populations quickly collapsed because of poaching, which resulted from the extremely high prices paid for rhino horns and elephant tusks in certain wealthy countries. Even though Zambian park wardens made courageous and highly motivated conservation efforts under difficult circumstances, it proved impossible to control the poaching. The astronomical value of horn and ivory has spawned a well-organized and effective chain of poaching, smuggling, and sale.

In spite of these sorts of problems, some tropical countries are developing a real commitment to the protection of their threatened biodiversity. In Central America and the Caribbean, for example, Belize, Costa Rica, and the Dominican Republic have relatively progressive policies on the conservation and protection of natural ecosystems. As of 2004, 29% of the area of Belize had been given park or reserve status, as had 9% of Costa Rica, and 23% of the Dominican Republic (World Resources Institute, 2005). For perspective, we should note that the relative areas of protected land in those Latin American nations are greater than in Canada (5.3%) and the U.S. (8.4%), in spite of their comparative poverty (these data are for IUCN categories 1–5; see Global Focus 26.2). Such vigorous conservation activities are badly needed in the region: during 1990–2000, the deforestation was 13% in Costa Rica and 21% in Belize.

In other Latin American countries, conservation efforts have been disrupted by civil war and other political instabilities and by different governmental and social priorities. For example, in 2004, the percentage of the national territory with protected status as parks or ecological reserves was only 0.1% in Jamaica, 0.2% in El Salvador, 0.3% in Haiti, 0.6% in Mexico, and 4.8% in Trinidad and Tobago (World Resources Institute, 2005).

The world's greatest expanses of tropical rainforest occur in equatorial Africa, southern and southeastern Asia, Central America, western South America, and the basin of the Amazon River. The latter region, known as Amazonia, contains the most extensive rainforest and may support 30% of the biodiversity of Earth (Mongabay, 2005). This rich tropical region is still extensively covered by old-growth rainforest that has been little affected by modern agriculture, lumbering, or other influences of industrial society (although virtually all of Amazonia has supported indigenous cultures for thousands of years).

However, the exploitation and devastation of the Amazonian forest is proceeding rapidly. Great expanses of rainforest are being converted into cattle ranches and soybean farms. In addition, large areas have been deforested by poor farmers who have migrated from heavily populated regions of Amazonian countries in search of "new" agricultural land. Some Amazonian forest has been degraded by hydroelectric developments, lumbering, and the harvesting of trees to manufacture charcoal as a fuel for the production of iron.

Most of Amazonia lies in northern Brazil. The population in that region has increased enormously in recent decades to several million people, mostly because of the migration of landless peasants from other parts of Brazil. This, along with the development of industrial agriculture, has resulted in rapid deforestation in Amazonian

Global Focus 26.1

CITES and the International Trade in Endangered Species

Many endangered species are extremely valuable for one reason or another. Some are avidly sought by private collectors or by public zoos or botanical gardens, many of which may be willing to pay large sums for living specimens to add to their collections. Some animal and plant tissues are extremely valuable, a circumstance that may result in endangered species being killed for their fur, ivory, horn, fine-grained wood, or other body parts. For example, rhinoceros horn is extremely valuable in Yemen for manufacturing into dagger handles, and in eastern Asia as an ingredient in traditional medicine. Similarly, bile from the gallbladder of bears is a precious commodity in traditional medicine in eastern Asia, as are tiger bones and the underground rhizome of ginseng, particularly if the plant was collected from a wild habitat. Elephant ivory is valued for carving and other crafts in Asia and elsewhere. Other costly products of endangered species include rare furs, trade in which has seriously affected large predators, especially cats such as tiger, cheetah, leopard, and jaguar.

The Convention on International Trade in Endangered Species, often referred to by its acronym CITES, is an international treaty that commits signatory nations to controlling or preventing the trade in threatened species. CITES was established in 1973 in association with the United Nations Environment Programme (UNEP). Its most important function is to monitor the international trade in endangered species and to control or prevent that trade as much as possible. For these purposes, the status of species as extinct, endangered, vulnerable, or rare is assigned by the International Union for the Conservation of Nature (IUCN). The actual trade in species is monitored by the World Wildlife Fund (WWF)/IUCN "Traffic" network worldwide. The world headquarters of CITES, IUCN, and WWF are all in Switzerland.

International trade in about 529 species of animals and 298 species of plants is prohibited by CITES (so-called Appendix I species). In addition, the trade in about 4466 animals and 28 074 plants (Appendix II) requires a CITES permit and is monitored by the World Conservation Monitoring Centre (WCMC) of Cambridge, U.K. WCMC also publishes a series of so-called "red books" summarizing the status of, and commerce in, about 8300 plant and 7200 animal species. Canadian species listed by CITES include 63 species of mammals, 57 birds, 4 reptiles, 11 fish, and 43 plants (most are native species of orchids).

Canada is a member of CITES. Some of its responsibilities under the treaty are to monitor and report on its international trade in all species that fall under the purview of WCMC. In 2004, for example, the federal government of Canada issued 172 permits to import living CITES species or their parts (the living organisms are intended for zoological or botanical parks or the pet trade), and 28 943 export permits (Robillard, 2005). Legal exports of living specimens in 2004 included 6 black bears, 2 polar bears, 4 wolves, and certain other native species, plus many individuals of non-native CITES species that were being traded among zoos and botanical parks. There is also a substantial legal export from Canada of body parts of some indigenous CITES species, including 53 narwhal tusks, 3737 wolf skins, 15 305 black bear skins, 342 grizzly bear skins, 451 polar bear skins, 239 cougar skins, 4235 bobcat skins, and 4570 lynx skins.

Of course, these data refer only to the known, legal trade of species listed by CITES. There is also a flourishing illegal trade in Canada, particularly of animal parts such as bear gallbladders, caribou antlers, and certain kinds of furs. Further, there is an illegal trade in some living animals and plants, such as certain native species of orchids and gyrfalcons and peregrine falcons, which are extremely valuable in the Middle East for use in the sport of falconry. Most of the prohibited trade involves animals and plants that were illegally hunted or collected by poachers. In addition, there are large illegal imports of banned products into Canada. These include rare and endangered parrots, reptiles, fish, orchids, and other species that are valuable in the pet trade. There is also a burgeoning illegal trade of animal parts that are valuable in traditional medicine, particularly to service a market among North Americans interested in traditional Chinese medicine.

The illegal trade in rare and endangered species is responsible for an enormous international economy (about US$5 billion per year; reputedly second only to the illegal drug trade). This is why such commerce is flourishing in so many countries, including Canada. To some degree, governments can deal with the problem by more rigidly enforcing their laws governing the illegal trade and by imposing more severe penalties on convicted offenders. Ultimately, however, the illicit commerce is driven by a wealthy and enthusiastic marketplace. Obviously, for the sake of the endangered biodiversity, it is critical that the demand be curtailed as soon as possible. Ultimately, people's attitudes must be changed, and severe penalties must be imposed for the illegal possession of species or body parts banned by CITES.

Global Focus 26.2

Categories of Protected Areas

The International Union for the Conservation of Nature (IUCN) and the World Commission on Protected Areas (WCPA) recognize six categories of protected areas. Categories I, II, and III represent strong commitments to maintaining natural ecosystems within the protected area, while the other categories allow some degree of resource management or extraction.

Category	Description
I.	*Strict Nature Reserves and Wilderness Areas* include nature, ecological, and wilderness reserves. These are managed mainly to preserve their natural condition, although some use by scientists for research and monitoring may be allowed.
II.	*National Parks and Equivalent Reserves* consist of national, state, and provincial parks, plus areas under native, tribal, or other traditional ownership. These areas are managed primarily to protect ecosystems, although recreation is usually permitted.
III.	*Natural Monuments* include geological phenomena and archaeological sites and are intended to protect natural features of aesthetic or cultural importance.
IV.	*Habitat and Species Management Areas* consist of wetlands, wildlife refuges, and wildlife sanctuaries. These are intended to conserve through the protection and management of habitats. Hunting and other types of consumptive use may be allowed in many of these areas.
V.	*Protected Landscapes and Seascapes* include landscapes, marine areas, scenic rivers, waterways, recreational areas, trails, protected forests, and conservation areas in which interactions of humans and nature have produced areas of distinct character. These areas are managed to sustain use by both people and wild species and ecosystems.
VI.	*Managed Resource Protected Areas* contain areas of primarily natural ecosystems. These are managed to ensure the protection of biodiversity, while also providing a sustainable harvest of renewable resources and ecological services.

Brazil. Between 1978 and 2004, a total of 520 000 km² of tropical forest was cleared, equivalent to about 12% of Amazonia (Mongabay, 2005). The rate of deforestation has increased significantly in the past few years, mostly due to a rush to develop additional acreage for cattle ranching and soybeans, for which huge export markets have developed in China and Europe (in 2004, Brazil exported US$10 billion worth of soybeans, which are now the country's largest agricultural export). Between 2002 and 2005 the annual rate of deforestation was 25 400 km²/y, compared with 17 600 km²/y in the preceding decade. By 2004, at least 20% of Amazonia had been deforested. And the process continues.

For various reasons, including pressures exerted by international environmental organizations, the government of Brazil has committed itself to conserving its Amazonian biodiversity, even while vigorously "developing" the economy of the region. Up to 2004, the government of Brazil had established about 210 000 km² of parks and ecological reserves (IUCN categories I–II), another 119 000 km² of areas with less protection (categories III–V; the permitted land-uses do not include deforestation), plus 115 000 km² of anthropological reserves, which are intended to protect the traditional homelands and cultures of indigenous peoples (World Resources Institute, 2005). Almost all of these protected areas are in Amazonia; however, as with protected areas everywhere, these areas often suffer from poaching, illegal mining and agricultural settlement, and other kinds of prohibited activities that degrade their ecological values (and also threaten Aboriginal cultures and land tenure).

Species Declines

Recently, numerous species of certain groups of organisms have been suffering intense and widespread declines in their populations, with many of them becoming endangered. These organisms include large carnivores, reptiles, amphibians, predatory birds, and migratory songbirds. For example, of the 49 species and geographically distinct populations of birds that are listed as endangered, threatened, or of special concern in Canada, 45 are migratory (COSEWIC, 2005). We will examine the problem of species declines using the example of North American songbirds.

Within the past decade or so, ecologists and birdwatchers have been reporting alarming declines in the populations of many species of so-called neotropical migrants (i.e., species that spend most of the year in tropical habitats but migrate to higher-latitude regions to breed). Most of the declining species breed in mature temperate and boreal forest. Although the reasons for the songbird declines in North America are not totally understood, the most important factors are probably the following:

- extensive deforestation in their tropical wintering range
- disturbance of mature-forest habitat in the northern breeding range
- fragmentation of breeding habitat into "islands" that are too small to sustain populations over the long term, and that are easily penetrated by forest-edge predators and nest parasites (such as cowbirds—to be discussed later)
- loss of critical habitats for staging and migration
- effects of pesticides and other toxic chemicals
- possibly also new introduced diseases, such as the West Nile virus

Bachman's warbler (*Vermivora bachmanii*) appears to have become extinct recently because of the loss of its tropical wintering habitat. Bachman's warbler used to breed in mature, hardwood forest in the southeastern United States. Although suitable breeding habitat remains in that region, this warbler has not been seen since the mid-1950s and is undoubtedly extinct. Its extinction was likely caused by the clearing of its critical wintering habitat, believed to have been tropical forest in Cuba that was converted into sugar cane plantations.

Much of the evidence suggesting that populations of neotropical migrants are declining is *anecdotal*—skilled birders are not seeing as many individuals of some species as they used to, even where the local habitat has not changed greatly. Unfortunately, only a few studies have closely monitored bird populations for many years in mature forest habitat. One of the best, long-term data sets is for a tract of forest in West Virginia, where the breeding birds, particularly the migrants, have declined substantially over a 37-year period. During 1947–53, 25 to 28

species bred at that site, of which 14 to 16 were neotropical migrants. This decreased to only 15 species and 8 migrants breeding over 1973–83 (Terborgh, 1989). During that same period, the total abundance of birds decreased by 16%, and that of neotropical migrants by 37%. In another important census of forest birds, made at Hubbard Brook, New Hampshire, 70% of the breeding species declined in abundance between 1969 and 1984 (Holmes *et al.*, 1986).

An extremely important Canadian data set comes from a bird observatory located at the tip of Long Point, a 32-km-long peninsula that juts into Lake Erie in southern Ontario. Because of its shape and location, Long Point attracts large numbers of birds during their migrations. During their southward autumn migration, many birds begin their crossing of Lake Erie at the tip of Long Point, having been funnelled along the landform as they move through its habitats. During the northward migration in the spring, the tip is the first land seen during the open-water crossing of Lake Erie, and birds often landfall there in large numbers. Consequently, an observatory at Long Point provides a large and dependable sample of the enormous populations of birds that breed in the extensive habitats to the north. Data from Long Point show that, between 1961 and 1988, 29 species of neotropical migrants declined in abundance, while only four species increased (Hussell *et al.*, 1992).

Another important Canadian data set has been compiled by the Canadian Wildlife Service, based on information from a large number of breeding bird surveys. These are made annually at many locations across Canada, using a common methodology. Because so many widely spaced locations contribute to the database, it can be used to provide an indication of synoptic trends in the abundance of birds. The analysis in Figure 26.2 shows that the abundance of neotropical migrants breeding in Canada has declined markedly between 1971 and 2002.

The causes of the declines of neotropical migrants include the reduction of their breeding habitat in North America due to forestry activities and conversions into agricultural and urban areas. The amount of available high-quality habitat has declined greatly, while much of the remainder has been fragmented into small islands of natural forest. This change is important because birds have less success when breeding in small fragments of forest. In part, this is because their nests are more vulnerable to predation by such species as crows, jays, magpies, skunks, and foxes.

Many migratory species have also been seriously affected by nest parasitism by the brown-headed cowbird

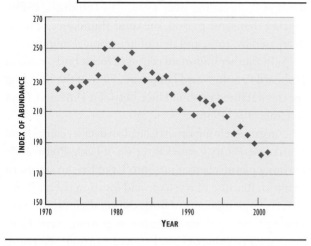

FIGURE 26.2 | Recent Changes in the Abundance of Neotropical Migrants in Canada

The index of abundance is based on the results of an annual analysis of a large number of breeding bird surveys at locations across the country.

Source: Data from Downes et al. (2003)

(*Molothrus ater*), which lays its eggs in the nests of other species. The foster parents raise the voracious cowbird chick, while their own young are neglected and usually die. The brown-headed cowbird has greatly expanded its range and abundance in North America, mostly because humans have provided it with suitable habitat by disturbing the formerly extensive forest. Cowbirds feed in open areas, and they are particularly efficient at parasitizing nests near forest edges.

Many bird species in the northern and eastern parts of the modern range of the cowbird are extremely vulnerable to nest parasitism (Freedman, 1995). They have only recently come in contact with this parasite and have not evolved an effective defence. For example, Kirtland's warbler (*Dendroica kirtlandii*), an endangered species, can suffer a parasitism rate of 70%. Each incidence leads to reproductive failure. A study in Illinois found that two-thirds of 75 nests of various host species were parasitized by cowbirds, including 76% of 49 nests of neotropical migrants. The rate of nest parasitism of white-crowned sparrows (*Zonotrichia leucophrys*) in California increased from 5% in 1975 to 40–50% in 1990–91, much more than the 20% rate that the sparrow population could sustain without declining.

The cowbird problem is a dilemma. This is because the only obvious way to help the threatened birds involves killing large numbers of the cowbird, itself a native species. Although distasteful, that action is required if humans wish to deal with the severe damage that this parasite is inflict-

ing on other species, as an indirect consequence of anthropogenic changes to its habitat.

Back from the Brink

Fortunately, dismal stories about extinctions and other grievous losses do not make up all the news about biodiversity (Freedman, 1995). There are also some success stories of conservation. These involve species that were taken perilously close to the brink of extinction, but have since recovered because they were given effective protection. In some cases, the recoveries have been vigorous enough that the species are no longer in imminent danger. Although these success stories are a distinct minority (the number of endangered species is increasing much more rapidly), they are nevertheless instructive. They illustrate that positive actions can yield great benefits, both for the species in question and for the humans that can exploit them as a potentially renewable resource.

The Northern Fur Seal and Some Other Seals

The northern fur seal (*Callorhinus ursinus*) lives in the northern Pacific Ocean. This seal was relentlessly exploited for its fur, and by 1920, it had been reduced from a population of several million to only about 130 000. Because the northern fur seal was believed to be in danger of extinction, an international treaty was signed that strictly regulated its harvest. The seal population responded vigorously to the conservation measures and rebounded to almost one million individuals. The species was again abundant enough to support a commercial hunt for its fur, leather, and oil. However, its numbers declined again and now there is only a subsistence hunt, equivalent to about 2000 animals per year since 1986. The northern fur seal has also been suffering considerable non-hunting mortality from entanglement in drift-nets used to fish in the north Pacific. In addition, oil spills and overfishing of its food pose new risks to its population.

Some other species of seals were also exploited excessively, but then rebounded in abundance after the hunt was stopped, or at least sensibly regulated. Two Canadian examples are the harp seal (*Phoca groenlandica*) of the north Atlantic Ocean, which now number about 5.9 million animals (see Chapter 14), and the grey seal (*Halichoerus grypus*) of temperate Atlantic waters. The grey seal numbered only about 5000 individuals as recently as the mid-1960s

Photo 26.2   Populations of humpback whales (*Megaptera novaeangliae*) were decimated worldwide by commercial whaling. However, this species is now protected and its numbers are increasing. Humpback whales, such as these animals off Newfoundland, spend much of the summer feeding on small fish in certain places off eastern Canada.

and was considered endangered. Since then, however, the grey seal has had remarkable population growth and now numbers more than 290 000 animals.

The Whaling Industry

Many populations of large whales were severely depleted during several centuries of unregulated exploitation (Chapter 14). Following protection, some whale populations have substantially recovered. The best example of such a recovery is the grey whale (*Eschrichtius robustus*) of the Pacific coast of North America, which was protected in the 1930s when its endangered population numbered only 1000–2000 animals. The grey whale now numbers more than 26 000 individuals, roughly its pre-exploitation population level. Although the grey whales of the eastern Pacific are no longer endangered, the population in the eastern Atlantic was extirpated several centuries ago, and another tiny stock in the western Pacific is critically endangered.

Other large species of whales were also depleted by commercial hunting. With few exceptions, these have been protected from exploitation since an international moratorium on whaling in 1986. Their populations are slowly

recovering, although not yet to the degree achieved by the grey whale. The sperm whale (*Physeter catodon*), for example, had a global pre-whaling abundance of about 2 million, but now numbers fewer than 1 million. Similarly, the finback whale (*Balaenoptera physalus*) initially numbered about 700 000, but now numbers 163 000, while the blue whale (*B. musculus*), initially numbering 250 000, now numbers only several thousand. The humpback whale (*Megaptera novaeangliae*) was about 100 000 and is now 22 000. These species will continue to recover their abundances as long as they remain protected from commercial hunting. There is intense pressure, however, for the moratorium to end for the most abundant species, particularly the minke whale (*Balaenoptera acutorostrata*), which number about 1 million.

Several other species of whales remain badly depleted and are recovering extremely slowly, if at all. One of these is the population of right whales (*Balaena glacialis*) of the western Atlantic, which numbers only a few hundred individuals. Another is the right whale of the eastern Pacific Ocean, with only a hundred or so animals. Yet another is the bowhead whale (*Balaena mysticetus*) of the Arctic, with a population of about 8000. Bowhead whales are still subjected to an Aboriginal hunt in northern coastal Alaska (no more than 67 can be struck per year; several have also been taken off Baffin Island in Canada since 1996). The most important causes of mortality of Atlantic right whales appear to be collisions with ships and entanglement in fishing nets.

The American Bison

Before the American bison, or buffalo (*Bison bison*), was subjected to an intensive commercial hunt, its population was an estimated 60 million. At that time, bison were the most abundant large, wild animals in North America, ranging over most of the continent.

Some biologists believe that there are several sub-species of bison. The eastern sub-species (*B. b. pennsylvanicus*), an animal of forests and glades, ranged over much of the eastern United States. It was hunted to extinction by the mid-1800s. The plains bison (*B. b. bison*) ranged throughout the prairies of North America and was by far the most populous sub-species. These animals migrated in enormous herds—one was described as being 80 km long and 40 km wide, another as 320 km long, and another as moving over a 160-km front! The plains bison were subjected to an intensive market hunt during the nineteenth century and were nearly exterminated. Apart from the money that was made by selling meat and hides, the eradication of the plains bison may have been encouraged by governments, likely for two reasons. First, the development of prairie agriculture was being disrupted by the bison herds, especially during their mass migrations. Second, since the bison were critical to the subsistence economy of the Plains Indians extermination of these abundant animals made it easier to displace Aboriginal tribes in favour of European colonists.

The most famous buffalo hunter was William F. Cody, or "Buffalo Bill," who was contracted in 1869 to provide meat for workers constructing the Union Pacific Railroad through the U.S. prairie. Cody reportedly killed 250 bison in a single day and more than 4000 during an 18-month period. Once the railways were built, special excursions were organized during which a train would stop near a herd of migrating buffalo, allowing passengers to shoot animals in a leisurely fashion through the windows of the coaches. Some of the tongues (a delicacy) would be cut from the dead animals; otherwise, the carcasses were left to rot. Such actions were a wanton destruction of a natural resource. More important damage, however, was caused by the market hunts made feasible by the new railroad—the meat could be shipped quickly to urban con-

sumers. Between 1871 and 1875, market hunters killed about 2.5 million bison per year. In addition, the Plains Indians had acquired rifles and horses by this time and were able to hunt bison much more effectively than before.

The unregulated exploitation of the plains bison was grossly unsustainable, and the species declined precipitously. By 1889 there were fewer than 1000 bison left in the United States, and only small herds survived in the Canadian prairies. Almost too late, a few closely guarded preserves were established, and some animals were captured for breeding programs. These and later actions have allowed the numbers of plains bison to increase to their present abundance of more than 50 000 animals. Of course, since almost all of the original habitat of the plains bison is gone, having been converted into agriculture, this animal will never recover its former abundance. However, the plains bison is no longer endangered.

The wood bison (*B. b. athabascae*) of the southern boreal forest of western Canada is a third sub-species. It was also hunted intensely. When this sub-species became endangered, governments protected the only remaining wild population in and around Wood Buffalo National Park in northern Alberta and the southwestern Northwest Territories. Unfortunately, the genetic integrity and health of this population has been degraded by interbreeding with plains bison, which were introduced to the area by misguided wildlife managers in the late 1920s. Fortunately, a previously unknown population of wood bison was discovered in 1960 in a remote area of Wood Buffalo National Park. It appears that these have not suffered from interbreeding with the plains sub-species. Some of these "pure" wood bison were used to establish another isolated population, northwest of Great Slave Lake. Regrettably, many of the wild-ranging bison of northwestern Canada have been exposed to introduced diseases of cattle, most notably tuberculosis and brucellosis. These, along with predation by humans and wolves, have taken their toll on the wood bison. The long-term viability of their population is cause for concern.

Agricultural interests within the federal government have proposed to exterminate virtually all of the bison in the vicinity of Wood Buffalo National Park, except for the "pure" wood bison occurring in isolated populations known to be free of bovine diseases. This slaughter is intended to prevent the spread of brucellosis and tuberculosis from bison to the cattle herds that are spreading northward in Alberta. A secondary reason for the proposed slaughter is to protect the genetic integrity of the wood bison sub-species, because it is the hybrid wood/plains animals that would be targeted for extermination, leaving the more isolated, non-diseased, pure wood bison to re-populate the cleared habitat. This proposal is highly controversial and, even if permitted, would probably not be successful. An enormous effort would be required to find each and every bison in the target area, which is a huge wilderness of boreal forest and muskeg.

In spite of continuing problems, it appears that vigorous conservation efforts have preserved the American bison. This large herbivore will survive, although in captivity and in relatively small populations in the wild.

Some Other Recoveries from Depleted Abundance

The sea otter (*Enhydra lutris*) lives on the west coast of North America. This mammal was subjected to a devastating eighteenth- and nineteenth-century hunt for its dense and lustrous fur. In fact, for decades, the sea otter was thought to be extinct, until small residual populations were discovered in the 1930s. The sea otter has rapidly recovered its abundance over much of the west coast. This recovery has been aided by deliberate re-introductions into areas from which it had been extirpated, such as the Pacific coast of Vancouver Island. Sea otters now number more than 100 000 individuals. However, the Canadian population is still small and vulnerable enough to remain officially designated as a threatened species.

The pronghorn antelope (*Antilocapra americana*) of the western plains of North America was severely over-hunted during the nineteenth century, and its population was reduced to about 20 000 individuals. Fortunately, strong conservation measures were implemented, and this species now numbers more than 500 000. It can again sustain a sport hunt.

The trumpeter swan (*Cygnus buccinator*) used to breed extensively in western North America, perhaps as far east as Ontario. Populations of this swan were devastated by hunting for its meat and skin. However, the trumpeter swan is now protected and has recovered somewhat in abundance; it now numbers more than 5000 individuals.

The wild turkey (*Meleagris gallopavo*) was widely extirpated from its natural range by hunting and habitat loss (of course, domestic varieties of this species are abundant in agriculture). Because of conservation measures and re-introductions to areas from which the species had disappeared, populations of wild turkeys have recovered substantially, for example in southern Ontario and Quebec. Many stocks of this large gamebird can again sustain a sport hunt.

Photo 26.3 Sea otters (*Enhydra lutris*) were decimated by hunting for their fur. Their populations have since recovered over much of their range, including parts of western Vancouver Island. Although no longer hunted, sea otters are still threatened by oil spills, habitat change caused by fishing, and illegal shooting by fishers who perceive that otters are eating "too many" valuable crustaceans and shellfish.
Source: C. Harvey-Clark

The wood duck (*Aix sponsa*) was greatly over-hunted for its beautiful feathers and as food. It also suffered from losses of habitat due to lumbering and wetland drainage. The recovery of the wood duck has been aided greatly by the widespread provision of nest boxes in wetlands used by this cavity-nesting species. Nest-box programs also benefit several other relatively uncommon cavity-nesting ducks, particularly the hooded merganser (*Lophodytes cucullatus*) and common goldeneye (*Bucephala clangula*). An unrelated program of providing terrestrial nest-boxes has helped to increase the abundance of eastern and western bluebirds (*Sialia sialis* and *S. mexicana*), which had been declining because of habitat loss.

The American beaver (*Castor canadensis*) was one of the most sought-after species in the fur trade, a commercial activity that stimulated much of the early exploration of Canada and the central and western United States. Beavers were over-harvested almost everywhere, causing the species to be extirpated from most of its natural range. However, conservation measures and decreased demand for its fur have allowed the beaver to recover its populations over most of its range where the habitat is still suitable. In fact, beavers are now considered to be "pests" in some of their recolonized habitats because of the flooding they cause.

Photo 26.4 The Labrador duck (*Camptorhynchus labradorium*) was a sea duck that used to winter on the Atlantic Coast of Canada and the northeastern U.S. and probably nested in coastal Labrador. Because of excessive hunting, the species became extinct around 1875. This is a photograph of carved models of a pair of Labrador ducks, replicated from old stuffed specimens that had been "collected" in Nova Scotia by a nineteenth-century naturalist.

Source: D. Josey

The whooping crane (*Grus americana*) is, it is hoped, an incipient success story of conservation. The whooping crane was never very abundant (likely around 1500 individuals), even before its populations were devastated by the combined effects of hunting, loss of its breeding habitat of prairie wetlands to agriculture, deterioration of its wintering habitat along the Gulf of Mexico, and egg and specimen collecting. These stressors drove the wild population down to the perilously low level of only 15 individuals (in 1941). Fortunately, since then, the whooping crane has been vigorously protected from hunting, while its major breeding habitat in Wood Buffalo National Park and its wintering habitat in coastal Texas have been conserved. These measures, along with a program of captive breeding and release, have allowed the population of whooping cranes to increase to about 453 animals (in 2005; 215 of these are in the migratory Wood Buffalo population; 45 in a new Wisconsin migratory group; 66 in a non-migratory Florida population; and 127 in captivity). There is now cautious optimism for the survival of this species, although it is still endangered.

Canadian Species and Ecosystems at Risk

The conservation status of species in Canada is assessed by the Committee on the Status of Endangered Wildlife in Canada (COSEWIC). COSEWIC is a consultative body with expert representatives from the federal government, the provinces and territories, universities, and non-governmental organizations, such as the World Wildlife Fund and the Canadian Nature Federation. It makes recommendations to the federal, provincial, and territorial governments, whose responsibility it is to actually designate conservation status.

Once a species is listed as endangered or threatened in Canada, a parallel body known as RENEW (REcovery of Nationally Endangered Wildlife) is mandated to prepare a plan that would ensure the recovery of its population to a safer level. As of 2004, recovery plans had been completed (25) or were in development (156) for 181 of the 500 species or populations that have been designated as at-risk in Canada.

COSEWIC recognizes five categories of risk, each of which has a specific meaning in terms of imminent threats to the future survival of species (COSEWIC, 2005).

Extinct refers to any species of wildlife that was formerly indigenous to Canada but no longer exists anywhere in the world. Canadian examples of extinct species are the great auk (*Pinguinus impennis*), passenger pigeon (*Ectopistes migratorius*), Labrador duck (*Camptorhynchus labradorium*), sea mink (*Mustela macrodon*), deepwater cisco (*Coregonus johannae*), longjaw cisco (*Coregonus alpenae*), and eelgrass limpet (*Lottia alveus*). Extinct sub-species are the Queen Charlotte caribou (*Rangifer tarandus dawsoni*), blue pike (*Stizostedion vitreum glaucum*), and Banff longnose dace (*Rhinichthys cataractae smithi*). As of 2005, 13 Canadian species or sub-species were extinct.

Extirpated refers to any species or sub-species that was formerly indigenous to Canada, but now survives in the wild only elsewhere (usually in the neighbouring U.S.). Examples include the black-footed ferret (*Mustela nigripes*), Atlantic grey whale (*Eschrichtius robustus*), Northwest Atlantic walrus (*Odobenus rosmarus*), greater prairie chicken (*Tympanuchus cupido*), pygmy short-horned lizard (*Phrynosoma douglassi*), paddlefish (*Polyodon spathula*), and blue-eyed mary (*Collinsia verna*). As of 2005, 22 taxa were extirpated in Canada.

Endangered refers to indigenous species that are faced with imminent extinction or extirpation throughout all or a significant portion of their Canadian range. As of 2005, 184 taxa were considered to be endangered in Canada. Examples include the Vancouver Island marmot (*Marmota vancouverensis*), bowhead whale (*Balaena mysticetus*), right whale (*Balaena glacialis*), whooping crane (*Grus americana*), Eskimo curlew (*Numenius borealis*), burrowing owl (*Speotyto cunicularia*), piping plover (*Charadrius melodus*), Blanchard's cricket frog (*Acris crepitans blanchardi*), blue racer snake (*Coluber constrictor foxii*), eastern prickly pear cactus (*Opuntia humifusa*), small white ladyslipper (*Cypripedium candidum*), thread-leaved sundew (*Drosera filiformis*), and seaside centipede lichen (*Heterodermia sitchensis*).

Threatened refers to any indigenous taxon that is likely to become endangered in Canada unless factors affecting its vulnerability are reversed. As of 2005, 129 taxa were considered threatened in Canada. Some examples include the wood bison (*Bison bison athabascae*), sea otter (*Enhydra lutris*), Pacific humpback whale (*Megaptera novaeangliae*), marbled murrelet (*Brachyramphus marmoratus*), massasauga rattlesnake (*Sistrurus catenatus*), and American chestnut (*Castanea dentata*).

Special concern refers to any indigenous species that is not currently threatened but is at risk of becoming so because of small or declining numbers, occurrence at the fringe of its range or in restricted areas, habitat fragmentation, or some other reason. As of 2005, 152 taxa or populations were considered to be of special concern in Canada. A few examples include the grizzly bear (*Ursus arctos*), polar bear (*Thalarctos maritimus*), blacktail prairie dog (*Cynomys ludovicianus*), long-billed curlew (*Numenius americanus*), ivory gull (*Pagophila eburnea*), spotted turtle (*Clemmys guttata*), and eastern prairie fringed orchid (*Platanthera leucophaea*).

It must be recognized that the designation of species at risk is a continuing and always incomplete process. For instance, since the conservation status of only a few species of invertebrates has been investigated, endangered species in this group are enormously under-represented in the COSEWIC list. Unfortunately, more rapid progress by COSEWIC is constrained by a shortage of funding for research and monitoring of endangered species in Canada and by a lack of specialists with the necessary taxonomic and ecological knowledge.

Of course, it is not sufficient merely to designate species as being at risk of extirpation or extinction. If their status in Canada is to be improved, the species and their habitats must also be protected. Remarkably, governments in Canada have not yet enacted effective legislation to protect endangered species and their habitat. However, this situation is starting to change. In 2002, the Government of Canada passed a Species at Risk Act, which provides some protection for species occurring on federal lands and otherwise within federal jurisdiction.

However, the federal legislation will have little direct influence on the status of the many at-risk species living on provincial, territorial, Aboriginal land claim, and private land in Canada. In particular, the Act does not fully address the protection of habitat of endangered species off federal land. To some degree, this critical deficiency is covered by legislation enacted or being prepared by provinces and territories. However, these legislations are also not very effective, particularly because they do not specifically protect the habitat of endangered species. Moreover, such a piecemeal approach results in uneven levels of protection for endangered species in Canada. This is unacceptable from the conservation viewpoint.

The effective protection of species at risk in Canada is raising controversy. Governments feel the need to demonstrate that they are making rapid progress toward sustainability, and an important component of that involves the protection of native species and their habitats. Unfortunately, the progress to date has been significantly lacking in that component and is not yet effective in protecting endangered biodiversity in Canada. Hopefully, the lobbying efforts of Canadian non-governmental organizations will result in appropriate changes to the currently weak legislation of all levels of government. Key national organizations in this regard are the Canadian Nature Federation (CNF), the Canadian Parks and Wilderness Society (CPAWS), the Sierra Legal Defence Fund, and the World Wildlife Fund—Canada (WWF).

Some of the natural ecosystems of Canada now occur only as small remnants of their former extent. Because of this, they are as endangered as the species they support. The most endangered of these at-risk ecosystems are the tall-grass prairie of southwestern Ontario and southeastern Manitoba, Carolinian forest of southern Ontario, dry coastal Douglas-fir and Garry oak forest types of southwestern British Columbia, semidesert of southeastern British Columbia, and various kinds of old-growth forest in all parts of forested Canada, but particularly in the east (see also Chapter 8). Some of these ecosystems, particularly the tall-grass prairie and Carolinian forest, are also very rich in endangered species. It is crucial that the remaining areas of these endangered ecosystems become preserved in parks, ecological reserves, and other kinds of protected areas.

The Importance of Protected Areas

Protected areas are parks, ecological reserves, and other tracts of land or water that are set aside from intensive development to conserve their natural ecological values. The intention is usually to protect threatened ecosystems, representative examples of widespread communities, or the habitat of endangered species. However, many protected areas also support certain human activities that do not severely threaten the conserved ecological values. Such activities may include ecotourism, other kinds of non-consumptive outdoor recreation, spiritual activities, education, scientific research, and, in some cases, even exploitative activities such as hunting, fishing, trapping, or timber harvesting.

It is important to understand that protected areas should never be regarded as the only, or even as the most important, way to conserve endangered species and ecosystems. Native species and other natural values should be accommodated as much as possible in all areas that humans use for economic purposes, such as agriculture, forestry, fishing, or mining. The role of protected areas is to ensure that species and ecosystems that are at risk in those "working" areas still have suitable refuges where they can maintain themselves.

A national system of protected areas in Canada would involve lands controlled by federal, provincial, or territorial governments; Aboriginal groups; and/or private interests. Ideally, the system of protected areas would be designed to sustain all native species and natural ecosystems over the long term, including terrestrial, freshwater, and marine systems. To ensure that all elements of indigenous biodiversity are adequately represented within a system of protected areas, all species and ecosystem types in the country or province must be identified, their abundance or extent determined, and their critical stressors understood. This information would allow all elements of natural-ecological heritage to be accommodated within a comprehensive *system plan* for a network of properly managed protected areas.

Of course, these are ideal criteria—no country has yet designed and implemented a comprehensive system of protected areas that sustains all native species and natural ecosystems. Moreover, many existing protected areas are relatively small. Most are threatened by stressors within their boundaries or by degrading influences from the surrounding area. In addition, the environmental factors that affect the protected species and ecosystems are often not well understood. Because of these and other problems, it is doubtful whether many of the smaller protected areas will be able to sustain their present ecological values over the long term. This will be especially true if a major environmental change occurs, such as global warming or a catastrophic disturbance (e.g., an extensive wildfire or disease epidemic).

The International Union for the Conservation of Nature (IUCN) recognizes six categories of protected areas (see Global Focus 26.2). In 2004, there were about 62 137 protected areas around the world, with a total area of 8.07 million km^2 (IUCN categories I–V; World Resources Institute, 2005). Of this total area, about 9568 sites comprising 3.96 million km^2 were fully protected (IUCN categories I and II) and could be considered as being true ecological reserves.

Protected Areas in Canada

National parks, provincial parks, and similar places are the largest and most important protected areas in Canada. A summary of areas protected by governments in Canada is provided in Table 26.2 and Figure 26.3. Note that the nationally protected area of about 8.4% is smaller than recommended by many conservation scientists, whose estimates range from 10 to 40% of the landmass.

As well, most parks serve additional purposes, particularly the support of economically important outdoor recreation and ecotourism. To some degree, the use of parks for these purposes challenges aspects of their function as ecological reserves. For example, strictly interpreted, the ecological values of national parks are not compatible with consumptive uses of their natural resources (e.g., sport fishing) or with the development within the parks of infrastructure supporting recreation and eco-

TABLE 26.2	Protected Areas in Canada in 2003	

Private and municipal protected areas are not included. The data include areas protected by legislation; industrial uses are prohibited.

PROVINCE OR TERRITORY	TOTAL AREA PROTECTED (10^3 km²)	PERCENTAGE OF JURISDICTION PROTECTED
Yukon	56.8	12.0
NWT and Nunavut	317.5	9.3
British Columbia	120.2	13.0
Alberta	80.1	12.3
Saskatchewan	22.4	3.5
Manitoba	54.0	8.5
Ontario	91.4	9.2
Quebec	52.2	3.5
New Brunswick	2.3	3.1
Nova Scotia	4.7	8.2
Prince Edward Island	0.15	2.6
Newfoundland and Labrador	17.0	4.3
Canada	818.8	8.4

Source: Statistics Canada (2004)

tourism (e.g., campgrounds, hotels, golf courses, ski facilities, roads, and interpretation facilities).

The ecological reserve function of many of Canada's protected areas is also threatened by land-use and management activities in their surrounding areas. Usually, the most important external stressors are associated with forestry, agriculture, mining, tourism, or hydroelectric

FIGURE 26.3	Protected Areas in Canada

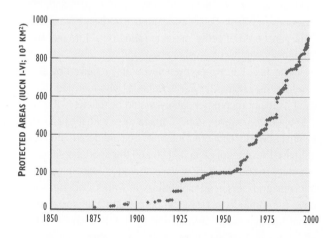

Source: Database of Canadian Council of Ecological Areas

development. In fact, all of the national parks in more southern regions of Canada are significantly threatened in this way. We can illustrate this problem with several well-known examples.

Point Pelee National Park is a small, 15.5-km² park in southwestern Ontario. This park contains some of the most important remnants of natural habitat left in the Carolinian zone of Canada (Chapter 8), most of which has been converted into agriculture or urbanized land uses. Consequently, Point Pelee National Park contains populations of many endangered species and ecosystems. However, this small park is used intensively for outdoor recreation, including birdwatching, boating, hiking, and picnicking on its beaches. To support these economically important activities, much of the park's limited area is maintained as paved roads, pathways, parking lots, campgrounds, information centres, lawns, and other infrastructure that does not enhance the protection of its ecological values.

In addition, the area next to the national park has been almost entirely converted into intensively managed agricultural lands, such as onion fields established on drained marshes, or into cottage and motel developments supporting tourism. These land-uses have isolated the relatively natural ecosystems of Point Pelee National Park; it is an ecological "island" surrounded by incompatible uses of the landscape. For these and other reasons, Point Pelee National Park is losing some of the natural features it is trying to protect. For example, the park has lost 10 of its original 21 species of reptiles, and 6 of 11 species of amphibians. Some of its habitats are being badly degraded by invasions of alien plants (such as garlic mustard, *Alliaria petiolata*), which crowd out native species. In fact, 37% of the species of vascular plants in the national park are non-native (Environment Canada, 1996).

Fundy National Park in New Brunswick is a similar case, although its ecological values are not as severely threatened as those of Point Pelee. Fundy National Park has an area of 206 km², but park ecologists believe that this is not large enough to sustain viable populations of some wide-ranging species, such as black bear, pine marten, and pileated woodpecker, or certain natural ecosystems such as old-growth forest (see also Canadian Focus 23.2). To some degree, these and other natural values are compromised by the development of tourism facilities within the national park, including a golf course, a saltwater swimming pool, campgrounds, interpretive facilities, and

Canadian Focus 26.2

Ecological Integrity in the Bow Valley Corridor

In 1885, Banff National Park was the first national park to be proclaimed in Canada. Banff is also the most famous of our national parks, because of its spectacular scenery, easily viewed large animals, and superb infrastructure supporting tourism and outdoor recreation. These values combine to attract visitors from across Canada and around the world.

Banff National Park covers a large area (6640 km^2) and thus plays an important role in protecting the natural ecological values of its region. This role is enhanced by the fact that Banff is bordered by several other protected areas, namely Jasper, Yoho, and Kootenay National Parks and Peter Lougheed Provincial Park, which collectively comprise an area of about 26 000 km^2.

Most of the native species and natural ecosystems of Banff National Park are well protected within its boundaries and in surrounding lands. Some others, unfortunately, are not. These natural values are threatened by a variety of stressors, some of which exert their influence within the national park while others make themselves felt outside its immediate boundaries.

Banff National Park hosts about five million tourists each year, generating more than $6 billion in economic activity. To service its many visitors, the park contains hotels, lodges, and campgrounds. To provide the tourists with interesting things to do, and to generate revenue and local employment, the park contains ski hills with associated lifts and lodges, golf courses, an extensive network of roads and trails, interpretation facilities, and two full-service settlements with more than 8000 permanent residents—the villages of Banff and Lake Louise. In addition, the Canadian Pacific Railway passes through the national park, as does the Trans-Canada Highway. These various facilities are developed especially intensely in the so-called Banff–Bow Valley corridor, a region that encompasses the major transportation routes through the park as well as the main tourist areas.

The tourism- and transportation-related infrastructure in the Banff–Bow Valley corridor provides important support for big-business tourism and the national system of ground transportation. These facilities do not, however, enhance the natural values of Banff National Park. In fact, local populations of timber wolf, grizzly bear, and other species are thought to be at risk in the greater Banff region, mostly because they are suffering unsustainably high death rates. The intense mortality results from collisions with vehicles on the highways and railroad, hunting outside the park, and the necessary killing of "problem" bears that become habituated to humans, particularly near campgrounds and frequently used trails. For example, a recent study of grizzly bears found that 90% of their deaths in Banff National Park occurred within 0.5 km of human infrastructure, and only 2 of 73 deaths were due to natural causes. In addition, the wilderness values of extensive areas have become significantly degraded by visual and noise pollution associated with traffic, highways, railroads, ski lifts, buildings, and large numbers of people.

The various environmental challenges to the ecological integrity of Banff National Park are an increasingly serious problem. Recently, a Task Force of five independent experts, appointed by Parks Canada, studied these challenges. The Task Force was given three objectives:

1. To develop a vision for the region that would integrate ecological, social, and economic values.
2. To undertake a comprehensive analysis of existing information, and to provide direction for future monitoring programs.
3. To recommend changes that would allow the Banff–Bow Valley region to be used as the basis for sustainable tourism and recreation industries, while continuing to protect its heritage of ecological values.

The Task Force reviewed a wealth of existing information, commissioned original research, and engaged in public consultations. Its final report concluded that intensive economic development in the Banff–Bow Valley region was quickly approaching an unsustainable level, and this was threatening the ecological integrity of the national park (Page *et al.,* 1996). The Task Force made many recommendations for specific actions and policies that would help to deal with the intensifying crisis. It strongly advised that the pace and intensity of development be strictly controlled, and in some cases reversed. In essence, the Task Force concluded that Banff National Park can be an effective protected area only if its use by humans is kept within sustainable bounds.

The Task Force report was favourably received by the minister responsible for Parks Canada, who affirmed that all of its major recommendations would be followed. If this is to happen, however, Parks Canada must take firm action against powerful economic interests that are determined to increase the amount of recreation and transportation infrastructure in the Banff–Bow Valley corridor. Hopefully, the minister and senior administrators in Parks Canada will have the fortitude to resist the compelling calls for additional "development" and will manage Banff National Park in a manner that makes its ecological integrity, not economic development, the bottom line.

extensive lawns, roads, and trails. Also important are industrial activities in the area surrounding the park, where natural forest is being converted into forestry plantations. These do not provide habitat for many of the native species of natural forest. Thus, the natural habitats of the park are becoming ecological islands within a modified landscape.

Banff National Park in southeastern Alberta was the first national park established in Canada (in 1885). The original intent was to protect some extremely scenic viewscapes and hot springs and to develop the area to enhance the economic benefits of tourism. It was not until several decades later that the philosophical underpinning of national parks in Canada shifted strongly toward the protection of natural values. In any event, the early development of Banff National Park featured the enthusiastic construction of large hotels, golf courses, skiing facilities, major highways, a transcontinental railroad, several towns, and other structures. Unfortunately, this pattern continues today with much ongoing and planned construction, coupled with rapid development of the area east of the park for tourism, residential neighbourhoods, forestry, and other uses. These facilities severely threaten the long-term viability of the natural values of Banff National Park. This development is engendering intense controversy and has been the subject of a commission of enquiry (see Canadian Focus 26.2).

Canada's provincial and territorial governments also have a responsibility to protect natural ecological values within their domain. These governments have designated numerous ecological reserves, supplemented by natural areas that are protected in provincial parks and conservation areas, which are also used for recreation, and sometimes for other purposes.

Some municipalities also have natural-area parks that provide habitat for native species. An outstanding example is the city of Windsor, Ontario, which is protecting some of Canada's most important remnants of tall-grass prairie and its many endangered species.

Some environmental non-governmental organizations (ENGOs) are also active in the protection of natural areas in Canada. At the national level, the Nature Conservancy of Canada is the organization that most actively protects land to conserve Canada's indigenous biodiversity, usually by purchasing or accepting donations of private properties or land-use rights (see Canadian Focus 26.3). Ducks Unlimited Canada plays a similar role, but with a focus on wetland habitat. At the provincial and more local levels, an increasing number of land trusts is also protecting natural areas.

Other national organizations, such as the World Wildlife Fund (Canada), the Canadian Nature Federation, the Canadian Parks and Wilderness Society, the Canadian Wildlife Federation, the Sierra Club, and Greenpeace, also play important roles in protecting biodiversity. However, they mostly do this through advocacy—these ENGOs lobby governments and the private sector to pursue more effective biodiversity agendas. Also, they engage in public campaigns and conduct research toward those ends. The World Wildlife Fund (Canada), for example, was the prime mover behind the Endangered Spaces Campaign, which was effective in convincing governments to preserve representative areas of their natural ecosystems within protected areas. The Canadian Council of Ecological Areas is an association of conservation experts in government, ENGOs, and universities, who are working to design a strategic plan for a national system of protected areas. More information about these various ENGOs, as well as many of their provincial and territorial counterparts, is provided by the Canadian Environmental Literacy Project (2005).

In spite of the diverse conservation-related activities of governments and private organizations in Canada, the existing network of protected areas is highly incomplete. There are three reasons for making this statement. First, the full breadth of Canada's natural heritage is not yet represented in protected areas. Second, there are many species at risk in Canada, many of which will have to be protected in ecological reserves that do not yet exist. Third, most of the protected areas are too small to protect their ecological values over the long term.

The latter consideration is important because small areas cannot sustain viable populations of some species of wildlife over the long term, even if they are protected. Small reserves also cannot sustain the ecological conditions required for certain communities to persist, particularly old-growth forest. In such cases, the protected area must be managed within the context of its surrounding landscape as a single, integrated ecosystem. Management activities in such "**greater protected areas**" should be designed to ensure the long-term viability of populations of species at risk, as well as natural communities at risk (see also Canadian Focus 23.2).

Design and Management of Protected Areas

The design of protected areas is an important field of research in conservation biology. The essential questions involve determining the size, shape, and positioning of protected areas to optimize their ability to protect biodiversity, while using limited funding as efficiently as possible. The least controversial recommendations of conservation biologists are that ecological reserves should be as large and as numerous as possible. Other aspects of the design of protected areas are being debated actively, and the controversies will not be resolved until more research is performed. These additional aspects of reserve design include the following.

The choice between size and number of protected areas: Is it preferable to have one large reserve or a number of smaller ones with the same total area (Figure 26.4a)? Conservation biologists identify this question with the acronym SLOSS—single large or several small. According to ecological theory, populations in larger reserves are expected to have a lower risk of local extinction compared with those in smaller areas. However, if separate populations occur in different reserves, the redundancy might protect against catastrophic loss of an endangered species in a larger region.

Larger reserves have more interior habitat: "Interior" habitat is not influenced by environmental conditions at *ecotones* (i.e., transitions between habitat types, such as a forest edge beside an adjacent field). Ecotonal habitats are often penetrated by invasive species, predators, and parasites (such as cowbirds), which can be important problems for some protected areas. In addition, many species require interior habitat for successful breeding. Larger reserves have proportionately more interior habitat, a factor that contributes to the protection of interior species (Figure 26.4a).

Circular reserves are better: A circle has a smaller ratio of edge to area than any other two-dimensional shape. To avoid extensive edge habitat in the design of a protected area, a roughly circular shape may be preferable (Figure 26.4b).

Reserves should be close together: If a population becomes extirpated in a protected area, the chances of natural recolonization may be improved if a nearby reserve has a surviving population. Consequently, it may be better to have unconnected reserves arranged relatively close to each other, rather than far apart (Figure 26.4c).

Reserves should be clumped: Similar reasoning suggests that it is better to aggregate reserves than to arrange them in a linear fashion. This would minimize the average inter-reserve distance (Figure 26.4d).

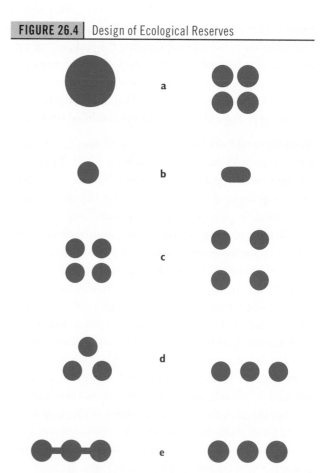

FIGURE 26.4 | Design of Ecological Reserves

This figure summarizes the basic principles of conservation biology for the design of protected areas. In each comparison, the design on the left is better than the design on the right (total areas of each comparison are assumed to be the same). See text for discussion.

Source: Modified from Simberloff (1988)

The role of corridors: A system of reserves connected by corridors of suitable habitat may provide better opportunities for gene flow and re-colonization after extirpation (Figure 26.4e). Admittedly, however, corridors might also make it easier for diseases, invasive species, and introduced predators to spread among reserves.

It is important to understand that the stewardship of biodiversity requires much more than simple declarations that tracts of natural areas are henceforth to be considered "protected." The integrity of those reserves must also be monitored, and proper management may be necessary. For example, if a protected area supports populations of endangered species, their status should be monitored. If

Conservation Charities—the Nature Conservancy of Canada

Governments throughout Canada have created extensive protected areas, but their actions are almost exclusively on so-called Crown land, which they already own. However, some of the most important properties of conservation value in Canada are privately owned by individuals or corporations. This is particularly the case of southern regions of the country, where most at-risk species and endangered ecosystems occur. Because of a lack of money, governmental agencies are usually reluctant to secure ecologically important habitat on privately owned lands. For this reason, conservation charities have formed for the purpose of raising funds to acquire private property in order to establish protected areas.

At the national level, the most important of these organizations is the Nature Conservancy of Canada (NCC). The focus of NCC is acquiring private property of high conservation value, which it does by purchasing or accepting donations of real estate, as well as rights of land-use. The latter involves a kind of private property called a conservation easement. If owned by NCC, a conservation easement can prevent current and future owners of the real estate from converting its natural habitat to residential lots or to cultivated agriculture, or from engaging in other proscribed activities that might threaten the natural values of the property. There are many other organizations, operating at local and provincial scales and usually known as land trusts, that also acquire private conservation lands and easements in Canada. However, NCC is the only national organization, and it is by far the biggest.

Since its origin in 1962, NCC has secured more than 1400 properties and has contributed to the protection of 7300 km^2 of natural habitat throughout Canada. In 2005, NCC raised (and spent) about $55 million to advance its conservation mission. Also in that year, it met the goals of its four-year "Campaign for Conservation," which raised $200 million, almost all of it from the private sector. About 30 000 Canadians contribute money to support the work of NCC.

The conservation actions of NCC are being guided by ecoregional plans, which help to identify the most important places where private action can make the most difference in protecting native species and natural ecosystems. These plans are developed in close partnership with governments, the U.S. Nature Conservancy, Ducks Unlimited Canada, provincial and local land trusts, industrial interests, and academic scientists. As of 2005, NCC had completed 10 ecoregional plans and had three others in progress, all for southern parts of Canada, which are the most imperilled from the conservation perspective. Eventually, NCC intends to have ecoregional plans for all regions of Canada. The results of the plans are used to identify focal areas for land assemblies—there are now about 50 of these key action areas, which NCC refers to as Natural Masterpiece Sites.

Successful conservation action requires more than just acquiring properties—the projects must also be properly stewarded to maintain or enhance their natural values. Stewardship actions range from posting signs at property boundaries to innovative, science-based, management actions needed to sustain particular species or ecological communities. For example, NCC routinely subjects its tall-grass prairie reserves in southeastern Manitoba to prescribed burns, which is necessary to prevent the endangered prairie from being degraded by incursions of shrubs and trees. At NCC reserves protecting endangered Garry-oak forest on southern Vancouver Island, stewardship volunteers spend many hours pulling alien weeds that threaten rare plants. One last example involves a protected area of rare Carolinean forest at Clear Creek in southern Ontario, where NCC is converting adjacent cornfields into natural forest in order to increase the size and enhance the viability of the conserved ecosystem. These kinds of stewardship activities must be advised by leading-edge scientific knowledge, which NCC is developing by hiring ecologists and by working in partnership with other organizations.

The Nature Conservancy of Canada is only one example of the many highly motivated and effective nongovernmental conservation organizations in Canada. Their work is crucial to sustaining the at-risk biodiversity of our country. Of course, being charities, private organizations like NCC can only spend money that they manage to raise, which is a good reason for citizens and companies to support their important work of protecting natural habitats.

Additional Information

The Nature Conservancy of Canada.
www.natureconservancy.ca/files/index.asp

any decline is observed, the environmental causes should be determined by research, and should then, if possible, be mitigated to prevent or repair the damage. Management activities can include, among other actions, patrols to prevent the poaching of animals and timber, modification of habitats to keep them suitable for species at risk, and captive breeding and release of endangered species.

Considered together, these stewardship actions represent an integrated program of monitoring, research, and management. The application of such a system is illustrated by the case of the endangered Kirtland's warbler (*Dendroica kirtlandii*). Monitoring has shown that this species has declined rapidly in abundance, and that its global population is now only a few hundred breeding pairs. Research has revealed that the breeding habitat of the warbler consists of jack pine (*Pinus banksiana*) stands of a particular age and structure. Many such stands have now been protected in the breeding range of Kirtland's warbler. However, as these stands get older, they are no longer suitable as breeding habitat. Consequently, management is actively developing appropriate breeding habitat by prescribed burning and planting of jack pine. In addition, research has shown that the endangered warbler is heavily parasitized by the brown-headed cowbird. Consequently, cowbird populations are being controlled in the warbler's breeding habitat. Additional research and monitoring are being directed to the environmental stresses that affect Kirtland's warbler during its little-known migrations and on its wintering range. Of course, these integrated activities of monitoring, research, and management must continue as long as Kirtland's warbler remains endangered.

International Conservation Activities

The conservation of wild species of plants and animals is now regarded by almost all societies as a worthwhile and important objective. As a result, in most countries, many people are becoming active in support of conservation. Evidence of these changes includes the fact that governments are becoming more involved in the conservation of indigenous and global biodiversity, while large numbers of non-governmental organizations are becoming more active at local, national, and international levels (CELP, 2005). In addition, more ecologists and other scientists are conducting biodiversity-related research and training in universities and other institutions.

All of these activities contribute to the greater agenda of biodiversity conservation, particularly by

- identifying and protecting the habitats of rare and endangered species and ecosystems, while also conserving representative areas of natural ecosystems;

- controlling illegal trade in the products of endangered species (such as elephant ivory, rhino horn, bear gallbladders, tiger bones and hides, and wild ginseng; refer to Global Focus 26.1);

- increasing the awareness of people about biodiversity issues and about the need to ensure adequate conservation of all of the Earth's species, ecosystems, and ecological processes;

- conducting necessary research into the biology and ecology of endangered species and ecosystems; and

- raising or providing funds for all of the above.

Not surprisingly, the intensity of these conservation activities is greatest, and increasing most quickly, in relatively wealthy, developed countries, such as Canada. Those countries can more easily afford to allocate significant funding and personnel to this worthwhile cause. Increasingly, however, signs of awareness of the importance of biodiversity issues, and actions to conserve those values, are also emerging in less developed countries. This reflects changes in the attitudes of people and governments in those countries and is reinforced by lobbying and funding provided by domestic and international aid agencies and non-governmental organizations. These changes are critically important because a large fraction of Earth's threatened biodiversity occurs in tropical, less developed countries.

Of course, a respect for nature has always been an integral component of most religions that developed in tropical countries, such as Buddhism, Hinduism, and Jainism. Nevertheless, this respect has not necessarily been translated into a real-world conservation ethic among the peoples of those or any other nations. As a result, wildlife and natural habitats have suffered badly, mostly because of the extensive conversion of natural ecosystems into agricultural ones, and for other reasons as well.

It is beyond the scope of this book to describe the many international agencies and organizations that are active in the protection of Earth's biodiversity. Some of the most important of them are the United Nations

Environment Programme (UNEP), the World Wildlife Fund, the International Union for the Conservation of Nature (or World Conservation Union; IUCN), the World Resources Institute, the Worldwatch Institute, and Conservation International (for more information see CELP, 2005). These organizations are active in protecting species and natural habitat, in education and lobbying, in research and monitoring, and in raising funds for the protection of biodiversity.

To illustrate the rapid development of international conservation activities, we will briefly examine a global program known as the Global Biodiversity Strategy (Reid *et al.*, 1992). This is a joint program of the World Conservation Union, the World Resources Institute, and the United Nations Environment Programme. The broad objectives of the Global Biodiversity Strategy are to maintain essential ecological processes and life-support systems on Earth, to preserve biodiversity, and to ensure the sustainable development of Earth's natural resources. Although these are rather general goals, they are important because they directly link the conservation of biodiversity with the sustainable development of global resources and human economies. One cannot occur without the other—a fact that must be acknowledged by any governments or agencies that support the Global Biodiversity Strategy.

Through the Global Biodiversity Strategy, all nations can initiate meaningful actions to conserve and protect their biodiversity for the benefit of present and future generations of people, as well as for reasons of intrinsic value. To achieve this end, 85 specific actions are recommended for implementation by countries committing themselves to the strategy. The following five actions by signatory countries are considered essential:

1. ratification and implementation of the recommendations of the international Convention on Biological Diversity, as presented in 1992 by the United Nations Environment Programme at the United Nations Conference on Environment and Development, held at Rio de Janeiro, Brazil (the "Earth Summit")

2. implementation of the actions detailed in the Global Biodiversity Strategy, with a focus on intensive efforts to conserve and protect the indigenous biodiversity of signatory nations

3. creation of an international administrative mechanism to ensure broad participation in decisions concerning global biodiversity, with representation from governments, the scientific community, citizens, industry, the United Nations, and non-governmental organizations

4. establishment of an international network, linked to the Convention on Biological Diversity, to monitor threats to biodiversity so that individuals and organizations can be alerted and take appropriate actions

5. integration of biodiversity considerations into planning processes for national development

Other key elements of the Global Biodiversity Strategy are summarized in Table 26.3, while essential elements of the Convention on Biological Diversity are listed in Table 26.4.

It is too soon to tell whether these international actions will be successful because the programs began only in the late 1970s (as an earlier program called the World Conservation Strategy). However, it is encouraging to know that this sort of comprehensive international effort exists and that almost all of Earth's nations are participating, including countries in all stages of economic development. Of course, it remains to be seen how effective the individual and collective actions will be.

Conclusions

If Earth's resources are to be used by humans on an ecologically sustainable basis, rare and endangered species and natural ecosystems must be protected. Clearly, an international program like the Global Biodiversity Strategy is needed to guide the process of sustainable development.

The modern predicament of extinction and endangerment of biodiversity is one of the most critical elements of the global environmental crisis. Hopefully, the increasing intensity of conservation activities worldwide will be sufficient to turn the tide, so future generations will regard these ongoing actions as a "success story" of global conservation. Any alternative result would be catastrophically tragic.

> *The one process ongoing in the 1990s that will take millions of years to correct is the loss of genetic and species diversity by the destruction of natural habitats. This is the folly that our descendants are least likely to forgive us.*

> E.O. Wilson (cited in Reid *et al.*, 1992)

TABLE 26.3	Key Elements of the Global Biodiversity Strategy

1. Catalyze action through international co-operation and national planning
2. Establish a national policy framework for conservation of biodiversity:
   - Reform existing public policies that invite the waste or misuse of biodiversity
   - Adopt new public policies and accounting methods that promote conservation and the equitable use of biodiversity
   - Reduce demand for at-risk biological resources
3. Create an international policy environment that supports national conservation of biodiversity:
   - Integrate biodiversity conservation into international economic policy
   - Strengthen the international legal framework for conservation to complement the Convention on Biological Diversity
   - Make the development-assistance process a force for biodiversity conservation
   - Increase funding for biodiversity conservation, and develop innovative, decentralized, and accountable ways to raise funds and spend them effectively
4. Create conditions and incentives for local conservation of biodiversity:
   - Correct imbalances in the control of land and resources that cause biodiversity losses, and develop new resource-management partnerships between government and local communities
   - Expand and encourage the sustainable use of products and services from the wild for local benefits
   - Ensure that those who possess local knowledge of genetic resources benefit appropriately when it is used
5. Manage biodiversity through the human environment:
   - Create the institutional conditions for bioregional conservation and development
   - Support biodiversity conservation initiatives in the private sector
   - Incorporate biodiversity conservation into the management of biological resources
6. Strengthen protected areas:
   - Identify national and international priorities for strengthening protected areas and enhancing their role in biodiversity conservation
   - Ensure the sustainability of protected areas and their contribution to biodiversity conservation
7. Conserve species, populations, and genetic diversity:
   - Strengthen capacity to conserve species, populations, and genetic diversity in natural habitats
   - Strengthen the capacity of off-site conservation facilities to conserve biodiversity, educate the public, and contribute to sustainable development
8. Expand human capacity to conserve biodiversity:
   - Increase appreciation and awareness of biodiversity values and their importance
   - Help institutions disseminate the information needed to conserve biodiversity and mobilize its benefits
   - Promote basic and applied research on biodiversity conservation
   - Develop human capacity for biodiversity conservation

Source: Modified from Reid *et al.* (1992)

TABLE 26.4	Key Elements of the Convention on Biological Diversity

- A commitment by governments to survey their natural living resources, both domesticated and wild, and to conserve sites noted for their rich biological diversity, as well as threatened species and domesticated varieties
- Recognition that both the conservation of biodiversity in wild nature and its preservation in captivity and gene banks are key tools in any effective biodiversity conservation strategy
- A commitment by governments to ensure that any use of biodiversity is sustainable and equitable
- Recognition that conservation of biodiversity is a common concern of all humankind and that nations have the sovereign right to use their biological resources
- Recognition that access to biodiversity is contingent upon prior informed consent of the country concerned, and that those who possess traditional knowledge about genetic resources, and farmers who have contributed to and maintained diversity in crops and livestock, deserve just compensation for the use of their knowledge or their varieties
- The establishment of a financial mechanism that would provide both technical and financial assistance to developing countries in need of support for surveying, characterizing, and conserving their indigenous biodiversity
- The establishment of an administrative structure giving equal control to developed and developing countries that are Parties to the Convention in the distribution of funds under the Convention, and ensuring participation of scientists, governments, and non-governmental organizations to advise on funding priorities
- Arrangements by which the commercial exploiters of biodiversity help finance much of its conservation in the countries that give it refuge
- Mechanisms to ensure access for developing countries to technologies for conserving and using biodiversity
- The establishment of a monitoring and early-warning system to alert governments and the public to potential threats to biodiversity

Source: Modified from Reid *et al.* (1992)

Key Terms

extinction

extirpation

mass extinction

endangered

endemic

protected area

greater protected area

Questions for Review

1. What are the greatest modern threats to global biodiversity?

2. What are the greatest modern threats to the native biodiversity of Canada?

3. List five examples of species that became extinct at any time during the past 500 years, and explain why they were lost.

4. List five examples of species that were endangered but have since recovered in abundance, and explain why this happened.

Questions for Discussion

1. How are the products of biodiversity important in your life? Compile a list of ways in which you use such products (include foods, materials, and medicines) in your daily routine. Are there substitutes for any or all of these uses?

2. Do you know of any species that are rare or endangered in the region in which you live? Find several examples, and identify the habitat needs of those species. Do you think that these rare or endangered species are being adequately protected? What more could be done? How can you help?

3. Find several examples of "endangered spaces" (endangered ecosystems) in your region and decide whether they are being adequately protected. What more could be done? How can you help?

4. We learned in this chapter that the greatest modern threat to Earth's biodiversity is posed by deforestation in tropical countries. Can you think of ways in which Canadians are economically linked with deforestation in the tropics? For example, do Canadian consumers provide a demand for certain tropical-forest products? Do Canadians hold some of the foreign debt of tropical countries? How might these circumstances contribute to tropical deforestation?

5. Everyone can help to protect endangered species and spaces. List some of the ways in which you can contribute to solving the problems of endangered biodiversity in the region where you live, in Canada, and internationally.

Exploring Issues

1. Your provincial government has committed to ensuring that its indigenous biodiversity will be conserved. Your services have been retained to provide advice on how to accomplish this goal. What would you tell the government to do in order to identify and conserve its indigenous species and ecosystems?

References

Beacham, W., F.V. Castronova, B. Freedman, and S. Sessine (eds.). 2001. *Beacham's Guide to International Endangered Species.* Farmington Hills, MI: Gale Group.

Blockstein, D.E. and H.B. Tordoff. 1985. Gone forever: a contemporary look at the extinction of the passenger pigeon. *Amer. Birds*, **39**: 845–851.

Canadian Council on Ecological Areas (CCEA). 2005. *Canadian Conservation Areas Database.* CCEA, Natural Resources Canada, and Environment Canada, Ottawa, ON.

Canadian Environmental Literacy Project (CELP). 2005. *Links to Organizations.* www.celp.ca/Links/LinkView.php?fid=stmain

COSEWIC. 2005. *Canadian Species at Risk.* Ottawa: Committee on the Status of Endangered Wildlife in Canada (COSEWIC). www.cosewic.gc.ca/

Day, D. 1989. *The Encyclopedia of Vanished Species.* Hong Kong: McLaren.

Diamond, J.M. 1982. Man the exterminator. *Nature*, **298**: 787–789.

Dobson, A.P. 1996. *Conservation and Biodiversity.* San Francisco, CA: W.H. Freeman & Co.

Downes, C.M., B.T. Collins and M. Damus. 2003. *Canadian Bird Trends.* Hull, PQ: Canadian Wildlife Service. www.cws-scf.ec.gc.ca/birds/trends/default_e.cfm

Ehrlich, P.R. and A. Ehrlich. 1981. *Extinction: The Causes and Consequences of the Disappearance of Species.* New York: Ballantine.

Eldredge, N. 1998. *Life in the Balance: Humanity and the Biodiversity Crisis.* Princeton, NJ: Princeton University Press.

Environment Canada. 1996. *The State of Canada's Environment, 1996.* Ottawa: Government of Canada.

Erwin, D.A. 1990. The end-Permian mass extinction. *Annu. Rev. Ecol. Syst.*, **21**: 69–91.

Feduccia, A. 1985. *Catesby's Birds of Colonial America.* Chapel Hill, NC: University of North Carolina Press.

Finch, D.M. 1991. *Population Ecology, Habitat Requirements, and Conservation Status of Neotropical Migrating Birds.* Fort Collins, CO: Rocky Mountain Forest and Range Experiment Station. USDA For. Serv. Gen. Tech. Rep. RM-205.

Fisher, J., N. Simon, and J. Vincent. 1969. *Wildlife in Danger*. New York: Viking.

Fitter, R. 1968. *Vanishing Wild Animals of the World*. London: Kaye & Ward.

Freedman, B. 1995. *Environmental Ecology*. 2nd ed. San Diego, CA: Academic.

Gaston, K.J. and J.I. Spicer. 2004. *Biodiversity: An Introduction*. 2nd ed. Oxford, UK: Blackwell Science.

Gould, S.J. 1989. *Wonderful Life: The Burgess Shale and the Nature of History*. New York: Norton.

Groombridge, B. and M.D. Jenkins. 2002. *World Atlas of Biodiversity: Earth's Living Resources in the 21st Century*. Berkeley, CA: University of California Press.

Heywood, V.H. (executive ed.). 1995. *Global Biodiversity Assessment*. Cambridge: Cambridge University Press.

Holmes, R.T., T.W. Sherry, and F.W. Sturges. 1986. Bird community dynamics in a temperate deciduous forest: long-term trends at Hubbard Brook. *Ecol. Monogr.*, **56**: 201–220.

Hussell, D.J.J., M.H. Mather, and P.H. Sinclair. 1992. Trends in numbers of tropical- and temperate-wintering landbirds in migration at Long Point, Ontario, 1961–1988. In: J.M. Hagan and D.W. Johnson, eds. *Ecology and Conservation of Neotropical Migrant Landbirds*. Washington: Smithsonian Institution Press. pp. 101–114.

International Whaling Commission. 2005. *Whale Population Estimates*. www.iwcoffice.org/conservation/estimate.htm

Leader-Williams, N., S.D. Albou, and P.S.M. Berry. 1990. Illegal exploitation of black rhinoceros and elephant populations: patterns of decline, law enforcement, and patrol effort in Luangwa Valley, Zambia. *J. Applied Ecol.*, **27**: 1055–1087.

Lovejoy, T.E. 1985. Amazonia, people and today. In: G.T. Prance and T.E. Lovejoy, eds. *Amazonia*. New York: Pergamon. pp. 328–338.

Martin, P.S. 1984. Catastrophic extinctions and late Pleistocene blitzkrieg: two radiocarbon tests. In: M.H. Nitecki, ed. *Extinctions*. Chicago: University of Chicago Press. pp. 153–189.

Martin, P.S. and H.E. Wright (eds.). 1967. *Pleistocene Extinctions: The Search for a Cause*. New Haven, CT: Yale University Press.

McClung, R.M. 1969. *Lost Wild America: The Story of Our Extinct and Vanishing Wildlife*. New York: William Morrow.

Mongabay. 2005. *Tropical Rainforests and the Perils They Face*. www.mongabay.com/home.htm

Myers, N. 1979. *The Sinking Ark: A New Look at the Problem of Disappearing Species*. Oxford: Pergamon.

Myers, N. 1988. Tropical forests and their species: going… going… In: E.O. Wilson, ed. *Biodiversity*. Washington, DC: National Academy Press.

Nettleship, D.N. and P.G.H. Evans. 1985. Distribution and status of the Atlantic Alcidae. In: D.N. Nettleship and T.R. Birkhead, eds. *The Atlantic Alcidae*. New York: Academic. pp. 54–154.

Nitecki, M.H. (ed.). 1984. *Extinctions*. Chicago: University of Chicago Press.

Norse, E.A. and L.B. Crowder (eds.). 2005. *Marine Conservation Biology: The Science of Maintaining the Sea's Biodiversity* Washington, DC: Island Press.

Norton, B.G. (ed.). 1986. *The Preservation of Species*. Princeton, NJ: Princeton University Press.

Page, J.D., Bayley, S.E., Good, D.J., Green, J.E., and Ritchie, J.P.B. 1996. *Banff–Bow Valley: At the Crossroads. Summary Report*. Ottawa: Supply and Services Canada. Report of the Banff–Bow Valley Task Force.

Perlman, D.L. and G. Adelson. 1997. *Biodiversity: Exploring Values and Priorities in Conservation*. Oxford, UK: Blackwell Science.

Peters, R.L. 1991. Consequences of global warming for biological diversity. In: R.L. Wyman, ed. *Global Climate Change and Life on Earth*. New York: Routledge, Chapman, & Hall. pp. 99–118.

Primack, R.B. 2004. *Essentials of Conservation Biology*. 3rd ed. Sunderland, MA: Sinauer.

Raup, D.M. 1986. Biological extinctions in Earth history. *Science*, **231**: 1528–1533.

Reaka-Kudla, M.L., D.E. Wilson, and E.O. Wilson (eds.). 1997. *Biodiversity II: Understanding and Protecting Our Biological Resources*. Washington, DC: National Academy Press.

Reid, W., C. Barker, and K. Miller (principal authors). 1992. *Global Biodiversity Strategy*. Washington: World Resources Institute.

RENEW. 2004. *Recovery of Nationally Endangered Wildlife*. Ottawa, ON: Canadian Endangered Species Conservation Council. www.speciesatrisk.gc.ca/publications/AbstractTemplate.cfm?lang=e&ID=27

Robillard, J.R. 2005. *CITES Trade Data*. Ottawa, ON: Canadian Wildlife Service, Wildlife Trade and International Division. (personal communication).

Simberloff, D. 1988. The contribution of population and community biology to conservation science. *Annu. Rev. Ecol. Syst.*, **19**: 473–511.

Soule, M.E. (ed.) 1986. *Conservation Biology: The Science of Scarcity and Diversity*. Sunderland, MA: Sinauer Assoc.

Statistics Canada. 2004. *Human Activity and the Environment 2004*. Ottawa, ON: Statistics Canada. http://estat.statcan.ca.ezproxy.library.dal.ca/content/english/articles/other/0000416-201-XIE.pdf

Steadman, D.W. 1991. Extinction of species: Past, present, and future. In: R.C. Wyman, ed. *Global Climate Change and Life on Earth*. New York: Routledge, Chapman, & Hall. pp. 156–169.

Terborgh, J. 1989. *Where Have All the Birds Gone?* Princeton, NJ: Princeton University Press.

Townsend, C.R., M. Begon, and J.L. Harper. 2002. *Essentials of Ecology*. 2nd ed. Cambridge, UK: Blackwell Publishers.

Vitousek, P.M. 1988. Diversity and biological invasions of oceanic islands. In: E.O. Wilson, ed. *Biodiversity*. Washington: National Academy Press. pp. 181–189.

Wilson, E.O. (ed.). 1988. *Biodiversity*. Washington: National Academy Press.

Wood, G.L. 1972. *Animal Facts and Figures*. Enfield, U.K.: Guinness Superlatives.

World Resources Institute. 2005. *Earth Trends. The Environmental Information Portal*. Washington, DC: WRI. www.wri.org/

World Wildlife Fund. 1999. *Endangered Spaces Progress Report, 98–99*. Toronto: World Wildlife Fund.

Ziswiler, V. 1967. *Extinct and Vanishing Animals*. New York: Springer.

Informative Websites

Canadian Wildlife Service. www.cws-scf.ec.gc.ca/

The Canadian Wildlife Service (CWS), part of Environment Canada, handles wildlife matters that are the responsibility of the federal government, including protection and management of migratory birds, nationally significant habitat and endangered species, as well as work on other wildlife issues of national and international importance.

Conservation International.
www.conservation.org/xp/CIWEB/home

Conservation International is an organization dedicated to studying and conserving global biodiversity.

COSEWIC (Committee on the Status of Endangered Wildlife in Canada). www.cosewic.gc.ca/

COSEWIC determines the national status of wild Canadian species, sub-species, and separate populations suspected of being at risk. Their site includes lists of at-risk species, definitions and terms of risk categories, and other information.

Ecological Society of America. *Biotic Invasions: Causes, Epidemiology, Global Consequences and Control.*
www.esa.org/science/Issues/FileEnglish/issue5.pdf

This publication of the ESA explains how non-native invasive species are causing severe environmental problems.

Environment Canada. The Green Lane.
www.ec.gc.ca/envhome.html

This comprehensive site from Environment Canada features pages on biodiversity, climate change, clean air and water, as well as links to publications, news releases, and related sites.

Environmental Literacy Council. Biodiversity.
www.enviroliteracy.org/subcategory.php/4.html

This organization provides an array of materials about biodiversity.

Nature Conservancy of Canada (NCC).
www.natureconservancy.ca/

NCC is an environmental organization that acquires private property in order to set up protected areas. Learn about their mission and operations at this website.

Parks Canada. www.pc.gc.ca/index_e.asp

Take a virtual tour, read information about national parks, or visit the related links.

United Nations Environment Programme (UNEP).
www.biodiv.org/welcome.aspx

The United Nations Environment Programme is responsible for the international Convention on Biological Diversity. This website explains the convention and provides much useful information.

World Resources Institute. Biodiversity and Protected Areas. http://biodiv.wri.org/

The World Resources Institute provides information about biodiversity and other environmental issues.

World Resources Institute. Earth Trends. The Environmental Information Portal. earthtrends.wri.org/

The WRI is a leading environmental organization that provides excellent information about resource issues.

World Wildlife Fund Canada. www.wwfcanada.org/

Looking for a way to help Canada's wildlife? The World Wildlife Fund explains how.

Worldwatch Institute. www.worldwatch.org/

This international organization provides useful information on a wide range of topics, including biodiversity issues.

27 Ecologically Sustainable Development

CHAPTER OBJECTIVES

After completing this chapter, you will be able to:

1. Outline the process of an environmental impact assessment, and describe several Canadian examples.
2. Discuss how monitoring and research are crucial to understanding the causes and consequences of environmental damage.
3. Explain how environmental reporting and literacy are crucial to dealing with the environmental crisis.
4. Outline the roles of governments, non-governmental organizations, scientists, and citizens in designing and implementing an ecologically sustainable economy.

CHAPTER OUTLINE

- Introduction
- Environmental Impact Assessment
- Environmental Legislation
- Environmental Monitoring and Research
- Environmental Reporting and Literacy
- Ecological Sustainability
- Environment and Society
- Prospects for Canada and for Spaceship Earth

Introduction

The previous parts of this book dealt with relatively specific topics. This has allowed us to learn the subject matter of environmental science by examining key ideas and by analyzing a body of supporting information. In this final chapter, we bring many of these topics together in an interdisciplinary fashion.

In the first sections of the chapter, we will examine topics related to environmental management and protection at the broader societal level. These topics include environmental impact assessment, monitoring and research, environmental literacy, and sustainability. All of these are necessary for maintaining an acceptable level of environmental quality and healthy ecosystems—two necessary objectives for a truly sustainable socioeconomic system. We will also examine a range of actions that each of us can undertake to help resolve environmental problems.

In the concluding section of this chapter, we will briefly discuss the future prospects for advanced economies such as that of Canada, and for spaceship Earth.

Environmental Impact Assessment

An **environmental impact assessment** (EIA) is a planning process that is used to help identify and prevent environmental problems. Environmental impact assessments do this by identifying and evaluating the potential consequences that proposed developments may have for environmental quality. Because it can consider ecological, physical-chemical, and other environmental effects, as well as socio-economic consequences, an EIA is a highly multi- and interdisciplinary activity.

An environmental impact assessment may be conducted to examine various kinds of activities, or planned developments, that could affect environmental quality, such as the following:

1. an individual project, such as a proposal to construct a dam, smelter, power plant, airport, highway, or incinerator

2. an integrated scheme, such as a proposal to develop an industrial park, a pulp or lumber mill with its attendant wood-supply and forest-management plans, or other complex developments involving numerous projects

3. a governmental policy that carries a risk of substantially affecting the environment

The scale of environmental assessments can vary greatly, from the examination of a relatively small proposal to construct a building near a wetland, to a megaproject associated with natural resource development.

In Canada, environmental impact assessments for proposals that involve federal funding or jurisdiction are regulated under the Canadian Environmental Assessment Act (CEAA); see Canadian Environmental Assessment Agency, 2005). The Act is a law that requires federal decision makers, referred to as "responsible authorities," to consider the predicted environmental effects of a proposed project before it is allowed to go ahead. If significant adverse effects are predicted, the project is not allowed to proceed until the damages have been addressed by a change in design or through some sort of mitigation. Provinces and territories have similar sorts of legislated requirements, as do some local levels of government.

Any proposed project, program, or policy carries risks for human welfare and for other species and ecosystems. For example, a project may be proposed that will emit toxic chemicals into the environment. In such a case, it is necessary to determine if the anticipated emissions might exceed the regulated levels. The most stringent regulatory standards and guidelines are related to the maximum exposures that humans can tolerate without health risks; criteria to protect other species and ecosystems are less exacting. In addition, the project might cause disturbances, which could result in ecological damage, during its construction or operation. These disturbances should be identified and quantified, and the potential environmental damages evaluated, before permission is granted to start the project.

The process of environmental impact assessment is intended to examine these potential damages and to suggest ways of avoiding or mitigating them as much as possible. However, this does not necessarily mean that no damage will be caused by the proposed development. In almost all cases, some damage is inevitable.

Because most developments potentially affect a great variety of species and ecosystems, impact assessments are limited to predicting the effects on only a selection of so-called "**valued ecosystem components**" (**VECs**). These components are valued because society perceives them to be important for one or more of the following reasons:

1. They are an economically important resource, such as an agricultural crop, a commercial forest, or a stock of fish, mammals, or birds.

2. They are a rare or endangered species or ecological community.

3. They are of cultural or aesthetic importance.

The initial phase of the process of environmental
impact assessment is known as a "screening." The screening determines the level of assessment that a proposed
activity will undergo (i.e., whether a minor review or a full
assessment is appropriate). In fact, about 99% of environmental assessments in Canada are restricted to the
screening level; in general, only larger projects require a
more extensive, comprehensive assessment. The decision
about whether to proceed to a more comprehensive assessment is made by a responsible authority of the federal government (usually a department or agency with a mandate
or experience that is relevant to the proposed project). The
decision is based on the likelihood of the proposed development causing significant adverse environmental effects,
as well as on expressions of public concern.

A full EIA requires the proponent to prepare an environmental assessment report, which is a series of documents that describe the proposed undertaking as well as
studies of its potential environmental and socio-economic
effects. The proponent must also inform the public in various ways of its detailed plans, such as holding information meetings in local communities and making planning
documents available for review by individuals and concerned organizations. For the largest projects, a review
panel of experts may be appointed by the Minister of the
Environment to hear submissions from the proponents
as well as from individuals and organizations that want to
intervene in the process. Once the panel has considered
all written and verbal submissions, it delivers a summary
report and a list of recommendations to the responsible
authority and the Minister of the Environment, who make
the report public. The federal government must then
decide whether to allow the development to proceed as
proposed, or with required mitigations that would avoid
or lessen environmental effects that are deemed unacceptable. A follow-up program may also be required, such
as environmental monitoring and mitigation of unanticipated damages.

Once the level of assessment is decided, a "scoping"
exercise is undertaken. This identifies potentially important interactions between project-related activities on the
one hand, and human welfare or VECs on the other. In
essence, the scoping compares the predicted spatial (space)
and temporal (time) boundaries of the stressors associated
with the proposed development with the areas where people and VECs are found. If potential interactions are identified, the assessors must determine whether significant
damage might be caused.

Sometimes impact assessments are not well funded,
or they have to be completed relatively quickly. In such
cases, ecologists, toxicologists, sociologists, and other professionals may have to provide expert opinions about the
likely importance of interactions between project-related
stressors and human welfare or VECs. These professional
opinions should be based on the best-available scientific
information and understanding, while recognizing that
such knowledge is incomplete and that differences of opinion often arise between qualified specialists. When sufficient time and funding are available, it is possible to conduct
field, laboratory, and/or computer-based (simulation)
research to investigate the potential interactions identified during the screening process. It must be understood,
however, that even well-funded, properly designed, and
well-executed research may yield uncertain results, particularly about damage that might occur at low intensities
of exposure to project-related stressors.

Planning Options

If potentially important risks to human welfare or VECs
are identified, a number of planning options must be considered. There are three broad choices.

Prevent or Avoid: One option is to avoid the predicted damage by ensuring that there are no significant exposures
of people or VECs to damaging stressors related to the
project. This can be done by modifying the characteristics of the development or, in cases of severe conflicts with
human welfare or ecological values, by choosing to can-
cel the project. Because prevention and avoidance may
involve substantial costs, they are sometimes considered
to be less desirable options by the proponents of a development. Politicians and regulators may also dislike this
option, since it often involves intense controversy and substantial economic opportunities may be cancelled.
Nevertheless, there is always public and regulatory pressure to take as many precautions as possible before undertaking a proposed development.

Mitigation: Another option is the **mitigation** of any predicted damages—that is, to repair or offset them as much
as possible. Because any direct damage to humans is considered unacceptable (and therefore to be avoided), mitigation is mainly relevant to damage inflicted on VECs
or to indirect, low-level risks to people. For instance, if the

habitat of a valued species is threatened, it may be possible to move the population at risk to a suitable habitat elsewhere or to create or enhance a habitat at another place so that no net damage is caused. As another example, a wetland may be destroyed by some development, but the damage may be offset through the creation of a comparable wetland elsewhere. Mitigations are a common way of dealing with potential conflicts between project-related stressors and VECs. However, it is important to understand that mitigations are never complete, and there is often residual damage.

Accept the Damages: The third, and least acceptable, option (from the environmental perspective) is for decision makers to choose to allow a project to cause some or all of the predicted damages to human welfare or VECs. This choice is often considered tolerable by proponents of projects and by politicians (although such a preference would rarely be explicitly stated). Their rationale is due to their perception that the socio-economic benefits gained by proceeding with a threatening development would be greater than the cost of the environmental damage.

Environmental impact assessments often find that a proposed development carries risks of causing damage to environmental quality. Usually, the development is allowed to proceed in some form, with the predicted environmental damage being avoided or mitigated to the degree that is considered technologically and economically feasible. As noted previously, however, there are always residual risks that cannot be avoided or mitigated. The damage that may occur represents some of the environmental costs of development, which are real even if there is financial compensation or other kinds of offsets.

Once a project has begun, compliance monitoring is usually necessary to ensure that regulatory criteria for pollution or health hazards are not being exceeded. It is extremely useful, although not always required, that any ecological effects also be monitored. This tests the predictions of the impact assessment and identifies any unanticipated effects or "surprises."

Ideally, monitoring programs are begun before a project actually starts. This establishes baseline conditions. The monitoring should continue for some years after the project is completed, until it is determined that important damage is not being caused by the development. If unanticipated damage is shown by the ecological effects monitoring, it may be prevented, avoided by an adaptive change in the project design, mitigated, or accepted as an ecological "cost" of development.

Some Canadian Examples of Impact Assessments

Environmental impact assessments have been conducted in all regions of Canada, examining projects that varied widely in both scale and potential effects. Each of these unique cases is instructive—they illustrate the environmental implications of development projects and the role played by impact assessment. In the following sections, we briefly examine selected elements of some environmental impact assessments in Canada.

Diamond Mines in the Northwest Territories: This proposal involved the development of mines to extract diamonds from five deposits discovered about 300 km northeast of Yellowknife. A variety of environmental damages may arise from this project.

First, some of the diamond-bearing rock lies beneath lakes that would have to be drained to develop the mines. These aquatic ecosystems would be destroyed.

In addition, large amounts of gravel are needed to construct roads and other infrastructure. Much of this material would be obtained from long, sinuous surface features known as eskers, which provide critical denning habitat for grizzly bear, wolf, and other high-profile species.

Further, large numbers of caribou traverse the region during their seasonal migrations. These are potentially affected by the mine and its network of roads. Substantial damage to the caribou could harm the Aboriginal people in the region, who engage in a subsistence hunt for these animals. The Aboriginal people might also suffer from interference with their commercial harvest of fur-bearing mammals.

Finally, the proposed mines are located in a region that is currently a huge, roadless wilderness. Conservationists, led by the World Wildlife Fund, objected to the approval of the mine before a system of protected areas was set up for the preservation of natural ecosystems and native species, including such large carnivores as grizzly bear, wolf, and wolverine.

The diamond-mine proposal passed its environmental impact assessment and was allowed to proceed. It is subject to stringent requirements, however, such as the implementation of acceptable methods of disposal of mining and milling wastes and the protection of waterbodies and rivers (other than those that must unavoidably be damaged to develop the mines and dispose of tailings). A ban has been imposed on local hunting by project personnel. As well, a monitoring program must be implemented to ensure that unanticipated damage is not caused to air or water quality, or to wildlife. The mine must also meet socio-economic criteria, including several that deal with employment opportunities and other involvement of local people (including Aboriginals) in the development. As a measure outside the scope of the formal impact assessment, the government of the Northwest Territories committed to establishing protected areas in the larger region.

Destruction of Diseased Bison: Agriculture Canada proposed to slaughter almost all the bison in the southern region of Wood Buffalo National Park and its vicinity. Some of these animals are infected with bovine tuberculosis and brucellosis, and there are concerns over the potential spread of these diseases to herds of domestic cattle to the south and west of the area. The bison targeted for slaughter are hybrids between the indigenous wood bison and plains bison that were introduced to the region during the late 1920s. The proposal did not include the elimination of small populations of genetically "pure" wood bison living farther to the north, and in fact, these are predicted to receive a measure of protection from the potentially harmful effects of interbreeding with hybrid animals.

This proposal was made in support of commercially important agricultural interests, but it quickly engendered intense controversy. It was opposed by virtually all conservationists and by local Aboriginal people. Although this project passed successfully through the impact assessment process, it was later suspended by the federal Minister of the Environment, largely in recognition of the intense opposition from conservation and First Nation interests.

The Hibernia Offshore Oil Development: Several decades of exploration have resulted in the discovery of large reservoirs of petroleum in undersea geological formations on the Grand Banks, east of Newfoundland. An environmental impact assessment examined a proposal from a consortium of companies to develop this valuable resource. A system of underwater wells was proposed that would feed to a central collecting system on a huge platform located in 80-m-deep water. The petroleum would be delivered periodically to onshore refineries using tanker ships.

The offshore waters of the Hibernia field sometimes experience intense winds, and immense icebergs pass through the region during most years. Some icebergs scour the ocean floor. These natural forces pose risks to the production and storage facilities. As well, accidents may result from equipment failure or human error. Alone or in combination, these factors could cause a massive petroleum spill. Such an accident could result in enormous damage to the fishery, to abundant marine mammals and seabirds in the region, and to other ecological and economic values.

The Hibernia development includes a sophisticated system of weather and iceberg monitoring, coupled with stringent spill-prevention and control technologies. These measures have been accepted by regulators and politicians as providing an acceptable degree of environmental safety. Consequently, the Hibernia development passed through the impact assessment process, and it began producing petroleum in 1997.

Grande-Baleine Hydroelectric Complex: Some regions of Canada have an enormous potential for the development of hydroelectricity. One area in which this renewable source of energy is being vigorously developed is northwestern Quebec. Several large rivers flowing into James and Hudson Bays have been dammed, allowing the storage of immense reservoirs of water. Electricity is generated at times when consumer demand is greatest.

The Grande-Baleine Complex was a proposal to add to the hydroelectricity capacity of Quebec by constructing three generating stations, with a total capacity of 3212 MW, on the Grande Baleine River. The associated dams would have flooded 1667 km² of terrestrial habitat. Other disturbances would have included the construction of roads and transmission lines to deliver the power to southern markets.

This controversial development would have had important environmental impacts. The most critical of these was the ecological damage associated with the creation of such enormous reservoirs, including the loss of terrestrial and wetland habitat, changes in flow regimes, effects on the ecology of rivers, and effects on water quality and ecosystems in nearshore Hudson Bay. In addition, the local populations and movements of caribou and fur-bearing mammals would have been affected, with consequences for the livelihood of Aboriginal people living in the region.

These and other potential effects were considered during a detailed environmental impact assessment, and plans were made to avoid or mitigate the damage to the degree that was possible. Ultimately, however, the proposed development did not proceed, not so much because of environmental concerns, but as a result of insufficient commitments to purchase the electricity in the northeastern United States. Without access to that foreign market, the estimated $13 billion cost of the project's construction was not considered economically feasible.

A Municipal Incinerator: This was a proposal to construct a facility to incinerate large quantities of municipal waste from metropolitan Halifax, Nova Scotia. Some of the heat produced would have been used to generate about 16 MW of electricity (this is also known as a "waste-to-energy" facility). The incinerator would have been fitted with advanced technologies to control the emissions of potentially toxic chemicals, such as metals, gases, and organic particles and vapours, including polycyclic aromatic hydrocarbons, dioxins, and furans. Such emissions can never be totally eliminated, however, and there is controversy about the risks to human health inherent in even minute exposures to some chemicals, particularly dioxins and furans. As it turned out, the proposal to build the incinerator was turned down by the provincial Minister of the Environment—partly because it was considered too costly in comparison with alternative methods of disposal of municipal waste, but also for environmental reasons.

A Peat Mine: Peat mined from bogs is used as a horticultural material, and it can also be burned as a source of energy. This proposal would have developed a mine on a bog in Nova Scotia to provide peat as an industrial fuel. The impact assessment focused on the fact that the bog in question provides habitat for several rare species, including a carnivorous plant called the thread-leaved sundew (*Drosera filiformis*). This species is endangered in Canada and also in much of the rest of its range in the eastern United States. Because the bog harbours the largest of four known populations of the sundew in Canada, the provincial Minister of the Environment did not allow a mine to be developed on that site. This was a controversial decision because it cancelled a local development initiative in a region in which the economy is chronically depressed.

Environmental Legislation

Many activities that could potentially degrade environmental quality are regulated by legislation passed by various levels of government. In addition, Canada has signed a number of international treaties and protocols that deal with important environmental issues. We can appreciate the scope of environmental laws by examining the major elements of legislation at the federal level in Canada, summarized in Appendix B. Provincial/territorial, municipal, and Aboriginal jurisdictions have also enacted many environmental laws.

Environmental law in Canada is made extremely complex by jurisdictional overlaps and other factors. One problem is that of harmonization of related pieces of legislation among the provinces/territories and the federal government. In 1998, these governments adopted the Canada-Wide Accord on Environmental Harmonization, intended to achieve progress in this direction. This action has, however, been resisted by certain interest groups, including the Canadian Environmental Law Association (CELA). CELA views the Accord as a mechanism for devolving federal environmental roles and responsibilities to the provinces and territories, which could reduce the federal government's accountability as well as its ability to respond to environmental challenges.

Environmental law in Canada is changing rapidly as new legislation is passed and older laws are modified or more specifically interpreted by the courts. One important interpretive decision of the Supreme Court of Canada affecting environmental impact assessments (described in Chapter 20) was the Rafferty decision of 1989, which made it clear that an EIA was needed for any undertakings involving the federal government.

In 1999, the Supreme Court's Marshall decision involved a case in which an Aboriginal person had been convicted of catching fish out of season, without a licence and for commercial sale. This conviction was overturned on the basis of treaty rights, negotiated in 1760–61, that guaranteed Mi'kmac and Maliseet Indians the right to commercially harvest natural resources at any time of year within an extensive treaty area in the Maritime Provinces. The Supreme Court interpreted the modern resource-harvesting rights of these Aboriginal nations as being sufficient for individuals to earn a "moderate living." The Marshall decision restored to Aboriginal people the legal right to engage in fish and timber harvests that are not subject to the same seasonal and geographical restrictions as for non-Aboriginals. The Marshall decision has resulted in intense controversy and conflict with non-Aboriginal fishers and government agencies. In 2003, the Supreme Court extended aspects of the Aboriginal resource-access rights to Metis in Canada, ruling that these persons could freely hunt and fish for subsistence purposes. Some key issues were left unresolved, such as the definition of a Metis person as well as what restrictions could be imposed for the purposes of safety and resource conservation. These aspects are being resolved through ongoing negotiations with the federal, provincial, and territorial governments. The social and economic repercussions of these decisions by the Supreme Court of Canada will probably take years to work out.

The settlement of comprehensive land claims with indigenous nations in Canada (in effect, the modern equivalent of "treaties") includes the formulation of suites of environmental laws. For example, such settlements include provisions governing many aspects of resource harvesting and management, waste management, and protected areas within the settlement regions.

An important example of the need for effective legislation concerns the protection of species at risk and their habitat in Canada. Comparable legislation has existed in the U.S. since 1973 as the Endangered Species Act (ESA) administered by the Fish and Wildlife Service. As of 2005, 1078 species of animals and 749 plants were listed as endangered or threatened under the ESA (518 of the listed animals occur in the U.S. and 560 in other countries, while 748 of the plants grow in the U.S. and three elsewhere). In addition, approved recovery plans were in place for 416 of the listed U.S. animals and 615 of the plants.

In Canada, the conservation status of species is designated by a group of experts from government, conservation organizations, and academia, known as COSEWIC (the Committee on the Status of Endangered Wildlife in Canada; see Chapter 26). As of 2005, COSEWIC had assigned "at-risk" status to 500 indigenous species and other taxa (such as sub-species; only native taxa are designated). Moreover, in December 2002, a federal Species at Risk Act (SARA) became law. SARA has toughened the legal provisions in support of the protection of species listed by COSEWIC. Its provisions are particularly strong with respect to at-risk species and their habitat occurring on lands owned by the federal government or otherwise falling within its jurisdiction. However, the SARA legislation is weaker with respect to species and critical habitat occurring on lands beyond direct federal jurisdiction, such as areas owned by provincial, territorial, municipal, Aboriginal, or private interests. Although there are provisions in SARA for the federal government to intervene within such cases, and to provide compensation to affected landowners, it is not absolutely bound to do so. Many such interventions would inevitably be expensive and controversial, and it remains to be seen how enthusiastically they will be utilized to protect at-risk species in Canada. Most of the provinces and territories have also passed laws related to the protection of species-at-risk within their jurisdictions, or they are actively preparing such legislation.

Of course, it is not sufficient to simply pass good laws intended to regulate actions that might degrade the quality of the environment—it is also necessary to enforce them. Between 1991 and 2004, only 100 out of 168 prosecutions were successful (i.e., achieved convictions) in Canada under the Canadian Environmental Protection Act (CEPA) or the Fisheries Act (Statistics Canada, 2004; Environment Canada, 2005). There is, however, a much larger number of cases that can be resolved with softer regulatory actions, such as writing a warning letter to a non-compliant party. Consider, for example, the following compliance data for 2003–2004 (one fiscal year) pertaining to environmental laws for which Environment Canada is responsible:

- Environment Canada carried out a total of 4413 inspections under the provisions of CEPA, and took various kinds of regulatory actions in 728 cases (this is a compliance rate of 83% of cases, although some non-compliant cases involved more than one aspect). A total of 13 prosecutions was undertaken, with convictions being obtained in 2 cases.

- Similarly, Environment Canada carried out 4229 inspections under the Fisheries Act, with 381 actions undertaken (91% compliance), including 32 prosecutions (1 conviction).

- Under the CEPA or Fisheries Act provisions relevant to
  - the national pollutant release inventory, there were 227 inspections, with 152 actions subsequently undertaken (equivalent to only a 34% compliance rate; no prosecutions were undertaken).
  - storage of PCB materials, there were 293 inspections, with 142 actions undertaken (a 48% compliance rate).
  - the export and import of hazardous waste, there were 354 inspections, with 59 actions undertaken (a 93% compliance rate).
  - ozone-depleting substances, there were 387 inspections, with 93 actions undertaken (a 76% compliance rate).
  - pulp and paper effluents of dioxins and furans, there were 195 inspections, with 8 actions undertaken (a 96% compliance rate).

- Under the provisions of the Wild Animal and Plant Protection and Regulation of International Trade Act (WAPPRITA), Environment Canada carried out 9193 inspections, with 2032 actions undertaken, including 61 prosecutions and 50 convictions.

- Under the Migratory Bird Act, Environment Canada prosecuted 721 cases and achieved convictions in 647 of them.

Global Focus 27.1

Politics and the Environment

As noted elsewhere in this chapter, it is not enough to just understand the causes and consequences of environmental or other problems—it is also necessary to have the political judgment and will to deal with pressing issues. This requires that appropriate policies be developed and suitable legislation be enacted and enforced. Unfortunately, dysfunctional political milieus in some countries prevent society from dealing with crucial issues of population, food scarcity, and ecological damage.

Some countries, such as Afghanistan and Iraq, have suffered debilitating effects of warfare, resulting in a government little able to cope with the severe physical, social, and environmental damages. Such countries can manage to take care of their people and environment only if well supported by foreign aid.

A more complex case is Zimbabwe, a southern African country that has potentially great resources of human and natural capital but is afflicted by a badly functioning and corrupt political system and leadership. Zimbabwe was born in 1980 of Rhodesia, a former British colony, when negotiations ended a rebellion against a white-dominated government and established a parliamentary democracy. Zimbabwe now supports about 13 million people, with 2 million living in the capital, Harare. The largest indigenous cultural group is Shona (76% of the population), followed by Ndebele (18%) and other tribes. People of European or Asian heritage are a small minority (2%). Zimbabwe's area of 391 000 km^2 includes magnificent wildlife and spectacular scenery, including Victoria Falls. Until recently, Zimbabwe was regarded as an African "success" story because its relatively stable government provided security for its people, and the country was a major tourist destination and key exporter of tobacco, food, gold, and other commodities.

Since the late 1990s, however, political, social, and environmental affairs in Zimbabwe have badly deteriorated. Robert Mugabe, the President since independence in 1980, has been resolute about remaining in power. He has achieved this by bullying his political opposition, stifling the press, and staging controversial elections in 2002 and 2005 (which he won). Mugabe also unleashed economic and social turmoil by abruptly embarking on a campaign to confiscate most agricultural land owned by white Zimbabweans (most are of British origin but can trace their local ancestors back for several generations). Much of the best land was then awarded to Mugabe's black political supporters, and some to landless poor people. The official rationale for the uncompensated land seizures was the fact that whites owned almost all of the higher-quality arable land (7% of the country's area) and pasture (13%), while most poor rural blacks were landless. However, Mugabe did not pursue the reallocation until his popularity was waning and his regime was threatened by a growing political opposition—the land seizures appear to be a populist tactic aimed at staying in power. Although some compensated land reallocation was a key element of the pact by which Zimbabwe was born from Rhodesia, the process had been long delayed by a lack of funding to purchase white-owned land. This was mostly because of Zimbabwe's large and increasing foreign debt, which is mostly due to government policies, as well as the failure of donor nations (such as Britain, the former colonial power) to provide funds to support the promised redistribution.

In any event, Mugabe's ill-considered policies immediately rendered most of Zimbabwe's commercial agriculture non-productive at a time of drought and food shortage, while displacing thousands of workers. During 1999–2000, the per capita production of grains was 46% less than in 1979–81 (World Resources Institute, 2005). This catastrophic loss of food production was caused by a complex of factors, including the chaos of land distribution, which resulted in much less cropland being planted to commercial food staples, as well as drought and decreasing rural person-power because of an out-of-control AIDS epidemic in the country. Clearly, the prospects of Zimbabwe feeding itself have suffered a severe blow. Moreover, its ability to purchase foods abroad has been diminished by a waning national economy, an intensifying debt spiral, and increased difficulty in obtaining foreign loans and aid.

Moreover, the population of Zimbabwe has grown tremendously during the past half century, from about 2.7 million in 1950 to 13 million in 2005 (WRI, 2005). The population growth rate averaged 3.3% per year during 1950–90, sufficient to double in size in only 21 years, but because of the AIDS epidemic, it has now fallen to only 0.5% per year and is expected to be 0.1% per year during 2005–10. The fertility rate is 3.9 children per woman (in 2005), and 42% of the population is younger than 15 years. The foremost reason for the high birth rate is the predominantly agrarian culture that views children as useful for performing work on the farm and in the home, and for assisting their parents in old age.

Global Focus 27.1 (continued)

It is inevitable, however, that population growth will diminish when effects of the current AIDS epidemic become fully manifest. About 34% of Zimbabweans aged 14 to 15 (in 2001) were infected with HIV, and life expectancy has fallen to 43 years. Despite this furious assault by AIDS, the government has not taken effective action to contain the epidemic or treat its victims. The quandary is complicated by a cultural attitude that considers HIV/AIDS a "shameful" affliction, so people will not admit to being infected.

Zimbabwe has other daunting problems, both environmental and social, that are beyond the scope of this book. The key point to understand is that any responsible government must be informed about crucial issues of the day, including environmental ones, and then be determined to take effective action. Otherwise, progress will be lost and a vortex of increasing damage, inevitable.

Several non-governmental organizations have taken on the mandate of advocating improvements to environmental law and policy in Canada, while ensuring that the existing laws are rigorously applied. The most prominent of these are the Canadian Environmental Law Association and the Sierra Legal Defence Fund. These organizations lobby politicians and suggest specific changes to existing or proposed legislation. In some cases they also take government agencies to court in order to force them to enforce the existing laws or to seek an interpretation from a higher court such as the Supreme Court of Canada.

Environmental Monitoring and Research

For many reasons—only some of which we have examined—there are widespread and well-founded concerns about damage being caused to the quality of the environment. In response, many nations are implementing programs to monitor changes in environmental quality over time. Most of these programs are intended to document changes occurring over large regions or entire countries and to help predict future changes. They are much larger in scale and scope than programs that monitor whether particular industrial facilities are complying with regulations and guidelines. Most large-scale monitoring is conducted by government agencies or, in some cases, by non-governmental organizations. The resulting data and knowledge are used to guide decision making in government, to enhance the work of non-governmental organizations, and to provide material for programs in environmental education.

In the sense meant here, **environmental monitoring** involves repeated measurements of factors related to

either the inorganic environment or the structure and functioning of ecosystems. Successful programs of environmental monitoring depend on the careful choice of a limited number of representative indicators (because not everything can be monitored) and on the collection of reliable data. If a monitoring program detects important changes, the possible causes and consequences of those changes are usually researched.

Environmental indicators are relatively simple measurements used to represent complex aspects of environmental quality. Indicators are usually sensitive to changes in the intensity of stressors. For example, the levels of chemical residues in species high in the food web are often used as indicators of contamination of the larger ecosystem. This is why residues of chlorinated hydrocarbons (such as DDT and PCBs) are routinely monitored in herring gulls and cormorants on the Great Lakes, and in marine mammals in nearshore water of the Pacific, Atlantic, and Arctic Oceans (Chapter 22). Similarly, many lichens are known to be sensitive to gaseous pollutants and are therefore monitored as indicators of air quality over large regions, including cities.

Other indicators include species that are considered to represent the general health of the ecosystem of which they are a component. For instance, the population status of grizzly bears is considered a good indicator of the quality of their extensive ecosystem, as are populations of spotted owls for western old-growth rainforest, pileated woodpecker and pine marten in some other forests, salmon and trout in certain aquatic ecosystems, and orca and other whales in the marine realm.

Sometimes, composite indicators are monitored to track changes in environmental quality. In some respects these are environmental analogues of the composite indexes that are used to monitor complex trends in finance and economics, such as the Consumer Price Index (CPI) and the Toronto Stock Exchange (TSX) index. Because they allow complex changes to be presented in a simple manner, composite indictors are especially useful for reporting to the general public.

Composite indicators of air and water quality have been developed using data for various kinds of important pollutants, such as major gases, vapours, and particulates in the atmosphere. However, composite indicators of **environmental quality** (or of **ecosystem health** or **ecological integrity**; see In Detail 27.1) are not yet well developed. This is mostly because scientists have not yet agreed on what the component variables should be.

When a change in indicators is measured in an environmental monitoring program, or when one is predicted, it is necessary to understand its causes and consequences. This is generally done by using accumulated knowledge of the effects of environmental stressors on ecosystems,

along with research designed to address important questions that are not yet understood. We can examine the linkages between environmental monitoring and research by considering several examples.

Suppose that environmental monitoring has detected that precipitation has become acidified in some large region (see Chapters 16 and 19). The cause(s) of the acidification might be understood by determining the concentrations of chemicals in the precipitation and by investigating local emissions of gases and particulates to the atmosphere. Researchers must also understand the consequences of increased deposition of acidifying substances to freshwater and terrestrial ecosystems, as well as the implications for buildings and other features of cities and towns. At first, the research would examine existing knowledge of the causes and ecological effects of acidification in various kinds of habitats. However, existing knowledge is always

In Detail 27.1

Notions of Environmental Quality

Environmental quality, *ecosystem health*, and *ecological integrity* are important notions that help us understand the importance of changes in the environment. Like many other notions, these cannot be precisely defined. It is possible, however, to develop a general understanding of what they mean.

Because they integrate changes in many components of ecosystems and environments, all of these concepts involve complex phenomena. Environmental quality, for example, is related to the concentrations of potentially toxic chemicals and other stressors in the environment, to the frequency and intensity of disturbances, and to the effects of these on humans, other species, ecosystems, and economies. Of particular concern, of course, are stressors associated with human activities, because these have become so important in the modern world.

Ecosystem health and ecological integrity are rather similar to each other and, in many respects, to environmental quality. However, these indicators focus on changes that may be occurring in natural populations and ecosystems, rather than on effects on humans and their economy.

All of these notions involve many variables related to stressors and socio-economic or ecological responses. As a result, they are sometimes measured with so-called

composite indicators, which integrate many possible changes that are thought to be important. Composite indicators are not exact measurements of environmental quality, ecosystem health, or ecological integrity, but they do allow society to determine whether conditions are getting worse or better.

These ideas can be explained by using ecological integrity as an example. Obviously, most environmental stressors associated with human activities will enhance some species, ecosystems, and ecological processes, while at the same time damaging others. However, ecological theory suggests that systems with higher values for any or all of the following characteristics will have a greater degree of ecological integrity:

- The ecosystem is resilient and resistant (see Glossary) to changes in the intensity of environmental stressors.
- The system is rich in indigenous biodiversity values.
- The ecosystem is complex in its structure and function.
- Large species are present.
- Top predators are present.
- The ecosystem has controlled nutrient cycling (i.e., it does not "leak" nutrient capital).
- The ecosystem has a "natural" character and is self-maintaining, as opposed to being strongly affected by human influences and management.

incomplete, and therefore it must be supplemented with new research examining risks of acidification that are not yet understood. The accumulated information helps society to understand whether the causes of acidification can be controlled, and if so, to assess the potential environmental and economic benefits.

In another example, monitoring might indicate that the ecological character of a region is changing because natural forests are being extensively converted into plantations through industrial forestry. The ecological consequences would initially be interpreted in the light of existing knowledge of the effects of forestry, supplemented by additional research that investigates poorly understood issues. Specific research questions might address the effects of the ecological conversions on biodiversity, forest productivity, watershed hydrology and chemistry, and global environmental change through effects on carbon storage (Chapters 17 and 23). This information is needed to help decision makers evaluate whether they should permit further conversions of natural forest into plantations.

Environmental monitoring and research in Canada are carried out by various agencies. Environment Canada is the most active agency at the federal level. In addition, the Department of Fisheries and Oceans deals with fisheries and oceanic environments, Natural Resources Canada provides data about non-renewable and some renewable resources, the Canadian Forest Service provides information relevant to commercial forests, Parks Canada examines changes in national parks and their surrounding areas, and Health and Welfare Canada deals with influences of environmental quality on human health. Statistics Canada plays a key role in compiling information and making it available to governments, companies, and the public. All of the provincial and territorial governments of Canada also have comparable agencies that deal with environmental issues within their jurisdiction.

A few non-governmental organizations also undertake a considerable amount of environmental monitoring and research. For instance, the World Wildlife Fund of Canada has programs that fund work on endangered species and ecosystems. The Nature Conservancy of Canada is also active in this kind of research. Canadian universities also have considerable technical expertise in environmental issues. University personnel are not usually involved in long-term monitoring programs, but many professors and graduate students undertake research into the causes and consequences of environmental changes.

Environmental monitoring programs provide society with crucial information and knowledge. Both are nec-

essary for implementing effective programs to prevent further degradation of environmental quality and the health of ecosystems, and to repair existing damage. These actions are necessary if society is to conduct its economy in a truly sustainable manner.

Some Challenges and Successes

As we noted earlier, programs of monitoring and research should be capable of detecting recent changes in environmental quality, while also helping to predict future changes. Well-designed programs should deal with the most important stressors that are known or potential threats to environmental quality. They should measure or predict the effects on people and on sensitive ecosystems and species, particularly those that are economically or ecologically important.

These are the simple requirements of a sensible program for monitoring and investigating environmental problems. Unfortunately, these criteria are not well met by many existing programs. As a result, there are deficiencies in our understanding of some important environmental problems. Consequently, those problems are not being addressed effectively, and they could become worse in the future. Some examples selected from preceding chapters include those listed below:

What constitutes an acceptable exposure of humans to potentially toxic chemicals? Some toxins, such as metals and many biochemicals, occur naturally. By how much can anthropogenic emissions be allowed to increase exposures beyond the natural background levels? Is any increase in exposure acceptable for non-natural toxins, such as dioxins, furans, PCBs, synthetic pesticides, and radionuclides? Or are there acceptable thresholds of exposure to these substances?

Is a widespread decline of migratory, neotropical, forest-interior songbirds occurring in North America? If so, what are the causes, and how can we manage the responsible stressors to repair the damage and prevent further losses of these native birds?

Anthropogenic emissions of CFCs (chlorofluorocarbons) may be causing a depletion of stratospheric ozone, resulting in increased ground-level exposures to ultraviolet radiation. What risks does this change have for human health and for wild species and ecosystems? How can the damage be prevented and repaired?

What are the dimensions of the global extinction crisis? How is biodiversity important to the health of the biosphere and to human welfare? Which Canadian species and ecosystems are most at risk, and why? Should Canada expend more effort to help conserve tropical biodiversity, or should we focus on problems within our own boundaries? How are Canadians linked to biodiversity-depleting stressors in tropical countries?

Extensive declines and diebacks of forests have been reported in various parts of the world, including Canada. Are those damages being caused by natural environmental changes or by stressors associated with human activities? If anthropogenic stressors are important, how can they be managed to prevent and repair the forest damage?

What are the environmental consequences and costs of conventional and nuclear warfare? The effects of war are devastating to humans, their economy, and environmental quality. If these effects were better known, this inherently destructive behaviour might be avoided.

Is it possible to valuate the worth of species, communities, and ecological services (i.e., to measure their worth in dollars) so that these can be integrated into economic cost-benefit models?

How intensively can renewable resources be harvested and managed without causing unacceptable risks to their long-term sustainability and without inflicting unacceptable damage on other species and ecosystems?

To deal properly with these and many other important issues, we must improve our understanding through better monitoring and research. We can illustrate the achievable benefits by examining a few "success stories" in which monitoring, research, and effective actions helped to resolve important environmental problems:

Eutrophication of freshwater was identified as an important environmental problem during the 1960s and early 1970s. Research discovered that phosphate was the primary cause and that the damage could largely be avoided by constructing sewage-treatment facilities and by using low-phosphorus detergent.

Contamination with persistent chlorinated hydrocarbons, such as DDT, dieldrin, and PCBs, was found to be widespread in the 1960s and 1970s. Research showed that some species, such as predatory birds, were being seriously harmed and that there were possible effects on humans. The toxicological evidence has convinced decision makers to ban these chemicals in most countries, to the great benefit of the environment.

Acidification was recognized during the late 1970s and the 1980s as an extensive phenomenon causing many ecolog-

ical damages. Research showed that the problem was largely due to atmospheric depositions of sulphur and nitrogen compounds. This convinced decision makers to require reductions of industrial emissions.

Environmental Reporting and Literacy

Environmental literacy (i.e., a well-informed understanding of environmental issues) is an important social goal. Knowledge about the causes and consequences of environmental damage can influence the decisions and choices made by politicians, regulators, corporations, and individual citizens. If appropriate, these decisions and choices can influence environmental quality in a positive manner (Figure 27.1). People acquire this knowledge in various ways, the most important of which are environmental reporting and other forms of education.

Environmental literacy has a pervasive influence on the attitudes that people develop. Individuals who are knowledgeable about environmental issues will make more appropriate lifestyle choices and will influence decision makers to ensure that sensible policies are implemented. In contrast, poorly informed public opinion encourages less appropriate environmental choices, such as rampant consumerism and wasteful use of resources. Environmental illiteracy also fosters the development of controversial "red herrings" of key issues, which can divert attention from more important problems.

An example of an environmental red herring is the common misunderstanding of differences between contamination and pollution. Related syndromes are known as NIMBY (i.e., "not-in-my-backyard"), LULU ("locally unacceptable land use"), BANANA ("build absolutely nothing anywhere near anybody"), and NIMTO ("not in my term of office"). NIMBY, LULU, and BANANA are common views that many people have about developments that may affect their local environment, while NIMTO is a frequent political response. These attitudes can result, in part, from a lack of information about the risks that may be associated with developments in the neighbourhood. Alternatively, NIMBY, LULU, and BANANA may result when planners and developers are insensitive to the legitimate concerns of local people.

In addition to affecting the siting of commercial and industrial facilities, NIMBY, LULU, BANANA, and NIMTO cause huge problems for planners who are attempting to build certain kinds of environmental

FIGURE 27.1 | Influences on Environmental Quality

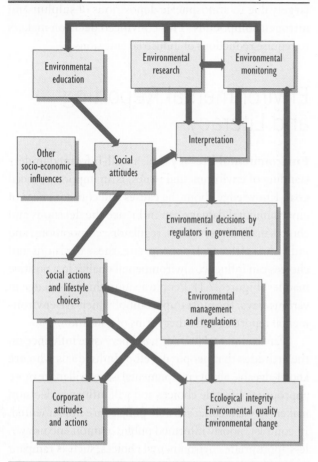

This is a conceptual model of the many influences on environmental quality, including the roles of monitoring, research, regulation, and literacy. Environmental monitoring and research provide an understanding of the causes and consequences of changes in conditions. Ideally, this understanding is based on objective information from monitoring and research programs, interpreted by environmental scientists and other qualified specialists (although the interpretations may be conditioned to some degree by social and cultural influences). This knowledge is communicated to decision makers in government, who may implement regulations and undertake management activities that affect environmental quality.

Knowledge about environmental and ecological changes is also communicated to the general public, through state-of-the-environment reporting, the educational system, activities of non-governmental organizations, and the mass media. Social attitudes regarding the environment are affected by environmental literacy, resulting in more appropriate choices of lifestyle and a public influence on the policies and actions of governments and corporations.

Source: Modified from Freedman (1995)

management facilities that society wants and needs. For example, even though all voters recognize that communities need facilities for the disposal of solid wastes and the treatment of sewage, few wish to have such works located in their own neighbourhood.

Decision makers in government and industry need objective cost-benefit analyses when dealing with environmental problems. Decision makers have the responsibility of making societal-level choices to avoid, mitigate, or accept environmental damage. Their choices are often based on their perceptions of the costs associated with environmental damage, offset by any economic benefits promised by the activity that is causing the degradation. Unfortunately, the perspective of many decision makers is that of conventional, short-term economics rather than ecological economics (see Chapter 12). Because many social controversies have resulted from seemingly nonbalanced choices, the role of decision makers is changing in Canada. In addition to, or even instead of, their actual making of choices, these people are increasingly being expected to create an appropriate climate for multilateral consultation and consensus-driven decision making.

Environmental reporting is one process for communicating information about changes in environmental quality to various interest groups. Such reporting should involve clear and objective presentations of information about changes in environmental quality and should also offer unbiased interpretations of the causes and consequences of those changes.

Environmental reporting is delivered to the broader public of Canada by various agencies, including government departments, educational institutions, non-governmental organizations, and the mass media. A governmental instrument that has been prominent in Canada since the mid-1980s is known as state-of-the-environment reporting. The federal government has released three well-regarded, comprehensive reports on the state of the Canadian environment (in 1986, 1991, and 1997). Most of the provinces have also released state-of-the-environment reports. Unfortunately, Environment Canada has now largely abandoned this function—in 1996 it closed down its division responsible for the preparation of comprehensive state-of-the-environment reports. Nevertheless, various federal agencies continue to make useful information about the environment available to the public. One excellent example is Statistics Canada, which publishes a wide range of useful information (e.g., Statistics Canada, 2004, 2005).

Of course, most people become informed about environmental issues through the mass media, such as news-

Canadian Focus 27.1

The Canadian Environmental Literacy Project

If complex environmental problems are to be addressed in a sensible way, our society needs a sound understanding of its socio-economic and natural systems and of the likely consequences of our actions. However, this knowledge is not just for environmental specialists—it must also be held by citizens, in the form of environmental literacy.

Environmental issues can be dealt with in schools, colleges, and universities by having specialized classes or by teaching the subject across the curriculum (i.e., in any kinds of classes). To help make this happen in Canada, it is useful to have teaching materials that deal with our issues in both regional and international contexts. Canadian textbooks, such as the one you are using, are helpful in this regard. Other useful resources include modular materials on various environmental topics that can be used by educators to prepare lectures, run semi-nars, and deliver experiential sessions (such as field trips). The Canadian Environmental Literacy Project (CELP) was started in order to help develop these sorts of modular resources for Canadian educators (see www.celp.ca).

CELP is a loose network of educators that aims to develop open-access materials to support the teaching of environmental studies in Canada. The focus is on modules that address Canadian issues within regional or international contexts. CELP began in 2003, using funding provided by a private Canadian foundation. Its materials are available at no cost to educators in the hope that by making it easier to teach environmental subjects, more will be taught. If the level of environmental literacy in Canada can be increased, citizens will understand critical issues on a personal level and may be more willing to support the costly actions required to prevent and repair damages. This is necessary if tangible progress is to be made toward an ecologically sustainable Canadian and global economy.

papers, magazines, radio, and television. These can be effective means of environmental education, but there are some drawbacks. Often, media presentations of issues are biased; sometimes they are inaccurate. The focus is frequently on controversies, especially those involving poorly resolved issues characterized by scientific uncertainty. This can result in high-profile disputes dominating the environmental agenda, which can detract from efforts to deal with some other important problems.

To some degree, this approach can be counterbalanced by providing the broader public with more objective information and by fostering a better understanding of the issues. One means of accomplishing this is to ensure that environmental issues are adequately, and objectively, dealt with in the education system. Ideally, this exposure would occur throughout the system—from primary and high schools, through colleges and universities, to continuing education for the working public.

Within all of these contexts (but particularly in schools, colleges, and universities), there are two broad ways of delivering environmental education. The first involves discrete, interdisciplinary classes in environmental studies or environmental science. Arguably, environmental issues are important enough to social literacy to justify their treatment as a primary subject area, comparable to mathematics, physics, biology, languages, literature, music,

Photo 27.1   Environmental literacy helps people to recognize the importance of environmental problems and to support appropriate actions by government, the private sector, and non-governmental organizations. Environmental literacy should be promoted at all levels of the education system. This scene shows naturalists learning about birds in Point Pelee National Park in southwestern Ontario.

and art. The second way of delivering environmental education is to integrate appropriate case material across the curriculum. Environment-related elements can be used to assist the teaching of virtually all disciplinary subjects, ranging from the physical sciences, through the other natural sciences and medicine, to the social sciences.

Measures to ensure that citizens are environmentally literate are a necessary part of any strategy designed to resolve environmental problems. If people understand these critical issues, they will be more willing to make personal sacrifices in support of the protection of environmental quality, biodiversity, and natural ecosystems.

Ecological Sustainability

We previously defined **sustainable development** as progress toward an economic system that is ultimately based on the wise use of renewable resources (Chapter 12). A sustainable economy would not deplete its capital of natural resources and would, therefore, not compromise the availability of resources for future generations of humans. We also noted that **ecologically sustainable development** would allow the human enterprise to continue, but without causing unacceptable damage to other species, natural ecosystems, or to other "non-resource" values.

By any of these criteria, modern industrial economies are clearly non-sustainable. There are two major reasons for this alarming conclusion. The first is the obsession that politicians, economists, and other managers of national and international economies have for rapid economic growth, both to keep up with an expanding population and to increase the standard of living. The second reason involves the likelihood that the present size of advanced economies (such as those of Canada, the U.S., the countries of Western Europe, and Japan) is already too large to be sustained for long. The rationale for these two statements is briefly explained in the following paragraphs (and has been further supported by more detailed discussions in earlier chapters).

Economic growth is typically achieved by forcing both non-renewable and potentially renewable resources through an economy, thereby making the economy larger. Since about 1990, leading industrial nations such as Canada, the U.S., and Japan were achieving economic growth rates of about 1–3% per year, which, if maintained, would double the size of their economies in only about 26 to 70 years. Rapidly developing economies, such as those of Brazil, China, Chile, India, Mexico, and Thailand, have recently been growing at up to 5–10% in some years, sufficient to double their economies in only 7 to 15 years.

As we learned earlier, these rapid economic growth rates can be achieved only as long as resources continue to be readily available. In Chapters 13 and 14, we examined numerous examples of rapidly depleting stocks of both non-renewable and potentially renewable resources. Such examples suggest that modern economic growth rates cannot be sustained and, in fact, will likely reverse themselves when crucial resources become depleted.

Moreover, many ecologists and environmentalists maintain that the present sizes of advanced economies (such as that of Canada) are already too large to be sustained. The arguments in support of this assessment are similar to those just noted—the large, "developed" economies are maintained by the forced throughput of mined resources, the supplies of which are rapidly becoming depleted.

It is common today for politicians, corporate spokespeople, and resource managers to assert publicly that they support progress toward sustainable development. However, almost all of these people are confusing genuine sustainable development, as it was defined at the beginning of this section, with "sustainable economic growth." In a resource-constrained world, unlimited economic growth can never be sustained over the long term. This is why ecologists and environmentally astute economists believe that further growth is undesirable: "Economic growth as it now goes on is more a disease of civilization than a cure for its woes" (Ehrlich, 1989).

It is important to understand that, although they are pushing society in an ill-advised direction, advocates of economic growth are not a malevolent force. Many of these people hope that growing economies will allow larger numbers of people to be productively employed, and thereby enjoy the benefits of an industrial, material society. These are, of course, highly desirable goals. Is it prudent, however, to seek to achieve a gigantic economy that would only temporarily support a large number of people? Or would it be better to limit the scale of the human enterprise to a level that can be supported by Earth's biosphere and resources over the long term? Fundamental considerations in a sustainable human economy are the numbers of people that must be supported, the total intensity of their resource use, the equitability of standards of living among the world's peoples, and the environmental damage that is caused.

Ultimately, an ecologically sustainable economy is limited by the carrying capacity of the planet for our species and its enterprises. Important elements of a sustainable economy will include controls over the population sizes of humans and their mutualistic species (such as cows and other domestic animals), as well as over per capita and total-population resource consumption. In part, the resolution of resource dilemmas will require a more equitable sharing of wealth among people living in today's poorer and richer countries. This would moderate the importance of poverty as a key factor in causing environmental degradation.

Environment and Society

All levels of society have a responsibility to protect the quality of the common environment. These obligations are a central aspect of the social contract by which enlightened communities operate.

The role of government is an overarching one, because it is empowered to regulate the activities of itself, the private sector, non-governmental organizations, and individuals. Of course, many activities of government and the private sector carry risks of causing environmental damage, and there is always an obligation to avoid or mitigate damage as much as possible.

The role of non-governmental environmental organizations is to lobby government and industry about issues, to raise public awareness, and increasingly (because of fiscally driven government cutbacks), to raise funds that can be used to prevent and repair environmental damage. Finally, all individual citizens have an obligation to live their lives in an environmentally responsible manner.

In the following sections, we will briefly examine the roles and activities of key environmental organizations (see also CELP, 2005).

International Organizations

The United Nations Environment Programme (UNEP) is the principal international organization dealing with environmental matters. UNEP is responsible for coordinating global environmental efforts with other agencies of the United Nations, national governments, and non-governmental organizations. UNEP also coordinates the development of multinational treaties and other agreements and periodically hosts global conferences on environmental themes.

Other agencies of the United Nations also have mandates that involve environmental issues. These include

Photo 27.2 The Nature Conservancy of Canada is a non-governmental organization whose activities focus on acquiring land or land-use rights for the protection of natural values. This project involved a donation by Shell Canada of almost 9000 ha of terrain around Mount Broadwood in southeastern British Columbia to develop a conservation area.

Source: L. J. Nuttall

the Food and Agriculture Organization of the United Nations (FAO), the United Nations Development Programme (UNDP), the United Nations Educational, Scientific, and Cultural Organization (UNESCO), the United Nations Population Fund (UNPF), the World Health Organization (WHO), and the International Labour Organization (ILO).

A wide range of non-governmental environmental organizations are also active on the international stage:

- Organizations involved in the international conservation of biodiversity include Conservation International, the Cousteau Society, the International Union for Conservation of Nature and Natural Resources, the Nature Conservancy (U.S.), the Smithsonian Institution, and the World Wildlife Fund.
- Organizations dealing with population issues include the Population Institute, the Population Reference Bureau, and Zero Population Growth.
- Organizations with more general mandates concerning resources and other environmental issues include the Earth Island Institute, the Environmental Policy Institute, Friends of the Earth, Greenpeace International, Resources for the Future, the Sierra Club, the World Resources Institute, and the Worldwatch Institute.

Canadian Organizations

At the federal level, Environment Canada plays a central role in preserving and enhancing environmental quality. The mandate of Environment Canada includes the protection of water, air, and soil quality; renewable resources; and indigenous biodiversity. Environment Canada's institutional objective is to foster a national capacity for sustainable development, in co-operation with international, provincial, territorial, municipal, and Aboriginal governments; other departments of the federal government; the private sector; and non-governmental organizations.

Environment Canada is divided into three major programs (or sections):

- The mandate of the Environmental Conservation Program involves ecosystem science, wildlife habitat, biodiversity, and related issues.

Photo 27.3 Ecotourism is an economically important activity that depends on the local availability of high-quality natural habitats. This is a view of part of a jungle lodge in southeastern Peru known as *Explorer's Inn*. It is one of the world's most famous birding places because of the extraordinary richness of tropical birds that can been seen there.

- The Environmental Protection Program deals with policy and regulatory matters pertaining to chemicals in the environment, atmospheric change issues, and federal preparedness for environmental emergencies.

- The Atmospheric Environment Service is responsible for atmospheric science, weather forecasting and modelling, and watershed management issues.

Other agencies of the federal government also have important environmental mandates:

- Natural Resources Canada deals with mineral and forest resources, including aspects of the environmental impacts of mining, the use of fossil fuels, and forestry.

- Health and Welfare Canada deals with environmental issues related to human health and also has primary jurisdiction over pesticide registrations.

- Agriculture and Agri-Food Canada deals with issues involving agricultural practices, including sustainability and pesticide registrations.

- Fisheries and Oceans Canada has a mandate to promote understanding, conservation, and beneficial use of aquatic resources.

- The Canadian Coast Guard helps to protect the marine environment through the prevention of pollution.

- Parks Canada, an agency of Heritage Canada, protects and manages national parks.

- The Department of Indian and Northern Affairs is responsible for environment and resource issues in extensive regions of northern Canada.

- The Canadian Environmental Assessment Agency conducts environmental assessments of projects involving the federal government.

- Statistics Canada compiles environment-related data and makes them available to other agencies and the public.

All of the provincial and territorial governments of Canada have agencies similar to those listed above for dealing with environmental responsibilities under their jurisdictions. Finally, the National Round Table on the Environment and the Economy is an integrated agency of federal, provincial, and territorial governments that examines important environmental issues and provides advice on ways to promote sustainable development in Canada.

Canada also has a wealth of non-governmental organizations that deal with environmental issues. National organizations that focus on the conservation of biodiver-

sity include the Canadian Nature Federation, the Canadian Parks and Wilderness Society, the Canadian Wildlife Federation, the Nature Conservancy of Canada, and the World Wildlife Fund of Canada. Organizations dealing with more general mandates concerning resources and other environmental issues include the Canadian Arctic Resources Committee, Canadian Ecology Advocates, Ducks Unlimited Canada, Energy Probe Research Foundation, Friends of the Earth, Greenpeace Canada, Pollution Probe, the Royal Society of Canada, the Sierra Club (Canada), the Tree Canada Foundation, and Wildlife Habitat Canada. In addition, all of the provinces and territories have non-governmental organizations that deal with environmental issues on a more regional basis. Many of these organizations are listed in CELP (2005).

Photo 27.4   A visit by U.S. President George W. Bush to Halifax in 2004 sparked a large public protest against his administration's policies related to foreign policy, economics, and the environment.

Environmental Citizenship

Although each of us individually has a relatively small effect on the environment, as a larger society our aggregate influence is enormous. If all Canadians were to pursue lifestyles that have softer effects on the environment, there would be great benefits for all of us, for future generations, and for other species. **Individual actions have relatively little effect, but many people working in concert can make a real difference.**

Environmental citizenship involves actions taken by people and families to lessen their impact on the environment. Individual acts of environmentalism involve making lifestyle choices that include having a small family, using less energy and material resources, and causing less damage to the natural world. In addition to the many "green" actions that people can undertake, they can also give moral and financial support to organizations that deal with environmental issues at international, national, and regional levels.

Libraries, bookstores, and websites stock many so-called "green" handbooks and pamphlets. These list hundreds of specific actions that people and families can take to lessen their effect on the environment. (Several of these books and websites are listed in the reference section of this chapter.) The diverse possibilities include shutting off lights when leaving a room, turning the thermostat down to 15° or less during the winter (while wearing warm slippers and a sweater!), avoiding wasteful travel habits (such as commuting alone in a car), avoiding the use of pesticides in lawn and garden care, planting trees (native species being strongly preferred) to store carbon on one's property and to provide wildlife habitat, becoming a vegetarian, and giving money and volunteer time to environmental charities (see In Detail 27.2).

Of course, few individual Canadians will make all of the green choices possible. To do so would be to voluntarily adopt an austere lifestyle, and most people are unwilling to choose this. Instead, most will undertake some positive actions, perhaps including recycling of many household wastes, riding a bicycle to school or work, not worrying about a weedy lawn, and supporting several environmental organizations. This would be "selective environmentalism" rather than a fully green lifestyle. However, if selective environmentalism is substantial enough, and is adopted by many people, there will be great benefits. Each of us is responsible for demonstrating our environmental citizenship by making as many green choices as possible and by encouraging relatives, friends, and acquaintances to do the same.

Photo 27.5   Each of us can choose to adopt a lifestyle that is less intensive in terms of its environmental impact. Being a "green" person involves many appropriate choices, such as commuting by bicycle instead of by automobile. You might want to make a list of other environmentally appropriate lifestyle choices.

Source: Dick Hemingway

If the citizens of Canada and other countries do not make these sensible, environmentally astute choices, the results will eventually be tragic.

Prospects for Canada and for Spaceship Earth

It is crucial that people understand how human activities cause environmental degradation, both directly and indirectly. We must also design procedures to prevent or effectively mitigate that damage. Over the long term, our society can prosper only if it institutes a sensible limitation on its population and ensures that its use of resources is truly sustainable.

The coupling of population control with sensible strategies of environmental management will be decisive in attaining a sustainable prosperity for humans, while accommodating other species and their natural communities on the only planet in the universe known to sustain life.

Try not to see things as they are,
but rather as how they should be.

A principle of Buddhist thought

In Detail 27.2

Environmental Choices

Each of us is confronted by many choices on how to live our life and how to influence our family, friends, and society at large. Many of our choices have significant environmental consequences in terms of resource use, pollution, and the conservation of the natural world. In this box, we examine a selection of "green" choices that can contribute to making our lifestyles and economy more sustainable by consuming and wasting less. Consider each of the suggested choices, and think about the environmental benefits that would result if large numbers of Canadians adopted them. Remember, according to Mahatma Gandhi, "You must be the change you wish to see in the world."

Green Themes

Reduce

- Do not purchase more than you really need.
- Avoid disposable or over-packaged products.
- Buy products that are durable and long-lasting.
- Do not discard items until they are truly worn out or cannot be fixed.

Reuse

- Be practical and creative in finding uses for used goods to avoid discarding them.
- Use empty glass and plastic containers to store bulk food and odds and ends.
- Reuse plastic shopping bags at the grocery store and for other purposes.
- Save cardboard, paper, string, and rubber bands for re-use.
- Pass along used clothing, toys, furniture, books, and magazines to family or friends, donate them to social service organizations, or sell them.

Recycle

- Discover what materials can be recycled in the area where you live, and then do so as fully as possible.
- Purchase products manufactured from recycled materials; this helps to develop a market for these goods.

Refuse (Avoid)

- Do not purchase goods or services produced at an unacceptable environmental cost in terms of the destruction of natural habitat or excessive pollution or resource consumption.

Support Environmental Initiatives

- If you think that companies, government bureaucracies, or politicians are not supporting environmentally sound initiatives or policies, complain regularly by writing letters or e-mail, or in other ways. If you think they are doing a good job, let them know that also.
- Support environmental organizations with your money and/or time (as a volunteer).

Lifestyle Choices

- Become a naturalist—learn to identify wild plants and animals and to understand their habitat needs and ecological relationships. Naturalists have a great empathy for wild places and the species that live there and support their conservation.
- Become a vegetarian. You will feed lower in the food web and be less involved in the economy of intensive livestock rearing and slaughter.
- Live more simply—consume fewer resources.

Some Specific Actions

Water and Sewage

- Use a flow-reducing attachment on faucets and showerheads to decrease water use.

Photo 27.6 Vegetarianism is a choice with implications for the conservation of natural areas that might otherwise be converted into pasture, and it protests against the cruelty with which livestock are often treated in industrial agriculture. Vegetarianism can also contribute to a healthier lifestyle.

In Detail 27.2 (continued)

- Turn off taps to reduce dripping, and ensure they are in good repair.
- Do not run water fast or continuously when hand-washing dishes, brushing your teeth, washing, or shaving.
- Only wash full loads in a dishwasher or washing machine, and use the energy-saver or shortest possible cycle.
- Keep a container of drinking water in the refrigerator instead of running the tap until the water gets cold.
- Put food scraps into the compost bin; otherwise discard them as garbage because using an in-sink disposal unit wastes water and adds excess organic matter to the sewage system.
- Reduce water use by about 20% by placing two 2-L plastic bottles filled with water into the toilet reservoir, or install a low-flush toilet.
- Insulate your water heater and pipes to obtain hot water more quickly and reduce energy wastage.
- Do not flush anything down the toilet that was not previously eaten (plus toilet paper)—cigarette butts, disposable diapers, dental floss, tampon holders, and condoms create problems at sewage treatment facilities and litter the environment.
- Use cleaning products that cause little environmental damage and avoid using bleach and fabric softener.
- If you are not hooked up to a central sewer system, use a composting toilet. This saves water and results in much less organic waste.

Energy Use

- Turn off lights, television, stereo, and radio when you leave a room.
- Use energy-efficient lights—a twin-tube 40-W fluorescent fixture produces about four times more light than a 100-W incandescent bulb and lasts 10 times longer.
- Where possible, use a pressure cooker or microwave instead of a regular oven; they cook food faster and use much less energy.
- In winter, set your thermostat to the lowest comfortable temperature and wear a sweater.
- Also, in winter, turn down the heat at night and when you are away during the day.
- If you use air conditioning in the summer, set your thermostat to the highest comfortable temperature.
- Ensure that storm windows and doors fit their frames snugly and that any crevices are caulked. These actions greatly reduce heat loss during winter and prevent cooling loss in summer.
- Install solar panels to produce heat and/or electricity for your house or office.

- If you are burning wood in a stove or furnace, only use well-seasoned fuel dried for at least six months. Use a high-efficiency burner, but do not excessively dampen the combustion because a smoldering burn pollutes the atmosphere. To further avoid pollution, do not burn painted wood, plastic, or garbage.

Use of Household Products

- Avoid using hazardous cleaning products; instead, use "old fashioned" alternatives such as baking soda, borax, and vinegar.
- To clean windows, mix 10 mL of vinegar with 1 L of water and wipe with newspaper, which can then be composted.
- Clean sink drains with hot water containing 60 mL of baking soda and 60 mL of vinegar per litre.
- Clean your oven with a pasty mixture of water and baking soda or pour salt onto fresh grease spots and wipe clean minutes later.
- Clean the toilet with baking soda and a mild detergent using a toilet brush.
- Clean sinks and counters with a pasty mixture of baking soda and water.
- Polish varnished furniture with a mixture of one part lemon juice and two parts olive or vegetable oil; for non-varnished furniture, use 15 mL lemon oil in 1 L mineral oil.
- If you must use hazardous household products, inquire about appropriate waste depots and special hazardous-waste collection days in your community.
- Always store hazardous products in their original containers so that handling and disposal instructions on labels can be followed.
- Store hazardous products in closed containers and in well-ventilated places, and do not store bleach close to acid or ammonia (if mixed, deadly chlorine gas is emitted).
- Use curtains, carpets, furniture, and other household items that contain minimal or no hazardous chemicals and materials such as formaldehyde.
- Use low-toxic paints, stains, varnishes, solvents, waxes, glues, adhesives, and cleaners.

In the Garden

- Water your garden only when necessary and in the coolest part of the day (early morning or late evening). Avoid over-watering and watering on windy days (to avoid excessive loss by evaporation).

In Detail 27.2 (continued)

- Cut the lawn to a height of 6–7 cm, as taller grass holds water better.

- Recycle your lawn clippings (e.g., leave them in place for in situ composting).

- Use a push mower, which saves fuel, avoids pollution, and provides exercise.

- Use a mulch of tree leaves, grass clippings, or wood chips to reduce water evaporation around garden plants, shrubs, and trees.

- Avoid using synthetic fertilizer and pesticides in your yard. Fertilize using compost. Use alternative pest-control products such as insecticidal soap and manual methods of control (such as digging weeds and hand-picking pest insects).

- Rotate species of vegetables and flowers in your garden from year to year and between locations to discourage soil diseases and pest insects.

- Plant basil, chives, chrysanthemums, garlic, horserad-ish, marigolds, mint, and thyme amongst garden plants; their natural odours and root secretions repel some pest insects.

- Maintain bird feeders in your yard, as birds contribute to natural insect control.

- Naturalize your garden—cultivate native plants instead of alien species and let commercial horti-cultural businesses know that this is what you want to buy.

- Compost as much of your organic discards as possi-ble. This greatly reduces the garbage put out for col-lection and provides an excellent organic fertilizer and soil conditioner. Many kitchen wastes can be composted, including vegetable and fruit peelings, coffee grounds, eggshells, tea leaves, wet paper, and uneaten food.

- To avoid pollution, use sand instead of salt to deal with ice on your sidewalk or driveway.

- Home gardeners can be efficient and productive food producers. If you do not have a backyard, then obtain a plot in your city's allotment site.

- Plant as many trees as possible to offset some of your CO_2 emissions.

- Plant well-positioned trees to cool your house instead of using air conditioning.

- Collect and use rainwater for watering the garden.

When Shopping

- Patronize small, local businesses and farmers' markets. This helps to avoid products that have been transport-ed long distances and keeps more money in the local economy.

- Buy products that are not over-packaged and are in returnable or recyclable containers.

- Buy storable products in bulk rather than in over-packaged smaller sizes, and store them in containers that you have saved.

- Avoid fruit or vegetables sold in blister or plastic pack-ages.

- Use a cloth-diaper cleaning service instead of buying disposable diapers.

- Buy products in paper containers instead of plastic or polystyrene.

- Buy unbleached, non-coloured, recycled paper products.

- Reuse plastic shopping bags or buy fabric shopping bags that can be reused.

The Family Vehicle

- Walk or use a bicycle whenever possible.

- If you must drive a car or truck, own one that is as small as possible; fuel consumption and overall resource use are strongly related to vehicle weight.

- Drive at moderate speeds—cars use about 10% less fuel when driven at 90 km/h rather than 100 km/h.

- Turn off the engine when waiting in your vehicle.

- Avoid carrying unnecessary weight, as it causes your vehicle to burn more fuel.

- Combine errands to reduce your total mileage.

- Keep your vehicle well serviced so it works efficiently.

- Use alternatives to the personal motor vehicle as often as possible, such as public transit, car or van pools, walking, or bicycling.

In the Office

- A laptop computer uses considerably less energy than a desktop computer.

- Ink-jet and dot-matrix printers use up to 95% less energy than laser printers.

- Make two-sided copies when photocopying and print-ing, and use machines that have an automatic "stand by" or "sleep" mode.

Key Terms

environmental impact assessment (EIA)

valued ecosystem components (VECs)

mitigation

environmental monitoring

environmental indicators

environmental quality

ecosystem health (ecological integrity)

environmental literacy

environmental reporting

sustainable development

ecologically sustainable development

environmental citizenship

Questions for Review

1. What are the circumstances that would trigger an environmental impact assessment in Canada, and how would the VECs (valued ecosystem components) be chosen for examination?

2. Define the following terms: economic growth, sustainable development, ecologically sustainable development.

3. Give an example of environmental legislation in Canada, describe the environmental problem it is intended to address, and clarify the roles and responsibilities of governments, the private sector, and individuals.

4. Make a list of 10 important choices that a Canadian student should consider making in order to soften her or his environmental impact.

Questions for Discussion

1. There has not yet been a full assessment of the environmental impacts of a broad government policy, such as entering into a free trade agreement with other countries. Does this mean that important environmental considerations are not being adequately considered when Canada's trade policies are developed?

2. Imagine that a large industrial development (e.g., a power plant, sewage-treatment plant, incinerator, pulp mill, or mine) is being proposed for the area where you live. Make a list of the important environmental considerations that you think should figure in an EIA of the proposed development.

3. Consider a landscape that is being managed for the harvesting of timber for a pulp mill. What economic and ecological values would have to be accommodated by an ecologically sustainable system of land-use in that area?

4. Considering all you know about environmental science, do you believe that there is a crisis in the region where you live, or in Canada, or on Earth? If you do believe that there is an environmental crisis, what are the core elements of a social strategy that would alleviate the damage?

Exploring Issues

1. Make a list of actions that you and your family could take in order to become less damaging in your environmental impact. For each action, consider the environmental benefits that would result, as well as the implications for your lifestyle.

2. You have just been elected to the position of "Benevolent Dictator" of Canada. You will have this position of power until you decide you no longer want it, and you have the responsibility to quickly make the Canadian economy operate according to the principles of ecological sustainability. What would be the central elements of such an economy? How would you choose to implement any changes necessary to achieve such a sustainable economy?

References

Abrams, R.H., W. Goldfarb, R.L. Graham, L. Heinzerling, D.A. Wirth, and Z.J.B. Plater (eds.). 2004. *Environmental Law and Policy*. Aspen, CO: Aspen Publishers.

Beanlands, G.E. and P.N. Duinker. 1983. *An Ecological Framework for Environmental Impact Assessment in Canada*. Halifax: Dalhousie University, Institute for Resource and Environmental Studies.

Canadian Environmental Assessment Agency. 2005. *Environmental Assessments*. www.ceaa-acee.gc.ca/index_e.htm

Canadian Environmental Assessment Research Council/National Research Council (CEARC/NRC). 1986. *Cumulative Environmental Effects*. Ottawa: CEARC/NRC. Board on Basic Ecology.

Canadian Environmental Literacy Project (CELP). 2005. *Links to Organizations*. www.celp.ca/Links/LinkView.php?fid=stmain

Canter, L.W. 1995. *Environmental Impact Assessment*. Columbus, OH: McGraw Hill.

Ehrlich, P.R. 1989. Facing the habitat crisis. *BioScience*, **39**: 480–482.

Environment Canada. 2005. *Environmental Law Enforcement Program*. www.ec.gc.ca/ele-ale/home/home_e.asp

Erickson, P.A. 1994. *A Practical Guide to Environmental Impact Assessment*. San Diego, CA: Academic.

Freedman, B. 1995. *Environmental Ecology*. 2nd ed. San Diego, CA: Academic.

Freedman, B., C. Staicer, and N. Shackell. 1993. *Recommendations for a National Ecological-Monitoring Program*. Ottawa: Environment Canada, State of the Environment Reporting Organization. Occ. Pap. Ser. No. 2.

Government of Canada. 1996. *The State of Canada's Environment*. Ottawa: Environment Canada, State of the Environment Reporting Organization.

Kubasek, N.K. and G.S. Silverman. 2004. *Environmental Law.* 5th ed. Englewood Cliffs, NJ: Prentice Hall.

Lawrence, D.P. 2003. *Environmental Impact Assessment: Practical Problems to Recurrent Problems.* New York: Wiley and Sons.

Marriott, B.B. 1997. *Environmental Impact Assessment: A Practical Guide.* Columbus, OH: McGraw-Hill Professional Publishing.

Morris, P. and R. Therivel (eds.). 2001. *Methods of Environmental Impact Assessment.* New York: Spons Architectural Price Book.

Statistics Canada. 2004. *Human Activity and the Environment 2004.* Ottawa, ON: Statistics Canada. http://estat. statcan.ca.ezproxy.library.dal.ca/content/english/ articles/other/0000416-201-XIE.pdf

Statistics Canada. 2005. *ESTA Database.* Ottawa, ON: Statistics Canada. http://estat.statcan.ca./

World Resources Institute. 2005. *Earth Trends. The Environmental Information Portal.* Washington, DC: WRI. www.wri.org/

Zygmunt, J.B.P., R.H. Abrams, W. Goldfarb, and R. Graham. 1998. *Environmental Law and Policy: A Coursebook on Nature Law and Society.* Wadsworth Pub., Belmont, CA.

Being a Green Canadian

Berthold-Bond, A. 1997. *The Green Kitchen Handbook: Practical Advice, References, and Sources for Transforming the Center of Your Home into a Healthful, Livable Place.* New York: Harper Perennial.

Co-op America's Green Pages On-Line. www.coopamerica.org/pubs/greenpages/

Environment Canada. *What You Can Do; Small Changes Make a Big Difference.* www.ec.gc.ca/eco/main_e.htm

Harris, M. 1991. *Ecological Gardening. Your Path to a Healthy Garden.* Toronto: Random House Canada.

National Round Table on the Environment and the Economy. 1991. *The National Waste Reduction Handbook.* Ottawa: National Round Table on the Environment and the Economy.

National Round Table on the Environment and the Economy. 1992. *Green Guide: A User's Guide to Sustainable Development for Canadian Colleges.* Ottawa: National Round Table on the Environment and the Economy.

Pollution Probe Foundation. 1991. *The Canadian Green Consumer Guide.* Toronto: McClelland & Stewart.

Trainer, T. 1995. *The Conserver Society: Alternatives for Sustainability.* London: Zed Books.

Yepsen, R. 1997. *1001 Old-Time Garden Tips: Timeless Bits of Wisdom on How to Grow Everything Organically, from the Good Old Days When Everyone Did.* Emmaus, PA: Rodale Press.

Informative Websites

Canadian Environmental Assessment Agency. www.ceaa.gc.ca/

The CEAA works on the leading edge of environmental assessment (EA) by investing in research and development, especially in what constitutes high-quality EA, and how best to carry it out in practice.

EcoLiving Center. www.ecolivingcenter.com/

This website provides much information about environmental issues and green lifestyles, and also many useful weblinks.

Ecological Monitoring and Assessment Network. www.eman-rese.ca

The Ecological Monitoring and Assessment Network (EMAN) is a national network of monitoring and research sites characterized by long-term, multidisciplinary studies. The network strives to facilitate co-operation and a holistic approach to ecological enquiry and ecosystem understanding.

EnviroLink. The Online Environmental Community. www.envirolink.org/

EnviroLink is dedicated to providing you with the most comprehensive, up-to-date environmental resources available. A good entry point for Web newcomers with an interest in all things ecological.

Environmental Jobs and Careers. www.ejobs.org/

E Jobs links to environmental opportunities in the USA and Canada. Employment includes careers such as environmental engineers, nature and wetlands scientists, chemists, geologists, policy and law, wildlife conservation, planning, education, wastewater treatment and operations, and program and project management.

Environmental Literacy Council. www.enviroliteracy.org/

The Environmental Literacy Council provides this wide-ranging website that provides information on many issues, with an aim to educate and foster environmental literacy.

Environmental Monitoring and Assessment Program. www.epa.gov/docs/emap/

The Environmental Monitoring and Assessment Program (EMAP) is a research program to develop the tools necessary to monitor and assess the status and trends of national ecological resources.

Resources for the Future. www.rff.org/

RFF is a non-profit and non-partisan think-tank located in Washington, DC that conducts independent research—rooted primarily in economics and other social sciences—on environmental and natural resource issues.

Revisiting Carrying Capacity: Area-Based Indicators of Sustainability. http://dieoff.org/page110.htm

Bill Rees, a professor from the University of British Columbia, wrote this essay about capacity.

The Science & Environmental Policy Project. www.sepp.org/

This page covers key issues such as global warming, ozone depletion, and regulatory excess, as well as project updates and current research.

Sierra Legal Defence Fund. www.sierralegal.org/

Working on behalf of concerned Canadians, the Sierra Legal Defence Fund protects the environment by upholding and enforcing the law. They provide free legal advice and free legal representation to individuals and groups fighting important environmental battles.

Smart Communities Network. www.sustainable.doe.gov/

The U.S. Department of Energy sponsors this page that is dedicated to informing the public about the many issues surrounding sustainable development.

Union of Concerned Scientists. *The Great Green Web Game.* http://go.ucsusa.org/game/

Test your knowledge of how your consumer choices affect the environment.

United Nations Development Programme. www.undp.org/

Focus areas of this page include poverty, gender, environment, and governance.

World Resources Institute. EarthTrends. The Environmental Information Portal. http://earthtrends.wri.org/

The WRI is a leading environmental organization that provides excellent information about resource issues.

Canadian Case 6

David Schindler—A Scientist and Citizen Environmentalist

David Schindler is a Professor in Biological Sciences at the University of Alberta, Edmonton. He is perhaps the leading ecologist in Canada, with a global reputation. He has won numerous awards, including the Stockholm Water Prize in 1991 (this is considered the equivalent of a Nobel Prize in aquatic science) and the Gerhard Herzberg Medal for Science and Engineering in 2001 (this is a Canadian award to the "scientist of the year"). Schindler studies aquatic systems, with specific interests in ecosystem-level studies, biogeochemistry, and experimental ecology. He has worked extensively on lakes and watersheds in the boreal, arctic, alpine, and montane biomes. He is perhaps most famous for his role in pioneering the use of whole-lake experimental studies in the Experimental Lakes Area of northwestern Ontario (see Canadian Focus 20.1).

David Schindler's research has focused on the effects of human activities on freshwater ecosystems and the resources they provide. His work has been highly interdisciplinary and it generally engages teams of scientists working on diverse aspects of some broader problem, such as the causes and effects of eutrophication, acidification, or climate change, or the cycling of persistent organochlorines and radioactive elements.

But Schindler has not only been an outstanding scientist—he has also worked hard to ensure that his work and that of his colleagues is used to inform decision makers and to formulate ecologically sound management policy in Canada, the U.S., and Europe. This willingness to engage in high-profile public debates about environmental policy and management practices sets Schindler aside from most scientists, who typically are not deeply involved in civic discussions about policies. Clearly, there is an important role for scientists to play as environmental citizens. There are even several societies organized to encourage this expert participation, such as the Union of Concerned Scientists, a non-governmental U.S. organization founded in 1969 and supported by 50 000 citizens and scientists, mostly in the United States.

Some of Schindler's advocacy has resulted in important changes that have yielded substantial benefits to environmental quality. This has included the removal of phosphorus from detergents and the construction of sewage-treatment plants to reduce eutrophication, and reductions of sulphur dioxide emissions to reduce acidification. In spite of these positive results, however, Schindler's advocacy about other important environmental issues has yet to yield the necessary economic and management changes. This has particularly been the case with respect to emissions of greenhouse gases implicated in global warming, and the control of organic and nutrient-laden effluents from intensive livestock-rearing facilities. These frustrations are highlighted in interviews with David Schindler in the video resource, Schindler's Way.

Question

1. Do you think that environmental scientists should actively participate in public debates involving their expert subject area? Or should they restrict their professional activities to their science interests, and allow public advocacy groups to lead the charge in terms of informing public policy?

Video Resource

"Schindler's Way." Country Canada, May 2002

Selected References

Dr. David W. Schindler. 2002. www.biology.ualberta.ca/ faculty/david_schindler/index.php?Page=1023

Union of Concerned Scientists. Citizens and Scientists for Environmental Solutions. 2002. www.ucsusa.org/

Appendix A
Units of Measurement and Conversions

Standard Units

Most of the world's scientists use the *International System of Units* (or SI). The SI system is based on seven primary units:

QUANTITY	NAME OF UNIT	SYMBOL
length	metre	m
mass	kilogram	kg
amount of substance	mole	mol
time	second	s
electric current	ampere	A
temperature	kelvin	K
luminous intensity	candela	cd

All other SI units are derived from the primary ones and are expressed in various forms of those units. For example, the SI unit for volume is the cubic metre (m^3), derived from the metre. Some common secondary SI units are the following:

QUANTITY	NAME OF UNIT	SYMBOL
area	square metre	m^2
volume	cubic metre	m^3
velocity	metre per second	m/s
density	kilogram per cubic metre	kg/m^3
acceleration	metre per second squared	m/s^2
frequency	hertz	Hz ($1 \text{ Hz} = 1 \text{ s}^{-1}$)
force	newton	N ($1 \text{ N} = 1 \text{ kg•m/s}^2$)
pressure and stress	pascal	Pa ($1 \text{ Pa} = 1 \text{ N/m}^2$)
energy or work	joule	J ($1 \text{ J} = 1 \text{ N•m}$)
power	watt	W ($1 \text{ W} = 1 \text{ J/s}$)
electric potential	volt	V ($1 \text{ V} = 1 \text{ W/A}$)

Some multiples of SI units have been given special names:

QUANTITY	NAME OF UNIT	SYMBOL	DEFINITION
area	hectare	ha	$1 \text{ ha} = 10^4 \text{ m}^2$
volume	litre	L	$1 \text{ L} = 10^{-3} \text{ m}^3$
	millilitre	mL	$1 \text{ mL} = 1 \text{ cm}^3 = 10^{-6} \text{ m}^3$
mass	tonne	t	$1 \text{ t} = 10^3 \text{ kg}$
amount of substance	mole	mol	6.02×10^{23} units of atoms, molecules, ions, electrons, photons, or other elementary entities
pressure	bar	bar	$1 \text{ bar} = 10^5 \text{ N/m}^2$
	millibar	mbar	$1 \text{ mbar} = 10^2 \text{ N/m}^2$
energy, work	kilowatt hour	kWh	$1 \text{ kW/h} = 3.6 \times 10^6 \text{ J}$
concentration of ions	equivalent	eq	molar concentration × number of charges on ion

The SI system specifies prefixes to denote multiples of units, in powers of ten:

PREFIX	SYM-BOL	EXPO-NENT	MULTIPLE	NUMBER
peta-	P	10^{15}	1 000 000 000 000 000	one quadrillion
tera-	T	10^{12}	1 000 000 000 000	one trillion
giga-	G	10^9	1 000 000 000	one billion
mega-	M	10^6	1 000 000	one million
kilo-	k	10^3	1 000	one thousand
hecto-	h	10^2	100	one hundred
deca-	da	10^1	10	ten
deci-	d	10^{-1}	0.1	one tenth
centi-	c	10^{-2}	0.01	one hundredth
milli-	m	10^{-3}	0.001	one thousandth
micro-	m	10^{-6}	0.000 001	one millionth
nano-	n	10^{-9}	0.000 000 001	one billionth
pico-	p	10^{-12}	0.000 000 000 001	one trillionth

Powers of Ten

Extremely large or small numbers can be written in a compact way that does not require large numbers of zeroes. Here are the basic rules for the "powers of ten" notation:

1. Any figure can be represented as a number between 1 and 10 followed by ten raised to a power (exponent).
2. If the power of 10 is positive, it means "move the decimal point this many places to the right."
3. If the power of 10 is negative, it means "move the decimal point this many places to the left."

examples: $4.26 \times 10^5 = 426\ 000$
$8.82 \times 10^{-4} = 0.000\ 882$

Conversions

Other types of units can be converted into SI units, and vice versa. The most common conversions are the following:

Length

1 inch = 25.4 mm = 2.54 cm

1 foot = 305 mm = 30.5 cm = 0.305 m

1 yard = 914 mm = 91.4 cm = 0.914 m

1 mile = 1.609 km

1 fathom = 1.83 m

1 nautical mile = 1.85 km

1 m = 39.37 in = 3.28 ft

1 km = 0.621 mile

Area

1 square inch = 645 mm^2 = 6.45 cm^2

1 square foot = 0.0929 m^2

1 square yard = 0.836 m^2

1 acre = 4050 m^2 = 0.405 ha

1 square mile = 2.59 km^2

1 m^2 = 10.8 ft^2 = 2.47 $\times$ 10^{-4} acre

1 ha = 2.47 acres

Volume

1 cubic inch = 16.4 cm^3

1 cubic foot = 0.0283 m^3

1 cubic yard = 0.765 m^3

1 m^3 = 35.3 ft^3 = 1.31 yd^3

Capacity

1 fluid ounce (Imp.) = 28.4 cm^3

1 fluid ounce (U.S.) = 29.5 cm^3

1 teaspoon = 4.93 cm^3

1 tablespoon = 14.8 cm^3

1 cup = 237 cm^3

1 pint (Imp.) = 568 cm^3

1 pint (U.S.) = 473 cm^3

1 quart (Imp.) = 1136 cm^3

1 quart (U.S.) = 946 cm^3

1 gallon (Imp.) = 4.55 L

1 gallon (U.S.) = 3.79 L

1 bushel (Imp.) = 0.0364 m^3

1 bushel (U.S.) = 0.0352 m^3

1 L = 0.220 Imp. gal = 0.264 U.S. gal

Mass

1 grain = 64.8 mg

1 ounce = 28.35 g

1 pound = 453.6 g = 0.454 kg

1 U.S. ton (short) = 907 kg

1 Imp. ton (long) = 1002 kg

1 kg = 35.27 oz = 2.2 lbs = 1.102 $\times$ 10^{-3} ton

1 tonne = 10^3 kg = 0.984 Imp. ton

Velocity

1 in/s = 25.4 mm/s

1 foot/s = 0.305 m/s

1 mile/hr = 0.447 m/s

1 knot = 0.515 m/s

1 m/s = 3.6 km/h = 3.28 ft/s = 199 ft/min = 2.24 mi/h

Pressure

1 lb/sq in = 6880 N m^{-2}

1 lb/sq ft = 47.8 N m^{-2}

1 inch of mercury (STP) = 3380 N/m^2

1 atm = 101 325 Pa = 1.01 bar = 14.7 psi = 760 mm Hg

Work

1 foot-pound = 1.36 J

Power

1 foot-pound/s = 1.36 W

1 horsepower = 746 W

Energy

1 British thermal unit (Btu) = 1.060 kJ

1 calorie = 4.187 J

Temperature

1 Fahrenheit degree (°) = 0.555 K

degrees Fahrenheit = 9/5 (degrees C) + 32

degrees Centigrade (Celsius) = 5/9 (degrees F – 32)

degrees Kelvin = (degrees Celsius + 273.15)

Actions which may affect environmental quality are regulated by legislation passed at the federal, provincial/territorial, and municipal levels. Canada is also a signatory to international treaties and protocols dealing with environmental issues. Environmental law, an extensive field in Canada, is made more complex by jurisdictional overlaps and other complicating factors. Unfortunately, we cannot explore these topics in detail in the limited space available. However, we can get an impression of the scope of environmental laws in Canada by briefly examining major elements of legislation at the federal level.

Federal Environmental Legislation

Arctic Waters Pollution Prevention Act (1985). This legislation was passed to regulate development related to the exploration and exploitation of natural resources in the Canadian Arctic. The Act is intended to ensure that while these economic activities take place, damage is not caused to the Inuit or other inhabitants of the region, or to the ecological balance of the marine ecosystem. The Act governs the deposition of domestic and industrial waste in arctic waters from ships or other sources.

Atomic Energy Control Act (1946). This law was passed because the safe development of nuclear energy was deemed essential to the national interest. The Atomic Energy Control Board (AECB) was established as the federal nuclear regulatory agency, responsible for ensuring that the use of nuclear energy in Canada does not pose undue risk to health, safety, security, or the environment. AECB establishes standards for uses of nuclear energy and radioactive materials (including manufacturing and international trade), and only licenses activities that meet its standards. Atomic Energy of Canada Ltd. was incorporated under the Act in 1952 to conduct research and development in support of the CANDU nuclear generating system.

Canada Petroleum Resources Act (1985). This legislation regulates activities related to the exploration, production, and transport of petroleum (including natural gas) resources in "frontier" lands (i.e., Yukon Territory, Northwest Territories, Nunavut, Sable Island, and marine and inland waters under federal jurisdiction). The Act regulates industrial activities to ensure resource conservation, protection of the environment, and safety of workers.

Canada Water Act (1970). This Act provides the framework for joint federal-provincial management of the freshwater resources of Canada, including research, planning, and implementation of programs relating to the conservation, development, and utilization of water.

Canada Wildlife Act (1985). This law regulates the conservation of wildlife (i.e., any wild organisms) occurring on habitat (terrestrial, inland waters, and territorial seas) under federal jurisdiction. The Act has discretionary provisions to encourage research, education, protection of endangered species, co-operation with other jurisdictions, and for establishing National Wildlife Areas and other kinds of protected areas (including marine).

Canadian Environmental Assessment Act (1995). This legislation establishes responsibilities and procedures for conducting environmental impact assessments for projects involving the federal government. The Act applies to projects for which the federal government holds decision-making authority as the proponent, land administrator, source of funding, or regulator. The Act establishes a process that helps responsible authorities determine the potential environmental effects of projects early in their planning stage. It has provisions for public involvement in the process, including unfettered access to relevant information. The Act is intended to promote sustainable development in Canada by encouraging economic activity that conserves and enhances environmental quality.

Canadian Environmental Protection Act (1999). This legislation is related to toxic substances in the environment and their potential effects on human health and environmental quality. The Act provides for the development of national environmental quality objectives, guidelines, and codes of practice for toxic substances. The Act contains provisions governing a wide variety of toxic substances and their possible release into the environment, including their development, manufacture, trade, transport, storage, use, and ultimate disposal as waste. The Act pertains to the practices of federal agencies, Crown corporations, and other elements of federal jurisdiction and is consistent with the Canada-Wide Accord on Environmental Harmonization signed by federal, provincial (except Quebec), and territorial ministers of the environment in 1998.

Drinking Water Materials Safety Act (proposed). This proposed legislation would provide enforceable standards for all materials that come into contact with drinking water. The Act is intended to protect human health by establishing nation-wide standards for treatment chemicals added to water, materials that come in contact with water from the point of collection to the point of distribution, and water-treatment devices used in the home.

Species At Risk Act (2002). This legislation includes provisions to protect designated at-risk species on land falling within the jurisdiction of the federal government. It confers less protection for habitat in areas of Canada beyond federal jurisdiction. The Act has provisions to aid in the recovery of designated species.

Fisheries Act (1985). This Act governs aspects of the fishing industry in Canada, such as (a) licensing; (b) fishing methods, effort, location, and disposition of the catch; (c) habitat protection (including pollution prevention and physical destruction); and (d) the powers of fisheries officers.

Food and Drug Act (1985). This legislation governs the safety of food intended for human consumption in Canada, including permissible residues of pesticides and other potentially toxic chemicals. It has provisions related to labelling, inspection, and residue criteria.

Forestry Act (1985). This legislation is intended to foster the sustainable development of the forest resource of Canada. The Act has provisions for the pursuit of that goal through (a) conducting relevant research, (b) promoting public co-operation in forest conservation; (c) entering into agreements with other governments or private interests; and (d) by providing forestry surveys, advice, and management for forest on lands within federal jurisdiction.

Great Lakes Fisheries Act (1955). This is enabling legislation for the Convention on Great Lakes Fisheries, a treaty between Canada and the United States (see below). The Act has provisions for developing a co-ordinated research and management program to sustain fish stocks in the Great Lakes and their tributary waters.

Hazardous Products Act (1985). This Act governs the import, export, and internal transportation of substances listed as "hazardous" in Canada. It contains provisions for prohibiting or restricting unsafe products, for labelling "controlled products," and for safe transportation.

Health of Animals Act (1990). This legislation governs the protection of animals in agriculture and as pets and has provisions for humane care in their rearing, transport, and slaughter. The Act also deals with diseases and toxic substances that may affect animals or that may be transmitted from animals to people.

International Boundary Waters Treaty Act (1909). This is enabling legislation related to a treaty signed with the United States in 1909 (the Boundary Waters Treaty), which deals with issues regarding inland waters shared by the two countries (see below). The Act prevents the unilateral damming or diversion of waters in Canada whose natural flow area includes U.S. territory.

International River Improvements Act (1985). This law provides a mechanism for the federal government to enact and enforce regulations and issue licences to develop and use water resources of international rivers (i.e., whose flow includes U.S. territory), including the construction of water-flow control structures.

Migratory Birds Convention Act (1917). This is enabling legislation for the Migratory Birds Convention, signed between Canada and the United States in 1917 to provide protection for migratory birds (see below). The Act provides for the protection and management of migratory bird species that inhabit Canada during all or any part of the year, including the establishment of migratory bird sanctuaries. The Act also prohibits the nonlicensed possession and commercial trade of a migratory bird, nest, or other products.

National Parks Act (1988). This legislation enables the federal government to commemorate, protect, and interpret places which are significant examples of the natural or cultural heritage of Canada. This is to be done for the benefit, education, and enjoyment of Canadians, and the parks are to be used in a manner that conserves the ecological and commemorative integrity of their heritage.

National Round Table on the Environment and the Economy Act (1993).   This law enables the establishment of a National Round Table on the Environment and the Economy. This is an advisory body whose purpose is to (a) be catalytic in explaining and promoting the principles and practices of sustainable development in Canada, (b) conduct research in relevant issues, and (c) advise governments and other sectors on ways of integrating environmental considerations and global issues of sustainable development into their decision-making processes.

Non-smokers' Health Act (1985).   This law regulates the smoking of tobacco products in federal workplaces and on common (Canadian-owned) carriers (such as public transit and airlines). The Act bans smoking in common areas under its jurisdiction but allows for the designation of enclosed, independently-ventilated smoking areas.

Oceans Act (1997).   This legislation commits the federal government to manage the oceans according to the principles of sustainable development, integrated management, and the precautionary approach. The Act replaces a previous, fragmented approach to oceans management with a collaborative, integrated approach, with the aim of optimizing economic benefits while ensuring the sustainability of marine resources. The Act allows for the development of an Oceans Management Strategy and contains provisions for the establishment of marine protected areas, maintenance of marine environmental quality, and implementation of integrated management.

Pest Control Products Act (1939).   This legislation regulates products used for the control of pests. The Act requires the registration of any pesticides imported, manufactured, sold, or used in Canada; regulates activities in the manufacturing, storage, distribution, display, and use of pest control products; has provisions related to the protection of human health and wildlife and to environmental quality; and interlocks with other relevant federal and provincial legislation concerning the safety of food and drugs and environmental protection. The prime considerations for product registration under the Act are human health, environmental health, and product efficacy.

Plant Protection Act (1990).   This law is intended to protect plant life and the agriculture and forestry sectors of the Canadian economy by preventing the importation, exportation, and spread of pests, and by providing for their control.

Wild Animal and Plant Protection and Regulation of International and Interprovincial Trade Act (1992).   This legislation controls the international and interprovincial transport and sale of certain wild species of animals and plants and their parts and derivatives. The Act pertains to Canadian and foreign species considered to be at risk. It also has provisions relating to the introduction of species potentially harmful to Canadian species and ecosystems.

International Accords, Agreements, Conventions and Protocols

Basel Convention on the Control of Transboundary Movements of Hazardous Wastes and Their Disposal (1989).   This agreement provides a framework for the regulation of the international trade in hazardous wastes. Signatory countries agree to transport hazardous wastes only to countries that have also signed the Convention (unless there are separate agreements that guarantee environmentally sound management), and not to send hazardous wastes to countries or regions that prohibit such imports.

Boundary Waters Treaty (1909).   This treaty deals with issues regarding inland waters shared by Canada and the United States. It prevents unilateral actions affecting water quantity and quality (such as the construction of dams and diversions) in waters whose natural flow area includes both countries.

Canada-US Agreement on Transboundary Movement of Hazardous Wastes (1986).   This binational agreement regulates the trade in hazardous wastes between Canada and the United States.

Convention on Biological Diversity (1992).   This agreement provides an international framework for the conservation of biological diversity, the sustainable use of its components, and the fair and equitable sharing of benefits arising out of the utilization of genetic resources.

Convention on Great Lakes Fisheries (1955).   This treaty between Canada and the United States is intended to conserve fish stocks in the Great Lakes and their tributary waters. The treaty is implemented by the binational Great Lakes Fishery Commission.

Convention on International Trade in Endangered Species of Wild Fauna and Flora (CITES) (1973).   This international agreement governs the trade in endangered species and their parts, in order to prevent their extinction.

Kyoto Protocol (1998) and the United Nations Framework Convention on Climate Change (1990).   These international agreements govern the emissions of substances that affect Earth's greenhouse effect.

London Convention on Ocean Dumping (1972). This international agreement regulates the disposal of waste materials into the oceans.

Migratory Birds Convention (1917). This treaty between Canada and the United States provides protection for migratory birds. The Act has provisions for the protection and management of migratory bird species, including the unlicensed possession of migratory birds or their products, and the establishment of sanctuaries.

Montreal Protocol on Substances that Deplete the Ozone Layer (1987). This international agreement governs the manufacturing, trade, and use of substances that deplete the stratospheric ozone layer.

North American Agreement on Environmental Cooperation (1994). This is an agreement between Canada, Mexico, and the United States that creates a framework to conserve, protect, and enhance the North American environment through co-operation and effective enforcement of environmental laws. This Agreement is a supplemental to the North American Free Trade Agreement (1994).

Appendix C
Detailed Data Tables

TABLE C.1	Population Growth in Selected Countries

COUNTRY	POPULATION (MILLIONS)				INTERVAL GROWTH RATE (%/Y)		
	1950	2004	2025	2050	1985-90	1995-2000	2005-10
RAPIDLY GROWING POPULATION							
Afghanistan	9	29	50	82	0.3	2.9	2.4
Bangladesh	42	141	205	280	2.0	1.7	1.6
Dem. Rep. of Congo	12	58	105	181	3.3	2.8	3.0
Egypt	22	73	103	127	2.5	1.9	1.6
Ethiopia	18	72	118	173	3.1	2.5	3.0
Iran	17	67	85	96	3.8	1.7	2.4
Iraq	5	26	42	58	3.3	2.8	2.6
Kenya	6	32	40	50	3.3	2.0	2.4
Madagascar	4	18	33	66	3.4	3.0	3.0
Nigeria	33	137	206	307	2.9	2.4	2.6
Pakistan	40	159	229	295	3.3	2.8	2.4
Tanzania	8	36	52	74	3.1	2.3	2.6
DECLINING RATE OF POPULATION GROWTH							
Brazil	54	179	211	221	1.8	1.2	1.1
China	555	1300	1476	1437	1.5	0.9	0.7
India	358	1087	1363	1678	2.1	1.6	1.3
Indonesia	79	219	276	309	1.8	1.5	1.1
Mexico	28	106	132	150	2.0	1.6	1.2
Philippines	21	84	118	147	2.1	2.0	1.6
Thailand	20	64	70	73	1.7	0.8	0.6
RELATIVELY SLOW RATE OF POPULATION GROWTH							
Australia	8	20	24	26	1.5	1.0	1.0
Canada	*14*	*32*	*36*	*37*	*1.4*	*1.0*	*0.7*
Korea, Dem. People's Rep. (North)	9	23	25	25	1.5	1.6	0.9
Korea, Rep. (South)	20	48	51	44	1.0	0.9	0.6
New Zealand	2	4	5	5	1.0	1.1	
South Africa	14	47	45	42	2.3	1.6	2.0
Sri Lanka	8	20	22	22	1.2	1.0	1.1
United States	158	294	349	420	1.0	0.8	0.8
RELATIVELY STABLE POPULATION							
Cuba	6	11	12	11	1.0	0.4	0.3
France	42	60	63	64	0.6	0.4	0.1
Germany	68	83	82	75	0.4	0.1	-0.1
Italy	47	58	58	52	0.1	0.0	-0.3
Japan	84	128	121	101	0.4	0.2	0.0
Sweden	7	9	10	11	0.5	0.3	0.2
United Kingdom	51	60	64	65	0.3	0.2	0.1
Russia	102	144	137	119	0.7	-0.2	-0.4

Sources: Data from World Resources Institute (1998, 2005) and Population Reference Bureau (2004)

| TABLE C.2 | Demographic Data for Selected Countries |

Note that birth rate minus death rate is equal to the intrinsic rate of population change. A difference of +10 units is equal to a 1% increase per year. Fertility rate is the number of children born to an average woman over her lifetime. Life expectancy is the average number of years lived, from birth.

COUNTRY	BIRTH RATE (BIRTHS/1000)		DEATH RATE (DEATHS/1000)		FERTILITY RATE (BIRTHS/WOMAN)		LIFE EXPECTANCY (YEARS)	
	1975-80	2004	1975-80	2004	1975-80	2004	1975-80	2004
RAPIDLY GROWING POPULATION								
Afghanistan	51	48	26	21	7.2	6.8	40	43
Bangladesh	47	30	21	9	6.7	3.3	47	60
Dem. Rep. of Congo	48	46	19	15	6.5	6.8	48	49
Egypt	39	26	16	6	5.3	3.2	54	68
Ethiopia	49	41	23	18	6.8	5.9	42	46
Iran	45	18	15	6	6.5	2.5	59	69
Iraq	42	36	15	9	6.6	5.0	61	60
Kenya	54	38	17	15	8.1	5.0	53	51
Madagascar	47	43	19	12	6.6	5.8	50	55
Malawi	57	51	24	21	7.6	6.6	43	44
Nigeria	47	42	20	13	6.5	5.7	45	52
Pakistan	47	34	18	10	7.0	4.8	53	61
Tanzania	48	40	19	17	6.8	5.3	49	45
RELATIVELY SLOW RATE OF POPULATION GROWTH								
Australia	16	13	9	7	2.1	1.7	73	80
Brazil	33	20	10	7	4.3	2.2	62	71
Canada	*15*	*11*	*7*	*7*	*1.8*	*1.5*	*74*	*79*
China	22	12	9	6	3.3	1.7	65	71
India	35	25	16	8	4.8	3.1	53	62
Indonesia	35	22	17	6	4.7	2.6	53	68
Korea, Rep. (South)	24	10	5	5	2.9	1.2	65	77
Mexico	37	25	9	5	5.3	2.8	65	75
New Zealand	17	14	8	7	2.2	2.0	72	78
Philippines	36	26	10	6	5.0	3.5	60	70
Sri Lanka	29	19	8	6	3.8	2.0	67	72
Thailand	32	14	9	7	4.3	1.7	61	71
South Africa	37	24	14	13	5.1	2.8	56	53
United States	15	14	9	8	1.8	2.0	73	77
RELATIVELY STABLE POPULATION								
Cuba	17	11	7	7	2.1	1.6	73	76
France	14	13	11	9	1.9	1.9	74	79
Germany	10	9	12	10	1.5	1.3	73	78
Italy	13	10	10	10	1.9	1.3	74	80
Japan	15	9	7	8	1.8	1.3	76	82
Sweden	12	11	10	10	1.7	1.7	75	80
United Kingdom	12	12	12	10	1.7	1.7	73	78
Russian Federation	16	10	9	17	1.9	1.4	67	65

Sources: Data from World Resources Institute (1998, 2005) and Population Reference Bureau (2004)

TABLE C.3	Age Structure of the Populations of Selected Countries in 2004		

COUNTRY	PERCENTAGE OF POPULATION		
	<15	15–65	>65
RAPIDLY GROWING POPULATION			
Afghanistan	45	53	2
Bangladesh	37	60	3
Dem. Rep. of Congo	48	49	3
Egypt	36	59	5
Ethiopia	44	53	3
Iran	33	62	5
Iraq	42	55	3
Kenya	44	52	4
Madagascar	45	52	3
Malawi	46	51	3
Nigeria	44	53	3
Pakistan	42	54	4
Tanzania	45	52	3
RELATIVELY SLOW RATE OF POPULATION GROWTH			
Australia	20	67	13
Brazil	30	64	6
Canada	18	69	13
China	22	71	7
India	36	60	4
Indonesia	30	65	5
Korea (South)	20	72	8
Mexico	35	60	5
New Zealand	22	66	12
Philippines	37	59	4
South Africa	34	62	4
Sri Lanka	27	66	7
Thailand	23	70	7
United States	21	67	12
RELATIVELY STABLE POPULATION			
Cuba	21	69	10
France	19	65	16
Germany	15	68	17
Italy	14	67	19
Japan	14	67	19
Sweden	17	65	18
United Kingdom	19	65	16
Russia	16	71	13

Source: Data from Population Reference Bureau (2004)

TABLE C.4	Energy Consumption in Selected Countries in 2001

"Commercial energy" is produced by public and/or private utilities and in large industrial facilities, or is used as hydrocarbon fuels. National energy consumption reflects the size of a country's economy and its population, while per-capita data allow a comparison of the lifestyles of average citizens. % renewable refers to the energy consumption derived from renewable sources. Countries are arranged within groups in order of total per capita energy use.

COUNTRY	TOTAL ENERGY USE		USE OF COMMERCIAL ENERGY		
	NATIONAL (10^{18} joule)	PER CAPITA (10^9 J)	NATIONAL (10^{18} J)	PER CAPITA (10^9 J)	% RENEWABLE
RELATIVELY UNDEVELOPED COUNTRIES					
Afghanistan	0.08	4	0.02	1	75
Bangladesh	0.75	6	0.44	3	42
Ethiopia	0.76	12	0.05	1	94
Sudan	0.64	21	0.08	1	88
Dem. Rep. Congo	0.61	12	0.06	1	95
Tanzania	0.63	18	0.04	1	95
Nigeria	3.65	33	0.62	5	83
Pakistan	2.51	18	1.52	10	42
India	20.1	20	11.8	11	43
Kenya	0.62	20	0.12	4	83
Philippines	1.71	23	0.93	11	47
Indonesia	5.70	27	3.65	17	37
RAPIDLY DEVELOPING COUNTRIES					
China	45.6	36	36.7	28	21
Brazil	7.52	45	5.59	31	38
Thailand	2.95	48	2.36	37	20
Iran	4.34	63	4.30	64	1
Mexico	6.24	64	5.69	54	11
Malaysia	1.79	82	1.68	73	3
DEVELOPED COUNTRIES					
Italy	7.08	123	6.73	116	5
South Korea	7.59	164	7.50	156	1
Japan	22.0	170	21.2	166	3
United Kingdom	9.64	163	9.49	158	1
France	10.7	181	10.2	169	6
Germany	14.1	172	13.9	168	1
Russia	25.2	173	25.0	171	3
Sweden	2.14	242	1.79	199	28
Australia	4.52	239	4.29	215	6
Canada	*10.1*	*332*	*9.77*	*305*	*17*
United States	95.0	339	90.9	309	5

Source: Data from World Resources Institute (2005)

TABLE C.5	Water Use in Selected Countries in 2000			

COUNTRY	PER CAPITA USE (metre^3/year)	SECTORAL USE (%)		
		DOMESTIC	INDUSTRY	AGRICULTURE
ARID, LESS-DEVELOPED COUNTRIES				
Tanzania	57	6	1	93
Ethiopia	40	1	6	93
Kenya	52	30	6	64
Somalia	378	1	<1	99
India	635	8	6	86
Egypt	1013	8	14	78
Sudan	1187	3	<1	97
Iran	1097	7	2	91
Afghanistan	1087	2	<1	98
Pakistan	1187	2	2	96
HUMID, LESS-DEVELOPED COUNTRIES				
Republic of Congo	11	59	31	10
Nigeria	70	21	10	69
Indonesia	391	8	1	91
Bangladesh	576	3	1	96
Brazil	345	20	18	62
South Korea	397	36	16	48
Vietnam	914	8	24	68
China	494	7	25	68
Philippines	377	17	9	74
Malaysia	392	17	21	62
Mexico	791	17	6	77
DEVELOPED COUNTRIES				
United Kingdom	163	22	75	3
Germany	572	12	68	20
Japan	696	20	18	62
France	674	16	74	10
Russia	527	19	63	18
Italy	771	18	37	45
Australia	1250	15	10	75
Canada	*1494*	*20*	*68*	*12*
United States	1682	13	46	41

Source: Data from World Resources Institute (2005)

TABLE C.6	Agricultural Land in Selected Countries

Land areas are for 2002; % refers to percent change of 2002 relative to 1992. (A positive value indicates an increase.)

COUNTRY CROPLAND PASTURE				
	(10^6 hectare)	%	(10^6 ha)	%
RELATIVELY UNDEVELOPED COUNTRIES				
Bangladesh	8.4	1	0.6	0
Dem. Rep. Congo	7.8	−2	15	0
Ethiopia	10.7	1	20	0
Kenya	5.2	9	21.3	0
Nigeria	33.0	2	39.2	−2
Sudan	16.7	27	117.0	6
Tanzania	5.1	13	35.0	0
Viet Nam	8.9	33	0.6	94
RAPIDLY DEVELOPING COUNTRIES				
Argentina	35.0	15	142.0	0
Brazil	66.6	13	197.0	5
China	154.0	16	400.0	0
India	170.1	1	11.1	−5
Indonesia	29.6	−12	11.2	−5
Iran	17.1	−8	44.0	0
Iraq	6.1	9	4.0	0
Malaysia	7.4	−3	0.3	2
Mexico	27.3	4	80.0	2
Pakistan	22.1	5	5.0	0
Philippines	10.7	8	1.5	17
Thailand	19.4	−6	0.8	0
DEVELOPED COUNTRIES				
Australia	48.6	3	398.4	−5
Canada	*45.9*	*1*	*29.0*	*0*
France	19.6	2	10.0	−10
Germany	12.0	3	5.0	−5
Italy	11.1	−5	4.4	1
Japan	4.8	−8	0.4	−4
Russia	125.3	−6	91.4	4
United Kingdom	5.8	−12	11.1	−3
United States	178.1	−4	233.8	−2

Source: Data from World Resources Institute (2005)

TABLE C.7	International Trade of Agricultural Produce

Net trade is calculated as exports minus imports. Positive numbers are net exports, while negative numbers are net imports. Cereals include maize, rice, sorghum, and wheat. Pulses are seeds in the legume family, such as peas, beans, and soybean. Data are for 2002 and are in 10^6 tonnes per year.

	CEREALS			PULSES		
	EXPORTS	**IMPORTS**	**NET TRADE**	**EXPORTS**	**IMPORTS**	**NET TRADE**
REGION						
North America	96.9	9.6	87.3	1.97	0.35	1.62
Europe	89.6	61.0	28.6	2.06	2.02	0.04
Oceania	19.4	1.2	18.2	1.08	0.03	1.05
South America	21.1	19.0	2.1	0.34	0.48	−0.14
Africa (sub-Sahara)	1.9	21.0	−19.1	0.21	0.33	−0.12
Central America	0.9	22.9	−22.0	0.22	0.41	−0.19
Asia	46.3	80.0	−33.7	2.35	3.96	−1.59
Middle East & North Africa	3.5	58.3	−54.8	0.49	1.02	−0.53
LEADING EXPORTERS						
United States	82.2	5.0	77.2	0.55	0.26	0.29
France	27.9	1.6	26.3	0.99	0.12	0.87
Argentina	19.6	<0.1	19.5	0.25	0.01	0.24
Australia	19.3	0.1	19.2	1.06	0.01	1.05
Canada	*14.7*	*4.6*	*10.1*	*1.41*	*0.01*	*1.40*
India	9.6	<0.1	9.5	0.15	2.17	−1.02
China	15.0	9.4	7.6	0.86	0.20	0.66
Germany	11.0	3.6	7.4	0.10	0.08	0.02
Thailand	7.5	1.0	6.5	0.04	0.01	0.03
United Kingdom	3.0	3.5	−0.5	0.30	0.18	0.12
MAJOR IMPORTERS						
Russia	13.5	1.4	12.1	0.15	0.01	0.14
Ukraine	12.2	0.1	11.1	0.18	<0.01	0.18
Iran	1.8	6.6	−4.8	0.16	<0.01	0.16
Brazil	0.3	7.8	−7.5	0.02	0.12	−0.10
Indonesia	<0.1	7.9	−7.8	0.01	0.04	−0.03
Italy	1.8	9.8	−8.0	0.02	0.43	−0.41
Algeria	0.1	8.6	−8.5	0.00	0.17	−0.17
Egypt	0.5	10.3	−9.8	0.03	0.41	−0.38
Korea, Rep. (South)	<0.1	13.4	−13.4	0.00	0.06	−0.06
Mexico	0.6	14.1	−13.5	0.16	0.15	0.01
Japan	0.5	26.6	−26.1	0.00	0.16	−0.16

Source: Data from World Resources Institute (2005)

TABLE C.8	Indexes of Agricultural Production in Selected Countries

Data are for 2003; % refers to percent change between 1993 and 2003. The 1999–2001 value of the index of food production was assigned a value of 100, and the 2003 data are relative to that number.

COUNTRY	CEREALS			ROOTS & TUBERS			INDEX OF FOOD PRODUCTION	
	PRODUCTION (10⁶ tonne)	YIELD (tonne/hectare·year)	%	PRODUCTIVITY (10⁶ tonne)	YIELD (tonne/hectare·year)	%	TOTAL	PER CAPITA
RELATIVELY UNDEVELOPED COUNTRIES								
Bangladesh	39.7	3.3	25	3.7	13.2	26	104	98
Dem. Rep. Congo	1.5	0.8	−4	15.7	8.0	4	97	90
Egypt	19.2	7.3	21	2.3	24.0	11	102	96
Kenya	2.8	1.5	−2	2.0	7.8	−1	99	94
Nigeria	24.5	1.1	−8	66.6	8.4	−20	105	97
Sudan	6.4	0.6	28	0.2	2.6	−6	109	102
Tanzania	4.1	1.4	16	8.1	6.7	−16	103	97
Viet Nam	37.5	4.5	33	7.1	11.4	54	118	114
RAPIDLY DEVELOPING COUNTRIES								
Argentina	34.2	3.2	13	2.6	21.6	−47	103	100
Brazil	66.4	3.4	42	26.0	13.8	13	119	114
China	377.5	4.8	6	172.5	17.0	0	112	109
India	232.1	2.4	13	31.1	18.2	19	103	98
Indonesia	63.0	4.2	8	21.7	13.8	17	108	104
Iran	21.1	2.4	48	3.6	19.7	−5	101	107
Malaysia	2.2	3.2	5	0.5	9.2	−5	115	108
Mexico	30.6	2.8	7	1.9	24.9	42	105	101
Pakistan	27.8	2.3	18	2.4	16.4	24	105	98
Philippines	18.5	2.8	27	2.2	6.3	−8	112	106
Thailand	31.7	2.6	16	18.7	17.4	24	106	103
DEVELOPED COUNTRIES								
Australia	38.0	2.1	5	1.3	30.5	4	99	96
Canada	*50.2*	*2.7*	*4*	*5.3*	*29.4*	*11*	*98*	*95*
France	54.9	6.1	−6	6.2	39.9	12	94	93
Germany	39.5	5.8	1	9.8	34.5	−12	93	93
Italy	18.1	4.4	−10	1.6	21.6	−4	91	91
Japan	10.8	5.4	23	4.6	27.8	15	96	96
Korea (South)	6.5	5.8	5	1.0	25.1	14	94	92
Russia	65.5	1.8	9	36.8	11.6	9	109	110
United Kingdom	21.5	6.0	9	5.9	40.8	−2	98	97
United States	348.6	7.0	40	21.6	39.6	12	101	98

Source: Data from World Resources Institute (2005)

TABLE C.9	Intensity of Agricultural Management in Selected Countries (2001 Data)				
	CROPLAND				
COUNTRY	AREA (10^6 hectare)	PER CAPITA (ha/person)	% IRRIGATED	FERTILIZER USE (kilogram/hectare of cropland)	NUMBER OF TRACTORS (ha/tractor)
RELATIVELY UNDEVELOPED COUNTRIES					
Bangladesh	9.4	0.063	47	171	1534
Dem. Rep. Congo	6.2	0.11	0	1	3243
Egypt	2.4	0.033	100	392	37
Kenya	4.1	0.13	1	29	411
Nigeria	3.7	0.029	1	7	1040
Sudan	7.5	0.22	12	5	1405
Tanzania	22.2	0.59	3	2	651
Viet Nam	10.7	0.13	41	226	52
RAPIDLY DEVELOPING COUNTRIES					
Argentina	36.8	0.95	6	25	117
Brazil	58.4	0.32	4	103	83
China	175.3	0.13	40	228	140
India	174.2	0.16	35	102	111
Indonesia	36.3	0.16	16	79	480
Iran	5.5	0.078	39	80	70
Malaysia	7.0	0.28	5	149	175
Mexico	19.4	0.18	24	68	84
Pakistan	23.8	0.15	82	133	69
Philippines	12.3	0.15	15	73	926
Thailand	27.2	0.43	26	92	83
DEVELOPED COUNTRIES					
Australia	49.0	2.46	5	47	161
Canada	29.0	0.91	2	54	63
France	40.0	0.66	11	213	16
Germany	26.9	0.33	4	217	12
Italy	14.0	0.24	24	128	7
Japan	4.4	0.034	55	282	2
Korea (South)	1.8	0.037	61	379	9
Russian Federation	152.6	1.07	4	13	160
United Kingdom	15.7	0.26	2	328	11
United States	114.7	0.39	13	111	37

Source: Data from World Resources Institute (2004, 2005)

TABLE C.10	Forest Resources and Forestry Production in Selected Countries

Forest cover data are for 2000; deforestation is the change in natural forest between 1990 and 2000 (a positive value means the forest area increased); net deforestation is % loss of original cover of natural forest; harvesting data are for 2002; percent increase refers to the increase of total harvest between 1992 and 2002.

COUNTRY	DEFORESTATION			FOREST HARVESTING			
	FORESTS (10^6 hectare)	RATE (%/year)	NET (%)	TOTAL (10^6 metre^3/y)	FUEL (10^6 m^3/y)	INDUSTRIAL (10^6 m^3/y)	PERCENT INCREASE
RELATIVELY UNDEVELOPED COUNTRIES							
Angola	69.8	−1.7	84.7	4.2	3.3	1.1	25
Bangladesh	1.3	−14.2	92.1	24.5	27.8	0.7	−1
Dem. Rep. Congo	135.2	−3.8	83.6	70.6	67.3	3.7	33
Cameroon	23.9	−8.5	57.6	12.9	9.3	2.2	10
Congo	22.1	−0.8	32.2	2.6	1.2	1.4	8
Kenya	17.1	−5.2	81.5	22.0	20.0	2.2	11
Myanmar	34.4	−13.1	59.4	39.8	35.4	5.9	80
Nigeria	13.5	−22.8	89.3	71.2	60.1	11.5	11
Sudan	61.6	−13.5	n.d.	18.9	17.1	2.2	5
Tanzania	38.8	−2.3	90.9	23.4	21.1	2.3	8
Venezuela	49.5	−4.2	16.4	5.7	3.7	1.9	14
Viet Nam	9.8	−5.5	82.8	31.9	26.6	7.2	−1
Zambia	31.2	−21.4	29.9	8.1	7.2	1.0	5
RAPIDLY DEVELOPING COUNTRIES							
Argentina	34.8	−7.6	40.5	13.4	4.0	8.2	9
Brazil	543.9	−4.1	33.6	235.3	134.5	130.5	5
China	163.5	12.4	78.4	308.5	191.1	127.2	−2
India	64.1	0.6	79.5	344.0	300.6	27.9	5
Indonesia	105.0	−11.1	34.4	144.7	82.6	52.1	−19
Iran	7.3	0.0	96.6	1.8	0.3	1.6	36
Malaysia	19.3	−10.9	36.2	61.2	3.3	29.3	−1
Mexico	55.2	−10.3	36.6	48.3	37.9	11.3	7
Pakistan	2.4	−14.3	94.2	29.2	25.0	4.2	13
Philippines	5.8	−13.3	94.0	17.7	13.3	3.5	−8
Thailand	14.8	−7.1	77.8	24.6	20.3	8.8	−5
DEVELOPED COUNTRIES							
Australia	154.5	−1.8	35.7	27.7	7.1	30.3	13
Canada	*244.6*	*0.0*	*8.8*	*229.4*	*3.0*	*271.2*	*−1*
France	15.3	4.2	83.5	49.1	2.4	49.6	−13
Germany	10.7	0.0	73.7	56.2	4.6	68.4	2
Italy	10.0	3.0	79.6	13.4	4.6	10.4	−2
Japan	24.1	0.1	41.8	62.8	0.1	34.4	0
Russia	851.4	0.2	31.3	273.6	48.8	273.6	−5
South Korea	6.2	−0.8	83.5	8.7	2.5	10.3	−2
Sweden	27.1	0.0	14.0	68.6	5.9	68.6	3
United Kingdom	2.8	6.5	94.0	10.4	0.2	10.4	0
United States	226.0	1.7	39.8	615.3	73.1	615.3	−3

Source: Data from World Resources Institute (2005)

TABLE C.11   Fish Catches and Aquaculture in Selected Countries

Data are in 10^6 t/y, averaged for 1999–2001, with percent increase since 1989–91 given in parentheses. Countries are listed in order of decreasing catches of marine fish.

| | | | AQUACULTURE | |
| | | | MARINE | FRESHWATER |
COUNTRY	MARINE FISH	FRESHWATER FISH	FISH	FISH
Global	85.16 (6)	8.67 (38)	14.24 (184)	21.38 (166)
China	14.70 (3)	2.22 (148)	9.36 (356)	15.11 (242)
Peru	8.99 (31)	0.04 (0)	<0.01	<0.01
Japan	4.90 (−48)	0.07 (−36)	0.71 (2)	0.10
United States	4.78 (−10)	0.03 (−29)	0.12 (15)	0.24 (−27)
Russia	3.65 (−49)	0.27 (−25)	<0.01	0.08 (−57)
Chile	4.38 (−25)	<0.01	0.41 (46)	<0.01
Indonesia	3.78 (65)	0.31 (7)	0.15 (28)	0.65 (75)
India	2.78 (23)	0.88 (79)	0.15 (27)	2.00 (91)
Thailand	2.71 (13)	0.21 (57)	0.45 (125)	0.27 (161)
Norway	2.67 (48)	<0.01 (0)	0.49 (247)	<0.01
Korea, Rep. (South)	1.97 (−15)	<0.01	0.29 (−21)	0.01 (−14)
Iceland	1.90 (41)	<0.01	<0.01	<0.01
Philippines	1.76 (10)	0.15 (−37)	0.08 (1)	0.31 (3)
Denmark	1.43 (−16)	<0.01	<0.01	0.04 (9)
Malaysia	1.26 (37)	<0.01	0.11 (130)	0.05 (360)
Mexico	1.21 (−5)	0.10 (−22)	0.04 (550)	0.02 (31)
Spain	1.09 (−4)	<0.01	0.28 (44)	<0.01
Canada	*0.99 (−35)*	*0.04 (−13)*	*0.04 (237)*	*0.01 (160)*
Argentina	0.94 (71)	0.03 (170)	<0.01	<0.01
United Kingdom	0.77 (−4)	<0.01	0.15 (284)	0.01 (−13)
South Africa	0.66 (3)	<0.01	<0.01	<0.01
France	0.60 (−2)	<0.01	0.21 (5)	0.05 (20)

Source: Data from World Resources Institute (2005)

TABLE C.12	Catches of Selected Species of Marine Fish in Canada

Catch biomass is in 10^3 tonne/year, and economic value of the catch is in millions of dollars.

SPECIES	ATLANTIC COAST				PACIFIC COAST				CANADA			
	QUANTITY		VALUE		QUANTITY		VALUE		QUANTITY		VALUE	
	1992	2003	1992	2003	1992	2003	1992	2003	1992	2003	1992	2003
GROUNDFISH												
Cod	186.5	22.7	152.0	33.5	10.1	0.8	5.5	1.1	196.6	23.5	157.5	34.6
Hake	38.3	15.1	17.7	10.6	97.2	69.1	16.0	17.4	135.5	84.2	33.8	27.9
Redfish	98.0	15.2	27.7	8.9	24.8	21.7	18.3	29.9	122.7	36.9	46.0	38.8
Flatfishes	48.5	23.0	29.2	19.1	7.8	6.1	5.7	7.1	56.3	29.1	35.0	26.2
Pollock	34.1	8.6	24.0	6.9	3.0	5.4	0.9	2.6	37.1	13.9	24.9	9.5
Turbot	22.5	15.8	19.3	26.1	3.5	4.3	0.9	1.3	26.0	20.2	20.1	27.4
Haddock	21.9	15.8	30.2	28.3	–	0.0	–	0.0	21.9	15.8	30.2	28.3
Total	461.3	129.1	313.8	156.9	159.7	127.8	93.8	127.2	621.0	256.9	407.6	284.1
PELAGIC AND OTHER FINFISH												
Herring	215.4	201.3	27.8	42.9	34.5	28.8	46.4	40.4	249.9	230.1	74.2	83.3
Salmon	0.3	0.0	1.1	0.0	64.9	38.4	161.3	48.1	65.1	38.4	162.4	48.1
Capelin	31.0	23.5	4.8	3.1	–	0.0	–	0.0	31.0	23.5	4.8	3.1
Mackerel	25.9	44.8	7.1	15.2	0.01	0.01	0.18	<0.01	25.9	44.8	7.1	15.2
Total	282.6	277.3	67.3	86.6	103.3	70.2	210.3	94.0	385.9	347.5	277.6	180.5
SHELLFISH												
Scallop	91.3	93.5	99.6	124.3	–	0.04	–	0.2	91.3	93.5	99.6	124.5
Shrimp	39.2	141.7	81.2	239.9	3.5	3.4	10.9	33.2	42.7	145.2	92.1	273.1
Lobster	41.6	48.5	314.0	646.7	–	0.0	–	0.0	41.6	48.5	314.0	646.7
Crab	37.9	97.4	58.8	525.4	2.5	7.1	9.3	38.2	40.4	114.4	68.2	563.5
Clams	16.8	39.2	15.4	35.9	4.0	12.8	18.6	38.0	20.8	42.0	34.0	73.9
Oysters	0.6	3.0	1.0	7.6	5.0	70.0	4.0	0.0	5.6	3.0	5.0	7.6
Total	233.1	443.8	575.0	1591.7	28.9	19.7	57.0	120.3	261.9	463.5	631.9	1712.0
TOTAL MARINE	977.0	850.3	966.5	1835.1	291.8	217.6	369.3	341.5	1269	1068	1336	2176.6
TOTAL INLAND	–	–	–	–	–	–	–	–	64.9		63.0	

Sources: Data from Statistics Canada (2000) and Fisheries and Oceans Canada (2005)

TABLE C.13   Per Capita and National Emissions of Carbon Dioxide by Selected Countries

Data are per capita emissions in units of tonnes of CO_2 per person·year in 2001, or total national emissions in 2001 (10^9 t/y). Percent increase since 1990 is given in parentheses.

COUNTRY	EMISSIONS (t/y PER CAPITA)	NATIONAL EMISSIONS (10^9 t/y)
GLOBAL AVERAGE	3.9 (−2)	24,000 (14)
Qatar	55.6 (87)	33 (137)
United Arab Emirates	26.5 (29)	76 (82)
United States	19.8 (4)	5702 (18)
Australia	18.1 (18)	350 (35)
Canada	16.5 (9)	512 (22)
Saudi Arabia	11.8 (34)	269 (85)
Czech Rep.	12.0 (−18)	123 (−18)
Germany	10.5 (−14)	865 (−11)
Russia	10.5 (−27)	1521 (−29)
United Kingdom	9.4 (−6)	553 (−2)
Korea, Rep. (South)	9.4 (71)	443 (88)
Japan	9.3 (9)	1184 (13)
Norway	7.9 (18)	35 (25)
Poland	7.7 (−16)	298 (−15)
Iran	7.4 (131)	498 (174)
Italy	7.4 (6)	426 (7)
France	6.3 (−2)	375 (3)
Venezuela	4.9 (−9)	121 (15)
Sweden	5.5 (−4)	49 (0)
Mexico	3.7 (3)	372 (24)
Thailand	2.7 (80)	166 (104)
China	2.4 (14)	3085 (27)
Brazil	1.8 (29)	313 (50)
Indonesia	1.4 (75)	300 (106)
India	1.0 (43)	1033 (74)
Philippines	0.9 (50)	69 (89)
Guatemala	0.8 (100)	9 (168)
Viet Nam	0.6 (100)	48 (139)
Nigeria	0.5 (25)	59 (71)
Kenya	0.3 (0)	9 (32)
Bangladesh	0.2 (100)	28 (158)
Cameroon	0.2 (0)	3 (32)
Haiti	0.2 (100)	2 (134)
Sudan	0.2 (0)	6 (29)
Zambia	0.2 (−33)	2 (−14)
Tanzania	0.1 (0)	4 (36)

Source: Data from World Resources Institute (2005)

TABLE C.14	Petroleum Production, Reserves, and Use in Selected Countries in 2003			
COUNTRY	PRODUCTION OF PETROLEUM (10^6 tonne/year)	PROVEN RESERVES OF PETROLEUM (10^9 t)	CONSUMPTION OF PETROLEUM (10^6 t/y)	NET EXPORTS/ IMPORTS (10^6 t/y)
Saudi Arabia	475 (10)	36.1	67 (29)	408
Russia	421 (19)	7.5	125 (−34)	296
United States	341 (−14)	4.2	914 (16)	−573
Iran	190 (3)	1.8	54 (6)	136
Mexico	189 (23)	2.3	83 (13)	106
China	169 (18)	3.2	275 (96)	−106
Norway	153 (34)	1.4	10 (1)	143
Venezuela	153 (14)	11.2	24 (23)	129
Canada	*141 (39)*	*2.3*	*96 (25)*	*45*
United Arab Emirates	118 (3)	13.0	15 (−13)	103
Kuwait	110 (14)	13.3	14 (174)	96
Nigeria	107 (10)	4.6	11 (−18)	96
United Kingdom	106 (5)	0.6	77 (−9)	29
Algeria	79 (37)	1.4	10 (10)	69
Brazil	77 (133)	1.5	84 (34)	−7
Libya	70 (6)	0.4	19 (23)	51
Iraq	66 (196)	15.5	27 (8)	39
Indonesia	58 (−25)	0.6	54 (43)	4
Kazakhstan	52 (127)	1.2	10 (−39)	42
Angola	44 (76)	1.2	2 (18)	42
Qatar	41 (95)	2.0	2 (125)	39
Oman	41 (5)	0.8	4 (6)	37
Argentina	39 (25)	0.5	18 (−11)	21
Malaysia	39 (25)	0.5	24 (53)	15
Egypt	37 (−23)	0.5	26 (20)	11
India	37 (27)	0.7	113 (81)	−76
Azerbaijan	16 (50)	1.0	4 (−46)	12
Italy	5 (−18)	0.1	92 (−1)	−87
Germany	3	<0.1	125 (−8)	−125
France	3	<0.1	94 (3)	−94
Japan	<1	<0.1	249 (−1)	−248
Korea South	<1	<0.1	106 (33)	−106
World	3697 (16)	156.7	3637 (16)	60

Sources: British Petroleum (2004) and World Resources Institute (2005)

Glossary of Key Terms

accuracy: The degree to which a measurement or observation reflects the actual value. Compare with **precision**.

acid rain: The wet deposition only of acidifying substances from the atmosphere. See also **acidifying deposition**.

acid shock: An event of relatively acidic surface water that can occur in the springtime when the snowpack melts quickly but the ground is still frozen.

acid sulphate soil: Acidic soil conditions caused when certain wetlands are drained and sulphide compounds become oxidized.

acid-mine drainage: Acidic water and soil conditions that develop when sulphide minerals become exposed to the atmosphere, allowing them to be oxidized by *Thiobacillus* bacteria.

acid-neutralizing capacity: The quantitative ability of water to neutralize inputs of acid without becoming acidified. See also **buffering capacity**.

acidification: An increasing concentration of hydrogen ions (H^+) in soil or water.

acidifying deposition: Both the wet and dry deposition of acidifying substances from the atmosphere.

acute toxicity: Toxicity associated with short-term exposures to chemicals in concentrations high enough to cause biochemical or anatomical damages, even death. Compare with **chronic toxicity**.

aerobic: Refers to an environment in which oxygen (O_2) is readily available. Compare with **anaerobic**.

aesthetic pollution: Substantially a matter of cultural values, this commonly involves images that are displeasing to many (but not necessarily all) people.

afforestation: Establishment of a forest where one did not recently occur, as when trees are planted on agricultural land.

age-class structure: The proportions of individuals in various age classes of a population.

agricultural site capability: See **site capability**.

agroecosystem: An ecosystem used for the production of food.

agroforestry: The cultivation of trees in plantations, typically using relatively intensive management practices.

algal bloom: An event of high phytoplankton biomass.

ammonification: Oxidation of the organically bound nitrogen of dead biomass into ammonium (NH_4^+).

anaerobic: Refers to an environment in which oxygen (O_2) is not readily available. Compare with **aerobic**.

angiosperm: Flowering plants that have their ovules enclosed within a specialized membrane and their seeds within a seedcoat. Compare with **gymnosperm**.

anthropocentric world view: This considers humans as being more worthy than other species and uniquely disconnected from nature. The importance and worth of everything is considered in terms of the implications for human welfare. Compare with **biocentric world view** and **ecocentric world view**.

anthropogenic: Occurring as a result of a human influence.

applied ecology: The application of ecological principles to deal with economic and environmental problems.

aquaculture: The cultivation of fish and other aquatic species.

aquifer: Groundwater resources in some defined area.

artificial selection: The deliberate breeding of species to enhance traits that are viewed as desirable by humans.

artificial wetland: An engineered wetland, usually constructed to treat sewage or other organic wastes.

aspect: The direction in which a slope faces.

assimilation efficiency: In an animal, the percentage of the energy content of ingested food that is absorbed across the gut wall. In plants, the percentage of solar visible light that is fixed by photosynthesis. The term may also be used to refer to the percentage assimilation of ingested inorganic nutrients (such as nitrate or phosphate) by plants or animals, or of drugs by animals.

atmosphere: The gaseous envelope surrounding the Earth, held in place by gravity.

atmospheric inversion (temperature inversion): A relatively stable atmospheric condition in which cool air is trapped beneath a layer of warmer air.

atmospheric water: Water occurring in the atmosphere, in vapour, liquid, or solid forms.

autecology: The field within ecology that deals with the study of individuals and species. Compare with **synecology**.

autotroph: An organism that synthesizes its biochemical constituents using simple inorganic compounds and an external source of energy to drive the process. See also **primary producer**, **photoautotroph**, and **chemoautotroph**.

available concentration: The concentration of metals in an aqueous extract of soil, sediment, or rocks, simulating the amount available for organisms to take up from the environment. Compare with **total concentration**.

baby boom: A period of high fecundity during 1945–1965 that occurred because of social optimism after the Second World War.

binomial: Two latinized words that are used to name a species.

bioaccumulation (bioconcentration): The occurrence of chemicals in much higher concentrations in organisms than in the ambient environment. Compare with **food-web magnification**.

biocentric world view: This considers all species (and individuals) as having equal intrinsic value. Humans are not considered more important or worthy than any other species. Compare with **anthropocentric world view** and **ecocentric world view**.

bioconcentration: See **bioaccumulation**.

biodegradation: The breakdown of organic molecules into simpler compounds through the metabolic actions of microorganisms.

biodiversity: The richness of biological variation, including genetic variability as well as species and community richness.

biological control: Pest-control methods that depend on biological interactions, such as diseases, predators, or herbivores.

biological oxygen demand (BOD): The capacity of organic matter and other substances in water to consume oxygen during decomposition.

biomagnification: See **food-web magnification**.

biomass energy: The chemical potential energy of plant biomass, which can be combusted to provide thermal energy.

biome: A geographically extensive ecosystem, occurring throughout the world wherever environmental conditions are suitable.

biosphere: All life on Earth, plus their ecosystems and environments.

birth control: Methods used to control fertility and childbirth.

BOD: See **biological oxygen demand**.

bog: An infertile, acidic, unproductive wetland that develops in cool but wet climates. Compare with **fen**.

boreal coniferous forest: A northern forest dominated by coniferous trees, usually species of fir, larch, pine, or spruce. See also **boreal forest**.

boreal forest (taiga): An extensive biome occurring in environments with cold winters, short but warm growing seasons, and moist soils, and usually dominated by coniferous trees.

broad-spectrum pesticide: A pesticide that is toxic to other organisms as well as the pest.

browse: Broad-leaved shrubs that are eaten by herbivores such as hares and deer.

bryophyte: Simple plants that do not have vascular tissues nor a cuticle on their foliage.

buffering capacity: The ability of a solution to resist changes in pH as acid or base is added.

calorie: A standard unit of energy, defined as the amount of energy needed to raise the temperature of one gram of pure water from 15°C to 16°C. Compare with **joule**.

carbon credits: Actions that help reduce the atmospheric concentration of CO_2, such as fossil-fuel conservation and planting trees.

carnivore (secondary consumer): An animal that hunts and eats other animals.

carrying capacity: The abundance of a species that can be sustained without the habitat becoming degraded.

chaparral: A shrub-dominated ecosystem that occurs in south-temperate environments with winter rains and summer drought.

chemoautotroph: Microorganisms that harness some of the potential energy of certain inorganic chemicals (e.g., sulphides) to drive their fixation of energy through chemosynthesis. Compare with **photoautotroph**.

chemosynthesis: Autotrophic productivity that utilizes energy released during the oxidation of certain inorganic chemicals (such as sulphides) to drive biosynthesis. Compare with **photosynthesis**.

chromosome: Subcellular unit composed of DNA and containing the genetic information of eukaryotic organisms.

chronic toxicity: Toxicity associated with exposure to small or moderate concentrations of chemicals, sometimes over a long period of time. The damages may be biochemical or anatomical, and may include the development of a lethal disease, such as cancer. Compare with **acute toxicity**.

clear-cutting: The harvesting of all economically useful trees from an area at the same time.

climate: The prevailing, long-term, meteorological conditions of a place or region, including temperature, precipitation, wind speed, and other factors. Compare with **weather**.

climate change: Long-term changes in air, soil, or water temperature; precipitation regimes; wind speed; or other climate-related factors.

coal: An organic-rich, solid fossil fuel mined from sedimentary geological formations.

coarse woody debris: Logs lying on the forest floor.

commensalism: A symbiosis in which one of the species benefits from the interaction, while the other is not affected in either a positive or negative way.

commercial energy production: The use of solid, liquid, and gaseous fuels, plus all electricity. Does not include the use of traditional fuels. See also **total energy production** and **traditional fuels**.

commercial extinction: Depletion of a natural resource to below the abundance at which it can be profitably harvested.

common-property resource: A resource shared by all of society, not owned by any particular person or interest.

community: In ecology, this refers to populations of various species that are co-occurring at the same time and place.

community-replacing disturbance: A disturbance that results in the catastrophic destruction of an original community, and its replacement by another one. Compare with **microdisturbance**.

compaction: A decrease in the pore space of soil (or increased bulk density) caused by the passage of heavy machinery.

compartment: A reservoir of mass in a nutrient or material cycle.

competition: A biological interaction occurring when the demand for an ecological resource exceeds its limited supply, causing organisms to interfere with each other.

competitor: A species that is dominant in a habitat in which disturbance is rare and environmental stresses are unimportant, so competition is the major influence on evolution and community organization.

compost: Partially decomposed, well-humified organic material

composting: The processing of discarded organic material by encouraging decomposition processes under warm, moist, oxygen-rich conditions. The product, known as compost, is a useful fertilizer and soil conditioner.

conservation: Wise use of natural resources. Conservation of nonrenewable resources involves recycling and other means of efficient use. Conservation of renewable resources includes these means, in addition to ensuring that harvesting does not exceed the rate of regeneration of the stock.

contamination: The presence of potentially damaging chemicals in the environment, but at concentrations less than those required to cause toxicity or other ecological damages. Compare with **pollution**.

control (control treatment): An experimental treatment that was not manipulated, and is intended for comparison with manipulated treatments.

conventional economics: Economics as it is commonly practised, which includes not accounting for costs associated with ecological damages and resource depletion. Compare with **ecological economics**.

conversion: See **ecological conversion**.

core: Earth's massive interior, made up of hot molten metals.

Coriolis effect: An influence of Earth's west-to-east rotation, which makes winds in the Northern Hemisphere deflect to the right and those in the Southern Hemisphere to the left.

creationist: A person who rejects the theory of evolution in favour of a literal interpretation of Genesis, the first book of the Old Testament of the Bible. See also **scientific creationist**.

critical load: A threshold for pollutant inputs, below which it is thought ecological damages will not be caused.

crude oil: See **petroleum**.

crude oil washing (COW) method: A method of washing a tanker's oil-storage components with a spray of crude oil before the next cargo is loaded. This eliminates the use of wash-water and avoids an important cause of marine oil pollution.

crust: The outermost layer of Earth's sphere, overlying the lithosphere and composed mostly of crystalline rocks.

cultural eutrophication: Eutrophication caused by anthropogenic nutrient inputs, usually through sewage dumping or fertilizer runoff. See also **eutrophication**.

cultural evolution: Adaptive evolutionary change in human society, characterized by increasing sophistication in the methods, tools, and social organizations used to exploit the environment and other species. Compare with **evolution**.

decay: The decomposition or oxidation of dead biomass, mostly through the actions of microorganisms.

decomposer: See **detritivore**.

deductive logic: Logic in which initial assumptions are made and conclusions are then drawn from those assumptions. Compare with **inductive logic**.

deep drainage: Soil water that has drained to below the lower limits of plant roots.

deforestation: A permanent conversion of forest into some other kind of ecosystem, such as agriculture or urbanized land use.

demographic transition: A change in human population parameters from a condition of high birth and death rates to one of low birth and death rates.

denitrification: The microbial reduction of nitrate (NO_3^-) into gaseous N_2O or N_2.

desert: A temperate or tropical biome characterized by prolonged drought, usually receiving less than 25 cm of precipitation per year.

desertification: The increasing aridity of drylands; an environmental change that can make agriculture difficult or impossible.

detritivore: A heterotroph that feeds on dead organic matter.

developed countries: Relatively wealthy countries, whose average citizens have a healthy and materialistic lifestyle, more so than in less-developed countries.

development (economic development): An economic term that implies improving efficiency in the use of materials and energy in an economy, and progress toward a sustainable economic system. Compare with **economic growth**.

disturbance: An episode of destruction of some part of a community or ecosystem.

DNA: The biochemical deoxyribonucleic acid, the main constituent of the chromosomes of eukaryotic organisms.

domestication: The genetic, anatomic, and physiological modification of crops and other species from their wild, progenitor species, through the selective breeding of preferred races (or cultivars).

dose-response relationship: The quantitative relationship between different doses of a chemical and a biological or ecological response.

doubling time: The time it takes for something to increase by a factor of two (as in population growth).

drift: Movement of applied pesticide off the intended site of deposition through atmospheric or aquatic transport.

dry deposition: Atmospheric inputs of chemicals occurring in intervals between rainfall or snowfall. Compare with **wet deposition**.

dumping: The long-term disposal of disused material, for example, by placing solid waste into a sanitary landfill, or by discarding liquid waste into a waterbody.

earthquake: A trembling or movement of the earth, caused by a sudden release of geological stresses at some place within the crust.

ecocentric world view: This incorporates the biocentric world view but also stresses the importance of interdependent ecological functions, such as productivity and nutrient cycling. In addition, the connections among species within ecosystems are considered to be invaluable. Compare with **anthropocentric world view** and **biocentric world view**.

ecofeminism: A philosophical and political movement that applies feminist ideas to environmental concerns.

ecological conversion: A long-term change in the character of the ecosystem at some place, as when a natural forest is converted into an agricultural land use.

ecological economics: A type of economics that involves a full accounting of costs associated with ecological damages and resource depletion. Compare with **conventional economics**.

ecological footprint: The area of ecoscape (i.e., landscape and seascape) required to supply a human population with the necessary food, materials, energy, waste disposal, and other crucial goods and services.

ecological integrity (ecosystem health): A notion related to environmental quality, but focusing on changes in natural populations and ecosystems, rather than effects on humans and their economy. See also **environmental quality**.

ecological justice: A worldview in which all species (i.e., not just humans) have a right to equitable access to the necessities of life and happiness. See also **social justice**.

ecological pyramid: A model of the trophic structure of an ecosystem, organized with plant productivity on the bottom, that of herbivores above, and carnivores above the herbivores.

ecological service: An ecological function that is useful to humans and to ecosystem stability and integrity, such as nutrient cycling, productivity, and control of erosion.

ecological stress: See **stressors**.

ecological sustainability: See **ecologically sustainable development**.

ecologically sustainable development: This considers the human need for resources within an ecological context, and includes the need to sustain all species and all components of Earth's life-support system. Compare with **sustainable development**.

ecologically sustainable economic system: An economic system that operates without a net consumption of natural resources, and without endangering biodiversity or other ecological values. Ultimately, ecologically sustainable economic systems are supported by the wise use of renewable resources.

ecologically sustainable economy: An economy in which ecological goods and services are utilized in ways that do not compromise their future availability and do not endanger the survival of species or natural ecosystems.

ecology: The study of the relationships between organisms and their environment.

economic development: See **development**.

economic growth: A term that refers to an economy that is increasing in size over time, usually due to increases in both population and per capita resource use. Compare with **development**.

ecosystem: A general term used to describe one or more communities that are interacting with their environment as a defined unit. Ecosystems range from small units occurring in micro-habitats, to larger units such as landscapes and seascapes, and even the biosphere.

ecosystem approach: A holistic interpretation of the natural world that considers the web-like interconnections among the many components of ecosystems.

ecosystem health: See **ecological integrity**.

ecotoxicology: Study of the directly poisonous effects of chemicals in ecosystems, plus indirect effects such as changes in habitat or food abundance caused by toxic exposures. Compare with **toxicology** and **environmental toxicology**.

ecotype: A population specifically adapted to coping with locally stressful conditions, such as soil with high metal concentrations.

ecozone: The largest biophysical zones in the national ecological classification of Canada.

electromagnetic energy: Energy associated with photons, comprising an electromagnetic spectrum divided into components, including ultraviolet, visible, and infrared.

endangered: In Canada, this specifically refers to indigenous species threatened with imminent extinction or extirpation over all or a significant portion of their Canadian range.

endemic: An ecological term used to describe species with a local geographic distribution.

energy: The capacity of a body or system to accomplish work, and existing as electromagnetic, kinetic, and potential energies.

energy budget: An analysis of the rates of input and output of energy to a system, plus transformations of energy among its states, including changes in stored quantities.

energy production: See **total energy production**.

entropy: A physical attribute related to the degree of randomness of the distributions of matter and energy.

environmental citizenship: Actions taken by individuals and families to lessen their impacts on the environment.

environmental degradation: Refers to pollution, disturbance, resource depletion, lost biodiversity, and other kinds of environmental damage; usually refers to damage occurring accidentally or intentionally as a result of human activities (see also **anthropogenic**), but can also be caused by natural disasters or stressors.

environmental discrimination (environmental prejudice): Discrimination against any defined group that results in them suffering a disproportionate amount of degradation or pollution of their living or work environment. See also **environmental racism**.

environmental ethics: These deal with the responsibilities of the present human generation to ensure continued access to adequate resources and livelihoods for future generations of people and other species.

environmental impact assessment (EIA): A process used to identify and evaluate the potential consequences of proposed actions or policies for environmental quality. See also **socioeconomic impact assessment**.

environmental indicators: Relatively simple measurements that are sensitive to changes in the intensity of stressors, and are considered to represent complex aspects of environmental quality.

environmental literacy: The degree to which people have a well-informed understanding of environmental issues.

environmental monitoring: Repeated measurements of indicators related to the inorganic environment or to ecosystem structure and function.

environmental quality: A notion related to the amounts of toxic chemicals and other stressors in the environment, to the frequency and intensity of disturbances, and to their effects on humans, other species, ecosystems, and economies.

environmental racism: Discrimination against a group of people defined by racial attributes, which results in them suffering a disproportionate amount of degradation or pollution of their living or work environment. See also **environmental discrimination**.

environmental reporting: Communication of information about changes in environmental quality to interest groups and the general public.

environmental risk: A hazard or probability of suffering damage or misfortune because of exposure to some environmental circumstance.

environmental risk assessment: A quantitative evaluation of the risks associated with an environmental hazard.

environmental science: An interdisciplinary branch of science that investigates questions related to the human population, resources, and damages caused by pollution and disturbance.

environmental security: The protection of people and the public interest from environmental risks, particularly those associated with anthropogenic activities and accidents, but may also include natural dangers.

environmental stressor: See **stressor**.

environmental toxicology: The study of environmental factors influencing exposures of organisms to potentially toxic levels of chemicals. Compare with **toxicology** and **ecotoxicology**.

environmental values: Perceptions of the worth of environmental components, divided into two broad classes: utilitarian and intrinsic.

environmentalist: Anyone with a significant involvement with environmental issues, usually in an advocacy sense.

erosion: The physical removal of rocks and soil through the combined actions of flowing water, wind, ice, and gravity.

estuary: A coastal, semi-enclosed ecosystem that is open to the sea and has habitats transitional between marine and freshwater conditions.

ethics: The perception of right and wrong. The proper behaviour of people toward each other and toward other species and nature.

eukaryote: Organisms in which the cells have an organized, membrane-bound nucleus containing the genetic material. Compare with **prokaryote**.

eutrophic: Pertains to waters that are highly productive because they contain a rich supply of nutrients. Compare with **oligotrophic** and **mesotrophic**.

eutrophication: Increased primary productivity of an aquatic ecosystem, resulting from nutrient inputs.

evaporation: The change of state of water from a liquid or solid to a gas.

evapotranspiration: Evaporation of water from a landscape. See also **transpiration**.

evolution: Genetically based changes in populations of organisms, occurring over successive generations.

experiment: A controlled test or investigation designed to provide evidence for, or preferably against, a hypothesis about the natural or physical world.

exposure: In ecotoxicology, this refers to the interaction of organisms with an environmental stressor at a particular place and time.

exposure assessment: An investigation of the means by which organisms may encounter a potentially toxic level of a chemical or other environmental stressor.

extinct (extinction): A condition in which a species or other taxon no longer occurs anywhere on Earth.

extirpated (extirpation): A condition in which a species or other taxon no longer occurs in some place or region, but still survives elsewhere.

fact: An event or thing known to have happened, to exist, or to be true. See also **hypothesis**.

fen: A wetland that develops in cool and wet climates, but is less acidic and more productive than a bog because it has a better nutrient supply. Compare with **bog**.

first law of thermodynamics: A physical principle stating that energy can undergo transformations among its various states, but it is never created or destroyed; thus, the energy content of the universe remains constant. See also **second law of thermodynamics**.

First Nations: The Aboriginal people(s) originally living in some place. This term is often used in reference to the original inhabitants of the Americas, prior to the colonization of those regions by Europeans, and their modern descendants.

fission reaction: Nuclear reaction involving the splitting of heavier, radioactive atoms into lighter ones, with the release of large quantities of energy.

fitness: The proportional contribution of an individual to the progeny of its population.

flow-through system: A system with an input and an output of energy or mass, plus temporary storage of any difference.

flux: A movement of mass or energy between compartments of a material or energy cycle.

food chain: A hierarchical model of feeding relationships among species in an ecosystem.

food web: A complex model of feeding relationships, describing the connections among all food chains within an ecosystem.

food-web magnification (food-web accumulation, food-web concentration): The tendency for top predators in a food web to have the highest residues of certain chemicals, especially organochlorines. Compare with **bioaccumulation**.

forest floor: Litter and other organic debris lying on top of the mineral soil of a forest.

forestry: The harvesting of trees and management of post-harvest succession to foster the regeneration of another forest.

fossil fuel: Organic-rich geological materials, such as coal, petroleum, and natural gas.

frontier world view: This asserts that humans have a right to exploit nature by consuming natural resources in boundless quantities. See also **sustainability world view** and **spaceship world view**.

fungicide: A pesticide used to protect crop plants and animals from fungi that cause diseases or other damages.

fusion reaction: Nuclear reaction involving the combining of light nuclei, such as those of hydrogen, to make heavier ones, with the release of large quantities of energy. Fusion reactions occur under conditions of intense temperature and pressure, such as within stars and in hydrogen bombs.

Gaia hypothesis: A notion that envisions Earth's species and ecosystems as a "superorganism" that attempts to optimize environmental conditions toward enhancing its own health and survival.

gene: A region of a chromosome, containing a length of DNA that behaves as a particulate unit in inheritance and determines the development of a specific trait.

genotype: The genetic complement of an individual organism. See also **phenotype**.

geography: The study of the features of the surface of the Earth, including topography, landforms, soil, climate, and vegetation, as well as the intersections of these with the economic interests of humans.

geothermal energy: Heat in Earth's crust, which can sometimes be used to provide energy for heating or generation of electricity.

glaciation: An extensive environmental change associated with an extended period of global climatic cooling and characterized by advancing ice sheets.

glacier: A persistent sheet of ice, occurring in the Arctic and Antarctic and at high altitude on mountains.

greater protected area: A protected area plus its immediately surrounding area, co-managed to sustain populations of indigenous species and natural communities.

green manure: Living plant biomass that is grown and then incorporated into the soil by tillage.

green revolution: Intensive agricultural systems involving the cultivation of improved crop varieties in monoculture, and increased use of mechanization, fertilizers, and pesticides.

greenhouse effect: The physical process by which infrared-absorbing gases (such as CO_2) in Earth's atmosphere help to keep the planet warm.

greenhouse gas: See **radiatively active gas**.

gross domestic product (GDP): The total annual value of all goods and services produced domestically within a country. GDP is equivalent to gross national product minus net investment income from foreign countries. See also **gross national product (GNP)**.

gross national product (GNP): The total annual value of all goods and services produced domestically by a country, including net foreign investment income. See also **gross domestic product (GDP)**.

gross primary production (GPP): The fixation of energy by primary producers within an ecosystem. See also **respiration**, **net primary production**, and **autotroph**.

groundwater: Water stored underground in soil and rocks.

groundwater drainage: The drainage of water to storage places in the ground, occurring under the influence of gravity.

growth: Refers to an economy or economic sector that is increasing in size over time. Compare with **development**.

gymnosperm: Vascular plants such as conifers, which have naked ovules not enclosed within a specialized membrane, and seeds without a seedcoat. Compare with **angiosperm**.

habitat: The place or "home" where a plant or animal lives, including the specific environmental factors required for its survival.

hazardous waste: Wastes that are flammable, explosive, toxic, or otherwise dangerous. See also **toxic waste**.

herbicide: A pesticide used to kill weeds. See also **weed**.

herbivore (or **primary consumer**): An animal that feeds on plants.

heterotroph: An organism that utilizes living or dead biomass as food.

hidden injury: A reduction in plant productivity caused by exposure to pollutants, but not accompanied by symptoms of acute tissue damages.

hormone: A biochemical produced in an endocrine gland (and transported by the blood) that functions to regulate a metabolic process. Some chemicals in food may mimic the function of hormones produced naturally in the body.

humidity: The actual concentration of water in the atmosphere, usually measured in mg/m^3. Compare with **relative humidity**.

humus: Amorphous, partially decomposed organic matter. An important and persistent type of soil organic matter, it is very important in soil tilth and fertility.

hydrocarbons: Molecules composed of hydrogen and carbon only.

hydroelectric energy: Electricity generated using the kinetic energy.

hydrologic (water) cycle: The movement between, and storage of water in, various compartments of the hydrosphere. See also **hydrosphere**.

hydrosphere: The parts of the planet that contain water, including the oceans, atmosphere, on land, in surface waterbodies, underground, and in organisms.

hyperaccumulator: A species that bioaccumulates metals or other chemicals to extremely high concentrations in their tissues. See also **bioaccumulation**.

hypereutrophic: Extremely eutrophic waters; usually considered to be a degraded ecological condition. See also **eutrophic**.

hypersensitivity: An extreme sensitivity to exposure to some environmental factor, resulting in a biological response such as asthma, disease, or even death. It may be expressed at the species or individual level, and it involves responses at relatively low intensities of exposure that the great majority of species or individuals could tolerate.

hypothesis: A proposed explanation for the occurrence or causes of natural phenomena. Scientists formulate hypotheses as statements, and test them through experiments and other forms of research. See also **fact**.

igneous rock: Rock such as basalt and granite, formed by cooling of molten magma.

impoundment: An area of formerly terrestrial landscape that is flooded behind a dam.

incineration: The combustion of mixed solid wastes to reduce the amount of organic material present.

indicator: See **environmental indicator**

indigenous culture: A human culture existing in a place or region prior to its invasion, or other significant influence, by a foreign culture.

individual organism: A genetically and physically discrete living entity.

inductive logic: Logic in which conclusions are objectively developed from the accumulating evidence of experience and the results of experiments. See also **deductive logic**.

inequitable: Not equitable or fair.

inhumane: Reflecting a lack of pity or compassion; most commonly refers to the cruel treatment by humans of other animals.

insecticide: A pesticide used to kill insects that are considered pests. See also **pesticide** and **pest**.

integrated forest management: Forest management plans that accommodate the need to harvest timber from landscapes, while also sustaining other values, such as hunted wildlife, outdoor recreation, and biodiversity.

integrated pest management (IPM): The use of a variety of complementary tactics toward pest control, with the aim of having fewer environmental and health risks.

interdisciplinary: Encompassing a wide diversity of kinds of knowledge.

intrinsic population change: Population change due only to the balance of birth and death rates.

intrinsic value: Value that exists regardless of any direct or indirect value in terms of the needs or welfare of humans.

invasive: Refers to non-native species that survive in wild habitats and possibly aggressively out-compete native species or cause other kinds of ecological damage.

inversion: see **atmospheric inversion**.

invertebrate: Any animal that lacks an internal skeleton, and in particular a backbone.

joule: A standard unit of energy, defined as the energy needed to accelerate 1 kg of mass at 1 m/s^2 for a distance of 1 metre. Compare with **calorie**.

K-selected: Refers to organisms that produce relatively small numbers of large offspring. A great deal of parental investment is made in each progeny, which helps to ensure their establishment and survival. Compare with **r-selected**.

keystone species: A dominant species in a community, usually a predator, with an influence on structure and function that is highly disproportionate to its biomass.

kinetic energy: Energy associated with motion, including mechanical and thermal types.

landscape: The spatial integration of ecological communities over a large terrestrial area.

landscape ecology: Study of the spatial characteristics and temporal dynamics of communities over large areas of land (landscapes) or water (seascapes).

laws of thermodynamics: Physical principles that govern all transformations of energy. See also **first law of thermodynamics** and **second law of thermodynamics**.

leaching: The movement of dissolved substances through the soil with percolating rainwater.

lentic ecosystem: A freshwater ecosystem characterized by non-flowing water, such as a pond or lake. Compare with **lotic ecosystem**.

less developed countries: Countries that are relatively poor and have not progressed far in terms of industrial and socioeconomic development.

life form: A grouping of organisms on the basis of their common morphological and physiological characteristics, regardless of their evolutionary relatedness.

life index (production life): The known reserves of a resource divided by its current rate of production.

liming: Treatment of a waterbody or soil to reduce acidity, usually by adding calcium carbonate or calcium hydroxide.

limiting factor: An environmental factor that is the primary restriction on the productivity of autotrophs in an ecosystem. See also **Principle of Limiting Factors**.

lithification: A geological process in which materials are aggregated, densified, and cemented into new sedimentary rocks.

lithosphere: An approximately 80-km thick region of rigid, relatively light rocks that surround Earth's plastic mantle.

load-on-top (LOT) method: A process used in ocean-going petroleum tankers to separate and contain most oily residues before ballast waters are discharged to the marine environment.

lotic ecosystem: A freshwater ecosystem characterized by flowing water, such as a stream or river. Compare with **lentic ecosystem**.

LRTAP: The long-range transport of atmospheric pollutants.

macroclimate: Climatic conditions affecting an extensive area. Compare with **microclimate**.

macroevolution: The evolution of species or higher taxonomic groups, such as genera, families, or classes. Compare with **microevolution**.

management system: A variety of management practices used in a coordinated manner.

manipulative experiment: An experiment involving controlled alterations of factors hypothesized to influence phenomena, conducted to investigate whether predicted responses will occur, thereby uncovering causal relationships. See also **experiment** and **natural experiment**.

mantle: A less-dense region that encloses Earth's core, and composed of minerals in a hot, plastic state known as magma.

marsh: A productive wetland, typically dominated by species of monocotyledonous angiosperm plants that grow as tall as several metres above the water surface.

mass extinction: An event of synchronous extinction of many species, occurring over a relatively short period of time. May be caused by natural or anthropogenic forces.

maximum sustainable yield (MSY): The largest amount of harvesting that can occur without degrading the productivity of the stock.

mechanization: The use of specialized machinery to perform work, instead of the labour of people or animals.

megacity: A large city, sometimes defined as having a population greater than 8 million people.

mesosphere: The layer of the atmosphere extending beyond the stratosphere to about 75 km above the surface of the Earth. See also **stratosphere**.

mesotrophic: Pertains to aquatic ecosystems of moderate productivity, intermediate to eutrophic and oligotrophic waters. Compare with **eutrophic** and **oligotrophic**.

metal: Any relatively heavy element that in its pure state shares electrons among atoms, and has useful properties such as malleability, high conductivity of electricity and heat, and tensile strength.

metamorphic rock: Rock formed from igneous or sedimentary rocks that have changed in structure under the influences of geological heat and pressure.

meteorite: An extraterrestrial rock-like object; very rarely, one may intersect with Earth's orbit and impact the planet.

microclimate: Climatic conditions on a local scale. Compare with **macroclimate**.

microdisturbance: Local disruptions that affect small areas within an otherwise intact community. Compare with **community-replacing disturbance**.

microevolution: Relatively subtle evolutionary changes occurring within a population or species, sometimes within only a few generations, and at most leading to the evolution of races, varieties, or subspecies. Compare with **macroevolution**.

mitigation: An action that repairs or offsets environmental damages to some degree.

monoculture: The cultivation of only one species while attempting to exclude others from the agroecosystem.

montane forest: A conifer-dominated forest occurring below the alpine zone on mountains.

MSY: See **maximum sustainable yield**.

mutagen: A chemical or physical agent (e.g., ultraviolet radiation) that is capable of inducing genetic mutations.

mutualism (mutualistic symbiosis): A symbiosis in which both partners benefit.

natural experiment: An experiment conducted by observing variations of phenomena in nature, and then developing explanations for these through analysis of potential causal mechanisms. See also **experiment** and **manipulative experiment**.

natural gas: A gaseous, hydrocarbon-rich mixture mined from certain geological formations.

natural population change: A change in population that is due only to the difference in birth and death rates, and not to immigration or emigration.

natural selection: A mechanism of evolution, favouring individuals that, for genetically based reasons, are better adapted to coping with environmental opportunities and constraints. These more fit individuals have an improved probability of leaving descendants, ultimately leading to genetically based changes in populations, or evolution.

net ecosystem productivity: The amount of ecosystem-level productivity that remains after respiration is subtracted from gross productivity.

net primary production (NPP): Primary production that remains as biomass after primary producers have accounted for their respiratory needs. See also **respiration** and **gross primary production**.

niche: The role of a species within its community.

nitrification: The bacterial oxidation of ammonium (NH_4^+) to nitrate (NO_3^-).

nitrogen fixation: The oxidation of nitrogen gas (N_2) to ammonia (NH_3) or nitric oxide (NO).

noise pollution: When the level of ambient sound becomes distracting to the normal activities of people. At a higher intensity it can cause hearing impairment.

non-governmental organizations: Organizations that operate at arm's length from government, either to pursue advocacy or to undertake environmental, public health, or social actions.

non-renewable resource (non-renewable natural resource): A resource present on Earth in finite quantities, so as it is used, its future stocks are diminished. Examples are metals and fossil fuels. Compare with **renewable resources**.

non-target damage: Damage caused by a pesticide to non-target organisms. See also **broad-spectrum pesticide** and **non-target organism**.

non-target organism: Organisms that are not pests, but which may be affected by a pesticide treatment. See also **broad-spectrum pesticide** and **non-target damage**.

nuclear fuel: Unstable isotopes of uranium (^{235}U) and plutonium (^{239}Pu) that decay through fission, releasing large amounts of energy that can be used to generate electricity.

null hypothesis: A hypothesis that seeks to disprove a hypothesis.

nutrient: Any chemical required for the proper metabolism of organisms.

nutrient budget: A quantitative estimate of the rates of nutrient input and output for an ecosystem, as well as the quantities present and transferred within the system.

nutrient capital: The amount of nutrients present in a site in soil, living vegetation, and dead organic matter.

nutrient cycling: Transfers and chemical transformations of nutrients in ecosystems, including recycling through decomposition.

ocean: The largest hydrological compartment, accounting for about 97% of all water on Earth.

old-growth forest: A late-successional forest characterized by the presence of old trees, an uneven-aged population structure, and a complex physical structure.

oligotrophic: Pertains to aquatic ecosystems that are highly unproductive because of a sparse supply of nutrients. Compare with **eutrophic** and **mesotrophic**.

omnivore: An animal that feeds on both plant and animal materials.

organic agriculture: Systems by which crops are grown using natural methods of maintaining soil fertility, and pest-control methods that do not involve synthetic pesticides.

orographic precipitation: Precipitation associated with hilly or mountainous terrain that forces moisture-laden air to rise in altitude and become cooler, causing water vapour to condense into droplets that precipitate as rain or snow.

outer space: Regions beyond the atmosphere of Earth.

over-harvesting (over-exploitation): Unsustainable harvesting of a potentially renewable resource, leading to a decline of its stocks.

oxidizing smog: An event of air pollution rich in ozone, peroxy acetyl nitrate, and other oxidant gases.

paradigm: A pattern or model; a collection of assumptions, concepts, practices, and values that constitutes a way of viewing reality, especially for an intellectual community that shares them.

parameter: One or more constants that determine the form of a mathematical equation. In the linear equation $Y = aX + b$, a and b are parameters, and Y and X are variables. See also **variable**.

parasitism: A biological relationship involving one species obtaining nourishment from a host, usually without causing its death.

persistence: The nature of chemicals, especially pesticides, to remain in the environment before eventually being degraded by microorganisms or physical agents such as sunlight and heat.

pest: Any organism judged to be significantly interfering with some human purpose.

pesticide: A substance used to poison pests. See also **pest, fungicide**, **herbicide**, and **insecticide**.

pesticide treadmill: The inherent reliance of modern agriculture and public-health programs on pesticides, often in increasing quantities, to deal with pest problems.

petroleum (crude oil): A fluid, hydrocarbon-rich mixture mined from certain geological formations.

phenotype: The expressed characteristics of an individual organism, due to genetic and environmental influences on the expression of its specific genetic information. See also **genotype**.

phenotypic plasticity: The variable expression of genetic information of an individual, depending on environmental influences during development.

photoautotroph: Plants and algae that use sunlight to drive their fixation of energy through photosynthesis. See also **chemoautotroph** and **photosynthesis**.

photochemical air pollutants: Ozone, peroxy acetyl nitrate, and other strongly oxidizing gases that form in the atmosphere through complex reactions involving sunlight, hydrocarbons, oxides of nitrogen, and other chemicals.

photosynthesis: Autotrophic productivity that utilizes visible electromagnetic energy (such as sunlight) to drive biosynthesis.

phytoplankton: Microscopic, photosynthetic bacteria and algae that live suspended in the water of lakes and oceans.

plantation: In forestry, these are tree-farms managed for high productivity of wood fibre.

point source: A location where large quantities of pollutants are emitted into the environment, such as a smokestack or sewer outfall.

political ecology: This integrates the concerns of ecology and political economy to consider the dynamic tensions between natural and anthropogenic change, and also the consideration of damage from both natural and anthropogenic perspectives; the latter includes the broad range of concerns from individual people to all of society.

pollution: The exposure of organisms to chemicals or energy in quantities that exceed their tolerance, causing toxicity or other ecological damages. Compare with **contamination**.

population: In ecology, this refers to individuals of the same species that occur together in time and space.

potential energy: The stored ability to perform work, capable of being transformed into electromagnetic or kinetic energies. Potential energy is associated with gravity, chemicals, compressed gases, electrical potential, magnetism, and the nuclear structure of matter.

potentially renewable natural resource: An alternate phrase for renewable natural resource, highlighting the fact that these can be overexploited, and thereby treated as if they were nonrenewable resources. See also **renewable resource**.

ppb (part per billion): A unit of concentration, equivalent to 1 microgram per kilogram ($\mu g/kg$), or in aqueous solution, 1 μg per litre ($\mu g/L$).

ppm (part per million): A unit of concentration, equivalent to 1 milligram per kilogram (mg/kg), or in aqueous solution, 1 mg per litre (mg/L).

prairie: Grassland ecosystems occurring in temperate regions.

precautionary principle: An approach to environmental management, adopted by many countries at the 1992 Earth Summit, which essentially states that scientific uncertainty is not a sufficient reason to postpone control measures when there is a threat of harm to human health or the environment.

precipitation: Deposition of water from the atmosphere as liquid rain, or as solid snow or hail.

precision: The degree of repeatability of a measurement or observation. Compare with **accuracy**.

prevailing wind: Wind that blows in a dominant direction.

primary consumer: A herbivore, or a heterotrophic organism that feeds on plants or algae.

primary pollutants: Chemicals that are emitted into the environment. Compare with **secondary pollutants**.

primary producer: An autotrophic organism. Autotrophs are the biological foundation of ecological productivity. See also **primary production**.

primary production: Productivity by autotrophic organisms, such as plants or algae. Often measured as biomass accumulated over a unit of time, or sometimes by the amount of carbon fixed.

primary sewage treatment: The initial stage of sewage treatment, usually involving the filtering of larger particles from the sewage wastes, settling of suspended solids, and sometimes chlorination to kill pathogens.

Principle of Limiting Factors: A theory stating that ecological productivity (and some other functions) is controlled by whichever environmental factor is present in least supply relative to the demand.

production: An ecological term related to the total yield of biomass from some area or volume of habitat.

production life: See **life index**.

productivity: An ecological term for production standardized per unit area and time.

prokaryote: Microorganisms without an organized nucleus containing their genetic material. Compare with **eukaryote**.

protected area (reserve): Parks, ecological reserves, and other tracts set aside from intense development to conserve their natural ecological values. See also **greater protected area**.

r-selected: Refers to organisms that produce relatively large numbers of small offspring. Little parental investment is made in each offspring, but having large numbers of progeny helps ensure that some will establish and survive. Compare with **K-selected**.

radiatively active gases (RAGs): Atmospheric gases that efficiently absorb infrared radiation and then dissipate some of the thermal energy gain by reradiation.

reclamation: Actions undertaken to establish a self-maintaining ecosystem on degraded land, as when a disused industrial site is converted into a permanent cover of vegetation, such as a pasture. Compare with **restoration** and **remediation**.

recycling: The processing of discarded materials into useful products.

relative humidity: The atmospheric concentration of water, expressed as a percentage of the saturation value for that temperature.

remediation: Specific actions undertaken to deal with particular problems of environmental quality, such as the liming of acidic lakes and rivers to decrease their ecological damage. Compare with **restoration** and **reclamation**.

renewable resource (renewable natural resource): These can regenerate after harvesting, and potentially can be exploited forever. Examples are fresh water, trees, agricultural plants and livestock, and hunted animals. Compare with **nonrenewable resources**.

replacement fertility rate: The fertility rate that results in the numbers of progeny replacing their parents, with no change in size of the equilibrium population.

replication: The biochemical process occurring prior to cellular division, by which information encoded in DNA is copied to produce additional DNA with the same information.

reserve: (1) Known quantities of resources that can be economically recovered from the environment. (2) An alternative word for a protected area. See **protected area**.

residue: Lingering concentrations of pesticides and certain other chemicals in organisms and the environment.

resilience: The ability of a system to recover from disturbance.

resistance: The ability of a population or community to avoid displacement from some stage of ecological development as a result of disturbance or an intensification of environmental stress. Changes occur after thresholds of resistance to environmental stressors are exceeded.

respiration: Physiological processes needed to maintain organisms alive and healthy.

response: In ecotoxicology, this refers to biological or ecological changes caused by exposure to an environmental stressor.

restoration: Establishment of a self-maintaining facsimile of a natural ecosystem on degraded land, as when abandoned farmland is converted back to a native prairie or forest. Compare with **reclamation** and **remediation**.

restoration ecology: Activities undertaken by ecologists to repair ecological damage, such as establishing vegetation on degraded habitat, increasing the populations of endangered species, and decreasing the area of threatened ecosystems.

reuse: Finding another use for discarded materials, usually with relatively little modification.

risk: See **environmental risks**.

risk assessment: See **environmental risk assessment**.

RNA: The biochemical ribonucleic acid, which is important in translation of the genetic information of DNA into the synthesis of proteins. RNA also stores the genetic information of some viruses.

ruderal: Short-lived but highly fecund plants characteristic of frequently disturbed environments with abundant resources.

run-of-the-river: A hydroelectric development that directly harnesses the flow of a river to drive turbines, without creating a substantial impoundment for water storage.

salinization: The buildup of soluble salts in the soil surface, an important agricultural problem in drier regions.

sanitary landfill: A facility where municipal solid waste is dumped, compacted by heavy machines, and covered with a layer of clean dirt at the end of the day. Some have systems to contain and collect liquid effluent, known as leachate.

science: The systematic and quantitative study of the character and behaviour of the physical and biological world.

scientific creationist: A creationist who attempts to explain some of the discrepancies between his or her beliefs (which are based on a literal interpretation of Genesis) and scientific understanding of the origin and evolution of life. See also **creationist**.

scientific method: This begins with the identification of a question involving the structure or function of the natural world, usually using inductive logic. The question is interpreted in terms of a theory, and hypotheses are formulated and tested by experiments and observations of nature.

seascape: A spatial integration of ecological communities over a large marine area.

second law of thermodynamics: A physical principle stating that transformations of energy can occur spontaneously only under conditions in which there is an increase in the entropy (or randomness) of the universe. See also **first law of thermodynamics** and **entropy**.

secondary consumer: A carnivore that feeds on primary consumers (or herbivores).

secondary pollutants: Pollutants that are not emitted, but form in the environment by chemical reactions involving emitted chemicals. Compare with **primary pollutants**.

secondary sewage treatment: Treatment applied to the effluent of primary sewage treatment, usually involving the use of a biological technology to aerobically decompose organic wastes in an engineered environment. The resulting sludge can be used as a soil conditioner, incinerated, or dumped into a landfill. See also **primary sewage treatment**.

sedimentary rock: Rock formed from precipitated minerals such as calcite, or from lithified particles eroded from other rocks such as sandstone, shale, and conglomerates.

sedimentation: A process by which mass eroded from elsewhere settles to the bottom of rivers, lakes, or an ocean.

selection harvesting: Harvesting of only some trees from a stand, leaving others behind and the forest substantially intact.

sewage treatment: The use of physical filters, chemical treatment, and/or biological treatment to reduce pathogens, organic matter, and nutrients in waste waters containing sewage.

significant figures: The number of digits used when reporting data from analyses or calculations.

silvicultural management: The application of practices that increase tree productivity in a managed forest, such as planting seedlings, thinning trees, or applying herbicides to reduce the abundance of weeds.

silviculture: The branch of forestry concerned with the care and tending of trees.

site capability (site quality): The potential of land to sustain the productivity of agricultural crops.

slope: The angle of inclination of land, measured in degrees (0° implies a horizontal surface, while 90° is vertical).

sludge: A solid or semi-solid precipitate that settles from polluted water during treatment; sludge is produced during the treatment of sewage and also in pulp mills and some other industrial facilities. It may be disposed of in a landfill, but if organic, can be used as a beneficial soil amendment.

smog: An event of ground-level air pollution.

snag: A standing dead tree.

social justice: A worldview that calls for equality of consideration for all members of a society, regardless of colour, race, socioeconomic class, gender, age, or sexual preference. See also **ecological justice**.

socio-economic impact assessment: A process used to identify and evaluate the potential consequences of proposed actions or policies for sociological, economic, and related values. See also **environmental impact assessment**.

soil: A complex mixture of fragmented rock, organic matter, moisture, gases, and living organisms that covers almost all of Earth's terrestrial landscapes.

soil profile: The vertical stratification of soil on the basis of colour, texture, and chemical qualities.

solar energy: Electromagnetic energy radiated by the sun.

solar system: The sun, its nine orbiting planets, miscellaneous comets, meteors, and other local materials.

spaceship Earth: An image of Earth as viewed from space, which illustrates the fact that, except for sunlight, resources needed by humans are present only on that planet.

spaceship world view: This focuses on sustaining only those resources needed by humans and their economy, and it assumes that humans can exert a great degree of control over natural processes and can pilot "spaceship Earth." See also **frontier world view** and **sustainability world view**.

species: An aggregation of individuals and populations that can potentially interbreed and produce fertile offspring, and is reproductively isolated from other such groups.

speciesism: Discrimination (by humans) against other species purely on the basis that they are not human, especially as manifested by cruelty to or exploitation of animals, or merely by a lack of consideration of their interests.

species richness: The number of species in some area or place.

stratosphere: The upper atmosphere, extending above the troposphere from 8–17 km to as high as about 50 km. See also **troposphere**.

stress-tolerator: Long-lived plants adapted to habitats that are marginal in terms of climate, moisture, or nutrient supply, but are infrequently disturbed and therefore stable, such as tundra and desert.

stressor: An environmental factor that constrains the development and productivity of organisms or ecosystems.

succession: A process of community-level recovery following disturbance.

surface flow: Water that moves over the surface of the ground.

surface water: Water that occurs in glaciers, lakes, ponds, rivers, streams, and other surface bodies of water.

sustainability world view: This acknowledges that humans must have access to vital resources, but it asserts that the exploitation of resources should be governed by appropriate ecological, aesthetic, and moral values, and should not deplete the necessary resources. See also **frontier world view** and **spaceship world view**.

sustainable development: Progress toward an economic system based on the use of natural resources in a manner that does not deplete their stocks nor compromise their availability for use by future generations of humans. Compare with **ecologically sustainable development**.

sustainable economic system (sustainable economy): An economic system that can be maintained over time without any net consumption of natural resources.

swamp: A forested wetland, flooded seasonally or permanently.

symbiosis: An intimate relationship between different species. See also **mutualism**.

synecology: The study of relationships among species within communities. Compare with **autecology**.

system: A group or combination of regularly interacting and interdependent elements, which form a collective entity, but one that is more than the sum of its constituents. See also **ecosystem**.

taiga: See **boreal forest**.

tectonic force: Force associated with crustal movements and related geological processes that cause structural deformations of rocks and minerals.

temperate deciduous forest: A forest occurring in relatively moist, temperate climates with short and moderately cold winters and warm summers, and usually composed of a mixture of angiosperm tree species.

temperate grassland: Grass-dominated ecosystems occurring in temperate regions with an annual precipitation of 25–60 cm per year; sufficient to prevent desert from developing but insufficient to support forest.

temperate rainforest: A forest developing in a temperate climate in which winters are mild and precipitation is abundant year-round. Because wildfire is rare, old-growth forests may be common.

temperature inversion: See **atmospheric inversion**.

teratogen: A chemical or physical agent that induces a developmental abnormality (i.e., a birth defect) in an embryo or fetus.

tertiary sewage treatment: Treatment applied to the effluent of secondary sewage treatment, usually involving a system to remove phosphorus and/or nitrogen from waste waters. See also **primary sewage treatment** and **secondary sewage treatment**.

theory: A general term that refers to a set of scientific laws, rules, and explanations supported by a large body of experimental and observational evidence, all leading to robust, internally consistent conclusions.

thermal pollution: An increase in environmental temperature sufficient to result in ecological change.

thermosphere: The layer of the atmosphere extending beyond the mesosphere to 450 km or more above the surface of the Earth. See also **mesosphere**.

threatened: In Canada, this refers to any indigenous taxa likely to become endangered (in Canada) if factors affecting their vulnerability are not reversed.

tidal energy: Energy that develops in oceanic surface waters because of the gravitational attraction between Earth and the Moon, and can potentially be used to generate electricity.

tilth: The physical structure of soil, closely associated with the concentration of humified organic matter. Tilth is important in water- and nutrient-holding capacity of soil, and is generally beneficial to plant growth.

tolerance: In ecotoxicology, this refers to a genetically based ability of organisms or species to not suffer toxicity when exposed to chemicals or other stressors.

total concentration: The concentrations of metals in soil, sediment, rocks, or water, as determined after dissolving samples in a strongly acidic solution. Compare with **available concentration**.

total energy production: The use of commercial energy plus traditional fuels in an economy. See also **traditional fuels**.

toxic waste: Waste that is poisonous to humans, animals, or plants. See also **hazardous waste**.

toxicology: The science of the study of poisons, including their chemical nature and their effects on the physiology of organisms. Compare with **environmental toxicology** and **ecotoxicology**.

traditional fuels: The noncommercial use of wood, charcoal, animal dung, and other biomass fuels for subsistence purposes, primarily for cooking food and heating homes. See also **total energy production** and **commercial energy production**.

transcription: A biochemical process by which the information of double-stranded DNA is encoded on complementary single strands of RNA, which are used to synthesize specific proteins.

translation: A biochemical process occurring on organelles known as ribosomes, in which information encoded in messenger RNA is used to synthesize particular proteins.

transpiration: The evaporation of water from plants. Compare with **evapotranspiration**.

trophic structure: The organization of productivity in an ecosystem, including the roles of autotrophs, herbivores, carnivores, and detritivores.

troposphere: The lower atmosphere, extending to 8–17 km.

tundra: A treeless biome occurring in environments with long, cold winters and short, cool growing seasons.

urban forest: Urban areas having a substantial density and biomass of trees, although often most are non-native species.

urban planning: An active process of designing better ways of organizing the structure and function of cities, including an orderly siting of land uses and activities.

urbanization: The development of cities and towns on formerly agricultural or natural lands.

utilitarian value: The usefulness of a thing or function to humans.

valued ecosystem components (VECs): In environmental impact assessment, these are components of ecosystems perceived to be important to society as economically important resources, as rare or endangered species or communities, or for their cultural or aesthetic significance.

variable: A changeable factor believed to influence a natural phenomenon of interest or that can be manipulated during an experiment.

vascular plant: Relatively complex plants with specialized, tube-like vascular tissues in their stems for conducting water and nutrients.

VECs: See **valued ecosystem components**.

vector: Species of insects and ticks that transmit pathogens from alternate hosts to people or animals.

vertebrate: Animals with an internal skeleton, and in particular a backbone.

virgin field: In epidemiology, this is a population that is hypersensitive to one or more infectious diseases to which it has not been previously exposed.

volcano: An opening in Earth's crust from which magmic materials, such as lava, rock fragments, and gases, are ejected into the atmosphere or oceanic waters.

waste: Any discarded materials. See also **hazardous waste** and **toxic waste**.

waste management: The handling of discarded materials using various methods. See also **dumping, incineration, recycling, composting, reuse**, and **waste reduction**.

waste prevention: See **waste reduction**.

waste reduction: Practices intended to reduce the amount of waste that must be disposed of. Also known as **waste prevention**.

water cycle: See **hydrologic cycle**.

watershed: An area of land from which surface water and groundwater flow into a stream, river, or lake.

wave energy: The kinetic energy of oceanic waves, which can be harnessed using specially designed buoys to generate electricity.

weather: The short-term, day-to-day or instantaneous meteorological conditions at a place or region. Compare with **climate**.

weathering: Physical and chemical processes by which rocks and minerals are broken down by such environmental agents as rain, wind, temperature changes, and biological influences.

weed: An unwanted plant that interferes with some human purpose.

wet deposition: Atmospheric inputs of chemicals with rain and snow. Compare with **dry deposition**.

wetland: An ecosystem that develops in wet places and is intermediate between aquatic and terrestrial ecosystems. See also **bog, fen, marsh**, and **swamp**.

whole-lake experiment: The experimental manipulation of one or more environmental factors in an entire lake.

wind: An air mass moving in Earth's atmosphere.

wind energy: The kinetic energy of moving air masses, which can be tapped and utilized in various ways, including the generation of electricity.

work: In physics, work is defined as the result of a force being applied over a distance.

working hypothesis: A hypothesis being tested in a scientific experiment or another kind of research. See also **hypothesis** and **null hypothesis**.

zero population growth (ZPG): When the birth rate plus immigration equal the death rate plus emigration.

zooplankton: Tiny animals that occur in the water column of lakes and oceans.

Credits

Table 1.1: World Resources Institute, Washington D.C.

Canadian Focus 3.1: Adapted from *The Climates of Canada*, Environment Canada, 1991. Reproduced with the permission of the Minister of Public Works and Government Services Canada, 2005.

Figure 8.3: Ecological Stratification Working Group. A National Ecological Framework for Canada, http://www.ec.gc.ca/soer-ree/English/Framework/Nardesc/canada_e.cfm, Agriculture and Agri-food Canada, Research Branch, Centre for Land and Biological Resources Research, Environment Canada, State of the Environmental Directorate, Ecozones Analysis Branch, 1996. Reproduced with the permission of the Minister of Public Works and Government Services, 2005.

Figure 9.4: C.J. Krebs. *Ecocology: The Experimental Analysis of Distribution and Abundance*, Harper & Row, New York, 1985.

Figure 10.1: Population Reference Bureau.

Figure 10.3: World Resources Institute, Washington, DC.

Figure 10.4: Population Reference Bureau.

Figure 10.5: Population Reference Bureau.

Table 10.1: Population Reference Bureau.

Table 10.3: World Resources Institute, Washington D.C.

Table 10.4: Population Reference Bureau

Table 10.5: Population Reference Bureau

Table 10.6: Population Reference Bureau

Table 10.7: Population Reference Bureau

Table 10.8: The United Nations is the author of the original material.

In Detail 10.3: World Health organization, 1999. Global HIV/AIDS and STD Surveillance, www.who.int/emc-hiv/global_report/slides/index.html. With permission of the World Health Organization.

Table 11.1: Adapted in part from the Statistics Canada publication "Report on the Demographic Situation in Canada 1997: current demographic analysis," Catalogue 91-213, 1994; "Annual Demographic Statistics," Catalogue 91-213, revised edition 2004.

Figure 11.1: Adapted from the Statistics Canada publications "Postcensal Annual Estimates of Population by Martial Status, Age, Sex, and Components of Growth in Canada, provinces and Territories", catalogue 91-210, 1992, "Population Projections", 1993-2016, Catalogue 91-520 and "Annual Demographic Statistics", Catalogue 91-203, revised edition 2004.

Table 11.2: Adapted in part from the Statistics Canada publication "Annual Demographic Statistics, catalogue 91-213, revised edition 2004.

Table 11.3: Adapted from the Statistics Canada publication "Human Activity and the Environment", Catalogue 11-509, 1994.

Table 11.4: Adapted from the Statistics Canada publications "Postcensal Annual Estimates of Population by Martial Status, Age, Sex, and Components of Growth in Canada, Provinces, and Territories", Catalogue 91-210, 1992; "Quarterly Demographic Statistics", Catalogue 91-002, Fourth Quarter 1995, vol. 09 no. 4; from "Quarterly Demographic Statistics," Catalogue 91-002, Third Quarter 1998, vol. 12 no.3; and from the Statistics Canada publication "Annual Demographic Statistics," Catalogue 91-213, revised edition 2004.

Table 11.5: Adapted from the Statistics Canada publication "Annual Demographic Statistics," Catalogue 91-213, revised edition 2004.

Table 11.6: Adapted from the Statistics Canada publication "Annual Demographic Statistics", Catalogue 91-213, revised edition 2004.

Table 11.7: Adapted from the Statistics Canada publications "Historical Statistics of Canada", Catalogue 11-516, 1983; "Human Activity and the Environment", Catalogue 11-509, 1994; "A National Overview: Population and Dwelling Counts, 1996 Census," Catalogue 93-357, March 1997; and "A National Overview: Population and Dwelling Counts, 2001 Census," Catalogue 93-360, May 31, 2002.

Table 11.8: Adapted from the Statistics Canada publications "A National Overview: Population and Dwelling Counts, 1996 Census," Catalogue 93-357, March 1997; "A National Overview: Population and Dwelling Counts, 2001 Census," Catalogue 93-360, May 31, 2002; Statistics Canada publication "Annual Demographic Statistics," Catalogue 91-213, revised edition 2004.

Figure 11.2: Adapted from the Statistics Canada publication "Annual Demographic Statistics", Catalogue 91-213, revised edition 2004.

Figure 12.3: Adapted from the Statistics Canada CANSIM database http://cansim2.statcan.ca, Series V1992259.

Table 13.2: Canadian Minerals Yearbook, 2003 Review and Outlook. Natural Resources Canada, Minerals and Metals Sector, 2004. Reproduced with the permission of the Minister of Public Works and Government Services Canada, 2005.

Table 13.3: Mineral Production of Canada, by Province and Territory, http://mmsd1.mms.nrcan.gc.ca/mmsd/production/default_e.asp. Natural Resources Canada, Minerals and Metals Sector, Minerals and Mining Statistics Division, 2005.

Table 13.4: http://www.bp.com/genericsection.do?categoryId=92&contentId=7005893. BP Statistical Review of World Energy 2005.

Table 13.5: http://www.bp.com/genericsection.do?categoryId=92&contentId=7005893. BP Statistical Review of World Energy 2005.

Table 13.6: http://www.bp.com/genericsection.do?categoryId=92&contentId=7005893. BP Statistical Review of World Energy 2005.

Table 13.7: Adapted from the Statistics Canada CANSIM database, http://cansim2.statcan.ca, Tables 126-0001, 131-0001, and 303-0016.

Table 13.8: World Resources Institute, Washington D.C.

Table 13.9: Adapted in part from the Statistics Canada publication "Human activity and the environment," Catalogue 11-509, 1994, and the World Resources Institute, Washington, D.C.

Table 13.10: World Resources Institute, Washington D.C.

Figure 14.1: Adapted from the Statistics Canada publication "Human Activity and the Environment", Catalogue 16-201, 2004.

Table 14.1: World Resources Institute, Washington D.C.

Figure 14.2: Adapted from the Statistics Canada publication "Human Activity and the Environment", Catalogue 16-201, 1994.

Table 14.2: World Resources Institute, Washington D.C.

Table 14.3: Environment Canada, 2004.

Table 14.4: Adapted from the Statistics Canada publication "Human Activity and the Environment", Catalogue 11-509, 2000.

Table 14.5: Adapted from the Statistics Canada publication "Human Activity and the Environment", Catalogue 11-509, 2000.

Table 14.6: World Resources Institute, Washington D.C.

Table 14.7: World Resources Institute, Washington D.C.

Table 14.8: World Resources Institute, Washington D.C.

Table 14.9: World Resources Institute, Washington D.C.

Table 14.10: Adapted from the Statistics Canada publication "Human Activity and the Environment," Catalogue 11-509, 1994, and from Statistic Canada's E-STAT, http://estat.statcan.ca.

Table 14.11: Adapted from Statistic Canada's E-STAT, http://estat.statcan.ca.

Table 14.12: World Resources Institute, Washington D.C.

Table 14.13: Canadian Council of Forest Ministers.

Table 14.14: World Resources Institute, Washington D.C.

Table 14.15: Fisheries and Oceans Canada (1999). Reproduced with the permission of Her Majesty the Queen in Right of Canada, 2000.

Canadian Focus 14.4: Reproduced with the permission of Her Majesty the Queen in Right of Canada, 2005.

Table 15.4: Adapted from the Statistics Canada CANSIM database, http://cansim2.statcan.ca, Table 102-0540.

Table 17.2: World Resources Institute, Washington D.C.

Figure 17.6: *The State of Canada's climate: Monitoring variability and change.* SOE Report No. 95-1, Environment Canada, 1995. Reproduced with the permission of the Minister of Public Works and Government Services, 2005.

Figure 19.1: Ro, C. U. and R. J. Vet 2005. Analyzed Data Fields from the National Atmospheric Chemistry Database and Analysis Facility. Toronto, ON: Air Quality Research Branch, Environment Canada. www.msc-smc.ec.gc.ca/natchem. Reproduced with the permission of the Minister of Public Works and Government Services Canada, 2005.

Figure 19.3: Reproduced with permission of Environment Canada.

Figure 19.7: Reproduced with permission of Environment Canada.

Table 20.2: The State of Canada's Environment, from http://www.ec.gc.ca. Reproduced with the permission of the Minister of Public Works and Government Services, 2003. Neilson, M.S., L'Italien, V. Glumac, D. Williams, and P. Bertram, 1994. Nutrients and Trends and System Response in *State of the Lakes Ecosystem Conference* (SOLEC), 1994. Ottawa: Environment Canada.

Figure 20.2: "Phytoplankton Density in Lake Erie," Edsall, T. and M. Charlton. 1997. *Nearshore Waters of the Great Lakes.* Environment Canada.

Figure 20.3: "Large scale impacts of hydroelectric development. Environmental Reviews, 5:27-54. Reproduced with permission of NRC Research Press.

Figure 20.4: "Large scale impacts of hydroelectric development. Environmental Reviews, 5:27-54. Reproduced with permission of NRC Research Press.

Table 21.1: http://www.bp.com/genericsection.do?categoryId=92& contentId=7005893 BP Statistical Review of World Energy 2005.

Figure 22.2: Modified from Kettela (1983) with permission.

Table 22.4: *Toxic contaminants in the environment: persistent organochlorines*, National Environmental Indicator Series, SOE Bulletin No. 91-1. Environment Canada, 1993. Reproduced with the permission of the minister of Public Works and Government Services, 2003.

Table 24.1: Adapted from the Statistics Canada CANSIM database, http://cansim2.statcan.ca, Tables 001-0010 and 011-0014.

Table 24.2: Reproduced with the permission of the Minister of Public Works and Government Services, 2005.

Figure 24.2: The Health of our Soil: Toward Sustainable Agriculture in Canada, Agriculture and Agri-food Canada, 1995. Reproduced with the permission of the Minister of Public Works and Government Services, 2003.

Figure 24.3: The Health of our Soil: Toward Sustainable Agriculture in Canada, Agriculture and Agri-food Canada, 1995. Reproduced with the permission of the Minister of Public Works and Government Services, 2003.

Figure 25.1: Greenhouse Gas Emissions from Urban Transportation: Backgrounder. Prepared by IBI Group and Management Technology Services under the directions of the NRTEE Task Force on Sustainable Transportation. Ottawa: National Round Table on the Environment and the Economy, 1998. Reproduced with permission of the Minister of Public Works and Government Services, 2005.

Figure 25.2: *Air quality trends in Canadian cities*, 1979-1992, http://www.etcentre.org/organization/aaqd/adfact_e.html, State of the Environment Reporting, Environment Canada, 1999. Reproduced with the permission of the Minister of Public Works and Government Services, 2003.

Table 25.2: Greenhouse Gas Emissions from Urban Transportation: Backgrounder. Prepared by IBI Group and Management Technology Services under the directions of the NRTEE Task Force on Sustainable Transportation. Ottawa: National Round Table on the Environment and the Economy, 1998. Reproduced with permission of the Minister of Public Works and Government Services, 2005.

Table 25.3: Greenhouse Gas Emissions from Urban Transportation: Backgrounder. Prepared by IBI Group and Management Technology Services under the directions of the NRTEE Task Force on Sustainable Transportation. Ottawa: National Round Table on the Environment and the Economy, 1998. Reproduced with permission of the Minister of Public Works and Government Services, 2005.

Figure 25.3: Reproduced with permission of Environment Canada.

Table 25.4: Transportation in Canada, Transport Canada, 2004. Reproduced with the permission of the Minister of Public Works and Government Services, 2005.

Table 25.6: Adapted from the Statistics Canada publication "Waste Management Industry Survey: Business and Government Sectors," Catologue 16F0023, 2002.

Figure 25.7: Urban Water Indicators: Municipal Water Use and Wastewater Treatment, http://www.ec.gc.ca/soer-ree/English/Indicators/Issues/Urb_H20/default.cfm, Environment Canada, 2001, National Indicators and Reporting Office, Reproduced with the permission of the Minister of Public Works and Government Services, 2003.

Table 25.8: National Sewage Report Card-Number Three, Sierra Legal Defence Fund, 1999.

Table 26.1: World Resources Institute, Washington D.C.

Figure 26.2: Reproduced with permission of Environment Canada.

Table 26.2: Adapted from the Statistics Canada publication "Human activity and the environment: annual statistics," Catalogue 16-201, 2004.

Appendix E, Tables 1-3, 5, 9, 10, 13 and 14: World Resources Institute, Washington, D.C.

Index